FISHES OF ALABAMA
AND THE MOBILE BASIN

5/28/97

To Hall —

Happy B'day

From your B'day Buddy

Fink

FISHES OF ALABAMA
AND THE MOBILE BASIN

Maurice F. Mettee, Patrick E. O'Neil, and J. Malcolm Pierson

Illustrations by
Karl J. Scheidegger

A cooperative effort of the Geological Survey of Alabama,
Game and Fish Division of the Alabama Department of Conservation
and Natural Resources, and the Region 4 Office
of the U.S. Fish and Wildlife Service

Published by Oxmoor House, Inc., book division of Southern Progress Corporation
P.O. Box 2463 Birmingham, Alabama 35201
Printed in the United States of America
First printing 1996

Library of Congress Cataloging-in-Publication Data
Mettee, Maurice F., 1943—
Fishes of Alabama and the Mobile basin

Bibliography: p.
Includes Index.
1. Freshwater Fishes—Alabama. 2. Freshwater Fishes—Alabama—Mobile Watershed. 3. Freshwater
Fishes—Alabama—Identification. 4. Freshwater Fishes—Alabama—Mobile River Watershed—Identification.
I. O'Neil, Patrick E. 1955—, II. Pierson, J. Malcolm, 1949— III. Title
QL628.A2M47 1996 597.092'9671—dc20 96-33100 ISBN: 0-8487-1485-7

Unless otherwise indicated, photographs are by Patrick E. O'Neil, J. Malcolm Pierson, and Maurice F. Mettee.
Unless otherwise indicated, illustrations were prepared by Karl J. Scheidegger. Financial support for preparation
of the illustrations provided by the Tennessee Valley Authority.

Field sampling and manuscript preparation were supported with Sport Fish Restoration Funds provided by the
U.S. Fish and Wildlife Service to the Game and Fish Division of the Alabama Department of Conservation and
Natural Resources and the Geological Survey of Alabama.

Production supported with Sport Fish Restoration Funds provided by the U.S. Fish and Wildlife Service to the Game
and Fish Division of the Alabama Department of Conservation and Natural Resources and Oxmoor House, Inc.

This book is listed as Monograph 15 of the Geological Survey of Alabama, Tuscaloosa, Alabama.

Oxmoor House, Inc.
Editor-in-Chief: Nancy Fitzpatrick Wyatt
Senior Homes Editor: Mary Kay Culpepper
Senior Editor, Editorial Services: Olivia Kindig Wells
Art Director: James Boone

Fishes of Alabama and the Mobile Basin
Editor: Brenda Waldron Kolb
Assistant Editor: Susan Hernandez Ray
Associate Art Director: Cynthia R. Cooper
Designer: Melissa Jones Clark
Copy Editor: Sally Antrobus
Proofreader: Michael Allocca
Editorial Assistants: Karly Benson, Barzella Estle, Jill Hasty,
    Neely Jones, Christina Wynn
Production and Distribution Director: Phillip Lee
Associate Production Manager: Vanessa Cobbs Richardson
Production Assistant: Valerie Heard
Publishing Systems Administrator: Rick Tucker

To our parents, who guided us through our early years, sparked our interest
in nature, and instilled in us a sense of responsibility and fair play;

to our wives and families, who shared our professional enthusiasm, encouraged
our work, and showed patience while we were in the field;

to our colleagues, who joined us in long but enjoyable hours of
field sampling, contributed their own field observations and data,
and suggested improvements in this publication;

and to future generations of young naturalists with an inexhaustible curiosity about
living creatures. They are the future of our science and guardians of our planet.

CONTENTS

PREFACE

Freshwater Fishes of Alabama, by W. F. Smith-Vaniz (1968), was a landmark work. Though brief by current standards, this first book on Alabama fishes contained 211 pages of taxonomic keys, black-and-white photographs, and descriptions of 282 freshwater and marine species, many of which occur throughout the eastern United States. The "Alabama fish book," as it came to be called, has become a standard reference for fisheries biologists, ichthyologists, environmental professionals, professors, and graduate students.

Much has happened in the 28 years since the publication of Smith-Vaniz's work. As a result of a better understanding of phylogenetic relationships, at least two dozen new species have been described, and the names of dozens more have changed (Robins et al., 1991). Tremendous quantities of new information have been compiled on the distributions, habitats, and life histories of southeastern fishes, resulting in a number of recent studies, including *Freshwater Fishes of Louisiana* (Douglas, 1974), *A Distributional Atlas of Kentucky Fishes* (Burr and Warren, 1986), *Fishes of Arkansas* (Robison and Buchanan, 1988), *A Field Guide to Freshwater Fishes* (Page and Burr, 1991), *The Freshwater Fishes of North Carolina* (Menhinick, 1991), *The Fishes of Tennessee* (Etnier and Starnes, 1993), and *Freshwater Fishes of Virginia* (Jenkins and Burkhead, 1993).

In 1990, the Game and Fish Division of the Alabama Department of Conservation and Natural Resources and the Region 4 Office of the U.S. Fish and Wildlife Service contracted the Geological Survey of Alabama to prepare the current work. Together, we set a twofold goal. For anglers, students, and general readers, we hoped to enrich the understanding of Alabama's diverse fish fauna and unique aquatic habitats. For ichthyologists and fisheries biologists, we wanted to provide such usable information as new species records, color maps relating species distributions to physiographic setting, and personal observations on species habitats and life histories.

The entire effort, from field work to bound book, was accomplished in only six years. The project has been a highlight in our careers, but we realize that this is by no means the final word on Alabama fishes. Even now, multiple-use conflicts over water quality and quantity are increasing, and in the next two decades, fisheries scientists, natural resource regulators, and industry representatives will be making decisions that affect the biological diversity of Alabama and the United States. We hope that the information in this book will assist these individuals and the public in fulfilling their responsibilities to future generations.

Preparing this book was a labor of love, but we could not have completed it alone. We built upon the work of scores of professors, students, fisheries biologists, and naturalists who over the past 150 years have methodically collected fishes, placed them in natural history museums, and published their observations. We have also relied on friends and colleagues who participated in hours of tedious sampling, suggested new collection localities, freely shared their field notes and expertise, and constructively commented on the final manuscript.

Current and former colleagues at the Geological Survey of Alabama who deserve our thanks include Bennett Bearden, Steve Harris, Carla Howard, Peggy Marsh, Beth McCullough, Stuart McGregor, Meredith Mettee, Jolanta Nunley, Alexander Sartwell, Tom

Shepard, Lee Smith, W. Everett Smith, Irene Thompson, and Kathy Webb.

For their leadership in this effort, our sincerest appreciation goes to Charles Kelley and Fred Harders of the Alabama Game and Fish Division and to Wally Walquist of the U.S. Fish and Wildlife Service. At the Alabama Game and Fish Division, we received enthusiastic support from Joe Addison, Claude Boyd, Dan Catchings, Doug Darr, Phil Ekema, Keith Floyd, Jay Haffner, Fred Hamilton, Jon Hornsby, Dickey Huey, Larry Johnson, Phillip Kilpatrick, Jim McHugh, Jerry Moss, Mike Newman, Nick Nichols, William Reeves, Rob Sherer, Gary Spray, Dan Thompson, William Tucker, Jack Turner, Ken Weathers, and Joe Zolczynski.

Alabama Power Company monitors the water quality and biological integrity of its hydroelectric reservoirs on the Coosa and Tallapoosa river systems. Together with coauthor J. Malcolm Pierson, Steve Krotzer, Ed Tyberghein, and Jim Lochamy collected fishes for these projects and allowed us to use some of their data.

Others who assisted in collecting or donating fishes include Dan Butterfield of Butterfield Fish Farms; Jim Williams of the National Biological Survey; Steve Moore of the National Park Service; Mike Howell and Robert Stiles of Samford University; Rick Bivens of the Tennessee Wildlife Resources Agency; Hank Bart, Royal D. Suttkus, and Michael Taylor of Tulane University; Jim Barkuloo, Laura Jenkins, Pledger Moon, and Frank Parauka of the U.S. Fish and Wildlife Service; Bernard Kuhajda of the University of Alabama; Bud Freeman and David Walters of the University of Georgia; and John Burke, Stephanie Puleo, and C. A. Schultz. Wayne Ford provided statistics on catfish production in Alabama.

A number of colleagues supplied collection data and allowed us to examine specimens housed in museums under their care. We would like to thank Henry Bart and John Ramsey, formerly of Auburn University; Julian Humphries of Cornell University; Ronald Altig of Mississippi State University; Jeffrey Williams of the Smithsonian Institution; Ellen Hammond, Larry Kay, Ed Scott, and Peggy Shute of the Tennessee Valley Authority; Herbert Boschung and Richard Mayden of the University of Alabama; Carter Gilbert of the University of Florida; Reeve Bailey and Douglas Nelson of the University of Michigan; and David Etnier of the University of Tennessee.

We are especially grateful to Royal Suttkus, professor emeritus at Tulane University, for his continuing contributions to our effort. An esteemed naturalist and treasured friend, Suttkus has personally collected nearly 2,000 samples of Alabama fishes, many of which he took single-handedly with a 10-foot minnow seine. His reviewing of parts of our manuscript is only the latest example of his generosity and commitment to this project and his intense interest in Alabama fishes. Others who reviewed parts of the manuscript were Robert Cashner, Robert Jenkins, Stephen Krotzer, Jerry Moss, and Bruce Thompson.

Except where noted, the photographs of Alabama fishes were taken by Patrick E. O'Neil or, in a few cases, by the other coauthors. Candy Crawford and Richard Pospisil of the University of Alabama Department of Educational Media processed most of our film and provided invaluable technical assistance. To help complete the photographic sequence for the species accounts and to show natural habitats for certain species, a number of colleagues generously loaned their transparencies. Richard Bryant and Wayne Starnes contributed the lake sturgeon, spotfin chub, amber darter, Conasauga logperch, and snail darter. Noel Burkhead provided the popeye shiner, silver shiner, Etowah darter, and Cherokee darter. William Pflieger of the Missouri Department of Conservation offered the goldeye; Peggy and John Shute, the ashy darter; and Bruce Bauer, the trispot darter. William Roston provided beautiful photographs of living species in their natural habitats. Gaylyn Gwin of *Outdoor Alabama* opened the magazine's archives and allowed us to use several photographs taken by Dan Brothers. John Van Swearingen provided several excellent photographs of cave environments in Alabama. Elizabeth Speer of the Elmore County Historical Society and John Hall of the Alabama Museum of Natural History provided old photographs of large fishes caught in Alabama.

Karl Scheidegger created all of the illustrations appearing in the taxonomic keys and in the accounts of the Alabama cavefish and the whiteline topminnow. Karl's contribution is especially valuable in that it combines his considerable drawing abilities with his experience in collecting and identifying Alabama fishes when he was a graduate student at Auburn University. We would also like to thank Wayne Starnes, who allowed us to use his line drawing of the extinct harelip sucker.

The color distribution and other resource maps—the first such maps ever printed in a state fish book—were produced using Intergraph MGE geographic information software. The authors managed the collection data for the 9,244 samples, but the real magic of turning the data files into printed maps was accomplished by Gary Crawford, Bonita Brennan, Phillip Henderson, Michael Szabo, Ruth Turner, and Donald Wheat at the Geological Survey of Alabama. Julie Luckett at NEC Incorporated was responsible for registering the computer map files.

Throughout this project, the authors felt a strong obligation to write a book that would excite and educate the public about an important group of animals that are difficult to observe in nature. Oxmoor House has carried our aspirations far beyond our greatest expectations. We extend our heartiest thanks to Bruce Akin, executive vice president of Southern Progress Corporation. As vice president and general manager of Oxmoor House, he assigned the team of dedicated professionals who transformed a scientific presentation into a beautiful, usable book. Major players in this effort were Nancy Wyatt, James Boone, Brenda Kolb, Richard Tucker, Melissa Clark, Mary Kay Culpepper, Susan Ray, Vanessa Richardson, Jill Hasty, Christina Wynn, Neely Jones, and Karly Benson. Sally Antrobus, copy editor, and Michael Allocca, proofreader, proved indispensable in making a scientific report more interesting and informative for the general reader. In our admittedly biased opinion, these individuals created a new standard in state fish books, one that could help to form the long-needed link between the scientific community and the public.

INTRODUCTION

Fishes are an extremely important natural resource to Alabama, its state and local economies, the welfare of its citizens, and the environmental integrity of its rivers and streams. Recreational fishing is a popular sport in Alabama, and its economic benefits to the state are considerable. Resident and nonresident anglers spend millions of dollars each year on boats and motors, fishing supplies, gasoline, accommodations, food, and other goods and services. Fishing license revenues and a portion of the federal excise taxes collected on the sales of fishing-related equipment are returned to the state of Alabama in the form of Sport Fish Restoration Funds. The Alabama Department of Conservation and Natural Resources uses these funds to monitor fish populations in state waters, build and maintain public boat ramps, and educate citizens about fishes and fishing opportunities in Alabama.

Commercial fishing is another important aspect of Alabama's fishery-related economy. Alabama is second only to Mississippi in the production and processing of pond-raised channel catfish. In 1995, Alabama catfish farmers produced 75 million pounds of catfish, most of which was processed in Hale County and was valued at $57 million (Wayne Ford, 1995, personal communication). Using legal gill nets, baskets, and trotlines, commercial anglers annually harvest thousands of pounds of catfishes, buffalo, and carpsuckers. Some of their catch is sold locally, but most is sent to wholesalers and shipped to northern U.S. markets. A growing awareness of the rewards of eating healthy foods will no doubt stimulate the market for high-nutrient, low-fat fresh fish.

The benefits of fishes far exceed obvious financial considerations. Recreational and subsistence anglers catch and eat thousands of pounds of sunfishes, catfishes, and suckers in Alabama annually. Most fishing is concentrated in Alabama's rivers, reservoirs, and public lakes, but some anglers prefer to fish in over 134,000 acres of private ponds scattered across the state.

In addition to their economic benefits, fishes help professionals judge and maintain the environmental quality of the state's aquatic habitats. Over the past two decades, scientists have recognized that fish communities are excellent indicators of water quality. Fishes are relatively long-lived aquatic creatures, and because many species require precise habitat and water-quality conditions, their patterns of abundance and occurrence indicate the health of the streams in which they live. As a general rule, minor environmental changes (whether natural or manmade) produce only slight deviations in normal fish communities. More serious environmental changes, especially those resulting from pollution and extreme habitat disturbance, can cause fish populations to be substantially altered or even eliminated. Making use of these observable patterns, many industries and government agencies now incorporate fish sampling into their programs for monitoring water quality.

The freshwater fishes of Alabama are a fascinating subject of study in their own right, and they have interested amateurs and professionals alike for more than 150 years. In the 19th century, many of the early species descriptions were based on specimens that physicians and naturalists had collected, preserved in salt or alcohol, and shipped by rail to large museums in the North. Hoping to learn more about the fish fauna of the Southeast, natural history museums in Philadelphia, Washington, and Cambridge, Massachusetts, initiated several sampling surveys, most of which were complicated by bad weather and unreliable transportation. In 1845, in a short article in *The Proceedings of the Boston Society of Natural History*, David Humphreys Storer published the first report on Alabama's freshwater fishes, describing seven species collected from the Tennessee River near Florence.

At about this time, Louis Agassiz, the renowned Harvard ichthyologist, began studying the fishes of the Southeast. In 1854 he published an article on fishes collected in the southern bend of the Tennessee River in Alabama. He later sought the help of the Geological Survey of Alabama, which may have been the first state agency involved in sampling freshwater fishes in Alabama. In a letter dated 11 July 1853 and addressed to state geologist Michael Tuomey, Agassiz asks for "separate collections from the headwaters of the Black Warrior, from its lower course, from the headwaters of the Tombigby [*sic*], from its middle course above its junction with the Black Warrior, from its lower course above its junction with the Alabama, also a collection from the Cahawbah [*sic*], one from the Coosa, (or even two, one from its headwaters and the other from its lower course) and one from the Tallapoosa." Agassiz also indicates that he had borrowed several fish samples from Tuomey, which the latter may have collected during his surveys of Alabama's bivalve mollusk fauna.

Investigations of Alabama fishes continued, and by 1900, nearly half of the state's fish species were described. Much of the information then available on the taxonomy and distribution of species was summarized in *The Fishes of North and Middle America*, by David Starr Jordan and Barton Warren Evermann (1896–1900).

Intensive surveys of Alabama fishes waned until the 1950s, when Ralph Chermock began his teaching career at the University of Alabama. Within a few years, Chermock's students completed studies on the marine fishes of coastal Alabama (Boschung, 1957), Alabama minnows of the genus *Notropis* (Howell, 1957), and the fishes of the lower Coastal Plain of Alabama (Hemphill, 1960). Chermock took the lead in creating the fish and mammal collections at the University of Alabama.

The fish collection at Auburn University (then Alabama Polytechnic Institute) had been established by Frank Guyton in 1930, and in the 1950s Homer Swingle and Jack Dendy greatly expanded it. The collection is particularly valuable because it contains not only substantial holdings from the Chattahoochee and Coosa river systems, but also many large river samples taken before the construction of navigational locks and dams on the Alabama and lower Tombigbee rivers.

The second generation of Alabama ichthyologists came of age under the tutelage of Herbert Boschung at the University of Alabama and John Ramsey at Auburn University. With the guidance of these two scientists, graduate students methodically surveyed the state's streams and rivers, having armed themselves only with nylon seines and a burning desire to learn more about the distributions and habits of these descrete and often beautiful aquatic creatures. The students' enthusiasm did not go unrewarded. From 1960 through 1985, knowledge of species' distributions, habitats, and life histories had expanded by several orders of magnitude. Many of Boschung's and Ramsey's former students, including the authors of this book, are still involved in sampling Alabama's fish fauna today.

ALABAMA'S NATURAL SETTING

Alabama's abundant water resources, varied topography, and subtropical climate sustain one of the richest fish faunas in North America. The state's remarkably diverse aquatic habitats—including springs, swamps, caves, streams, rivers, reservoirs, and wetlands—support a correspondingly diverse number of fish species. To understand why Alabama has such a variety of fishes, it is useful to have some sense of its waterways, climatic regimes, and landforms.

WATERWAYS AND DRAINAGE BASINS

Alabama is known throughout the world for its trophy fish–producing lakes and reservoirs, but they represent only a small part of the vast network of rivers and stream systems that drain the state and provide habitat for its varied fish fauna. Alabama ranks first in the nation in navigable channels, with 1,438 miles of waterways which include 16 lock and dam structures on six river systems. Twenty-one hydroelectric production facilities and more than 20 public water supply impoundments on smaller streams are scattered throughout the state. The total surface area of its major lakes, ponds, and reservoirs is 563,000 acres, and an average of about 33.5 trillion gallons of water flow through Alabama's river systems each year. Of perhaps greater interest is the fact that groundwater supplies are estimated to be near 553 trillion gallons. About 3.6 million acres of wetlands, from fresh to saline, are associated with Alabama waterways, providing yet another significant source of habitat for fishes.

It is easier to appreciate the uniqueness of Alabama's water resources and aquatic habitats when they are compared to other river systems in the United States. One basis of comparison is the daily water yield per square mile of drainage basin. The Mobile basin yields an average of 0.94 million gallons per day per square mile (mgd/mi^2) of drainage basin. That is more than the 0.34 mgd/mi^2 for the Mississippi River and 0.70 mgd/mi^2 for the Columbia River as it enters the Pacific Ocean, and it is considerably more than that of the Colorado River, which yields only 500 gallons per day/mi^2 of drainage area. Similar to the Mobile basin is the Apalachicola basin, which yields 0.86 mgd/mi^2 after draining the Piedmont, Valley and Ridge, and Coastal Plain provinces in Georgia and Alabama.

Even though total basin areas and average flows are greater for the Mississippi and Columbia rivers than for the Mobile basin, their yields of water per unit of drainage area are only about 30 and 60 percent, respectively, that of the Mobile basin. These figures are not unexpected since the Mississippi drains parts of the semi-arid Plains and Southwest, and the Columbia drains the wetter Pacific Northwest. As the comparison to these two areas shows, Alabama is an abundantly watered state, a fact that, together with its diverse physiographic template and stable climate, set the stage for its diverse fish heritage.

Approximately 77,000 miles of river and stream channels are carved into Alabama's landscape. About 61 percent flow throughout the year, while the remaining 39 percent flow intermittently only during the wetter seasons. Three drainage groups occur within the state: the Tennessee River drainage in north Alabama, the Mobile basin in north-central and central Alabama, and the coastal drainages stretching from the Escatawpa River, which lies west of the Mobile basin, to the Chattahoochee River, which forms part of the Alabama-Georgia state line. Our area of study encompasses not just those drainages that fall within Alabama's state line, but the entire Mobile basin. As a single, interconnected hydrologic unit, this watershed contains more species of fishes than any other drainage basin of comparable size and is one of the greatest natural faunistic regions in North America.

Tennessee River Drainage

The Tennessee River originates in Virginia, North Carolina, and Tennessee, makes a U-shaped bend across northern Alabama, and then flows northward to join the Ohio River in western Kentucky. It drains approximately 6,826 mi^2, or 13 percent, of Alabama's 51,677 mi^2 surface area. Major northern tributaries of the river in Alabama include Cypress Creek, Shoal Creek, the Elk River, Limestone Creek, the Flint River, and the Paint Rock River; southern tributaries include Bear Creek, Spring Creek, Big Nance Creek, Clear Creek, and Flint Creek. The average flow of the Tennessee River entering Alabama is over 37,600 cubic feet per second (cfs). An additional 14,000 cfs are added as the river crosses the state, producing an average exit flow of 51,600 cfs. The entire length of the river in Alabama is impounded to form, from west to east, Pickwick Lake, Wilson Lake, Wheeler Lake, and Guntersville Lake. The Tennessee Valley Authority manages the reservoirs for flood control, electrical power generation, navigation, and recreation. The TVA also manages the smaller reservoirs on Cedar Creek, Little Bear Creek, and Bear Creek in Franklin, Marion, and Winston counties.

The Tennessee River supports some of the finest smallmouth bass, largemouth bass, and sauger fishing in the United States. It is also home to several uncommon or rare fish species, including the palezone shiner, flame chub, Alabama and southern cavefishes, spring pygmy sunfish, blenny darter, slackwater darter, Tuscumbia darter, boulder darter, and snail darter.

Several species previously found in the Alabama section of the Tennessee drainage may have been extirpated from the state. The spotfin chub, last collected in 1937, and the ashy darter, last collected in

Reservoir	Acreage
CHATTAHOOCHEE RIVER	
1. George W. Andrews	1,540
2. Walter F. George	45,180
3. Lake Harding	5,850
4. West Point (in Alabama)	2,300
CONECUH RIVER	
5. Point A	900
6. Gantt	2,770
ESCATAWPA RIVER	
7. Big Creek	3,600
ALABAMA RIVER	
8. Claiborne	5,930
9. William "Bill" Dannelly	17,000
10. R. E. "Bob" Jones	12,510
TALLAPOOSA RIVER	
11. Thurlow	585
12. Yates	1,980
13. Martin	40,000
14. R. L. Harris	10,660
COOSA RIVER	
15. Jordan/Bouldin	6,800
16. Mitchell	5,850
17. Lay	12,000
18. Logan Martin	15,263
19. Neely Henry	11,200
20. Weiss	30,200
LOWER TOMBIGBEE RIVER	
21. Coffeeville	8,500
22. Demopolis	10,000
UPPER TOMBIGBEE RIVER	
23. Gainesville	6,400
24. Aliceville	8,300
BLACK WARRIOR RIVER	
25. Selden	7,800
26. Oliver	790
27. Tuscaloosa	5,880
28. Holt	3,300
29. Bankhead	9,200
30. Lewis Smith	21,200
TENNESSEE RIVER	
31. Pickwick	43,100
32. Cedar Creek	4,200
33. Little Bear Creek	1,560
34. Lower Bear Creek	670
35. Upper Bear Creek	1,850
36. Wilson	15,930
37. Wheeler	67,100
38. Guntersville	69,100
TOTAL ACREAGE	516,998

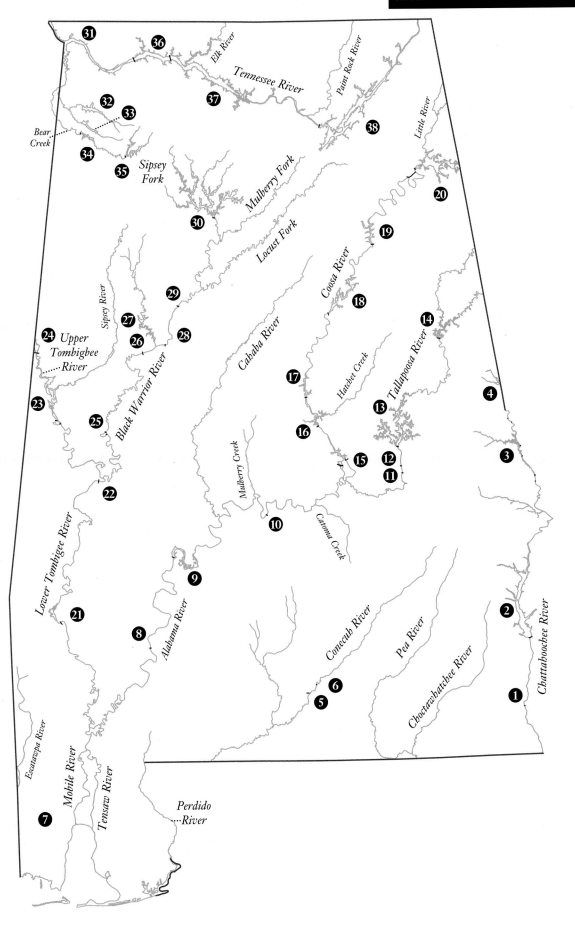

1845, still occur farther upstream in the drainage. Limited populations of the lake sturgeon and shovelnose sturgeon appear to have been eliminated from the drainage in Alabama, although both species still exist in the upper Mississippi basin. The harelip sucker and the whiteline topminnow, both last recorded from Alabama in 1889, are now considered to be extinct, probably as a result of modification and siltation of their preferred habitats.

Mobile Basin

The Mobile basin drains an area of 43,683 mi^2 in Alabama, Mississippi, Tennessee, and Georgia. In Alabama, the basin drains approximately 32,207 mi^2, or 62 percent, of the state's land area.

The western Mobile basin is comprised of the upper Tombigbee River (9,097 mi^2), the Black Warrior River (6,228 mi^2), and, below the confluence of these two river systems, the lower Tombigbee River (4,659 mi^2). This entire area contains more than 81,000 surface acres of impoundments. With more than 21,000 acres, Lake Lewis Smith on the Sipsey Fork is the largest of these impoundments; deep and clear, it is known for its spotted and striped bass. The series of impoundments created by the completion of the Tennessee-Tombigbee Waterway are narrow and shallow outside the navigation channel, providing excellent fishing for largemouth bass and crappie. The upper Tombigbee River skirts the Fall Line Hills, while the lower Tombigbee River slices through the lower Coastal Plain before its confluence with the Alabama River. The Black Warrior River system drains a portion of the Cumberland Plateau in Jefferson, Cullman, Walker, and Tuscaloosa counties and the upper Coastal Plain.

The eastern Mobile basin is drained by the Alabama River (6,023 mi^2), Cahaba River (1,818 mi^2), Coosa River (10,161 mi^2), and Tallapoosa River (4,675 mi^2). This part of the basin contains more than 170,000 surface acres of impoundments—more than double the area found in the western Mobile basin. The largest of these are Lake Martin (40,000 acres) on the Tallapoosa River and Lake Weiss (30,200 acres) on the Coosa River. Impoundments on the Coosa and Tallapoosa Rivers were constructed for hydroelectric and flood control purposes, and neither river is navigable by commercial traffic.

The Cahaba, Coosa, and Tallapoosa rivers flow over the carbonaceous and metamorphic terrain of the Valley and Ridge and the Piedmont physiographic provinces. These rivers, therefore, have waters of a higher minerality and clarity than those flowing over the shale and sandstone of the Cumberland Plateau and sands of the Coastal Plain. The Alabama River flows almost entirely within the Coastal Plain before meeting the lower Tombigbee to form the Mobile River. Downstream, the expansive Mobile Delta begins where the Mobile River splits into a braided network of four distributaries—the Mobile, Middle, Tensaw, and Blakely rivers—which daily contribute an average of more than 41 billion gallons of fresh water to Mobile Bay.

Coastal Rivers

The free-flowing nature of Alabama's coastal rivers and streams produces some of the most beautiful aquatic habitats in the state. Many of them have darkly stained waters meandering through forested swamps or flowing over extensive sand and gravel shoals—all areas locally known as blackwaters.

The coastal rivers include, from west to east, the Escatawpa (767 mi^2), Perdido (840 mi^2), Conecuh (3,848 mi^2), Blackwater (148 mi^2), Yellow (507 mi^2), Choctawhatchee (3,130 mi^2), and Chattahoochee (2,832 mi^2) river systems, which drain about 25 percent of Alabama's land area. Because the topography of coastal drainages is unsuited for reservoir development, only a few have been constructed. Impoundments of significant size are Point A and Gantt lakes (about 3,670 acres combined) on the Conecuh River near Andalusia, Walter F. George (45,180 acres) on the Chattahoochee River northeast of Dothan, and Big Creek Lake (3,600 acres) in Mobile County.

Some of the most interesting fish species inhabiting these rivers, streams, and backwaters are the pygmy and bluefin killifish, the spring-dwelling redeye chub, the Alabama shad, and the gulf sturgeon. Only eight species of darters occur with any frequency, partly because coastal drainages lack the hard substrates and moderate gradients that these fishes prefer. In the Apalachicola basin, several endemic species occur in the Chattahoochee drainage in Alabama: the bluefin stoneroller, the bluestripe shiner, the broadstripe shiner, the greater jumprock, the undescribed "grayfin redhorse," and the undescribed "shoal bass," which resembles the smallmouth bass of the Tennessee River drainage.

CLIMATE

For the past 10,000 years, Alabama's stable, humid, subtropical climate has been controlled by several factors, including the state's position on the earth (between 31° and 35° north latitude), its lack of major mountain ranges, and its proximity to the Gulf of Mexico. Summers are hot, with high temperatures of around 90°F and lows of around 70°. The moist Gulf air frequently produces afternoon thunderstorms, especially in the summer. In late summer and fall, the driest times of the year, many upland streams cease to flow or go completely dry. Winters are typified by series of cold fronts that create patterns of rainy days alternating with clear periods; daytime high temperatures average between 45° and 50°F and nighttime lows between 30° and 40°. Rainfall is generally greatest from December to March, but early and middle summer may also be quite wet, particularly in July. Regional rainfall varies from 50 to 54 inches in the Tennessee Valley and from 60 to 65 inches along the coast.

Alabama's climate today is much the same as it was 280 to even 345 million years ago. The climate then was warm and moist, rather as today's tropical and subtropical environments are. These conditions encouraged the growth of massive swamps containing many plant species now long extinct. One difference from the climatic tendencies of the past 3 million years (when ice sheets flowed throughout much of the northern hemisphere) is that the climate then was more unstable, drifting back and forth between temperate and cooler regimes.

The last great glaciation, the Wisconsinan, lasted from 100,000 to 10,000 years ago. Even though Alabama had no ice cover, the event significantly influenced the distribution of fishes in the state, for it displaced to the south species that had previously occurred only in the north.

PHYSIOGRAPHY

Physiography concerns the structure and type of underlying geologic formations, as well as the local geologic and climatic forces that shape the landscape. Along with several other factors, an area's physiography determines the natural water-quality conditions of local streams, rivers, and lakes and in many cases the distribution of species occurring in the area.

Across geologic time in Alabama, powerful tectonic forces created chains of mountains, which were gradually eroded into plateaus, foothills, and valleys by the variable and relentless forces of wind, rain, and temperature. Rivers changed direction and migrated across the state, intersecting and capturing other streams along the way. As climatic changes triggered the advances and retreats of great continental ice sheets, coastlines ebbed and flowed many times, even extending as far inland as Tuscaloosa, Montgomery, and Phoenix City.

These climatic and geologic events in Alabama have been a major force behind the natural selection processes that have created new fish species, driven others into extinction, and isolated some populations. Today, Alabama's moderate climate regimes and diverse physiography sustain a variety of aquatic habitats—from coastal marshes to high-gradient, boulder-laden mountain streams—and correspondingly diverse biological forms.

In Alabama, five major physiographic sections are recognized: the Highland Rim, the Cumberland Plateau, the Alabama Valley and Ridge, the Piedmont Upland, and the East Gulf Coastal Plain. Further delineations of districts within these sections recognize yet other unique physical areas, illustrating the broad and diverse physiographic character of the state. In the following descriptions of physiography, we have relied on Harper (1920, 1942, 1943), Johnson (1930), Fenneman (1938), Pierce (1966), and Sapp and Emplaincourt (1975), and our personal observations.

Highland Rim

The Highland Rim in its entirety extends from the glacial boundary in Indiana south through Nashville to the Tennessee River in Alabama. The Highland Rim in Alabama is located in the northwestern portion of the state and is drained exclusively by the Tennessee River. Valley floors are predominantly limestone at altitudes of 500 feet, while ridges are typically composed of sandstone and are nearly 1,000 feet. The three districts delineated in the Highland Rim—the Tennessee Valley, Little Mountain, and Moulton Valley—all slope gently to the west and eventually disappear beneath Coastal Plain deposits. Most streams in the southern portion of the Highland Rim originate in the Pottsville escarpment of the Warrior basin, flow northward through Moulton Valley, and proceed through Little Mountain in narrow valleys deeply cut through sandstone beds.

The Tennessee Valley, which comprises the red-clay lands on both sides of the Tennessee River, is the largest district in the Highland Rim. The level parts of the valley contain numerous springs, small ponds, lime sinks, and caves formed by solution of the underlying limestone. Found exclusively in the Highland Rim are several species closely associated with these habitats, including the Tuscumbia darter, the spring pygmy sunfish, and the Alabama cavefish.

The Tennessee Valley, Little Mountain, and Moulton Valley districts are drained by the Tennessee River and its tributaries: to the north of the river, Elk River, Cypress Creek, Butler Creek, Limestone Creek, and Bluewater Creek, and to the south, Town Creek, Spring Creek, Big Nance Creek, and Flint Creek. During times of drought, water from springs often augments streamflows, and some springs, such as Tuscumbia Spring, supply drinking water. Streams draining south to the Tennessee River usually flow year-round, and many have exceptionally good water quality. Small headwater streams flowing north through the Little Mountain and Moulton Valley districts are dry channels or stagnant pools during late summer. Some of these streams receive agricultural runoff and permitted wastewater discharges, which can lead to water-quality degradation during low streamflows.

Cumberland Plateau

The Cumberland Plateau is an undulating surface of sandstone and shale that is frequently dissected by valleys and hollows. Elevations range from 600 feet at Tuscaloosa to nearly 1,700 feet in the Jackson County Mountains northeast of Huntsville and at Lookout Mountain near Mentone. Eight districts have been described in the Cumberland Plateau: the Warrior Basin, Jackson County Mountains, Sand Mountain, Sequatchie Valley, Blount Mountain, Murphrees Valley, Wills Valley, and Lookout Mountain. Most of the Cumberland Plateau consists of the Warrior Basin and Sand Mountain, and the plateau's predominant drainage features are the Black Warrior River and its tributaries.

The Warrior Basin is an 80-mile-wide, dissected plateau of sandstone and shale in Winston, Cullman, Walker, Jefferson, and Tuscaloosa counties. During summer months, flow in the large streams is usually sustained, but many headwater tributaries go dry because of low recharge from aquifers. The dominant drainage features are the upper Black Warrior River and its tributaries—Locust Fork, Mulberry Fork, Sipsey Fork, and North River—which drain through steep-sided, often gorgelike valleys. The basin is inhabited by the uncommon Warrior, Tuskaloosa, and undescribed "muscadine" darters, which are limited to upland streams having good water quality.

Located in the northeast corner of Alabama, the Jackson County Mountains district is a plateau of high relief characterized by mesa-like mountaintops of sandstone and stream valleys cut into limestone. The principal drainage features are the Paint Rock River and portions of the Flint River, both of which flow to

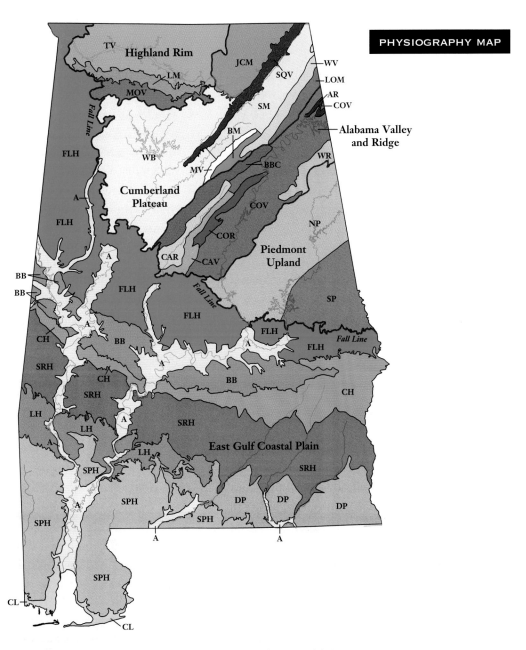

PHYSIOGRAPHY MAP

Major Division	Province	Physiographic Section	District
Interior Plains	Interior Low Plateau	Highland Rim	Tennessee Valley (TV), Little Mountain (LM), Moulton Valley (MOV)
Appalachian Highlands	Appalachian Plateau	Cumberland Plateau	Warrior Basin (WB), Jackson County Mountains (JCM), Sand Mountain (SM), Sequatchie Valley (SQV), Blount Mountain (BM), Murphrees Valley (MV), Wills Valley (WV), Lookout Mountain (LOM)
	Valley and Ridge	Alabama Valley and Ridge	Coosa Valley (COV), Coosa Ridges (COR), Weisner Ridges (WR), Cahaba Valley (CAV), Cahaba Ridges (CAR), Birmingham-Big Canoe Valley (BBC), Armuchee Ridges (AR)
	Piedmont	Piedmont Upland	Northern Piedmont Upland (NP), Southern Piedmont Upland (SP)
Atlantic Plain	Coastal Plain	East Gulf Coastal Plain	Fall Line Hills (FLH), Black Belt (BB), Chunnenuggee Hills (CH), Southern Red Hills (SRH), Lime Hills (LH), Dougherty Plain (DP), Southern Pine Hills (SPH), Coastal Lowlands (CL)
		Alluvial-deltaic Plain (A)	

the Tennessee River. The Paint Rock River supports a rich aquatic fauna, including such uncommon fishes as the snail darter and blotchside logperch, the pale-zone shiner, the undescribed "sawfin shiner," and many uncommon unionid mussel species. Somewhat more widespread are the streamline and blotched chubs and the telescope, warpaint, and mountain shiners, but they require undisturbed habitats for survival.

The Sand Mountain district is a large plateau of sandstone and shale ranging in width from eight to 18 miles. Approximately 80 miles long, this district gradually merges with the Warrior basin in the southwest and Blount Mountain in the southeast. Major stream systems on Sand Mountain are Short Creek, South Sauty Creek, and Town Creek (all of which drain to the Tennessee River) and the headwater streams of the Locust Fork. Many streams cut deep gorges through or fall precipitously over the edge of Sand Mountain. Of concern is poor streamwater quality, the result of runoff from agricultural and livestock facilities and permitted discharges from small communities and industries. Both the upland nature of streams on Sand Mountain and degraded water quality contribute to a low diversity of fish species. The distribution of such species as the rosefin shiner and banded sculpin is interesting because their common occurrence in the Tennessee and Black Warrior rivers suggests past connections between the drainages.

The Lookout Mountain district is a flat, narrow (3- to 7-mile-wide) remnant of the Cumberland Plateau extending from Chattanooga, Tennessee, to Gadsden, Alabama, a distance of 75 miles. Lookout Mountain is composed of sandstones and shales and resembles Sand Mountain in topography and character. The two major drainage features are Little River and Black Creek. Little River originates on the mountain in Georgia, flows southwest over a series of spectacular falls and through a deep gorge, and joins the Coosa River near Weiss reservoir. Diversity is low in upper Little River, whereas the lower river has a relatively diverse fish fauna, including one of the few remaining populations of the threatened blue shiner.

A pronounced topographic feature in Tennessee, the Sequatchie Valley district has its southwestern extent near the community of Blount Springs, Alabama. The northeastern part of the valley in Alabama is occupied by the Tennessee River where it enters the state downstream to Guntersville, while the southwestern third of the Sequatchie Valley ultimately drains into the Black Warrior River. No fishes are uniquely distributed in the Sequatchie Valley.

The Wills Valley district extends approximately 70 miles southwest across DeKalb and Etowah counties, ending near Gadsden. The valley averages about 5 miles wide and is composed of three limestone valleys separated by sandstone ridges of low relief. The primary drainage feature of Wills Valley is Big Wills Creek, which follows the valley through its entire course before entering the Coosa River near Gadsden. Many springs and spring seeps enter Big Wills Creek from Sand and Lookout mountains, providing a variety of aquatic habitats. Big Wills Creek and its tributaries are affected by agricultural runoff and permitted discharges from small industries and communities.

A remnant of the Cumberland Plateau, the Blount Mountain district is underlain with sandstones and shales. This saucer-shaped region is about 35 miles long and 4 to 6 miles wide. It is drained by Inland and Highland lakes, which are water-supply impoundments on Blackburn Fork, a tributary of the Locust Fork. Blackburn Fork traverses Murphrees Valley before entering the Locust Fork. In the past, rainbow trout have been stocked in Inland Lake and they are still occasionally hooked by fishermen. Several species that are common in the Coosa River system (including the rainbow shiner, riffle minnow, black redhorse, banded sculpin, and redeye bass) also occur occasionally in the upper reaches of Blackburn Fork, suggesting past connections between the two drainage systems.

Alabama Valley and Ridge

The Alabama Valley and Ridge consists of a series of folded and faulted parallel ridges and valleys that trend northeast-southwest and that have elevations ranging from 600 to 2,100 feet. Ridges are made of sandstone and chert, while valleys are generally developed on limestone and shale. Seven districts are described in the Alabama Valley and Ridge: Coosa Valley, Coosa Ridges, Weisner Ridges, Cahaba Valley, Cahaba Ridges, Birmingham–Big Canoe Valley, and Armuchee Ridges. Over half of the area within the Valley and Ridge is occupied by the Coosa Valley. Species that are limited to the Valley and Ridge above the Fall Line include the Conasauga logperch, amber darter, trispot darter, coldwater darter, and pygmy sculpin.

The Coosa Valley district extends for about 100 miles from Cherokee County to Chilton County and averages about 20 miles wide. The Coosa Valley is a shale and limestone plain with ridges of low relief. The primary drainage feature is the Coosa River, which is impounded along most of its length in Alabama. The common occurrence of the flame chub, mountain shiner, and blacknose dace in both the Coosa and the Tennessee river drainages suggests past stream connections.

The Coosa Ridges district, which consists of a belt of folded, parallel ridges, is about 5 miles wide and 50 miles long and extends across St. Clair and Shelby counties. The district is characterized by sandstone ridges separated by shale valleys. The most prominent mountain ridges are Oak, Double Oak, and Backbone. Streams originating in this district drain to either the Coosa or the Cahaba River and demonstrate a typical "trellised" drainage pattern: the tributaries follow the strike of the formation as closely as possible, running along beds of softest rock and then crossing the harder belts only occasionally. This pattern can be seen in Kelley Creek, Beaver Creek, Shoal Creek, and the upper Cahaba River.

The Weisner Ridges district consists of a series of dissected mountains of extreme relief rising some 900 feet above the Coosa Valley. The Weisner Ridges extend for 40 miles from the Alabama-Georgia line to Coldwater Mountain at Anniston. Major streams draining the Weisner Ridges are Choccolocco Creek, Cane Creek,

Nances Creek, and Tallasseehatchee Creek.

The Cahaba Valley district lies between the Cahaba Ridges and Coosa Ridges districts and extends for approximately 75 miles across Bibb, Jefferson, Chilton, Shelby, and St. Clair counties. It averages about 10 miles wide and is developed on dolomites, erodible shales, resistant chert beds, and weathered, soluble limestones. Streams that drain the Cahaba Valley and flow into the Cahaba River include the upper Little Cahaba River, Lake Purdy, Cahaba Valley Creek, Buck Creek, and the lower Little Cahaba River near Centreville.

The Cahaba Ridges district, which lies between the Cahaba Valley and the Birmingham–Big Canoe Valley, is about 65 miles long and 5 miles wide. It is characterized by several parallel ridges that trend northeast-southwest and are formed by massive sandstone and conglomerate beds. This area is drained by the Cahaba River, which meanders back and forth through the ridges. The Cahaba Ridges and Cahaba Valley are extensively developed for residential and commercial use, and as a result, streams receive significant amounts of nonpoint-source pollution, including nutrients and sediments. The Cahaba is home to several distinctive species, including the skygazer shiner, Cahaba shiner, and goldline darter.

The Birmingham–Big Canoe Valley district ranges from 4 to 8 miles in width and extends from Etowah County to Tuscaloosa County, a distance of some 90 miles. The valley is developed on soluble limestones and dolomites, shales, sandstones, and chert. The northeastern portion of the district is drained by streams flowing to Big Canoe Creek, which empties into the Coosa River near Gadsden, whereas the southwest portion is drained by headwaters to Turkey, Valley, Village, Fivemile, and Davis creeks. Because many of its springs originate in the carbonaceous terrain of the Birmingham Valley, this district contains distinctive aquatic habitats that support biological forms found nowhere else. The watercress darter, for example, occurs in only three spring areas in this region, and the vermilion darter is known only from Turkey Creek. The commercial and residential development in the Birmingham Valley has adversely affected the water quality and fish fauna of this region.

Piedmont Upland

The Piedmont Upland section is the nonmountainous section of the "older Appalachians" as described by Fenneman (1938). This undulating plain is created by surface rocks of long-term degradation and underlying rocks that are severely deformed and angled to the surface. The Piedmont Upland section in Alabama is a wedge-shaped feature bounded on the south by Coastal Plain sediments and on the north by the Alabama Valley and Ridge. Piedmont geology is complex, consisting of high- and low-grade metamorphic and igneous rocks, including quartzite, phyllite, slate, schist, amphibolite, and gneiss.

The Piedmont Upland section is divided into two districts—the Northern Piedmont Upland and the Southern Piedmont Upland. Elevations in the Northern Piedmont Upland range from 1,000 to 1,200 feet in the northeast and from 500 to 600 feet in the southwest. In the northern portion, the Talladega and Rebecca mountains form a prominent ridge system that trends northeast and encompasses Cheaha Mountain, at 2,407 feet the highest point in the state. The Tallapoosa River is the major system draining the Northern Piedmont Upland and is impounded along its middle reaches for hydroelectric power generation. The lower reaches of the Coosa River, including Mitchell and Jordan lakes, flow through the southern end of the district into the Alabama River just after it enters the Coastal Plain. Numerous small springs and clear upland streams occur throughout the district, providing aquatic habitats for fish species found nowhere else. The lined chub, Etowah darter, lipstick darter, Tallapoosa darter, and Tallapoosa shiner, for example, are restricted to the Piedmont in either the Tallapoosa River or the upper reaches of the Coosa River in Georgia.

The Southern Piedmont Upland district consists of a flat surface with little topographic relief. The area is cut by tributaries of the Tallapoosa and Chattahoochee rivers. Some of the most interesting aquatic habitats of

the area are located on the Fall Line, where streams cut through the edge of the Piedmont as they enter the Coastal Plain, dropping into a series of rapids or spectacular falls over the basal Piedmont rocks. The undescribed "shoal bass," the highscale and bandfin shiners, and the bluefin stoneroller can be found in this region.

East Gulf Coastal Plain

The East Gulf Coastal Plain is characterized by gentle rolling hills, sharp ridges, prairies, and broad, alluvial floodplains. Rocks underlying the Coastal Plain are of sedimentary origin and consist of sand, gravel, porous limestone, chalk, marl, and clay. These strata dip underground to the southwest at 35 to 40 feet per mile and generally strike in east-west belts. Some strata are more resistant to erosion and underlie broad, sawtoothed ridges, known as cuestas, that slope gently to the south and have steep north-facing slopes. The East Gulf Coastal Plain, which represents over 50 percent of the land area in Alabama, occurs south and southwest of the Fall Line and comprises eight physiographic districts: the Fall Line Hills, Black Belt, Chunnenuggee Hills, Southern Red Hills, Lime Hills, Dougherty Plain, Southern Pine Hills, and Coastal Lowlands.

The Fall Line divides Alabama into two regions—the upland and the lowland—and is the zone of contact between the hard rocks of the Appalachians and Interior Plateau and the soft, unconsolidated sediments of the Coastal Plain. Streams above the Fall Line are generally swift and have high gradients, reflecting the hard base rocks and high elevations of the area. Streams below the Fall Line are generally slow, have muddy or sandy bottoms, and have the lower gradients associated with flat topography.

The Fall Line is the most significant physical feature affecting the distribution of fishes in Alabama. Species that are cosmopolitan in distribution are unrestricted by this natural barrier. But because of the limitations stemming from life-history traits, morphological adaptations, or lack of invasion routes, many species are limited to either above or below the Fall Line.

The Fall Line Hills district is a wide, crescent-shaped band extending from the Tennessee River in northwest Alabama, traversing the middle portion of the Mobile basin, and ending near the Chattahoochee River in east Alabama. The Fall Line Hills form a boundary to the Highland Rim, Cumberland Plateau, Alabama Valley and Ridge, and the Piedmont Upland. Streams draining the Fall Line Hills are well sustained, even in the driest years, because of extensive sand and gravel aquifers. Topography can be fairly rugged with many steep slopes, particularly near streams. In the western part of the district, the Fall Line exists as an irregular transition belt about 15 miles wide where rocks of the Cumberland Plateau and Coastal Plain commingle. This contrasts with the eastern part of the district, where the Fall Line is a sharp transition between coastal sediments and Piedmont rocks. In the Tennessee River, the suckermouth minnow, slenderhead darter, and brindled madtom are limited to the Fall Line Hills. For reasons that are unknown, one species within the Mobile basin—the bluntnose minnow—avoids streams draining the Fall Line Hills.

The Black Belt district is an undulating, deeply weathered plain developed primarily on chalk and marl characterized by concentrations of soft, white-gray limestone. This bedrock material erodes into fertile soils that bake hard in summer heat and become adhesive when wet, making them difficult to cultivate. Because of its thin soils and impermeable rocks, the Black Belt represents a unique and clearly defined hydrologic region in the state. Many streams have eroded to chalk bedrock and are noted for their high rates of runoff and variability of flow during storms. Small streams often go dry, and large streams frequently exhibit reduced flow. As Harper (1943) notes, the Black Belt is one of the driest regions in the state, and natural prairie grasslands once covered up to 10 percent of the area. Because of these hydrologic and water-quality factors, the Black Belt is a significant distributional barrier, and several species that are widespread in the Mobile basin are absent in the Black Belt, including the bluehead chub, rough shiner, and black madtom. On the other hand, species such as the backwater darter seem to thrive in the unique environmental conditions of Black Belt streams.

The Chunnenuggee Hills district consists of a series of pine-forested sand hills developed on hardened beds of clay, sandstone, siltstone, and chalk. The north-facing slope in the western part of the district is known as the Ripley Cuesta and rises abruptly 100 to 200 feet above the Black Belt. This district widens in the eastern part of the state, includes several more cuestas, and encompasses about 2,200 square miles in Alabama. The rocks in the district are more permeable than chalk in the Black Belt but are still relatively poor aquifers. The Tombigbee and Alabama rivers of the Mobile River basin traverse the Chunnenuggee Hills. The headwaters of the Conecuh, Pea, and Choctawhatchee rivers originate here.

The 50-mile-wide belt known as the Southern Red Hills district narrows in southwest Alabama and broadens considerably in the east. Two subdistricts—the Flatwoods and the Buhrstone Hills—are delineated in the western part of the district. The Flatwoods subdistrict in southern Sumter and central Marengo counties. It is developed on dark clays and marls that weather to stiff, plastic soils. Few ponds and springs are found in the area, and potable groundwater is difficult to find.

The Southern Red Hills proper are characterized by cuestalike ridges with steep, serrate north slopes and gentle back slopes. The Buhrstone Hills subdistrict along the southern edge of the Southern Red Hills proper is characterized by rugged terrain of resistant claystone and sandstone. The greatest topographic relief in the Coastal Plain occurs in the Buhrstone Hills, where ridges rise 300 to 400 feet above stream valleys. Streams in this area acquire such upland characteristics as high gradients, hard-rock bottoms, and swifter flows.

The Tombigbee and Alabama rivers traverse the Southern Red Hills in the west, while a significant portion of the Conecuh, Pea, and Choctawhatchee rivers drain the district in the east. Three species with interesting distributions in this district are the southern studfish, burrhead shiner, and rainbow shiner. They are most common in upland habitats above the Fall Line in the Mobile basin, but sizable populations are also found in the Buhrstone Hills and Southern Red Hills.

The rugged Lime Hills occur over resistant limestones in Choctaw, Clarke, Monroe, and Conecuh counties. The Hatchetigbee dome subdistrict is in the southern end of the Lime Hills and is a geologic feature exposing the Tallahata Buhrstone. Interesting habitats develop where streams cut through alluvial sediments down to limestone, resulting in streambeds with upland characteristics like those seen in the Buhrstone Hills. These habitats support populations of some species, such as the banded sculpin and Alabama shiner, that are known most commonly above the Fall Line. Mineral springs occur in the Hatchetigbee area, and some, with salt domes near the surface, are quite briny. With respect to the distribution of fish species in the Coastal Plain, the southern edge of the Lime Hills where they meet the Southern Pine Hills represents a significant barrier to distribution.

The Dougherty Plain, or wiregrass region, extends from the southeast corner of the state west to Conecuh County, where it forms the eastern edge of the Lime Hills. It is an extension of a Georgia upland composed of limestone, sand, and clay. Active solution of the underlying limestone produces many shallow, flat-bottomed depressions that dot the landscape. Small headwater streams are noticeably absent from the Dougherty Plain because active solution transfers many of the drainages to underground channels. The name *wiregrass* refers to the needlerush that commonly grows in the area's wet, shallow depressions. In Alabama the only species known to occur exclusively in the Dougherty Plain is the bluefin killifish. The redeye chub favors spring-influenced habitats in both the Dougherty Plain and Southern Red Hills.

The Southern Pine Hills district in southwest Alabama has low-relief topography with broad, rounded ridges and V-shaped valleys of sand and clay sediments. Unlike the Dougherty Plain, this region is not subject to solution and the boundary between the two districts is sometimes a distinct escarpment. Flat uplands with shallow ponds, bogs, and marshes occur throughout the district, and many of the saucerlike valleys are perpetually wetted by seepage from nearby hills. The abundance of warm summer rains is a major factor in leaching fertility from the soil and favoring the growth of pines in this region. Streams are well sustained by groundwater flows in summer. These streams, and especially those streams originating in the Pine Hills proper, are called blackwater creeks because the dissolved organic matter suspended in the water makes it appear tea-colored.

Major streams draining the Southern Pine Hills include the Conecuh and Perdido rivers, the lower reaches of the Tombigbee and Alabama rivers, the Mobile Delta, and the Escatawpa River. The Mobile Delta is about 40 miles long and from 5 to 10 miles wide. It is a large, mature, forested wetland that is tidally influenced during low river flows and is transected by numerous small stream channels connecting the larger rivers. The mature swamp habitat prevalent in the upper delta changes to an emergent type of wetland near the head of Mobile Bay. Many species representing several families of fishes appear to be distributed exclusively in the Southern Pine Hills district. Examples include the bluespotted sunfish, banded sunfish, banded topminnow, golden topminnow, rainwater killifish, least killifish, flagfin shiner, coastal shiner, and brighteye darter.

Between the Southern Pine Hills and the Gulf of Mexico lie the narrow Coastal Lowlands (generally less than 5 miles wide), consisting of ancient sea level terraces, dunes, beaches, and barrier islands. The region contains extensive salt and brackish marshes bordering inland bays and estuaries; here fresh water merges into the tidal zone, which supports many largely marine fish species that use such marshlands as nursery areas.

In sum, Alabama's five major physiographic regions and their varying subdivisions provide a wide range of aquatic habitats, from estuaries to tiny springs, and from wide, sluggish rivers to whitewater gorges. Such diversity of habitats is a key reason for the state's rich fish fauna.

DATA COLLECTION AND ANALYSIS

The data base for this book comprises information from 9,244 samples collected at 3,716 stations in Alabama, Georgia, Mississippi, and Tennessee from 1845 to 1994. Though few in number when compared to later collections, the earliest records provide important information on species no longer inhabiting the Tennessee River drainage (including the extinct harelip sucker and whiteline topminnow and the extirpated lake sturgeon, shovelnose sturgeon, spotfin chub, and ashy darter). About 36 percent of the samples were collected by the authors from 1980 to 1994, and many others were contributed by colleagues at the University of Alabama (2,049 samples collected from 1948 to 1983), Tulane University (1,513 samples from 1938 to 1994), and Auburn University (815 samples from 1938 to 1984).

CHRONOLOGY FOR 9,244 SAMPLES COLLECTED AT 3,716 STATIONS, 1845-1994

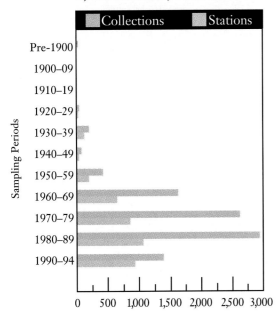

Our sampling efforts for this book were designed to accomplish four goals: to collect new information from incompletely surveyed areas (especially riverine habitats); to verify the existence of species with marginal occurrence in Alabama; to confirm the presence of species last reported in state waters several decades ago; and to collect and photograph representative individuals of each species in the state. Surveys in remote areas of several drainages were rewarding, occasionally yielding as many as 40 or more species, with some samples producing new state or drainage records.

The development of safe, reliable backpack and boat electrofishing gear has enhanced sampling in small streams and large rivers in the last 20 years. Backpack electrofishing units are fitted with handheld electrodes and powered by either a rechargeable battery or a small gasoline-powered motor. Boat electrofishing units are usually equipped with a gasoline-powered generator and electrodes mounted on long booms projecting forward from the boat's bow. Control boxes on backpack and boat units are capable of producing AC or DC current, although DC current is safer when properly regulated.

Sampling duration at a particular station was influenced by habitat diversity, stream size, and sampling method. It takes about 45 to 90 minutes to collect a sample in small to medium-sized streams. Obtaining an objective sample in large streams and rivers requires two to four hours of intense sampling with two or three types of gear. Repeated sampling, particularly during months of low streamflow, yields the most complete data for both streams and rivers.

The type of sampling gear used is determined by sampling environment (river, reservoir, small stream),

stream conditions (stream width and depth, streamflow, and substrate type), and project needs. Small streams can be sampled with bottom-weighted nylon seines. Large streams, rivers, and reservoirs generally require both nets and boat electrofishing gear to obtain a representative sample. Seining works well on shallow gravel bars, especially at night. Large-mesh gill nets and trammel nets are effective for collecting open-water species that are more active at night.

In recent years, ichthyologists have adopted an increasingly conservation-oriented attitude toward collecting fish, identifying them, and then returning them to their natural environment. Unless it is absolutely necessary to keep them, individual fishes are identified to species, tabulated, and released unharmed. Visual surveys, using either snorkels or scuba gear, have proven reliable for observing the habits and habitats of threatened and endangered species under optimum, clear water conditions. Nevertheless, certain circumstances still warrant that entire collections or voucher specimens of non-

endangered species be retained for scientific study. Such samples are preserved in 10 percent formalin, created by adding one part 37 percent formaldehyde to nine parts of water. Accurate records are essential, and field data sheets like the one reproduced below are invaluable aids for recording details about the sample and sampling location. The field sheet is then stored with the preserved sample.

Distribution maps in the species accounts were produced with Intergraph geographic information software. All collection data (locality, date and time, ecological observations, species' names and numbers, and so on) were stored on a personal computer for later analysis. Individual sample locations were initially plotted on county highway maps and later transferred into digitized map files. Intergraph software was used to create individual layers of digitized map information (the stream base and separate outlines for the United States, Alabama, and Alabama's physiographic districts). The dots representing species distributions were produced by linking PC output files to the digitized map files.

GEOLOGICAL SURVEY OF ALABAMA ICTHYOLOGICAL SURVEY DATA SHEET

Survey_____ Field No._____ Accession No._____

Drainage System_____ Station No. _____

Locality_____

Township_____ Range_____ Section_____ Date_____

County_____ Quadrangle_____

State_____ Elevation_____

Water Color_____ Width_____

Flow_____ Depth_____

Bottom_____ Shore_____

Stream order_____ Physio district_____

Vegetation _____

Weather _____

Temperature: Air_____ Water_____ Time_____

Capture method_____ Capture depth_____

Notes _____

Original fixative_____

Collected by_____ Identified by_____

Species collected_____ Specimens collected_____

LOWER TOMBIGBEE RIVER, CHOCTAW COUNTY

Environmental studies frequently include water-quality and biological monitoring to assess the impact of commercial or industrial development. Recently collected information should be reliable, whereas older data may require review and additional sampling. In analyzing data for this book, we found that information on several river systems in Alabama is becoming dated. Only 37 percent of all stations have been sampled at least once since 1985, and new sampling efforts are needed in the Black Warrior, Tombigbee, Blackwater, Chattahoochee, Coosa, Escatawpa, and Yellow river systems.

We also analyzed species collection data to determine the collection of stations for each species (also at the bottom of each distribution map) and the number of stations sampled since 1985 (noted in the drainage checklist beginning on page 28). These data reveal that, despite intensive sampling efforts, we know little about the distribution and occurrence of many species. Because populations are dynamic, moving in response to daily life rhythms and environmental extremes and pollution stresses, samples from 50 or even 10 years ago are often inadequate for assessing population status today.

DATES OF LAST COLLECTION FOR 3,716 STATIONS			
Drainage Areas/River Systems	**Stations Sampled (%)**		**Total Stations**
	Pre-1985	**1985-94**	
TENNESSEE RIVER			
	380 (61)	248 (39)	628
MOBILE BASIN			
Mobile Delta[1]	25 (21)	97 (79)	122
Lower Tombigbee	155 (70)	65 (30)	220
Upper Tombigbee	352 (93)	26 (7)	378
Black Warrior	272 (64)	153 (36)	425
Alabama	149 (47)	171 (53)	320
Cahaba	98 (55)	81 (45)	179
Coosa	461 (70)	199 (30)	660
Tallapoosa	192 (60)	126 (40)	318
COASTAL DRAINAGES			
Escatawpa	34 (97)	1 (3)	35
Perdido	6 (19)	26 (81)	32
Conecuh	25 (22)	88 (78)	113
Blackwater	6 (86)	1 (14)	7
Yellow	20 (91)	2 (9)	22
Choctawhatchee	59 (60)	40 (40)	99
Chattahoochee	114 (72)	44 (28)	158
GRAND TOTAL	2,348 (63)	1,368 (37)	3,716

1— Includes major freshwater tributaries to the eastern and western sides of Mobile Bay.

FISH DISTRIBUTIONS

The freshwater rivers in Alabama and the Mobile basin tributaries in adjacent states are inhabited by 404 species of fishes—more than in most other states or provinces in North America. Alabama's freshwater fish fauna includes 306 native species (described and undescribed) and 13 non-native species. New collections supplemented with information provided by Boschung (1992), Shipp (1986), Swingle (1971), and Swingle and Bland (1974) document at least 85 marine and estuarine species in the Mobile Delta and freshwater tributaries of Mobile Bay. Tennessee's 302 to 319 freshwater species currently outnumber Alabama's (Etnier and Starnes, 1993), but Tennessee's marine fauna is limited to the Atlantic needlefish, an apparent transient into the Tennessee River through the Tennessee-Tombigbee Waterway. Totals in some other southern states are 215 species in Arkansas (Robison and Buchanan, 1988); 242 species in Kentucky (Burr and Warren, 1986); 210 species in Virginia (Jenkins and Burkhead, 1993); and 148 species in Louisiana (Douglas, 1974).

In terms of the diversity of southeastern fishes, Alabama's importance is evidenced by the fact that 61 species in the study area are endemic—that is, each of these species' range is limited to a particular spring or stream, river system, or basin. The Mobile basin has 41 endemic species. Of the 35 endemic species that Etnier and Starnes (1986) recognize in the Tennessee River drainage, 14 occur in Alabama.

Seventy-three of the described species discussed in the accounts that follow (or 24 percent) have type localities in the study area—more than in any other area of similar size in North America. (A type locality is the place where specimens were taken for the original scientific description.) At least four species—the Alabama shad,

whiteline topminnow, ashy darter, and boulder darter—have apparently disappeared from their type localities. The anadromous Alabama shad still makes annual spawning runs upstream into the Choctawhatchee and Conecuh rivers. Collections of single individuals below the Claiborne and Millers Ferry locks and dams in 1994–95 provide some hope that limited numbers still enter the Alabama River and lower Mobile basin. The whiteline topminnow is presumed to be extinct. The ashy darter may have been extirpated from Cypress Creek in Lauderdale County, but populations remain in the Tennessee and Cumberland river drainages (Etnier and Starnes, 1993). Future sampling may rediscover the boulder darter at Shoal Creek in Lauderdale County; a population persists in the Elk River near the Alabama-Tennessee border in Limestone County.

Because fishes live underwater and are rarely seen, most people are unaware of the large number of species that occur in Alabama, or of the unique and sometimes restricted habitats they occupy. Many would likely name the sunfishes as the most diverse group of Alabama fishes, but that family accounts for only 21 species. The family Cyprinidae is actually the largest group, with over 90 species of minnows and carps. The family Percidae is second, with 78 species of darters, including the yellow perch, walleye, and sauger. The family Catostomidae is third, containing 23 species, including the commercially important carpsuckers, buffalo, and redhorses. Although the family Ictaluridae is represented by 19 species of catfishes, anglers are likely to encounter only nine of them; most of the remaining 10 species are madtoms that are less than 5 inches long and live in streams.

Many species survive in a broad spectrum of habitats, while others occur in specialized habitats that are

OTTER POND, CONECUH NATIONAL FOREST

well represented throughout the state; a few are restricted to highly specialized habitats, destruction of which may lead to the species' extinction. Large rivers and reservoirs support sizable populations of paddlefish, bowfin, gars, herrings and shad, carps, suckers, bullhead catfishes, sunfishes, and the freshwater drum. Many small to large streams not only contain flourishing populations of minnows, madtoms, topminnows, livebearers, smaller sunfishes, and darters, but are also spawning sites for lampreys, suckers, catfishes, and sunfishes. Swamps and oxbow lakes are often home to gars, bowfin, carps, suckers, catfishes, and sunfishes. They serve as important refuges for riverine fishes during floods.

Springs and caves offer specialized habitats for some of Alabama's most restricted and least understood fish species. The Alabama cavefish is one of the rarest species in the Northern Hemisphere, and its habitat is protected by the Tennessee Valley Authority. The southern cavefish, on the other hand, is widely distributed in cave environments throughout the Appalachian Mountains and occurs at 47 locations in Alabama. The only known location for the spring pygmy sculpin—Coldwater Spring in Calhoun County—is protected by the city of Anniston as a public water supply. The spring pygmy sunfish inhabits only two spring systems in north Alabama; indeed, from 1937 to 1973, this species was believed to be extinct. Many other examples of habitat-restricted species are discussed in the species accounts.

DISTRIBUTION BY DRAINAGE

The 16 river systems draining Alabama and parts of adjacent states are divisible into three major drainage groups. The Tennessee River drainage flows across northern Alabama, draining 6,826 mi^2 (or 13 percent) of the state's approximately 51,000 mi^2 of surface area. The Mobile basin encompasses 43,683 mi^2 and contains eight major river systems, the Mobile Delta, and small freshwater tributaries to Mobile Bay; it drains 32,207 mi^2 in Alabama and 11,476 mi^2 in Georgia, Mississippi, and Tennessee. The coastal group contains seven small rivers that drain 12,073 mi^2 across south Alabama before entering Florida or Mississippi.

The Alabama portion of the Tennessee River drainage is represented by 176 species, of which the harelip sucker and whiteline topminnow are presumed to be extinct. The single record of the harelip sucker is from an 1884 sample collected in Cypress Creek, near Florence in Lauderdale County (Gilbert, 1891). The whiteline topminnow was described in 1889 based on specimens collected at Spring Creek (Gilbert, 1891), a small stream draining the Huntsville area and Redstone Arsenal in Madison County. Of the 14 endemic species known to occur in the Tennessee River drainage, we collected 10: the spring pygmy sunfish, blenny darter, slackwater darter, crown darter, black darter, blueside darter, lollipop darter, blackfin darter, Tuscumbia darter, and boulder darter. Endemic species not collected are the Alabama cavefish, snail darter, spotfin chub (possibly extirpated), and whiteline topminnow (extinct).

For all its natural diversity, the Tennessee River drainage has received only limited study in recent years, and therefore the distributions of many species (including some reaching southern range limits) are based on samples collected 50 or 60 years ago. Our goals were to verify the continued existence of as many species as possible and, using modern sampling equipment, to expand our knowledge of their ranges. Over 300 samples collected in the drainage from 1991 through 1994 provided a great deal of new information, including the first state records of the mountain madtom and bluebreast darter in the Elk River system.

The occurrence and distributions of 29 poorly known species in the Tennessee River drainage were confirmed, and in many cases, their distributions in Alabama were expanded. These include the Ohio lamprey, chestnut lamprey, mooneye, American eel, streamline chub, blotched chub, speckled chub, palezone shiner, ribbon shiner, channel shiner, "sawfin shiner," suckermouth minnow, stargazing minnow, river carpsucker, quillback, highfin carpsucker, blue sucker, bigmouth buffalo, black buffalo, silver redhorse, river redhorse, shorthead redhorse, stonecat, brindled madtom, fringed darter, gilt darter, and slenderhead darter. Species whose continued existence could not be confirmed include the lake sturgeon, shovelnose sturgeon, shortnose gar, goldeye, spotfin chub, popeye shiner, silver shiner, elegant madtom, ashy darter, and snail darter.

The Mobile basin is inhabited by one of the richest fish faunas in North America, numbering 236 species. Robison (1986) estimated that the Mississippi basin contained 260 species, but its drainage area—1,243,600 mi^2—is nearly 28 times larger than the 43,683 mi^2 for the Mobile basin. Two other southeastern systems recognized for their faunal richness are the Tennessee River (which drains approximately 40,550 mi^2 in Alabama, Kentucky, Mississippi, Tennessee, and Virginia, and contains from 225 to 240 species) and the Cumberland River (which drains approximately 18,000 mi^2 in Kentucky and Tennessee, and contains from 172 to 186 species) (Burr and Warren, 1986; Etnier and Starnes, 1986, 1993).

The number of species contained in any one of the eight major rivers that form the Mobile basin ranges from 123 species in the upper Tombigbee River system to 147 species in the Coosa River system. Collection records of the slough darter are limited to two localities in Mississippi; the yellowfin shiner, brook trout, Etowah darter, Cherokee darter, amber darter, and Conasauga logperch are restricted to the upper Coosa River system in Georgia. The trispot darter was originally described from a single specimen collected at Cowens Creek. This small Cherokee County stream was eliminated by completion of Weiss reservoir in 1960, but populations of the trispot darter still exist in Georgia.

The Mobile Delta and freshwater tributaries to Mobile Bay contain 131 species, 30 of which are marine. Many marine species are confined to estuarine areas of coastal Alabama for much of the year, but individuals of some species make occasional forays into fresh water, particularly during late summer as flow from the Mobile and Tensaw rivers diminishes and a saltwater wedge formed by tidal influence moves slowly upstream.

At least six of the seven marine species collected 100 or more miles inland in Alabama may exist as naturally reproducing freshwater populations. The Atlantic needlefish occurs farther inland in Alabama than any other marine species. Freshwater spawning is evidenced by our collections of small individuals measuring 1 to 3 inches in the Alabama River above Claiborne Lock and Dam and in the Black Warrior and upper Tombigbee rivers above Demopolis Lock and Dam. Striped mullet are abundant in the Alabama and lower Tombigbee rivers and less common in the Black Warrior and upper Tombigbee rivers. But they apparently do not spawn in fresh water. Mettee et al. (1989) established a new inland record for the bay anchovy, collecting 99 specimens in the Black Warrior River below Armisted I. Selden Dam—270 river miles upstream of Mobile Bay. Collections of the rainwater killifish and least killifish (two small, short-lived species reaching adult sizes of only 1 to 2 inches) in the Alabama and lower Tombigbee rivers document progressive upstream movement and reproduction in freshwater environments. Populations of the southern flounder and hogchoker exist inland to the tailwaters of Claiborne Lock and Dam on the Alabama River and Coffeeville Lock and Dam on the lower Tombigbee River. Collections of large numbers of small hogchokers, even upstream of Claiborne Lock and Dam, suggest spawning in both river systems.

The seven coastal river systems in south Alabama are inhabited by 137 species. Only 21 species are known from the headwaters of the Blackwater River system (148 mi^2), but future sampling could add several species. The fish fauna of the Conecuh River system was incompletely known until recently. Bailey et al. (1954) reported 57 species in Alabama, and later sampling added another five to 10 species. Our collection of 101 samples at 88 stations from 1990 through 1994 increased the state total to 95 species. Similar efforts may supplement the list of 92 known species in the Chattahoochee River system.

In Alabama, coastal drainages provide important habitats for several species that are absent or have limited distributions elsewhere in the state. The brighteye darter occurs at only two locations, both of which are in the Escatawpa River system. Similarly, the banded sunfish is limited to the Perdido River system in Baldwin County. The largest remaining populations of anadromous Gulf sturgeon and Alabama shad occur seasonally in the Choctawhatchee River system in Geneva County. Recent records of these species also exist from the Conecuh

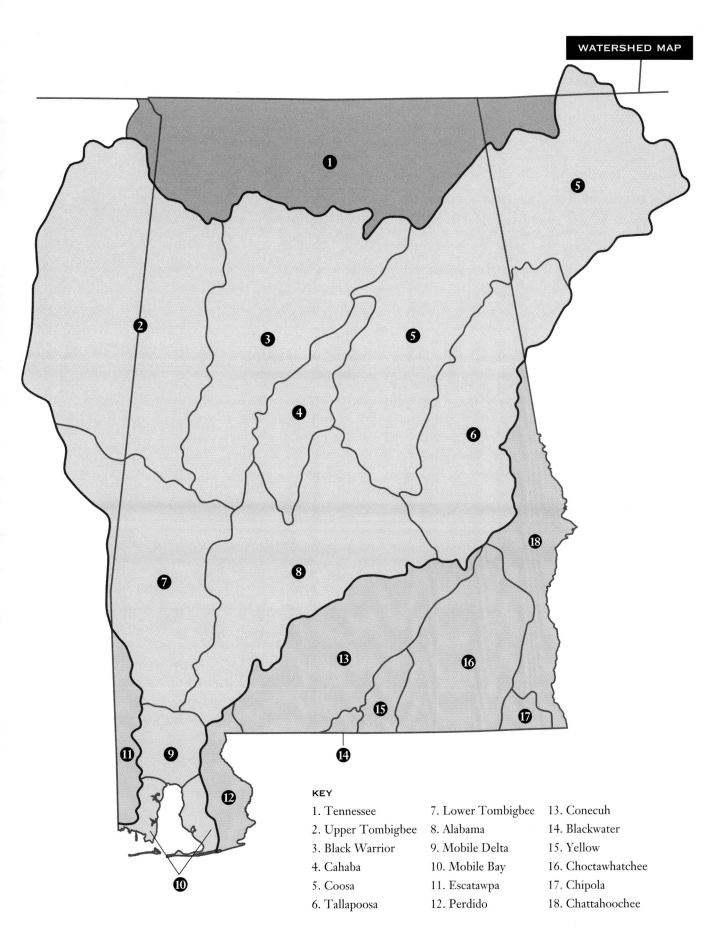

KEY

1. Tennessee
2. Upper Tombigbee
3. Black Warrior
4. Cahaba
5. Coosa
6. Tallapoosa
7. Lower Tombigbee
8. Alabama
9. Mobile Delta
10. Mobile Bay
11. Escatawpa
12. Perdido
13. Conecuh
14. Blackwater
15. Yellow
16. Choctawhatchee
17. Chipola
18. Chattahoochee

River system, Mobile Delta, and Alabama River drainage. Populations of the bluefin stoneroller, bluestripe shiner, broadstripe shiner, greater jumprock, "grayfin redhorse," and "shoal bass" are limited to the Chattahoochee River system.

DISTRIBUTION ACROSS DRAINAGES

Species have crossed drainage divides at several locations in Alabama. The largest and perhaps most intriguing area lies in northwestern Alabama and involves species migration from the upper Tombigbee River system into the Tennessee River drainage and the Black Warrior River system. New collection data, supplemented with information in Wall (1968) and Boschung (1992), document populations of 11 upper Tombigbee species in headwater tributaries of Bear Creek: the pretty shiner, bluehead chub, striped shiner, silverstripe shiner, weed shiner, blacktail shiner, Dixie chub, black madtom, tadpole madtom, harlequin darter, and speckled darter. Similarly, isolated populations of 17 upper Tombigbee species are distributed in tributaries of the Sipsey Fork and the Black Warrior River proper, below the junction of Mulberry and Locust forks: the pretty shiner, clear chub, striped shiner, bluehead chub, orangefin shiner, rough shiner, mimic shiner, Dixie chub, Alabama hog sucker, golden redhorse, speckled madtom, pirate perch, shadow bass, goldstripe darter, rock darter, dusky darter, and river darter.

Previous studies propose various theories to explain species relationships among these three systems. Wall (1968) and Etnier and Starnes (1986) suggest stream piracy. Smith-Vaniz (1968) speculates that Little Bear Creek previously existed as an upper Tombigbee River tributary and was subsequently captured by Bear Creek. Swift et al. (1986) discuss sea level fluctuations and their effects on drainage configurations and species distribution patterns. Judging from the distribution of Coastal Plain sediments as mapped by Osborne et al. (1989), we suspect fish species may have moved between Bear Creek and tributaries of the Black Warrior and upper Tombigbee rivers when broad areas in northwestern Alabama were inundated by lower-salinity, interglacial seas. Afterward, when the polar ice caps refroze, the sea levels

LONGNOSE GAR

declined, and the surface eroded, some populations became isolated across today's drainage divides, where they still exist in limited numbers.

Species occurrence across an area from the Sipsey Fork to the Coosa River system in northern Alabama indicates more faunal exchange between the Mobile basin and Tennessee River and intrabasin exchange among the Black Warrior, Cahaba, and Coosa river systems. Six Tennessee River species have entered the Mobile basin: The rosyfin shiner, steelcolor shiner, blacknose dace, and black redhorse occur at one or more stations at Sipsey, Mulberry, and Locust forks, and the flame chub and blacknose dace are found in the Coosa River system. In a region extending from Turkey Creek to Blackburn Fork of the Locust Fork, the consistent appearance of six species— the rainbow shiner, tricolor shiner, Alabama hog sucker, black redhorse, rock darter, and speckled darter—would seem to suggest a past connection among the Black Warrior, Cahaba, and Coosa river systems. A single Mobile basin species, the rainbow shiner, is known from two Tennessee River tributaries in Marshall and Dekalb counties.

The Mobile basin has contributed species to two of Alabama's seven coastal drainages. In Alabama tributaries of the Chattahoochee River system, we collected five species that commonly occur in the Tal-

lapoosa River system: the Tallapoosa shiner, striped shiner, bluehead chub, rough shiner, and redfin darter. The possibility of past connections between upper Chattahoochee River tributaries and the Coosa River system is suggested by populations of an undescribed chub, longnose shiner, bandfin shiner, and snail bullhead in the Etowah River system in Georgia.

The Alabama and Conecuh river systems have exchanged species across several areas in southern Alabama. A probable connection or connections in southern Monroe and Conecuh counties allowed the largescale stoneroller, striped shiner, bluehead chub, and rough shiner to enter the Escambia Creek system. This connection may also have assisted the river redhorse, crystal darter, and harlequin darter in reaching the Conecuh River proper, where populations currently exist. At about the same time, the Everglades pygmy sunfish may have entered seepage headwater areas of several Alabama River tributaries, although it is now limited to Wallers Creek in Monroe County. The bluntnose minnow's occurrence in the Conecuh River system implies a connection between Pine Barren and Cedar creeks (Alabama River system) and Persimmon Creek (Conecuh River system) in northern Butler County. However, the origin of two widely scattered populations of the cypress minnow in the Conecuh River system cannot be explained. A single population of the blacktip shiner in

the Mobile basin resulted when a small Conecuh River tributary in Bullock County was diverted into Town Creek, a southern tributary to the Tallapoosa River.

EFFECTS OF URBANIZATION

At least two dozen species are conspicuously absent in lower reaches of the Mulberry and Locust fork tributaries of the Black Warrior River system. During the last century the area has seen extensive industrial and urban development, much of it in the days before environmental regulations. One outcome may be the elimination of fish species that still inhabit surrounding headwater tributaries. These species include the Alabama shiner, striped shiner, burrhead shiner, Alabama hog sucker, Warrior darter, vermilion darter, Tuskaloosa darter, watercress darter, coal darter, blackside darter, blackbanded darter, and "Mobile logperch." Additional surveys are needed to determine if these species are present in the area.

SPECIES DATA BY COUNTY

The complete listing of fish species in the Appendix of the book is intended to assist planners, resource managers, and consultants in preparing local and regional impact statements involving aquatic habitats in Alabama's 67 counties.

An analysis of our data files revealed that Baldwin County is inhabited by 142 species—the largest number reported for any of the 105 counties included in the study area. With few exceptions, 109 are freshwater species that principally inhabit rivers and streams. The remaining 33 species are usually found in marine or estuarine waters but occasionally, individuals intrude into freshwater environments.

Because of its excellent water quality and a diversity of aquatic habits, Lauderdale County supports the most diverse freshwater fish fauna in the study area, numbering 138 species plus the Atlantic needlefish. The fact that only 34 species have been recorded from Dekalb County is largely due to the fact that much of the county is occupied by upland areas of Sand and Lookout mountains.

State	County	Species	County	Species	County	Species
Alabama	Autauga	94	Dallas	117	Marion	72
	Baldwin	142	Dekalb	34	Marshall	92
	Barbour	59	Elmore	121	Mobile	120
	Bibb	115	Escambia	92	Monroe	127
	Blount	59	Etowah	65	Montgomery	102
	Bullock	52	Fayette	65	Morgan	87
	Butler	53	Franklin	98	Perry	123
	Calhoun	70	Geneva	73	Pickens	105
	Chambers	60	Greene	111	Pike	46
	Cherokee	67	Hale	93	Randolph	73
	Chilton	86	Henry	61	Russell	72
	Choctaw	108	Houston	78	St. Clair	82
	Clarke	131	Jackson	101	Shelby	87
	Clay	58	Jefferson	86	Sumter	115
	Cleburne	59	Lamar	77	Talladega	86
	Coffee	39	Lauderdale	139	Tallapoosa	92
	Colbert	104	Lawerence	100	Tuscaloosa	119
	Conecuh	47	Lee	106	Walker	62
	Coosa	81	Limestone	123	Washington	108
	Covington	66	Lowndes	80	Wilcox	128
	Crenshaw	56	Macon	96	Winston	77
	Cullman	47	Madison	99		
	Dale	56	Marengo	98		
Georgia	Bartow	62	Floyd	43	Muarry	80
	Carroll (P)	47	Forsyth (P)	8	Paulding (P)	31
	Chattooga	46	Gilmer	37	Pickens	42
	Cherokee	55	Gordon	67	Polk	27
	Cobb (P)	16	Haralson	46	Walker (P)	41
	Dawson	43	Lumpkin (P)	27	Whitfield (P)	65
	Fannin	3				
Mississippi	Chickasaw (P)	26	Lee	30	Pontotoc (P)	10
	Choctaw (P)	26	Lowndes	105	Tishomingo (P)	56
	Clay	79	Monroe	101	Union (P)	16
	Itawamba	91	Noxubee	97	Webster (P)	7
	Kemper	28	Oktibbeha	60	Winston (P)	55
	Lauderdale	35	Prentiss (P)	45		
Tennessee	Bradley (P)	65	Polk (P)	52		

Total fish species per county, based on 9,244 samples collected at 3,716 stations in Alabama, Georgia, Mississippi, and Tennessee from 1845 through 1994 (P) = partially drained county.

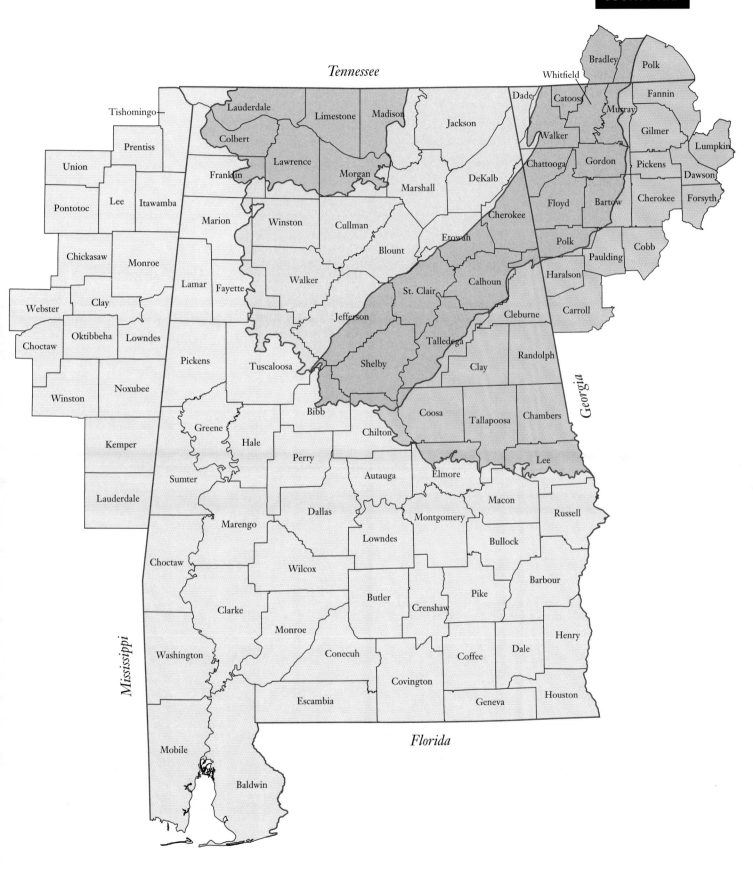

Tennessee

Florida

Mississippi

Georgia

Tishomingo
Prentiss
Union
Lee
Itawamba
Pontotoc
Chickasaw
Monroe
Webster
Clay
Choctaw
Oktibbeha
Lowndes
Winston
Noxubee
Kemper
Lauderdale

Lauderdale
Colbert
Franklin
Marion
Lamar
Fayette
Walker
Tuscaloosa
Pickens
Greene
Hale
Sumter
Marengo
Choctaw
Clarke
Washington
Mobile
Baldwin

Lawrence
Limestone
Madison
Morgan
Winston
Cullman
Blount
Jefferson
Shelby
Bibb
Perry
Dallas
Wilcox
Monroe
Conecuh
Escambia

Jackson
Marshall
DeKalb
Cherokee
Etowah
St. Clair
Calhoun
Chilton
Coosa
Autauga
Elmore
Lowndes
Butler
Crenshaw
Covington

Dade
Whitfield
Catoosa
Walker
Chattooga
Floyd
Polk
Haralson
Cleburne
Talladega
Clay
Tallapoosa
Chambers
Lee
Macon
Montgomery
Bullock
Pike
Coffee
Geneva

Bradley
Polk
Fannin
Murray
Gilmer
Lumpkin
Gordon
Pickens
Dawson
Bartow
Cherokee
Forsyth
Paulding
Cobb
Carroll
Randolph
Russell
Barbour
Dale
Henry
Houston

SPECIES BY DRAINAGE GROUP AND RIVER SYSTEMS

Unless preceded by an asterisk, each species is described in an account in the appropriate family chapter.
For species followed by note numbers, see notes on page 39.

| | DRAINAGE GROUP AND RIVER SYSTEMS | | | | | | | | | | | | | | | | STATIONS | |
| | MOBILE BASIN | | | | | | | | | COASTAL RIVERS (WEST TO EAST) | | | | | | | 1985–1994 | TOTAL |
	TR	MD	LT	UT	BW	AL	CA	CO	TA	ES	PE	CN	BL	YE	CH	CT	(% of total)	
PETROMYZONTIDAE LAMPREYS																		
Ichthyomyzon bdellium, Ohio lamprey	N																8 (62)	13
I. castaneus, chestnut lamprey		N	N	N	N	N	N										27 (47)	58
I. gagei, southern brook lamprey	N	N	N	N	N	N	N	N	N	N	N	N	N		N	N	97 (46)	212
I. greeleyi, mountain brook lamprey	N																2 (100)	2
Lampetra aepyptera, least brook lamprey	N	N	N	N	N	N	N	N	N			N					37 (25)	147
L. appendix, American brook lamprey	N																2 (50)	4
CARCHARHINIDAE REQUIEM SHARKS																		
*Carcharhinus leucas, bull shark		M															1 (50)	2
DASYATIDAE STINGRAYS																		
*Dasyatis sabina, Atlantic stingray		M															1 (100)	1
ACIPENSERIDAE STURGEONS																		
Acipenser fulvescens, lake sturgeon	N							N									0 (0)	5
A. oxyrinchus desotoi, gulf sturgeon		N					N	N			N		N				7 (70)	10
Scaphirhynchus platorynchus, shovelnose sturgeon	N																0 (0)	2
S. suttkusi, Alabama sturgeon (MBE)				N	N	N	N										3 (15)	20
POLYODONTIDAE PADDLEFISH																		
Polyodon spathula, paddlefish	N	N	N	N	N	N	N	N	N								37 (59)	63
LEPISOSTEIDAE GARS																		
Lepisosteus oculatus, spotted gar	N	N	N	N	N	N	N	N	N	N	N	N			N	N	255 (74)	349
L. osseus, longnose gar	N	N	N	N	N	N	N	N	N		N	N			N	N	150 (54)	278
L. platostomus, shortnose gar	N																1 (33)	3
L. spatula, alligator gar		N						N				N					8 (67)	12
AMIIDAE BOWFIN																		
Amia calva, bowfin	N	N	N	N	N	N	N	N	N			N					105 (60)	174
HIODONTIDAE MOONEYES																		
Hiodon alosoides, goldeye	N																0 (0)	4
H. tergisus, mooneye	N	N	N	N	N	N	N	N									22 (32)	69

TR MD LT UT BW AL CA CO TA   ES PE CN BL YE CH CT

ABE—Apalachicola basin endemic
AL—Alabama River
BL—Blackwater River
BW—Black Warrior River
CA—Cahaba River
CH—Choctawhatchee River
CN—Conecuh River
CO—Coosa River
CT—Chattahoochee River
ES—Escatawpa River
EX—extinct
I—introduced freshwater or marine species
LT—Lower Tombigbee River
M—native marine species
MBE—Mobile basin endemic
MD—Mobile Delta, Mobile Bay tributaries
N—native freshwater species
PE—Perdido River
TA—Tallapoosa River
TR—Tennessee River
TDE—Tennessee drainage endemic
UT—Upper Tombigbee River
YE—Yellow River

DRAINAGE GROUP AND RIVER SYSTEMS — STATIONS

MOBILE BASIN									COASTAL RIVERS (WEST TO EAST)							1985–1994	TOTAL
TR	MD	LT	UT	BW	AL	CA	CO	TA	ES	PE	CN	BL	YE	CH	CT	(% of total)	
ELOPIDAE — TARPONS																	
Elops saurus, ladyfish	M															5 (100)	5
ANGUILLIDAE — FRESHWATER EEL																	
Anguilla rostrata, American eel — N	N	N	N	N	N	N	N	N		N	N			N	N	111 (50)	186
OPHICHTHYIDAE — SNAKE EELS																	
Myrophis punctatus, speckled worm eel	M															1 (20)	5
CLUPEIDAE — HERRINGS																	
Alosa alabamae, Alabama shad		N	N		N	N	N				N			N		13 (25)	53
A. chrysochloris, skipjack herring — N	N	N	N	N	N	N	N	N			N			N	N	113 (65)	174
Brevoortia patronus, gulf menhaden	M	M														17 (71)	24
Dorosoma cepedianum, gizzard shad — N	N	N	N	N	N	N	N	N			N			N	N	320 (56)	574
D. petenense, threadfin shad — N	N	N	N	N	N	N	N	N	N		N			N	N	220 (63)	349
ENGRAULIDAE — ANCHOVIES																	
Anchoa mitchilli, bay anchovy	M	M		M	M											23 (59)	39
CYPRINIDAE — CARPS AND MINNOWS																	
Campostoma oligolepis, largescale stoneroller — N		N	N	N	N	N	N	N			N					474 (33)	1443
C. pauciradii, bluefin stoneroller (ABE)															N	5 (9)	53
Carassius auratus, goldfish — I					I	I	I				I					1 (8)	12
Clinostomus funduloides, rosyside dace — N																34 (42)	81
Ctenopharyngodon idella, grass carp — I	I	I	I	I		I	I	I		I				I	I	42 (91)	46
Cyprinella caerulea, blue shiner (MBE)						N	N									5 (12)	41
C. callistia, Alabama shiner (MBE)		N	N	N	N	N	N	N								202 (38)	538
C. callitaenia, bluestripe shiner (ABE)															N	2 (15)	13
C. galactura, whitetail shiner — N																15 (26)	57
C. gibbsi, Tallapoosa shiner								N							N	62 (40)	155
C. lutrensis, red shiner						I									I	2 (20)	10
C. monacha, spotfin chub (TDE) — N																0 (0)	2
C. spiloptera, spotfin shiner — N																74 (51)	144
C. trichroistia, tricolor shiner (MBE)		N	N	N	N											110 (33)	330
C. venusta, blacktail shiner	N	N	N	N	N	N	N	N	N	N	N		N	N	N	490 (34)	1444
C. whipplei, steelcolor shiner — N			N													30 (29)	102

TR MD LT UT BW AL CA CO TA ES PE CN BL YE CH CT

Column groups — **MOBILE BASIN:** TR, MD, LT, UT, BW, AL, CA, CO, TA · **COASTAL RIVERS (WEST TO EAST):** ES, PE, CN, BL, YE, CH, CT · **STATIONS 1985–1994 (% of total)** · **TOTAL**

CYPRINIDAE — CARPS AND MINNOWS

	TR	MD	LT	UT	BW	AL	CA	CO	TA	ES	PE	CN	BL	YE	CH	CT	(% of total)	TOTAL
Cyprinus carpio, common carp	I	I	I	I	I	I	I	I	I	I					I	I	212 (65)	325
Ericymba buccata, silverjaw minnow		N	N	N		N	N	N	N	N	N			N	N	N	203 (36)	562
Erimystax dissimilis, streamline chub	N																3 (100)	3
E. insignis, blotched chub	N																13 (100)	13
Hemitremia flammea, flame chub	N							N									35 (42)	84
Hybognathus hayi, cypress minnow	N		N	N	N	N	N	N	N			N					11 (13)	84
H. nuchalis, Mississippi silvery minnow	N		N	N	N	N	N	N	N								32 (12)	273
Hybopsis amblops, bigeye chub	N																28 (51)	55
H. lineapunctata, lined chub (MBE)								N	N								31 (21)	149
H. winchelli, clear chub			N	N	N	N	N	N	N	N							62 (27)	229
H. sp. cf. *winchelli*[1]								N			N	N		N	N	N	61 (43)	143
*Hypopthalmichthys molitrix, silver carp				I					I								1 (50)	2
*H. nobilis, bighead carp				I					I								1 (50)	2
Luxilus chrysocephalus, striped shiner	N	N	N	N	N	N	N	N	N			N				N	365 (30)	1221
L. coccogenis, warpaint shiner	N																3 (75)	4
L. zonistius, bandfin shiner						N	N									N	20 (23)	88
Lythrurus ardens, rosefin shiner	N			N													65 (36)	179
L. atrapiculus, blacktip shiner							N					N		N	N	N	58 (40)	145
L. bellus, pretty shiner	N	N	N	N	N	N	N	N	N								226 (25)	917
L. fumeus, ribbon shiner	N																1 (11)	9
L. lirus, mountain shiner						N	N										36 (31)	116
L. roseipinnis, cherryfin shiner		N	N		N					N							14 (26)	53
Macrhybopsis aestivalis, speckled chub	N																3 (100)	3
M. storeriana, silver chub	N	N	N	N	N	N	N	N	N								73 (36)	205
M. sp. cf. *aestivalis* (MBE)[2]		N	N	N		N	N	N	N								49 (33)	150
M. sp. cf. *aestivalis*[3]												N		N	N		14 (82)	17
Nocomis leptocephalus, bluehead chub	N		N	N	N	N	N	N	N			N				N	195 (30)	647
N. micropogon, river chub	N							N									11 (46)	24
Notemigonus crysoleucas, golden shiner	N	N	N	N	N	N	N	N	N	N	N	N		N	N	N	138 (23)	595
Notropis albizonatus, palezone shiner	N																4 (100)	4
N. ammophilus, orangefin shiner		N	N	N	N	N	N	N	N								174 (30)	574
N. ariommus, popeye shiner	N																0 (0)	1
N. asperifrons, burrhead shiner (MBE)					N	N	N	N	N								49 (26)	187
N. atherinoides, emerald shiner	N	N	N	N	N	N	N	N	N								152 (46)	329

TR MD LT UT BW AL CA CO TA   ES PE CN BL YE CH CT

ABE—Apalachicola basin endemic   CA—Cahaba River   CT—Chattahoochee River
AL—Alabama River   CH—Choctawhatchee River   ES—Escatawpa River
BL—Blackwater River   CN—Conecuh River   EX—extinct
BW—Black Warrior River   CO—Coosa River   I—introduced freshwater or marine species

CYPRINIDAE — CARPS AND MINNOWS	TR	MD	LT	UT	BW	AL	CA	CO	TA	ES	PE	CN	BL	YE	CH	CT	1985–1994 (% of total)	TOTAL
Notropis baileyi, rough shiner	N		N	N	N	N	N	N	N			N				N	186 (31)	597
N. boops, bigeye shiner	N																20 (63)	32
N. buchanani, ghost shiner	N																0 (0)	8
N. cahabae, Cahaba shiner (MBE)							N										7 (39)	18
N. candidus, silverside shiner (MBE)			N	N	N	N	N	N	N								97 (59)	164
N. chalybaeus, ironcolor shiner			N			N				N	N		N	N	N		1 (7)	14
N. chrosomus, rainbow shiner	N			N	N	N	N										38 (19)	202
N. cummingsae, dusky shiner																N	2 (12)	17
N. edwardraneyi, fluvial shiner (MBE)			N	N	N	N	N	N	N								57 (39)	147
N. harperi, redeye chub												N	N	N	N		11 (33)	33
N. hypsilepis, highscale shiner																N	3 (12)	26
N. leuciodus, Tennessee shiner	N																11 (92)	12
N. longirostris, longnose shiner			N				N		N	N	N		N	N	N		79 (42)	187
N. lutipinnis, yellowfin shiner							N										9 (50)	18
N. maculatus, taillight shiner			N	N	N	N				N					N	N	15 (41)	37
N. petersoni, coastal shiner			N			N				N	N					N	20 (71)	28
N. photogenis, silver shiner	N																0 (0)	1
N. rubellus, rosyface shiner	N																2 (17)	12
N. stilbius, silverstripe shiner	N		N	N	N	N	N	N	N								162 (30)	543
N. telescopus, telescope shiner	N																29 (69)	42
N. texanus, weed shiner	N	N	N	N	N	N	N	N	N	N	N	N		N	N	N	300 (34)	892
N. uranoscopus, skygazer shiner (MBE)						N	N	N									39 (54)	72
N. volucellus, mimic shiner	N																10 (50)	20
N. wickliffi, channel shiner	N																3 (100)	3
N. xaenocephalus, Coosa shiner (MBE)							N	N									96 (30)	321
N. sp. cf. *volucellus* (MBE)[4]			N	N	N	N	N	N	N								74 (27)	270
N. species, "sawfin shiner"[5]	N																14 (100)	14
Opsopoeodus emiliae, pugnose minnow	N	N	N	N	N	N	N	N	N	N		N			N	N	99 (27)	361
Phenacobius catostomus, riffle minnow (MBE)					N	N	N	N	N								82 (40)	204
P. mirabilis, suckermouth minnow	N																1 (25)	4
P. uranops, stargazing minnow	N																1 (20)	5
Phoxinus erythrogaster, southern redbelly dace	N																9 (25)	36
Pimephales notatus, bluntnose minnow	N		N	N	N	N		N				N					152 (24)	639
P. promelas, fathead minnow	I			I	I	I		I								I	9 (25)	36

TR MD LT UT BW AL CA CO TA   ES PE CN BL YE CH CT

LT—Lower Tombigbee River
M—native marine species
MBE—Mobile basin endemic
MD—Mobile Delta, Mobile Bay tributaries

N—native freshwater species
PE—Perdido River
TA—Tallapoosa River
TR—Tennessee River

TDE—Tennessee drainage endemic
UT—Upper Tombigbee River
YE—Yellow River

	MOBILE BASIN									COASTAL RIVERS (WEST TO EAST)							1985–1994 (% of total)	TOTAL
	TR	MD	LT	UT	BW	AL	CA	CO	TA	ES	PE	CN	BL	YE	CH	CT		
CYPRINIDAE — CARPS AND MINNOWS																		
Pimephales vigilax, bullhead minnow	N	N	N	N	N	N	N	N									194 (33)	587
Pteronotropis euryzonus, broadstripe shiner (ABE)																N	5 (20)	25
P. hypselopterus, sailfin shiner			N	N		N				N	N	N	N	N	N		69 (45)	154
P. signipinnis, flagfin shiner			N	N		N				N	N	N	N	N			22 (27)	81
P. welaka, bluenose shiner			N	N		N	N					N		N	N	N	1 (5)	22
Rhinichthys atratulus, blacknose dace	N				N			N									34 (20)	169
Semotilus atromaculatus, creek chub	N		N	N	N	N	N	N	N								217 (23)	949
S. thoreauianus, Dixie chub	N	N	N	N	N	N	N	N	N			N		N	N	N	56 (29)	190
CATOSTOMIDAE — SUCKERS																		
Carpiodes carpio, river carpsucker	N																6 (86)	7
C. cyprinus, quillback[6]	N	N	N	N	N	N	N	N	N			N			N	N	83 (70)	118
C. velifer, highfin carpsucker[7]	N	N	N	N	N	N	N	N	N			N			N		146 (58)	250
Catostomus commersoni, white sucker	N																9 (35)	26
Cycleptus elongatus, blue sucker[8]	N		N	N		N	N	N	N								18 (50)	36
Erimyzon oblongus, creek chubsucker	N		N	N	N	N	N	N	N							N	86 (28)	305
E. sucetta, lake chubsucker		N	N	N	N	N	N	N	N	N	N	N	N	N	N	N	14 (16)	90
E. tenuis, sharpfin chubsucker		N	N	N	N	N	N	N	N	N	N	N	N	N	N	N	56 (48)	116
Hypentelium etowanum, Alabama hog sucker		N	N	N	N	N	N	N	N							N	314 (33)	963
H. nigricans, northern hog sucker	N							N						N			73 (46)	160
Ictiobus bubalus, smallmouth buffalo	N	N	N	N	N	N	N	N									162 (60)	270
I. cyprinellus, bigmouth buffalo	N						I										7 (27)	26
I. niger, black buffalo	N																12 (43)	28
Lagochila lacera, harelip sucker	EX																0 (0)	1
Minytrema melanops, spotted sucker	N	N	N	N	N	N	N	N	N	N	N	N	N	N	N	N	240 (45)	536
Moxostoma anisurum, silver redhorse	N																12 (75)	16
M. carinatum, river redhorse	N		N	N	N	N	N	N	N			N					62 (56)	111
M. duquesnei, black redhorse	N			N	N	N	N	N	N								175 (41)	423
M. erythrurum, golden redhorse	N			N	N	N	N	N	N	N							111 (30)	376
M. lachneri, greater jumprock (ABE)																N	6 (15)	39
M. macrolepidotum, shorthead redhorse	N																12 (46)	26
M. poecilurum, blacktail redhorse		N	N	N	N	N	N	N	N	N	N	N		N	N		325 (49)	663
M. species, "grayfin redhorse" (ABE)[9]																N	6 (36)	17
ICTALURIDAE — BULLHEAD CATFISHES																		
Ameiurus brunneus, snail bullhead							N									N	5 (22)	23

TR MD LT UT BW AL CA CO TA   ES PE CN BL YE CH CT

ABE—Apalachicola basin endemic	CA—Cahaba River	CT—Chattahoochee River
AL—Alabama River	CH—Choctawhatchee River	ES—Escatawpa River
BL—Blackwater River	CN—Conecuh River	EX—extinct
BW—Black Warrior River	CO—Coosa River	I—introduced freshwater or marine species

	MOBILE BASIN									COASTAL RIVERS (WEST TO EAST)							STATIONS 1985–1994	TOTAL
DRAINAGE GROUP AND RIVER SYSTEMS	TR	MD	LT	UT	BW	AL	CA	CO	TA	ES	PE	CN	BL	YE	CH	CT	(% of total)	
ICTALURIDAE BULLHEAD CATFISHES																		
Ameiurus catus, white catfish	I	I				I	I	I							I	N	17 (81)	21
A. melas, black bullhead	N	N	N	N	N	N	N	N			N			N			19 (11)	178
A. natalis, yellow bullhead	N	N	N	N	N	N	N	N	N	N	N	N	N	N	N	N	149 (36)	418
A. nebulosus, brown bullhead	N	N	N		N	N	N	N			N			N	N	N	29 (33)	89
A. serracanthus, spotted bullhead															N		3 (50)	6
Ictalurus furcatus, blue catfish	N	N	N	N	N	N	N	N	N		N						97 (57)	170
I. punctatus, channel catfish	N	N	N	N	N	N	N	N	N	N	N				N	N	326 (50)	655
Noturus elegans, elegant madtom	N																1 (25)	4
N. eleutherus, mountain madtom	N																1 (100)	1
N. exilis, slender madtom	N																10 (40)	25
N. flavus, stonecat[10]	N																3 (75)	4
N. funebris, black madtom	N	N	N	N	N	N	N	N		N	N			N	N	N	125 (37)	337
N. gyrinus, tadpole madtom	N	N	N	N	N	N		N		N	N	N		N		N	59 (21)	276
N. leptacanthus, speckled madtom		N	N	N	N	N	N	N		N	N	N	N	N	N	N	258 (36)	709
N. miurus, brindled madtom	N																2 (33)	6
N. munitus, frecklebelly madtom			N				N	N	N								8 (10)	81
N. nocturnus, freckled madtom	N		N	N	N	N	N			N							9 (20)	45
Pylodictis olivaris, flathead catfish	N	N	N	N	N	N	N	N	N	N	N						125 (50)	251
ARIIDAE SEA CATFISHES																		
* Arius felis, hardhead catfish		M									M						4 (100)	4
* Bagre marinus, gafftopsail catfish		M															0 (0)	1
ESOCIDAE PIKES																		
Esox americanus, redfin pickerel	N	N	N	N	N	N	N	N	N	N	N	N	N	N	N	N	110 (28)	388
* E. masquinongy, muskellunge								I									1 (100)	1
E. niger, chain pickerel	N	N	N	N	N	N	N	N	N	N	N	N		N	N	N	106 (32)	332
SALMONIDAE TROUTS AND CHARS																		
Oncorhynchus mykiss, rainbow trout				I			I	I									13 (33)	39
Salmo trutta, brown trout							I										0 (0)	6
Salvelinus fontinalis, brook trout							I										0 (0)	2
APHREDODERIDAE PIRATE PERCH																		
Aphredoderus sayanus, pirate perch	N	N	N	N	N	N	N	N	N	N	N		N	N	N	N	117 (30)	395
AMBLYOPSIDAE CAVEFISHES																		
Speoplatyrhinus poulsoni, Alabama cavefish (TDE)	N																0 (0)	1

TR MD LT UT BW AL CA CO TA   ES PE CN BL YE CH CT

LT—Lower Tombigbee River
M—native marine species
MBE—Mobile basin endemic
MD—Mobile Delta, Mobile Bay tributaries
N—native freshwater species
PE—Perdido River
TA—Tallapoosa River
TR—Tennessee River
TDE—Tennessee drainage endemic
UT—Upper Tombigbee River
YE—Yellow River

	MOBILE BASIN									COASTAL RIVERS (WEST TO EAST)							STATIONS 1985–1994 (% of total)	TOTAL
	TR	MD	LT	UT	BW	AL	CA	CO	TA	ES	PE	CN	BL	YE	CH	CT		
AMBLYOPSIDAE CAVEFISHES																		
Typhlichthys subterraneus, southern cavefish	N								N								17 (36)	47
BELONIDAE NEEDLEFISH																		
Strongylura marina, Atlantic needlefish	M	M	M	M	M	M	M	M	M			M			M	M	91 (71)	129
CYPRINODONTIDAE KILLIFISH																		
* Cyprinodon variegatus, sheepshead minnow		M															3 (38)	8
FUNDULIDAE TOPMINNOWS																		
Fundulus albolineatus, whiteline topminnow (TDE)	EX																0 (0)	1
F. auroguttatus, banded topminnow		N										N	N				3 (60)	5
F. bifax, stippled studfish (MBE)							N	N									13 (62)	21
F. blairae, southern starhead topminnow			N	N													7 (100)	7
F. catenatus, northern studfish	N																24 (44)	55
F. chrysotus, golden topminnow		N															7 (64)	11
F. dispar, northern starhead topminnow			N	N	N	N	N										10 (48)	21
F. escambiae, russetfin topminnow											N	N	N	N	N		9 (31)	29
* F. grandis, gulf killifish		M															8 (80)	10
F. notatus, blackstripe topminnow	N	N	N	N		N											14 (13)	110
F. notti, bayou topminnow		N	N	N		N				N							23 (26)	87
F. olivaceus, blackspotted topminnow	N	N	N	N	N	N	N	N	N	N	N	N			N	N	477 (34)	1410
F. stellifer, southern studfish (MBE)						N	N	N									49 (35)	140
Leptolucania ommata, pygmy killifish											N						1 (33)	3
Lucania goodei, bluefin killifish															N		1 (100)	1
L. parva, rainwater killifish			N	N													7 (54)	13
POECILIIDAE LIVEBEARERS																		
Gambusia affinis, western mosquitofish[11]	N	N	N	N	N	N	N	N	N	N								
G. holbrooki, eastern mosquitofish[11]	N	N									N	N	N	N	N		97 (8)	1259
Heterandria formosa, least killifish			N	N	N										N		7 (100)	7
* Poecilia latipinna, sailfin molly		M															2 (40)	5
ATHERINIDAE SILVERSIDES																		
Labidesthes sicculus, brook silverside	N	N	N	N	N	N	N		N	N	N	N			N	N	196 (49)	398
Menidia beryllina, inland silverside		N			N						N						19 (79)	24
SYNGNATHIDAE PIPEFISHES																		
* Syngnathus scovelli, gulf pipefish		M															3 (43)	7
GASTEROSTEIDAE STICKLEBACKS																		
* Culaea inconstans, brook stickleback	I																0 (0)	1

TR MD LT UT BW AL CA CO TA ES PE CN BL YE CH CT

ABE—Apalachicola basin endemic	CA—Cahaba River	CT—Chattahoochee River
AL—Alabama River	CH—Choctawhatchee River	ES—Escatawpa River
BL—Blackwater River	CN—Conecuh River	EX—extinct
BW—Black Warrior River	CO—Coosa River	I—introduced freshwater or marine species

	MOBILE BASIN									COASTAL RIVERS (WEST TO EAST)							1985–1994 (% of total)	TOTAL
	TR	MD	LT	UT	BW	AL	CA	CO	TA	ES	PE	CN	BL	YE	CH	CT		
COTTIDAE — SCULPINS																		
Cottus bairdi, mottled sculpin	N						N										16 (37)	43
Cottus carolinae, banded sculpin	N		N			N	N	N	N								272 (35)	784
C. pygmaeus, pygmy sculpin (MBE)						N											2 (100)	2
MORONIDAE — STRIPED BASSES																		
Morone chrysops, white bass	N	N	N	N	N	N	N	N				N				N	73 (54)	135
M. mississippiensis, yellow bass	N	N	N	N								N					55 (85)	65
M. saxatilis, striped bass	M	M	M		M	M	M	M	M					M	M		55 (72)	76
M. chrysops x *saxatilis*, palmetto bass	I	I	I	I	I	I	I	I	I			I		I	I		68 (94)	72
ELASSOMATIDAE — PYGMY SUNFISHES																		
Elassoma alabamae, spring pygmy sunfish (TDE)	N																4 (80)	5
E. evergladei, Everglades pygmy sunfish		N					N			N				N			11 (92)	12
E. zonatum, banded pygmy sunfish		N	N	N	N	N	N	N	N	N	N	N	N	N	N	N	90 (29)	311
CENTRARCHIDAE — SUNFISHES																		
Ambloplites ariommus, shadow bass		N	N	N	N	N	N	N	N	N	N	N		N	N	N	123 (36)	346
A. rupestris, rock bass	N																23 (58)	40
Centrarchus macropterus, flier		N	N	N	N	N	N	N	N		N			N	N	N	20 (22)	90
Enneacanthus gloriosus, bluespotted sunfish		N	N							N	N						6 (50)	12
E. obesus, banded sunfish												N					1 (50)	2
Lepomis auritus, redbreast sunfish	N						N	N						N	N		198 (45)	443
L. cyanellus, green sunfish	N	N	N	N	N	N	N	N	N	N		N		N	N		394 (30)	1313
L. gulosus, warmouth	N	N	N	N	N	N	N	N	N	N	N	N	N	N	N	N	252 (36)	695
L. humilis, orangespotted sunfish	N		N	N	N	N		N	N								22 (19)	116
L. macrochirus, bluegill	N	N	N	N	N	N	N	N	N	N	N	N	N	N	N	N	783 (39)	2035
L. marginatus, dollar sunfish	N	N	N	N	N	N	N	N		N	N	N	N	N	N	N	33 (26)	127
L. megalotis, longear sunfish	N	N	N	N	N	N	N	N	N	N	N	N	N	N	N	N	707 (40)	1766
L. microlophus, redear sunfish	N	N	N	N	N	N	N	N	N	N	N	N		N	N	N	332 (49)	678
L. miniatus, redspotted sunfish	N	N	N	N	N	N	N	N	N	N	N	N		N	N	N	213 (38)	562
Micropterus coosae, redeye bass					N		N	N	N								176 (37)	482
M. dolomieu, smallmouth bass	N				I		I	I	I								35 (83)	42
M. punctulatus, spotted bass	N	N	N	N	N	N	N	N	N	N	N	N	N	N	N	N	349 (42)	823
M. salmoides, largemouth bass	N	N	N	N	N	N	N	N	N	N	N	N				N	554 (43)	1284
M. species, "shoal bass" (ABE)[12]														N			0 (0)	14
Pomoxis annularis, white crappie	N	N	N	N	N	N	N	N	N	N		N		N	N		139 (44)	315
P. nigromaculatus, black crappie	N	N	N	N	N	N	N	N				N		N	N	N	166 (41)	401

TR MD LT UT BW AL CA CO TA   ES PE CN BL YE CH CT

LT—Lower Tombigbee River   N—native freshwater species   TDE—Tennessee drainage endemic
M—native marine species   PE—Perdido River   UT—Upper Tombigbee River
MBE—Mobile basin endemic   TA—Tallapoosa River   YE—Yellow River
MD—Mobile Delta, Mobile Bay tributaries   TR—Tennessee River

PERCIDAE — PERCHES AND DARTERS

Column groupings: **MOBILE BASIN** = TR MD LT UT BW AL CA CO TA; **COASTAL RIVERS (WEST TO EAST)** = ES PE CN BL YE CH CT; Stations **1985–1994 (% of total)** and **TOTAL**.

Species	TR	MD	LT	UT	BW	AL	CA	CO	TA	ES	PE	CN	BL	YE	CH	CT	1985–1994 (% of total)	TOTAL
Ammocrypta beani, naked sand darter		N	N	N	N	N		N		N							39 (24)	166
A. bifascia, Florida sand darter											N	N		N	N		32 (65)	49
A. meridiana, southern sand darter (MBE)		N	N	N	N	N		N									27 (18)	153
Crystallaria asprella, crystal darter		N	N	N		N	N	N	N		N						29 (31)	93
Etheostoma bellator, Warrior darter (MBE)					N												4 (22)	18
E. blennioides, greenside darter	N																25 (47)	53
E. blennius, blenny darter (TDE)	N																6 (60)	10
E. boschungi, slackwater darter (TDE)	N																9 (53)	17
E. brevirostrum, holiday darter (MBE)								N									5 (27)	18
E. caeruleum, rainbow darter	N																57 (46)	123
E. camurum, bluebreast darter	N																3 (100)	3
E. chermocki, vermilion darter (MBE)				N													2 (67)	3
E. chlorosomum, bluntnose darter		N	N	N	N		N										18 (13)	143
E. chuckwachatte, lipstick darter (MBE)								N									28 (90)	31
E. cinereum, ashy darter	N																0 (0)	1
E. colorosum, coastal darter								N			N	N	N	N	N		59 (66)	90
E. coosae, Coosa darter (MBE)								N									75 (28)	272
E. corona, crown darter (TDE)	N																12 (43)	28
E. crossopterum, fringed darter	N																3 (60)	5
E. davisoni, Choctawhatchee darter								N				N		N	N		33 (47)	71
E. ditrema, coldwater darter (MBE)								N									6 (23)	26
E. douglasi, Tuskaloosa darter (MBE)				N													9 (32)	28
E. duryi, black darter (TDE)	N																86 (49)	177
E. edwini, brown darter												N	N	N	N	N	20 (24)	84
E. etowahae, Etowah darter (MBE)								N									6 (60)	10
E. flabellare, fantail darter	N																36 (68)	53
E. fusiforme, swamp darter		N	N	N		N				N	N	N		N	N		16 (49)	33
E. gracile, slough darter				N													0 (0)	2
E. histrio, harlequin darter	N	N	N	N	N	N		N			N						13 (25)	57
E. jessiae, blueside darter (TDE)	N																23 (79)	29
E. jordani, greenbreast darter (MBE)							N	N	N								76 (42)	181
E. kennicotti, stripetail darter	N																26 (70)	37
E. lachneri, Tombigbee darter (MBE)		N	N	N	N												48 (18)	265
E. lynceum, brighteye darter											N						1 (50)	2

TR MD LT UT BW AL CA CO TA   ES PE CN BL YE CH CT

ABE—Apalachicola basin endemic
AL—Alabama River
BL—Blackwater River
BW—Black Warrior River
CA—Cahaba River
CH—Choctawhatchee River
CN—Conecuh River
CO—Coosa River
CT—Chattahoochee River
ES—Escatawpa River
EX—extinct
I—introduced freshwater or marine species

	DRAINAGE GROUP AND RIVER SYSTEMS																STATIONS	
	MOBILE BASIN									COASTAL RIVERS (WEST TO EAST)							1985–1994 (% of total)	TOTAL
PERCIDAE PERCHES AND DARTERS	TR	MD	LT	UT	BW	AL	CA	CO	TA	ES	PE	CN	BL	YE	CH	CT		
Etheostoma neopterum, lollipop darter (TDE)	N																2 (67)	3
E. nigripinne, blackfin darter (TDE)	N																44 (39)	112
E. nigrum, johnny darter	N		N	N	N	N	N		N								61 (18)	338
E. nuchale, watercress darter (MBE)				N													2 (67)	3
E. parvipinne, goldstripe darter[13]	N		N	N	N	N	N	N	N	N	N	N		N	N	N	30 (20)	153
E. proeliare, cypress darter		N	N	N	N							N					26 (16)	168
E. ramseyi, Alabama darter (MBE)		N						N	N								67 (42)	159
E. rufilineatum, redline darter	N																42 (62)	68
E. rupestre, rock darter (MBE)			N	N	N	N	N	N									84 (25)	336
E. scotti, Cherokee darter (MBE)								N									10 (71)	14
E. simoterum, snubnose darter	N																49 (69)	71
E. stigmaeum, speckled darter	N	N	N	N	N	N	N	N	N	N	N	N					296 (36)	825
E. swaini, gulf darter		N	N	N	N	N	N	N	N	N		N		N	N	N	130 (33)	389
E. tallapoosae, Tallapoosa darter (MBE)									N								65 (48)	135
E. trisella, trispot darter (MBE)								N									1 (7)	15
E. tuscumbia, Tuscumbia darter (TDE)	N																1 (9)	11
E. wapiti, boulder darter (TDE)	N																3 (75)	4
E. whipplei, redfin darter			N	N	N	N	N	N	N							N	85 (19)	451
E. zonale, banded darter	N																16 (88)	18
E. zonifer, backwater darter			N	N		N	N		N							N	29 (33)	87
E. zonistium, bandfin darter[14]	N			N													3 (13)	23
Perca flavescens, yellow perch	I	N		I						I	I						49 (82)	60
Percina antesella, amber darter (MBE)								N									2 (18)	11
P. aurolineata, goldline darter (MBE)							N	N									10 (37)	27
P. austroperca, southern logperch											N			N			10 (77)	13
P. brevicauda, coal darter (MBE)					N		N	N									15 (38)	40
P. burtoni, blotchside logperch	N																1 (50)	2
P. caprodes, logperch	N																46 (49)	94
P. evides, gilt darter	N																8 (80)	10
P. jenkinsi, Conasauga logperch (MBE)								N									0 (0)	3
P. lenticula, freckled darter			N	N		N	N	N	N								13 (25)	52
P. maculata, blackside darter	N		N	N	N	N			N								14 (11)	123
P. nigrofasciata, blackbanded darter[15]			N	N	N	N	N	N	N	N	N	N	N	N	N	N	511 (36)	1416
P. palmaris, bronze darter (MBE)								N	N								104 (48)	218

TR MD LT UT BW AL CA CO TA   ES PE CN BL YE CH CT

LT—Lower Tombigbee River   N—native freshwater species   TDE—Tennessee drainage endemic
M—native marine species   PE—Perdido River   UT—Upper Tombigbee River
MBE—Mobile basin endemic   TA—Tallapoosa River   YE—Yellow River
MD—Mobile Delta, Mobile Bay tributaries   TR—Tennessee River

		MOBILE BASIN								COASTAL RIVERS (WEST TO EAST)							STATIONS 1985–1994 (% of total)	TOTAL
DRAINAGE GROUP AND RIVER SYSTEMS	TR	MD	LT	UT	BW	AL	CA	CO	TA	ES	PE	CN	BL	YE	CH	CT		
PERCIDAE — PERCHES AND DARTERS																		
Percina phoxocephala, slenderhead darter	N																2 (20)	10
P. sciera, dusky darter	N		N	N	N	N											20 (12)	166
P. shumardi, river darter	N		N	N	N	N	N	N									24 (23)	105
P. tanasi, snail darter (TDE)	N																0 (0)	1
P. vigil, saddleback darter	N		N	N	N	N	N		N		N						35 (22)	161
P. species, "gulf logperch" (MBE)		N	N	N	N	N	N										8 (19)	43
P. species, "Mobile logperch" (MBE)		N	N	N	N	N	N										154 (35)	436
P. species, "muscadine darter" (MBE)			N				N										63 (44)	142
Stizostedion canadense, sauger	N																14 (52)	27
S. vitreum, walleye	N		N	N	N	N	N	N			N						15 (22)	69
LUTJANIDAE — SNAPPERS																		
* Lutjanus griseus, gray snapper		M															3 (75)	4
GERREIDAE — MOJARRAS																		
* Eucinostomus argenteus, spotfin mojarra		M															9 (100)	9
SPARIDAE — PORGIES																		
* Archosargus probatocephalus, sheepshead		M															17 (94)	18
* Lagodon rhomboides, pinfish		M									M						5 (100)	5
SCIAENIDAE — DRUMS																		
Aplodinotus grunniens, freshwater drum	N	N	N	N	N	N	N	N									219 (61)	362
* Bairdiella chrysoura, silver perch		M															0 (0)	1
Cynoscion nebulosus, spotted seatrout		M															3 (100)	3
* Leiostomus xanthurus, spot		M									M						18 (82)	22
* Micropogonias undulatus, Atlantic croaker		M															5 (83)	6
* Pogonias cromis, black drum		M															2 (67)	3
Sciaenops ocellatus, red drum		M															11 (100)	11
CICHLIDAE — CICHLIDS																		
* Oreochromis aureus, blue tilapia								I								I	1 (50)	2
MUGILIDAE — MULLETS																		
Mugil cephalus, striped mullet		M	M	M	M	M	M	M		M	M				M		95 (84)	113
* Mugil curema, silver mullet		M															11 (100)	11
ELEOTRIDAE — SLEEPERS																		
* Dormitator maculatus, fat sleeper		M															3 (75)	4
* Eleotris pisonis, spinycheek sleeper		M															2 (100)	2
BOTHIDAE — LEFTEYE FLOUNDERS																		
Paralichthys lethostigma, southern flounder		M	M				M				M						20 (69)	29

TR MD LT UT BW AL CA CO TA   ES PE CN BL YE CH CT

	MOBILE BASIN									COASTAL RIVERS (WEST TO EAST)							1985–1994 (% of total)	TOTAL
	TR	MD	LT	UT	BW	AL	CA	CO	TA	ES	PE	CN	BL	YE	CH	CT		
SOLEIDAE SOLES																		
Trinectes maculatus, hogchoker		M	M			M				M	M			M	M		25 (42)	59
SPECIES PER RIVER SYSTEM	176	131	133	123	130	144	135	147	134	51	59	95	21	49	80	92		
328 TOTAL				236									137					

ABE—Apalachicola basin endemic
AL—Alabama River
BL—Blackwater River
BW—Black Warrior River
CA—Cahaba River
CH—Choctawhatchee River
CN—Conecuh River

CO—Coosa River
CT—Chattahoochee River
ES—Escatawpa River
EX—extinct
I—introduced freshwater or marine species
LT—Lower Tombigbee River

M—native marine species
MBE—Mobile basin endemic
MD—Mobile Delta, Mobile Bay tributaries
N—native freshwater species
PE—Perdido River
TA—Tallapoosa River

TR—Tennessee River
TDE—Tennessee drainage endemic
UT—Upper Tombigbee River
YE—Yellow River

NOTES

1. Clear chub populations inhabiting coastal drainages east of the Mobile basin are a new species (Clemmer, 1979).

2. One, possibly two, new species of speckled chubs have been recognized in the Mobile basin.

3. Speckled chubs in the Choctawhatchee and Escambia Bay drainages have been recognized as a new species (Gilbert, 1992).

4. One, possibly two, new species of mimic shiners have been recognized in the Mobile basin.

5. The "sawfin shiner" will soon be described as a new species.

6. Quillback carpsuckers in the Choctawhatchee, Conecuh, and Chattahoochee river drainages are a new species.

7. Highfin carpsuckers in the Choctawhatchee and Conecuh river drainages are a new species.

8. Blue suckers in the Mobile basin have been recognized as a new species.

9. The "grayfin redhorse" in the Chattahoochee River drainage is a new species (Jenkins, 1970)

10. Based on our comparisons of color patterns and distributional data provided in Page and Burr (1991), stonecats in Shoal Creek and the Elk River may represent a new species.

11. Angus and Howell (1996) delineated the ranges of two species of mosquitofishes in Alabama. *Gambusia affinis* occurs in the Tennessee River drainage and the northern two-thirds of the Mobile basin; *G. holbrooki* occurs in coastal drainages lying east of the Mobile basin. Intergrades of both species occur in the lower reaches of the Alabama and lower Tombigbee drainages, the Mobile Delta and Mobile Bay tributaries, and the Perdido River drainage.

12. The "shoal bass" in the Chattahoochee River drainage is a new species (Gilbert, 1992).

13. Goldstripe darters in Doe Branch (Black Warrior River system) are a new species.

14. Populations of the bandfin darter from upper tributaries of Bear Creek (Tennessee River drainage) and Hubbard Creek (Black Warrior River system) may represent a new species.

15. Blackbanded darters in Uchee Creek (Chattahoochee River drainage) have been recognized as a distinct new species and may be more closely related to the bronze darter.

FISH ANATOMY AND STANDARDIZED MEASUREMENTS AND COUNTS

While some large fishes can readily be identified at first sight or by comparing fish-in-hand with a color photograph, many must be identified through the use of a taxonomic key because of their discrete physical characteristics. Such taxonomic keys can be found at the end of the family introductions. In order to use a taxonomic key effectively, users must be familiar with the anatomical features found on fishes and the standardized counts and measurements used to identify species. One of the first guides to standardize counting and measuring methods was *Fishes of the Great Lakes Region* (Hubbs and Lagler, 1958). This book created the standard that is still used today and modified when necessary. Recent publications with excellent accounts of anatomy are *The Fishes of Ohio* (Trautman, 1981) and *Freshwater Fishes of Virginia* (Jenkins and Burkhead, 1993).

BODY SHAPES AND STRUCTURES

Body size, shape, and color are the most obvious features used to identify fishes. The body of a fish is generally divided into three distinct parts: the *head*, the *caudal region*, and the *trunk*. The *head* extends from the tip of the snout to the rear edge of the gill covers (opercles). The *caudal region* begins at the urogenital opening and extends to the tip of the caudal or tail fin. The *trunk* includes the area between the head and the caudal region.

Fishes exhibit a variety of body forms which in most cases are adaptations to the habitats in which they live. Lampreys and the American eel have an *elongate or eel-like* body form when viewed from the side. Minnows and suckers have a *moderately elongate* shape, while sun-

fishes are *deep-bodied*. When viewed head-on, body forms may be *rounded* as in mullet, slightly to strongly *compressed* from side to side as in the sunfishes, or slightly to strongly *depressed* from top to bottom, such as in the flounders and other bottom-dwelling fishes.

Elongate or Eel-like

Moderately Elongate

Deep-Bodied

Most fishes possess two basic types of fins. *Median* or *unpaired fins* include the dorsal, anal, and caudal fins, and occur along the midline of the body. The *dorsal fin* can be single or double. It is supported by hard, sharp spines, soft flexible rays, or both, and its length and height vary among families and genera. Mullets and silversides have a small dorsal *finlet* composed of spines anterior to their dorsal fin. Catfishes, trout, salmon, and char have a small fleshy flap of skin called an *adipose fin* on the dorsal midline of the body between the dorsal and caudal fins.

The *caudal* or *tail fin* may be forked or unforked. All caudal fins can be classified according to shape. The upper and lower lobes of the *homocercal tail* characteristic of most fish species are generally the same length, although one may be slightly larger than the other. Caudal fins may be *rounded* outward, *truncate* or flat along the margin, or *forked* with two well-defined lobes. The upper lobe of the *heterocercal tail* found on sturgeons and the paddlefish is larger and longer than the lower lobe.

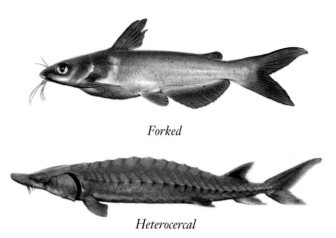

Forked

Heterocercal

Homocercal

Rounded

Truncate

Most fish species have two kinds of *paired fins*. The *pectoral fins* occur near the middle of the body behind the gill opening, or in a lower position closer to the breast. The *pelvic fins* may be located in a thoracic position below the paired pectoral fins or abdominally between the anal and pectoral fins.

The *frenum* is a fleshy bridge connecting the upper lip to the snout. Presence or absence is determined by passing a fine dissecting pin along the groove between the upper lip and snout.

Barbels are fleshy olfactory appendages around the mouth. Their size, location, and number are important diagnostic features in several families. A *terminal barbel* is located in the posterior corner of the mouth, whereas a *preterminal barbel* occurs just anterior to the mouth corner, often concealed in the lip groove, and is generally small in size.

Tubercles and *contact organs* are hard, conelike structures of various sizes that develop on breeding individuals of certain fish species during the spawning season. Tubercles occur on the head, body, or fins and function for tactile stimulation, aggressive display, mate recognition, and friction for maintaining body contact during reproduction.

Fin types and *shapes* generally refer to the posterior margin of a fin. A *convex* fin is rounded outward and a *concave* fin is rounded inward. A *falcate* fin is deeply concave or sickle-shaped.

The *anal fin* arises on the body's ventral surface, usually posterior to the *urogenital vent* (a structure with anal and genital pores) and in front of the caudal fin.

Dorsal fin position usually refers to the dorsal fin origin compared to the pelvic or anal fin origin.

Mouth position refers to the mouth location on the head. Terms used to describe mouth position are *inferior, subterminal, terminal, supraterminal, and superior*.

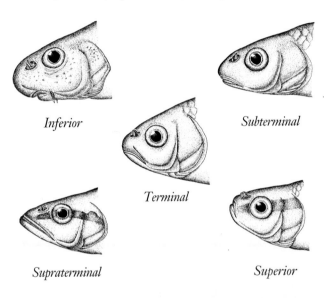

Inferior

Subterminal

Terminal

Supraterminal

Superior

Color and *pigmentation* are important for protection, recognition, reproduction, and communication. Colors vary with age, size, reproductive state, habitat, and water clarity. Colors disappear quickly with preservation to leave only the melanistic patterns. Several terms are used to describe color and pigmentation patterns. *Bars* are generally vertical or oblique in orientation, whereas *stripes* are horizontal. *Eye* or *ocular bars* are located near the eye. Small to large marks of various size and shape known as *blotches* occur along the sides of the body. Dorsal *saddles* exist as dark bands along the back and sometimes connect with side blotches. Fin pigmentation may consist of one or more continuous or interrupted *bands* running parallel to the fin margin or as *streaks* running parallel to the spines and rays. *Mottling* refers to a reticulated pattern of dark and light markings. *Spotted, flecked,* and *speckled* refer to distinct small spots. *Stitching* refers to the visual effect of two small dashes associated with each lateral line pore.

Immaculate and *pale* indicate very few darkened melanophores or spots; *dusky* and *dark* indicate greater melanophore concentration and spotting.

MEASUREMENTS

Measurements are usually taken on the left side of the body. Body proportions are often described in relation to the standard length.

Standard length (SL) is the distance from the tip of the snout to the hypural plate, a series of fused bones at the end of the vertebral column. The end of the hypural plate is evident as a crease when the caudal fin is bent forward. Standard length is preferred over total length because it is not influenced by broken caudal rays, which may affect total length measurements.

Total length (TL) is the distance from the tip of the snout to the posterior end of the longest caudal fin ray.

Fork length (FL) is the distance from the tip of the snout to the deepest part of the fork.

Head length is the distance from the tip of the snout to the rear margin of the operculum.

Snout length is the distance from the tip of the snout to the anterior rim of the orbit.

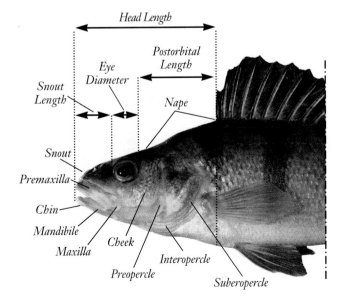

ANATOMICAL FEATURES

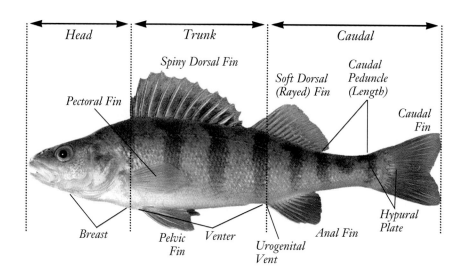

Head | Trunk | Caudal

Spiny Dorsal Fin

Pectoral Fin

Soft Dorsal (Rayed) Fin

Caudal Peduncle (Length)

Caudal Fin

Breast

Pelvic Fin

Venter

Urogenital Vent

Anal Fin

Hypural Plate

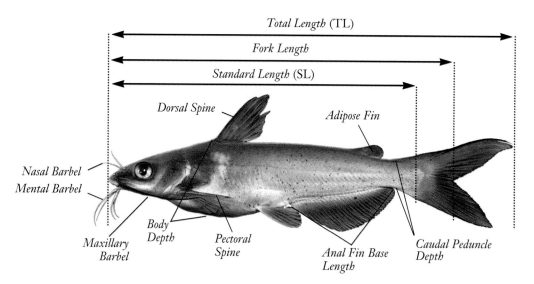

Total Length (TL)

Fork Length

Standard Length (SL)

Dorsal Spine

Adipose Fin

Nasal Barbel
Mental Barbel

Body Depth

Pectoral Spine

Maxillary Barbel

Anal Fin Base Length

Caudal Peduncle Depth

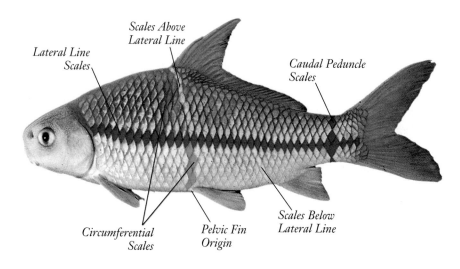

Scales Above Lateral Line

Lateral Line Scales

Caudal Peduncle Scales

Circumferential Scales

Pelvic Fin Origin

Scales Below Lateral Line

Eye diameter or *orbit width* is the maximum distance across the orbital rim.

Postorbital length is the distance from the posterior margin of the orbital rim to the rear margin of the operculum.

Gape width is the distance across the mouth where the upper and lower jaws are hinged.

Maximum body depth is usually measured at the deepest part of the body.

Caudal peduncle length is measured from the posterior end of the anal fin base to the middle of the hypural plate (see standard length for location of plate).

Caudal peduncle depth is measured at the shallowest part of the caudal peduncle.

COUNTS

Scale counts should be made on a series of specimens rather than one individual to assess variability for a specific feature. Alabama fishes may have one of four types of *scales*. Small *placoid scales* found on sharks and related species have a characteristic "sandpaper" texture. *Ganoid scales* found on gars and other primitive fishes form hard impenetrable plates. *Cycloid scales* on more advanced fishes develop annual growth rings used to age specimens. Still other fishes have *ctenoid scales*, which are named for minute spines on exposed scale margins, producing a rough texture. Counting scales is easy on large fishes but becomes more difficult on smaller species. Allowing smaller specimens to dry for a short time will cause their scales to curl upward and increase scale counting efficiency and accuracy.

Lateral line scales are the pored or unpored scales contained in a continuous line along the side of the body extending from the shoulder girdle to the posterior end of the hypural plate at the caudal fin base. The most anterior scale to be counted is the first one touching the shoulder girdle. The end of the hypural plate is determined by a crease that develops when the caudal fin is flexed forward. A scale lying over the crease is included only if one-half or more of the scale length lies anterior to the crease. Scales extending onto the caudal fin are excluded from the count. All scales in a *complete lateral line* have a tiny pore. An *incomplete lateral line* contains pored and unpored scales, unless otherwise defined in the key.

Circumferential scale counts involve making two counts, adding them, and adding 2. The dorsal count is determined by counting scale rows in a vertical plane across the back and in front of the dorsal fin, starting and ending with the scale row immediately above the lateral line. Small scales concentrated in front of the dorsal fin are usually excluded. The ventral count starts and ends with the scale row below the lateral line and extends vertically across the ventral midline, usually in front of the pelvic fins. Dorsal and ventral scale counts are summed and added to 2 (for the lateral line scales) to yield the total count.

Scales above lateral line refers to the number of scale rows along one side of the body, beginning at the dorsal fin origin and extending downward at an oblique angle to the row of scales immediately above the lateral line scale.

Scales below lateral line refers to the number of scale rows along one side of the body, beginning at a ventral fin origin and extending upward and obliquely to the scale row directly below the lateral line scale. This count begins at the pelvic fin origin in primitive species and at the anal fin origin on advanced fishes.

Caudal peduncle scales refers to all scale rows covering the least depth of the caudal peduncle.

Predorsal scales and scale rows include all scales touching the midline anterior to the dorsal fin. Predorsal scale rows include only those scales in natural rows anterior to the dorsal fin. It excludes all scales lying between natural rows.

Fin rays and spines are fin-support structures found on all fishes. Fin rays are composed of two fused units that are flexible and segmented (articulated) throughout their length. They may be branched or unbranched. *Principal rays* extend to the distal fin margin and in many species, the first principal ray is unbranched. *Rudimentary rays* usually occur at the leading edge of median fins and do not reach the distal fin margin. *Spines* are typically pointed, unsegmented, and unbranched, and their bony construction usually makes them stiff and sharp. Flexible spines, known as *soft spines*, may be confused with unbranched rays. Spines and rays can occur in separate fins or mixed in the same fin, with spines preceding the rays. The fins on small fishes must be spread and backlit to count spines and rays accurately through a dissecting microscope. Fatty tissue around the fins of catfishes must be dissected near the fin base in order to count fin elements accurately.

Pectoral and *pelvic fin ray counts* include all branched and unbranched rays near the fin base.

Dorsal and *anal fin ray counts* involve only principal rays. The last two rays are counted as one when they arise from the same point. The first principal ray is usually unbranched. All anterior rudimentary rays are included in the count on pikes, catfishes, and trout because distinguishing principal and rudimentary status is difficult. The anterior rudimentary rays of the median fins in most families are not counted because their lengths differ distinctly from those of the principal rays.

Caudal fin ray counts include all principal rays unless otherwise specified. The caudal fin ray count equals the number of branched rays plus 2.

Branchiostegal rays are long, thin bones that support the gill membranes beneath the head. Ray counts are completed by bending the opercle or head to expand the branchiostegal area. Counting the ray nearest the opercle requires careful scrutiny.

The cephalic lateralis system includes *cephalic pores* and *canals* on the surface of the head, both of which are useful characters for darter and topminnow identification. Drying or wetting may be necessary to locate specific canals and pores.

Infraorbital canal (IO)—the IO pore count starts anterior to the eye, follows the ventral rim of the orbit rising along the posterior rim, and ends with the last pore before the junction with the supraorbital and lateral canal systems. The IO canal may be interrupted, in which case the count is given by indicating the anterior portion + the posterior portion.

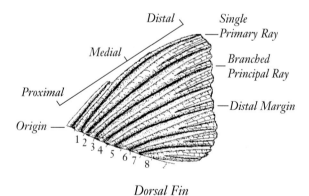

Dorsal Fin

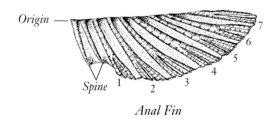

Anal Fin

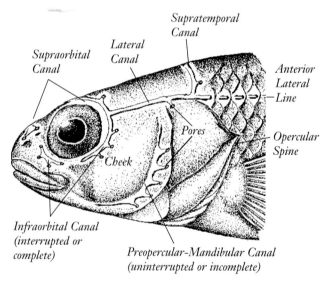

Preopercular mandibular canal (POM) pores are counted in the POM canal, which follows the posterior margin of the preopercle ventral edge, ending on the underside of the lower jaw.

Gill arches are located beneath the gill covers and support two important morphological structures. Thin, red gill filaments on the outside of the arch are important respiratory organs. Thicker, less numerous, white to cream-colored gill rakers on the inside of the gill arch are used for capturing food particles. Gill rakers are typically counted on the first arch on the right side of the body to avoid damage to the left side. It is sometimes necessary to count rakers on the upper or lower limb, which lie above and below the angle of the gill arch, respectively. Any raker on the angle is included in the lower limb count.

Pharyngeal throat teeth are bony modifications of the fifth gill arch located at the beginning of the throat that serve to crush food before it enters the stomach. Their structure is important in the identification of many minnow and sucker species. After the pharyngeal arches are removed and cleaned, they must be examined with a dissecting microscope so that the row(s) of teeth can be counted. To remove the arch, first bend the gill cover forward and insert fine-pointed forceps into the gill chamber in front of the cleithrum, the large sickle-shaped bone located at the rear of the gill chamber. Once the pharyngeal arch is detected, forceps are used to grasp the top attachment and break it free from the surrounding tissue. The same process is repeated with the lower attachment, after which the arch is lifted free of the body. Although the arches may be broken during extraction, tooth sockets are usually visible and can be counted. Pharyngeal arches bear 1 to 3 rows of teeth. The major row contains the largest and greatest number of teeth. A dentition formula of 2, 4-4, 2 means that the left arch has 2 teeth in the minor row and 4 teeth in the major row. The right arch has 4 teeth in the major row and 2 in the minor row. Phyaryngeal tooth counts are generally symmetrical, but exceptions do exist; therefore, modal counts are advised.

KEY TO THE FAMILIES OF FISHES

This taxonomic key uses obvious physical characteristics to identify the 29 families of freshwater and marine fishes included in the species accounts in this book. Most morphological features in the key are easily distinguishable, but the reader can consult the Fish Anatomy section and Glossary for unfamiliar terms.

1a. Pectoral and pelvic fins absent; seven small round pores on side of head serve as gill openings; one nostril on top of head between eyes; circular mouth lacks jaws . . . . lampreys, Family Petromyzontidae

1b. Pectoral fins always present, pelvic fins present or absent; a single operculum or gill cover occurs on either side of the head, rear margin usually unattached and can be lifted to expose the gill arches and red gill filaments; two nostrils, one located on either side of the head and in front of the eye; prominent mouth with jaws located at end of or below snout. . . . . go to 2

1a. least brook lamprey

2a. Caudal fin base arches upward, making the caudal fin asymmetrical when viewed laterally . . . . go to 3

2b. Upper and lower parts of the caudal fin and fin base symmetrical. . . . . go to 6

2a. asymmetrical caudal fin

2b. symmetrical caudal fin

3a. Caudal fin rounded . . . . go to 4

3b. Caudal fin forked, the upper lobe substantially larger than the lower lobe . . . . go to 5

4a. Snout long and beaklike; body covered with rows of hard, nonoverlapping rhomboid scales; dorsal fin short and near caudal fin base . . . . gars, Family Lepisosteidae

4b. Snout short, not beaklike; body covered with oval, overlapping scales; dorsal fin long, extending over most of back . . . . bowfin, Family Amiidae

4a. gar

4b. bowfin

5a. Snout distinctly paddle shaped with two small barbels on lower surface in front of mouth; gill covers elongated and pointed at rear margin; back and sides smooth, without bony plates . . . . paddlefish, Family Polyodontidae

5b. Snout shovel shaped with 4 large barbels; gill covers not elongated and pointed; back and sides covered with 5 rows of prominent bony plates . . . . sturgeons, Family Acipenseridae

5a. paddlefish

5b. gulf sturgeon

6a. Pelvic fins ususlly absent . . . . go to 7

6b. Pelvic fins usually present; greatly reduced or missing in soles . . . . go to 8

7a. Eyes degenerate; body white, lacking pigmentation; anus located near throat. . . . .

. . . . cavefishes, Family Amblyopsidae

7b. Eyes present; body color olivaceous; anus in front of anal fin . . . . freshwater eel, Family Anguillidae

7a. southern cavefish

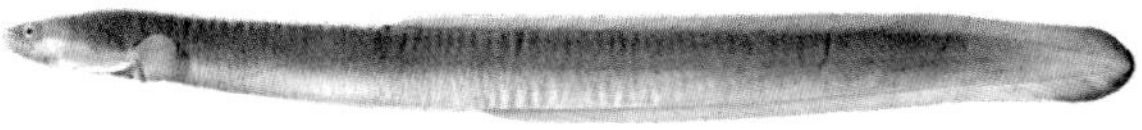

7b. American eel

8a. Pelvic fins located closer to anal fin than to pectoral fins. . . . . go to 9

8b. Pelvic fins just beneath or slightly behind pectoral fins . . . . go to 22

8a. pelvic fins closer to anal fin    8b. pelvic fins beneath pectoral fin

9a. Pectoral fins with a well-developed spine; body without scales. . . . . . . bullhead catfishes, Family Ictaluridae

9b. Pectoral fins lack a well-developed spine; body with scales . . . . go to 10

9a. freshwater catfishes: spotted bullhead (left), channel catfish (right) and frecklebelly madtom (bottom)

10a. Head without scales . . . . go to 11

10b. Head partially covered with scales . . . . go to 17

11a. Scales along midline of venter meet at an acute angle, forming a sawtooth or knifelike edge . . . . . go to 12

11b. Scales along midline of venter smooth and rounded with no sawtooth or knifelike edge . . . . go to 14

12a. Mouth very large, upper jaw extending well behind the eye . . . . anchovies, Family Engraulidae

12b. Mouth small, upper jaw not extending behind eye . . . . go to 13

12a. bay anchovy

13a. Dorsal fin origin located in front of anal fin origin; lateral line absent . . . . herrings, Family Clupeidae

13b. Dorsal fin origin over or slightly behind anal fin origin; lateral line present . . . .
. . . . mooneyes, Family Hiodontidae

13a. threadfin shad   13b. mooneye

14a. Adipose fin present; axillary process present at base of pelvic fin . . . . . trouts and chars, Family Salmonidae

14b. Adipose fin absent; axillary process absent . . . . go to 15

14a. brook trout

15a. Dorsal and anal fins each with a stout serrated spine . . . . carps and minnows, Family Cyprinidae (in part)

15b. Dorsal and anal fin origins without a stout serrated spine . . . . go to 16

15a. carps and minnows: common carp (left) and goldfish (right)

16a. Dorsal fin with 9 or fewer soft rays; anal fin origin located about equidistant from eye and caudal fin origin
. . . . carps and minnows, Family Cyprinidae (in part)
16b. Dorsal fin with 10 or more soft rays; anal fin origin distinctly closer to caudal fin base than to eye . . . .
. . . . suckers, Family Catostomidae

16a. carps and minnows: speckled chub (left) and blacktail shiner (right)

16b. suckers: highfin carpsucker (left), Alabama hog sucker (right), and spotted sucker (bottom)

17a. Spiny dorsal fin located in front of soft dorsal fin. . . . . go to 18
17b. Spiny dorsal fin absent . . . . go to 19

18a. Dorsal fin pronounced with large, stiff spines; anal rays 8 to 9 . . . . mullets, Family Mugilidae
18b. Dorsal finlet small with slender, flexible spines; anal rays 14 to 23 . . . . silversides, Family Atherinidae

18a. striped mullet

18b. brook silverside

19a. Long needle-shaped mouth filled with slender sharp teeth; lateral line scales number 275 to 300 . . . .
. . . . needlefish, Family Belonidae
19b. Jaws not needle-shaped; fewer than 150 lateral line scales . . . . go to 20

19a. Atlantic needlefish

20a. Snout broad and shaped like a duck's bill; caudal fin forked . . . . pikes, Family Esocidae

20b. Snout not broad or duck-billed; caudal fin rounded . . . . go to 21

20a. redfin pickerel

21a. Dorsal fin base over anal fin base; third anal fin ray branched . . . . topminnows, Family Fundulidae

21b. Dorsal fin base mostly (females) or entirely (males) behind anal fin base; third anal fin ray unbranched . . .

. . . . livebearers, Family Poeciliidae

21a. blackstripe topminnow   21b. mosquitofish

22a. Both eyes located on one side of head; body flattened . . . . go to 23

22b. One eye on each side of head; body not flattened . . . . go to 24

23a. Both eyes on left side of body; pectoral fins present . . . . lefteye flounders, Family Bothidae

23b. Both eyes on right side of body; pectoral fins absent . . . . sole, Family Soleidae

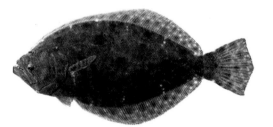 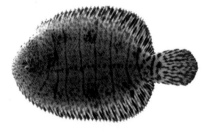

23a. southern flounder   23b. hogchoker

24a. Dorsal fin with 3 spines; anus at throat between gill covers . . . . pirate perch, Family Aphredoderidae

24b. Dorsal fin with 4 or more spines; anus immediately in front of anal fin . . . . go to 25

24a. pirate perch

25a. Body naked . . . . sculpins, Family Cottidae
25b. Body covered with scales . . . . go to 26

25a. banded sculpin

26a. Soft dorsal rays 24 or more . . . . drums, Family Sciaenidae
26b. Soft dorsal rays 15 or fewer . . . . go to 27

26a. freshwater drum

27a. Dorsal fins separated by a deep notch; several continuous or broken dark horizontal stripes along silvery body; gill covers with a sharp spine . . . . striped basses, Family Moronidae
27b. Dorsal fins joined or if notched, fish lacks dark horizontal stripes on silvery body; gill covers lack sharp spine . . . .
. . . . go to 28

27a. yellow bass

28a. Total dorsal spines and rays 15 or fewer; lateral line absent; adult total length less than 50 mm . . . .
. . . . pygmy sunfishes, Family Elassomatidae
28b. Total dorsal spines 16 or more; lateral line present, complete or incomplete; adult total length more than 60 mm . . . . go to 29

28a. banded pygmy sunfish

29a. One or two anal spines . . . . perches and darters, Family Percidae

29b. Three or more anal spines . . . . sunfishes, Family Centrarchidae

29a. perches and darters: Alabama darter (top), blackbanded darter (middle), and walleye (bottom)

29b. sunfishes: bluegill (left), white crappie (right), and largemouth bass (bottom)

CHOCTAWHATCHEE RIVER, GENEVA COUNTY

FAMILY AND SPECIES ACCOUNTS

Three hundred species representing 29 families of freshwater and marine fishes are discussed in the main body of the book. Families are arranged in phylogenetic order, from the primitive lampreys through the advanced soles. Genera and species are arranged alphabetically within families. Most common and scientific names of species conform to recommendations in Robins et al. (1991), with exceptions of a few genera and species in the minnow family, Cyprinidae; the topminnow family, Fundulidae; the striped bass family, Moronidae; and the pygmy sunfish family, Elassomatidae.

Each family treatment contains three components: an introduction, an illustrated taxonomic key to species, and one or more species accounts. Species within a family are distinguished with an illustrated taxonomic key placed at the end of the family introduction. Each taxonomic key provides a series of either/or choices that draw the user's attention to characteristics useful in fish identification.

The two-page species accounts are designed to communicate scientific information in an attractive, interesting, and predictable format. Color photographs of representative individuals are included for most species. Photographs illustrating various habitats are incorporated throughout the book in an effort to increase awareness of species-habitat relationships that exist in nature.

❶ MAP PAGE: The left page of each account contains two distribution maps. Dots on the large map show specific collection sites and provide a visual perspective of distribution patterns as related to physiography. The small inset map shows the native distribution species in the 48 states. Inset maps for introduced North American fishes, including trout, catfishes, and sunfishes, usually reflect native range and part or all of the known introduced range. Inset maps for non-native (introduced) species are blank because their distributions are not completely known.

❷ SPECIES IDENTIFICATION: Common and scientific species names, the last name(s) of the individual(s) who described the species, the publication date of the original description, and the etymology (origin) of the scientific names are placed in the upper right-hand corner. The genus name always appears first; it begins with a capital and is italicized; the species name is italicized and always appears in lower case. The last name of the species author may or may not be enclosed in parenthesis. An author's name not enclosed in parentheses signifies that the scientific name has remained unchanged since the original description. Conversely, a name enclosed in parenthesis signifies that the scientific name has changed due to a later revisionary study. These author citations are reflected in the Literature Cited. An additional reference is included in the Characteristics section of some accounts when the name of the describer differs from that of the author of the publication in which the description occurred.

Most species included in the book were collected in Alabama and photographed shortly thereafter. Selected minnow and darter species were purposefully photographed during peak breeding season to show dazzling body colors. Several colleagues allowed us to use their slides of rare species. A few other species were collected in adjacent states. A caption beneath each color photograph provides the location and county of capture, date of capture, length, sex, and the Geological Survey of Alabama (GSA) collection number.

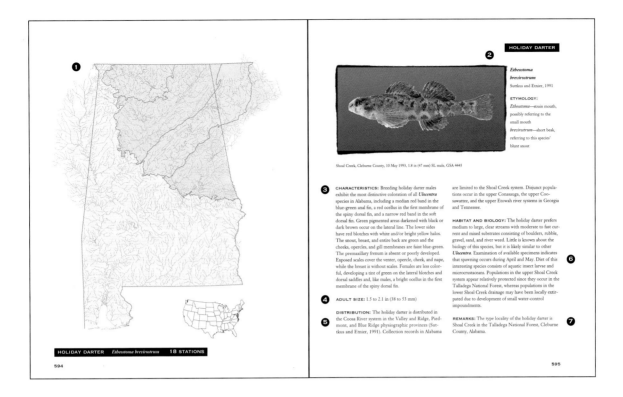

3 CHARACTERISTICS: This section provides morphological data and color notes for use in confirming identifications from the taxonomic keys. With few exceptions, characteristics are derived from examination of fishes collected in the study area and from literature references.

4 ADULT SIZE: Adult size refers to the standard length in inches (in) and millimeters (mm) or meters (m) of adult individuals observed in Alabama. State angling records are provided for appropriate species. See center illustration on page 44 for standard length.

5 DISTRIBUTION: This section explains distribution patterns in the United States and in the study area. The influence of physical environment and physiographic setting on the dispersion of species across Alabama and the southeastern United States is indicated when known. Range extensions and new collections of marginally known or infrequently collected species receive special mention.

6 HABITAT AND BIOLOGY: We compiled much of this information from personal notes and observations during some 60 years among the three of us of sampling fishes in Alabama. Terms of relative abundance are as follows:

Abundant implies the species is collected in large numbers.

Widespread means that it inhabits numerous different habitat types and is regularly encountered during sampling.

Common species can be collected regularly but only within their preferred habitats.

Uncommon implies lower density within a preferred habitat, and more intensive sampling is required to document a species' presence.

Rare means either that a species is restricted to only a few specific locations or that its density, even within its preferred habitat, is so low that collection is not assured, intensive sampling effort notwithstanding. Habitat descriptions refer to microhabitat or the immediate area from which the species was collected.

7 REMARKS: Here specialized information is given for selected species. When available, harvest data is provided for fishes of sport and commercial importance. Species that are protected by the Endangered Species Act or Rules and Regulations of the Alabama Department of Conservation and Natural Resources are identified. Alabama type localities are also given in this section.

LAMPREYS

Petromyzontidae

Although lampreys and eels have similar body shapes, the two can be separated by mouth structure. While eels have hinged jaws, lampreys possess oval buccal cavities surrounded by small, fleshy projections called cirri, making them the most primitive fishes in Alabama. Teeth, if present, usually surround the oral opening in concentric rings leading into the digestive tube. The lamprey is scaleless, with one median nostril located on top of the head and seven pairs of gill pores. Its skeleton is made of cartilage rather than bone. Paired pectoral and pelvic fins are absent, and the dorsal and caudal fins are fused to form one continuous fin.

Six species of lampreys inhabit Alabama. The Ohio lamprey, ***Ichthyomyzon bdellium***, and chestnut lamprey, ***I. castaneus***, are parasitic and occur throughout the Tennessee River drainage. The chestnut lamprey is now the only parasitic species native to the Mobile basin, but Ohio lampreys could eventually move through the Tennessee-Tombigbee Waterway and into the upper Tombigbee River. The four remaining species are nonparasitic; of these, two occur throughout Alabama, two only in the Tennessee drainage. As adults, parasitic lampreys are larger (6 to 14 inches) than nonparasitic lampreys (4 to 8 inches). Parasitic lampreys typically inhabit large streams or rivers, while nonparasitic forms live in smaller streams.

Adult parasitic lampreys feed on the blood of other fishes, primarily carp and various species of suckers and sunfishes. To feed, a lamprey fastens its buccal cavity on a host fish and rasps a circular hole through the victim's skin. It then injects an anticoagulant into the wound to keep the host's blood flowing. After feeding, the lamprey detaches itself and remains free-living until it needs to feed again. The host is usually not killed outright, but it may later bleed to death from the effects of the anticoagulant or die from an infection in the wound.

It had been thought that lampreys do not parasitize other lampreys. However, on 21 May 1993, at the Flint River in Madison County, we collected an 11-inch (279 mm) Ohio lamprey bearing three wounds that had obviously been caused by another lamprey. We could not identify the parasitizing lamprey, but several colleagues examined the host fish and confirmed our assessment of what could be the first observed case of one lamprey parasitized by another.

It is possible, though not probable, that an angler would encounter a lamprey parasitizing a game fish. Such an occurrence is most likely in the Tennessee River— there, samplings and observations of recently parasitized hosts indicate that chestnut and Ohio lampreys are more widespread than previously believed. Parasitic activity is greatest from March through June, probably because the cool water temperatures make host fishes lethargic and thus more easily preyed upon by lampreys.

Adult parasitic lampreys spawn at the same time of year and favor the same kinds of habitats. In late winter, they gather around the mouths of streams and migrate upstream into small, clear tributaries. Spawnings typically occur in riffles, or shallows, where currents are moderate to swift and substrates consist of gravel and sand. Working together, males and females move pebbles with their mouths to build a shallow, oval nest that is several inches wide. Spawning by multiple partners follows, which can last for several hours or up to three days. The eggs deposited in the nest number in the hundreds or sometimes the thousands. Exhausted, the adults usually die shortly after spawning. How many of the eggs actually hatch depends on several factors, including streamflow, water quality, and predation of eggs.

Lampreys pass through two life stages. After hatching, the small, blind larvae, called ammocoetes, are swept downstream into pools where currents are slow and bottoms consist of mud, silt, and leaf litter. Depending on the species, they remain there from one to seven years, eating microscopic organisms in the soft substrates.

During the fall and winter of the appropriate year, ammocoetes metamorphose into adults. They develop eyes, and their oral hoods are absorbed and replaced by the characteristic buccal cavities. Parasitic adults migrate downstream into large streams or rivers and participate in the spawning cycle within a year or two. Nonparasitic adults do not migrate but continue to inhabit the stream where they were hatched; interestingly, after their metamorphosis, they stop feeding.

To the naked eye, ammocoetes of the various species look the same, so they are difficult to identify. The adults of the two lamprey genera found in Alabama can be reliably identified by their different dorsal fins; determining their species usually requires a microscope and careful observation.

KEY TO ADULT LAMPREYS

1a. Dorsal fin deeply notched to form distinct anterior and posterior parts . . . . go to 2, *Lampetra*

1b. Dorsal fin may be notched but not divided into two parts . . . . go to 3, *Ichthyomyzon*

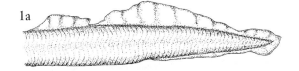 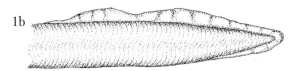

Dorsal fins of 1a, *Lampetra,* and 1b, *Ichthyomyzon*

2a. Myomeres from last gill cleft to cloaca usually 54 to 60 . . . . least brook lamprey, *L. aepyptera*

2b. Myomeres usually 64 to 75 . . . . American brook lamprey, *L. appendix*

3a. Oral disc on fresh individuals equal to or wider than head width; teeth sharp and well developed . . . .
. . . . go to 4

3b. Oral disc on fresh individuals narrower than head width; teeth blunt, absent, or poorly developed . . . . . .
. . . . go to 5

4a. Myomeres 49 to 56; body olive to brown, grading to cream or white on venter; fins butterscotch to olive . . .
. . . . chestnut lamprey, *I. castaneus*

4b. Myomeres 53 to 62; body and fins always light to dark gray . . . . Ohio lamprey, *I. bdellium*

5a. Myomeres 57 to 60; body tan to light gray, grading from gray to white mottling on venter; lateral line organs black on back, unpigmented on venter . . . . mountain brook lamprey, *I. greeleyi*

5b. Myomeres 49 to 59; back olive to yellow, grading to light tan or white on venter; lateral line organs black on back and venter . . . . southern brook lamprey, *I. gagei*

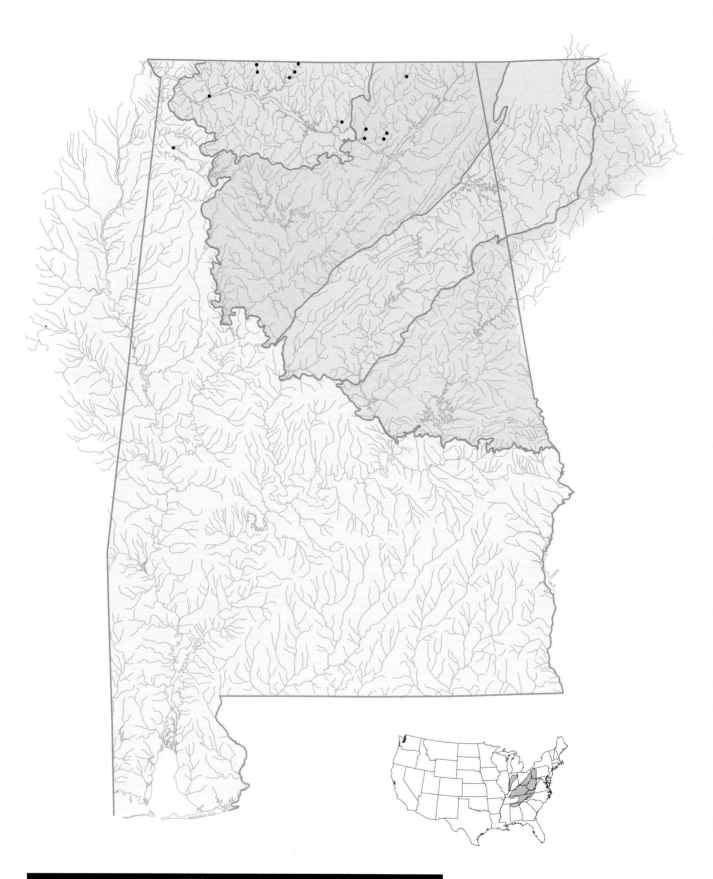

Ichthyomyzon bdellium

(Jordan, 1885)

ETYMOLOGY:

Ichthy—fish

myzon—sucking

bdello—leech, in Greek

Paint Rock River, Marshall County, 18 May 1993, 9.6 in (245 mm) TL male, GSA 4511

CHARACTERISTICS: Because the Ohio and chestnut lampreys share so many physical features, they are difficult to distinguish (Burr, 1980; Jenkins and Burkhead, 1993). Hubbs and Trautman (1937) report 53 to 62 myomeres between the last gill slit and the anus on specimens of *Ichthyomyzon bdellium* (54 on one specimen from Alabama) and 49 to 56 myomeres on *I. castaneus*. The Ohio lampreys we collected in Alabama were intermediate in myomere count, ranging from 52 to 56. Page and Burr (1991) suggest that body and fin colors are useful in distinguishing the two species. Live individuals of *I. bdellium* have blue to slate gray backs, white to mottled gray venters, and gray fins. Live individuals of *I. castaneus* have yellow to tan backs and venters and yellow-olive fins. More study is needed to resolve the uncertainties in identifying Southern populations of Ohio and chestnut lampreys. See Jordan (1885a) for original description.

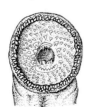

Ventral view of the buccal cavity

ADULT SIZE: 6 to 12 in (152 to 300 mm)

DISTRIBUTION: Rohde and Lantrigne-Courchene (1979) mapped four collection localities for Ohio lampreys in Alabama. From 1991 to 1993, we collected individuals at seven new localities—three in the Elk River, three in the Paint Rock River, and one in the Flint River. Future sampling will undoubtedly increase this species' known range in the Tennessee River drainage and may provide more insight into its life history in Alabama.

HABITAT AND BIOLOGY: Adult Ohio lampreys are normally found in medium or large streams or in small rivers with moderate to slow currents and debris or gravel and sand substrates. They infrequently inhabit small streams. Most of the Ohio lampreys we have collected were parasitizing carp, but we also found one attached to the snout of a longnose gar, *Lepisosteus osseus*, and several more attached to the heads and shoulders of smallmouth buffalo, *Ictiobus bubalus*. Little is known of the life history of the Ohio lamprey in Alabama. General spawning activities are described in the Lampreys family introduction. Rohde and Lantrigne-Courchene (1979) report that the larval stage lasts for up to four years.

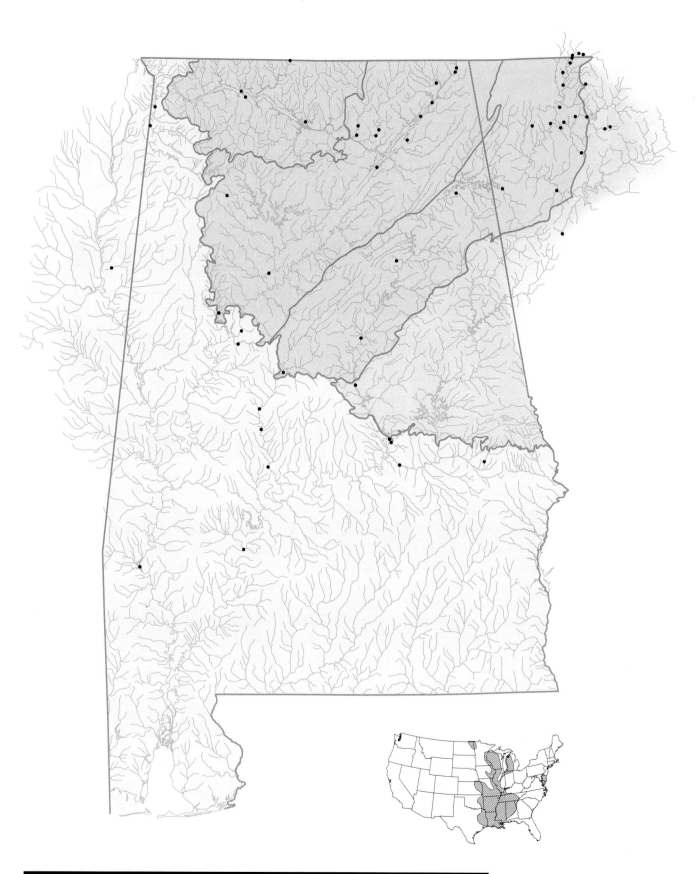

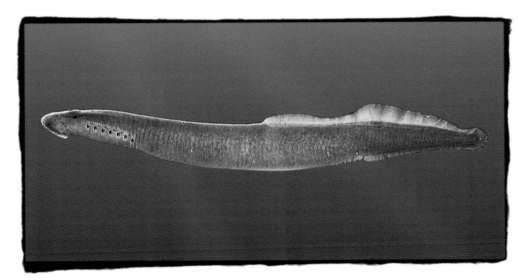

Ichthyomyzon castaneus

Girard, 1858

ETYMOLOGY:

Ichthy—fish

myzon—sucking

castaneus—chestnut, referring to body color

Paint Rock River, Marshall County, 19 May 1993, 12.2 in (310 mm) TL female, GSA 4475

CHARACTERISTICS: The dorsal fin is slightly notched but is not divided into two distinct fins. In live individuals, the expanded oral disc is as wide as or wider than the head. Teeth—two or three supraorals and four or five bicuspid teeth on each side of the oral opening— are large and well developed. On the trunk, myomeres between the last gill opening and the anus number from 49 to 56. Lateral line organs on the head and ventral side are black. Color differences between chestnut and Ohio lampreys are discussed under Characteristics for Ohio lamprey, *Ichthyomyzon bdellium*. See Girard (1858a) for original description.

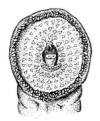

Ventral view of the buccal cavity

ADULT SIZE: 8 to 14 in (203 to 356 mm)

DISTRIBUTION: Rohde and Lantrigne-Courchene (1978a) map chestnut lampreys at two locations in the Tennessee River drainage in Alabama and at nine localities in the Mobile basin. Mayden et al. (1989) expand the number of Mobile basin localities to 17. From 1991 to 1993, we collected individuals at 13 new stations in the Tennessee River drainage. During the same period, the Alabama Game and Fish Division collected individuals at two new locations in the Cahaba River. The collection of a single individual from the mouth of Pursley Creek is the first occurrence of this species below the Fall Line and in the Alabama River system.

HABITAT AND BIOLOGY: Chestnut lampreys usually inhabit rivers, reservoirs, and medium or large streams. We collected several free-swimming individuals; those in the parasitic mode were attached to carp and buffalo. Adults begin migrating into smaller streams in February and spawn in April or May. Spawning behavior is described in the Lampreys family introduction. The larval stage lasts for two or three years.

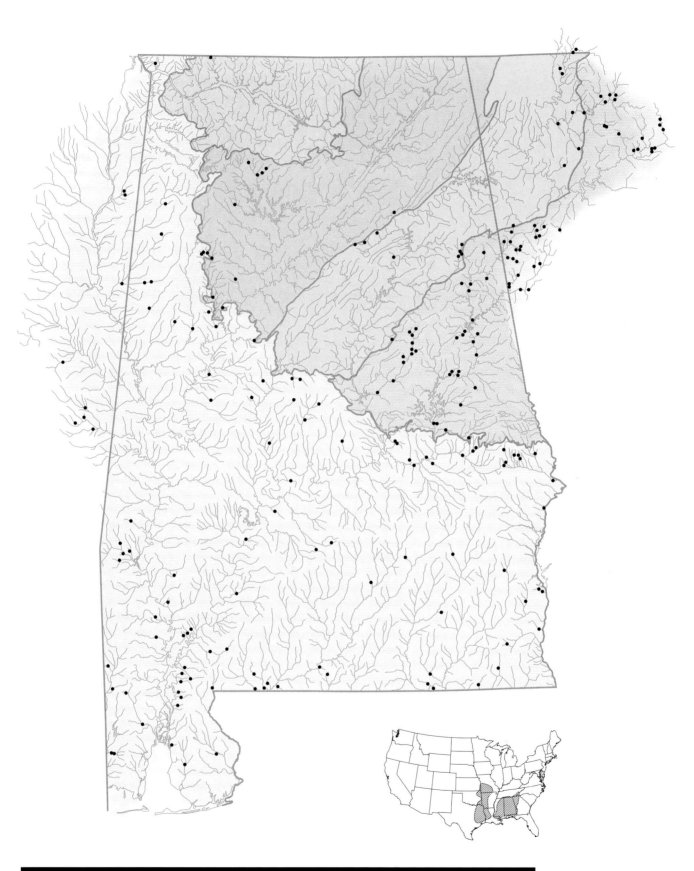

SOUTHERN BROOK LAMPREY *Ichthyomyzon gagei* **212 STATIONS**

Ichthyomyzon gagei

Hubbs and Trautman, 1937

ETYMOLOGY:

Ichthy—fish

myzon—sucking

gagei—in honor of

S. H. Gage, who studied

lampreys

Butler Creek, Lauderdale County, 24 February 1993, 6.3 in (160 mm) TL female, GSA 4358

CHARACTERISTICS: The dorsal fin is slightly notched but is not divided into two distinct fins. On live individuals, the oral disc is narrower than the head. The teeth—two or three supraoral teeth and three or four bicuspid teeth on each side of the oral opening—are blunt and poorly developed. On most individuals, myomeres between the last gill opening and the anus number from 49 to 59. Lateral line organs on the back and venter are black. The body is olive to yellow on the back, grading to light tan or white on the venter. The fins are light tan to white.

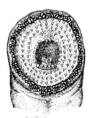

Ventral view of the buccal cavity

ADULT SIZE: 3.9 to 7.9 in (100 to 200 mm)

DISTRIBUTION: Although collected in every major river system in the Mobile basin, this nonparasitic species is rare in the Tennessee River drainage. We collected single specimens in Lauderdale County at Bumpass Creek and Little Butler Creek. Individuals avoid the unfavorable habitats and poor water conditions of streams draining the Black Belt and Southern Pine Hills.

HABITAT AND BIOLOGY: Southern brook lampreys inhabit small or medium streams having moderate to swift currents over sand and gravel substrates. Dendy and Scott (1953) report that, in Alabama, spawning occurs from March through July. We observed spawning in the Cahaba and upper Tallapoosa river systems in March. We also observed nest building in a Cahaba River tributary in late May: Two males and a female moved gravel to the upper end of a riffle, building a nest about 8 inches in diameter, 2 or 3 inches deep, and in about 4 inches of water. Ammocoetes metamorphose into adults in about three years. Spawning usually occurs in the spring following metamorphosis.

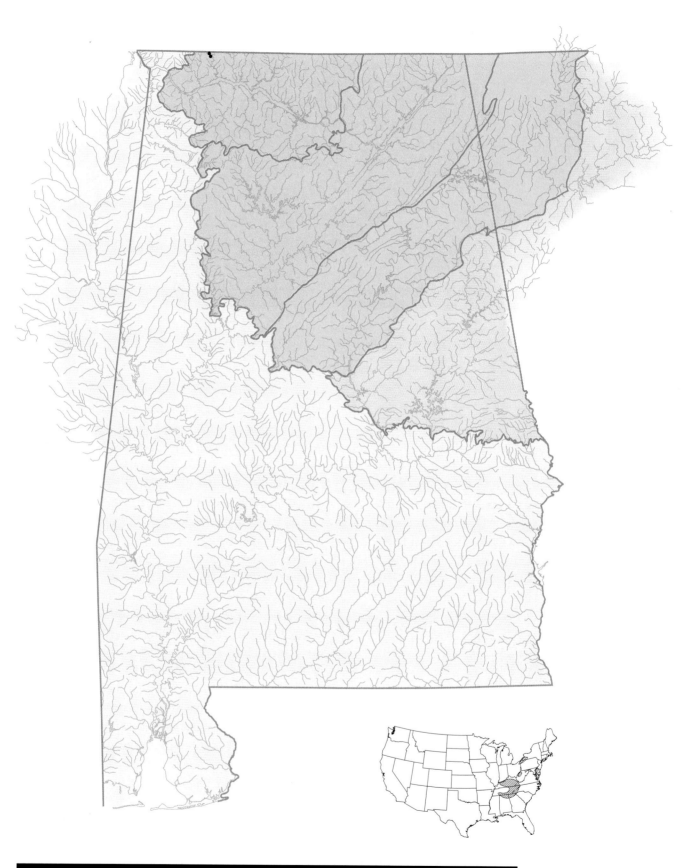

MOUNTAIN BROOK LAMPREY   *Ichthyomyzon greeleyi*   **2 STATIONS**

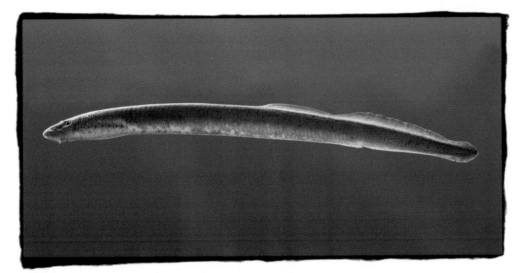

Ichthyomyzon greeleyi
Hubbs and Trautman, 1937

ETYMOLOGY:

Ichthy—fish

myzon—sucking

greeleyi—in honor of
John R. Greeley,
who discovered the species

Butler Creek, Lauderdale County, 31 March 1992, 6.5 in (165 mm) TL female, GSA 4241

CHARACTERISTICS: The dorsal fin is slightly notched but is not divided into two distinct fins. On live individuals, the expanded oral disc is narrower than the head. This species is the only nonparasitic lamprey in Alabama that has sharp, well-developed teeth. The buccal cavity has two or three supraoral teeth above the oral opening and three to five bicuspid teeth on either side. Myomeres between the last gill opening and the anus number from 57 to 60. Lateral line organs are black on the back and unpigmented on the venter, a characteristic that separates this species from all other lampreys in Alabama. The body is tan to light gray above and gray to white mottling on the venter. All fins are tan to butterscotch.

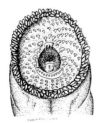

Ventral view of the buccal cavity

ADULT SIZE: 4.5 to 7.1 in (115 to 180 mm)

DISTRIBUTION: The Tennessee River drainage forms the southern range limit for the mountain brook lamprey. Rohde and Lantrigne-Courchene (1978b) include only one collection station in Alabama. At Shoal Creek in Lauderdale County, we recently collected individuals at two stations. Although future sampling conducted in early spring may reveal a slightly larger range, we believe this species' occurrence is limited in Alabama.

HABITAT AND BIOLOGY: The mountain brook lamprey normally inhabits small, clear, high-gradient streams, where it occurs over gravel and sand in moderate currents. In Alabama this species' spawning time and behavior are unstudied. In Tennessee, Etnier and Starnes (1993) observed spawning activity in early May. For lampreys in western North Carolina, Beamish and Austin (1985) estimate that the larval stage lasts from five to seven years.

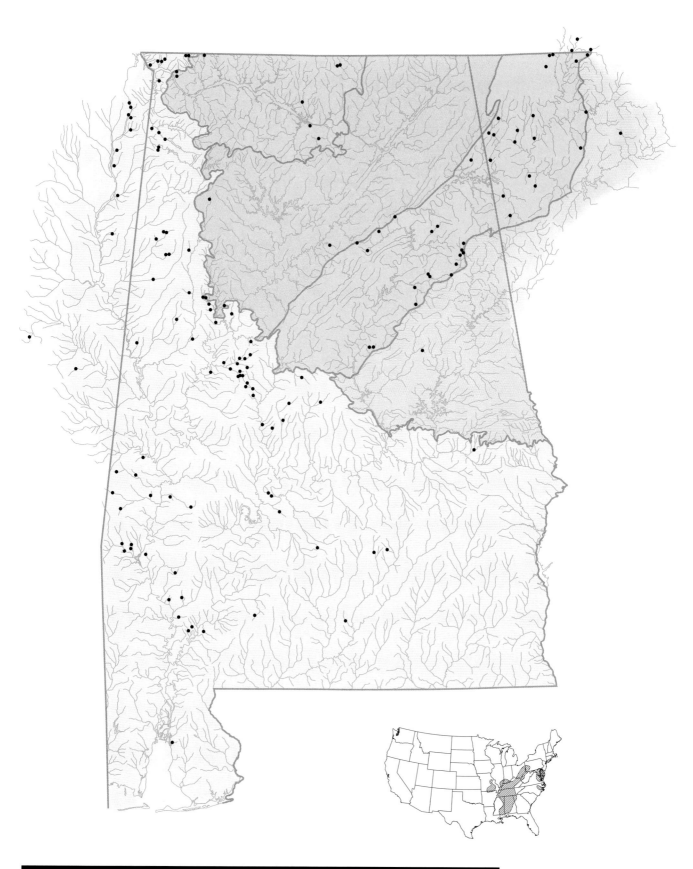

LEAST BROOK LAMPREY   *Lampetra aepyptera*   **147 STATIONS**

Lampetra aepyptera

(Abbott, 1860)

ETYMOLOGY:

Lampetra—sucker of stones

aepyptera—high fin

Buck Branch, Colbert County, 28 March 1991, 3.6 in (91 mm) TL male, GSA 5360

CHARACTERISTICS: The anterior and posterior of the dorsal fin are separated by a distinct notch. On live individuals, the expanded oral disc is narrower than the head. Two widely separated supraoral teeth lie above the oral opening, and three unicuspid or bicuspid teeth lie on either side. Myomeres between the last gill opening and the anus usually number from 54 to 60. Lateral line organs are usually unpigmented. The body is dark to light tan above, blending to light tan to white below. Fins are light tan to cream.

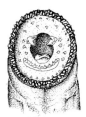

Ventral view of the buccal cavity

ADULT SIZE: 3.5 to 6.5 in (89 to 165 mm)

DISTRIBUTION: This species, though found in scattered locations around the state, has not been collected in the streams of the Black Belt and Southern Pine Hills. Collections in coastal drainages are limited to three upstream sites in the Conecuh River system.

HABITAT AND BIOLOGY: Members of this nonparasitic species usually inhabit small to medium streams with moderate currents over sand and gravel substrates. Spawning occurs from February in south Alabama to April in north Alabama. On 6 February 1980, we collected a spawning aggregation of 34 individuals over sandy substrates at Thornton Branch, a small tributary of the lower Tombigbee River in southern Sumter County. Several females were filled with eggs, an indication that spawning would occur soon. On 28 March 1991, we collected another spawning aggregation of 34 individuals at Buck Branch, in Colbert County. Because the abdomens of several females were distended with eggs, spawning was either imminent or in progress.

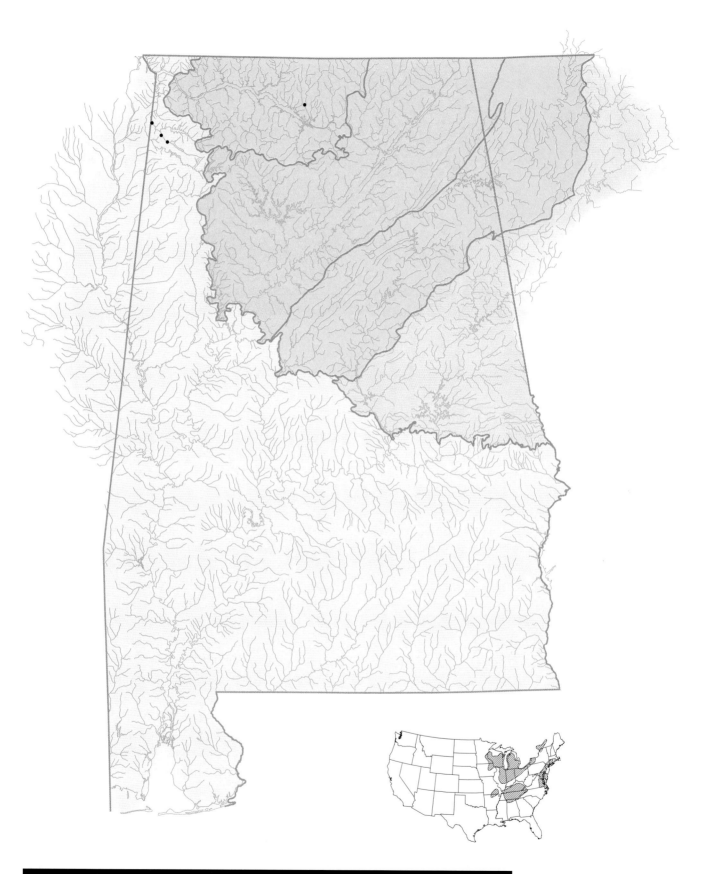

Lampetra appendix

(DeKay, 1842)

ETYMOLOGY:

Lampetra—sucker of stones

appendix—appendage, possibly referring to the tubular process emerging from the vent of this and other lampreys

Little Bear Creek, Franklin County, 25 February 1993, 6.1 in (155 mm) TL female, GSA 4363

CHARACTERISTICS: The high dorsal fin is deeply divided into two distinct parts. On live individuals, the expanded oral disc is about as wide as the head. Two large supraoral teeth are found above the oral opening, and three bicuspid teeth are located on either side. Unlike other lamprey species, whose teeth radiate around the oral opening, the American brook lamprey's remaining teeth occur in small clusters. Myomeres between the last gill opening and the anus usually number from 64 to 75. The back is medium to dark blue-gray, shading to light gray or cream on the venter.

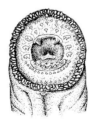

Ventral view of the buccal cavity

ADULT SIZE: 5.9 to 7.9 in (150 to 200 mm)

DISTRIBUTION: In Alabama, this species is recorded from only four localities in two Tennessee River tributaries. Wall (1968) collected 28 specimens in Little Bear Creek in 1966. We collected individuals just downstream of his station and also in Cedar Creek. The only other collection came from French Mill Creek, a tributary to Piney Creek in eastern Limestone County.

HABITAT AND BIOLOGY: The American brook lamprey occurs in small to medium streams. Individuals seem to prefer clean gravel substrates and fast currents. Seagle and Nagel (1982) report a spawning in March in northeastern Tennessee, while Etnier and Starnes (1993) cite a spawning in early April in Citico Creek. Seagle and Nagel (1982) estimate that the larval stage lasts five or six years. Transformed adults usually spawn the next spring and die soon afterward.

STURGEONS

Acipenseridae

The Atlantic sturgeon's Gulf subspecies, ***Acipenser oxyrinchus desotoi,*** holds the record as the largest fish ever caught in Alabama fresh waters. A 400-pound specimen measuring 9.5 feet (3 m) in length and 20 inches (510 mm) across the head was landed from the Coosa River near Coopers, Alabama, and pictured in the *Birmingham News* on 15 June 1924. Even as late as 23 April 1941, a fish weighing 360 pounds and measuring 8 feet (2.4 m) in length was caught on a trotline in the Cahaba River about a mile above Centreville. In an accompanying article, John P. Kennedy, the angler, reported that spawning runs of sturgeon were once common in Alabama. (By "sturgeon," he presumably meant Gulf sturgeon.) Kennedy's father remembered that in the 1880s he caught 27 sturgeon weighing from 350 to 850 pounds in an illegal fish trap in the Cahaba River. Because the sturgeon were so huge, they had to be dragged from the river by a team of mules.

At that time, sturgeon were indeed abundant in Alabama, according to records kept by the U. S. Commission of Fish and Fisheries. A 1905 report states that 100,000 pounds of sturgeon and 5,000 pounds of sturgeon roe, caviar's main ingredient, were harvested from the Mobile River in 1903. Again, these were presumably Gulf sturgeon. An 1898 report records that 42,900 pounds of shovelnose sturgeon were caught in 1896—39,500 pounds from the Alabama River, 2,300 pounds from the Black Warrior River, and 1,100 pounds from the Tennessee River. (Fish from the Alabama and Black Warrior rivers were later described as Alabama sturgeon; see below.)

Today, unfortunately, sturgeon are not nearly as plentiful or as widely distributed as they once were.

Concerned, the Alabama Game and Fish Division has prohibited the taking of any sturgeon from Alabama waters. Reasons often given for its dwindling populations and shrinking distributions are the overfishing that took place around the turn of the century and, more recently, pollution or destruction of its habitats. Also, the construction of locks and dams disrupts the spawning runs of most anadromous species, including the Gulf sturgeon and Alabama shad, ***Alosa alabamae.*** Only two of the four species originally recorded in Alabama—the Gulf sturgeon and Alabama sturgeon—still exist in the state.

However, their future may be brighter. Fisheries biologists in several northern states, including Wisconsin, Minnesota, and South Dakota, are artificially spawning and rearing both lake and shovelnose sturgeon. If this success continues, fisheries biologists in other regions will undoubtedly emulate the practice, for it may be the only way to restore these impressive creatures to their former place in the environment.

Such a restoration is clearly desirable, for the sturgeon's tremendous size is only one aspect of its distinctiveness. Certain physical characteristics reveal that it is also among the oldest, most primitive fishes in Alabama. The elongate skeleton is made of cartilage rather than bone, and the vertebral column extends into the dorsal lobe of the heterocercal tail, much as a shark's does. On the ventral side of the duckbill snout is a protractile mouth with lobed lips; in front of the mouth dangle four barbels. In cross section, the sturgeon is pentamerous, or five-sided. Its body is covered, not with scales, but with leathery skin and five rows of dermal plates, or scutes: one row along the dorsal midline, one row along each side, and one row along each ventrolateral surface.

Sturgeon typically live on the bottoms of medium or large rivers, feeding on worms, aquatic insect larvae, and other creatures inhabiting the first few inches of sand and mud. Because sturgeon have few predators, they have unusually long lives—the large ones can live for more than 100 years. Sturgeon do not reproduce until they are between eight and 20 years old, depending on the species. Only part of the population reproduces in any given year, which buffers the species against times when few eggs hatch or offspring survive.

Shovelnose sturgeon inhabiting rivers of the Mobile basin have been described as Alabama sturgeon, *Scaphirhynchus suttkusi*, by Williams and Clemmer (1991); shovelnose sturgeon from the Tennessee River are *S. platorynchus*. A few lake sturgeon, *Acipenser fulvescens*, were collected in the Coosa and Tennessee river systems in the 1950s, but this species is now believed to have been extirpated in Alabama. Although not native to Alabama, white sturgeon, *A. transmontanus*, have been collected in Weiss Reservoir and below Logan Martin Dam on the Coosa River (and two small specimens were purchased from a local department store in 1994). Two characteristics distinguish the white sturgeon from both lake sturgeon and Gulf sturgeon: The white sturgeon lacks scutes behind the dorsal and anal fins, and its barbels are located closer to the tip of its snout than to its mouth.

KEY TO STURGEONS

1a. Lower lip with two lobes; spiracles present; no filament on upper lobe of caudal fin . . . . . go to 2, *Acipenser*
1b. Lower lip with four lobes; spiracles absent; upper lobe of caudal fin on younger fish with a long filament . . . . go to 3, *Scaphirhynchus*

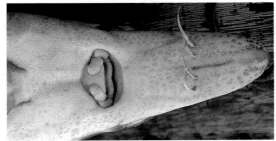 

Lower lips of 1a, *Acipenser,* and 1b, *Scaphirhynchus*

2a. Snout long, V-shaped, and frequently upturned at end; mouth width less than 55 percent of distance between eyes; viscera pale white to cream; preanal fin dermal plates in two rows . . . . Gulf sturgeon, *A. oxyrinchus desotoi*
2b. Snout short, rounded, broad, and not upturned at end; mouth width greater than 60 percent of distance between eyes; viscera dark ; preanal fin dermal plates in a single row . . . . lake sturgeon, *A. fulvescens*

3a. Eye large, its length going into head width 6.5 to 8.2 (usually 7.0 to 8.0) times; 27 to 32 (usually 29 to 30) lateral plates on side of body in front of dorsal fin origin; body color orangish yellow . . . . Alabama sturgeon, *S. suttkusi*
3b. Eye small, its length going into head width 7.7 to 14.4 (usually 9.0 to 11.0) times; 23 to 31 (usually 27) lateral plates on side of body in front of dorsal fin origin; body is light gray on back and white to cream on venter but rarely orangish yellow. . . . . shovelnose sturgeon, *S. platorynchus*

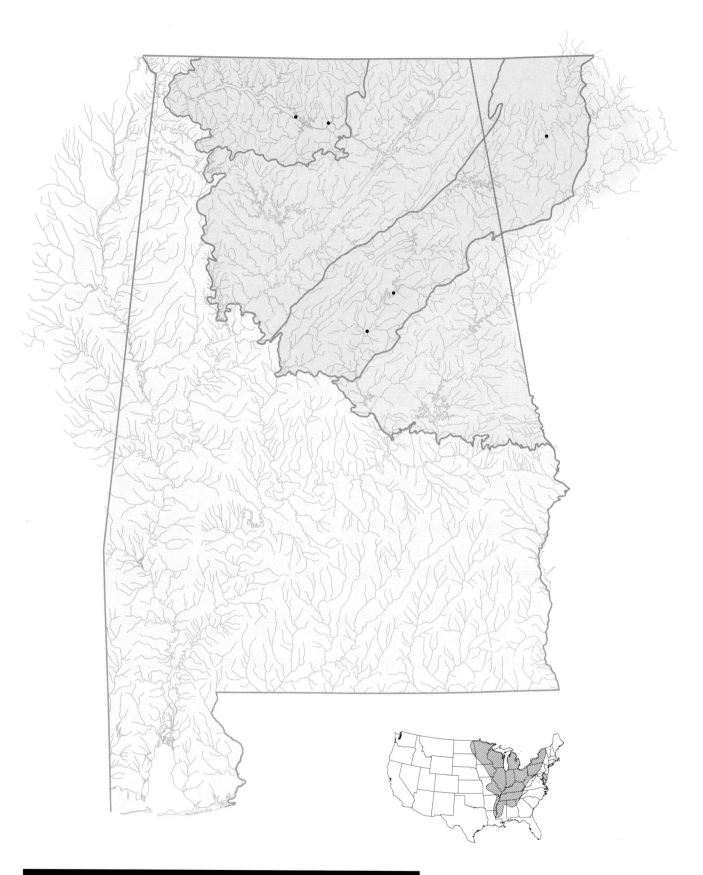

LAKE STURGEON *Acipenser fulvescens* **5 STATIONS**

Acipenser fulvescens

Rafinesque, 1817

ETYMOLOGY:

Acipenser—sturgeon

fulvescens—yellowish

Wolf River, Shawano County, Wisconsin, 8.3 in (210 mm) TL. Photograph courtesy of Richard T. Bryant and Wayne C. Starnes.

CHARACTERISTICS: In the lake sturgeon, the snout is rounded, and a small spiracle is present above and behind each eye. The barbels are smooth, not fringed. The caudal peduncle is not completely covered with dermal plates. The lower lip has two lobes. The back may be light tan to moderate brown, grading to cream color on the venter. Fins are similarly colored. See Rafinesque (1817a) for original description.

ADULT SIZE: 7 to 9 ft (2.1 to 2.7 m)

DISTRIBUTION: The major populations of lake sturgeon are widespread in northern latitudes of the United States and Canada. In Alabama, its collection at only four locations—two in the Tennessee River, two in the Coosa River—coupled with the lack of recent collections indicates that the fish has been extirpated from state waters. Even so, the species is not in immediate jeopardy, because adults have been artificially spawned and reintroduced into the species' former range in the Missouri and upper Mississippi river systems.

HABITAT AND BIOLOGY: Little is known about this species' life history in Alabama. According to studies of northern populations by Scott and Crossman (1973) and Becker (1983), lake sturgeon live on the bottoms of rivers and large streams that have gravel and sand substrates and moderate or swift currents. They feed on benthic (bottom-living) invertebrates, including crayfish, aquatic insect larvae, and mollusks. Only a portion of the adult population migrates upstream into larger streams and spawns in any one year; the time between spawns ranges from four to nine years. Spawning occurs from April into June and lasts for one or two days. Adults congregate in shallow water over gravel in moderate or strong currents, where two males generally spawn with a single female. Some 50,000 to 700,000 eggs are deposited per spawn; larger females may deposit as many as one to three million eggs. Adults leave the spawning site soon afterward to avoid being trapped by summer's lower water levels.

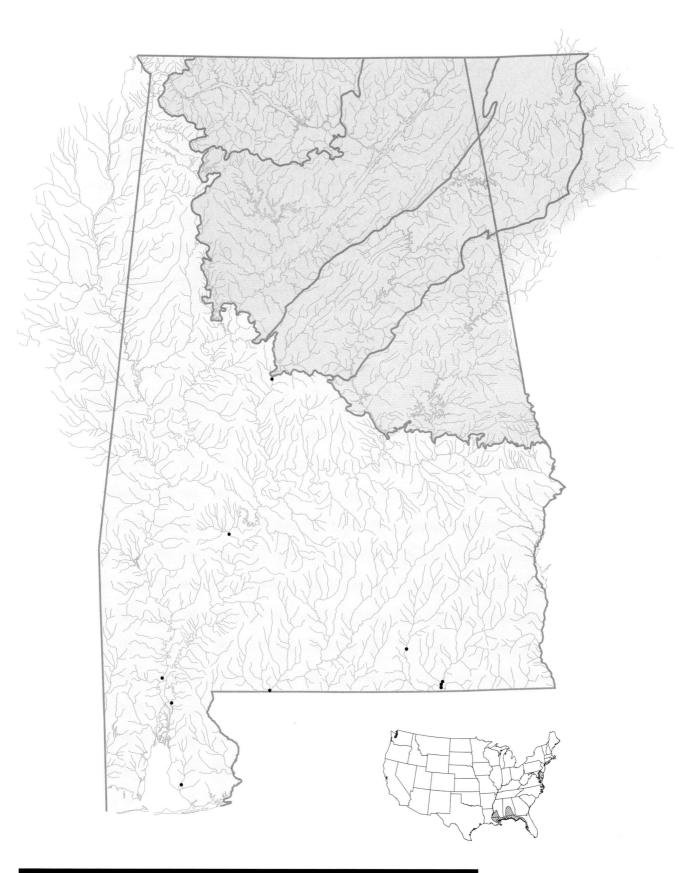

Acipenser oxyrinchus desotoi

(Vladykov, 1955)

ETYMOLOGY:

Acipenser—sturgeon

oxyrinchus—sharp snout

desotoi—in honor of Hernando de Soto

Choctawhatchee River, Geneva County, 25 April 1995, 54 in (1,360 mm) SL male, GSA 4832

CHARACTERISTICS: The Gulf subspecies of the Atlantic sturgeon, *Acipenser oxyrinchus desotoi*, is distinguished from the lake sturgeon, *A. fulvescens*, by a narrower mouth (less than 55 percent of interorbital width in the former, compared to more than 62 percent in the latter) and paired postdorsal and preanal scutes (one row in the lake sturgeon). Other characteristics include a V-shaped snout that is frequently upturned at the tip, a small spiracle behind and slightly above the eye, and a bilobed lower lip. The back is medium to light brown, grading into cream on the belly. Fins are light tan to cream. We follow Gilbert's (1992) recommendation of the spelling *oxyrinchus* as originally used by Mitchill (1815).

ADULT SIZE: 7 to 14 ft (2.1 to 4.3 m)

DISTRIBUTION: The best viable population of Gulf sturgeon in Alabama is in the Choctawhatchee River near Geneva, where we have observed more than two dozen individuals between 1991 and 1994. In 1991 and 1992, the Alabama Game and Fish Division examined live specimens from the Fish River on the eastern side of Mobile Bay and also in the Mobile Delta.

HABITAT AND BIOLOGY: Gulf sturgeon are anadromous, living in salt water and spawning in fresh water. From November through January, individuals reside in estuaries and near shores, where they feed on amphipods, isopods, midges, crabs, and shrimp. Upstream spawning runs usually begin in February. Our collections of males indicate April spawning in the Choctawhatchee River in Geneva County. After spawning, adults retreat to deeper pools and remain there until August or September, when they return downstream. When these fishes are in fresh water, feeding apparently ceases. Huff (1975) reports that migrating sturgeon in the Suwannee River reach sexual maturity between nine and 12 years of age. Spawning sites vary from river to river, but members of a single population probably return to the same general spawning area, much as Pacific salmon do.

REMARKS: On 30 September 1991, the Gulf sturgeon was listed as a threatened species by the U. S. Fish and Wildlife Service. It is also protected under Rules and Regulations of the Alabama Game and Fish Division.

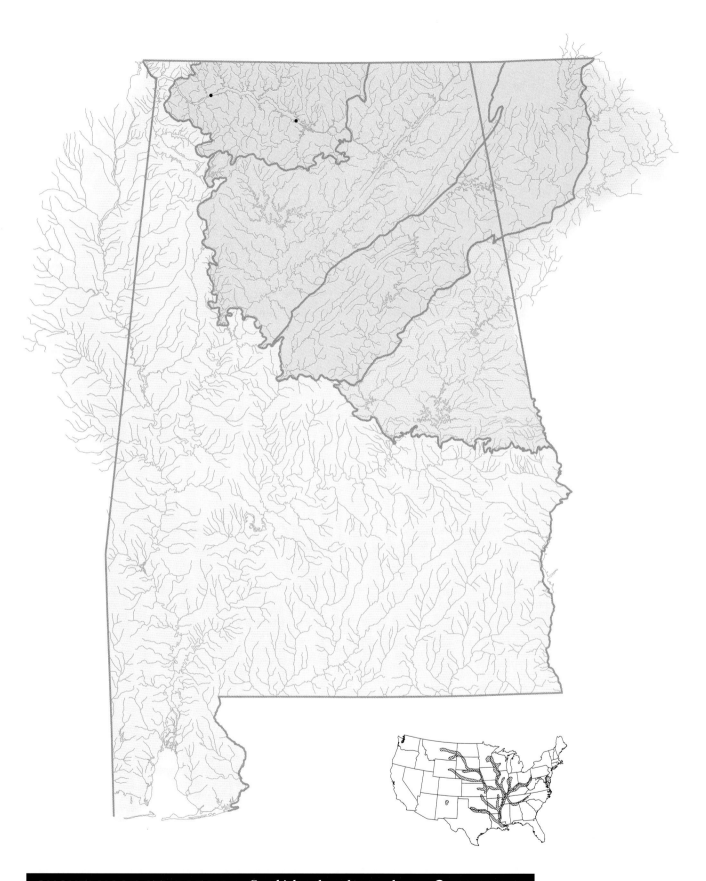

SHOVELNOSE STURGEON   *Scaphirhynchus platorynchus*   **2 STATIONS**

Scaphirhynchus platorynchus

(Rafinesque, 1820)

ETYMOLOGY:

Scaphirhynchus—spade-shaped snout

platorynchus—broad snout

Mississippi River, Lake County, Tennessee, January 1994, 25 in (630 mm) SL

CHARACTERISTICS: As its common name indicates, this species has a shovel-shaped snout. Both the shovelnose and the Alabama sturgeon, ***Scaphirhynchus suttkusi***, are distinguished from members of the genus *Acipenser* by four lobes on the lower lip and fringed barbels in front of the mouth. The shovelnose sturgeon's eye is somewhat smaller than the Alabama sturgeon's; its eye length goes 7.7 to 14.4 (usually 9.0 to 11.0) times into head width. Lateral plates anterior to the origin of the dorsal fin number 23 to 31, dorsal plates 13 to 19, and plates between the caudal fin base and the caudal peduncle seven to 10 (usually nine). The top on this fish is light to medium gray or brown, grading to cream or white on the venter.

ADULT SIZE: 2 to 3 ft (0.6 to 0.9 m)

DISTRIBUTION: In Alabama, shovelnose sturgeon were first collected in the Tennessee River near Wilson Dam in 1937 and near Decatur in 1940 (Bailey and Cross, 1954). These specimens were later deposited in the University of Michigan Museum of Zoology and the Smithsonian Institution. Although this species seems to have been extirpated in Alabama, recent collections were reported in Kentucky by Warren et al. (1986) and in Arkansas by Robison and Buchanan (1988). Etnier and Starnes (1993) report that shovelnose sturgeon are often taken by commercial fishermen in western Tennessee.

HABITAT AND BIOLOGY: Little is known about the habitat of this species in Alabama. Hurley et al. (1987) record collecting upper Mississippi basin specimens, at depths of 14 to 40 feet in large rivers with swift currents and sand and gravel substrates. Individuals usually seek cover behind wing dams and other structures during high water and remain in deeper channels during the summer. In Arkansas, Robison and Buchanan (1988) report that adults spawn over rocky substrates when water temperatures reach 68° to 71°F (19.5° to 21.1°C). Individuals are fairly active during the spring, probably because they are searching for spawning partners. Rafinesque (1820) reports that Alabama shad, paddlefish, and shovelnose sturgeon were all collected below the falls of the Ohio River, an indication that the three species may use the same area for spawning.

REMARKS: Shovelnose sturgeon have been spawned in captivity and the offspring released into the upper Mississippi River basin. Hopes are that one day this can be done to restock Alabama waters as well.

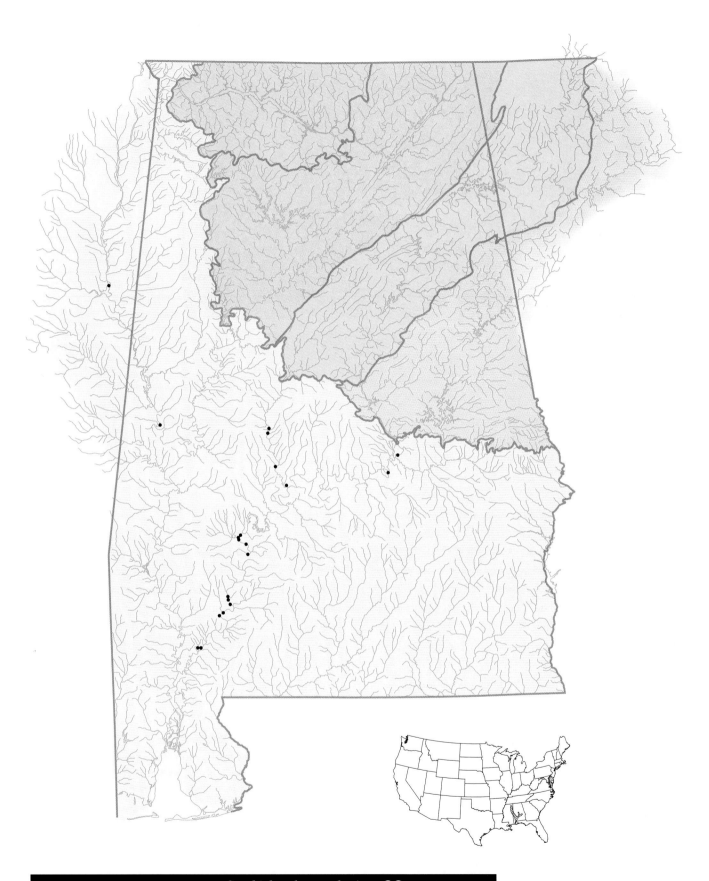

ALABAMA STURGEON *Scaphirhynchus suttkusi* **20 STATIONS**

Scaphirhynchus suttkusi
Williams and Clemmer,
1991

ETYMOLOGY:
Scaphirhynchus—spade-shaped snout
suttkusi—in honor of Royal D. Suttkus, noted ichthyologist and collector of southeastern fishes

Alabama River, Monroe County, 2 December 1993, 25.6 in (650 mm) SL male, GSA 4583

CHARACTERISTICS: In the Alabama sturgeon, the eye is large, its length going 6.5 to 8.2 (usually 7.0 to 8.0) times into the head width (Williams and Clemmer, 1991). Lateral plates behind the dorsal fin usually number 27 to 32, dorsal plates 15 to 21, and plates between the anal fin base and the caudal peduncle seven or eight. The back and most of the dorsal, pectoral, and caudal fins are brownish orange. The sides of the body near the lateral row of scutes are light tan to golden yellow. The belly, pelvic fin, and most of the anal fin are creamy white.

ADULT SIZE: 2.3 to 2.6 ft (.7 to .8 m)

DISTRIBUTION: This species is endemic to the Mobile basin. The original description was based on only 32 museum specimens from the Alabama, Cahaba, Coosa, and upper Tombigbee rivers. Burke and Ramsey (1985) collected five specimens in the lower Alabama River system. Since 1993, three individuals have been collected in the Alabama River, all from downstream of Claiborne Lock and Dam.

HABITAT AND BIOLOGY: Burke and Ramsey (1985) observe that this species prefers deep, swiftly moving currents over permanent sand and gravel substrates. Williams and Clemmer (1991) note that larval insects were the most abundant food items in the specimens they examined. The collection of 12 individuals (including two gravid females) at the mouth of the Cahaba River on 21 March 1969 (Burke and Ramsey, 1985, 1995) indicated that this species spawns in late March or early April; Alabama River females examined in April and May 1985 had not ovulated, which suggests a later spawn.

REMARKS: The type locality for the Alabama sturgeon is Smith Lake, Monroe County, Alabama. The continued existence of this species, which is unique to the Mobile basin, may depend upon cooperative efforts to conduct spawning in captivity and to release the offspring into suitable habitats. This strategy has already been successful for shovelnose sturgeon in the upper Mississippi.

PADDLEFISH

Polyodontidae

The paddlefish—a prehistoric fish that is represented by only two species worldwide—looks like a big-mouthed shark with a boat paddle for a nose. These unique physical features have inspired a number of colorful but scientifically incorrect descriptive names, including freshwater shark, spoonbill cat, and spoonbill sturgeon. Even Walbaum (1792), in his original description of the species, classified the paddlefish as a shark because of its relatively large size, heterocercal tail, and cartilaginous skeleton. In fact, the paddlefish's closest relatives are not sharks or catfishes, but sturgeons.

The American paddlefish, *Polyodon spathula*, reaches lengths of 6 to 7 feet, and although its size is intimidating, it is a docile creature. Since it is planktivorous (plankton-feeding), the paddlefish routinely cruises near the water surface, its mouth open and its gill filaments screening the water for plankton; from time to time, it closes its mouth to swallow the plankton mass deposited on the filaments. The paddlefish is also known for its spectacular jumps, particularly in late afternoon. Though not completely understood, the jumps may be a way for the fish to free itself of parasites.

The only other paddlefish species occurs in China. The Chinese paddlefish, *Psephurus gladius*, is characterized by a snout that resembles a sword rather than a paddle: The end is pointed, and the median axis is thick, tapering to thinner lateral edges. This species is piscivorous (fish-eating), and it grows to be much larger than its American relative, reaching lengths of up to 20 feet. Like other commercial fishes, Chinese paddlefish have been greatly overfished in recent years. Concerned, the Chinese government recently classified *P. gladius* as an endangered species. The government has also introduced the American paddlefish into many of China's rivers to ease the impact of commercial fishing on its native counterpart.

Paddlefish have long been prized as a food fish in Alabama, but their planktivorous feeding habits make them difficult to catch. Commercial fishermen have caught them using trotlines soaked in oil-based liquids and, more recently, gill nets. Paddlefish have also been snagged below dams during spawning runs, although this method has been used more effectively in the Mississippi River. The species' historical importance for commercial fishing is evidenced by an 1898 report by the U.S. Commission of Fish and Fisheries: In 1894, 8,250 pounds of paddlefish (valued at $185) were snagged in the Alabama and Black Warrior rivers. Nearly a century later, Malvestuto et al. (1983) claim that in 1980 and 1981, fishermen harvested 93,885 pounds from the Mobile Delta and lower Tombigbee River.

Paddlefish are in demand partly because their roe is being used for caviar. Traditionally, sturgeon roe has been preferred, but declining sturgeon populations make paddlefish roe an attractive alternative. Many state conservation agencies have cautioned that now paddlefish are being overfished, a problem compounded by the fact that paddlefish require many years to reach sexual maturity (seven to nine years for males, nine to 11 years for females). In 1987, the Alabama Game and Fish Division banned all paddlefish harvesting in the state. Since then, we have noted an increase in our encounters with paddlefishes of all sizes—an encouraging sign that the moratorium is having a positive effect.

TOMBIGBEE RIVER, CLARKE COUNTY

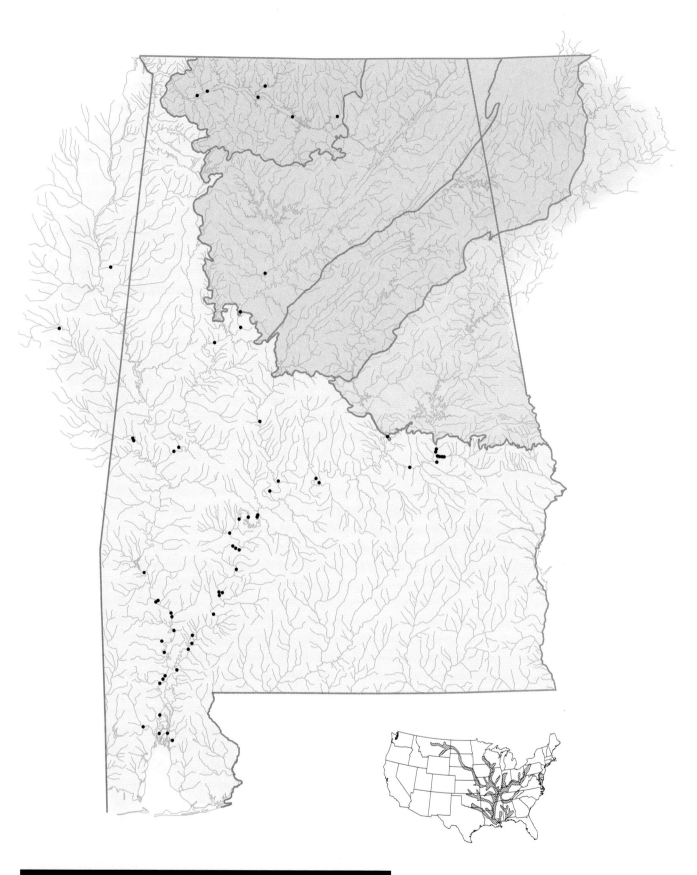

PADDLEFISH *Polyodon spathula* **63 STATIONS**

Polyodon spathula

(Walbaum, 1792)

ETYMOLOGY:

Polyodon—many teeth, referring to the numerous gill rakers
spathula—spatula, referring to the paddle-shaped snout

Tombigbee River, Marengo County, 30 April 1992, 20.4 in (519 mm) TL male, GSA 4226

CHARACTERISTICS: This fish's long, paddle-shaped snout accounts for about one-third of its total body length. The snout helps to stabilize the fish as it swims, and it also contains specialized cells that assist in detecting the plankton swarms upon which this species feeds. The skin is smooth. Small individuals are pink on the back and white on the venter; for larger individuals around 10 to 12 inches, the body color changes to bluish gray on the back and cream on the venter. The eyes are tiny compared to the rest of the head and body. On the underside of the snout are two minute barbels in front of a large, toothless mouth. When viewed through the mouth, the gills are large and show the many closely spaced filaments that trap microscopic food. On each side, a gill cover extends posteriorly, ending in a long, pointed flap. The skeleton is composed of cartilage rather than bone. The end of the vertebral column extends into the upper lobe of the heterocercal tail, much as a shark's does.

ADULT SIZE: 3.9 to 5.9 ft (1.2 to 1.8 m). The state angling record (52 lb, 12 oz) was caught below Wilson Dam on the Tennessee River in 1982.

DISTRIBUTION: Paddlefish occur primarily below the Fall Line in the Mobile basin. They are absent in our coastal rivers. Due to overfishing, this species has all but disappeared from the Tennessee River. On 9 September 1994, we received a photograph of a 19-inch-long paddlefish that was caught and released below Wilson Dam near Florence, Alabama.

HABITAT AND BIOLOGY: Paddlefish are generally found in open water, but we have collected individuals as long as 3 to 4 feet in relatively small streams, such as Isaac Creek (Monroe County), Chickasaw Creek (Mobile County), and Three Rivers Creek (Washington County). A migratory species, paddlefish congregate below dams to spawn during March and April. Spawning between one female and several males is believed to occur in open water. Floating downstream with the current, eggs drift to the bottom and stay there until hatching. Newly hatched individuals grow rapidly, reaching 12 to 14 inches by the end of their first year. Paddlefish are long-lived. Examinations of growth rings on the dentary bones indicate life spans of 20 to 30 years.

GARS

Lepisosteidae

Growing to lengths of 4 to 6 feet, gars are among the largest freshwater fishes found in Alabama. This vicious-looking fish has a bony head, a moderate to long snout, and numerous sharp teeth. The cylindrical body is covered with rough, hard, diamond-shaped, nonoverlapping ganoid scales, giving the fish an armor-plated appearance. The dorsal and anal fins are situated in the rear half of the body, just in front of the rounded caudal fin.

The feeding habits of these creatures are as their looks suggest. Motionless, they linger along a bank or at the edge of aquatic vegetation, darting out occasionally to grab unsuspecting prey (usually a smaller sunfish or shad). They swallow their prey whole, head first.

Other than the alligator gar, *Lepisosteus spatula*, members of this family are usually not sought by fishermen in Alabama. Contrary to local legends, gars are not known to attack people. Nevertheless, if they are caught, gars should be handled with great care. With their needlelike teeth and the sharp plates on their heads, gars can inflict nasty wounds and even damage boats.

Gars "roll" on the water's surface, particularly in late summer, when water temperatures rise and dissolved oxygen content decreases. As a gar breaks the surface, it swallows air that is forced into the air bladder inside the gut cavity. Oxygen absorbed into the blood through a rich supply of blood vessels surrounding the air bladder supplements oxygen obtained through the gills during normal respiration.

Our field observations indicate that gars generally spawn from late March into early June. Small schools of one female and one to several males swim about in shallow water, occasionally thrashing the surface with their tails. During this process, sperm and large adhesive eggs are released. Fertilized eggs settle to the bottom, where they stick to the substrate, aquatic vegetation, and limbs or other debris. Etnier and Starnes (1993) indicate that gar eggs may be toxic, thereby reducing egg mortality by predation. After mating, adults return to deeper water. Larval gars are not strong swimmers. They spend their first few days attached to vegetation or tree roots by means of an adhesive spot at the tip of the snout. Young gars have a long dorsal filament on the caudal fin that vibrates constantly; its function is unknown, and the filament disappears with age.

The alligator gar is one of the largest fish species in Alabama. Adult specimens weighing more than 100 pounds and reaching lengths exceeding 6 feet are occasionally caught by anglers in the Mobile Delta and tributaries to Mobile Bay. Somewhat migratory in nature, alligator gars once ranged throughout most Coastal Plain rivers of the Mobile basin. Inland records have diminished dramatically in recent years, apparently because this gar cannot easily make its way through navigational locks and dams. Biologists with the Alabama Game and Fish Division note that a growing demand for alligator gar meat in several southeastern states has prompted increased commercial fishing in Alabama's coastal waters, with an estimated several hundred gars being caught annually. Because populations of this long-lived species could be damaged by overfishing, harvest seasons and size limits, or both, may be required.

The longnose gar, *L. osseus,* often reaches lengths of 4 to 5 feet and weights of 30 or more pounds. This species seems to prefer moving water, especially tailwater areas below dams. Probably the most abundant and widespread gar in Alabama, the spotted gar, *L. oculatus*, thrives in rivers and reservoirs and also ventures into moderate to small streams.

Gar species can usually be distinguished by snout shape and body color. The spotted gar has a short, moderately broad snout, and most individuals are brown on the back and cream to light tan, with small darker spots on the venter and conspicuous black spots on the snout,

back, and fins. (We have also collected melanistic, or essentially black, spotted gars and have seen one xanthic, or bright orange, specimen from south Alabama.) The longnose gar has a long, slender snout and is olive green on the back and white to cream on the venter. The spotted gar and the shortnose gar, *L. platostomus*, have similar snout shapes and body colors, except that the uncommon shortnose has few, if any, spots. The alligator gar is distinguishable from the spotted gar by having a shorter, wider snout and a heavier body.

KEY TO GARS

1a. Snout long and narrow, its width going 10 or more times into its length . . longnose gar, *Lepisosteus osseus*
1b. Snout short and broad, its width going fewer than 10 times into its length . . . . go to 2

2a. Distance from tip of snout to corner of mouth shorter than from corner of mouth to back edge of gill cover; gill rakers number 60 or more on the gill arch . . . . alligator gar, *L. spatula*
2b. Distance from tip of snout to corner of mouth longer than from corner of mouth to back edge of gill cover; gill rakers number 30 or fewer on the gill arch . . . . go to 3

3a. Head and anterior part of body with scattered black spots; lateral line scales number 54 to 58; predorsal scales usually 45 to 54 . . . . spotted gar, *L. oculatus*
3b. Head and anterior part of body without black spots; lateral line scales number 59 to 64; predorsal scales usually number 51 to 55 (occasionally 50) . . . . shortnose gar, *L. platostomus*

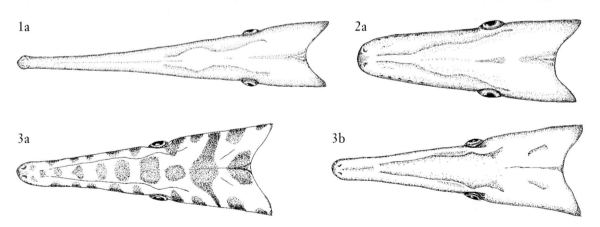

Snouts of 1a, *L. osseus*; 2a, *L. spatula*; 3a, *L. oculatus*; 3b, *L. platostomus*

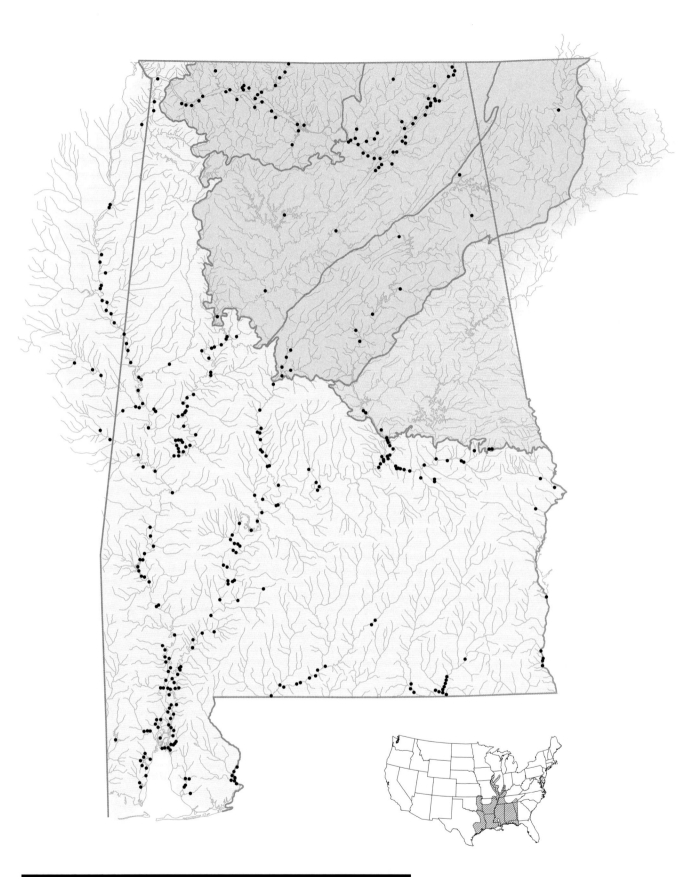

Lepisosteus oculatus
(Winchell, 1864)

ETYMOLOGY:
Lepisosteus—bony scale
oculatus—eyed, referring to
the round spots on the body
and fins

Choctawhatchee River, Geneva County, 6 May 1993, 15.4 in (390 mm) SL male, GSA 4441

CHARACTERISTICS: A spotted gar has from 54 to 58 lateral line scales and 17 to 20 diagonal scale rows, counting obliquely from the anal fin origin upward to the dorsal midline. Predorsal scales generally number from 45 to 54. The head, back, and sides are medium brown with scattered round, darker brown spots. The venter varies from light brown to cream. The fins are light yellow to brown with round brown or black spots.

ADULT SIZE: 2.9 to 3.9 ft (0.9 to 1.2 m). The state angling record (8 lb, 12 oz) was caught in Cotaco Creek, a Tennessee River tributary, in 1987.

DISTRIBUTION: Our sampling efforts, supplemented with data from the Alabama Game and Fish Division and Tulane University, indicate that spotted gars are widespread and occasionally abundant in the Mobile basin and larger coastal drainages. We collected this species at 58 stations in the Tennessee River drainage

and observed dozens of individuals in Bear Creek in Colbert County on 6 June 1993. The range of the spotted gar will be expanded by future surveys of Alabama's riverine faunas.

HABITAT AND BIOLOGY: Our samplings over the past 10 years indicate that this is the most widespread and abundant gar species in Alabama, probably because it is adaptable to a broader range of habitats than other gars. We have collected individuals in rivers and reservoirs, large and small streams, swamps, and oxbow lakes. Unlike longnose gars, which prefer flowing water, spotted gars seem to like areas of little or no current. They are also frequently associated with floating and attached aquatic vegetation and other heavy cover. A spawning aggregation of adults was observed on 18 May 1989 in Hatchet Creek, a major tributary of the Coosa River. Eggs and larvae of this species in Alabama are described by Simon and Tyberghein (1991).

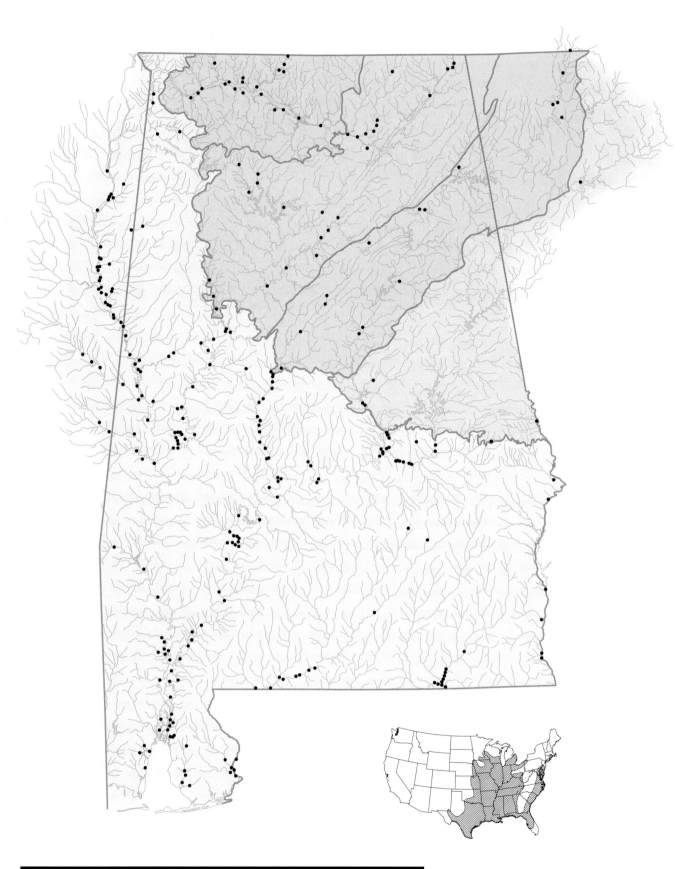

LONGNOSE GAR   *Lepisosteus osseus*   **278 STATIONS**

Lepisosteus osseus

(Linnaeus, 1758)

ETYMOLOGY:

Lepisosteus—bony scale

osseus—bony

Choctawhatchee River, Geneva County, 6 May 1993, 15 in (380 mm) SL male, GSA 4441

CHARACTERISTICS: Longnose gars have from 58 to 64 lateral line scales and 20 to 23 diagonal scale rows counting obliquely from the anal fin origin to the dorsal midline. The width of the snout at the nostrils is less than the eye diameter. The body is olive green to light brown on the back, cream to white on the venter, and has 57 to 64 lateral scales. Predorsal scale rows usually number from 47 to 55. The fins are light gray to clear with a few scattered dark spots.

ADULT SIZE: 3.9 to 5.9 ft (1.2 to 1.8 m). The state angling record (32 lb, 14 oz) was caught in Jordan Reservoir on the Coosa River in 1985.

DISTRIBUTION: Longnose gars occur in every river system in Alabama except the Escatawpa. Reports by Wiley (1979) and Boschung (1992) provide limited longnose gar records in the Tennessee River system. However, information obtained from Tennessee Valley Authority biologists and supplemented by our 1991–93 collection data from 23 stations indicates that the species is more common than was previously believed.

Several dozen individuals up to 4 feet in total length were observed suspended at the water surface in both Paint Rock River and Bear Creek during our 1993 boat electrofishing efforts. Future sampling, particularly in the Tennessee River drainage, should increase the known range of this species in Alabama.

HABITAT AND BIOLOGY: Longnose gars inhabit rivers and reservoirs, large streams, and swamps. They seem to prefer flowing water, and during the spring spawning season, we have observed large numbers of gravid adults congregated in tailwater areas below every lock and dam in the Mobile basin. This species also ventures into brackish and even salt water, where it is infrequently landed by anglers. Pflieger (1975) reports that longnose gars spawn from early May into June in Missouri. We observed spawning aggregations of adult males and females in May. Individuals were congregated in a slow to moderate current of rocky riffles and runs of the lower Coosa River main channel in Elmore County. A few days later, adhesive gar eggs were found on cobble and rubble substrate in this same riffle area.

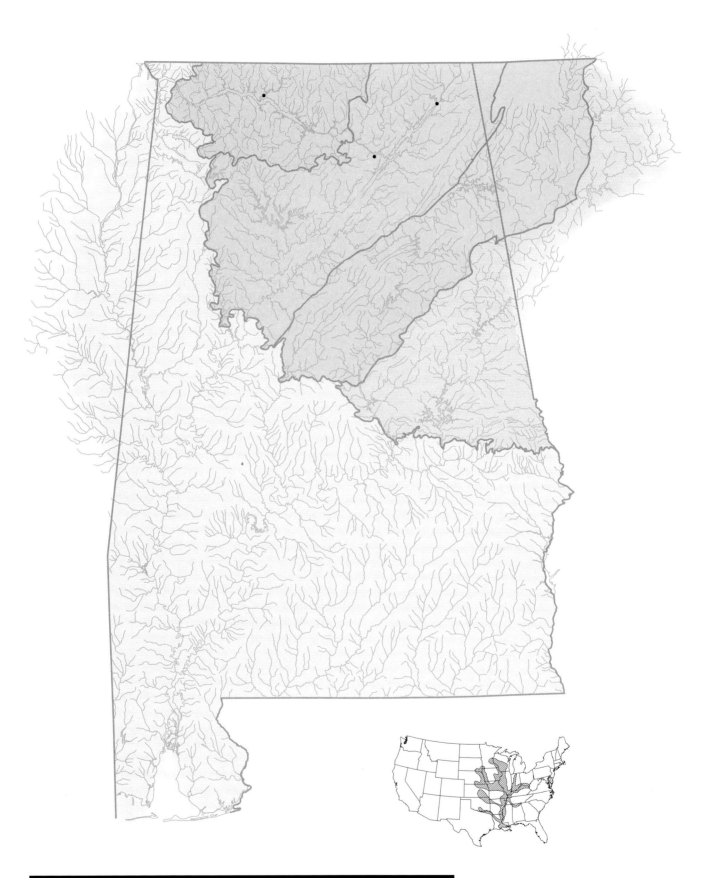

SHORTNOSE GAR *Lepisosteus platostomus* **3 STATIONS**

Mississippi River, West Feliciana Parish, Louisiana, 14 December 1978, 12.6 in (320 mm) SL, TU 110918

CHARACTERISTICS: The shortnose gar's body has 59 to 64 lateral line scales, 20 to 23 rows of diagonal scales between the anal fin origin and the dorsal midline, and 51 to 55 predorsal scale rows. The presence or absence of spots on the snout and anterior body will usually separate spotted from shortnose gars. Spotted gars have dark round spots on the snout and anterior regions of the back; shortnose gars usually lack spots except on the body and vertical fins.

ADULT SIZE: 1.7 to 2.6 ft (.5 to .8 m). No state angling record exists for this species.

DISTRIBUTION: We have included the shortnose gar with some reservations. Jandebeur (1972) and Lee (1978a) report the same collection location from the lower Elk River in Alabama. Biologists from the Tennessee Valley Authority record an occasional individual from above and below Guntersville Reservoir, but our attempts to locate voucher specimens have been unsuccessful. Boschung (1992) cites David A. Etnier (personal communication) in reporting collections from Pickwick, Wheeler, and Guntersville pools. However, Etnier and Starnes (1993) provide no records from the Tennessee River near the Alabama state line. They further comment that upstream reports of the species in the Tennessee River drainage (which ends in Alabama on their inset map) could be based upon identification of poorly marked spotted gars. We examined many dozens, if not hundreds, of short-snouted gars from 1991 through 1993 during boat electrofishing in the Tennessee River system. All suspicious-looking individuals were placed in a live tank, examined, and released unharmed. Without exception, all acquired snout spots in captivity. We cannot say that shortnose gars do not occur in Alabama, but we do believe they are extremely rare.

HABITAT AND BIOLOGY: This species appears to have a higher tolerance to silt and high turbidity than do other gar species. Although it inhabits rivers and reservoirs, Robison and Buchanan (1988) found it most abundant in quiet Arkansas backwaters characterized by sand and silt bottoms. Etnier and Starnes (1993) note that shortnose gar avoid both currents and rooted vegetation in Tennessee. In reviewing two earlier papers, Pflieger (1975) reports that their diet consists more of crayfishes and insects than fishes.

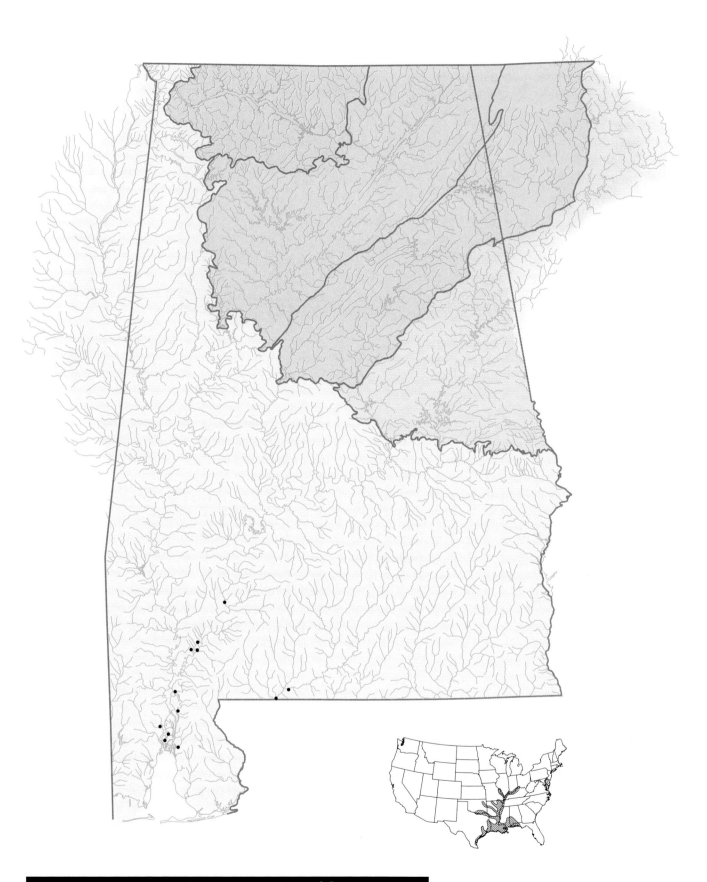

ALLIGATOR GAR   *Lepisosteus spatula*   12 STATIONS

Lepisosteus spatula
Lacepede 1803

ETYMOLOGY:

Lepisosteus—bony scale
spatula—spatula, referring
to the shape of the snout

Conecuh River, Escambia County, 24 March 1992, 39 in (990 mm) SL female, GSA 4195

CHARACTERISTICS: Alligator gars typically have from 57 to 62 lateral line scales and 23 diagonal scale rows between the anal fin origin and the dorsal midline. Adult gars always have two rows of teeth in the upper jaw, compared to one row in all other gar species. Younger individuals may have only one row. The back and sides of this species are green to gray, and the venter is white. The vertical fins are tan with varying numbers of round black spots.

ADULT SIZE: 5.9 to 9.8 ft (1.8 to 3 m). The state angling record (140 lb) was caught in Blakeley River in the Mobile Delta in 1983.

DISTRIBUTION: Alligator gars still inhabit the Mobile Delta and adjacent coastal waters, but recent reports indicate that inland occurrences are rare. One author (MFM) remembers that in the 1950s the *Demopolis Times* featured a photograph of a large alligator gar caught in either the Tombigbee or the Black Warrior River. A 140-pound specimen was caught in the Alabama River near Claiborne Ferry in Monroe

County on 5 July 1928 (John Hall, 1992, personal communication). In November 1991, we examined two alligator gars taken with bow and arrow in Chuckfee Bay north of the Mobile Causeway. One weighed 100 pounds, the other 120. Personal encounters with this species are limited to collections of several smaller individuals (18 to 30 inches total length) in the Mobile Delta and three larger specimens (45 to 50 inches total length) from the Conecuh River near Brewton. We have also examined photographs of several individuals collected with hook and line in Dog River, Fish River, and the Mobile Delta.

HABITAT AND BIOLOGY: Alligator gars live in Alabama's coastal estuaries as well as in its major rivers and large streams. The Conecuh River sites where we collected this species were characterized by a moderate current and predominantly sand and gravel substrates. Mobile Delta collections were from brackish water near Mobile Bay, where currents were slow and substrates were composed mainly of silt and mud. As with other gar species, spawning probably occurs in the spring.

BOWFIN

Amiidae

The bowfin family has only one extant genus and one species, **Amia calva**. This species is frequently caught by anglers in Alabama, who have given the bowfin such vernacular names as grindle, grinnel, mudfish, and dogfish.

The bowfin is a long, cylindrical fish with a prominent backbone that flexes upward into a rounded tail. It is the only freshwater fish in Alabama with a bony gular plate between its lower jaws on the underside of the head. The dorsal fin has 46 to 50 soft rays; it extends more than half the length of its back and is longer than that of any other fish species in Alabama except the American eel. The body is covered with cycloid scales, with 64 to 70 along the lateral line; the head is scaleless. Body color is mottled olive green to light brown on the back, grading to light green to cream on the venter. A prominent black spot—which is surrounded by a yellow or orange ring and located near the base of the caudal fin on young bowfins and adult males—is an excellent example of deceptive coloration. Resembling another eye, this physical feature sometimes confuses potential predators, causing them to strike at the tail rather than the head and thus allowing the bowfin to escape. The adult bowfin's large mouth possesses many sharp, canine teeth. Anglers have learned to be careful while handling these fish, which are slippery, strong, and capable of delivering a powerful bite.

Although we have collected bowfin in rivers and larger streams, they thrive in swamps, sloughs, borrow pits, backwater areas of reservoirs, and oxbow lakes such as those along the Black Warrior River in Greene County. They apparently prefer areas of standing water rather than current and often reach greatest abundance near aquatic vegetation. Fishes, including gizzard shad, golden shiners, and bullheads, compose much of the bowfin's diet (Robison and Buchanan, 1988). In March and April, males prepare a spawning site by cleaning an area within a stand of aquatic vegetation. After females deposit their eggs, males guard the nests until the eggs hatch. Young bowfin remain hidden for their first few days, after which they venture out in schools and eventually as individuals.

Although bowfin reach weights of more than 10 pounds and provide an excellent fight when hooked, local anglers usually disdain them as food. Even so, they occasionally appear in commercial markets: Malvestuto et al. (1983) report that commercial and sport fishermen caught more than 8,500 pounds of bowfin in the lower Tombigbee River and Mobile Delta in 1980 and 1981.

Horsehunter Creek, Noxubee County, 12 May 1995, 3.3 in (84 mm) SL juvenile, GSA 4645

BLACK WARRIOR RIVER, GREENE COUNTY

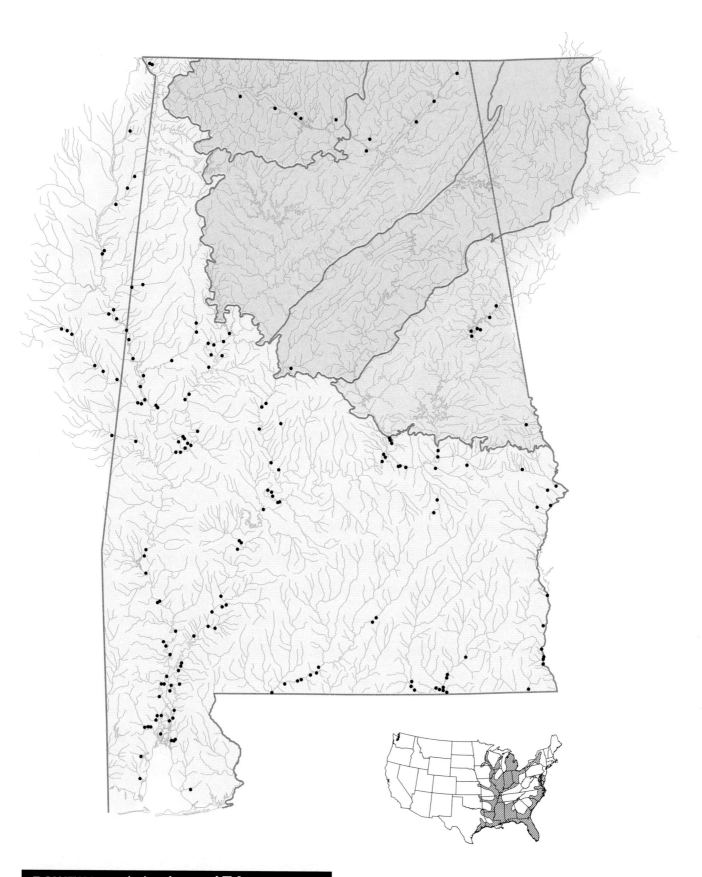

BOWFIN   *Amia calva*   **174 STATIONS**

Amia calva

Linnaeus, 1766

ETYMOLOGY:

Amia—in Greek, an
unidentified fish, possibly
a bonito
calva—smooth

Hatchechubbee Creek, Russell County, 8 April 1993, 14.4 in (365 mm) SL male, GSA 4416

CHARACTERISTICS: See Bowfin family introduction.

ADULT SIZE: 15 to 24 in (380 to 610 mm). The state angling record (17 lb, 12 oz) was caught in the Mobile Delta in 1978.

DISTRIBUTION: Knowledge of bowfin distribution in Alabama has increased substantially over the past 10 years. Burgess and Gilbert (1978) report fewer than 20 localities in Alabama. Boschung (1992) supplies records of four samples that were collected by the Tennessee Valley Authority in the Tennessee drainage in 1936 and 1937 and were housed at the University of Michigan Museum of Zoology. Page and Burr (1991) exclude the entire eastern Mobile basin from their report on freshwater fishes of the United States. The map on the facing page records the species at 174 stations, 60 percent of which have been collected since 1985. The Mobile Delta appears to be the bowfin's stronghold. On several occasions, we observed more than 100 bowfin in less than an hour of electrofishing. The absence of bowfin records from the Blackwater, Escatawpa, and Yellow rivers is probably due to insufficient sampling.

HABITAT AND BIOLOGY: Bowfin prefer quiet, clear, backwater areas, lingering along the margins of aquatic vegetation, in undercut banks, and around branches and other submerged structures. Pflieger (1975) reports spawning in April and May in Missouri. On 8 April 1993, in Hatchechubbee Creek in Russell County, we collected the most beautiful male bowfin we have ever observed. The above photograph shows the intense emerald green characteristic of male bowfin in high spawning condition. R. D. Suttkus collected a bright green male bowfin running milt in 58°F (14°C) water at Tait's Bar on the Alabama River, Wilcox County, on 28 February 1990. Small bowfin typically form dense schools and remain in or near aquatic vegetation until they reach 4 to 5 inches (102 to 127 mm) total length, when they become more solitary in lifestyle. We observed a large school of fry less than an inch long in backwater areas of the Black Warrior River system in April. The air bladder in this species functions as a lung does, extracting oxygen from air that is gulped at the water surface. Neill (1950) notes that bowfin estivate under certain conditions. Carlander (1969) reports a life span of 30 or more years.

MOONEYES

Hiodontidae

Members of this family have large, conspicuous eyes, with eye diameters that are nearly double those of any other Alabama fish species of similar size. At first glance, mooneyes seem to strongly resemble the herrings in the family Clupeidae, but several characters separate the two. First, all mooneyes have a lateral line system, while clupeids lack these structures. Also, mooneyes are piscivorous, feeding on small fishes; close examination reveals that their upper and lower jaws and even their tongues are equipped with many small, sharp teeth, which are useful in catching prey. In contrast, clupeids are planktivorous, and they lack teeth.

The mooneye family contains only two species, both of which occur in Alabama. The mooneye, **Hiodon tergisus**, occurs in all river systems of the Mobile basin and the Tennessee River drainage. (The Elk River, shown at right, is a tributary of the Tennesee River.) The goldeye, **H. alosoides**, a more northern species, was collected at four stations in the Tennessee River drainage in 1938 and has not been seen since, an ominous sign that the species may have been eliminated from the state's ichthyofauna. However, this species is presently distributed throughout the Mississippi basin from Louisiana northward to North Dakota and Montana, and eastward into the Ohio and Tennessee river drainages.

KEY TO MOONEYES

1a. Dorsal fin origin above or slightly behind anal fin origin; 9 to 10 dorsal fin rays; 29 to 34 anal fin rays; 56 to 62 lateral line scales; Tennessee River drainage . . . . goldeye, *Hiodon alosoides*

1b. Dorsal fin origin distinctly anterior to anal fin origin; 11 to 12 dorsal fin rays; 26 to 29 anal fin rays; 52 to 57 lateral line scales; Mobile basin and the Tennessee River drainage . . . . mooneye, *H. tergisus*

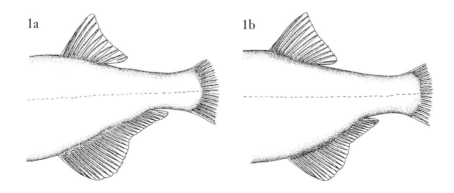

Dorsal and anal fin insertions in 1a, *H. alosoides*, and 1b, *H. tergisus*

PAINT ROCK RIVER, MARSHALL COUNTY

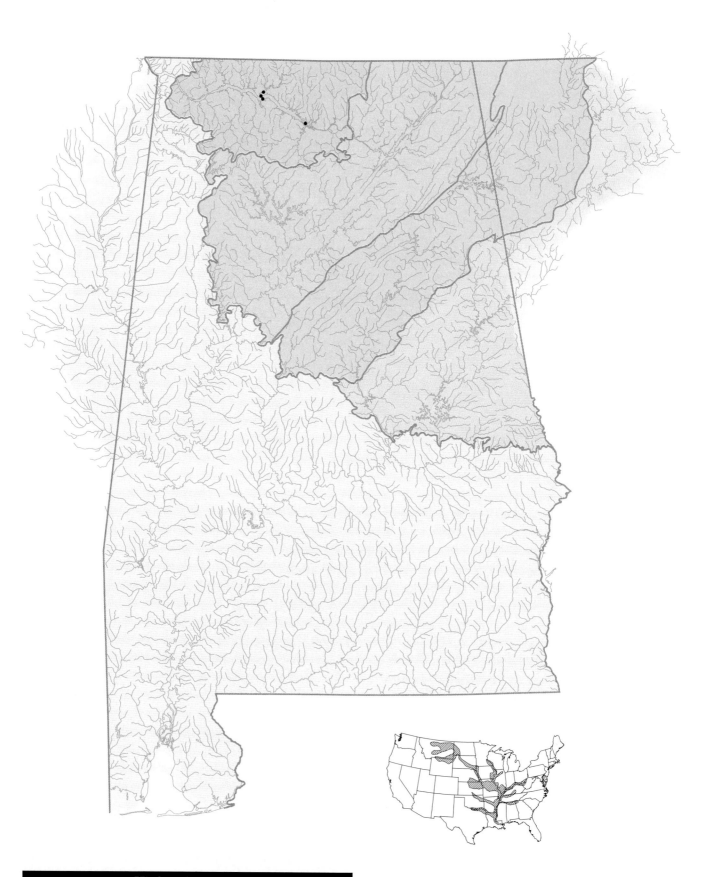

GOLDEYE   *Hiodon alosoides*   4 STATIONS

Hiodon alosoides

(Rafinesque, 1819)

ETYMOLOGY:

Hiodon—tongue tooth, referring to the tiny teeth on the tongue

alosoides—shadelike

Moniteau Creek, Moniteau County, Missouri, 5 August 1973, 7.6 in (193 mm) SL male. Photograph courtesy of William Pflieger.

CHARACTERISTICS: The goldeye is an elongate, compressed fish with a fairly small head but a distinctly large eye. In lateral view, the dorsal fin origin is directly above or slightly behind the anal fin origin. A fleshy keel extends from the pectoral fin base to the anus. The dorsal fin has nine to 10 rays. The anal fin contains 29 to 34 fin rays, making it one of the longest found on any Alabama fish species. The ends of the pectoral fins almost touch the pelvic fin bases. The mouth is large, with an upper jaw that extends backward to behind the pupil of the eye. Small, sharp, recurved teeth on both jaws and the tongue assist in holding prey until it can be swallowed. Anal fin structure separates the sexes. On males the anterior area of the anal fin margin is convex, whereas on females it is almost straight or concave (Cross, 1967). The back of a live goldeye is bluish green, and the venter is white. The sides have a distinct silvery appearance. On live individuals the eye is golden in color and covered with an adipose eyelid.

ADULT SIZE: 12 to 18 in (300 to 460 mm)

DISTRIBUTION: Collections housed at the University of Michigan Museum of Zoology show that goldeyes once occurred in Alabama. The lack of recent collections indicates that they no longer exist in the state. Etnier and Starnes (1993) include only one Tennessee River collection upstream of Alabama. They speculate that the species' disappearance from the Tennessee and upper Cumberland rivers is due to impoundments, even though goldeyes appear to be more tolerant of turbidity than their near relative, the mooneye.

HABITAT AND BIOLOGY: The goldeye is a surface feeder in large streams, rivers, and reservoirs. In Arkansas, spawning occurs in shoals and the backwaters of reservoirs, possibly at night, when water temperatures reach 50° to 55°F (10° to 13°C) (Robison and Buchanan, 1988). Females do not have oviducts, so their eggs are released directly into their body cavities before spawning. Etnier and Starnes (1993) report that at one year of age, fish vary from 30 to 128 mm in length. The maximum life span in Canada is 14 years (Scott and Crossman, 1973).

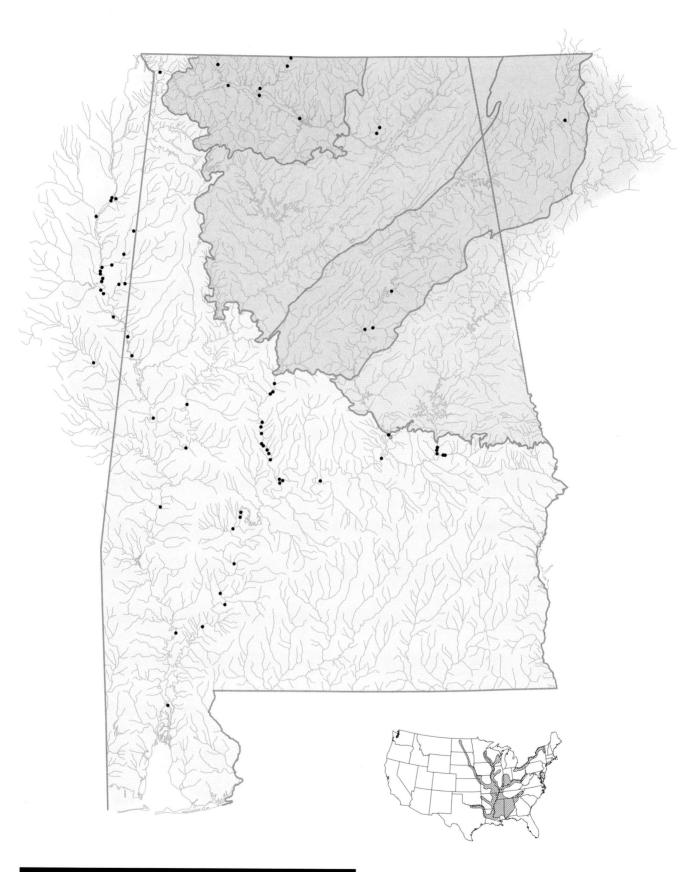

Hiodon tergisus
Lesueur, 1818

ETYMOLOGY:
Hiodon—tongue tooth, referring to the tiny teeth on the tongue
tergisus—polished

Cahaba River, Perry County, 12 May 1992, 8.1 in (205 mm) SL male, GSA 4237

CHARACTERISTICS: The mooneye is an elongate fish with a short head and a large, silvery eye covered with an adipose eyelid. The dorsal fin origin is distinctly anterior to the anal fin origin. The dorsal fin has 11 or 12 rays; the anal fin, 26 to 29 rays (fewer than the goldeye). The fleshy keel along the venter extends from the pelvic fin base to the anus. The upper jaw extends almost to the middle of the pupil. In live individuals the back varies from bluish green to silvery, and the sides and venter are glossy and silvery. See Lesueur (1818a) for original description.

ADULT SIZE: 12 to 18 in (300 to 460 mm)

DISTRIBUTION: The mooneye is an elusive species, and because it appears only infrequently in collections, its distribution in Alabama is incompletely known. Previous reports stated that mooneye had not been collected in the Tennessee River drainage since 1938 and 1941. However, we collected them at five stations in 1993: two in the Elk River, two in the Paint Rock River (where the species was fairly abundant), and one in

Shoal Creek. Biologists with the Tennessee Valley Authority reported mooneye from the Elk River in 1980 and the Tennessee River in 1962 and 1976. Jandebeur (1972) collected a single specimen with a trammel net in the lower Elk River in 1968. We have collected mooneye in the Alabama, Cahaba, Coosa, and Tallapoosa river systems below the Fall Line in the Mobile basin.

HABITAT AND BIOLOGY: Mooneyes are surface feeders in large streams and rivers. They thrive in greatest abundance in the swift tailwaters of locks and dams. Spawning occurs in March and April, probably in swift water over sand and gravel substrates. Several male and female mooneye in "running ripe" condition were collected in a hoop net from Bull Mountain Creek, a tributary to the upper Tombigbee River in northeastern Mississippi, in May. Females of this species do not have oviducts, meaning that eggs are released directly into the body cavity before spawning. Etnier and Starnes (1993) report that mooneye grow rapidly in Tennessee, with year-old fishes reaching 8 inches (200 mm).

FRESHWATER EEL

Anguillidae

The American eel, **Anguilla rostrata**, is the only member of this family in North America, and its life history has been closely studied over the last 70 years. Although many questions remain unanswered, information summarized by Smith (1968 and 1989) confirms that this is one of the most distinctive fish species in Alabama.

Much of the mystery surrounding eels concerns their reproductive habits. Called a catadromous species, eels spend six or seven years of their lives in fresh water but move out to sea to breed. As they reach adult size and are stimulated to spawn, they begin a long, one-way migration that takes them downstream into the Gulf of Mexico, around the tip of Florida, and into the Atlantic Ocean. Actual spawning occurs sometime during mid- to late winter but has never been observed. Opinions differ as to the exact spawning area, but judging from field studies, ichthyologists speculate that it is near the Sargasso Sea and the island of Bermuda. Robins et al. (1979) report that a possibly gravid female American eel was photographed off the Bermuda Islands at a depth of about 6,000 feet. The European eel, **Anguilla anguilla**, resembles the American eel and is believed to spawn in the same general area, perhaps at a different time of year.

After the eels spawn, they die. The pelagic eggs float in the water column until they hatch into what are called leptocephalus larvae. The aimless voyage of young eels lasts from 12 to 18 months, during which time they undergo successive physical changes to become "glass eels" and finally "elvers." Most elvers reach the estuaries along the Atlantic Coast and in winter and spring begin ascending the major rivers to begin their freshwater existence. Some, however, continue their voyage into the Gulf of Mexico and are delivered (via the Gulf Stream and nearshore currents) to the Choctawhatchee Bay system and other coastal areas east of the Mississippi River, where they migrate inland during winter and spring. Vladykov (1971) suggests that American elvers may return to the same rivers that their parents occupied.

As it matures, the American eel takes on its distinctive appearance. Its snakelike body is covered with tiny embedded scales. On the head are paired eyes and nostrils. The mouth has movable jaws with many sharp teeth. The dorsal, caudal, and anal fins are fused into one long fin extending around the posterior of the body. The upper half of the body is olive green to brown, grading from pale yellow to white on the venter. Eels resemble lampreys, but the former are distinguished by their hinged jaws with well-developed teeth, paired eyes and nostrils, paired pectoral fins, and single gill slit on each side of the head. Pelvic fins are absent on this species.

Although its popularity has waned, the eel was once an important food fish in North America. Trautman (1981) provides an interesting account of how, around the turn of the century, commercial fishermen in Ohio used large wooden barrels as traps for catching live eels. To make the traps, the fishermen drilled a dozen or so two-inch-wide holes in the sides of each barrel and then tacked a woman's stocking, its toe area removed, over each hole. The fishermen filled the barrels with cheese, meat, and even garbage; attached them to floats; and submerged them in deep river pools. Following the scent of the bait, the eels entered the holes in the barrels and swam through the stockings, which collapsed behind them. The fishermen checked their traps every day or two, either selling the live eels at market or pickling their catch for later consumption.

TOMBIGBEE RIVER, CHOCTAW COUNTY

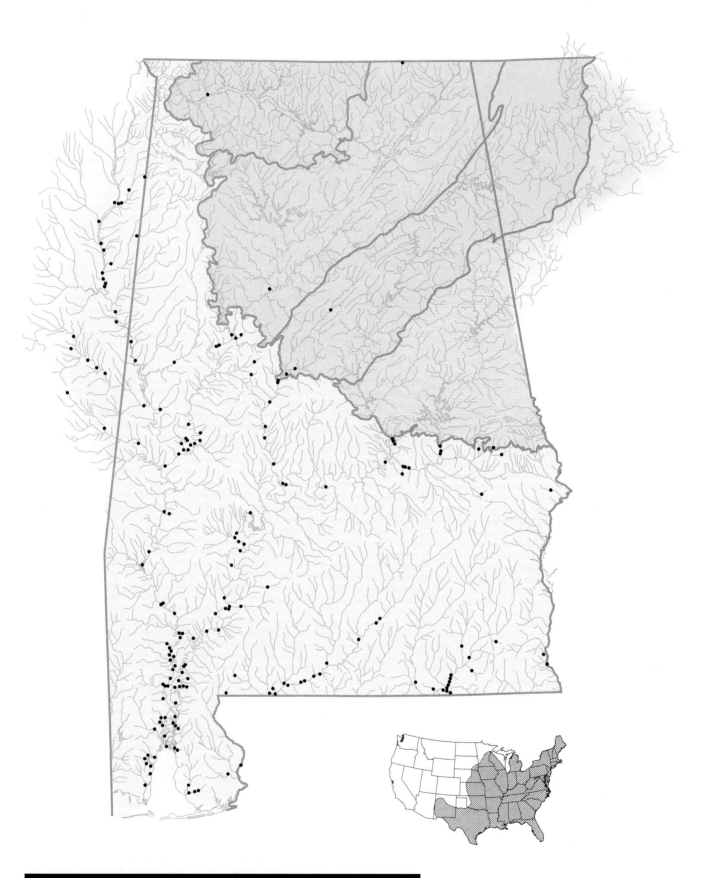

AMERICAN EEL *Anguilla rostrata* **186 STATIONS**

Anguilla rostrata

(Lesueur, 1817)

ETYMOLOGY:

Anguilla—eel

rostrata—long nose

Choctawhatchee River, Geneva County, 6 May 1993, 13.2 in (335 mm) TL, GSA 4441

CHARACTERISTICS: Information on eel characteristics is included in the Freshwater Eel family introduction. See Lesueur (1817a) for original description.

ADULT SIZE: 2.9 to 4.9 ft (0.9 to 1.4 m). The state angling record (5 lb, 8 oz) was caught in Lake Shechi in Chilton County in 1989.

DISTRIBUTION: Recent records of American eels in the Tennessee River of Alabama are rare. Lee (1978b) included one record from a southern tributary. Feeman (1987) reported a specimen from the Paint Rock River downstream of the junction of Estill Fork and Hurricane Creek in Madison County. In 1993, we collected and released American eels at two stations in the drainage, one in Estill Fork of the Paint Rock River and another in the lower reaches of Cypress Creek in Lauderdale County. American eels have been collected from every river system in the Mobile basin as well as from several coastal drainages in southeastern Alabama. Although eels are known from downstream, none were collected in the Escatawpa River system in Alabama, probably due to limited boat access and insufficient sampling with proper

gear. Inland distributions of American eels and several other fish species may have declined in recent years because of their inability to navigate over or through high-lift locks and dams. The greatest eel concentrations occur in the southern half of the state, particularly in the Mobile Delta. Angler reports supplemented by sampling efforts indicate a progressive decline in abundance with each upstream dam.

HABITAT AND BIOLOGY: Most individuals of this species have been collected around aquatic vegetation and from undercut banks in rivers, reservoirs, and large streams. Migrations, spawning, and life history are discussed in the Freshwater Eel family introduction. American eels are common in rocky shoals of tailwater areas below Jordan and Thurlow dams on the Coosa and Tallapoosa rivers, respectively. During our 1992 and 1993 sampling efforts in the Mobile Delta, we saw many American eels of all sizes around beds of aquatic vegetation and along undercut mud banks. Wenner and Musick (1975) report that American eels feed on small fishes, crayfishes, and insects in fresh water and on small crustaceans, bivalves, and polychaete worms in coastal areas.

HERRINGS

Clupeidae

The herring family contains nearly 200 species, most of them marine. Characteristics include a strongly compressed but fairly short (12 inches or less) silver body covered with easily shed cycloid scales. Most species in this family, called clupeids, have a keel made of sharp, tooth-shaped projections that point posteriorly along the midventral line. Herrings do not have scales on the head or a lateral line. Their eyes are covered with adipose eyelids—transparent coverings with vertical slits. The caudal fin is deeply forked, and several species have a small flap of skin, called an axillary process, at the base of each pelvic fin.

Five clupeids occur in Alabama. The gizzard shad, **Dorosoma cepedianum**, and threadfin shad, **D. petenense**, are important as forage species for several native game fishes, including striped basses and several species of catfishes and sunfishes. Live gizzard shad fished with some type of float (balloon or cork) or on the lake bottom are a favorite bait for catching striped bass at Lewis Smith Lake near Jasper and also below several dams on the Coosa and Tallapoosa rivers. Trotline and jug anglers frequently use cast nets or homemade wire scoop nets on long poles to catch threadfin shad along the wingwalls of most inland dams. The Alabama shad, **Alosa alabamae**, was described from four individuals collected at Tuscaloosa in 1896 (Evermann, 1896). It is an anadromous species, with adults living in salt water and migrating into major rivers along the Gulf Coast to spawn in fresh water. Inland occurrence of Alabama shad has declined substantially in the past 20 years, possibly because high-lift dams have effectively blocked migration routes to upstream spawning areas. Skipjack herring, **Alosa chrysochloris**, occur throughout Alabama. Because of physical similarities, this species and Alabama shad have often been confused, even by ichthyologists. The largescale menhaden, **Brevoortia patronus**, is one of the most abundant herrings found along the Gulf Coast, and like its freshwater relatives, it is an important forage species for many marine game fishes. In addition to its angler-related uses, menhaden by the millions of pounds are harvested and processed into cat food annually.

Clupeids are an open water species, occasionally visible to fishermen as large rippling schools at the water surface. Mass spawnings involving entire schools of a particular species occur in the spring and early summer. Fertilization is accomplished when adults release clouds of eggs and sperm into the water column. Because they contain tiny oil droplets, the eggs remain buoyant until the larvae hatch. Schools of very small gizzard and threadfin shad are often encountered along the downstream edges of permanent sand and gravel bars. Accumulations of fine silts and associated microscopic organisms in these areas may serve as important food sources until individuals can feed on plankton in open-water environments.

KEY TO HERRINGS

1a. Top midline in front of dorsal fin covered with scales; dorsal fin containing 16 or more rays, none of them elongated; axillary process present at pelvic fin base . . . . go to 2

1b. Top midline in front of dorsal fin not covered with scales; dorsal fin containing 14 or fewer rays, with last dorsal ray elongated into a slender filament; no axillary process . . . . go to 4, *Dorosoma*

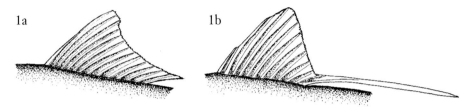

Dorsal fins of 1a, *Alosa*, and 1b, *Dorosoma*

2a. A prominent row of enlarged scales extending along back in front of dorsal fin; pelvic fin containing 7 rays. . . . . largescale menhaden, *Brevoortia patronus*

2b. No enlarged scales along back in front of dorsal fin; pelvic fin containing 8 or 9 rays . . . . . . go to 3, *Alosa*

3a. Lower jaw protrudes far in front of upper jaw when jaws are closed and viewed from side; maximum depth measured at dorsal fin origin goes 4.6 or more times into total length; 20 to 24 rakers on lower limb of first gill arch . . . . skipjack herring, *A. chrysochloris*

3b. Lower jaw protrudes little, if any, in front of upper jaw when jaws are closed and viewed from side; maximum depth measured at dorsal fin origin goes 4.5 or fewer times into total length; 42 to 48 rakers on lower limb of first gill arch . . . . Alabama shad, *A. alabamae*

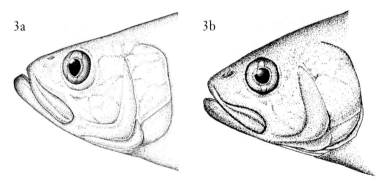

Lower jaws of 3a, *A. chrysochloris*, and 3b, *A. alabamae*

4a. Anal rays number 29 to 35; mouth inferior, with upper jaw notched in center; 59 to 67 lateral scales. . . . . gizzard shad, *D. cepedianum*

4b. Anal rays number 20 to 28; mouth terminal, with upper jaw not notched in center; 42 to 48 lateral scales. . . . . threadfin shad, *D. petenense*

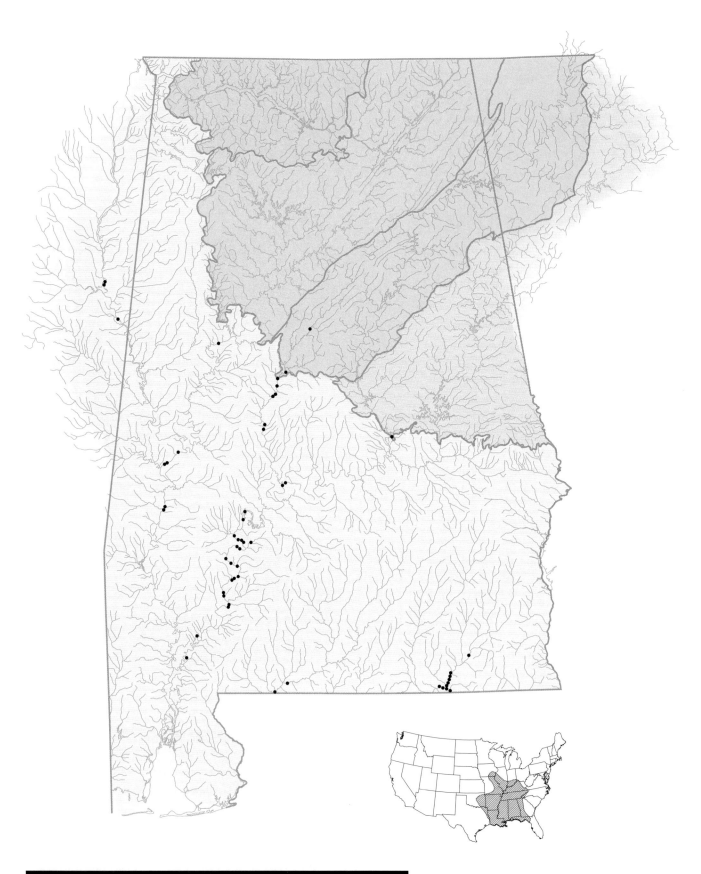

ALABAMA SHAD *Alosa alabamae* **53 STATIONS**

Alosa alabamae

Jordan and Evermann, 1896

ETYMOLOGY:

Alosa—shad

alabamae—from Alabama

Choctawhatchee River, Geneva County, 6 May 1993, 8.7 in (220 mm) SL male, GSA 4441

CHARACTERISTICS: The Alabama shad is an elongate, silvery fish with 55 to 60 scales in the lateral series. The dorsal fin has 15 to 17 rays; the anal fin has 18 to 19 rays. The back of a live Alabama shad is greenish blue; the rest of the body is silvery. Fins are generally clear. The dorsal and caudal fins have a slightly darker margin. See Evermann (1896) for original description.

ADULT SIZE: 12 to 18 in (300 to 460 mm)

DISTRIBUTION: In the past, Alabama shad inhabited most Gulf Coast drainages from the Mississippi River east to the Suwannee River in Florida. During the last 20 years, inland distribution and abundance have greatly declined due to the construction of dams, which block annual spawning runs, and to water pollution and habitat alteration. The largest remaining population is in the Apalachicola River system below Jim Woodruff Dam. Each year, shad still enter the Choctawhatchee and Conecuh river systems in southeastern Alabama to spawn. Recent Mobile basin records are limited to collections of single adults in the Alabama River below Claiborne (1993) and Millers Ferry (1995) locks and dams.

HABITAT AND BIOLOGY: The Alabama shad is the only anadromous clupeid species in Alabama. Adults live in salt water but migrate upstream into free-flowing rivers to spawn. The authors' ongoing studies indicate that shad arrive in the Alabama reach of the Choctawhatchee and Conecuh rivers in March. Adults spawn in April, when water temperatures reach 65° to 68°F (18° to 20°C), and migrate downstream shortly thereafter. Actual spawning has not been observed, but it probably occurs in open, flowing water over sand bars in the late afternoon or at night. Readings of otoliths from specimens collected in 1994 and 1995 indicate that male Alabama shad were one to four years old. Females were two to six years old, two years older than reported by Laurence and Yerger (1967) and three years older than determined by Mills (1972) using scale readings.

REMARKS: The type locality of the Alabama shad is the Black Warrior River at Tuscaloosa, Tuscaloosa County. Ironically, the four specimens used for the scientific description of this species are the only known records from this river system.

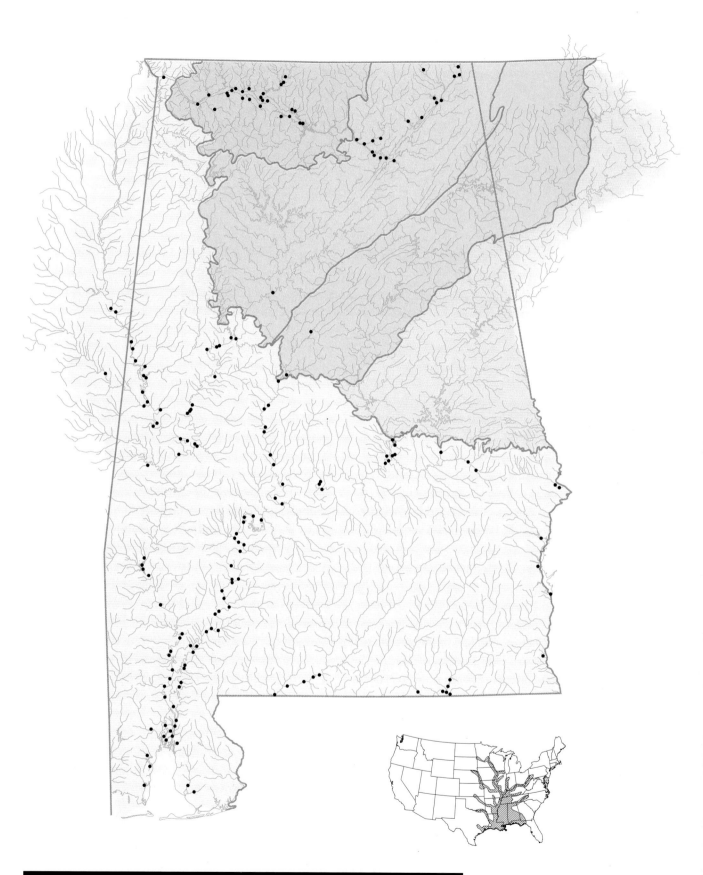

Alosa chrysochloris

(Rafinesque, 1820)

ETYMOLOGY:

Alosa—shad

chrysochloris—gold-green, referring to the greenish color of the backs of live individuals

Tombigbee River, Marengo County, 30 April 1992, 13.2 in (335 mm) SL male, GSA 4226

CHARACTERISTICS: Particularly as young individuals, skipjack herring and Alabama shad closely resemble one another and are often confused, but several characteristics separate the two. Skipjack herring are not as deep-bodied as Alabama shad; their maximum body depth at the dorsal fin origin goes 4.6 or more times into the total length (fewer than 4.5 times on Alabama shad). When viewed from the side, the skipjack's lower jaw, the edge of which is completely pigmented, protrudes considerably in front of its upper jaw. The last ray of the dorsal fin is not elongated into a filament—a useful character for separating species of *Alosa* from species of the genus *Dorosoma*. Lateral scales number from 53 to 60; the lateral line is absent. Hildebrand (1963) states that skipjack herring lack dark spots along the side, but he may have based his conclusions on preserved museum specimens. We have observed that large live skipjack frequently have one to three dark spots, but they fade shortly after death.

ADULT SIZE: 12 to 15 in (300 to 370 mm)

DISTRIBUTION: Skipjack herring have been collected from almost all river systems in Alabama. The lack of records from the Escatawpa River in Alabama is probably due to sampling with improper gear and the inability to use boat electrofishing gear in the area.

HABITAT AND BIOLOGY: An inhabitant of surface and midwater areas, this species occurs in rivers, reservoirs, and large streams. Skipjack herring migrate both upstream and downstream in rivers, and individuals will occasionally enter the saline waters of the Mobile Delta. Large numbers of adults congregate in swift-flowing tailrace areas below dams in late March and early April, presumably to spawn. Young individuals are more widely distributed and usually occur alone. As many fishermen know, skipjack will readily strike a small spoon or jig and provide a good battle for their relatively small size. Jigging for skipjacks is a popular sport below Claiborne and Millers Ferry locks and below dams on the Alabama River.

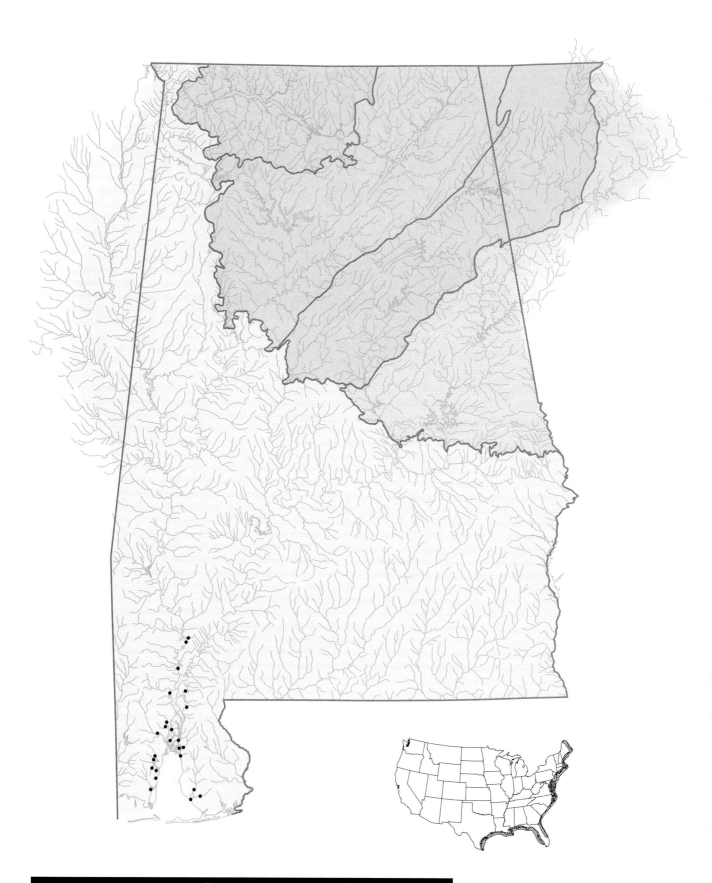

GULF MENHADEN   *Brevoortia patronus*   **24 STATIONS**

Brevoortia patronus
Goode, 1878

ETYMOLOGY:

Brevoortia—in honor of
James Carson Brevoort
patronus—protector

Weeks Bay, Baldwin County, 20 August 1992, 6.2 in (158 mm) SL male, GSA 4471

CHARACTERISTICS: The Gulf menhaden's scales overlap so much that their exposed margins are much taller than they are wide. Most individuals have a prominent black shoulder spot and several small spots beneath the dorsal fin. This fish's lateral profile is unlike that of any other species in Alabama: The deepest part of the body is about midway between the pectoral fin base and tips. The pelvic fin has seven rays; the pectoral fin has an axillary process at its base. Gulf menhaden are fast-swimming, planktivorous fishes with gill structures modified to enhance their feeding efficiency. Individual gill rakers on the lower limb of each gill arch are two to three times longer than the gill filaments, and they are equipped with many small, hook-shaped appendages that, when attached, presumably hold the rakers in place. Raker length and structure provide an ingenious filtering system for catching the vast quantities of food these mobile fishes need. The back is grayish black; the sides vary from light green to orange; the venter is white. The fins vary from clear to lemon yellow.

ADULT SIZE: 5.1 to 7.9 in (130 to 200 mm)

DISTRIBUTION: Gunter (1945) indicates that Gulf menhaden were never collected in waters of low salinity, a characteristic of estuaries or partially tidal waters. We have collected this species in salt water, in Chickasaw Creek (a western tributary to the Mobile Delta), and in several tributaries to the lower Tombigbee River. Because of this fish's apparent ability to enter fresh water, future sampling may document its presence in the lower Alabama River, particularly during periods of salt-water intrusion in late summer.

HABITAT AND BIOLOGY: Most inland records of this species are from large rivers. Small individuals have been taken by seining along sandbars at night. Available information indicates that mass spawnings may occur in late winter or early spring in open water. Young menhaden generally migrate near shore to feed and grow, as evidenced by their abundance in these areas in late summer.

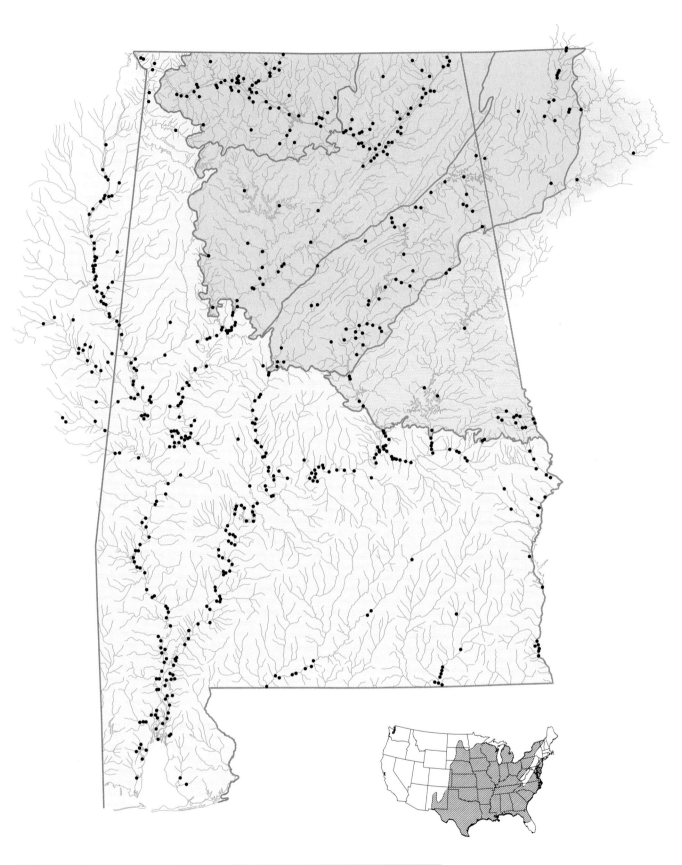

GIZZARD SHAD   *Dorosoma cepedianum*   571 STATIONS

120

Dorosoma cepedianum

(Lesueur, 1818)

ETYMOLOGY:

Dorosoma—lance-shaped body

cepedianum—in honor of Citoyen Lacépède, the French ichthyologist

Cypress Creek, Lauderdale County, 16 July 1992, 5.8 in (148 mm) SL, GSA 4282

CHARACTERISTICS: The last dorsal fin ray on both the gizzard and threadfin shad is elongated and whip-like. The gizzard shad, however, is the only member of this family with a blunt snout and an inferior mouth. The ventral edge of the upper jaw is deeply notched. Lateral scales number between 59 and 67; a lateral line is lacking. The anal fin has 29 to 35 fin rays; the dorsal fin, 10 to 13. The back is bluish gray. Freshly caught individuals may have a greenish or silver tinge overall, as well as several darker, horizontal bars along the sides. The venter is milky white to silver. The color of the vertical fins is variable, from nearly black during the spawning season to clear with irregular black blotches in the fall. See Lesueur (1818a) for original description.

ADULT SIZE: 7.9 to 12 in (200 to 305 mm)

DISTRIBUTION: Gizzard shad are abundant throughout the Tennessee and Chattahoochee rivers and the Mobile basin. They are much less abundant in the Choctawhatchee and Conecuh rivers. Their absence from the Escatawpa, Perdido, Yellow, and Blackwater rivers may be real or only apparent, the result of riverine sampling conducted without proper gear.

HABITAT AND BIOLOGY: This schooling, pelagic species feeds primarily on plankton. Although individuals occasionally enter large streams, they occur in greatest abundance (frequently estimated at 2,000 to 4,000 pounds per acre) in open, quiet waters in rivers and reservoirs. The species can endure moderate salinity, as evidenced by our collections in the Dog and Fowl river systems in Mobile County and in the Fish and Magnolia river systems in Baldwin County. Mass spawnings occur primarily at night in open water from April through June. The tiny adhesive eggs float on the currents, where they remain until the larvae hatch. Gizzard and threadfin shad are sensitive to abrupt changes in temperature and dissolved oxygen content. This species is prone to large-scale, unexpected die-offs in late summer.

REMARKS: When using gizzard shad as live bait, protect them from physical stress by keeping them in the circulating water of round live wells.

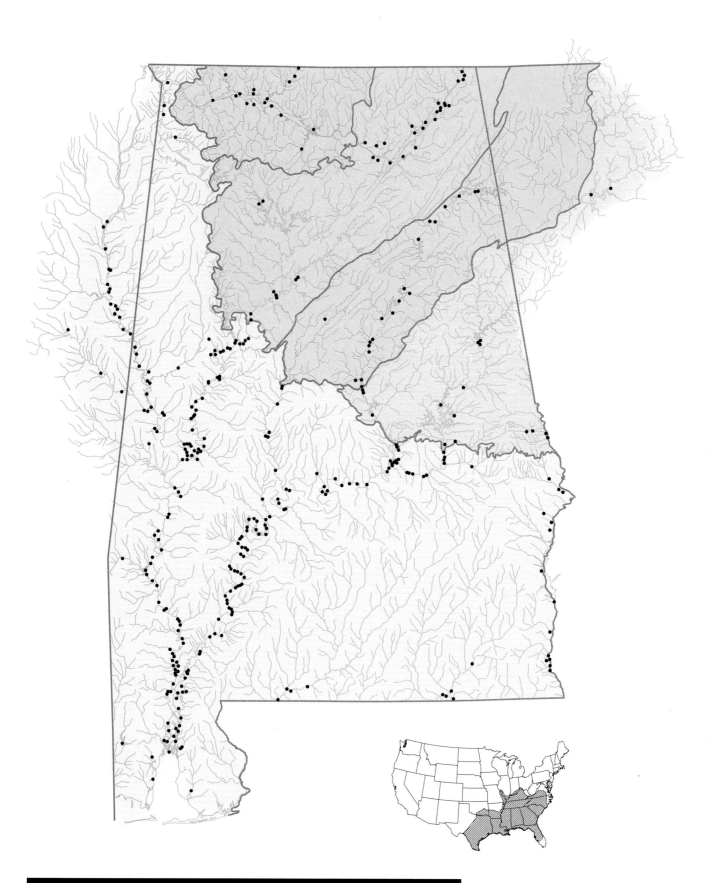

THREADFIN SHAD   *Dorosoma petenense*   349 STATIONS

Dorosoma petenense
(Günther, 1867)

ETYMOLOGY:

Dorosoma—lance-shaped body

petenense—from Lake Peten, Yucatan, the type locality

Black Warrior River, Tuscaloosa County, 16 June 1992, 4.3 in (110 mm) SL female, GSA 4262

CHARACTERISTICS: Like the gizzard shad, the threadfin shad has an elongated posterior dorsal ray, but its mouth is terminal and the lower margin of its upper jaw is not notched. The anal fin has 20 to 28 rays; the dorsal, 10 to 13. Lateral scales number 42 to 48; no lateral line is present. The back is bluish gray with a persistent black or purple shoulder spot. The venter is silver to creamy white. The caudal fin is distinctly yellow (hence the local name "yellowtails"). Other fins may be light yellow, dusky, or clear.

ADULT SIZE: 5.1 to 7.1 in (130 to 180 mm)

DISTRIBUTION: Threadfin shad are abundant in the Tennessee River and in all rivers of the Mobile basin. We encountered small numbers of threadfin shad in the Conecuh, Choctawhatchee, and Chattahoochee rivers. A purposeful introduction could explain the single collection from Big Creek Lake, a municipal reservoir of Mobile and a tributary to the Escatawpa River system. We have no records from the Perdido, Yellow, or Blackwater rivers, but future sampling will probably expand the species' known range in these systems.

HABITAT AND BIOLOGY: This pelagic, plankton-feeding species occurs in large, often single-size schools and with gizzard shad. The greatest numbers occur in rivers, reservoirs, and large streams, where they can be seen rippling the surface at dawn and dusk. Only rarely have we taken them in moderate and small streams. In Missouri, Pflieger (1975) notes that spawning occurs from dawn to sunrise, when water temperatures reach 70°F (21.3°C). Threadfin shad are sensitive to sudden changes in water temperature and oxygen content; for this reason, they frequently experience die-offs in late summer and winter.

REMARKS: Alhough the threadfin shad is native to Alabama, it has been widely introduced both here and elsewhere throughout the United States as a forage species for temperate basses and sunfishes.

ANCHOVIES

Engraulidae

Anchovies have had a long and colorful history as a food fish. They are the fish mentioned most often in old Greek writings, and they were used as all-purpose seasoning by the ancient Romans.

Before pollution caused their extinction, Mediterranean anchovies were prized; those landed at the French port of Collioure were reputed to be the best in the world. Today, anchovies are found in the Atlantic as far north as southern Norway and in the Pacific off the western coasts of North and South America. In texture and flavor, the American anchovy is coarser than its European counterpart.

Distinctive head characteristics easily separate members of the anchovy family from their nearest relatives, the herrings. The anchovy has a large mouth that opens wide and extends well behind the rear edge of the eye; on all herrings in Alabama (even *Alosa* species), the mouth is smaller and fails to reach even the inside edge of the eye. The anchovy has a conical snout with a long, pointed upper jaw. On the anchovy, the lower jaw is much shorter, weaker in structure, and less conspicuous, while most herrings have jaws of nearly equal size (an exception being the skipjack herring, in which the lower jaw is longer than the upper jaw).

Anchovies are distributed in warm shore waters around the world. Most species live in marine habitats of tropical regions, but a few live in temperate regions, and several are known from fresh water. In Alabama, five species occur in estuarine and nearshore marine waters. The bay anchovy, *Anchoa mitchilli*, is the only species that intrudes into freshwater rivers in the state. Our 1986 collection of 99 bay anchovies below Armisted I. Selden Dam on the Black Warrior River in Greene County is a new inland record for the species in the United States and, though unsubstantiated to date, may be the first indication that this species spawns in strictly fresh water.

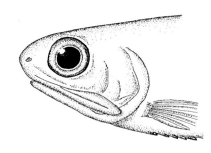

Mouths of (left) bay anchovy, *Anchoa mitchilli*, and (right) Alabama shad, *Alosa alabamae*

BYRNES LAKE, MOBILE DELTA

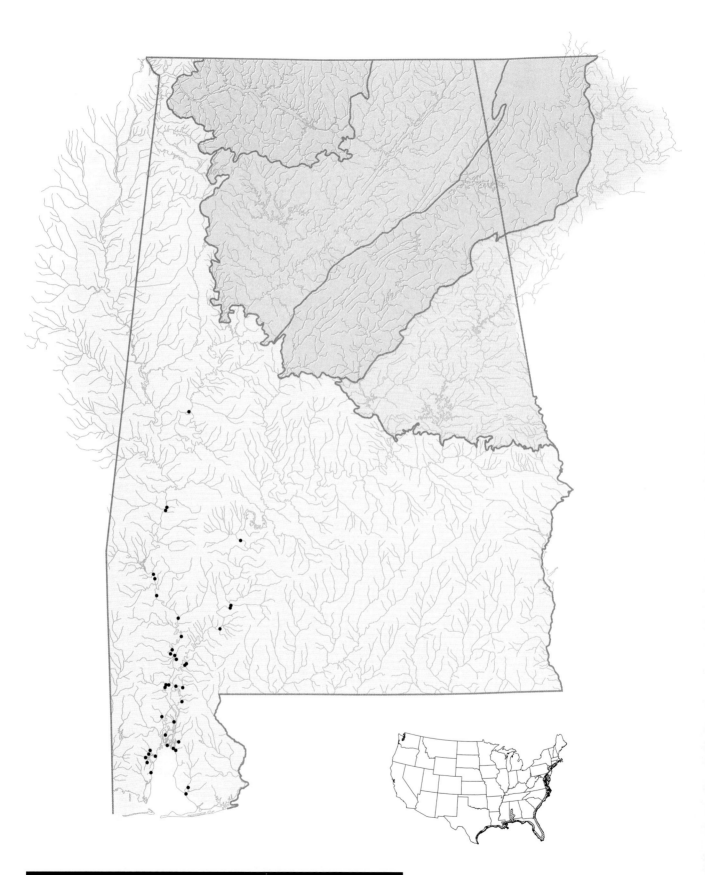

BAY ANCHOVY *Anchoa mitchilli* **39 STATIONS**

Anchoa mitchilli

(Valenciennes, 1848)

ETYMOLOGY:

Anchoa—herringlike

mitchilli—in honor of

Dr. Samuel L. Mitchill,

senator from New York

and author of several papers

on North American fishes

Weeks Bay, Baldwin County, 17 June 1993, 1.8 in (47 mm) SL female, GSA 4487

CHARACTERISTICS: On this small fish, the dorsal fin origin is located directly above the anal fin origin. It contains 12 to 14 rays, and the anal fin has 24 to 27 rays. The snout is short—about the same length as the eye. On the large mouth, the upper jaw extends backward almost to the gill opening, and the lower jaw is slightly included in the upper jaw. The body is covered with small, deciduous, easily shed scales. Lateral scales number 36 or 37; no lateral line is present. A small, axillary process is located at the base of each pectoral fin. A live bay anchovy is silver to greenish in color, with a distinctive silver stripe running the length of its body. See Cuvier and Valenciennes (1848) for original description.

ADULT SIZE: 2 to 3 in (51 to 76 mm)

DISTRIBUTION: The bay anchovy is predominantly a marine species, but we have collected numerous individuals in tributaries on both sides of Mobile Bay as well as in the Alabama and lower Tombigbee rivers. Our collection of 99 individuals from the Black Warrior River (below Armisted I. Selden Dam, Greene County, 22 August 1986) is a new inland record for the species. Although freshwater spawning is unsubstantiated to date, it is highly unlikely that the individuals we collected, with an estimated life span of only one or two years, could have traveled 270 miles upstream from Mobile Bay and negotiated two locks and dams having a combined lift of 70 feet.

HABITAT AND BIOLOGY: Bay anchovies are abundant in Alabama's estuarine areas, where a single haul of a seine can capture several hundred individuals. In inland rivers, however, they are uncommon to rare. Most of the bay anchovies we observed in the Alabama and lower Tombigbee rivers were collected along the margins of aquatic vegetation and around tree limbs and other emergent structures with boat electrofishing gear. We also caught anchovies by seining along clean sand and gravel banks. Spawning occurs in estuaries from April into early June. Anchovies eat small copepods and isopods, and they are in turn eaten by predacious fishes and shorebirds.

CARPS AND MINNOWS

Cyprinidae

The family Cyprinidae is a large, diverse group of soft-finned, freshwater fish species found on almost every continent. More than 200 genera and 2,000 species of cyprinids have been described (Berra, 1981; Nelson, 1994) and collected in Asia, Africa, Europe, and North America. (Interestingly, cyprinids are absent in South America, which is inhabited by the ecologically similar and equally diverse characins.) Among fish families in Alabama, cyprinids contain the most species—almost 90 described and recognized but as yet undescribed forms.

Carps and minnows occupy a variety of habitats—swamps, springs, streams of all sizes, lakes, reservoirs, and large, flowing rivers. Their diets also vary, depending on the species and its preferred habitat. Minnows generally eat organic debris and aquatic insects. Grass carp eat mostly aquatic vegetation but will also take aquatic insects and small fishes. Common carp are bottom feeders, foraging for insects and detritus in the mud, while silver and bighead carp are planktivores, straining microscopic plants and animals from the water.

Cyprinids' spawning habits are extraordinarily diverse (Johnston and Page, 1992). Some species of the genus *Cyprinella* deposit their eggs in crevices of wood or rock substrate in flowing water. Minnows of the genus *Pimephales* spawn by turning upside down and depositing their eggs under flat objects, afterward remaining nearby to guard the eggs. Several species in the genus *Nocomis* use their mouths to build 8- to 10-inch-high gravel mounds as spawning sites. The eggs they deposit in the mounds' crevices are protected and require no parental care. Other minnow species also utilize these *Nocomis* mounds as spawning sites, usually with no adverse effect to any of the species. Members of

the genera *Hybognathus*, *Luxilus*, *Lythrurus*, *Notropis*, and *Phoxinus* simply spawn in close association in open water, with the fertilized eggs settling to the bottom. Large species like carp generally spawn in open water, broadcasting their eggs over vegetation or roots and allowing them to drift with the currents.

Equally varied are adult sizes—from less than 2 inches for some minnows to more than 3 feet for large carps. In other respects, however, their physical appearances are similar. Most cyprinids have smooth, cycloid scales. They lack jaw teeth, but most species have one to three rows of pharyngeal teeth, which are located near the pharynx and are important taxonomic characters for identifying many minnow species. All species have a single dorsal fin located in front of the anal fin.

The cyprinids are closely related to the suckers (family Catostomidae), but the two can be easily distinguished. On most cyprinids, the mouth is located at the

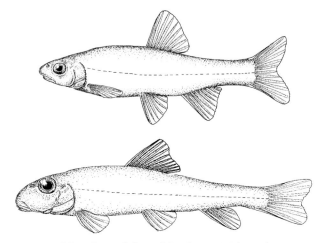

Mouths and fins of (top) cyprinids and
(bottom) catostomids

tip of the snout or only slightly beneath it, and the lips are always thin and well defined. On suckers, the mouth is always located distinctly below and behind the snout, and the lips are either plicate (ridged) or papillate (composed of small, fleshy projections called papillae). Whereas the cyprinid's anal fin is slightly behind the dorsal fin, the sucker's anal fin is placed well behind the dorsal fin and much closer to the caudal fin.

Minnows and carps also share certain physical characteristics with catfishes. Both families have what is known as the Weberian apparatus—a series of ligaments and small bones that connect the air bladder to the ear. The Weberian apparatus aids the fish's sensory perception by transmitting pressure changes (from either sound waves or water depth) from the air bladder to the ear. Like catfish, carp and goldfish have pronounced spines in their dorsal and anal fins, and carp have two pairs of fleshy barbels around their mouths.

Of the cyprinid species found in Alabama, at least six have been introduced as a result of their commercial use elsewhere in the United States. The golden shiner, *Notemigonus crysoleucas*, and the fathead minnow, *Pimephales promelas*, are native to North America, but partly because they have been cultivated and sold as bait, their ranges have increased substantially. In 1877, the common carp, *Cyprinus carpio*, was brought from Europe and introduced into the United States as a game and food fish. As reproducing populations became established, carp spread throughout most river systems in the United States, northern Mexico, and southern Canada. In 1963, the Asian grass carp, *Ctenopharyngodon idella*, was introduced into Arkansas (Pflieger, 1975) as a biological means of controlling aquatic weeds in private and public waters. By 1978, commercial distribution and accidental loss had allowed the grass carp to spread into the river systems of 34 states, including Alabama (Guillory, 1978). Although laws require dealers of grass carp to sterilize fry to prevent them from reproducing, Pflieger (1975) reports the collection of both larvae and ripe males and females in Arkansas. Not included in this study are two Asian imports—silver carp, *Hypopthalmichthys molitrix*, and bighead carp, *H. nobilis*—which have also been introduced to control

aquatic vegetation. The extent of their distributions in the United States is not completely known, but our records indicate that both occur in Alabama, particularly in the Mobile basin.

The relationships of several groups of minnows have been and are still being investigated, and as a result, the genus and species names of many family members have changed. Some changes we applaud; others we question, either here or in the species accounts that follow. For example, some groups of minnows previously included in the genus *Notropis* are now thought to have derived from single ancestral forms; Mayden (1989) therefore removes these species from *Notropis* and elevates them to previously recognized subgenera— *Cyprinella*, *Lythrurus*, *Luxilus*, and *Pteronotropis*. Other species previously included in the genus *Hybopsis* are elevated to separate genera—namely, *Erimystax* and *Macrhybopsis*. Several ichthyologists now believe that some *Hybopsis* may be more closely related to *Notropis*, but since these relationships are not yet clearly defined, we have kept the *Hybopsis amblops* group in *Hybopsis* and kept both *Notropis ammophilus* and *N. longirostris* in *Notropis*. However, because most ichthyologists recognize that the minnows in *Notropis* may have more than one origin, the coming years will probably bring name changes that reflect more natural relationships.

Our study area contains many species within the unsettled *Notropis* complex, and some are likely candidates for systematic revision and unique generic recognition. For instance, males of the subgenus *Hydrophlox* (Swift, 1970)—including *Notropis baileyi*, *N. chrosomus*, *N. leuciodus*, and *N. lutipinnis*—develop characteristic bright red or orange breeding colors, indicating that these species may be closely related. The subgenus *Alburnops* is represented by only one species, *Notropis edwardraneyi*, of unknown affinities in *Notropis*. The subgenus *Notropis* of the genus *Notropis* is represented by a number of species in Alabama (including *N. ariommus*, *N. atherinoides*, *N. candidus*, *N. photogenis*, *N. stilbius*, and *N. telescopus*). Two other well-defined species groups have also been identified. The *volucellus* species group contains *N. buchanani*, *N. cahabae*, *N. volucellus*, *N. wickliffi*, and the "sawfin shiner," whereas

N. *maculatus* and *Opsopoeodus emiliae* may ultimately form a distinct group. The *texanus* species group contains **N. boops**, **N. chalybaeus**, **N. petersoni**, **N. texanus**, and **N. xaenocephalus**. Swift (1970) also includes **N. asperifrons** and **N. hypsilepis** in this group.

At this writing, the relationships of several remaining cyprinid species are unknown. These species include the barbled **Notropis harperi**, the endangered **N. albizonatus**, the unusual **N. uranoscopus**, and **N. cummingsae**. As investigation into these and other species continues, ichthyologists may one day regroup and rename some of them to reflect more natural relationships among the species.

The key to the carps and the minnows, which begins below, distinguishes the three most speciose genera—**Cyprinella**, **Lythrurus**, and **Notropis**—and also identifies the remaining species in the family. The key to the genus **Cyprinella** begins on page 138, the key to the genus **Lythrurus** on page 140, and the key to the genus **Notropis** on page 140.

KEY TO CARPS AND MINNOWS

1a. Dorsal fin with 13 or more rays; serrate dorsal and anal spines present . . . . go to 2
1b. Dorsal fin with fewer than 13 rays; no serrate dorsal or anal spines present . . . . go to 3

2a. Two barbels on each side of upper jaw; pharyngeal teeth in 3 rows . . . . common carp, **Cyprinus carpio**
2b. No barbels on upper jaw; pharyngeal teeth in 1 row . . . . goldfish, **Carassius auratus**

3a. Anal fin located posteriorly on peduncle; distance from anal fin origin to caudal base goes into distance from anal fin origin to snout more than 2.5 times; pharyngeal teeth with parallel grooves . . . .
. . . . grass carp, **Ctenopharyngodon idella**
3b. Anal fin located more anteriorly; distance from anal fin origin to caudal base goes into distance from anal fin origin to snout fewer than 2.5 times; pharyngeal teeth without prominent grooves . . . . go to 4

Anal fin locations of 3a, **Ctenopharyngodon idella**, and 3b, minnow

4a. Lower jaw with cartilaginous, horizontal shelf, which is prominent and protrudes beyond lower lip; long intestine coiled several times around swim bladder . . . . go to 5, **Campostoma**
4b. Lower jaw without prominent cartilaginous shelf; intestine not coiled around swim bladder . . . . go to 6

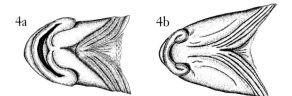

Mouth structures of 4a, **Campostoma**, and 4b, **Phenacobius**

5a. Gill rakers usually 20 to 28; breeding males with 10 to 22 cephalic tubercles and, in live individuals, pinkish orange to orange dorsal and anal fins . . . . largescale stoneroller, *C. oligolepis*

5b. Gill rakers usually 12 to 16; breeding males with 23 to 27 cephalic tubercles and, in live individuals, blue-green dorsal and anal fins; Chattahoochee River drainage . . . . bluefin stoneroller, ***C. pauciradii***

6a. Barbels present (single or paired), may be small and inconspicuous in ***Semotilus*** . . . . go to 7

6b. Barbels absent . . . . go to 21

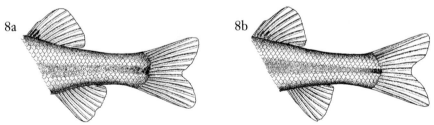

Semotilus barbel   ***Nocomis*** barbel   ***Macrhybopsis*** barbel   ***Erimystax*** barbel

7a. Small, fleshy barbel preterminal, not present at tip of maxilla, often hidden in groove below maxilla, and well anterior of mouth corner (poorly developed in young); upper lip wider at midline than on sides . . . .
. . . . go to 8, ***Semotilus***

7b. Barbel terminal, present at tip of maxilla and in corner of mouth; width of upper lip uniform. . . . . . go to 9

8a. Deep-bodied fish with fewer than 52 lateral line scales; basicaudal spot a triangular or vertical bar separate from broad lateral band; breeding males with yellow fins. . . . . Dixie chub, *S. thoreauianus*

8b. More slender fish with more than 52 lateral line scales; basicaudal spot quadrate and connected to narrower lateral band; breeding males with pinkish to reddish fins . . . . creek chub, *S. atromaculatus*

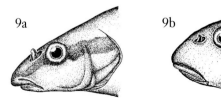

Caudal spot shapes of 8a, ***S. thoreauianus***, and 8b, ***S. atromaculatus***

9a. Snout with frenum; premaxillae not protractile; upper jaw not separated from snout by continuous groove .
. . . . blacknose dace, ***Rhinichthys atratulus***

9b. Snout without frenum; premaxillae protractile; upper jaw separated from snout by continuous groove. . . . .
. . . . go to 10

Snouts of 9a, ***Rhinichthys*** (with frenum), and 9b, ***Nocomis*** (without frenum)

10a. Diameter of orbit much less than distance from posterior rim of orbit to dorsal attachment of operculum; in live individuals, caudal fin colored . . . . go to 11, *Nocomis*

10b. Diameter of orbit approximately equal to distance from posterior rim of orbit to dorsal attachment of operculum; caudal fin generally uncolored . . . . go to 12

11a. Breeding males with 4 to 6 large tubercles on head; lateral line downcurved anterior to dorsal fin . . . . bluehead chub, *N. leptocephalus*

11b. Breeding males with up to 35 small tubercles on head; lateral line straight or only slightly downcurved anterior to dorsal fin; Tennessee River drainage and extreme upper Coosa River system . . . . river chub, *N. micropogon*

12a. Barbel small, detectable with magnifying glass; conspicuous lateral stripe extending to surround snout; light median streak on frontal area; red spot in dorsal part of eye . . . . redeye chub, *Notropis harperi*, go to key on page 140

12b. Barbel larger, easily seen by unaided eye; lateral stripe absent or, if present, not extending to surround snout; no light median streak on frontal area . . . . go to 13

13a. On depressed dorsal fin, tips of anterior rays extending well beyond tips of posterior rays; dark lateral band typically present . . . . go to 14, *Hybopsis*

13b. On depressed dorsal fin, tips of anterior rays not extending well beyond tips of posterior rays; lateral band faint or absent . . . . go to 17

Dorsal fin shapes of 13a, *Hybopsis*, and 13b, *Cyprinella*

14a. Above dark lateral band, pale band with few or no melanophores; lateral band expanded into diamond-shaped spot at tail base; Tallapoosa and upper Coosa river systems . . . . . . lined chub, *H. lineapunctata*

14b. Above dark lateral band, pale band with abundant melanophores; lateral band only slightly expanded at tail base or, if pale band present, then caudal spot of same height as lateral band . . . . go to 15

15a. Pelvic fin origin slightly anterior to dorsal fin origin; Tennessee River drainage . . . . bigeye chub, *H. amblops*

15b. Pelvic fin origin either below or slightly posterior to dorsal fin origin. . . . . go to 16

16a. Slender chub; caudal spot not extending onto rays of caudal fin and formed by ventral expansion of lateral band at caudal base; Mobile basin . . . . clear chub, *H. winchelli*

16b. More deep-bodied chub; caudal spot distinct, wedge-shaped, and separated from lateral band; coastal drainages from Perdido River east to Chattahoochee River . . . . undescribed chub, *H.* sp.

17a. Lateral line scales 52 or more; posterior membranes of dorsal fin darkened with melanophores . . . . spotfin chub, *Cyprinella monacha*, go to key on page 138

17b. Lateral line scales fewer than 52; membranes of dorsal fin lacking pigmentation . . . . go to 18

18a. Modal number of anal fin rays 8. . . . . go to 19, *Macrhybopsis*

18b. Modal number of anal fin rays 6 or 7; Tennessee River drainage. . . . . go to 20, *Erimystax*

19a. Body pale; when present, melanophores arranged regularly; in live individuals, ventral edge of caudal fin milky white; dorsal fin origin above or slightly anterior to pelvic fin origin . . . .
. . . . silver chub, *M. storeriana*

19b. Body with large, randomly scattered melanophores; dorsal fin origin distinctly posterior to pelvic fin origin; barbel single or double . . . . speckled chub, *M. aestivalis*

20a. Lateral line scales usually 43 or fewer; silver lateral stripe with vertical, elongate rectangles distinctly larger than pupil of eye. . . . . blotched chub, *E. insignis*

20b. Lateral line scales usually 46 or more; darker lateral stripe with horizontal, elongate ovals about same size as pupil of eye . . . . streamline chub, *E. dissimilis*

20a   20b

Lateral blotches of 20a, *E. insignis*, and 20b, *E. dissimilis*

21a. Between pelvic fins, ventral surface shaped into sharp, fleshy keel . . . .
. . . . golden shiner, *Notemigonus crysoleucas*

21b. Between pelvic fins, ventral surface rounded, with no fleshy keel . . . . go to 22

Ventral keel of 21a, *Notemigonus crysoleucas*

22a. Lips formed into fleshy lobes in corners of mouth, creating suckerlike appearance; lobes of caudal fin unequal, with ventral portion usually smaller and rounded . . . . go to 23, *Phenacobius*

22b. Lips not formed into fleshy lobes; lobes of caudal fin equal in size . . . . go to 25

23a. Lateral line scales fewer than 51; Tennessee River drainage . . . . suckermouth minnow, *P. mirabilis*

23b. Lateral line scales 52 or more. . . . . go to 24

24a. Lateral line scales from 59 to 69; predorsal scale rows from 25 to 27; narrow lateral stripe; Mobile basin
. . . . riffle minnow, *P. catostomus*

24b. Lateral line scales from 52 to 59; predorsal scale rows from 21 to 25; much wider lateral stripe; Tennessee River drainage . . . . stargazing minnow, *P. uranops*

25a. Predorsal scales smaller anteriorly than posteriorly, particularly behind head; in adults, short ray of dorsal fin stout, blunt at tip, and separated from first principal ray by membrane; predorsal area broad and flattened; in males, large breeding tubercles confined to front of snout and chin. . . . . . . go to 26, ***Pimephales***

25b. Predorsal scales about same size anteriorly as posteriorly; in adults, short ray of dorsal fin slender and not separated from first principal ray by membrane; predorsal area not broad and flattened; in males, breeding tubercles not confined to snout and chin . . . . go to 28

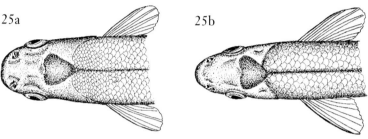

Predorsal scale configurations of 25a, ***Pimephales***, and 25b, ***Notropis***

26a. Mouth oblique, not overhung by snout; lateral line usually incomplete. . . . . fathead minnow, *P. promelas*
26b. Mouth horizontal, overhung by snout; lateral line complete . . . . go to 27

27a. Peritoneum silvery, with black speckles; pharyngeal teeth strongly hooked; breeding males with 9 tubercles; anterior end of lateral line upcurved to dorsal attachment of operculum. . . . bullhead minnow, *P. vigilax*
27b. Peritoneum black; pharyngeal teeth straight or slightly hooked; breeding males with 16 tubercles; anterior end of lateral line straight behind operculum . . . . bluntnose minnow, *P. notatus*

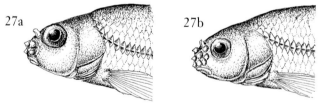

Tubercle and lateral line configurations of 27a, *P. vigilax*, and 27b, *P. notatus*

28a. Underside of head flat, with tubular channels seen as light streaks. . . silverjaw minnow, ***Ericymba buccata***
28b. Underside of head shaped normally, without tubular channels . . . . go to 29

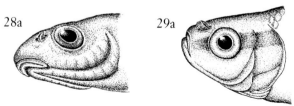

Tubular head channels of 28a, *E. buccata*; mouth shape of 29a, *O. emiliae*

29a. Mouth small and very oblique; dorsal rays 9 . . . . pugnose minnow, ***Opsopoeodus emiliae***
29b. Mouth of normal size; dorsal rays 7 or 8 . . . . go to 30

30a. Scales small, generally 70 or more in lateral series, and barely visible in small specimens. . . . . go to 31
30b. Scales larger, fewer than 70 in lateral series, and visible to unaided eye . . . . go to 33

31a. Lateral line scales from 70 to 95; modal number of anal rays 8; small fishes less than 3 inches in length. . .
. . . . southern redbelly dace, ***Phoxinus erythrogaster***
31b. Lateral line scales from 85 to 100; modal number of anal rays 12; large rivers or culture ponds . . . .
. . . . go to 32, ***Hypopthalmichthys***

32a. Ventral keel extending from vent to pelvic fin base; gill rakers comblike; sides with many small, irregularly
shaped blotches . . . . bighead carp, ***H. nobilis***
32b. Ventral keel extending from vent to isthmus; gill rakers fused into a porous plate; sides uniform, without
dark blotches. . . . . silver carp, ***H. molitrix***

33a. Pharyngeal teeth in principal row 5– 4. . . . . go to 34
33b. Pharyngeal teeth in principal row 4 – 4 . . . . go to 35

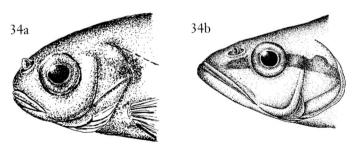

2, 5– 4, 2   4 – 4   1, 4 – 4, 1   2, 4– 4, 2

Pharyngeal tooth formulas

34a. Lateral line scales 36 to 41; small caudal spot distinct and separate from lateral band; mouth normal;
Tennessee River drainage and Coosa River system . . . . flame chub, ***Hemitremia flammea***
34b. Lateral line scales 43 to 57; no caudal spot; mouth enlarged, oblique . . . .
. . . . rosyside dace, ***Clinostomus funduloides***

34a   34b

Mouth shapes of 34a, ***H. flammea***, and 34b, ***C. funduloides***

35a. On side of head, groove extending from behind angle of jaw and continuing dorsoanteriorly to snout, its length about twice mouth width; intestine coiled; peritoneum usually black . . . . . . go to 36, *Hybognathus*

35b. Groove absent from side of head and snout or, if present, not distinctly wider than mouth; intestine with single, S-shaped loop; peritoneum usually silver. . . . . go to 37

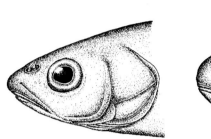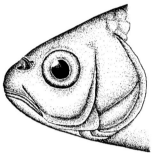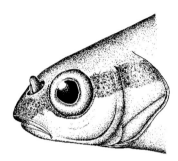

Mouth grooves for (left) *Hybognathus*, (center) *Luxilus*, and (right) *Notropis*

36a. Snout length less than or equal to eye diameter; front of upper lip about level with middle or bottom of eye; body form compressed and angular in profile; on front of sides, scales with distinct dark edges forming diamond pattern; predorsal stripe thin . . . . cypress minnow, *H. hayi*

36b. Snout length greater than eye diameter; front of upper lip below eye; body form subterete and rounded in profile; on front of sides, scales without distinct dark edges; predorsal stripe moderately wide. . . . .
. . . . Mississippi silvery minnow, *H. nuchalis*

36a 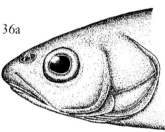 36b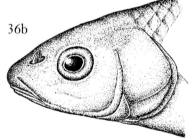

Heads of 36a, *H. hayi*, and 36b, *H. nuchalis*

37a. Predorsal scales tiny and crowded, more than 20 rows; modal number of anal rays 10 or 11; origin of dorsal fin behind pelvic fin origin . . . . *Lythrurus*, go to key on page 140

37b. Predorsal scales larger, 20 or fewer rows; modal number of anal rays 10 or fewer; origin of dorsal fin over or near pelvic fin origin. . . . . go to 38

38a. Melanophore concentrations confined to posterior membranes of dorsal fin (more widely pigmented in *Cyprinella callistia* and *C. lutrensis*); body typically deep and compressed, with black-edged scales forming rhomboid or diamond-shaped pattern along sides; pharyngeal teeth 1,4 – 4,1 (4 – 4 in *C. lutrensis* and *C. monacha*); anal fin rays modally 8 or 9 . . . . *Cyprinella*, go to key on page 138

38b. Interradial membranes of dorsal fin lacking melanophores or totally pigmented; body normally not compressed; pigment on scales not forming rhomboid pattern; pharyngeal tooth count and anal ray count variable . . . . go to 39

Scale configurations, body shapes, and dorsal fins of (top) *Cyprinella*,
(bottom left) *Notropis*, and (bottom right) *Luxilus*

39a. Height of exposed lateral line scales at least more than twice their width; modally 9 anal rays; pharyngeal
teeth 2,4 – 4,2 . . . . go to 40, *Luxilus*

39b. Height of exposed lateral line scales twice or less than twice their width; anal rays variable in number; pharyngeal teeth variable in number . . . . go to 42

40a. Dorsal fin without black diagonal band; base of caudal fin typically pigmented . . . .
. . . . striped shiner, *L. chrysocephalus*

40b. Dorsal fin with black diagonal band; base of caudal fin unpigmented, resulting in white band or large white
spots . . . . go to 41

41a. On dorsal fin, black band nearly parallel to distal margin; fork of caudal fin with wide black border; in live
individuals, red bar on opercle and on first few dorsal rays; no caudal spot; Tennessee River drainage . . . .
. . . . warpaint shiner, *L. coccogenis*

41b. On dorsal fin, black band beginning at lower third of anterior margin and ending at center of posterior rays;
fork of caudal fin without black border; in adults, caudal spot present . . . . bandfin shiner, *L. zonistius*

42a. Body deep, with wide, blue-black lateral band (less wide on *Pteronotropis welaka*), which divides into body
depth fewer than 3 times; in nuptial males, dorsal and anal fins enlarged and well pigmented . . . .
. . . . go to 43, *Pteronotropis*

42b. Body tapers toward ends; when present, lateral band variable in intensity, its width dividing into body depth
3 or more times. . . . . *Notropis*, go to key on page 140

43a. Pharyngeal teeth 1,4 – 4,1; in breeding males, snout blue . . . . bluenose shiner, *P. welaka*

43b. Pharyngeal teeth 2,4 – 4,2; snout not blue . . . . go to 44

44a. Predorsal stripe faint on dark background; in live individuals, 2 large, yellow spots on base of caudal fin, and red coloration on anal, caudal, and dorsal fins; breeding tubercles (22 to 32) on outer edge of mandible usually small and directed laterally in saw-toothed pattern . . . . flagfin shiner, *P. signipinnis*

44b. Predorsal stripe distinct on light background; small, red spots on base of caudal fin, and/or a clear "window" along median rays of orange caudal fin; breeding tubercles (7 to 16) on outer edge of mandible not forming a saw-toothed pattern (pattern on *P. euryzonus* intermediate between *P. signipinnis* and *P. hypselopterus*) . . . . go to 45

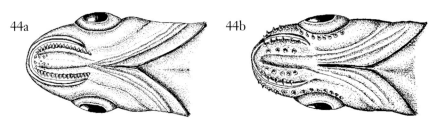

Lower jaw tubercle patterns of 44a, *P. signipinnis*, and 44b, *P. hypselopterus*

45a. In breeding individuals, caudal fin bright orange; membranes of median 4 or 5 caudal rays unpigmented, producing a clear "window"; in breeding males, edge of extended dorsal fin convex, anterior rays of depressed dorsal fin equal to or slightly longer than posterior rays, and membranes evenly pigmented across fin, except for distal tips; Chattahoochee River drainage. . . . . broadstripe shiner, *P. euryzonus*

45b. In breeding individuals, caudal fin olive yellow to dusky yellow; base and tips of caudal ray membranes clear, with dark crescent in center and no "window"; in breeding males, edge of extended dorsal fin concave; anterior rays of depressed dorsal fin equal to or shorter than posterior rays. . . . . sailfin shiner, *P. hypselopterus*

KEY TO THE MINNOWS OF THE GENUS *Cyprinella*

1a. Barbel present . . . . spotfin chub, **Cyprinella monacha**

1b. Barbel absent . . . . go to 2

2a. Body depth divides into standard length 3.5 or fewer times in adults and 3.8 times in juveniles; anal rays 8 or 9, with mixed frequency in a series of specimens; dark pigment uniformly distributed in dorsal fin; pharyngeal teeth 4–4 . . . . red shiner, *C. lutrensis*

2b. Body depth divides into standard length more than 3.5 times in adults and more than 3.7 times in juveniles; anal rays always either 8 or 9 in a series of specimens; dark pigment confined to posterior of dorsal fin (uniformly pigmented in *C. callistia*); pharyngeal teeth 1,4–4,1. . . . . go to 3

3a. Modal number of anal rays 8 . . . . go to 4

3b. Modal number of anal rays 9 . . . . go to 8

4a. Lateral band very dark and of uniform width (about width of eye) from operculum to caudal peduncle, enlarging slightly to form caudal spot; Coosa and Cahaba river systems. . . . . blue shiner, *C. caerulea*

4b. Lateral band darker and wider on caudal peduncle, fading anteriorly . . . . go to 5

5a. Lateral band widens into indistinct caudal spot; Tennessee River drainage . . . . spotfin shiner, *C. spiloptera*
5b. Prominent black caudal spot noticeably wider than lateral band . . . . go to 6

Caudal spots of (left) *C. spiloptera* and (right) *C. ventusa*

6a. Diffuse, narrow lateral band extending from caudal spot to operculum; snout rounded, with subterminal mouth; Alabama and Tombigbee river drainages . . . . Alabama shiner, *C. callistia*
6b. Lateral band on peduncle, fading anteriorly; drainages south of Tennessee River . . . . go to 7

Heads of (left) *C. callistia*, (center) *C. callitaenia*, and (right) *C. venusta*

7a. Snout blunt; caudal spot small, contrasting with metallic-blue lateral stripe in live individuals; on upper lip of adults, maxillary groove well developed; Chattahoochee River drainage. . . . bluestripe shiner, *C. callitaenia*
7b. Snout sharp; caudal spot large, contrasting with light, dusky lateral stripe; in adults, maxillary groove smaller . . . . blacktail shiner, *C. venusta*

8a. Basal third of anterior dorsal fin membranes with melanophores; lateral band widens above anal fin, narrows, and widens again to form distinct caudal spot . . . . go to 9
8b. Basal third of anterior dorsal fin membranes not darker than distal areas; no distinct caudal spot . . . go to 10

9a. On heads of males, breeding tubercles scattered, small, and numerous, with tip of snout slightly overhanging lower lip. . . . . Tallapoosa shiner, *C. gibbsi*
9b. On heads of males, breeding tubercles linear, coarse, and less numerous, with normally shaped snout . . . . tricolor shiner, *C. trichroistia*

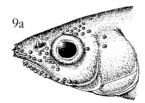 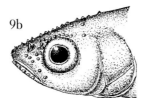

Head tubercles and snouts of 9a, *C. gibbsi*, and 9b, *C. trichroistia*

10a. Caudal fin rays completely outlined with melanophores; lateral line scales 37 to 38; Tennessee River drainage and upper Black Warrior system. . . . . steelcolor shiner, *C. whipplei*
10b Base of exposed caudal rays unpigmented, forming a conspicuous dorsal and ventral light spot; lateral line scales 39 to 42; Tennessee River drainage. . . . . whitetail shiner, *C. galactura*

KEY TO THE MINNOWS OF THE GENUS *Lythrurus*

1a. At base of anterior dorsal rays, prominent dusky blotch appearing as distinct spot when viewed from above and usually spilling onto membranes of anterior rays . . . . rosefin shiner, *Lythrurus ardens*

1b. At base of anterior dorsal rays, no prominent blotch . . . . go to 2

2a. Interradial membranes of dorsal and anal fins with little or no dark pigment . . . . go to 3

2b. Interradial membranes of dorsal and anal fins variously pigmented . . . . go to 4

3a. Anal rays 10; body depth goes 5 or more times into standard length; postanal streak dark and well developed; on head and predorsal region, breeding tubercles prominent and abundant; chin with little or no pigment . . . . mountain shiner, *L. lirus*

3b. Anal rays usually 11; body depth goes fewer than 5 times into standard length; postanal streak absent or vague; breeding tubercles small, difficult to see with unaided eye; chin somewhat pigmented; Tennessee River drainage . . . . ribbon shiner, *L. fumeus*

4a. On dorsal and anal fins, pigmentation confined to distal half of first 3 or 4 rays; on pelvic and pectoral fins, few scattered melanophores on first few rays . . . . cherryfin shiner, *L. roseipinnis*

4b. On dorsal and anal fins, pigmentation on nearly all rays; pelvic and pectoral fins more heavily pigmented . . . . go to 5

5a. On dorsal and anal fins, pigmentation band uniform in width and intensity throughout; Mobile basin . . . . pretty shiner, *L. bellus*

5b. On dorsal and anal fins, pigmentation band narrowing posteriorly, resulting in triangular pattern (somewhat intermediate between *L. roseipinnis* and *L. bellus*); coastal drainages east of Mobile basin . . . . blacktip shiner, *L. atrapiculus*

Fin pigmentation of (left) *L. roseipinnis*, (center) *L. bellus*, and (right) *L. atrapiculus*

KEY TO THE MINNOWS OF THE GENUS *Notropis*

1a. Minute barbel in corner of mouth . . . . redeye chub, *Notropis harperi*

1b. Barbel absent . . . . go to 2

2a. Pharyngeal teeth in 2 rows (2,4 – 4,2 or 1,4 – 4,1); tooth sometimes missing from lesser row . . . . . . go to 3
2b. Pharyngeal teeth in 1 row on each arch (4 – 4) . . . . go to 23

3a. Pharyngeal teeth 1,4 – 4,1. . . . . go to 4
3b. Pharyngeal teeth 2,4 – 4,2 . . . . go to 7

4a. Lateral line pores with black spots or bars located dorsally and ventrally of each pore (may be weakly developed in some individuals or preserved specimens); Tennessee River drainage . . . . go to 5
4b. Lateral line pores without black spots or bars . . . . go to 6

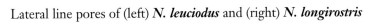

Lateral line pores of (left) *N. leuciodus* and (right) *N. longirostris*

5a. Lateral band on snout touching tip of lower jaw; body somewhat compressed . . . . bigeye shiner, *N. boops*
5b. Lateral band not continuing onto lower jaw; body more cylindrical . . . . . . Tennessee shiner, *N. leuciodus*

6a. Modal number of anal rays 10; dark lateral band from snout to caudal fin. . . . .
. . . . dusky shiner, *N. cummingsae*
6b. Modal number of anal rays 7; no dark lateral band; in live breeding males, fins yellow . . . .
. . . . longnose shiner, *N. longirostris*

7a. Modal number of anal rays 10 or more. . . . . go to 8
7b. Modal number of anal rays 9 or fewer . . . . go to 12

8a. Dorsal fin origin well behind origin of pelvic fins . . . . go to 9
8b. Dorsal fin origin directly (or nearly so) above origin of pelvic fins . . . . go to 10

9a. Expanded anal fin with concave margin; tip of anterior dorsal fin ray pointed, extending beyond posterior rays when depressed; discrete spots for lateral band anterior of dorsal fin . . . .
. . . . emerald shiner, *N. atherinoides*
9b. Expanded anal fin with straight margin; tip of anterior dorsal fin ray not extending past tip of posterior rays when depressed; lateral band anterior of dorsal fin shaded in appearance. . . . .
. . . . rosyface shiner, *N. rubellus*

Anal fins of 9a, *N. atherinoides*, and 9b, *N. rubellus*

10a. Predorsal scale rows 16 or fewer; each dorsolateral scale with dark margin or short bar . . . .
. . . . telescope shiner, *N. telescopus*
10b. Predorsal scale rows 17 or more; each dorsolateral scale pale, with single, dark, marginal concentration of melanophores . . . . go to 11

11a. Pelvic fin rays 8; anterodorsal margin of lateral band straight; Mobile basin . . . .
. . . . silverstripe shiner, *N. stilbius*
11b. Pelvic fin rays 9; anterodorsal margin of lateral band bluntly saw-toothed; Tennessee River drainage . . . .
. . . . silver shiner, *N. photogenis*

Lateral bands of 11a, *N. stilbius*, and 11b, *N. photogenis*

12a. Modal number of anal rays 9 . . . . go to 13
12b. Modal number of anal rays 7 or 8. . . . . go to 14

13a. Eye very large, width equal to interorbital width and longer than snout length. . . . .
. . . . popeye shiner, *N. ariommus*
13b. Eye small, width less than interorbital width and about equal to snout length. . . . .
. . . . silverside shiner, *N. candidus*

Eyes and snouts of 13a, *N. ariommus*, and 13b, *N. candidus*

14a. Lateral stripe diffuse and dusky; basicaudal spot, if present, only faint and disjunct . . . .
. . . . fluvial shiner, *N. edwardraneyi*
14b. Dark lateral stripe well developed; basicaudal spot present or weakly developed. . . . . go to 15

15a. Middorsal stripe dark and unbroken, encircling dorsal fin base and continuing to caudal fin base; dark lateral stripe of uniform intensity, extending to eye . . . . go to 16
15b. Middorsal stripe variously developed, not encircling dorsal fin base; dark lateral stripe of variable intensity, interrupted behind eye . . . . go to 17

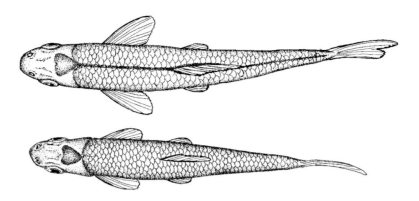

Midddorsal stripes of (top) *N. baileyi* and (bottom) *N. asperifrons*

16a. Caudal spot distinct and well pigmented; anal rays 7; on live individuals, fins yellow . . . .
. . . . rough shiner, *N. baileyi*
16b. Caudal spot lacking, faint dark streak extending posteriorly on caudal rays to fork; anal rays 8; fins reddish
yellow to red; upper Coosa system. . . . . yellowfin shiner, *N. lutipinnis*

17a. Predorsal dark stripe absent or much reduced; mouth inferior . . . . go to 18
17b. Predorsal dark stripe typically well developed; mouth terminal. . . . . go to 19

18a. Basicaudal spot small, wedge-shaped, and separated from dark lateral stripe; Chattahoochee River drainage
. . . . highscale shiner, *N. hypsilepis*
18b. Basicaudal spot large, quadrate, and both connected to and wider than lateral stripe; Mobile basin . . . . . .
. . . . burrhead shiner, *N. asperifrons*

19a. All anal rays clear or with only few melanophores near margin on last 2 rays . . . . go to 20
19b. Last 3 or 4 anal rays outlined with melanophores or all anal rays pigmented (extent of pigmentation varying in populations of *N. petersoni* and *N. chalybaeus*). . . . . go to 21

Anal fin pigmentation of (left) *N. xaenocephalus* and (right) *N. texanus*

20a. Dark lateral stripe deeper anterior to anal fin than on caudal peduncle, with pale stripe above deepest on
caudal peduncle; anal rays modally 7; Coosa and Tallapoosa river systems. . . . .
. . . . Coosa shiner, *N. xaenocephalus*
20b. Dark lateral stripe and pale stripe above uniform in width from caudal fin to head; anal rays modally 8
. . . . rainbow shiner, *N. chrosomus*

21a. Inside of mouth pigmented; anal rays modally 8 . . . . ironcolor shiner, *N. chalybaeus*
21b. Inside of mouth not pigmented; anal rays modally 7 . . . . go to 22

22a. Last 3 or 4 rays outlined with melanophores; basicaudal spot quadrate and connected to lateral stripe; mid-dorsal stripe expanded immediately before dorsal fin origin to form dark blotch . . . . weed shiner, *N. texanus*

22b. All anal rays edged with melanophores (may be indistinct in some populations); basicaudal spot wedge-shaped and separated from lateral stripe; middorsal stripe not expanded before dorsal fin origin. . . . . coastal shiner, *N. petersoni*

23a. Modal number of anal rays 7 . . . . go to 24

23b. Modal number of anal rays 8 or more . . . . go to 26

24a. Narrow, dark lateral band from caudal fin through eye and around snout; pale dorsolateral band, 1.5 scale rows wide; scales above dark lateral band lacking pigment; Tennessee River drainage. . . . . palezone shiner, *N. albizonatus*

24b. Lateral band present on peduncle but fading anteriorly; all scales above lateral stripe with dark edges . . . . go to 25

25a. Eye small, shorter than snout; basicaudal spot either absent or indistinct. . . . . orangefin shiner, *N. ammophilus*

25b. Eye moderate, longer than snout; basicaudal spot small and wedge-shaped; pair of dark crescents between nostrils; eyes elongate and placed high on head . . . . skygazer shiner, *N. uranoscopus*

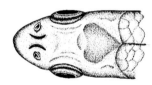

Nostril crescents of 25b, *N. uranoscopus*

26a. Lateral line incomplete, with pored scales not extending beyond origin of dorsal fin; anterior lateral line scales not noticeably elevated; small dusky triangle at upper and lower edge of caudal base; in breeding males, snout red or bright pink. . . . . taillight shiner, *N. maculatus*

26b. Lateral line complete; anterior lateral line scales much taller than wide . . . . go to 27

27a. Coloration pallid; lateral band and caudal spot either faint or absent; vertical band of small melanophores near caudal base; body laterally compressed; infraorbital canal absent; tips of pelvic fins extending to anal fin; Tennessee River drainage . . . . ghost shiner, *N. buchanani*

27b. Coloration much darker, with obvious lateral band on peduncle, triangular caudal spot, and dark edging on scales; body cylindrical; infraorbital canal complete . . . . go to 28

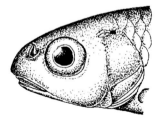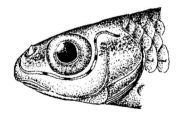

Heads and infraorbital canal structures of (left) *N. buchanani* and (right) *N. volucellus*

28a. Only anterior 4 rays of dorsal fin outlined with melanophores; on live individuals, front third of dorsal, anal, pelvic, and pectoral fins with orange to russet-orange pigment; Tennessee River drainage . . . . "sawfin shiner," *N.* sp.
28b. All rays of dorsal fin outlined with melanophores . . . . go to 29

29a. Lateral stripe on caudal peduncle with straight upper and lower margins, not expanded into ventrally deflected lobe; Cahaba River system . . . . Cahaba shiner, *N. cahabae*
29b. Lateral stripe on caudal peduncle expanded into ventrally deflected lobe . . . . go to 30

Caudal spots of 29a, *N. cahabae*, and 29b, *N. volucellus*

30a. Scales along dorsal part of caudal peduncle uniformly pigmented; circumferential scales usually 11; predorsal stripe lightly pigmented to nonexistent; Tennessee River drainage . . . . channel shiner, *N. wickliffi*
30b. Scales along dorsal part of caudal peduncle more heavily pigmented posteriorly than anteriorly; circumferential scales usually 9 . . . . mimic shiner, *N. volucellus*

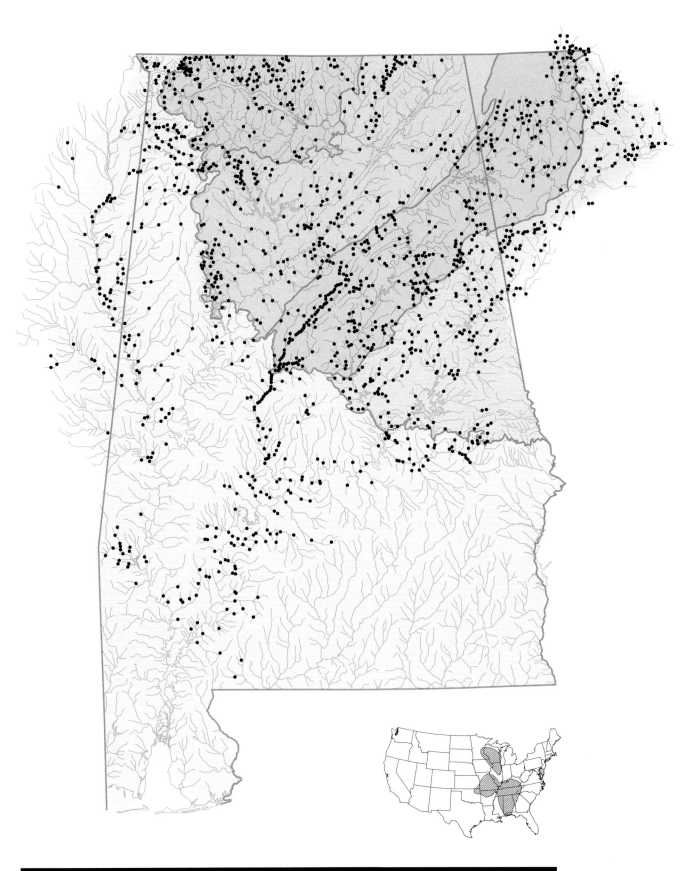

LARGESCALE STONEROLLER *Campostoma oligolepis* **1,443 STATIONS**

Campostoma oligolepis
Hubbs and Greene, 1935

ETYMOLOGY:

Campostoma—curved
mouth
oligolepis—few scales

Butler Creek, Lauderdale County, 31 March 1992, 4.9 in (124 mm) SL male, GSA 4241

CHARACTERISTICS: Each of the species of the genus *Campostoma* has a cartilaginous ridge on the lower jaw and a greatly elongate intestine, which is usually more than twice the standard length. The largescale stoneroller is distinguished from the bluefin stoneroller, *C. pauciradii*, by having more gill rakers (usually 20 to 28) and more lateral line scales (usually 48 to 53) (Burr and Cashner, 1983). It also has fewer breeding tubercles on the head (10 to 22) than the bluefin stoneroller (23 to 27). The breeding male is brassy yellow along the back and upper sides, grading to white or light yellow along the venter. The dorsal, anal, pelvic, and pectoral fins are orange to pinkish orange, and the dorsal fin has a distinct black band.

ADULT SIZE: 3 to 6.9 in (75 to 175 mm)

DISTRIBUTION: *Campostoma oligolepis* is common in the Mississippi River basin. It also occurs in the Mobile basin and the Tennessee River drainage. Our collections at two locations in the Conecuh River drainage in south

Alabama provide additional evidence of historical faunal exchange between it and the Alabama River system.

HABITAT AND BIOLOGY: Widespread and often abundant, stonerollers prefer upland habitats above the Fall Line. Ideal habitats are small to medium-sized clear streams with substrates of gravel, cobble, boulders, or bedrock in riffles or moderately deep riffle runs. Juveniles frequently favor slower currents over sand and silt. Stone-rollers are herbivorous, feeding on algae that they scrape off rocks with a cartilaginous ridge on their lower jaws. The elongate intestines characteristic of *Campostoma* help them to digest this plant material. Stonerollers spawn from early March through April. Males excavate spawning pits in shallow water by moving stones with their mouths or pushing them with their heads. Located near riffles with adjacent deep pools, the pits may be up to 12 inches deep. Stonerollers are considered "pollution tolerant" because they persist in streams that contaminants have made unsuitable for other species.

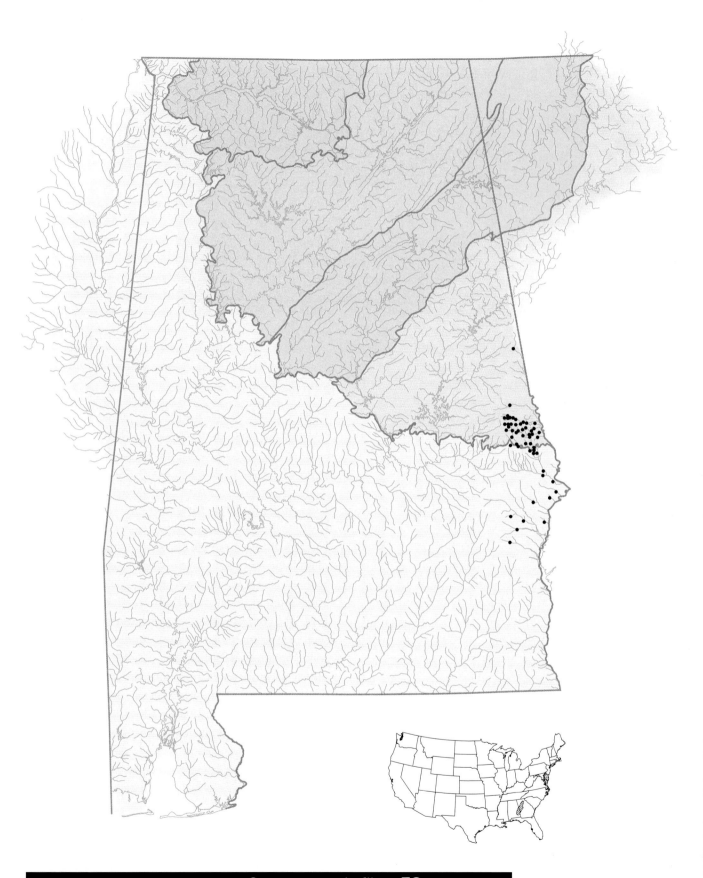

BLUEFIN STONEROLLER *Campostoma pauciradii* **53 STATIONS**

148

Campostoma pauciradii
Burr and Cashner, 1983

ETYMOLOGY:

Campostoma—curved mouth

pauciradii—referring to the low number of gill rakers on the first arch

Little Uchee Creek, Lee County, 19 February 1993, 3.9 in (98 mm) SL male, GSA 4375

CHARACTERISTICS: Small to moderate in size, the bluefin stoneroller is distinguished from the largescale stoneroller, *Campostoma oligolepis*, by having fewer gill rakers (usually 12 to 16), blue-green breeding colors in the dorsal and anal fins, and a higher number of breeding tubercles (Burr and Cashner, 1983). The bluefin stoneroller also has fewer lateral line scales (from 42 to 49). In breeding males, the gill covers have numerous small white tubercles, while the head develops large tubercles on the sides. Most of the body scales have at least one tubercle, particularly on the back and upper sides. Breeding males are dark olive on the back, yellowish green to steel-blue on the head and upper sides of the body, brassy yellow on the lower sides, and white or light cream on the venter.

ADULT SIZE: 3.9 to 5.9 in (100 to 150 mm)

DISTRIBUTION: This species is limited to the Apalachicola and Altamaha river systems in Georgia, and in Alabama it is most common above the Fall Line. Burr and Cashner (1983) report sympatry with **C. oligolepis** in headwater tributaries of the Tallapoosa, Etowah, and Tennessee river drainages in Georgia (not shown on the facing map). In the Chattahoochee River in Alabama, **C. pauciradii** is found only in tributaries that are immediately above and below the Fall Line—most frequently in Lee, Russell, and Chambers counties.

HABITAT AND BIOLOGY: Like other *Campostoma* species, the bluefin stoneroller prefers the shoal areas, riffles, and riffle runs of small to moderate streams characterized by clear, flowing water and gravel and sand substrates. We observed spawning in April in a small Coastal Plain stream typical of its preferred habitat. Located in about 8 inches of water, the spawning nest was a circular depression in white sand and fine gravel, with a thin layer of dark silt on top. To feed, this species uses its cartilaginous ridge on the lower jaw to scrape algae and other organisms from rocks and other hard structures.

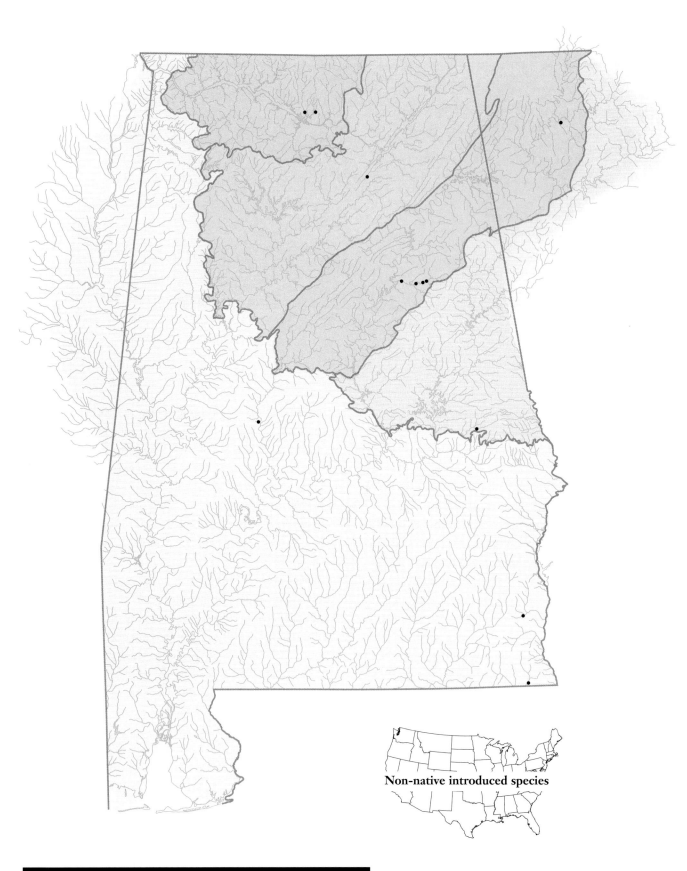

Non-native introduced species

GOLDFISH   *Carassius auratus*   **12 STATIONS**

Carassius auratus

(Linnaeus, 1758)

ETYMOLOGY:

Carassius—from the Greek word *karass*, the common name for these fishes in Eurasia
auratus—gilded

Marion Fish Hatchery, Perry County, 22 March 1995, 6.7 in (170 mm) SL male, GSA 4637

CHARACTERISTICS: Like the common carp, the goldfish has a long dorsal fin and a saw-toothed spine in front of the dorsal and anal fins. This species does not have barbels, and it has fewer than 30 lateral line scales. Goldfish sport a variety of colors—scarlet, red, pink, orange, silver, brown, white, gray, black—that can occur singly or in combination. Most common, however, is a color combination of medium to dark olive brown on the back, blending to light yellow and cream on the belly.

ADULT SIZE: 3.9 to 15 in (100 to 380 mm)

DISTRIBUTION: The goldfish is native to China and eastern Europe. Now widely distributed in the United States, this exotic species became an introduced one after it escaped or was released from fish hatcheries, ponds, home aquariums, and bait buckets. Though collections in Alabama have been few, the goldfish's range is wide, stretching from the Tennessee to the Chattahoochee rivers.

HABITAT AND BIOLOGY: Goldfish prefer quiet waters with extensive aquatic vegetation—conditions similar to those in most home aquariums. Adults favor plankton, but they will feed on a variety of animal and plant matter. Breder and Rosen (1966) report that, in Alabama, spawning occurs from February through November and is similar to that of the common carp. (In fact, goldfish sometimes hybridize with the common carp.) Goldfish are unusually long-lived; in captivity, they sometimes live for 30 years.

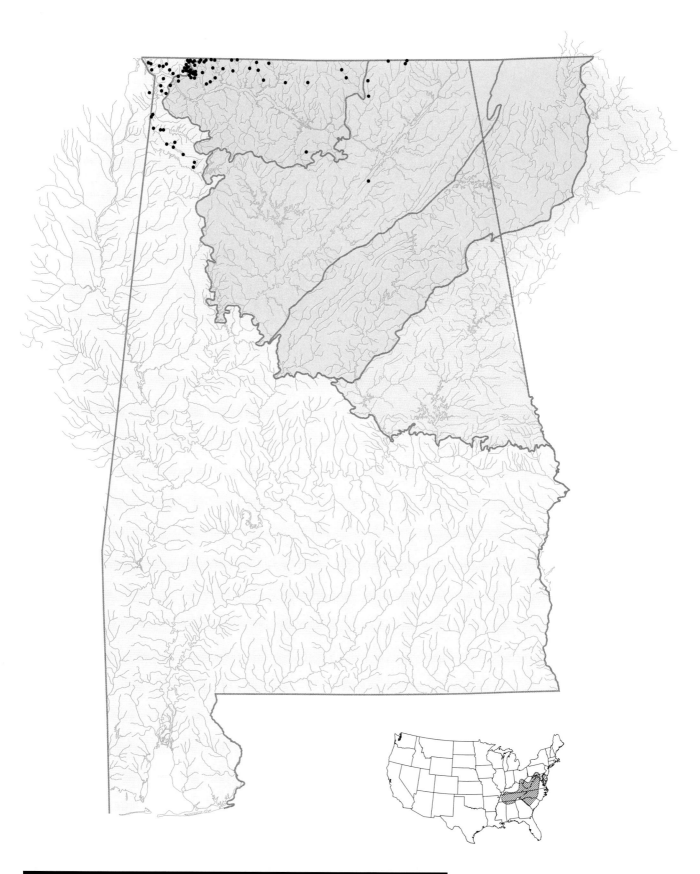

Clinostomus funduloides
Girard, 1856

ETYMOLOGY:

Clinostomus—inclined mouth

funduloides—like a fundulus, or any fish of the genus *Fundulus*

Wilson Branch, Lauderdale County, 2 April 1993, 3.0 in (75 mm) SL male, GSA 4405

CHARACTERISTICS: The rosyside dace has a deep, compressed body; a large, oblique mouth; and 5–5 or 5–4 principal teeth on the pharyngeal arches. Breeding individuals are quite colorful, with both sexes ranging from olive to light brown or golden yellow. Breeding males also develop a rose red streak that is broad (4 to 6 scale rows wide) and extends from the gill covers to the caudal fin. Females have a golden brown to tan lateral band with black mottling along the sides.

ADULT SIZE: 2 to 3 in (50 to 75 mm)

DISTRIBUTION: *Clinostomus funduloides* occurs in upland Atlantic slope drainages from the Chesapeake Bay south to the Savannah, Tennessee, and Cumberland rivers. It also occurs infrequently in tributaries to the Ohio River in West Virginia and Ohio. In Alabama the rosyside dace is restricted to the Tennessee River drainage and is most frequent in the Bear Creek system and in stream systems north of the Tennessee River.

HABITAT AND BIOLOGY: This species frequents both pools and riffles of clear, cool, medium-sized upland streams flowing over gravel, cobble, or bedrock. It is found most often in runs and chutes below riffles or in

pools below small waterfalls. Because of its large mouth, it can consume a variety of prey, including terrestrial insects. A typical life span is four years. Individuals in nuptial condition and color have been collected from late February through May, and as Etnier and Starnes (1993) report, rosyside dace will spawn over the nests of some other species, such as stonerollers.

Spawning aggregation of rosyside dace. Photograph courtesy of William N. Roston.

153

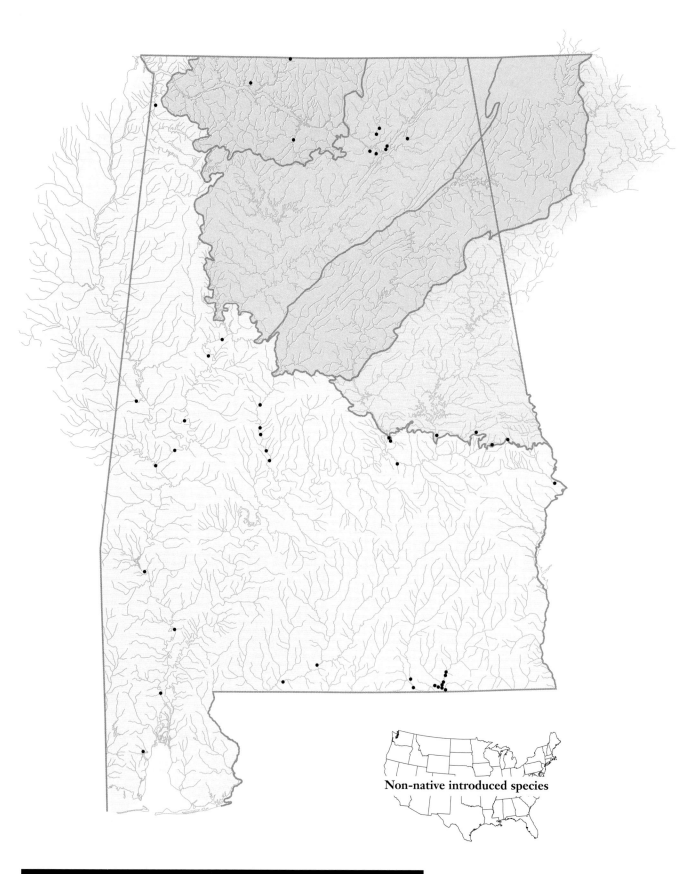

GRASS CARP   *Ctenopharyngodon idella*   46 STATIONS

Ctenopharyngodon idella
(Valenciennes, 1844)

ETYMOLOGY:

Ctenopharyngodon—comb-like pharyngeal teeth
idella—from the Greek word *ideo*, meaning "distinctive"

Butterfield Farms, Tuscaloosa County, 18 March 1994, 10 in (253 mm) SL adult, GSA 4620

CHARACTERISTICS: Also known as white amur, grass carp are characterized by a thick, mulletlike body; a small, blunt head; and an anal fin placed on the caudal peduncle and well behind the dorsal fin. Distinct parallel grooves are located on the pharyngeal teeth. The scales are prominently edged in black on the sides and back. Grass carp are generally silvery to olive on the back, grading to white on the venter. See paper by Cuvier and Valenciennes (1844) for original description.

ADULT SIZE: This is a large species, with adults ranging from 2.6 to 4.3 ft (0.8 to 1.3 m) in length and up to 51 lb in weight.

DISTRIBUTION: The grass carp is an exotic species native to the Pacific slope of Asia and imported to the United States in 1963 at Stuttgart, Arkansas (Guillory, 1978). This species is extensively stocked throughout the United States to control aquatic vegetation, and one consequence of the practice has been the grass carp's rapid proliferation in native waters. The Tennessee Valley Authority, for example, has stocked Guntersville Reservoir with thousands of grass carp fingerlings. Our frequent encounters with grass carp in the Choctawhatchee River are the result of their accidental introduction when the dam of a catfish pond failed and the pond's contents spilled into the river.

HABITAT AND BIOLOGY: The grass carp is a large, strong-swimming species that makes spectacular jumps when it is frightened or confined in a small area. Juveniles have been reported to feed on small invertebrates and crustaceans, while adults feed primarily on macroscopic aquatic vegetation, consuming up to their weight in food each day. Growth can be rapid, reaching 20 inches or more each year. Sexually mature individuals spawn in areas of increased velocity in large rivers, producing eggs that are suspended in the water column (Breder and Rosen, 1966). The proliferation of the species is cause for concern. Because the grass carp competes with native species for space and food, and may even destroy fish and wildlife habitat, it could reduce the populations of other fish species. In order to control the species' population size and its spread throughout southeastern rivers and lakes, stocking is now permitted only with sterile grass carp.

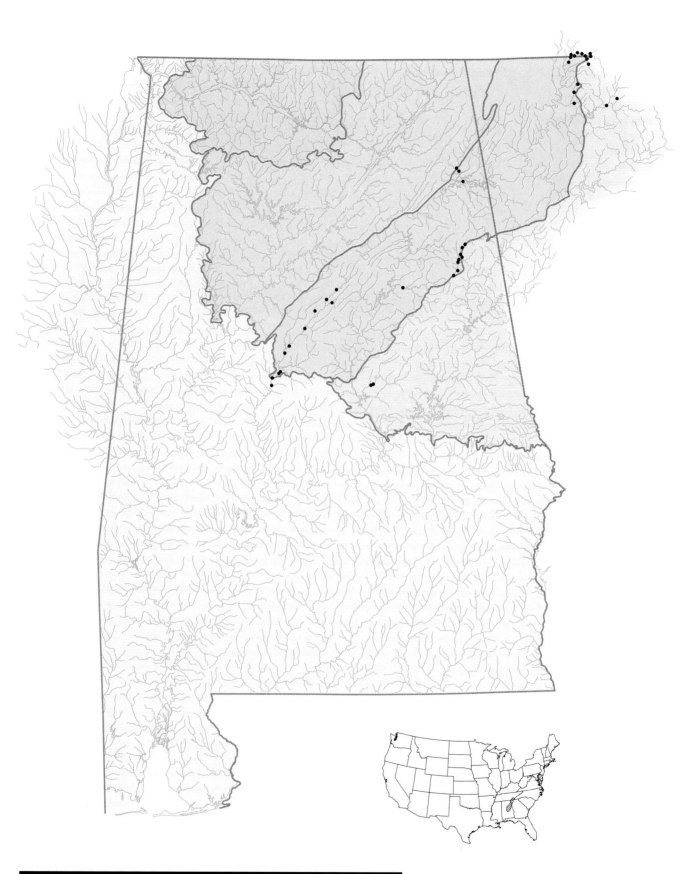

BLUE SHINER *Cyprinella caerulea* **41 STATIONS**

Cyprinella caerulea

(Jordan, 1877)

ETYMOLOGY:

Cyprinella—diminutive of
Cyprinus, the carp
caerulea—blue

Weogufka Creek, Coosa County, 24 June 1992, 2.0 in (50 mm) SL female, GSA 4308

CHARACTERISTICS: The body of *Cyprinella caerulea* is narrow and elongate, and its head is relatively small and triangular in shape. The mouth is terminal to subterminal and oblique. In breeding males, the dorsal fin is greatly expanded, and the snout protrudes slightly. Females and nonbreeding males are generally plain, with a steel-blue or dark silver body above the lateral stripe. Breeding males have a similar appearance, except their entire bodies acquire a more intense metallic blue color. The lateral stripe is bright blue-green, the fins are either bright yellow or orange edged in white, and the dorsal fin membranes are dark. See Jordan (1877a) for original description.

ADULT SIZE: 2 to 2.8 in (50 to 70 mm)

DISTRIBUTION: This species is endemic to the Mobile basin above the Fall Line in the upper Coosa River system. In Alabama it is restricted to the lower reaches of Little River, Weogufka Creek, and Choccolocco Creek (Pierson and Krotzer, 1987). Dobson (1994) recently reported a 3-mile range extension upstream in Little River. The species was formerly known from the Cahaba River system but has not been reported there since 1971.

HABITAT AND BIOLOGY: Blue shiners prefer clear, medium or large streams and are found in shallow pools with slow currents or in backwaters over sand and gravel substrates. They consume terrestrial insects and, to a lesser extent, immature aquatic insects. Spawning in the upper Coosa River system occurs from late April to late July (Krotzer, 1984).

REMARKS: The type locality of the blue shiner is tributaries to the Oostanaula River, near Rome, Floyd County, Georgia. The U.S. Fish and Wildlife Service has listed the blue shiner as a threatened species.

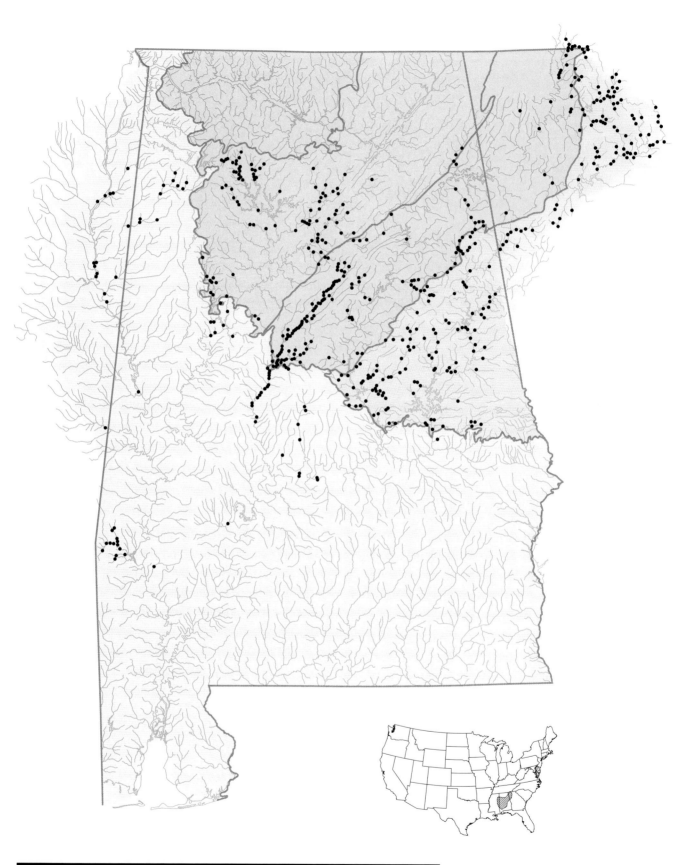

ALABAMA SHINER   *Cyprinella callistia*   538 STATIONS

158

Cyprinella callistia
(Jordan, 1877)

ETYMOLOGY:

Cyprinella—diminutive of
Cyprinus, the carp
callistia—beautiful sail,
referring to the bluish black
dorsal fin

Hatchet Creek, Coosa County, 24 June 1992, 3.3 in (84 mm) SL breeding male, GSA 4320

CHARACTERISTICS: The Alabama shiner has a somewhat stout, moderately elongate body that is slightly compressed. The head is triangular and large, and the mouth is relatively large, horizontal, and located on the bottom of the head. Breeding males are beautiful, with a blue-black caudal spot and steel-blue back and sides grading to a cream venter. Fins have milky white shading, while the dorsal fin is bright red in the front and has a large black spot on the back. (In breeding males, the dorsal fin is expanded.) The caudal fin is bright red edged in white and yellow. See Jordan (1877a) for original description.

ADULT SIZE: 2.6 to 3.5 in (65 to 90 mm)

DISTRIBUTION: *Cyprinella callistia* is endemic to the Mobile basin and is found most frequently above the Fall Line. The Alabama shiner is one of the dominant minnow species found in the Cahaba, Coosa, and Tallapoosa river systems. Mettee et al. (1987) report isolated populations of Alabama shiners in Okatuppa and

Tuckabum creeks (two lower Tombigbee River tributaries in the western Lime Hills) and also give the first account of the species from this region.

HABITAT AND BIOLOGY: The Alabama shiner is the most common cyprinid in the main channel of the Tallapoosa River. Adults favor moderate to swift flowing runs and riffles over boulder, cobble, and gravel substrates, whereas juveniles prefer shallow waters with slow to moderate current. Spawning individuals have been collected from April to early July, usually at the head of swift riffles or in chutes within riffles. Ferguson (1989) reports crevice spawning for Alabama shiners living in aquariums. This species feeds on aquatic insect larvae and other bottom-dwelling animals, and snails have been found in the digestive tracts of some individuals.

REMARKS: The type locality for the Alabama shiner is tributaries to the Oostanaula and Etowah rivers, near Rome, Floyd County, Georgia.

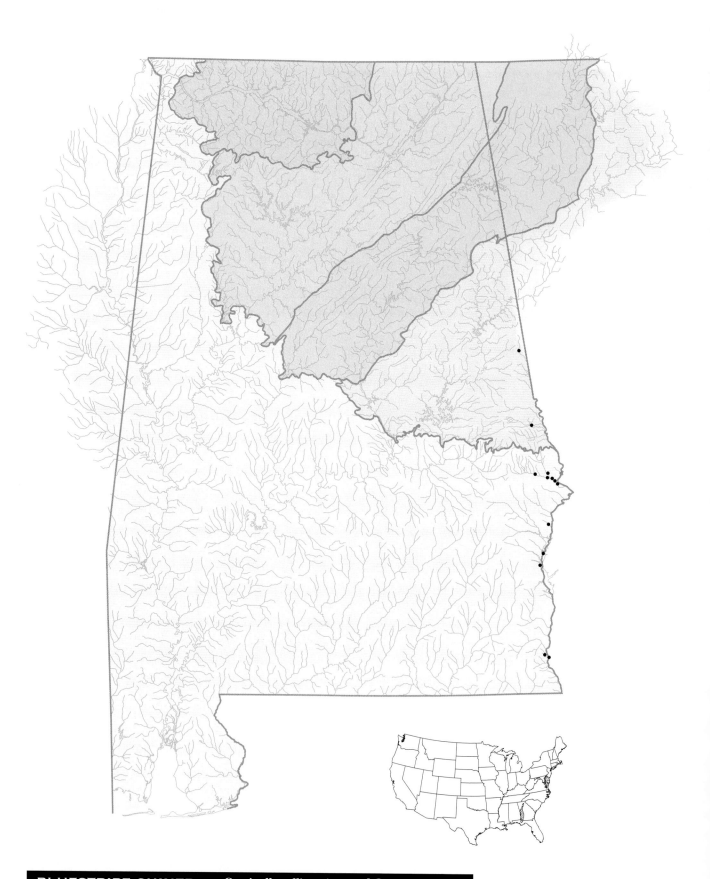

Cyprinella callitaenia

(Bailey and Gibbs, 1956)

ETYMOLOGY:

Cyprinella—a diminutive of *Cyprinus*, the carp *callitaenia*—beautiful band or ribbon, referring to the blue lateral stripe

Farley Service Water Cooling Lake, Houston County, 10 May 1994, 2.7 in (68 mm) SL male, GSA 4627

CHARACTERISTICS: The bluestripe shiner is an elongate, slender minnow with a slightly compressed body. The head is small, with an inferior, oblique mouth and a long, blunt snout. Breeding males are steel-blue with iridescent pink flecks above the lateral stripe. The dorsal fin is iridescent green in the center and is edged in blue and then white. The paired fins and caudal fin are edged in white, as is the greenish yellow anal fin.

ADULT SIZE: 2 to 3 in (50 to 75 mm)

DISTRIBUTION: This species is endemic to the Apalachicola River basin, where it occurs in the Chattahoochee and Flint river drainages. In Alabama it is found only in the Chattahoochee River drainage, including Halawakee and Uchee creeks. In a recent survey of the lower Chattahoochee River drainage, Shepard et al. (1995) report that bluestripe shiners are not as common there as they once were. The authors found shiners in Omusee, Abbie, Cheneyhatchee, and

Little Barbour creeks. Interestingly, they also found good populations from a few sites in Walter F. George Reservoir, a habitat that was previously considered unfavorable for bluestripe shiners. One of the largest known breeding populations of bluestripe shiners in Alabama occurs in the cooling lake for the Joseph M. Farley nuclear power plant in Houston County.

HABITAT AND BIOLOGY: *Cyprinella callitaenia* lives in rivers, reservoirs, and large tributaries with slow to moderate currents over sand and gravel substrates. Its diet has not been studied but is presumed to consist of drifting insects or plant matter. Spawning occurs from May to June, primarily over rocky crevices or other hard substrates. Like some other species of *Cyprinella*, the bluestripe shiner is a fractional crevice spawner—that is, at intervals throughout the extended spawning season, it deposits its eggs in the crevices of submerged logs or fractured rocks. Wallace and Ramsey (1981) report spawning from April to August in Uchee Creek, with peak activity in June.

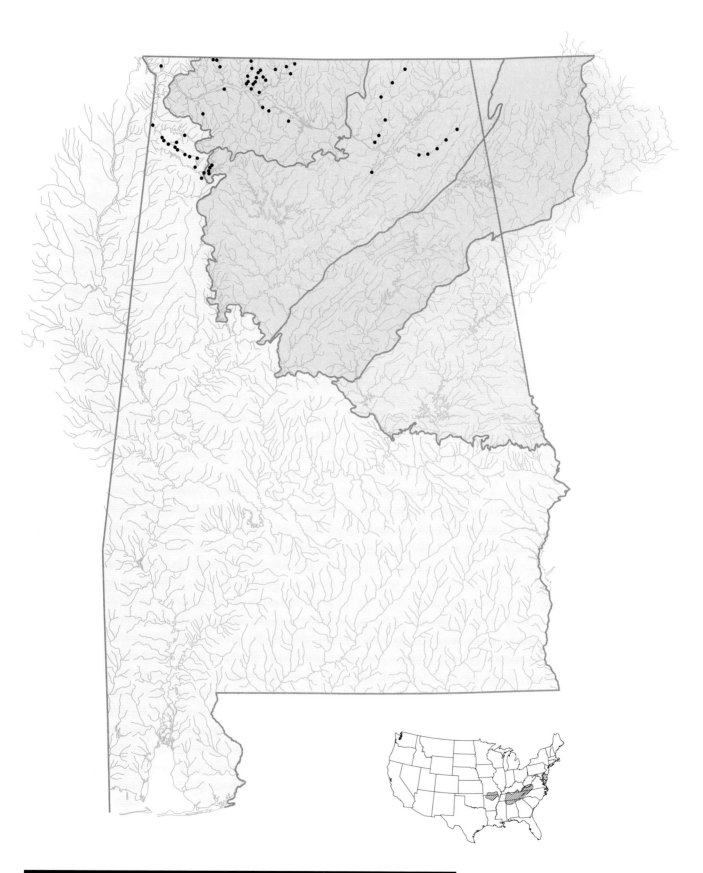

Cyprinella galactura
(Cope, 1868)

ETYMOLOGY:

Cyprinella—diminutive of *Cyprinus*, the carp *galactura*—milk tail, referring to the white areas on the caudal fin

Sour Branch, Lauderdale County, 24 February 1993, 3.5 in (90 mm) SL male, GSA 4375

CHARACTERISTICS: The whitetail shiner is easily recognized by the two milky white spots at the base of its caudal fin. It is a large species, with a terete, elongate, slightly compressed body. In breeding males, the back is an iridescent bluish silver, and the dorsal fin is greatly expanded. The head is large and elongate, with a protruding snout and a distinctly subterminal mouth; both the snout and lips are bright red. The anal fin and paired fins are milky white, while the caudal fin is white at the base, red in the center, and black along the margin. Small whitetail shiners may be confused with the spotfin shiner, *Cyprinella spiloptera*; the steelcolor shiner, *C. whipplei*; or the warpaint shiner, *Luxilus coccogenis*. *Cyprinella galactura* has more predorsal and lateral line scales than do *C. spiloptera* or *C. whipplei* and a much smaller mouth than does *L. coccogenis*. See Cope (1868a) for original description.

ADULT SIZE: 3 to 5.1 in (75 to 130 mm)

DISTRIBUTION: The whitetail shiner is widely distributed on both sides of the Mississippi River. To the west it occurs in the Ozark Plateau and Ouachita Mountain region, while to the east it occurs in the Tennessee and Cumberland river drainages and in the upper Savannah and Santee river drainages. In Alabama this species occurs in the Tennessee River drainage, most frequently in the Bear Creek, Town Creek, Elk River, Bluewater Creek, Second Creek, and Paint Rock River systems.

HABITAT AND BIOLOGY: *Cyprinella galactura* is found in small to moderate, high-gradient, clear, flowing streams with hard, stable substrates. Its diet is diverse, consisting of drifting insects, insect larvae, and occasionally plant material. Outten (1958) reports a diet of mayflies, diptera, and beetles for individuals in the upper French Broad River in North Carolina. Outten indicates that whitetail shiners live for two or three (but sometimes as many as four) years. In Alabama reproduction occurs from June to August, and the behavior is described as fractional crevice spawning (Pflieger, 1975)—that is, at intervals throughout the breeding season, the shiner deposits its eggs in the crevices of submerged logs or fractured rocks.

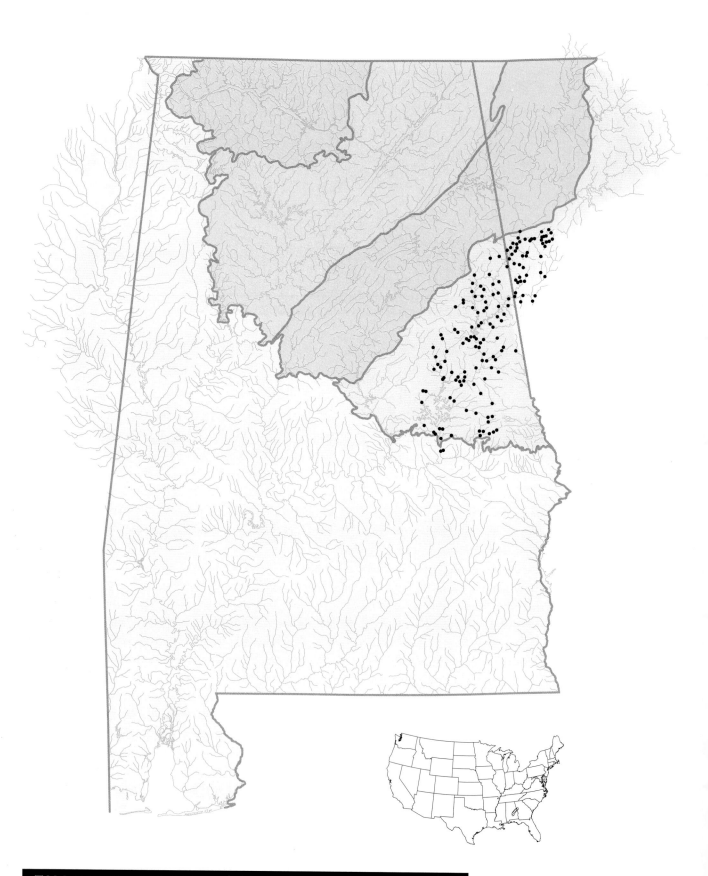

Cyprinella gibbsi

(Howell and Williams, 1971)

ETYMOLOGY:
Cyprinella—diminutive of *Cyprinus*, the carp
gibbsi—in honor of Robert H. Gibbs, U.S. National Museum, recognizing his studies of the genus *Cyprinella*

Josie Leg Creek, Tallapoosa County, 24 June 1992, 2.5 in (64 mm) SL male, GSA 4322

CHARACTERISTICS: *Cyprinella gibbsi* has an elongate, robust, moderately deep, and only slightly compressed body. Its head is moderate in size and triangular, with a long, pointed snout, particularly in breeding males. Its mouth is large, terminal, and oblique. Breeding males are brilliantly colored, with a blue-black to steel-blue back and sides and a copper lateral stripe. The dorsal fin (which is not greatly expanded in breeding males) is red-orange in the front and dark in the back, with white shading throughout. Paired fins and the anal fin are red-orange in the front and white in other areas. The caudal fin has milky white tips, red-orange membranes, and a black margin. Though their ranges do not overlap, the Tallapoosa shiner is most closely related to the tricolor shiner, *C. trichroistia*. Males of the two species can be distinguished by breeding tubercle patterns and snout shapes (see the key for the genus *Cyprinella* on pages 138–39).

ADULT SIZE: 2 to 2.6 in (50 to 65 mm)

DISTRIBUTION: The Tallapoosa shiner is distributed almost exclusively in the Tallapoosa River system above the Fall Line. A recent collection of several specimens from Wehadkee Creek in Randolph County is the first record of *C. gibbsi* from the Chattahoochee River system, indicating stream capture between the Tallapoosa and Chattahoochee river systems.

HABITAT AND BIOLOGY: The Tallapoosa shiner is the most common minnow species collected in tributaries of the Tallapoosa River system above the Fall Line. It is most frequently found in medium-sized streams with sand, silt, or rock substrates. Swift areas and shoals downstream of riffles appear to be preferred, although individuals have been reported from eddies and pools with slow currents. Little information is available about the life history of this species. However, as with other *Cyprinella* species, spawning likely occurs from late April through June. Ferguson (1989) reports crevice spawning for *C. gibbsi* in aquariums. Diet probably consists of stream drift composed of terrestrial insects and aquatic insect immatures with occasional plant matter.

REMARKS: The type locality of the Tallapoosa shiner is Enitachopco Creek, a tributary to Hillabee Creek, Clay County, Alabama.

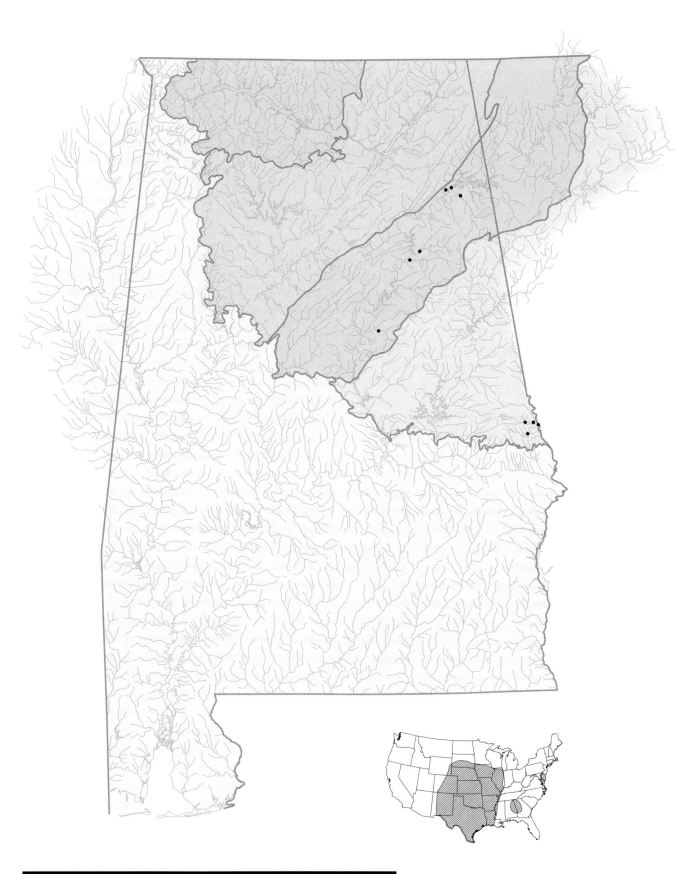

Cyprinella lutrensis

(Baird and Girard, 1853)

ETYMOLOGY:

Cyprinella—diminutive of *Cyprinus*, the carp

lutrensis—otter, referring to Otter Creek, Arkansas, where this species was first found

Red River, Rapides Parish, Louisiana, 3 June 1995, 2.1 in (54 mm) SL male, TU 174960

CHARACTERISTICS: The red shiner is a relatively deep-bodied species with a highly arched back. The head is large and deep, with a pointed snout and large mouth. Breeding males are brightly colored. The back is blue or blue-green, while the back of the head is red, and the opercles are pink or reddish orange. The sides are light blue with a dark, crosshatched pattern. The paired fins are reddish orange with white margins, while the anal fin is red in the center with a white margin. The dorsal fin is typically not expanded. *Cyprinella lutrensis* typically has nine anal rays and 4–4 pharyngeal teeth. However, this species readily hybridizes with the blacktail shiner, *C. venusta*, and the hybrids frequently have eight or nine anal rays. Hybrids may also have a faint caudal spot. See Baird and Girard (1853a) for original description.

ADULT SIZE: 1.2 to 3 in (30 to 75 mm)

DISTRIBUTION: The native range of *C. lutrensis* is the Mississippi River basin and Gulf coastal drainages west of the Mississippi River. Commonly sold as bait, the red shiner has escaped or been released into the Coosa and Chattahoochee river systems, and in some cases it is probably hybridizing with *C. venusta*. Timmons (1982) includes a record from the upper Tombigbee River drainage, but because we were unable to examine the specimen, we did not include the record in the distribution map on the facing page.

HABITAT AND BIOLOGY: The red shiner is found in a variety of habitats, from still backwaters to flowing streams. It appears to prefer moderately large creeks with some flow over sand, silt, or gravel, although it also seems to tolerate siltation, turbidity, and other extreme habitat conditions. Spawning reportedly occurs from April to September in the South and Midwest, with individuals living for more than two years (Lewis and Gunning, 1959). The species has been observed spawning in crevices (Gale, 1986) as well as broadcasting gametes in open water and depositing eggs over sunfish beds (Minckley, 1959). The red shiner's diet includes algae and terrestrial and aquatic insects.

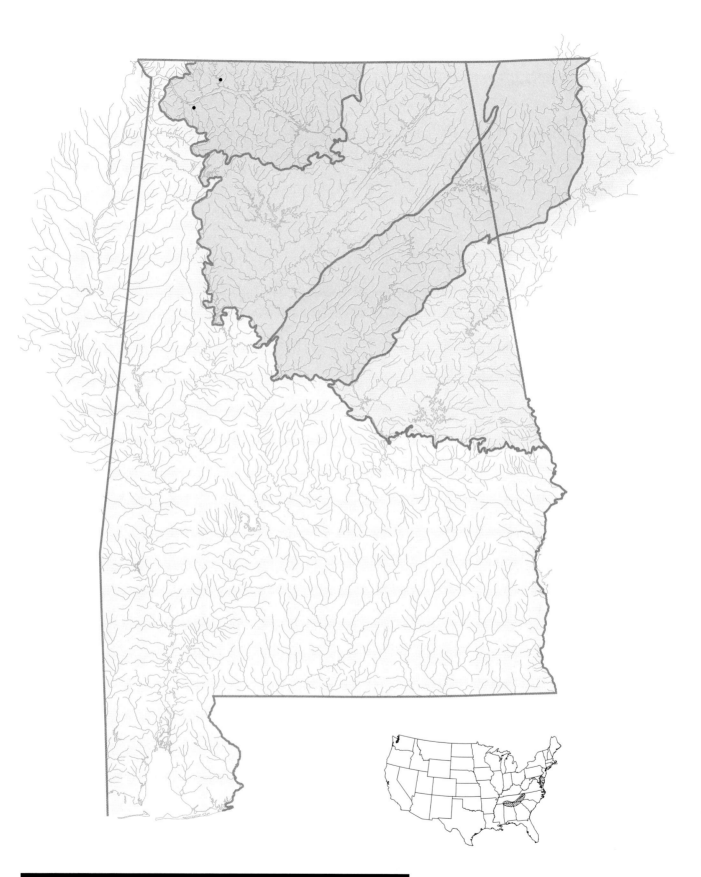

SPOTFIN CHUB *Cyprinella monacha* **2 STATIONS**

168

Cyprinella monacha
(Cope, 1868)

ETYMOLOGY:
Cyprinella—diminutive
of *Cyprinus*, the carp
monacha—solitary,
reflecting the discoverer's
perception of its rarity

Emory River, Morgan County, Tennessee, 10 June 1991, 3.0 in (75 mm) SL. Photograph courtesy of Richard T. Bryant and Wayne C. Starnes.

CHARACTERISTICS: The body form of *Cyprinella monacha* is elongate, terete, and somewhat triangular in cross section. The head is triangular and small in side view, with a distinctly inferior mouth. The spotfin chub was formerly referred to the genus *Hybopsis* because of its barbel. It is readily distinguished from other *Cyprinella* species not only by its barbel but also by its 4 – 4 pharyngeal teeth and more than 50 lateral line scales (most other species in the genus have 1,4 – 4,1 teeth and around 40 lateral line scales). Breeding males have a brilliant turquoise–royal blue color along the back, side of the head, and upper part of the sides. During peak nuptial activity, the fins are tipped with milky white. See Cope (1868b) for original description.

ADULT SIZE: 2.2 to 3.3 in (55 to 85 mm)

DISTRIBUTION: This species is endemic to the Tennessee River drainage in upland habitats of Alabama, Tennessee, Georgia, North Carolina, and Virginia, but it has not been found for some time in Alabama and Georgia. In any case, its occurrence is rare throughout its range. In Alabama it has been collected at only two locations: in Little Bear Creek near Tuscumbia, Colbert County (one specimen), and in Shoal Creek near Florence, Lauderdale County (three specimens). The Little Bear Creek collection was made in 1937, the Shoal Creek collection in 1884—in both cases before the Tennessee Valley Authority impounded the Tennessee River. The species' current presence in Alabama is in doubt, though acceptable habitat may occur in the upper Shoal Creek, Elk River, or Paint Rock River systems.

HABITAT AND BIOLOGY: The spotfin chub prefers clear, medium-sized upland rivers with moderate or swift current over boulder substrates. Adults are found in swift current, while juveniles are often found in slow current over gravel (Jenkins and Burkhead, 1984). The species feeds primarily on immature aquatic insects (such as midges, blackflies, mayflies, and caddisflies) and lives for more than three years. The spotfin chub reportedly reproduces from late May to August and is a fractional crevice spawner on rocks, logs, and other similar cover.

REMARKS: The U.S. Fish and Wildlife Service has listed the spotfin chub as a threatened species.

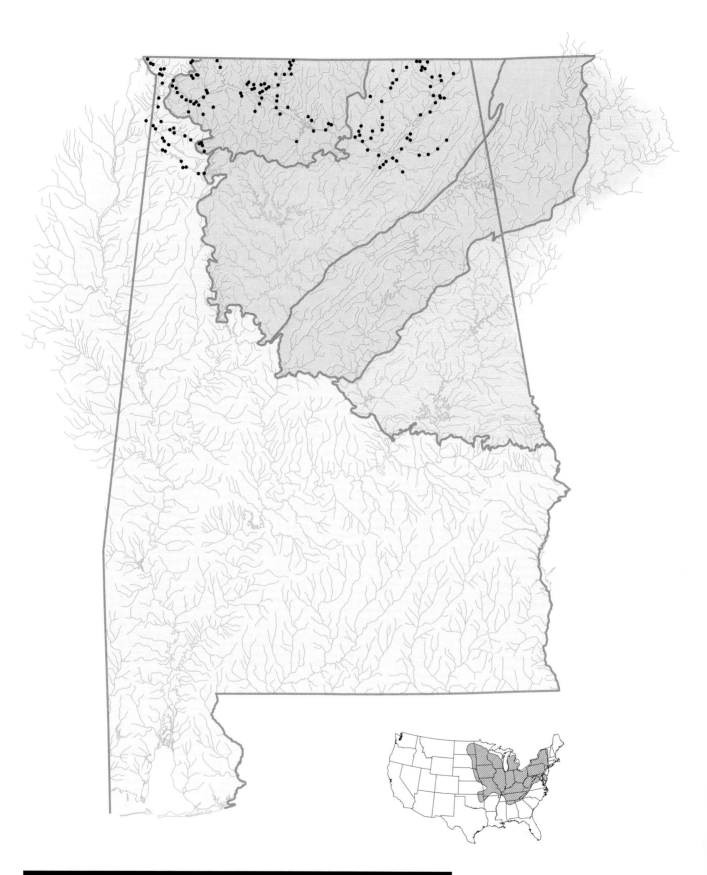

Coon Creek, Jackson County, 11 June 1992, 3.1 in (80 mm) SL male, GSA 4257

Cyprinella spiloptera
(Cope, 1868)

ETYMOLOGY:

Cyprinella—diminutive of *Cyprinus*, the carp *spiloptera*—spot fin or spot wing, referring to the spot at the end of the dorsal fin

CHARACTERISTICS: The body of the spotfin shiner is elongate and somewhat compressed. The head is small, with a conical, protruding snout and a moderately large, oblique, and terminal mouth. This species lacks a distinct caudal spot, and adults have a blotch on the last two or three rays of the dorsal fin. Breeding males usually have a steel-blue back and sides and a yellow snout. The paired fins and anal fin are yellow, and all fins are edged in white. Species of *Cyprinella* likely to be confused with *C. spiloptera* include the whitetail shiner, *C. galactura*, and the steelcolor shiner, *C. whipplei*. *Cyprinella galactura* has two white caudal spots and a less oblique mouth, in addition to a break in the lateral stripe just anterior to the caudal fin. Etnier and Starnes (1993) list several useful characters for separating *C. whipplei* from *C. spiloptera*. In *spiloptera* the lateral stripe on the caudal peduncle extends only slightly above the midline and has a distinct dorsal edge, while in *whipplei* the lateral stripe extends well above the midline and is less distinct on the upper margin. Also, the *spiloptera* breeding male has a normally shaped dorsal fin with melanophores only on the posterior membranes, while *whipplei* has an enlarged dorsal fin with melanophores throughout all membranes. See Günther (1868) for description.

ADULT SIZE: 1.8 to 3.9 in (45 to 100 mm)

DISTRIBUTION: *Cyprinella spiloptera* is distributed throughout the upper Atlantic slope drainages, the Great Lakes basin, and the Mississippi River basin from northern Minnesota south to Arkansas and east to the Ohio and Tennessee rivers. This species occurs widely and commonly throughout the Tennessee River drainage.

HABITAT AND BIOLOGY: The spotfin shiner occurs in clear to somewhat turbid streams of moderate size; it prefers flowing pools, but it is also found in larger rivers and impoundments. Spawning occurs from late May to mid-August. Pflieger (1965) reports that eggs are laid in crevices and on the underside of logs, and he also indicates that *C. spiloptera* spawns earlier than *C. whipplei*. Male spotfin shiners have been observed producing sounds during courtship behavior, perhaps as a means of communicating with females of the same species or antagonizing intruding males of other species (Gale and Gale, 1977). Spotfin shiners consume stream drift composed of adult and immature aquatic insects, plant material, occasional small fish, and terrestrial insects.

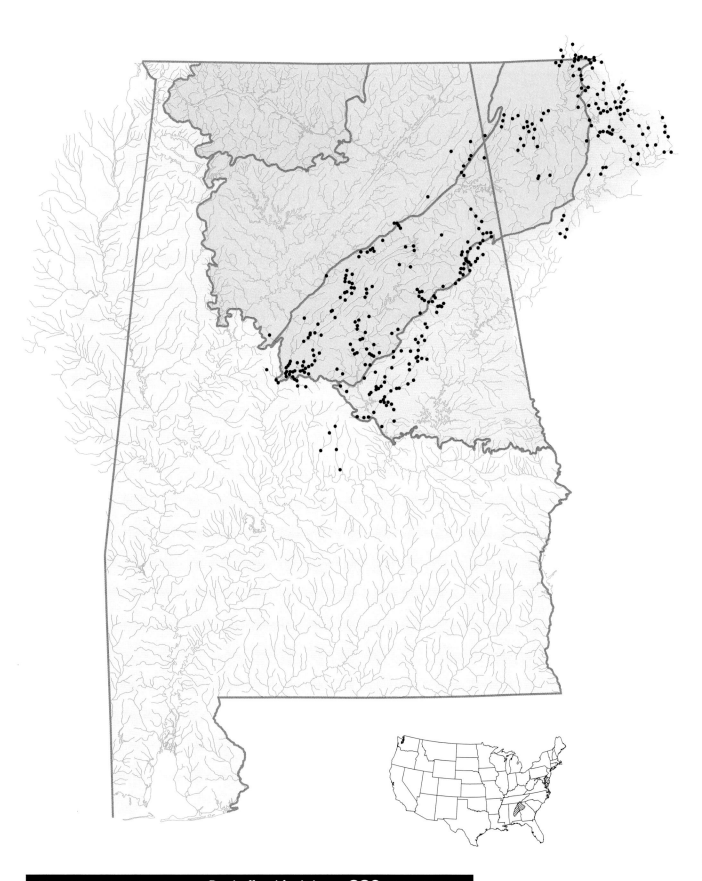

TRICOLOR SHINER   *Cyprinella trichroistia*   330 STATIONS

172

Cyprinella trichroistia
(Jordan and Gilbert, 1878)

ETYMOLOGY:
Cyprinella—diminutive of
Cyprinus, the carp
trichroistia—tricolored sail,
referring to the tricolored
dorsal fin on breeding males

Wash Creek, Chilton County, 21 April 1993, 2.2 in (55 mm) SL male, GSA 4437

CHARACTERISTICS: A moderately sized, slightly compressed, elongate fish, the tricolor shiner has a large, triangular head with a long, pointed snout. The mouth is large, terminal, and oblique. Breeding males have a dark blue-gray lateral band bordered above by a narrow stripe. The anterior part of the dorsal fin is orange, while the posterior membranes are black, contrasting with the white fin rays. The predominantly orange caudal fin has white tips and a diffuse quadrate spot at its base. The anal, pelvic, and pectoral fins are orange anteriorly and milky white elsewhere. (This contrasts with the red-orange color of these fins in the closely related Tallapoosa shiner, **Cyprinella gibbsi**.) See paper by Jordan and Brayton (1878) for original description.

ADULT SIZE: 2.6 to 3.1 in (65 to 80 mm)

DISTRIBUTION: The tricolor shiner is endemic to the Mobile basin and is almost completely confined to the Cahaba and Coosa river systems above the Fall Line. Isolated populations are known to occur in Swift and Little Mulberry creeks of the Alabama River drainage and in Davis and Turkey creeks in the Black Warrior River system. The Black Warrior populations apparently gained access through headwater stream capture from tributaries of the Cahaba and Coosa river systems.

HABITAT AND BIOLOGY: *Cyprinella trichroistia* is common throughout its range, occurring in flowing, cool streams over boulders, cobble, or gravel. Juveniles prefer quiet waters over sand or sand-gravel substrates. Diet includes stream drift composed of adult and immature aquatic insects, plant matter, and terrestrial insects. Spawning occurs from mid-May through August. Ferguson (1989) reports crevice-spawning behavior for this species, with pairs swimming horizontally along a crevice as they release and fertilize eggs down its length. To attract females, males perform mock spawning runs along the crevices.

REMARKS: The type locality of this species is a tributary of the Etowah River, near Rome, Floyd County, Georgia.

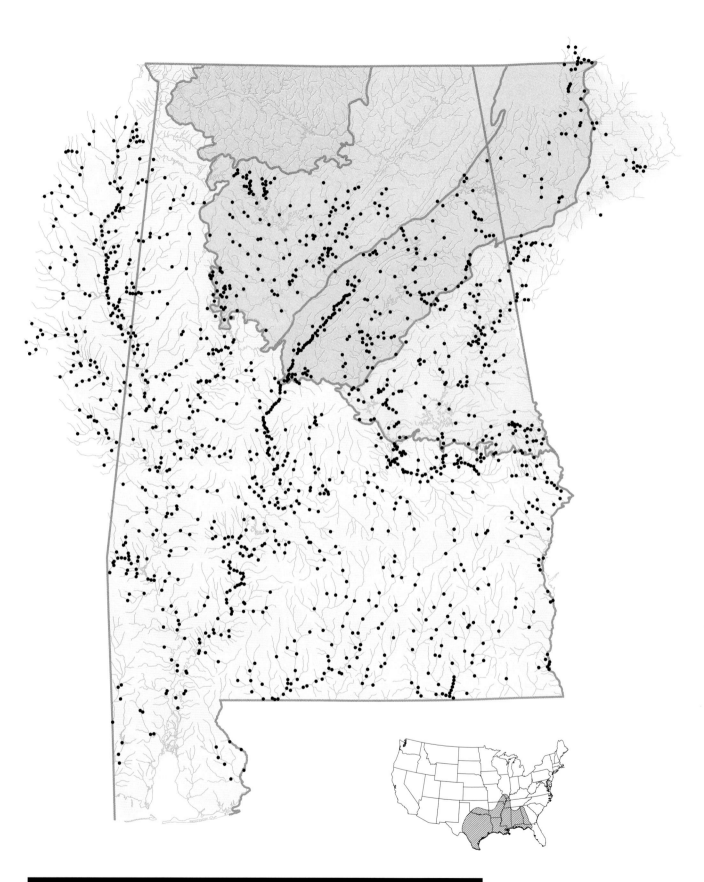

Cyprinella venusta

Girard, 1856

ETYMOLOGY:

Cyprinella—diminutive of *Cyprinus*, the carp *venusta*—Venus, the Roman goddess of love

Choctawhatchee River, Geneva County, 13 April 1992, 3.5 in (90 mm) SL male, GSA 4216

CHARACTERISTICS: The blacktail shiner is one of the largest and most common *Cyprinella* species, with a slender body form that is elongate to moderately deep. The head is moderately large, with a sharp snout and a terminal, large, and oblique mouth. A large, distinct spot at the base of the caudal fin is characteristic of this species and is the basis of its common name. Breeding males have an intense steel-blue back and a large, well-developed caudal spot. The anal and caudal fins are light yellow, and all fins are edged in white.

ADULT SIZE: 2.6 to 5.9 in (65 to 150 mm)

DISTRIBUTION: *Cyprinella venusta* occurs from the Rio Grande basin in Texas, east to the Suwannee River, and north through the Mississippi River basin to the confluence of the Ohio River. Two of the three recognized subspecies (Gibbs, 1957) occur in Alabama: The slender blacktail shiner, *C. v. stigmaturus*, is found in the upper Mobile basin (most frequently above the Fall Line), while the eastern blacktail shiner, *C. v. cercostigma*, occurs in the lower Mobile basin and coastal rivers draining the state. Intergradation between these subspecies has been recognized in the Alabama, Cahaba, and Tallapoosa river systems.

HABITAT AND BIOLOGY: The blacktail shiner is a common and abundant inhabitant of many different aquatic habitats, from headwaters, river channels, and swift riffle-run chutes to slow backwater areas and reservoirs. Our most successful collections of *C. venusta* have been in impoundments, large rivers, and large streams in swift chutes below riffles. Breeding adults more than 4 inches long are regularly captured in Alabama's rivers in June and July. Spawning occurs from June to August; in June we have observed nuptial behavior over fractured bedrock in Upatoi Creek, Georgia. The diet of this species consists of drifting adult and immature aquatic insects, plant material, and terrestrial insects.

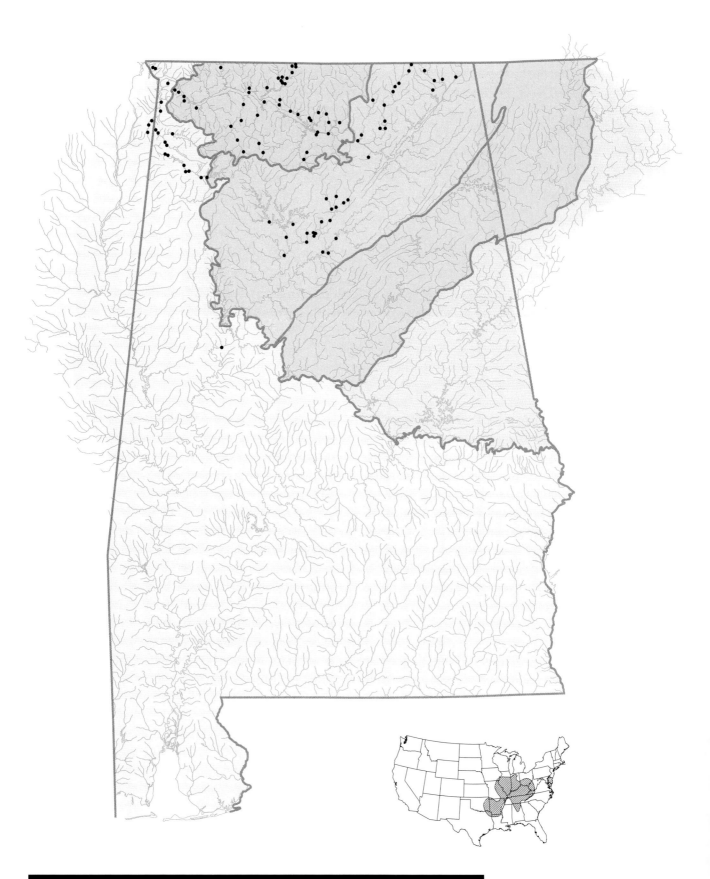

Cyprinella whipplei

Girard, 1856

ETYMOLOGY:

Cyprinella—diminutive of *Cyprinus*, the carp

whipplei—in honor of Lieutenant A. W. Whipple, the officer in charge of the expedition that discovered this species

Mallard Creek, Lawrence County, 14 July 1992, 3.4 in (87 mm) SL male, GSA 4269

CHARACTERISTICS: *Cyprinella whipplei* is slightly compressed and moderately deep, with a small, subconical head. The snout is red, short, and pointed; the mouth is terminal. In breeding males, the greatly expanded dorsal fin has melanophore stippling throughout all interradial membranes. The back is steel-blue, the sides an iridescent purple. All fins are lemon yellow with a milky white flush. The dorsal fin has a large spot near the back. The steelcolor shiner is easily confused with the spotfin shiner, *C. spiloptera*; for characteristics of the latter, see its account on pages 170–71.

ADULT SIZE: 1.6 to 5.3 in (40 to 135 mm)

DISTRIBUTION: *Cyprinella whipplei* ranges from the Ohio River basin south to the upper Black Warrior River system and west to the Missouri River drainage. It also occurs in the Ouachita and Red river drainages of Oklahoma and Arkansas. In Alabama the steelcolor shiner commonly occurs in the Tennessee River drainage and has become established in the Black Warrior River system in both the Mulberry and Locust fork systems. A record is available from the Black Warrior River near Tuscaloosa. Recent sampling efforts (1993) failed to yield the steelcolor shiner in selected parts of the upper Black Warrior system.

HABITAT AND BIOLOGY: The steelcolor shiner occurs in streams of moderate size and gradient, preferring flowing waters over hard bottoms and typically avoiding headwater streams. It spawns from June to August, depositing eggs in crevices or on the underside of logs and rocks (Pflieger, 1965). Individuals may live to be three years old, and their diet consists of drifting adult and immature aquatic insects, plant material, and terrestrial insects.

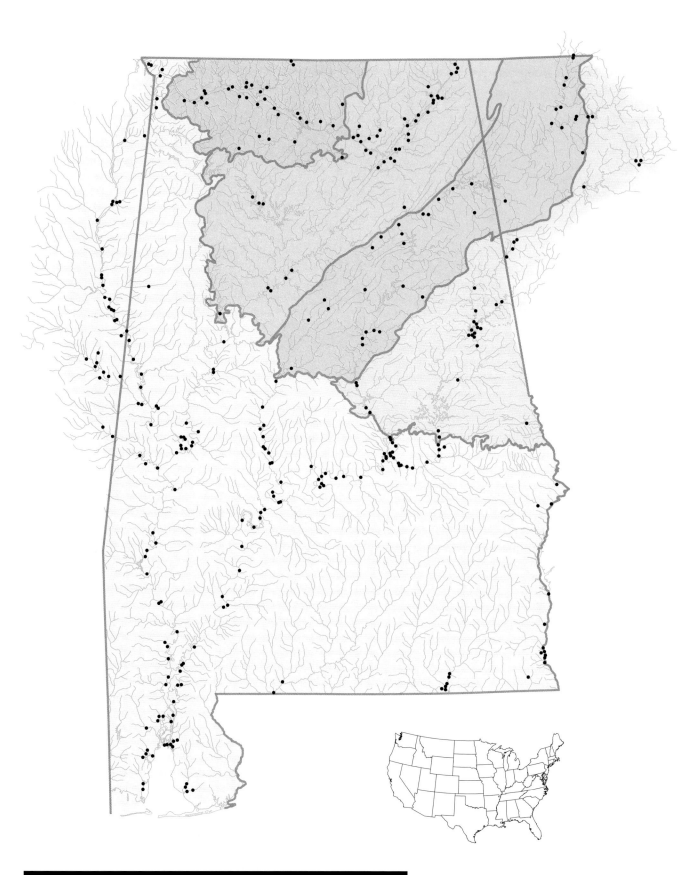

COMMON CARP   *Cyprinus carpio*   **325 STATIONS**

Cyprinus carpio
Linnaeus, 1758

ETYMOLOGY:

Cyprinus—carp (New Latin, from the Greek *kyprinos*)
carpio—carp (Late Latin)

Choctawhatchee River, Geneva County, 12 April 1992, 12.4 in (315 mm) SL, GSA 4214

CHARACTERISTICS: Unlike the similar goldfish, the common carp has two barbels on each side of the mouth and a long dorsal fin. The pharyngeal arch contains three rows of teeth. Like the goldfish, however, this species has saw-toothed spines preceding the dorsal and anal fins. The lateral line usually has 35 to 40 scales, and colors range from light olive on the back to yellow on the venter. The caudal fin is often a subdued red to reddish orange. Although the common carp is frequently confused with some species of suckers, such as buffalo (*Ictiobus*) and carpsuckers (*Carpiodes*), its barbels and saw-toothed spines easily distinguish it from the others.

ADULT SIZE: 12 to 26 in (305 to 660 mm). Large individuals approach 40 lb (18 kg).

DISTRIBUTION: The common carp is an introduced exotic species in the United States, originally established in 1877 by state fish commissions. Its natural range is throughout central Europe and Asia, and it occurs throughout Alabama in all major river drainages.

HABITAT AND BIOLOGY: Common carp are most abundant in large streams and impoundments, especially those made fertile by runoff and discharge of agricultural and domestic wastes. They frequent waters up to 20 feet deep with cover such as trees or other large structures. They feed mostly in the mud, consuming worms, insect larvae, and plankton. In Alabama reproduction occurs from early spring to summer in well-vegetated waters up to 6 feet deep. The adults' vigorous spawning in shallow waters stirs up sediment and causes the water to become turbid. Small, adhesive eggs attach to vegetation or sink into the mud after fertilization. It has been reported that a single female may contain up to 7 million eggs, but the average number of eggs is between 100,000 and 500,000 (Breder and Rosen, 1966). Because a female releases only about 500 to 1,000 eggs at a time, spawning occurs over a protracted period. Adults become sexually mature in three to five years. Our observations indicate that carp are particularly susceptible to predation by Ohio and chestnut lampreys in the Tennessee River drainage.

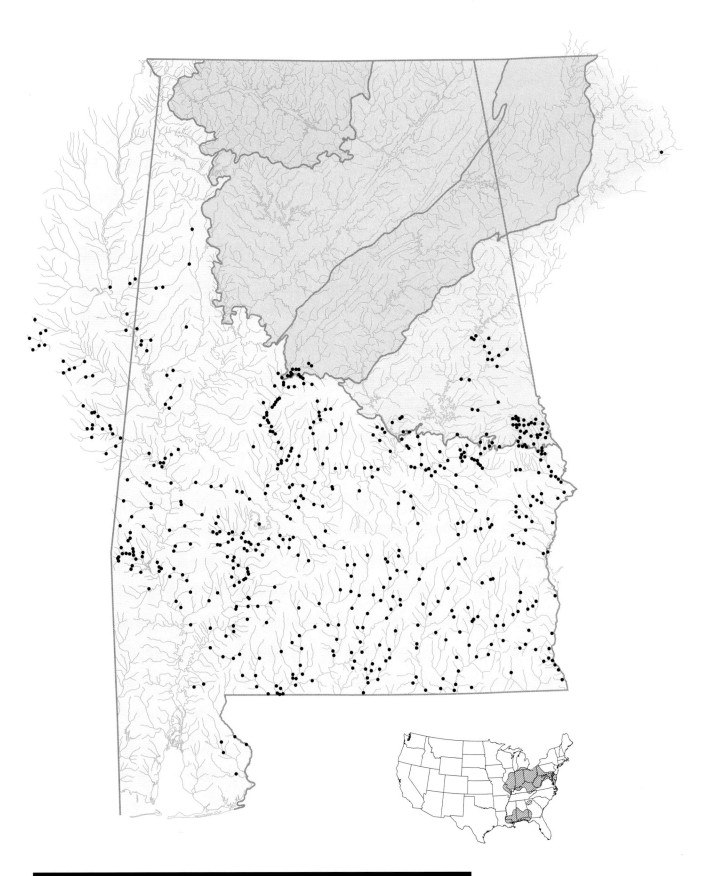

SILVERJAW MINNOW *Ericymba buccata* **562 STATIONS**

Ericymba buccata
Cope, 1865

ETYMOLOGY:
Ericymba—cavity
buccata—cheek, referring
to the exaggerated sensory
system of the head

Perdido River, Baldwin County, 19 August 1992, 2.7 in (69 mm) SL male, GSA 4466

CHARACTERISTICS: The silverjaw minnow is easily recognized by its extensive tubular sensory system, which appears on live individuals as silvery or translucent streaks on the underside of the head. The species has a pointed snout, a long head, and a compressed, slender body that is tapered at both ends. A small, horizontal mouth is located on the flattened ventral side of the head. Individuals are not colorful, being silver or straw color above and white below. Mayden (1989) refers this species to *Notropis*, and Robins et al. (1991) cite it as *N. buccatus*. Because of substantial morphological differences between this species and other cyprinids, we retain *Ericymba* as a distinctive genus, as do Boschung (1992) and Etnier and Starnes (1993). See Cope (1865a) for original description.

ADULT SIZE: 1.2 to 2.8 in (30 to 70 mm)

DISTRIBUTION: Two disjunct populations of the silverjaw minnow occur in the United States. One is located in Gulf slope drainages from the Apalachicola River basin west to the Pearl River drainage, generally below the Fall Line. The other is found in the Ohio River basin from the upper Cumberland River drainage north to the Great Lakes; on the Atlantic slope, it has invaded the Potomac River basin. In Alabama this species is both widespread and common throughout the Mobile basin below the Fall Line and in all Gulf Coast drainages. It also occurs well above the Fall Line in the Tallapoosa River system, and a disjunct population is known from the upper Etowah River in Georgia.

HABITAT AND BIOLOGY: The silverjaw minnow is an abundant and widespread inhabitant of shallow sand and gravel streams of the Coastal Plain, generally preferring larger, flowing streams. It also seems to tolerate some turbidity and stream degradation. Adults feed over algal layers, from which they extract immature insects, most commonly midge larvae and mayflies. Juveniles consume microcrustaceans. Wallace (1973) reports spawning from April to July in Indiana, with individuals living to be more than three years old. Spawning in Alabama occurs from March through June. Like the other "sand-loving" species, *Notropis ammophilus* and *N. longirostris*, the silverjaw minnow spawns over sand and gravel bars.

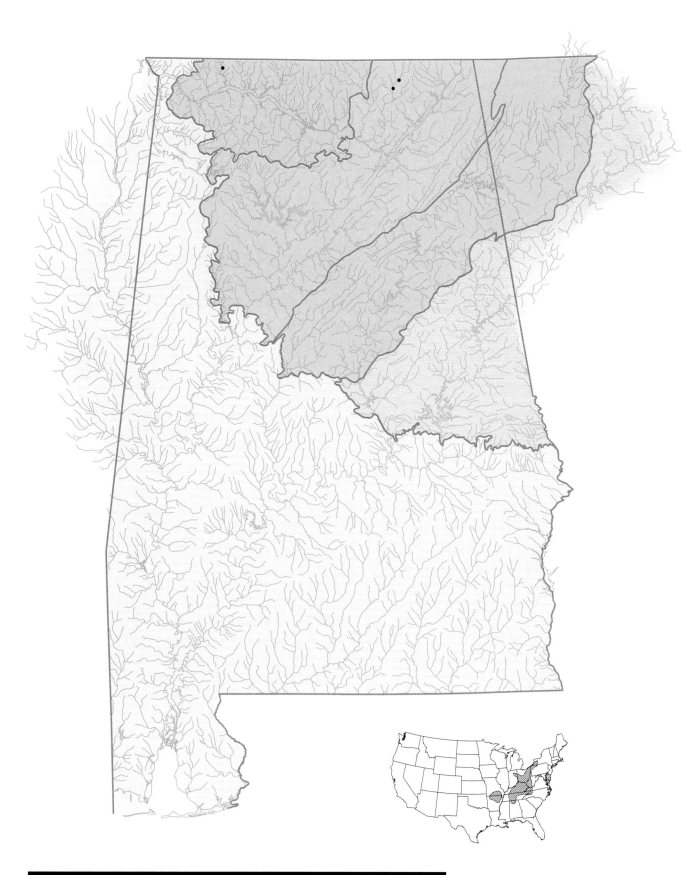

STREAMLINE CHUB   *Erimystax dissimilis*   3 STATIONS

Erimystax dissimilis
(Kirtland, 1840)

ETYMOLOGY:

Erimystax—loosely interpreted, large lip or mustache
dissimilis—dissimilar

Shoal Creek, Lauderdale County, 15 July 1992, 3.6 in (92 mm) SL male, GSA 4277

CHARACTERISTICS: *Erimystax dissimilis* has a slender, terete body that is slightly depressed in cross section. Its blunt, rounded snout extends beyond the upper lip, and its eye is smaller than the snout. The mouth is small, horizontal, and inferior, containing a small barbel in each corner. The sides are typically marked with nine or 10 dark, horizontally elongate blotches that are about the same size as the pupil of the eye, while lateral line scales usually number more than 46. This species is distinct from the similar blotched chub, *E. insignis*, which is shorter and more robust, has vertically elongate blotches, and usually has 43 or fewer lateral line scales.

ADULT SIZE: 2.6 to 4.5 in (65 to 115 mm)

DISTRIBUTION: Streamline chubs occur throughout the Ohio River basin from New York to the Tennessee River drainage. Their distribution in Alabama is limited to the Tennessee River drainage, where records are from only two systems—the Paint Rock River in Jackson County and Shoal Creek in Lauderdale County. Streamline chubs are uncommon and, when encountered, occur in low numbers. This species occurs sympatrically with *E. insignis*, with which it can be confused.

HABITAT AND BIOLOGY: *Erimystax dissimilis* prefers medium to large clear streams with moderate flow over clean gravel and cobble substrates. Individuals have been observed on the bottom in chutes below riffles. Harris (1986) reports a diet consisting of aquatic insects, particularly midges, mayflies, caddis flies, and organisms that live attached to underwater surfaces, suggesting a benthic life for this species. The streamline chub's reproductive cycle in Alabama is not known; however, spawning is reported to occur from mid-April through May in Tennessee (Harris, 1986), and it may run as late as early June in Alabama.

REMARKS: On 7 September 1995, after the creation of the distribution map on the facing page, we collected a series of 10 individuals in the Paint Rock River, at the community of Paint Rock. In only one net haul made in a pool about 3 feet deep, we captured five of these individuals over a sandy-silty bottom near a large, submerged log. We found the other five individuals in a plunge pool that also had a sandy bottom and that was located at the foot of a long riffle. This single collection has encouraged our hope that streamline chubs are retaining a foothold in Alabama.

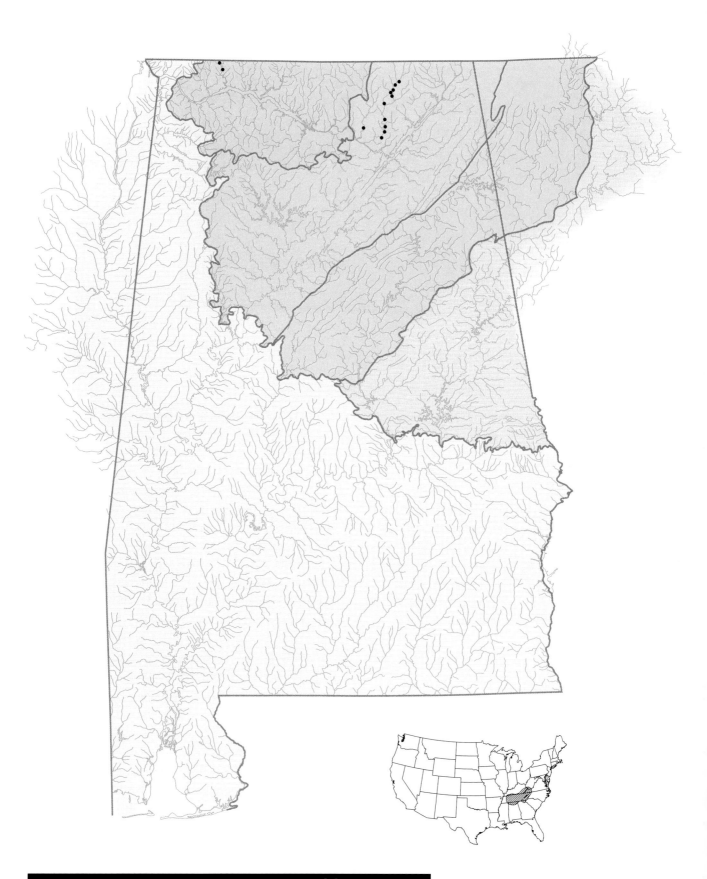

BLOTCHED CHUB *Erimystax insignis* **13 STATIONS**

Erimystax insignis
(Hubbs and Crowe, 1956)

ETYMOLOGY:
Erimystax—loosely interpreted, large lip or mustache
insignis—remarkable,
referring to the lateral
pigmentation

Paint Rock River, Marshall County, 20 May 1993, 2.9 in (74 mm) SL male, GSA 4476

CHARACTERISTICS: The blotched chub is often confused with the streamline chub, *Erimystax dissimilis*,
but the blotched chub is a shorter, generally deeper-
bodied species. It is characterized by a large eye, a
blunt, rounded snout overhanging the upper lip, and a
small, inferior mouth. The lateral blotches number
seven or eight, are vertically elongate, and are larger
than the pupil of the eye. A nuptial individual is light
golden to straw in color, with flecks of iridescent black
throughout. The caudal fin has two sulfur yellow spots
at its base, while the other fins are generally clear or
colored with a delicate yellow wash.

ADULT SIZE: 1.8 to 3 in (45 to 75 mm)

DISTRIBUTION: *Erimystax insignis* is found only in
the Tennessee and Cumberland river drainages from
Virginia to Alabama. In Alabama it is known from the
upper Shoal Creek system, Lauderdale County, and
more frequently (but still uncommonly) from the
Paint Rock and Flint river systems in northeast
Alabama.

HABITAT AND BIOLOGY: The blotched chub
prefers medium-sized or large, clear streams with
moderate flow over clean cobble and bedrock substrates. Individuals have been taken on the bottom in
chutes below riffles and in aquatic vegetation in the
middle of large shoals and riffles. Harris (1986)
describes *E. insignis* as a bottom feeder that consumes mostly midges, blackflies, mayflies, and organisms attached to underwater surfaces. Harris also
reports a spawning season in Tennessee that extends
from mid-April to early May. In Alabama nuptial
individuals from the Paint Rock River have been collected in mid-May.

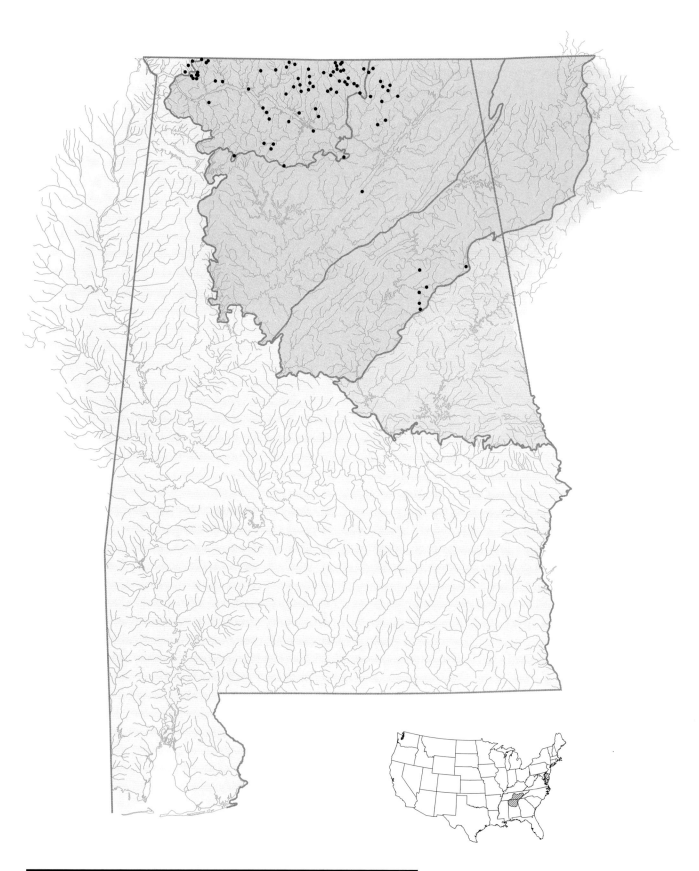

FLAME CHUB   *Hemitremia flammea*   84 STATIONS

186

Hemitremia flammea
(Jordan and Gilbert, 1878)

ETYMOLOGY:

Hemitremia—half aperture, referring to the incomplete lateral line
flammea—flaming, referring to the bright red colors in breeding males

Wilson Creek, Lauderdale County, 2 April 1993, 1.6 in (42 mm) SL male, GSA 4407

CHARACTERISTICS: *Hemitremia flammea* is a short species with a round body form in profile. The head is small, blunt, and rounded. Breeding males are striking, with lower sides that become flame red while their venters remain light. In each individual, the anterior base of the dorsal fin has a red spot, and the light olive back and sides are streaked with golden brown. A dark lateral band runs between the golden stripes, ending in a small but separate spot at the base of the caudal fin. See Jordan (1878a) for original description.

ADULT SIZE: 1.6 to 2.4 in (40 to 60 mm)

DISTRIBUTION: The flame chub is found only in the Tennessee, Cumberland, and Coosa river drainages. It regularly occurs throughout the Tennessee River drainage in the Cypress Creek, Elk River, Swan Creek, Flint River, and Paint Rock River systems, where it is most frequently encountered in springs, spring runs, and tributaries draining the Highland Rim. Isolated populations occur in tributaries to Choccolocco Creek in Calhoun and Talladega counties.

HABITAT AND BIOLOGY: This species prefers springs and small spring-fed streams, where it is sometimes abundant. It is an early spawner, beginning in January and continuing to early June. Spawning usually peaks in March, when we observed gravid individuals in association with slackwater darters, *Etheostoma boschungi*, in spring seeps flowing through pastures. Foods of the flame chub include midges, worms, snails, filamentous algae, and terrestrial insects (Sossamon, 1990).

Limestone spring run, Lauderdale County

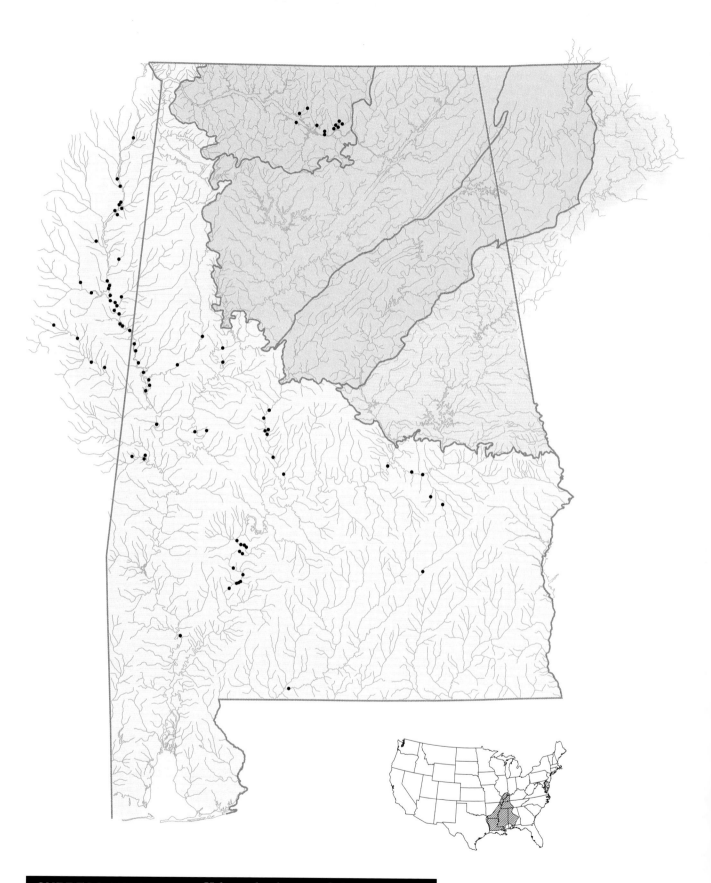

CYPRESS MINNOW *Hybognathus hayi* **84 STATIONS**

Hybognathus hayi
Jordan, 1885

ETYMOLOGY:

Hybognathus—swollen jaw
hayi—in honor of O. P. Hay,
noted ichthyologist and
discoverer of the species

Pearl River, Washington Parish, Louisiana, 23 February 1978, 2.3 in (59 mm) SL female, TU 106161

CHARACTERISTICS: The cypress minnow has a compressed body and an angular profile. The scales form a distinct diamond-shaped pattern on the sides; the melanophores on the front of the lateral band are small and only slightly larger than those on the upper sides and back. The broadly rounded snout does not project beyond the upper lip, and the mouth is upturned. The anal and dorsal fins are placed more anteriorly on the cypress minnow than those on the similar Mississippi silvery minnow, *Hybognathus nuchalis*. Fingerman and Suttkus (1961) and Burr and Mayden (1982a) provide additional information on differentiating *H. hayi* from *H. nuchalis*. See Jordan (1885b) for original description.

ADULT SIZE: 2.6 to 3.9 in (65 to 100 mm)

DISTRIBUTION: The cypress minnow is distributed throughout Gulf slope drainages from the Sabine River drainage east to the Escambia River basin, including the lower Mississippi River basin and portions of the Tennessee and Ohio river drainages. In Alabama the cypress minnow has been documented in the Mobile basin below the Fall Line, sporadically in the Conecuh River drainage, and in the Tennessee River drainage. It was frequently collected in the Tombigbee River before that river's impoundment, but its current status there is unknown. The status of populations in the Tennessee River drainage is also unknown, since all available records date from before the river's impoundment.

HABITAT AND BIOLOGY: *Hybognathus hayi* has been found in large, somewhat turbid streams and rivers, sloughs, and overflow pools. Kemp and Hubbs (1954) indicate that it generally prefers quiet waters with little or no flow over muddy bottoms. This contrasts with *H. nuchalis*, which occurs in both quiet pools and flowing streams (Fingerman and Suttkus, 1961). Little is known of the reproductive biology or diet of the cypress minnow in Alabama. R. D. Suttkus (personal communication) reports spawning from late December to early March in the Pearl River drainage, Mississippi, with adults congregating in December and January before moving to spawning areas. Aspects of the cypress minnow's ecology are similar to those of *H. nuchalis*, which spawns from January through March and feeds on a variety of organisms inhabiting muddy bottoms.

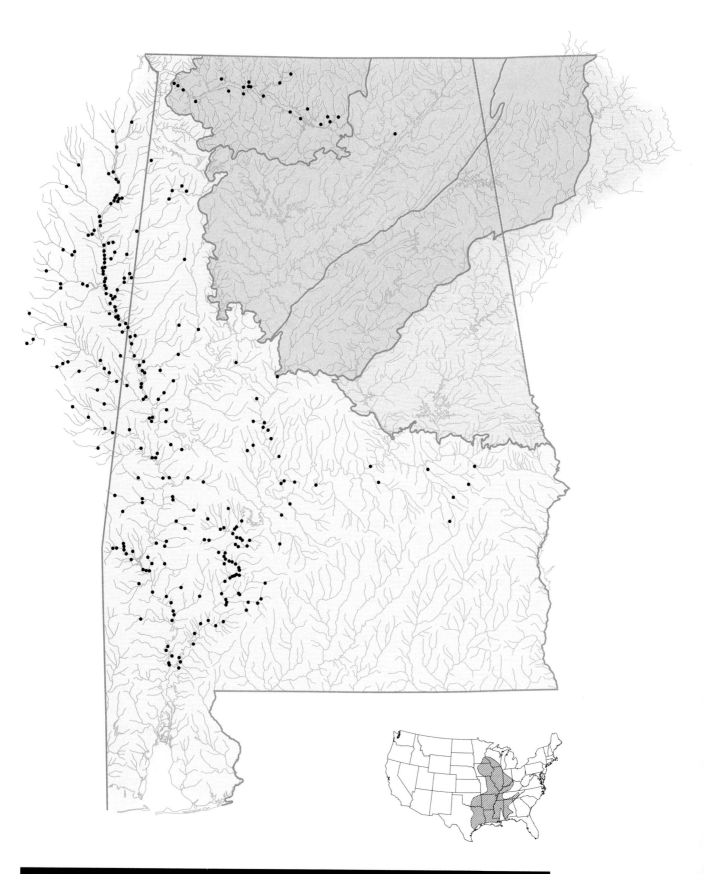

MISSISSIPPI SILVERY MINNOW *Hybognathus nuchalis* **273 STATIONS**

190

Hybognathus nuchalis

Agassiz, 1855

ETYMOLOGY:

Hybognathus—swollen jaw

nuchalis—nape

Beaver Creek, Marengo County, 18 June 1992, 3.0 in (75 mm) SL male, GSA 4454

CHARACTERISTICS: The Mississippi silvery minnow resembles the cypress minnow, *Hybognathus hayi*, but the former has a more cylindrical body and a rounded profile. Other differences include the melanophores on the anterior part of the lateral band, which are noticeably larger than those on the sides and back of *H. nuchalis*, and a snout that projects slightly beyond the upper lip. In *H. nuchalis* the dorsal and anal fins are placed more posteriorly than those in *H. hayi*. Also, the midline along the back is broader than the dorsal fin base. Burr and Mayden (1982a) report that, for all sizes, the eye-to-mouth distance (measured from the upper orbital rim down to a perpendicular line extending posteriorly from the mouth corner) is always greater in *H. nuchalis* than in *H. hayi*.

ADULT SIZE: 3 to 3.9 in (75 to 100 mm)

DISTRIBUTION: This species occurs throughout the Mississippi River basin, from Minnesota south to the Brazos River and east to the Mobile basin. It inhabits the Tennessee River drainage and the Mobile basin below the Fall Line. The status of the Tennessee River populations is unknown, because few individuals have been discovered there since the river was impounded in the 1930s (Etnier et al., 1979). It may be that the species has been extirpated from this drainage in Alabama.

HABITAT AND ECOLOGY: Mississippi silvery minnows are common in low-gradient rivers and streams. The fact that they are often abundant just upstream of where streams enter larger rivers or impoundments indicates a preference for flowing conditions. Fingerman and Suttkus (1961) report similar habitat requirements (which differ from those of *H. hayi*, which seems to inhabit only quiet, still backwaters and pools over muddy bottoms). *Hybognathus nuchalis* lives near silty, muddy bottoms, consuming the bottom ooze and digesting the plant and animal matter it contains. Spawning occurs from January through April in quiet waters along the margins of streams and in the backwaters and overflow pools of large rivers. The field notes of R. D. Suttkus indicate an early end to spawning in the Pearl River (January–March) and a later beginning in the Alabama River drainage (March–April). Juveniles are found from May through July. Spawning behavior is presumably similar to that of the eastern silvery minnow, *H. regius* (Raney, 1939), which releases nonadhesive eggs onto the bottoms of cove backwaters.

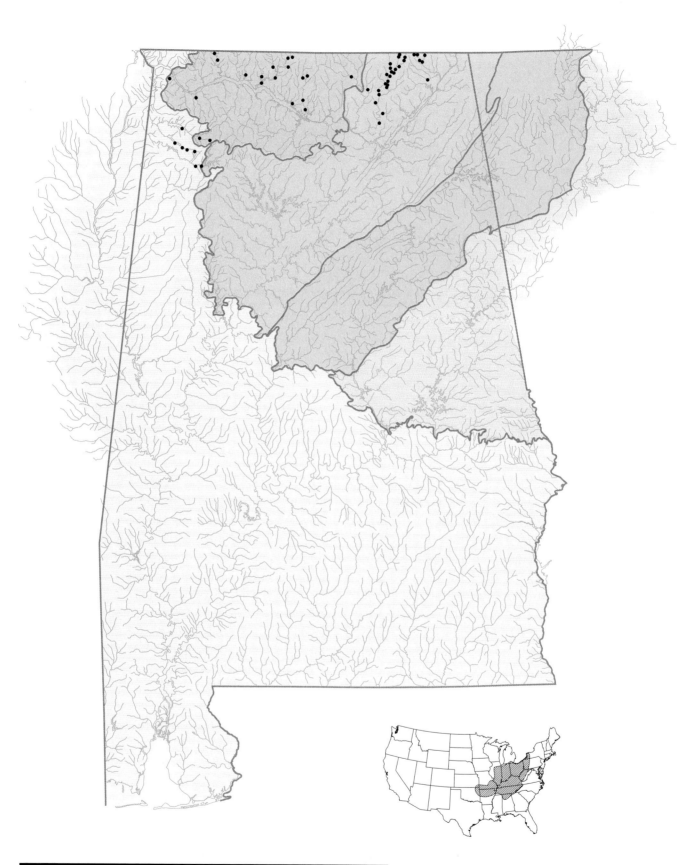

BIGEYE CHUB *Hybopsis amblops* **55 STATIONS**

Hybopsis amblops

(Rafinesque, 1820)

ETYMOLOGY:

Hybopsis—rounded face, referring to the blunt snout

amblops—blunt face

Estill Fork, Jackson County, 10 June 1992, 2.1 in (53 mm) SL female, GSA 4314

CHARACTERISTICS: The bigeye chub has a single mouth barbel, a weakly falcate dorsal fin, and a dark lateral band. Its body form is slender, and its snout is blunt, with a small, horizontal mouth. The eye is large, with a diameter slightly greater than the length of the snout. The back and sides are light greenish yellow. Similar species are the lined chub, *Hybopsis lineapunctata*, and the clear chub, *H. winchelli*, which occur in drainages south of the Tennessee River basin. The mimic shiner, *Notropis volucellus*, is likely to be confused with the bigeye chub, but the former lacks a mouth barbel. Species of the *H. amblops* group are geographically distinct, with *H. amblops* being found only in the Tennessee River drainage, *H. winchelli* in the Mobile basin and Escatawpa River, *H. lineapunctata* in the Tallapoosa and Coosa river systems, and the undescribed species in drainages east of the Mobile basin.

ADULT SIZE: 2 to 3 in (50 to 75 mm)

DISTRIBUTION: The bigeye chub is found in the upper Mississippi River basin from the Tennessee River north to the Great Lakes and west to the Ozarks in Arkansas and Missouri. In Alabama this species is restricted to the Tennessee River drainage, where it commonly occurs in the Paint Rock River, Elk River, and Bear Creek systems.

HABITAT AND BIOLOGY: The bigeye chub is frequently encountered in small or medium-sized streams of clear water over sandy, gravelly, or rocky bottoms. It is commonly found in pool areas near riffles and in quiet pools with little or no current. Gravid individuals have been observed in May and June. The diet consists of aquatic insects. Etnier and Starnes (1993) report specimens consuming equal numbers of midge larvae and large nymphs of mayflies and stoneflies. Little is known about the life history of this common, frequently occurring species in Alabama.

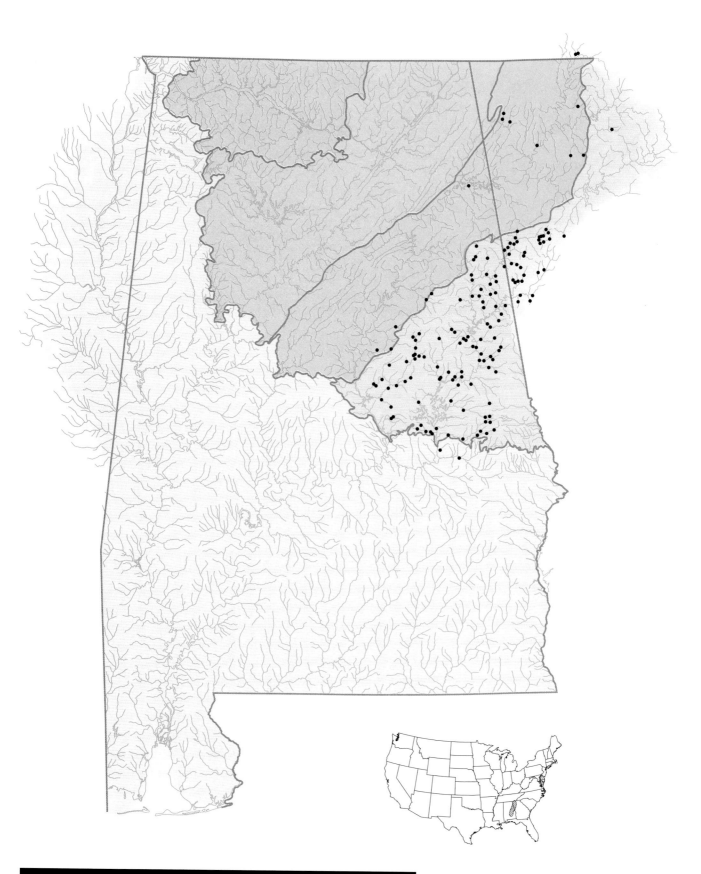

LINED CHUB   *Hybopsis lineapunctata*   149 STATIONS

Hybopsis lineapunctata
Clemmer and Suttkus, 1971

ETYMOLOGY:

Hybopsis—rounded face, referring to the blunt snout *lineapunctata*—line spot, referring to the dark lateral band and caudal spot

Josie Leg Creek, Tallapoosa County, 24 June 1992, 2.2 in (55 mm) SL female, GSA 4322

CHARACTERISTICS: The lined chub is a large minnow with a terete, compressed body and a long head. Its long, blunt snout overhangs an inferior, slightly oblique mouth which has a single barbel in each corner. A dark lateral band is well developed, extending from the gill opening to the caudal fin base—narrowing on the peduncle and expanding into a small but distinct caudal spot. This band is interrupted by the eyes but continues around the snout, and it is bounded above by a light band. The scales on the back are well pigmented. Live individuals are various shades of silvery white and yellow. The Coosa shiner, *Notropis xaenocephalus*, and the burrhead shiner, *N. asperifrons*, are similar species often encountered with the lined chub, and because their dark lateral bands are similar, they are often mistaken for one another. The easiest way to separate the species is to look for mouth barbels: The lined chub has them, whereas the Coosa and burrhead shiners do not.

ADULT SIZE: 2 to 2.6 in (50 to 65 mm)

DISTRIBUTION: This species is endemic to the Tallapoosa and Coosa river systems in the Mobile basin. It is most common above the Fall Line in the Tallapoosa River system and less common in the Coosa, where it is found in upland tributaries in Georgia and in the Hatchet Creek system.

HABITAT AND BIOLOGY: *Hybopsis lineapunctata* is commonly encountered in small or medium-sized flowing streams with pools and riffles over gravel, sand, or rubble substrates—all habitats often found in the Piedmont region of eastern Alabama. The lined chub's diet consists of aquatic and terrestrial insects. Clemmer and Suttkus (1971) indicate that spawning occurs from mid-May through early June, and extremely gravid females have been collected in June.

REMARKS: The type locality of the lined chub is Enitachopco Creek, near Ashland, Clay County, Alabama.

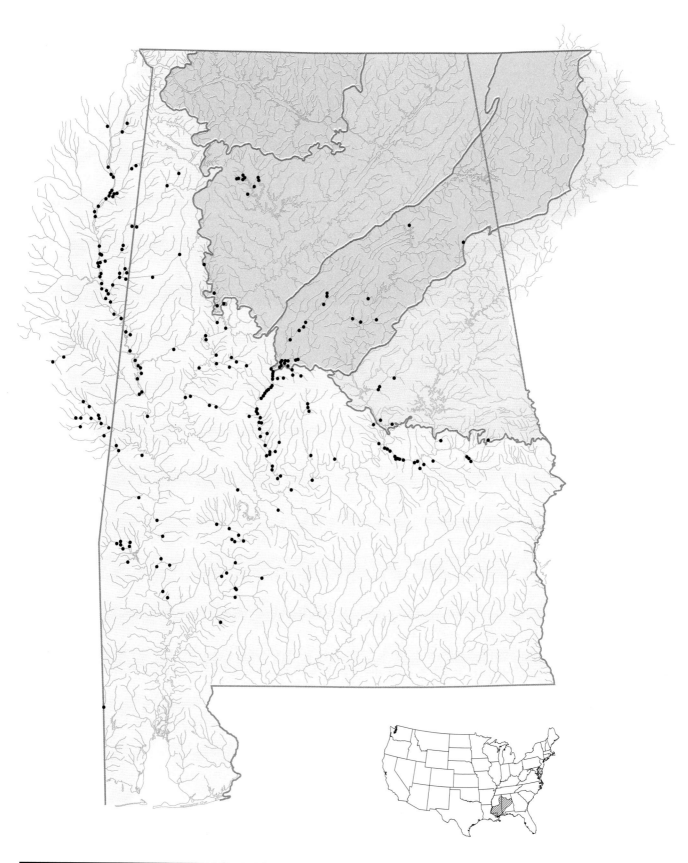

CLEAR CHUB *Hybopsis winchelli* **229 STATIONS**

196

Hybopsis winchelli

(Girard, 1856)

ETYMOLOGY:

Hybopsis—rounded face, referring to the blunt snout

winchelli—in honor of the late Alexander Winchell of the University of Michigan

Big Sandy Creek, Tuscaloosa County, 29 March 1993, 1.7 in (43 mm) SL female, GSA 4387

CHARACTERISTICS: The clear chub has a single mouth barbel, a weakly falcate dorsal fin, and a dark lateral band. Its body form is slender, and its snout is blunt, with a small, horizontal mouth. The eye is large, its diameter slightly greater than the length of the snout. The back and sides are light greenish yellow. Similar species occurring sympatrically and likely to be confused with the clear chub are the silverjaw minnow, *Ericymba buccata*, and the weed shiner, *Notropis texanus*; however, both of these species lack mouth barbels. An undescribed species similar to *Hybopsis winchelli* occurs in coastal drainages east of the Mobile basin (Clemmer, 1971). *Hybopsis winchelli* differs from the undescribed form in snout shape, mouth position, head length, and size and position of nuptial tubercles. Moreover, the caudal spot of *H. winchelli* is formed by a ventral expansion of the lateral band at the caudal fin base and does not extend onto the caudal rays. The caudal spot of the undescribed chub, on the other hand, is a distinct, wedge-shaped feature that is separate from the lateral band and that extends onto the caudal fin rays.

ADULT SIZE: 2 to 2.8 in (50 to 70 mm)

DISTRIBUTION: *Hybopsis winchelli* is found in eastern tributaries of the lower Mississippi River basin, east to and including the Mobile basin. In Alabama this species is found in the Mobile basin and in the Escatawpa River drainage. The undescribed species similar to *winchelli* is found from the Perdido River drainage east to the Apalachicola River basin.

HABITAT AND BIOLOGY: The clear chub appears to prefer small or moderately large streams of clear water over gravel, sand, or silt bottoms. It is often found in pool areas near riffles and in quiet pools with little or no current. For populations west of the Mobile basin, Clemmer (1980) indicates spawning occurs from late February to late March. However, ripe individuals have been observed later in the spring, and spawning in the Mobile basin is from March through May. Little is known about the feeding ecology of this species. It presumably eats stream drift composed of aquatic and terrestrial insects and possibly filamentous algae.

REMARKS: The type locality of the clear chub is the Black Warrior River (precise location unknown).

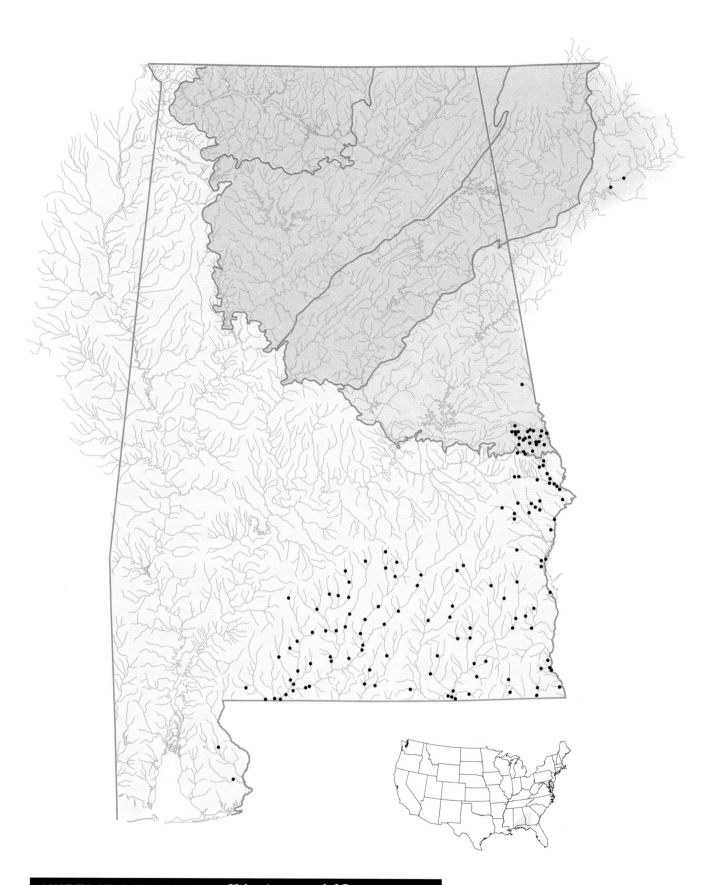

UNDESCRIBED CHUB   *Hybopsis* sp.   **143 STATIONS**

Hybopsis **sp.**

ETYMOLOGY:

Hybopsis—rounded face, referring to the blunt snout

Jordan Creek, Conecuh County, 4 May 1995, 1.9 in (47 mm) SL female, GSA 4643

CHARACTERISTICS: The undescribed chub, which resembles the clear chub, *Hybopsis winchelli*, has a single barbel, a falcate dorsal fin, and a dark lateral band. The body is slender, and the snout is blunt, with a small, horizontal mouth. The large eye has a diameter slightly greater than the length of the snout. The back and sides are light greenish yellow. Clemmer (1971) recognizes this species as a distinct form, and we follow his work here. The species differs from *H. winchelli* in snout shape, mouth position, head length, caudal spot shape, and size and position of nuptial tubercles. Also, the undescribed chub occurs with and is likely to be confused with two other similar species: the silverjaw minnow, *Ericymba buccata*, and the weed shiner, *Notropis texanus*, both of which lack mouth barbels.

ADULT SIZE: 2 to 2.8 in (50 to 70 mm)

DISTRIBUTION: This lowland chub occurs in coastal drainages from the Perdido River system east to the Apalachicola basin. Most collections are from drainages between the Perdido and Choctawhatchee rivers in south Alabama. Chattahoochee River populations cross the Fall Line and are widespread and occasionally abundant in Wacoochee and upper Uchee creeks.

HABITAT AND BIOLOGY: This species prefers small to large streams with clear or slightly turbid water over gravel, sand, or silt bottoms. It is found in pool areas near riffles and in quiet pools with little or no current. Large populations can be found over sand and gravel shoals in larger rivers, such as the Conecuh and upper Choctawhatchee. Gravid individuals have been collected in May, and spawning likely occurs from April to late June. Little is known about this species' feeding ecology, but it presumably eats aquatic and terrestrial insects and possibly filamentous algae.

Five Runs Creek, Covington County, Conecuh National Forest

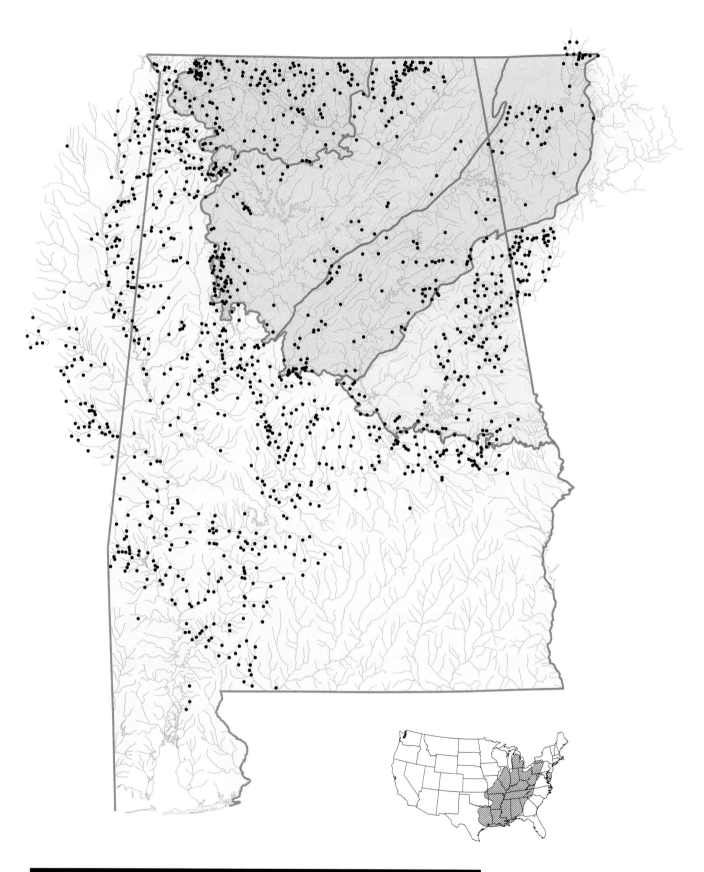

STRIPED SHINER   *Luxilus chrysocephalus*   1,221 STATIONS

Luxilus chrysocephalus
Rafinesque, 1820

ETYMOLOGY:
Luxilus—small light, hence the name *shiner*
chrysocephalus—golden head

Josie Leg Creek, Tallapoosa County, 22 April 1993, 4.8 in (122 mm) SL male, GSA 4438

CHARACTERISTICS: The striped shiner has a deep head and compressed body. Its large scales are generally much higher than they are wide on the sides, and the pigment on some scales forms crescent-shaped bars. The back has distinct parallel bars running lengthwise and ending in a V at the caudal fin. Breeding males turn rose red color on the snout, lower head, and venter, while their sides become scarlet. Dorsal and caudal fins are flushed with yellow, and the paired fins and anal fin are pink to scarlet with clear margins. Individuals taken outside the breeding season have little color.

ADULT SIZE: 2.6 to 5.9 in (65 to 150 mm)

DISTRIBUTION: This species occurs from the southern Great Lakes region south to Gulf slope drainages, east to the Ohio River basin, and west to Texas and the Ozark Mountains. Two subspecies of *Luxilus chrysocephalus* are recognized: the northern striped shiner, *L. c. chrysocephalus*, which occurs from the Tennessee River drainage in Alabama north of approximately 34 degrees north latitude; and the southern

striped shiner, *L. c. isolepis*, which occurs south of this line, generally below the Fall Line (Gilbert, 1964). In Alabama *L. c. chrysocephalus* is found in the Tennessee River drainage and the Coosa River system, while *L. c. isolepis* is found in the remaining drainages of the Mobile and the Escambia river basins. Intergrades of the two subspecies have been recognized in Blackburn Fork of the Black Warrior River.

HABITAT AND BIOLOGY: The striped shiner typically inhabits small to medium-sized streams with slow to moderate currents and alternating areas of pools and riffles. Small individuals are often found in moderately swift riffle runs; large adults prefer deeper pools with slower currents. From March through early May, spawning occurs over gravel and sand in rudimentary nests constructed by males and also over gravel pits dug by other species of Cyprinidae, including *Nocomis*, *Semotilus*, and *Campostoma* (Johnston and Page, 1992). This surface feeder eats stream drift containing aquatic and terrestrial insects and filamentous algae; it may also occasionally eat larger invertebrates.

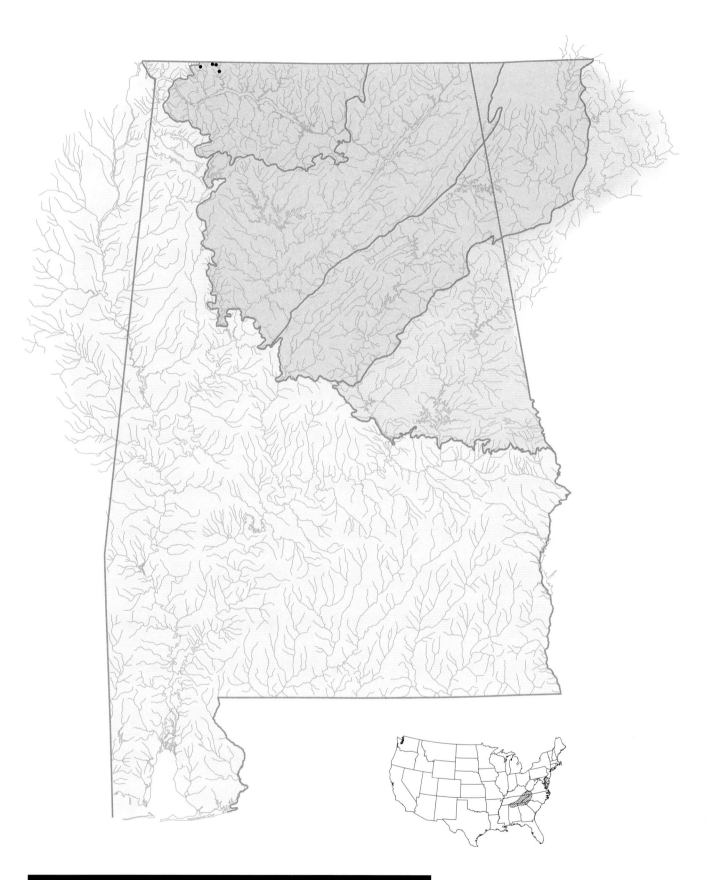

WARPAINT SHINER   *Luxilus coccogenis*   **4 STATIONS**

202

Luxilus coccogenis
(Cope, 1868)

ETYMOLOGY:
Luxilus—small light, hence the name *shiner*
coccogenis—berry red cheek

Sour Branch, Lauderdale County, 24 February 1993, 3.7 in (93 mm) SL male, GSA 4375

CHARACTERISTICS: This *Luxilus* species is fairly large and compressed, with scales generally higher than they are wide and a large head and mouth. The outer third of the dorsal fin has a wide black band parallel with the margin, and there is a wide black border near the margin of the caudal fin. In breeding males the snout and upper jaw are cherry red. The front margin of the opercle has a red orange bar, and the base of the dorsal fin has a cherry red spot. A well-developed black bar marks the gill openings. Each lobe of the caudal fin has a distinct pale zone extending about half the fin length, giving the appearance of pale caudal fin spots. The original description is given in Günther (1868).

ADULT SIZE: 3 to 3.9 in (75 to 100 mm)

DISTRIBUTION: The warpaint shiner is distributed throughout the Tennessee River drainage from Virginia to Alabama and occurs in the headwaters of a few Atlantic slope drainages (Gilbert, 1964). As shown on the facing page, we have collected this species from the Cypress and Shoal creek systems in the Tennessee

River drainage. On 6 September 1995, after the distribution map was created, we made two collections in the Lookout Creek system, a small drainage that originates near Valley Head, Alabama, and flows northwest to Georgia. These collections extend the warpaint shiner's range in Alabama to three stream systems.

HABITAT AND BIOLOGY: *Luxilus coccogenis* inhabits medium-sized to large upland streams with clear, cool water. They appear to prefer swift riffles and riffle runs over rock and gravel substrates. Spawning activity over nests of the river chub, *Nocomis micropogon*, was observed in the upper Tennessee River drainage from June to July (Outten, 1957). Spawning in Alabama may occur as early as April, since colorful males showing nuptial tubercles have been collected in the Shoal Creek system in March. Shallow, flowing water is required for spawning, which occurs over bottom cover, debris, and chub nests. The maximum reported age is more than four years (Outten, 1957). The diet is stream drift containing plant material, terrestrial insects, and adult and immature aquatic insects.

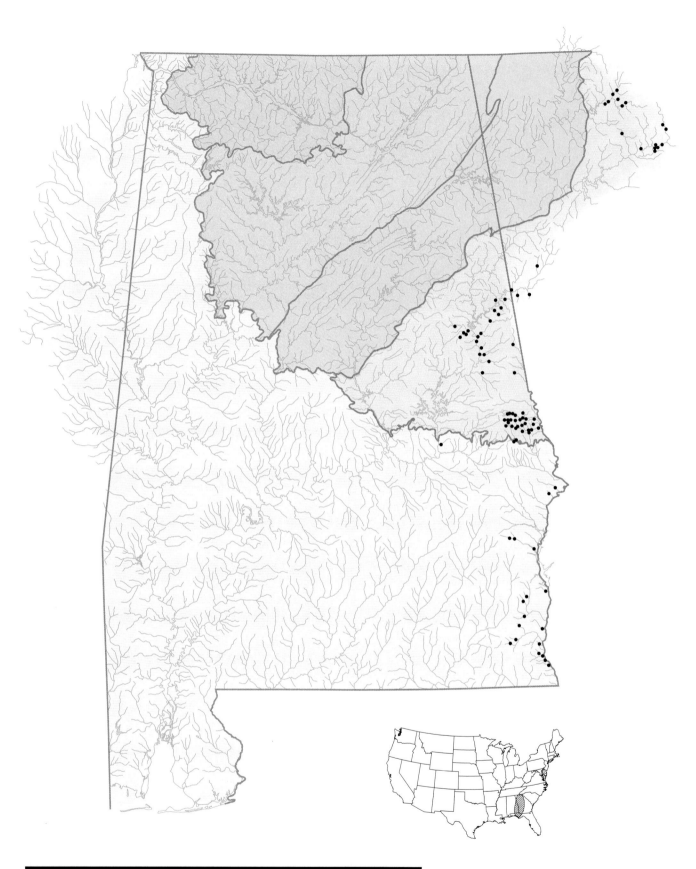

BANDFIN SHINER   *Luxilus zonistius*   **88 STATIONS**

Luxilus zonistius
Jordan, 1880

ETYMOLOGY:
Luxilus—small light, hence the name *shiner*
zonistius—banded, referring to the dorsal fin

Halawakee Creek tributary, Lee County, 6 April 1993, 2.6 in (66 mm) SL male, GSA 4408

CHARACTERISTICS: The bandfin shiner is among the smallest species of *Luxilus*, with a deep and compressed body. The dorsal fin has an oblique black band beginning much closer to the body than does that of the warpaint shiner, *L. coccogenis*. The bandfin shiner has a distinct caudal spot and a subdued red bar on the cheek. Body color is typically olive to steel-blue on the back, grading to a copper flush along the sides.

ADULT SIZE: 2.4 to 3 in (60 to 75 mm)

DISTRIBUTION: *Luxilus zonistius* is found in the Chattahoochee River drainage and upper portions of the Altamaha, Savannah, Coosa, and Tallapoosa river systems (Gilbert, 1964). In Alabama it occurs throughout the Chattahoochee drainage and in parts of the Tallapoosa and Coosa systems.

HABITAT AND BIOLOGY: The bandfin shiner prefers to inhabit small to medium-sized streams that have substrates of bedrock, gravel, rubble, or sand and that have no aquatic vegetation. The species is usually common when encountered. Johnston and Birkhead (1988) observed spawning in April in a Halawakee Creek tributary in Lee County. They also reported nuptial activity over the gravel nest of a bluefin stoneroller, *Campostoma pauciradii*, with shiners presumably depositing their gametes in the nest as well. These observations indicate that, for bandfin shiners in Alabama, spawning most likely occurs from March through May, the spawning season for other *Luxilus* species in the state. The diet of the bandfin shiner is probably stream drift composed of adult and immature aquatic insects, terrestrial insects, and plant matter.

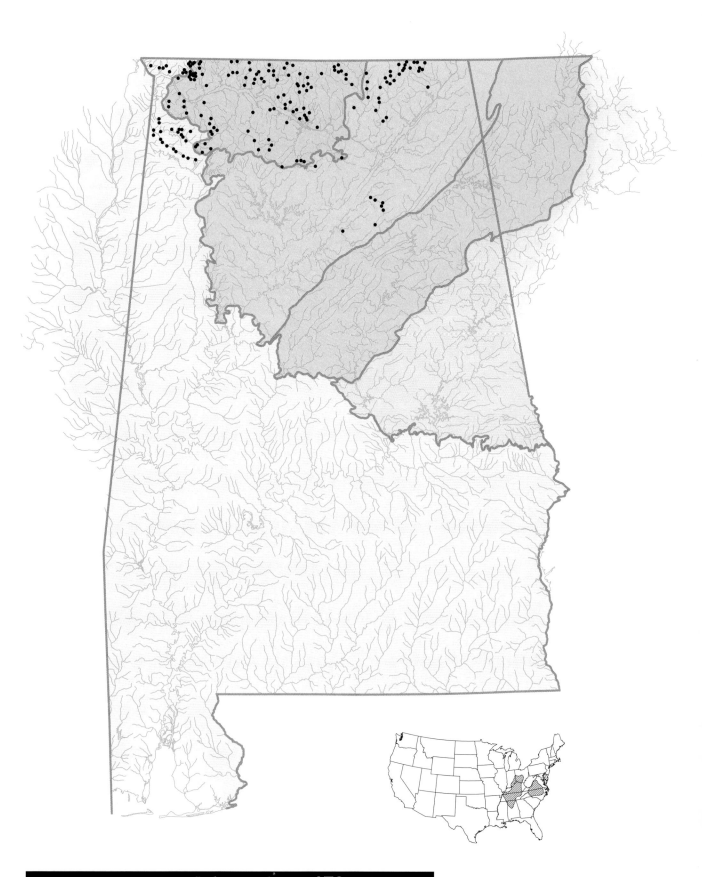

ROSEFIN SHINER   *Lythrurus ardens*   179 STATIONS

Lythrurus ardens

(Cope, 1868)

ETYMOLOGY:

Lythrurus—blood tail, perhaps referring to the bright
red breeding colors
ardens—burning

Second Creek, Lauderdale County, 1 July 1993, 2.6 in (66 mm) SL male, GSA 4496

CHARACTERISTICS: The rosefin shiner is a small to medium-sized cyprinid characterized by a deep, compressed body and a medium-sized head. The genus *Lythrurus* is characterized by small scales (generally 24 or more predorsal scale rows), more than 10 anal rays, and numerous small breeding tubercles on the head. The rosefin shiner has a distinct spot at the base of the dorsal fin and a dark lateral band extending from the caudal fin to the dorsal fin base. Breeding males have vertical bars of varying widths extending across the back to just below the lateral band. The body color of breeding males is blue-gray along the back and upper sides, changing to a golden yellow along the lower sides and venter, while the distal halves of the dorsal, anal, and caudal fins are orange. See Günther (1868) for original description.

ADULT SIZE: 1.8 to 3 in (45 to 75 mm)

DISTRIBUTION: Two populations of this species are recognized (Snelson, 1990). *Lythrurus a. ardens* occurs in Atlantic slope drainages in Virginia and North Carolina, and *L. a. fasciolaris* occurs in the Ohio basin from Ohio south to Alabama. In Alabama *L. ardens* occurs in the Tennessee River drainage and in Clear Creek and Blackburn Fork, two tributaries of Locust Fork in the Black Warrior River system. Fiorino (1991) elevates *L. a. fasciolaris* to species status, *L. fasciolaris*.

HABITAT AND BIOLOGY: The rosefin shiner inhabits small to medium-sized upland streams with slow to moderate current, usually over gravel and rubble substrates. Trautman (1981) indicates a marked preference for clear streams with moderate to high gradient and gravel substrates with little clay or silt. He also reports an intolerance of very turbid waters and stream reaches where siltation rapidly occurs. In Alabama spawning occurs from April through July, often over sunfish nests. Diet reportedly consists of algae, midges, mayflies, odonates, and terrestrial insects taken at the surface (Surat et al., 1982).

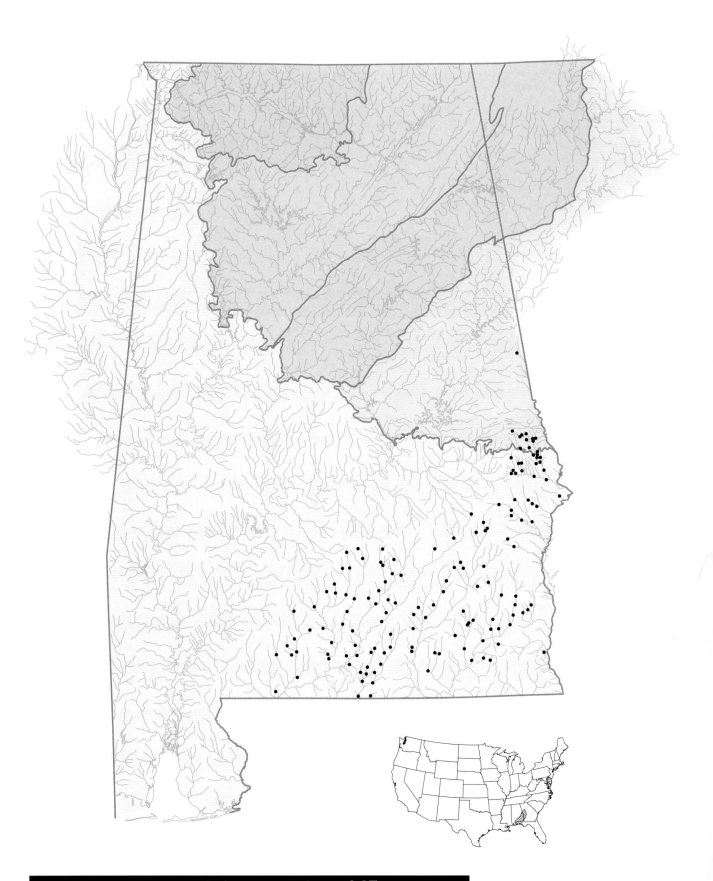

BLACKTIP SHINER *Lythrurus atrapiculus* **145 STATIONS**

Jordan Creek, Conecuh County, 4 May 1995, 2.1 in (52 mm) SL male, GSA 4643

Lythrurus atrapiculus
(Snelson, 1972)

ETYMOLOGY:

Lythrurus—blood tail, perhaps referring to the bright
red breeding colors
atrapiculus—black apex

CHARACTERISTICS: For most characteristics (particularly fin pigmentation), the blacktip shiner is weakly
differentiated from and typically intermediate between
the pretty shiner, **Lythrurus bellus**, and the cherryfin
shiner, **L. roseipinnis.** Pigmentation on the dorsal and
anal fins is wedged-shaped, narrowing from the distal
half of the first anterior rays to the tips of the posterior
rays. Pigment in the pelvic fins is concentrated at the
front but fades until it disappears at the back, and the
dorsal fin is light orange on the bottom half. The blacktip shiner does not occur with other **Lythrurus** species
in Alabama, but small individuals may be confused with
the golden shiner, **Notemigonus crysoleucas**, or the
weed shiner, **Notropis texanus**.

ADULT SIZE: 1.2 to 2.2 in (30 to 55 mm)

DISTRIBUTION: This species is found in Gulf Coast
drainages from the Escambia River basin east to the
Apalachicola basin (Snelson, 1972). In Alabama the
blacktip shiner is found in the Conecuh, Yellow,
Choctawhatchee, and Chattahoochee river drainages.
The only Mobile basin record of this species is from
Town Creek, a Tallapoosa tributary in Bullock County.

HABITAT AND BIOLOGY: Usually common when
encountered, this species prefers small to medium-sized
streams with sand bottoms and many backwaters and
pools. Snelson (1972) points out that one often finds no
L. atrapiculus in long stretches of shallow stream habitat but then discovers many individuals congregated in
long, deep pools. Little is known about the life history
of this species, except that gravid individuals have been
collected from May to July. Its diet likely consists of
drifting terrestrial and aquatic insects.

REMARKS: The type locality for the blacktip shiner is
Sikes Creek, near Clio, Barbour County, Alabama.

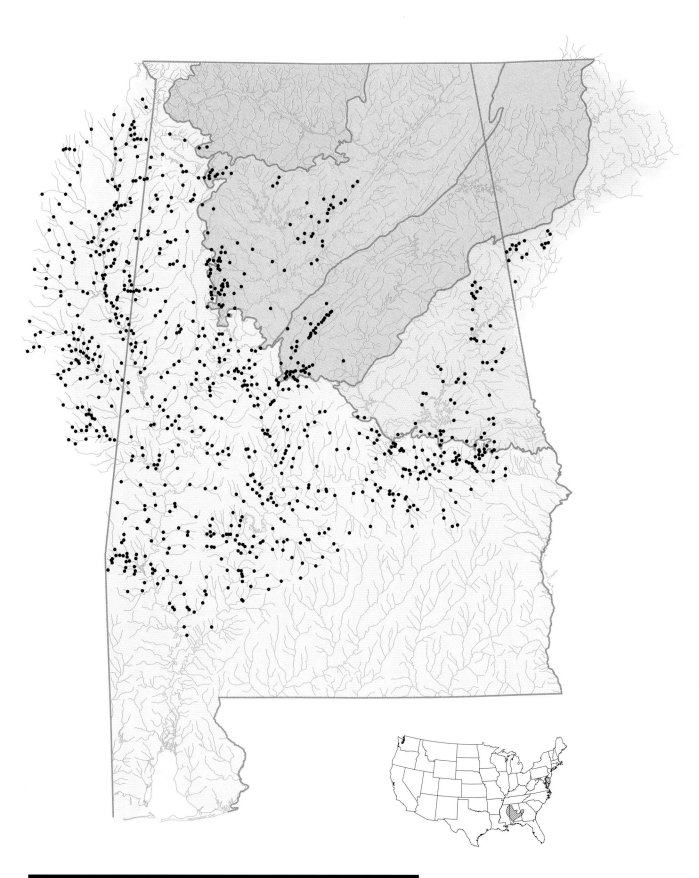

PRETTY SHINER   *Lythrurus bellus*   **917 STATIONS**

Lythrurus bellus
(Hay, 1881)

ETYMOLOGY:

Lythrurus—blood tail, perhaps referring to the bright red breeding colors
bellus—beautiful

Chilatchee Creek, Dallas County, 14 April 1993, 2.1 in (54 mm) SL male, GSA 4422

CHARACTERISTICS: A deep-bodied, compressed species, *Lythrurus bellus* is distinguished from the cherryfin shiner, *L. roseipinnis*, by its more intensely pigmented fin patterns. On each outside margin of the dorsal, anal, and pelvic fins is an orange band of uniform size that covers about one-third of the fin's depth. This contrasts with the wedge-shaped patterns in the blacktip shiner, *L. atrapiculus*, and the sparsely pigmented patterns in *L. roseipinnis*. Breeding males have a red flush in the dorsal fin, with a red-orange caudal fin of less intensity.

ADULT SIZE: 1.6 to 2.6 in (40 to 65 mm)

DISTRIBUTION: The pretty shiner is confined to the Mobile basin and to the Bear Creek system in the Tennessee River drainage. Though absent from the upper Coosa River system, it occurs commonly in the lower Coosa system and in the Cahaba and Tallapoosa river systems, which flank the Coosa watershed. Two subspecies have been recognized: *Lythrurus b. alegnotus*, which occurs in the upper Black Warrior River system, and *L. b. bellus*, which occurs at all other locations (Snel-son, 1972). A zone of intergradation between the two subspecies occurs in the North River drainage of the Black Warrior River system. Black Warrior populations of *L. bellus* need further investigation.

HABITAT AND BIOLOGY: A wide-ranging species, the pretty shiner is usually common throughout its range. It frequents many habitats, from small headwater streams to large rivers, but it appears to prefer flowing, medium-sized streams over sand, silt, and gravel substrates. Spawning occurs from April to June in shallow, flowing pools or in riffle runs with moderate current. Snelson (1972) reported large numbers of nuptial individuals, apparently a spawning aggregation, over longear sunfish nests in Calebee Creek, Macon County. Aggregating individuals in extreme breeding condition were collected during April in a riffle run behind an old bridge piling in Beaver Creek, Marengo County. The diet of this species consists of stream drift composed of adult and immature insects and plant material. The pretty shiner seems to tolerate a variety of degraded stream conditions, including siltation and enrichment.

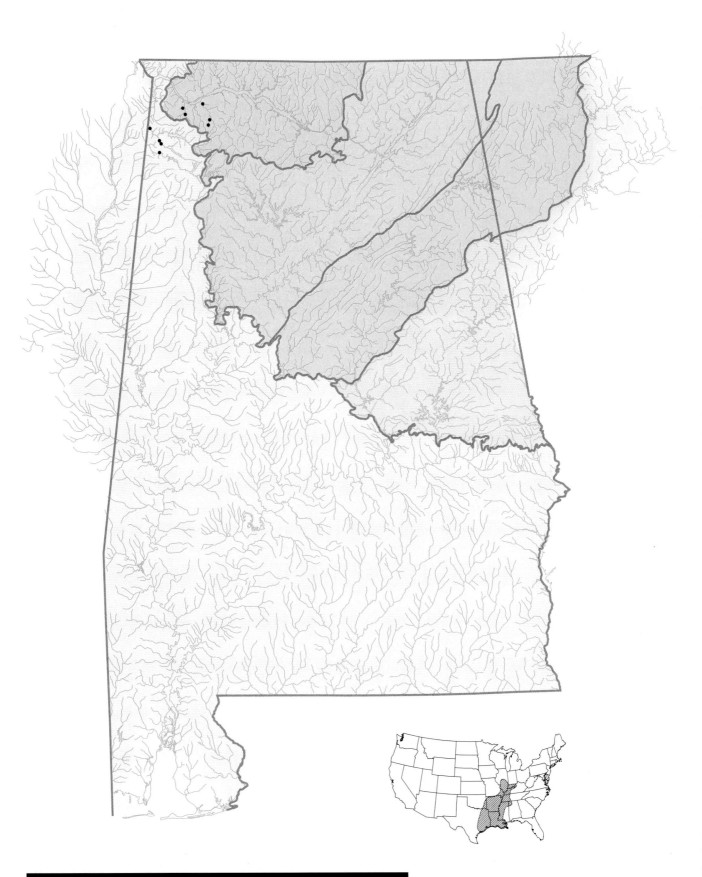

RIBBON SHINER *Lythrurus fumeus* **9 STATIONS**

Lythrurus fumeus

(Evermann, 1892)

ETYMOLOGY:

Lythrurus—blood tail, perhaps referring to the bright red breeding colors

fumeus—smoky

Spring Creek, Colbert County, 17 May 1995, 1.7 in (44 mm) SL female, GSA 4646

CHARACTERISTICS: The ribbon shiner is a pale, deep-bodied fish with a terminal and oblique mouth. It is distinguished from most species in *Lythrurus* by having little or no dark pigment in the dorsal and anal fins. It differs from the mountain shiner, *L. lirus*, by having a deeper body, a modal number of anal rays equal to 11, and pigment flecks on the chin. The back is pale olive yellow, and the sides are silvery, with a faint lateral stripe. Snelson (1973) reports yellow breeding pigments restricted to the fin rays. In other *Lythrurus* species, red or orange pigments are most intensely developed on the membranes, not the rays.

ADULT SIZE: 1.4 to 2.2 in (35 to 55 mm)

DISTRIBUTION: This species is widespread in lowland streams throughout the Mississippi basin, from Illinois to Louisiana. In Alabama it is documented only in the Bear, Cane, and Spring creek systems of the Tennessee River drainage in the northwest part of the state.

HABITAT AND BIOLOGY: *Lythrurus fumeus* inhabits lowland streams with reduced flow over sand, silt, or clay bottoms. Its reported tolerance of turbidity explains its abundance in disturbed streams in agricultural regions. Smith (1979) reports the ribbon shiner in low-gradient creeks flowing over clay, sand, or mud and identifies its preferred habitat as clear, vegetated pools with little current over sand. Gravid individuals found during May in Spring Creek were associated with beds of river weed near pool margins. Little else is known of the biology of the ribbon shiner, although Etnier and Starnes (1993) infer that spawning occurs from May through August in Tennessee populations. Diet likely consists of stream drift composed of terrestrial insects, aquatic insects, and plant material.

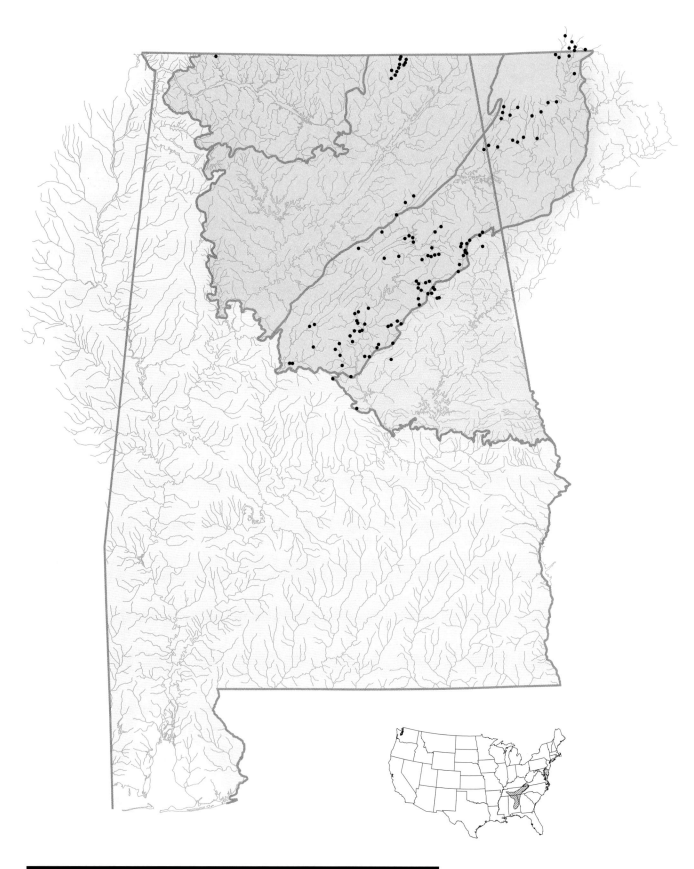

Lythrurus lirus

(Jordan, 1877)

ETYMOLOGY:

Lythrurus—blood tail, perhaps referring to the bright red breeding colors *lirus*—lily white

Larkin Fork, Jackson County, 18 May 1993, 2.0 in (50 mm) SL breeding male, GSA 4474

CHARACTERISTICS: The most slender of Alabama's *Lythrurus* species, the mountain shiner is also distinguished from the other members by having fins with reduced pigmentation. It also lacks the distinct dorsal fin spot found in the rosefin shiner, **L. ardens**. The body form is generally compressed but more rounded than those of other species of *Lythrurus*. The lateral band is widest in midbody, thinning toward the head and peduncle. In breeding males, tubercles are extremely concentrated on the head, and the body color observed in Larkin Fork individuals was light olive to yellow-green, with pale yellow-gold along the back and white on the venter. Snelson (1980) reports contrasting descriptions of male breeding color in the early literature on this species. See Jordan (1877a) for original description.

ADULT SIZE: 1.4 to 2.2 in (35 to 55 mm)

DISTRIBUTION: This species is confined to the Tennessee and Alabama river drainages in Virginia, Tennessee, Georgia, and Alabama (Snelson, 1980). In the Mobile basin, this species is found only in the Coosa and Cahaba river systems above the Fall Line. In the Tennessee River drainage, this species has been found in the Shoal Creek and Paint Rock River systems. Surprisingly, it is absent from the upper Black Warrior and Tallapoosa river systems.

HABITAT AND BIOLOGY: *Lythrurus lirus* inhabits cool, flowing, small to medium-sized streams, preferring clear waters by riffles and riffle runs over substrates ranging from boulders to sand and gravel. This species is not abundant, occurring in widely dispersed populations. Nuptial and tuberculate individuals have been captured in April and May. Spawning occurs from early May through July.

REMARKS: The type locality of this species is tributaries to the Etowah River near Rome, Floyd County, Georgia.

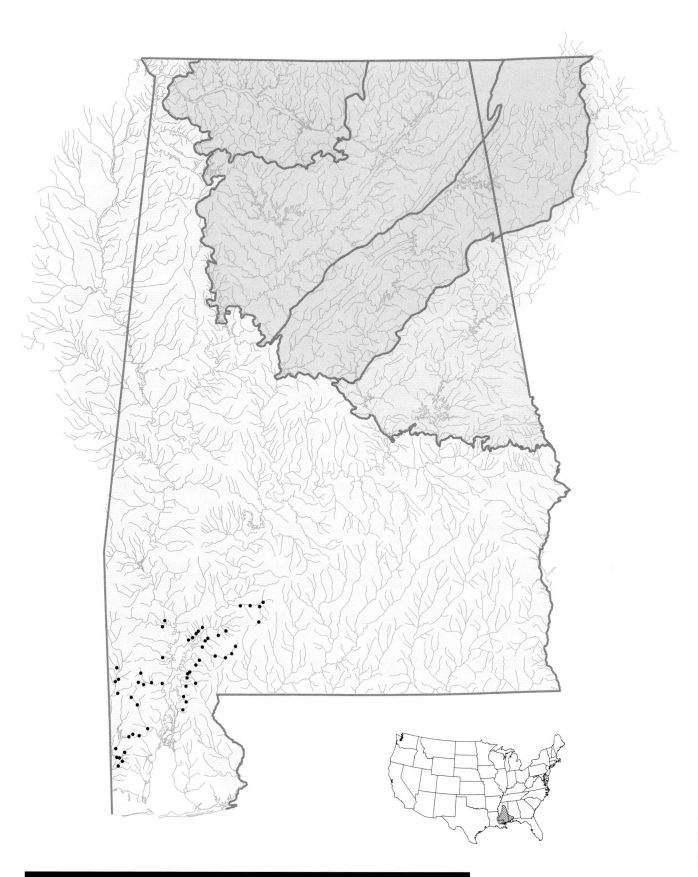

CHERRYFIN SHINER   *Lythrurus roseipinnis*   53 STATIONS

Lythrurus roseipinnis
(Hay, 1885)

ETYMOLOGY:
Lythrurus—blood tail,
perhaps referring to the
bright red breeding colors
roseipinnis—red fin

Puppy Creek, Mobile County, 3 May 1995, 1.9 in (47 mm) SL male, GSA 4642

CHARACTERISTICS: This species is easily confused with both the pretty shiner, *Lythrurus bellus*, and the blacktip shiner, *L. atrapiculus*. The cherryfin shiner, however, does not occur in the range of *L. atrapiculus*, which is confined to coastal drainages east of the Mobile basin. Also, dorsal and anal fins in the cherryfin shiner are less pigmented than those in the pretty and blacktip shiners, with melanophores confined to the interradial membranes near the tips of the first two to three rays of these fins. Snelson (1972) indicates that the cherryfin shiner has the most specific fin pigmentation pattern of the *L. roseipinnis* species complex, and consequently this is a good character for distinguishing the three species. The paired fins have little pigment (such is not the case in the pretty and blacktip shiners). The lateral band is well defined on the peduncle but dusky anteriorly. In breeding males the dorsal fin has a medial zone of red, while the anal fin and pelvic fins are flushed with cherry red over the back third to half. The caudal fin is delicately shaded with orange-red. Originally described by Hay (1881) as *Minnilus rubripinnis*, this species was assigned another name by Jordan (1885a) for original description.

ADULT SIZE: 1.2 to 2 in (30 to 50 mm)

DISTRIBUTION: *Lythrurus roseipinnis* is found in Gulf slope drainages from the Mobile basin west through Lake Pontchartrain and north through the Yazoo River drainage. Distribution in Alabama is confined to the lower Mobile basin near the confluence of the Alabama and Tombigbee rivers, south through the Mobile Delta, and west to the Escatawpa drainage. In the lower Alabama and Tombigbee rivers, there is a zone of distributional proximity between *L. roseipinnis* and *L. bellus*, but collections have indicated no sympatry between these species.

HABITAT AND BIOLOGY: The cherryfin shiner is a common inhabitant of medium-sized streams with slow to moderate flows. Substrates are typically sand, silt, or clay, with stream margins varying from heavily vegetated to clean. Local populations have been found in both heavy cover and open stream reaches. Heins and Bresnick (1975) report a spawning season extending from late March into August or September in Mississippi and a life span of more than one year. Ripe individuals have been collected from late March through August in Alabama; otherwise, little is known about the life history of this species.

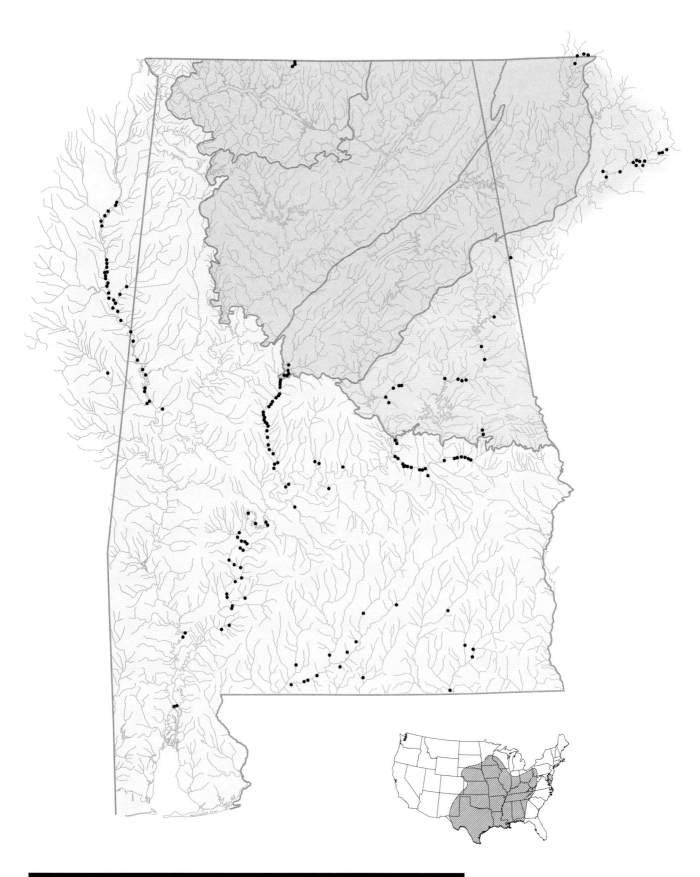

SPECKLED CHUB *Macrhybopsis aestivalis* **170 STATIONS**

Macrhybopsis aestivalis

(Girard, 1856)

ETYMOLOGY:

Macrhybopsis—long or large bodied minnows

aestivalis—of the summer

Elk River, Limestone County, 5 October 1993, 2.0 in (50 mm) SL female, GSA 4614

CHARACTERISTICS: This pale, slender species has an inferior, horizontal mouth and round black spots on the back and sides. The snout is long and blunt, projecting well beyond the upper lip. Individuals are pale yellow or silvery year-round. In drainages east of the Mobile basin, members of this species have two barbels in each corner of the mouth; in the Mobile basin and Tennessee River populations, they have only one barbel.

ADULT SIZE: 1.8 to 3 in (45 to 75 mm)

DISTRIBUTION: *Macrhybopsis aestivalis* is found in Gulf slope drainages from the Apalachicola basin to the Rio Grande basin and north to Minnesota. It seems to be restricted to large, flowing river channels, including the Alabama, Cahaba, Tallapoosa, lower Coosa, and upper Tombigbee rivers (before construction of the Tennessee-Tombigbee Waterway), generally near or below the Fall Line; the Conecuh, Pea, and Choctawhatchee rivers; and the extreme upper Coosa and Tallapoosa rivers. Carter R. Gilbert of the Florida Museum of Natural History will soon publish a report that recognizes three or four distinct species of speckled chubs in Alabama. One species is limited to the Tennessee River drainage. One or perhaps two new species will be described from the

Mobile basin. Another new species will be identified as a coastal form restricted to the Conecuh and Choctaw-hatchee drainages.

HABITAT AND BIOLOGY: Speckled chubs are confined to large, flowing river habitats and are found over gravel and sand bars in moderate to swift currents. Spawning occurs from late April to August, and large spawning aggregations have been observed in the lower Cahaba and Tallapoosa main channels during May and June and in the lower Pearl River in Mississippi during March and April. Etnier and Starnes (1993) also report a protracted spawning season for Tennessee populations—from early May to mid-August. Foods of this species include aquatic insect immatures, particularly midges (Starrett, 1950).

Choctawhatchee River, Dale County, 15 July 1993, 2.2 in (55 mm) SL, GSA 4606. Note the paired barbels.

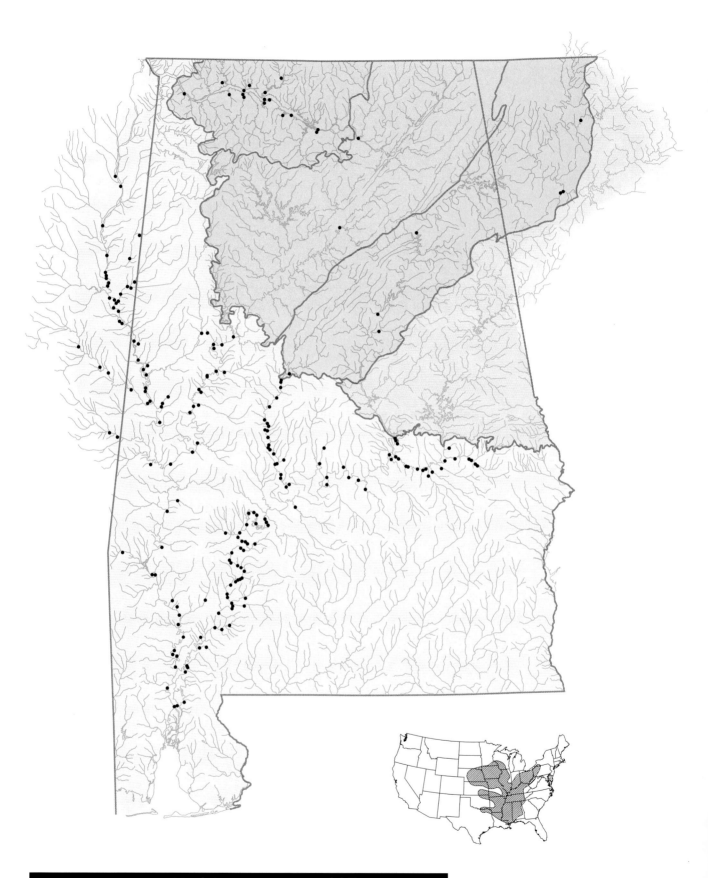

SILVER CHUB *Macrhybopsis storeriana* **205 STATIONS**

Trussels Creek, Greene County, 11 May 1994, 2.8 in (72 mm) SL female, GSA 4735

Macrhybopsis storeriana
(Kirtland, 1845)

ETYMOLOGY:

Macrhybopsis—long- or large-bodied minnows *storeriana*—in honor of David Humphreys Storer, author of the first synopsis of North American fishes (1846)

CHARACTERISTICS: The silver chub is a slender species with large eyes; its eye diameter is about equal to its snout length. The rounded snout is blunt and projects well beyond the upper lip. The mouth is small, inferior, and horizontal, with a single barbel in each corner. Life color is light olive to silvery, with the scales on the back faintly edged with melanophores. The lower caudal lobe is somewhat darker, with a milky white edge that contrasts with the dusky upper lobe. Edges of the dorsal and anal fins are falcate. Species likely to be confused with the silver chub are the silverside shiner, *Notropis candidus*; fluvial shiner, *N. edwardraneyi*; and Mississippi silvery minnow, *Hybognathus nuchalis*.

ADULT SIZE: 3.5 to 6.1 in (90 to 155 mm)

DISTRIBUTION: *Macrhybopsis storeriana* is widely distributed throughout the Mississippi, Ohio, and Mobile basins east to the Brazos River drainage in Texas. In the Mobile basin and Tennessee River drainage, this species is confined to large river channels and tributary streams.

HABITAT AND BIOLOGY: The silver chub appears to prefer sluggish waters of main river channels and large tributary streams, often with increased turbidities. Spawning occurs from April through June, most likely in open water. Three years is the maximum life span. The field notes of R. D. Suttkus record large spawning aggregations in the lower Pearl River, Mississippi, in February and March. In the Cahaba, Coosa, and Tallapoosa main channels, adults are often collected in moderate to fast current or in slow eddies adjacent to fast currents over sand or gravel substrate. Stream drift composed of adult and immature insects, plant material, and zooplankton are the food staples of this species. Etnier and Starnes (1993) report that the introduced Asian clam *Corbicula* is a principal food source for Tennessee individuals.

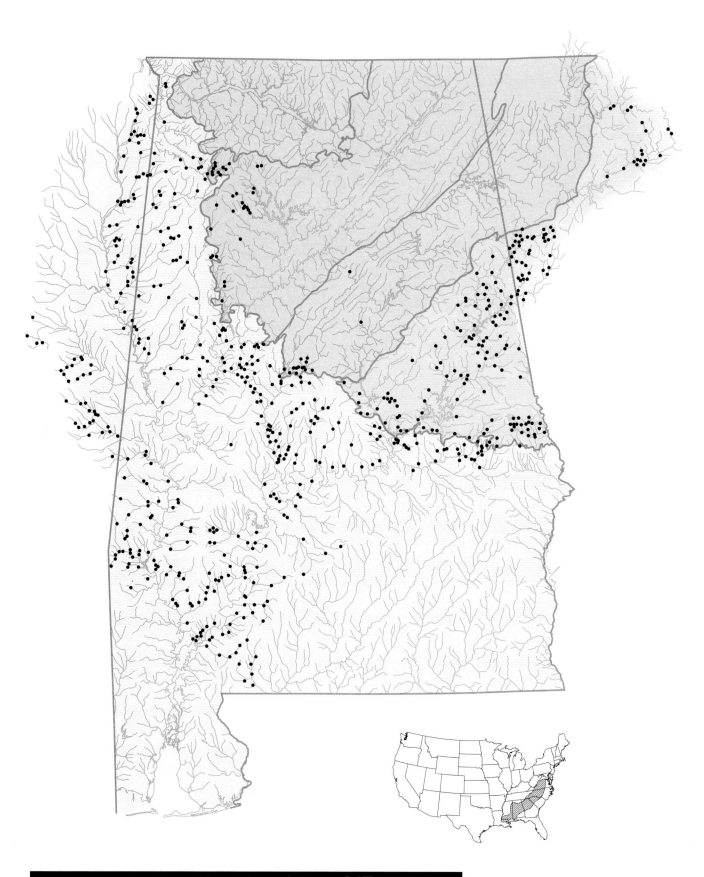

BLUEHEAD CHUB   *Nocomis leptocephalus*   647 STATIONS

Nocomis leptocephalus
(Girard, 1856)

ETYMOLOGY:
Nocomis—In Longfellow's *Song of Hiawatha*, name meaning "daughter of the moon"
leptocephalus—slender head

Josie Leg Creek, Tallapoosa County, 24 June 1992, 2.9 in (73 mm) SL female, GSA 4322

CHARACTERISTICS: The bluehead chub is a stout, short, relatively deep-bodied species. Fewer head tubercles on males—typically no more than 25 (Lachner and Jenkins, 1971)—distinguish this from other *Nocomis* species. The snout is short, the head generally large, and the mouth horizontal. Breeding males develop prominently swelled heads (a condition known as nuptial crests), which are typically blue on the sides. The lateral stripe is light tan to orange. The fins, all of which have rounded contours, are orange or red.

ADULT SIZE: 2.8 to 6.7 in (70 to 170 mm)

DISTRIBUTION: The bluehead chub is found in Atlantic slope drainages from the lower Chesapeake basin south to the Altamaha River drainage in Georgia. It occurs primarily above the Fall Line in the Apalachicola basin. *Nocomis leptocephalus* is found extensively in the Mobile basin below the Fall Line, with a sharp southern demarcation along the lower edge of the Lime Hills physiographic district. This species is notably absent from the Black Belt but occurs extensively above the Fall Line in the Tallapoosa River system; only

a few localities are known in the upper Coosa River. Individuals are also known from the Escambia basin in extreme south Alabama and from the Halawakee Creek system in the Chattahoochee River drainage. The bluehead chub has also invaded the Tennessee River drainage in the Bear Creek system.

HABITAT AND BIOLOGY: Species of *Nocomis* generally prefer clear streams of small to moderate size with moderate to high gradient. A substrate of gravel or small stones is usually required, because these materials are used for building nests that will protect fertilized eggs. Usually dome-shaped and sometimes containing up to 10,000 stones, nests are constructed from April to June (Lachner, 1952), with spawning occurring from late spring to midsummer. Lachner reports longevity of more than four years. Several species in Alabama are known to spawn in conjunction with *Nocomis* nests, including the largescale stoneroller, *Campostoma oligolepis*; striped shiner, *Luxilus chrysocephalus*; rosefin shiner, *Lythrurus ardens*; rainbow shiner, *Notropis chrosomus*; rosyface shiner, *N. rubellus*; southern redbelly dace, *Phoxinus erythrogaster*; and blackside darter, *Percina maculata*.

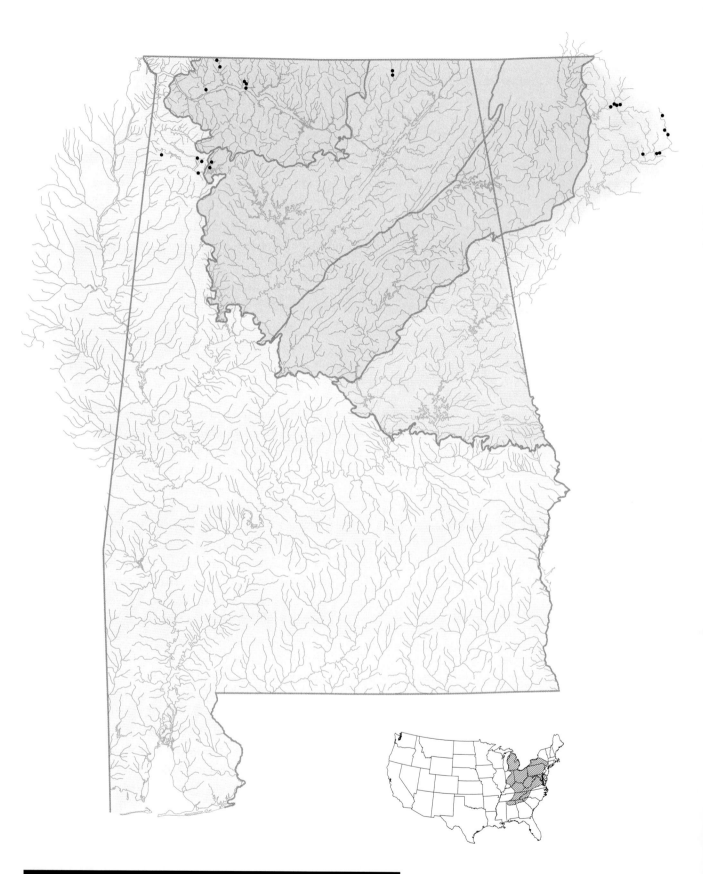

Nocomis micropogon
(Cope, 1865)

ETYMOLOGY:

Nocomis—In Longfellow's
Song of Hiawatha, name
meaning "daughter of the
moon"
micropogon—small beard,
referring to the small
barbels

Larkin Fork, Jackson County, 9 June 1992, 2.4 in (60 mm) SL male, GSA 4306

CHARACTERISTICS: Compared to the bluehead chub, *Nocomis leptocephalus*, which is stout and whose breeding males become blue, the river chub, *N. micropogon*, is less stout, and its breeding males become rosy red. The river chub's caudal, anal, and dorsal fins are reddish orange, while its paired fins are yellowish. Nonbreeding individuals are olive above and dusky yellow below. Lachner and Jenkins (1971) report that mean values for meristic characters are higher in *N. micropogon* than in *N. leptocephalus*. See Cope (1865a) for original description.

ADULT SIZE: 3.5 to 7.1 in (90 to 180 mm)

DISTRIBUTION: This species is found above the Fall Line in Atlantic slope drainages from the Susquehanna River south to the James River. It also occurs in the upper Santee, Savannah, and Coosa river drainages, throughout the Great Lakes area and the upper Ohio basin, and in the Tennessee River drainage. It is restricted to the upper Coosa River system in the

Mobile basin, and it is only sporadically found in the Tennessee River drainage in north Alabama.

HABITAT AND BIOLOGY: The river chub prefers small to medium-sized streams of moderate gradient and clear water over substrates ranging from gravel to boulders. Like *N. leptocephalus*, *N. micropogon* is a nest builder, constructing gravel mounds up to 3 feet (914 mm) wide and 12 inches (300 mm) high. During nest building, which occurs from late spring to early summer, males construct trenches for mating at the upstream end of the mounds (Jenkins and Burkhead, 1993). During the breeding season, male *Nocomis* develop a curious morphological feature called a nuptial crest. Swelling begins between the nares on the top of the head and eventually extends to the back of the nape, where it ends abruptly (Lachner, 1952). Lachner reports first spawning at three years of age and a life span of up to five years. River chubs feed opportunistically on immature aquatic insects, worms, crustaceans, mollusks, and fishes found near their bottom habitats.

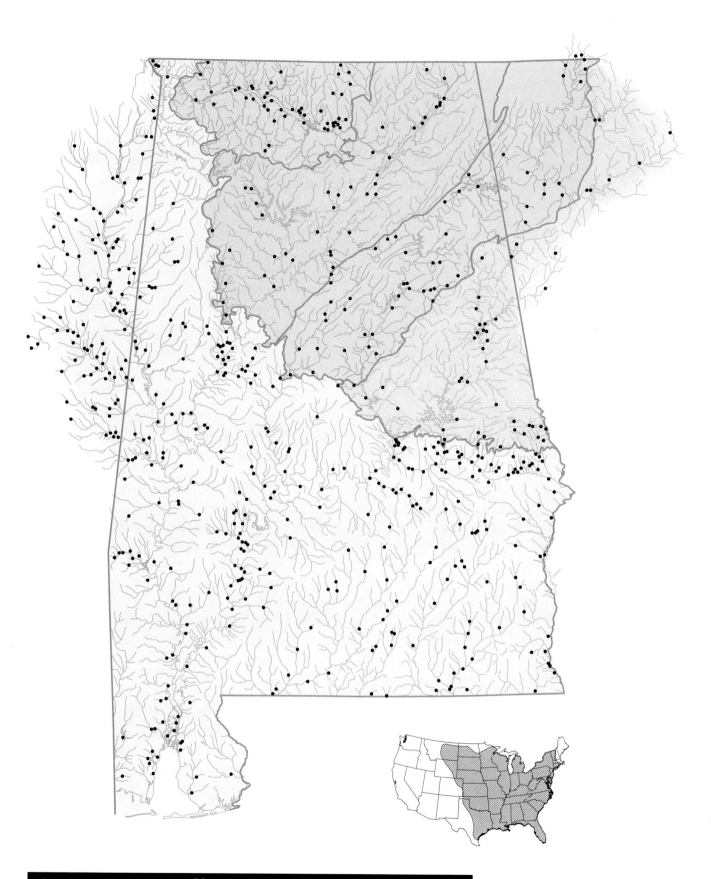

GOLDEN SHINER *Notemigonus crysoleucas* **595 STATIONS**

Notemigonus crysoleucas
(Mitchill, 1814)

ETYMOLOGY:
Notemigonus—angled back
crysoleucas—golden white,
referring to body color

Horselot Creek, Russell County, 7 April 1993, 2.6 in (66 mm) SL female, GSA 4414

CHARACTERISTICS: The body of the golden shiner is deep and laterally compressed, with a lateral line that curves toward the venter on the anterior part of the body. The venter has a sharp, fleshy keel extending from between the pelvic fins to the sickle-shaped anal fin. The head is small, with a small, upturned mouth. The back is light greenish olive to light orange; the sides are silvery, the venter white. Cavender and Coburn (1992) consider all North American species of the family Cyprinidae, except for those in the genus *Notemigonus*, to be of a single ancestral origin; these members are called phoxinins. *Notemigonus*, represented in North America only by the golden shiner, is considered to be more closely related to the European cyprinids known as leuciscins.

ADULT SIZE: 2 to 9.1 in (50 to 230 mm)

DISTRIBUTION: *Notemigonus crysoleucas* is found throughout Gulf and Atlantic slope drainages and the Mississippi basin and has been widely introduced in western states. It is widespread throughout Alabama, occurring in all major drainages.

HABITAT AND BIOLOGY: The golden shiner is a cultured bait species, which accounts for its wide distribution in the United States. It is commonly found in quiet backwaters, and it thrives in isolated areas of impoundments. Spawning occurs from April to July, with the females laying adhesive eggs over aquatic plants or the nests of other fish species. DeMont (1982) reports golden shiners spawning over nests of bluegill, while Kramer and Smith (1960) describe schools of 25 to 100 golden shiners depositing eggs over largemouth bass nests about one or two days after the bass had spawned. In July, in backwater pools of the lower Cahaba River, thousands of golden shiner juveniles have been collected in just a few net hauls. Crustaceans, filamentous algae, and stream drift consisting of adult and immature insects composes the diet of this species.

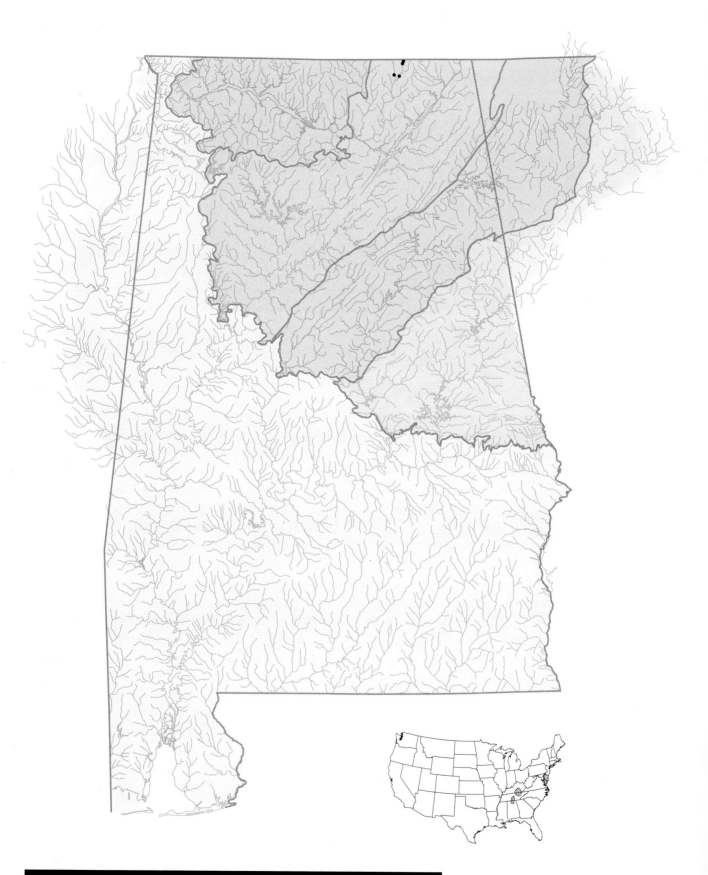

Notropis albizonatus
Warren and Burr, 1994

ETYMOLOGY:

Notropis—keeled back
albizonatus—white belt
or girdle, referring to the
immaculate stripe along
the side

Estill Fork, Jackson County, 30 June 1992, 1.8 in (45 mm) SL male, GSA 4492

CHARACTERISTICS: *Notropis albizonatus* has a slender, spindle-shaped body with a pointed snout and large eyes (typically larger than the snout). The narrow lateral band is dark and extends from the snout to the caudal fin. The anterior lateral line pores look as though they were stitched together by the dark melanophores located above and below each pore. A small, dark, wedge-shaped spot is at the base of the caudal fin, the top and bottom rays of which are lightly outlined with pigment. Two dark spots are obvious along the front and middle of the dorsal fin base. A pale lateral stripe occurs above the dark band—hence the name *palezone*. The only breeding color is a faint yellow wash at the base of the pectoral fin rays. Warren et al. (1994) postulate that the palezone shiner and the skygazer shiner, **N. uranoscopus**, along with **N. chihuahua**, **N. ludibundus**, and **N. procne** (the last three not occurring in Alabama), are all of a common ancestral origin. *Notropis albizonatus* belongs to a group of closely related species that include **uranoscopus** and **chihuahua**. See Warren et al. (1994) for original description.

ADULT SIZE: 1.2 to 2.4 in (30 to 60 mm)

DISTRIBUTION: Highly restricted in distribution, the palezone shiner is found only in the Tennessee River drainage in Alabama and Tennessee and disjunctly to the north in the Cumberland River drainage in Kentucky. It is uncommon and localized throughout its range. In Alabama, for example, it occurs only in the upper Paint Rock River system in Jackson County.

HABITAT AND BIOLOGY: This rare species, when found, usually occurs in moderately large, high-gradient, clear streams flowing over bedrock, cobble, or gravel mixed with clean sand; it prefers pools and pool runs below riffles. It is thought that spawning occurs from early June through July in Alabama, but Etnier and Starnes (1993) report that tuberculate individuals have been collected in May and June in Tennessee. Warren et al. (1994) indicate spawning from mid-May to early July, peaking in June, with individuals living between three and four years. Little else is known about the biology of this species.

REMARKS: The U.S. Fish and Wildlife Service has listed the palezone shiner as an endangered species.

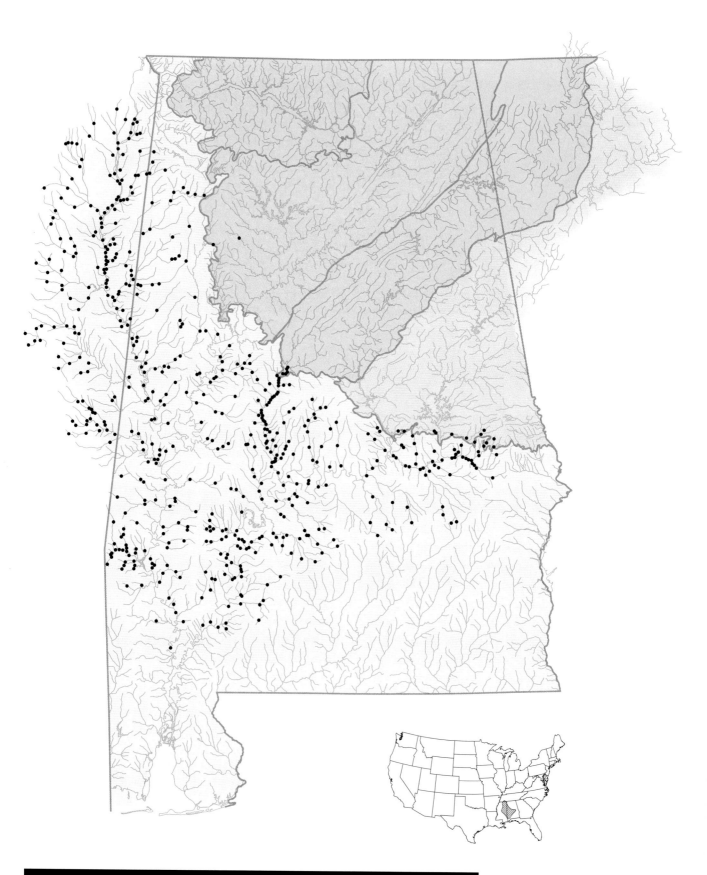

ORANGEFIN SHINER   *Notropis ammophilus*   574 STATIONS

Notropis ammophilus
Suttkus and Boschung, 1990

ETYMOLOGY:
Notropis—keeled back;
ammophilus—sand-loving

Deas Branch, Choctaw County, 18 June 1992, 1.7 in (43 mm) SL male, GSA 4456

CHARACTERISTICS: The orangefin shiner has a somewhat terete body and a markedly arched dorsal profile, which is more robust anteriorly and tapers toward the caudal fin. The mouth is inferior and almost horizontal. Breeding males have bright orange or reddish orange in all fins, a pinkish orange snout, and bright orange lips. The back is light olive yellow, fading on the sides to a faint lateral band represented by a melanophore above and below each lateral line pore. The venter is silvery white. In Alabama the orangefin shiner most closely resembles the longnose shiner, *Notropis longirostris*, but the latter species has a more southeasterly distribution.

ADULT SIZE: 1.6 to 2 in (40 to 50 mm)

DISTRIBUTION: *Notropis ammophilus* is widely distributed in the Mobile basin from the Fall Line south to near the northern edge of the Southern Pine Hills. A single collection from Lost Creek in Walker County represents the only Black Warrior record from above the Fall Line. Disjunct populations occur in the Yellow Creek and Hatchie River systems of the Tennessee River drainage and in the Skuna system of the Yazoo River drainage in Mississippi (Suttkus and Boschung, 1990).

HABITAT AND BIOLOGY: This species inhabits small to large streams with clear water and sand or sand-gravel substrates. Large schools numbering in the hundreds or thousands are often seen drifting in shallow water over sand shoals or bedrock. Spawning occurs from April through September. Heins et al. (1980) describe the spawning season as extending from mid-April to late September or early October in Uphapee Creek, with most individuals living about two years. This species' diet is unstudied, but it likely includes terrestrial insects, aquatic insects (such as midges), and plant material.

REMARKS: The type locality of the orangefin shiner is Chilatchee Creek, Dallas-Wilcox county line, Alabama.

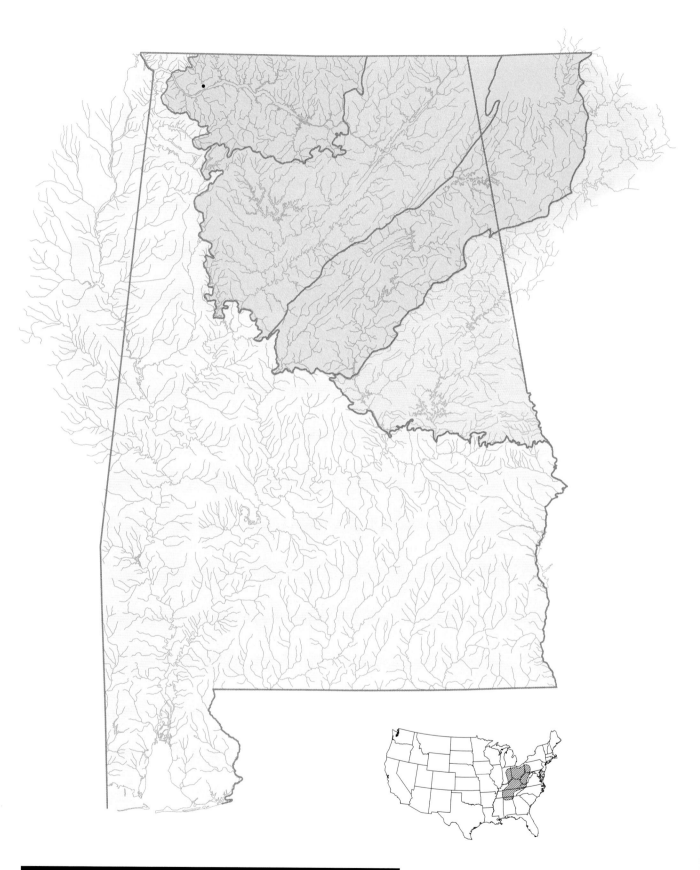

POPEYE SHINER *Notropis ariommus* **1 STATION**

Holston River, North Fork, Washington County, Virginia, 6 June 1984, 2.9 in (74 mm) SL male. Photograph courtesy of Noel M. Burkhead.

Notropis ariommus
(Cope, 1868)

ETYMOLOGY:

Notropis—keeled back
ariommus—large eye

CHARACTERISTICS: *Notropis ariommus* resembles the telescope shiner, *N. telescopus*, but the former is distinguished by a paler, more slab-sided appearance and much larger eyes. Its eye diameter—more than one and a half times its snout length—is proportionately larger than that of any other Alabama *Notropis*. The popeye shiner has a single line of melanophores edging the dorsolateral scales, compared to a double line in *N. telescopus*. Also, the front of the back and upper sides lack the crooked stripes characteristic of *N. telescopus*. Popeye shiners do not develop a distinctive breeding color; the body on the sides and venter is olive brown above and silvery below. See Cope (1868a) for original description.

ADULT SIZE: 1.8 to 3 in (45 to 75 mm)

DISTRIBUTION: *Notropis ariommus* is found in the Tennessee River drainage north to the Wabash River drainage in Indiana and east to the upper Ohio basin. In Alabama it is limited to the Tennessee River drainage

and was last collected in 1889 in Cypress Creek near Florence. Although there have been no recent records of this species in Alabama, continued sampling efforts in the Elk River and Shoal Creek systems may rediscover it, since Feeman (1987) reports its occurrence in the Elk River just north of the Alabama state line.

HABITAT AND BIOLOGY: Etnier and Starnes (1993) report a preferred habitat of shallow gravel flats and flowing pools in small rivers and large streams. Trautman (1981) states that this former inhabitant of Ohio waters prefers waters of great clarity. Before its disappearance in Ohio, it was associated with such species as sturgeon, mooneye, redhorses, harelip suckers, chubs, and several darters, all of which required clear waters to survive. Etnier and Starnes (1993) note a diet composed of a variety of aquatic insects, including beetles, midges, caddisflies, and mayflies. They also report a late spring spawning season, from early April through late June, in Tennessee.

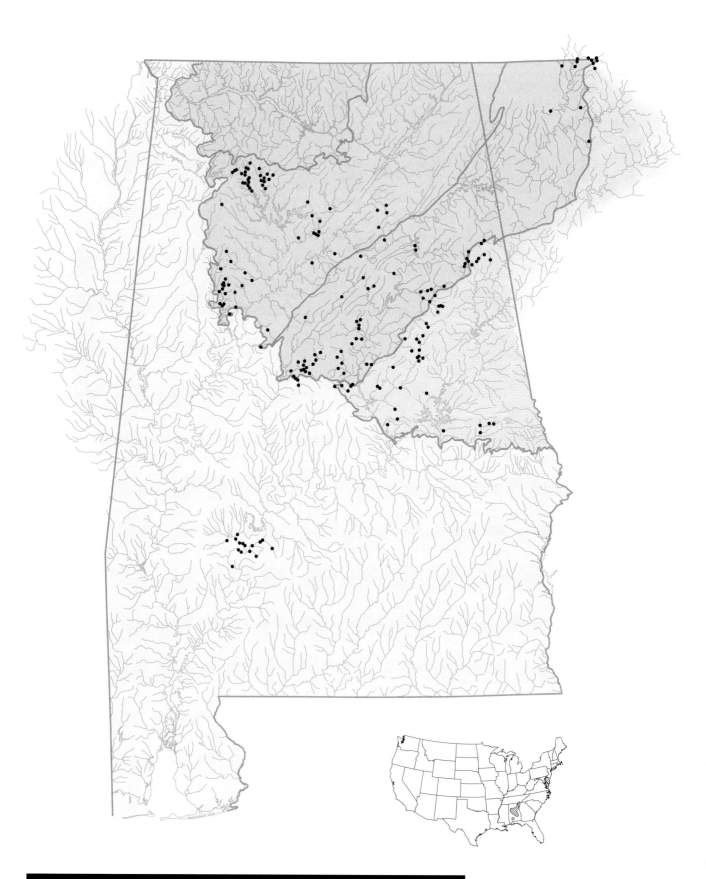

BURRHEAD SHINER *Notropis asperifrons* **187 STATIONS**

Notropis asperifrons

Suttkus and Raney, 1955

ETYMOLOGY:

Notropis—keeled back
asperifrons—rough fore-
head, referring to this
species' breeding tubercles

Wash Creek, Chilton County, 21 April 1993, 1.7 in (44 mm) SL female, GSA 4437

CHARACTERISTICS: The body form of the burrhead shiner is elongate and rounded in cross section. The head is somewhat triangular, with a blunt snout and inferior, horizontal mouth. A dark, narrow lateral band extends from the caudal fin and encircles the snout. An immaculate band is located immediately above the lateral stripe, extending from the tail to the gill opening. Although *Notropis asperifrons* resembles the Coosa shiner, *N. xaenocephalus*, the former lacks a predorsal stripe, whereas the latter has a well-defined one. Individuals do not develop vivid breeding colors, as do many other species in the family Cyprinidae. Swift (1970) indicates that this species is related to the *N. texanus* species group. See Suttkus and Raney (1955a) for original description.

ADULT SIZE: 1.8 to 2.4 in (45 to 60 mm)

DISTRIBUTION: *Notropis asperifrons*, a species that is endemic to the Mobile basin above the Fall Line, occurs from the upper Black Warrior River system to the Tallapoosa River system. An isolated population of *N. asperifrons* is found in Wilcox and Monroe counties, in the lower Alabama River drainage in the Lime Hills region.

HABITAT AND BIOLOGY: The burrhead shiner prefers clear woodland streams of small to moderate size with rubble, bedrock, and sand substrates. The spawning season likely occurs from April to June. Females heavy with eggs and tuberculate males have been collected from the upper Black Warrior system in April and May. Etnier and Starnes (1993) report *N. asperifrons* spawning in the Conasauga River from April through June. The biology of this handsome species is in need of further study.

REMARKS: The type locality of the burrhead shiner is Holly Creek, a tributary to the Conasauga River, near Ramhurst, Murray County, Georgia.

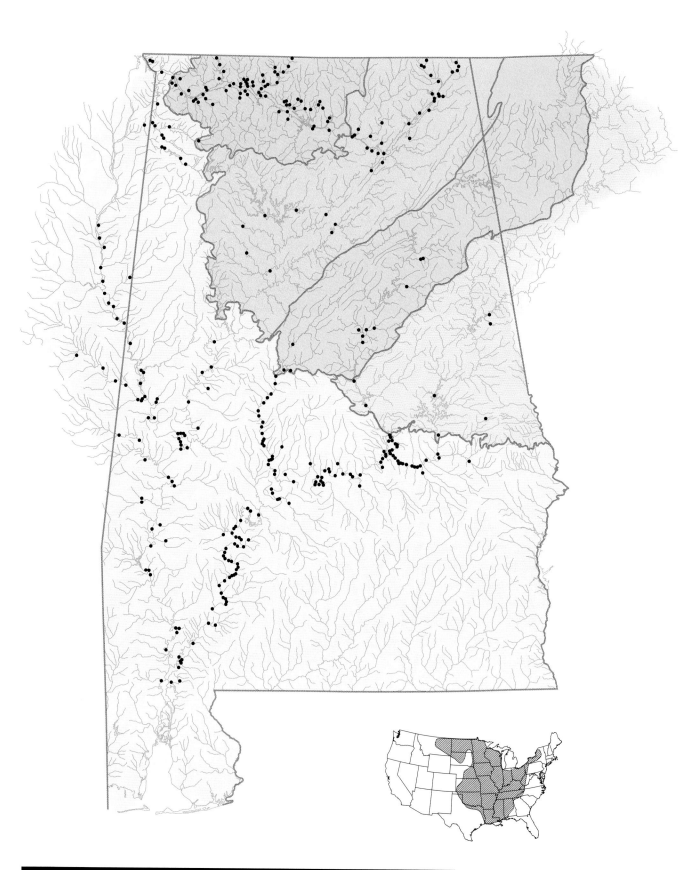

EMERALD SHINER   *Notropis atherinoides*   329 STATIONS

Notropis atherinoides
Rafinesque, 1818

ETYMOLOGY:

Notropis—keeled back
atherinoides—like a silverside of the family
Atherinidae

Tennessee River, Madison County, 13 July 1992, 3.1 in (78 mm) SL male, GSA 4268

CHARACTERISTICS: The emerald shiner is a stream-lined, elongate minnow with a small head and terminal, oblique mouth. The chin is extensively pigmented, while the fins are colorless. Dorsal and anal fins are pointed, and the anal fin is generally falcate. While silvery in appearance, this species has a pale yellow-olive back and a faint lateral stripe. The emerald shiner resembles *Notropis rubellus*, the rosyface shiner. The rosyface shiner is generally smaller and darker, with the lateral line completely outlined with melanophores and with straight-edged dorsal and anal fins. Other species that may be confused with *N. atherinoides* are the silverstripe shiner, *N. stilbius*, and the silverside shiner, *N. candidus*. See Rafinesque (1818a) for original description.

ADULT SIZE: 2 to 4.1 in (50 to 105 mm)

DISTRIBUTION: The emerald shiner is distributed from the Galveston Bay drainage in Texas east to the Mobile basin and north through the Mississippi basin.

This species also occurs throughout much of Canada. Our sampling efforts indicate that in Alabama emerald shiners are most abundant in main river channels below the Fall Line in the Mobile basin. We have also encountered them in lesser abundance above the Fall Line. The species is widespread and often abundant in the Tennessee River drainage.

HABITAT AND BIOLOGY: *Notropis atherinoides* is widespread and abundant in large, slow rivers and reservoirs and apparently tolerates a wide range of turbidity conditions and bottom types. It is also found in the lower reaches of larger tributaries in similar habitats. Breeding individuals have been found from April through July, and spawning has been reported to occur at night in quiet waters over sand and mud substrates (Becker, 1983). Prey of the emerald shiner consists of terrestrial and aquatic insects, algae, and microcrustaceans. Emerald shiners are important forage fish for sport and game species in large rivers and impoundments.

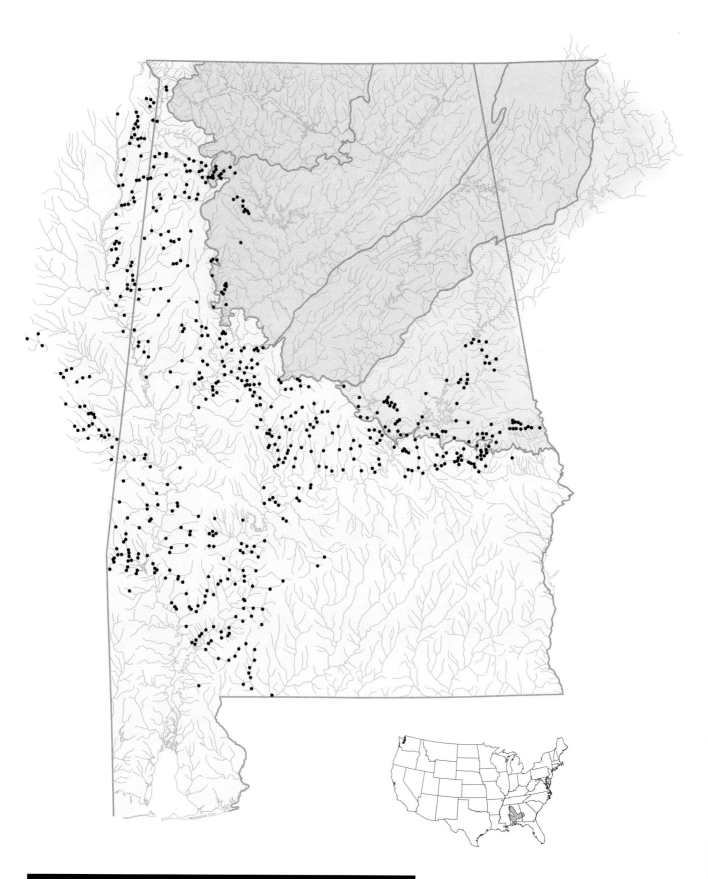

ROUGH SHINER   *Notropis baileyi*   **597 STATIONS**

Notropis baileyi

Suttkus and Raney, 1955

ETYMOLOGY:

Notropis—keeled back
baileyi—in honor of
Reeve M. Bailey, professor
emeritus and former curator
of the University of Michigan Museum of Zoology

Josie Leg Creek, Tallapoosa County, 24 June 1992, 2.1 in (54 mm) SL male, GSA 4322

CHARACTERISTICS: The rough shiner has a deep, stocky, somewhat compressed body and a terminal, oblique mouth. Breeding males have a slight hump along the back between the dorsal fin and the back of the head. The lateral band is black with a yellowish cast. Above the lateral band, the sides are reddish brown with a slight yellow tint. Below the lateral band, they are yellow grading to a silvery white venter. All fins are yellow. Red and yellow variants of this species are known, the yellow form occurring in the western Mobile basin and the red form in eastern portions of that basin. See Suttkus and Raney (1955b) for original description.

ADULT SIZE: 2 to 3 in (50 to 75 mm)

DISTRIBUTION: *Notropis baileyi* is widely distributed throughout the Mobile basin. It is particularly abundant below the Fall Line in the Southern Red Hills, Lime Hills, and Fall Line Hills. Substantial populations exist in the Bear Creek system of the Tennessee drainage; in Escambia Creek, a tributary to the Conecuh River; and

in Uchee and Halawakee creeks, which drain into the Chattahoochee. It is absent from sluggish, turbid streams that drain the Black Belt.

HABITAT AND BIOLOGY: This species prefers small to large flowing streams with sand and gravel substrates. Spawning occurs from early May to late September, peaking in May and June (Mathur and Ramsey, 1974a). Breeding aggregations have been observed over gravel nests of ***Nocomis*** and ***Campostoma*** (Johnston and Kleiner, 1994) and in depressions up to 2 feet deep in sandy substrates with a light silt cover. Mathur and Ramsey (1974b) record a diet of drift made up of terrestrial and aquatic insects and plant material. They attribute this species' ecological success throughout its range to its opportunistic feeding habits, long spawning season, and high reproductive potential.

REMARKS: The type locality is Sawacklahatchee Creek, a Tallapoosa River tributary near Society Hill, Macon County, Alabama.

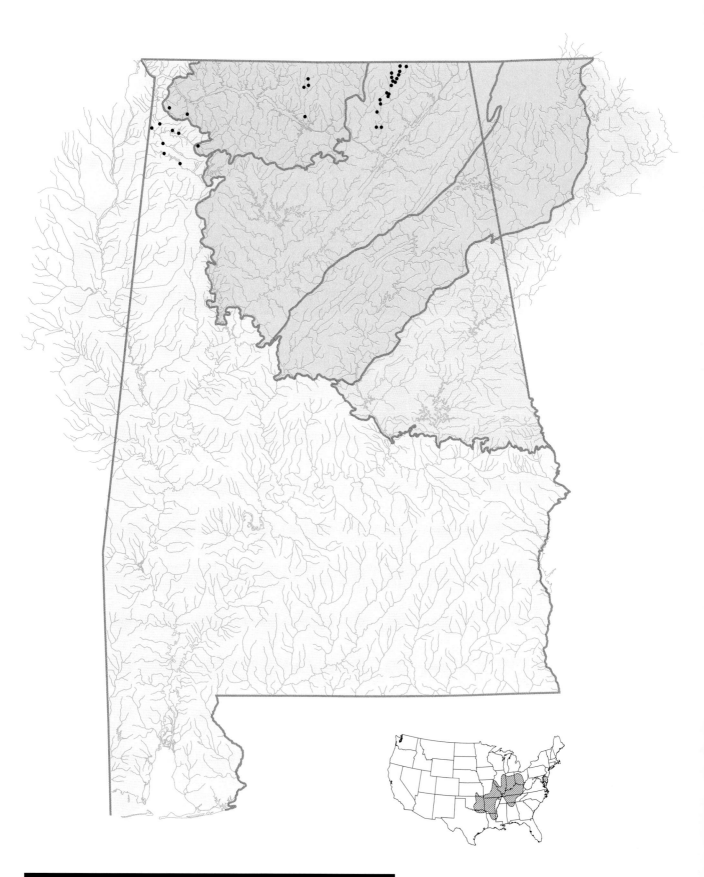

BIGEYE SHINER *Notropis boops* **32 STATIONS**

Notropis boops

Gilbert, 1884

ETYMOLOGY:

Notropis—keeled back
boops—ox eye, referring
to this species' large eye

Piney Creek, Limestone County, 20 May 1993, 2.3 in (58 mm) SL female, GSA 4477

CHARACTERISTICS: *Notropis boops* is a deep-bodied, somewhat compressed minnow with large eyes. The large, oblique mouth is at the end of the snout, while the end of the upper jaw extends past the front of the eye. The back is typically olive yellow, and the sides are silvery. The lateral band is dark and continues around the snout, touching the tip of the lower jaw. The pores of the lateral band are outlined with melanophores on the top and bottom. The bigeye shiner is similar to and found sympatrically with the Tennessee shiner, *N. leuciodus*, which lacks pigment on the tip of the lower jaw.

ADULT SIZE: 1.2 to 3.1 in (30 to 80 mm)

DISTRIBUTION: *Notropis boops* is generally confined to upland streams in the Mississippi basin from the Tennessee and Ohio river drainages west through Missouri and Arkansas. Its occurrence in Alabama is sporadic and is limited to the Tennessee River drainage,

with individuals having been taken from the Paint Rock River and Bear, Spring, and Piney creek systems.

HABITAT AND BIOLOGY: The bigeye shiner usually inhabits clear, small to medium-sized streams with pools over substrates of gravel, rock, or sand; it typically avoids fast waters. Little is known about the life history of this species in Alabama. In Oklahoma a protracted spawning season from late April to August has been recorded (Lentinen and Echelle, 1979), with most individuals spawning by their second summer of life. In Alabama spawning likely occurs from late May to August. The diet of *N. boops* probably consists of stream drift composed of terrestrial insects, adult and immature aquatic insects, and plant material. Trautman (1981) reports that this species is a sight feeder, preying on small insects hovering at the water surface. He also notes that bigeye shiners are sensitive to increased siltation and turbidity.

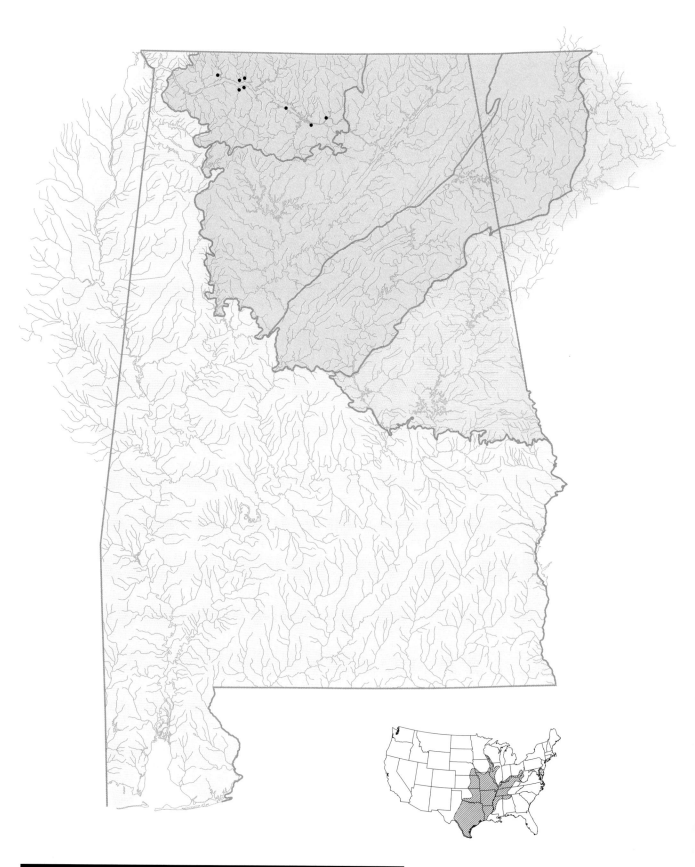

GHOST SHINER *Notropis buchanani* **8 STATIONS**

Notropis buchanani

Meek, 1896

ETYMOLOGY:

Notropis—keeled back
buchanani—in honor of
J. L. Buchanan, former
president of Arkansas Industrial University

Red River, Rapides Parish, Louisiana, 3 June 1995, 1.4 in (36 mm) SL male, TU 175009

CHARACTERISTICS: The ghost shiner is pale and has a deep, somewhat slab-sided body. Its arched back tapers to a small head, which has a small, slightly oblique mouth. Sensory canals under the eye are lacking or are reduced, while the dorsal fin is very high and pointed. *Notropis buchanani* is easily confused with the mimic shiner, *N. volucellus*, and channel shiner, *N. wickliffi*, which have more rounded body forms, complete sensory canals, and more pigment on their bodies. Also, the tips of the pelvic fins extend almost to the anal fin on *N. buchanani*, unlike those on *volucellus* and *wickliffi*.

ADULT SIZE: 1 to 2 in (25 to 50 mm)

DISTRIBUTION: *Notropis buchanani* is distributed from the Rio Grande basin east to the Mississippi basin and north to Minnesota. In Alabama this species is restricted to the Tennessee River drainage, with collections limited to stream mouths along the river. Several of the localities depicted on the facing page represent

preimpoundment collections made by the Tennessee Valley Authority in 1937 and 1938. Few recent collections have been taken in Alabama, although during the 1990s TVA biologists reported the ghost shiner from the impounded reaches of several large tributaries, including Second Creek, Lauderdale County, and the Elk River.

HABITAT AND BIOLOGY: The ghost shiner inhabits large, sluggish rivers, streams, and impoundments, preferring sloughs and backwaters. Little is known of its biology, but like most minnows, it probably eats stream drift composed of terrestrial and aquatic insects and plant material. Spawning has been reported to occur from late April to August in several states. Trautman (1981) indicates that ghost shiners definitely seek clean, quiet waters with the clean sand and gravel bottoms usually associated with aquatic plants. In contrast, Smith (1979) reports that ghost shiners are common in turbid waters over a bottom of silt and detritus, noting abundant populations in polluted reaches of the Illinois and Kaskaskia rivers.

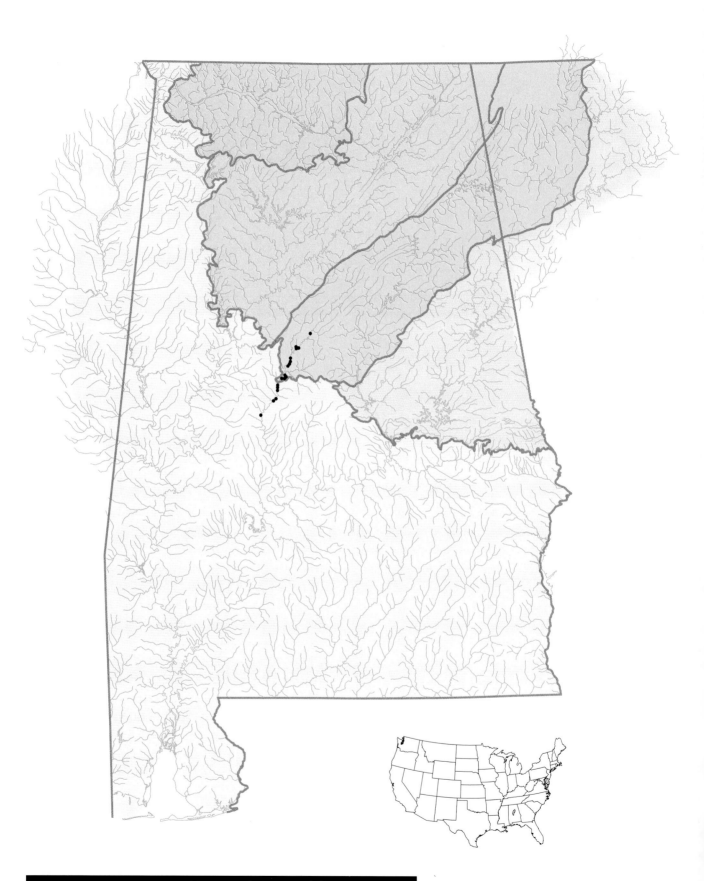

CAHABA SHINER *Notropis cahabae* **18 STATIONS**

Notropis cahabae

Mayden and Kuhajda, 1989

ETYMOLOGY:

Notropis—keeled back
cahabae—of the Cahaba
River, the range of this
species

Cahaba River, Bibb County, 8 May 1993, 1.5 in (38 mm) SL male, GSA 4446

CHARACTERISTICS: A member of the *Notropis volucellus* species group, *N. cahabae* is a long-known but only recently described species (Mayden and Kuhajda, 1989). It has an elongate but somewhat robust body and a head with large eyes and a slightly oblique mouth. Though similar in appearance to the mimic shiner, *N. volucellus*, the channel shiner, *N. wickliffi*, and an undescribed species similar to *N. volucellus* known from the Mobile basin, the Cahaba shiner has a lateral stripe with straight dorsal and ventral edges on the caudal peduncle, no well-defined predorsal stripe or spot, and a breast usually characterized by embedded or exposed scales. In the other three species, the lateral stripe is expanded ventrally, forming a distinct caudal spot. Adult Cahaba shiners are light olive above and silvery below and do not develop vivid breeding colors.

ADULT SIZE: 1.4 to 1.8 in (35 to 45 mm)

DISTRIBUTION: *Notropis cahabae* is endemic to the main channel of the Cahaba River of the Mobile basin.

The historic range of the Cahaba shiner included about 76 river miles from Centreville upstream to Helena, but recent studies (Shepard et al., 1994) indicate that the species is now limited to about 15 river miles from Centreville upstream to Piper Bridge. In the Cahaba River it occurs sympatrically with the undescribed "Mobile mimic shiner" (see page 283).

HABITAT AND BIOLOGY: The preferred habitat of the Cahaba shiner is the main channel of the Cahaba River, in areas of shallow shoals up to 5 feet deep and downstream of riffles composed of clean sand or a sand-gravel mix. Individuals have also been observed in shallow waters flowing through beds of the emergent aquatic vegetation *Justicia*. Spawning occurs from mid-May through early July, with peak activity in June. Little is known of the species' feeding biology.

REMARKS: The type locality of this species is the Cahaba River, near Centreville, Bibb County, Alabama. The U.S. Fish and Wildlife Service has listed the Cahaba shiner as an endangered species.

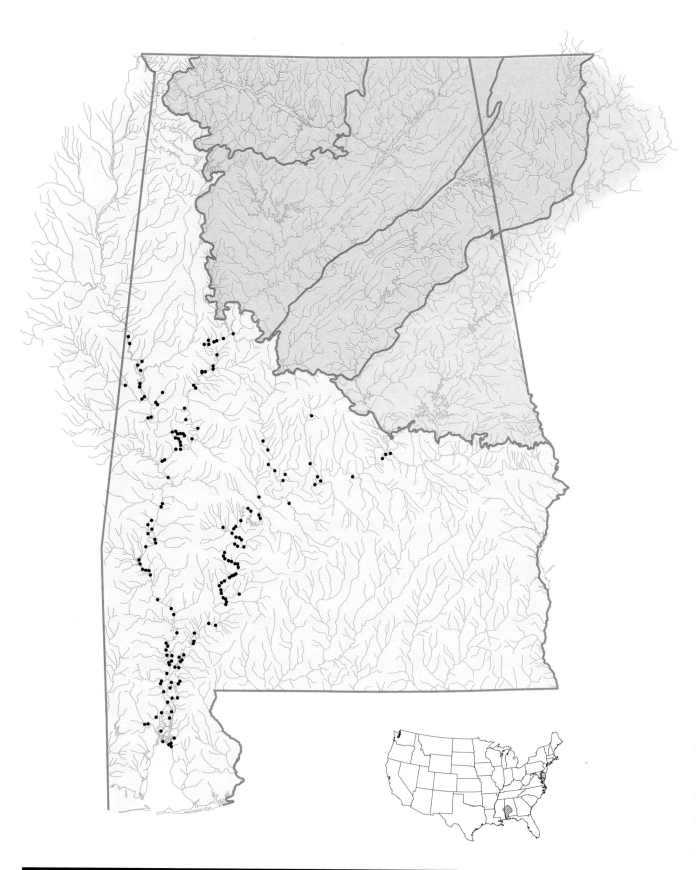

Notropis candidus

Suttkus, 1980

ETYMOLOGY:

Notropis—keeled back
candidus—glittering white,
referring to this species'
white sides

Black Warrior River, Tuscaloosa County, 16 June 1992, 2.8 in (72 mm) SL female, GSA 4262

CHARACTERISTICS: This slender species has a compressed body and an eye diameter that is about equal to the length of the pointed snout. The lateral stripe, lightly outlined above and below with melanophores anterior to the dorsal fin, is darkest on the peduncle and fades toward the head. This species is sometimes confused with the sympatric emerald shiner, *Notropis atherinoides*, and silverstripe shiner, *N. stilbius*, but is distinguished from them by its lack of dark pigment on the mouth.

ADULT SIZE: 1.6 to 3.1 in (40 to 80 mm)

DISTRIBUTION: This species is endemic to main-channel habitats in the Alabama, Black Warrior, Tombigbee, Cahaba, and Tallapoosa rivers and the lower portions of large tributaries in the lower Mobile basin. There are no records above the Fall Line. Specimens have been taken in tidally influenced rivers in the lower Mobile Delta.

HABITAT AND BIOLOGY: *Notropis candidus* is an abundant shiner that favors large, clear to turbid rivers and impoundments. It is commonly found in water up to 5 feet deep over sand and gravel bars. Large schools of silverside shiners are often captured close to river-banks in 1 or 2 feet of water. R. D. Suttkus (1980) describes this species' diurnal movements, from deeper habitats during the day to shallower areas during the night. Spawning occurs in open water, probably over hard sand to fine gravel, from June to mid-August. Few individuals live for more than two or three years. Little is known about the silverside shiner's feeding habits, but it presumably eats stream drift composed of terrestrial insects, adult and immature aquatic insects, and plant material.

REMARKS: The type locality of the silverside shiner is the Alabama River near Holly Ferry crossing, Wilcox County, Alabama.

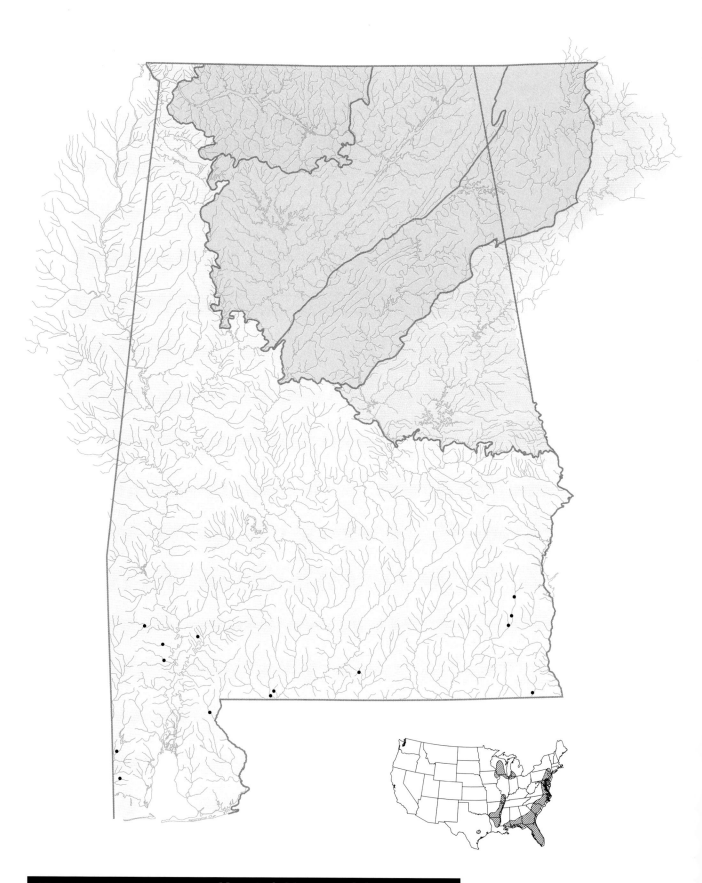

IRONCOLOR SHINER   *Notropis chalybaeus*   **14 STATIONS**

Notropis chalybaeus
(Cope, 1869)

ETYMOLOGY:
Notropis—keeled back
chalybaeus—iron-colored

Wilder Branch, Escambia County, Florida, 8 May 1986, 1.4 in (34 mm) SL male.

CHARACTERISTICS: This small species of *Notropis* has a deep, compressed body and a dark, pronounced lateral band extending from the tail to the snout. The inside of the mouth is intensely pigmented, a feature that separates this species from the weed shiner, *N. texanus*; coastal shiner, *N. petersoni*; and bluenose shiner, *Pteronotropis welaka*. Breeding males have a bright orange stripe above the lateral band, and the back is reddish brown with an olive cast. Orange "windows" appear above and below the caudal spot, with an orange cast extending onto the tail. Melanophores outline the anal rays.

ADULT SIZE: 1.6 to 2.2 in (40 to 55 mm)

DISTRIBUTION: The ironcolor shiner is found in Atlantic and Gulf slope drainages from Maine to Texas, generally in the lower Coastal Plain and infrequently up the Mississippi basin to Michigan. It is distributed sporadically in south Alabama from the Chipola River system west to Big Creek in Mobile County.

HABITAT AND BIOLOGY: *Notropis chalybaeus* inhabits small, slow, acidic blackwater streams draining swamps and other types of vegetated wetlands of the Southern Pine Hills and lower Dougherty Plains. Marshall (1947) describes its habitat in Florida as sluggish streams with small, quiet pools and shallow, swift blackwaters. This shiner is a sight feeder, consuming adult and immature insects and plant material drifting in the stream. Marshall (1947) reports a protracted spawning season in Florida, from early April through September. Spawning in Alabama likely occurs from April to August. During spawning, females broadcast their eggs in the water column over sand-bottom pools, where the eggs adhere to sand and gravel particles.

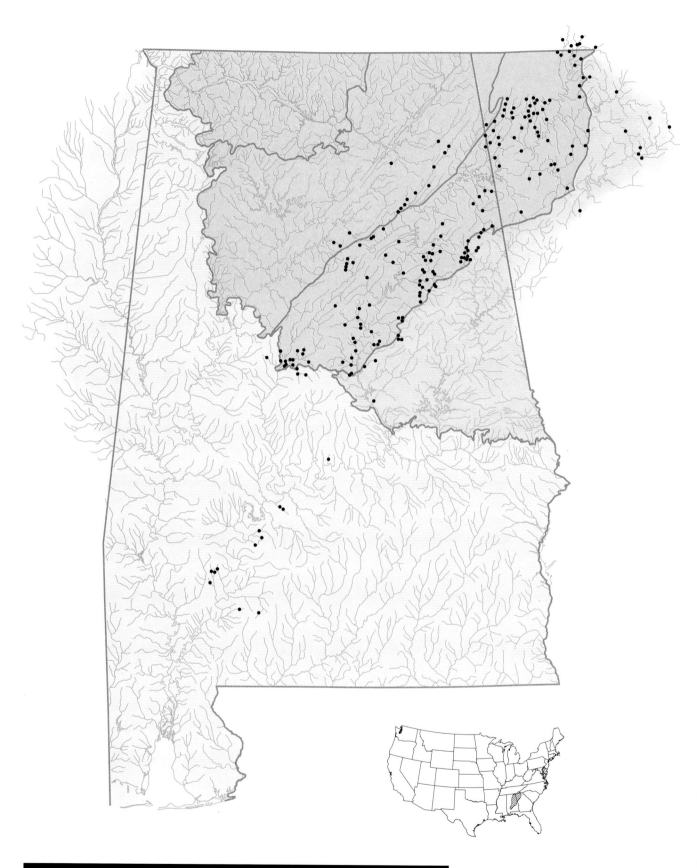

RAINBOW SHINER *Notropis chrosomus* **202 STATIONS**

Notropis chrosomus

(Jordan, 1877)

ETYMOLOGY:

Notropis—keeled back

chrosomus—colored body

Little Schultz Creek, Bibb County, 13 May 1993, 1.9 in (49 mm) SL male, GSA 4473

CHARACTERISTICS: *Notropis chrosomus* is a robust, moderately compressed minnow species with a slender peduncle and short fins. A black lateral band extends from the gill opening to the tail. Breeding males are quite beautiful, with a light reddish purple stripe above the lateral band and iridescent violet flecks along the back and the dorsal, pectoral, and caudal fins. The sides below the purple stripe are iridescent powder blue, changing to silver on the venter. The dorsal and anal fins have bright red spots in the center of the front rays. The dorsal half of the eye is bright red. In both sexes, small breeding tubercles cover the head and a large part of the body (Swift, 1970). The rainbow shiner is placed in the colorful subgenus *Hydrophlox* of *Notropis*, along with *N. baileyi*, *N. leuciodus*, *N. lutipinnis*, and *N. rubellus* in our study area. See Jordan (1877a) for original description.

ADULT SIZE: 1.6 to 2.4 in (40 to 60 mm)

DISTRIBUTION: The rainbow shiner is almost exclusively confined to the Mobile River basin above the Fall Line in the Alabama Valley and Ridge. It is commonly found throughout the Coosa River system and parts of the Cahaba River system, but it is strangely absent in the Tallapoosa River system. Isolated populations are found in the lower Alabama River drainage, in upland tributaries of the Black Warrior River system adjacent to the Alabama Valley and Ridge, and in the Short and Town creek systems of the Tennessee River drainage.

HABITAT AND BIOLOGY: This species is typically found in small, low-turbidity headwater streams flowing over gravelly and sandy riffles and pools. Spawning occurs from April through June or July, frequently over gravel nests constructed by fish species of the genus *Nocomis* or *Campostoma*; we have observed rainbow shiners spawning over *Nocomis* mounds in Little Schultz Creek, a Cahaba River tributary in Bibb County in early May. With their reddish purple backs and neon blue pectoral fins, males are quite prominent in spawning aggregations. Like other *Notropis*, the rainbow shiner is most likely a drift feeder, consuming aquatic insects and plant material. Surprisingly, considering this fish's striking appearance, its life history has received little study.

REMARKS: The type locality of the rainbow shiner is tributaries to the Etowah River near Rome, Floyd County, Georgia.

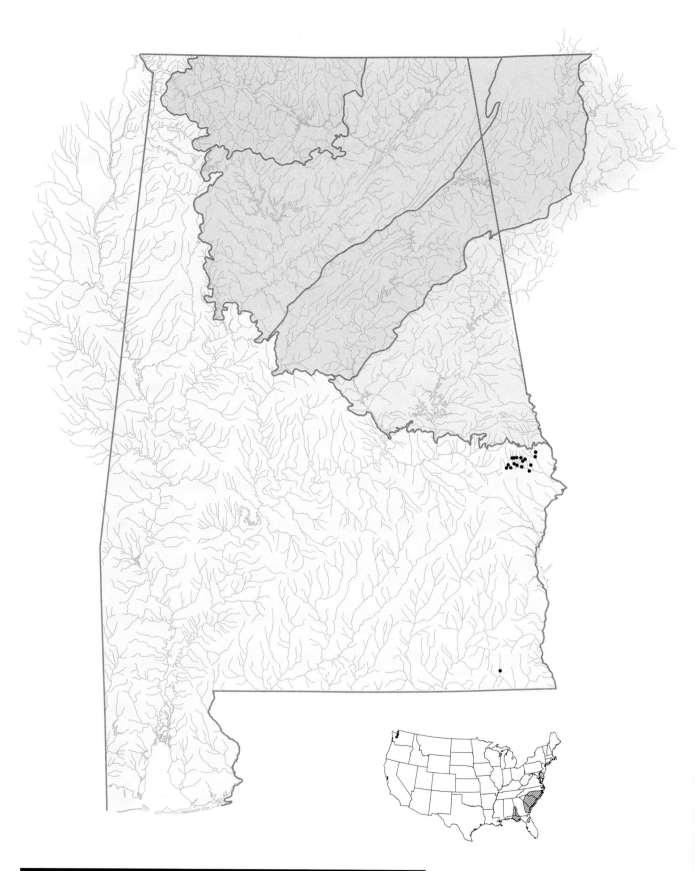

DUSKY SHINER *Notropis cummingsae* **17 STATIONS**

Notropis cummingsae
Myers, 1925

ETYMOLOGY:
Notropis—keeled back
cummingsae—in honor
of Mrs. J. H. Cummings,
of Wilmington, North Car-
olina, a researcher of local
flora and fauna, and George
Myers's host during his field
investigations

Snake Creek, Russell County, 7 April 1993, 1.7 in (44 mm) SL female, GSA 4410

CHARACTERISTICS: The dusky shiner is a somewhat short and compressed species characterized by a wide black band extending from the tip of the snout to the caudal fin base. The caudal fin base has a distinct spot, with pigment streaking toward the back of the fin. The somewhat oblique mouth is near the tip of the snout. The color of breeding males is dusky yellow-brown on the back, with a light yellow to orange stripe above the lateral band; fin color varies from clear to light yellow. *Notropis cummingsae* can be confused with the ironcol-or shiner, *N. chalybaeus*, which usually has eight anal rays and a heavily pigmented mouth.

ADULT SIZE: 1.2 to 2.4 in (30 to 60 mm)

DISTRIBUTION: *Notropis cummingsae* is found in Atlantic and Gulf slope drainages from the Tar River in North Carolina to the Choctawhatchee River in south Alabama and northwest Florida. Its range in Alabama is limited to the Uchee Creek system, a tributary to the

Chattahoochee River, and a tributary to the Chipola River in Houston County. Hubbs and Raney (1951) divide *N. cummingsae* into two subspecies: **N. c. collis**, which occurs in northern South Carolina and central North Carolina, and **N. c. cummingsae**, which occurs throughout the remainder of the species' range.

HABITAT AND BIOLOGY: Dusky shiners are found in lowland streams of the Uchee Creek drainage, where low gradients and saturated soils have stimulated the exten-sive growth of forested wetlands. This area is demarcated in the Uchee Creek area, where bedrock upland streams at the Fall Line abruptly change to slow wetland streams over sand, detritus, and mud. This species prefers slower pools and backwaters with flow. Schools of several hun-dred dusky shiners have been observed in deep, flowing pools with a thick growth of submerged aquatic vegeta-tion. The biology of the dusky shiner is poorly known. Spawning presumably occurs from May through July, and diet is assumed to include insects and plant material.

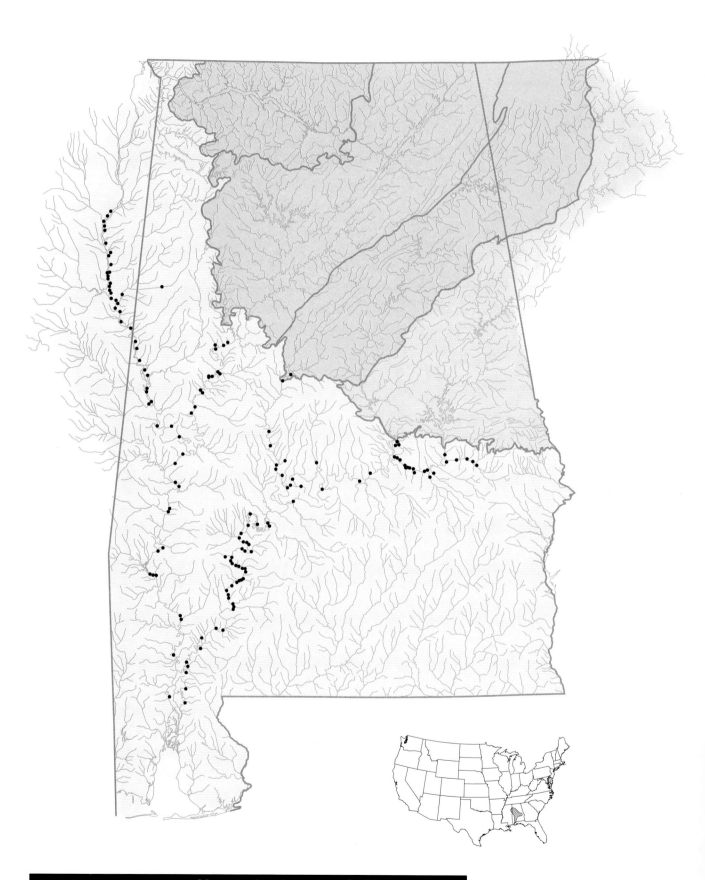

FLUVIAL SHINER   *Notropis edwardraneyi*   **147 STATIONS**

Notropis edwardraneyi

Suttkus and Clemmer, 1968

ETYMOLOGY:

Notropis—keeled back
edwardraneyi—in honor
of Edward C. Raney,
Cornell University

Black Warrior River, Tuscaloosa County, 16 June 1992, 2.1 in (54 mm) SL male, GSA 4262

CHARACTERISTICS: The body form of the fluvial shiner is stocky, with a characteristic blunt snout bending sharply downward near the tip of the mouth. The mouth is terminal and oblique, extending almost to the front of the eye, which is generally larger than the snout. Body color is silvery, with a diffuse, dusky lateral band extending along the caudal peduncle to the base of the caudal fin, where some individuals develop a faint, disjunct, wedge-shaped spot. The underside is devoid of pigment. Lateral line scales are bounded above and below by a single row of faint melanophores. In their description of *Notropis edwardraneyi*, Suttkus and Clemmer (1968) may have achieved a new record for systematic thoroughness: They examined 32,493 specimens collected in the Alabama and Tombigbee rivers from 1957 to 1968.

ADULT SIZE: 1.8 to 2.4 in (45 to 60 mm)

DISTRIBUTION: *Notropis edwardraneyi* is endemic to the Mobile basin below the Fall Line, where it is generally restricted to the main river channels and lower reaches of large rivers, impoundments, and tributaries. It has recently been documented from the main channel of the Coosa River at the Fall Line near Wetumpka.

HABITAT AND BIOLOGY: The fluvial shiner is commonly and abundantly found over hard sand, gravel, or mud bars in impoundments, flowing channels of main rivers, and mouths of large tributaries. Spawning occurs from May through June. Although little is known about this relatively abundant species' biology, it is presumably a drift feeder, consuming plant material and aquatic and terrestrial insects.

REMARKS: The type locality is the Alabama River near Holly Ferry crossing, Wilcox County, Alabama.

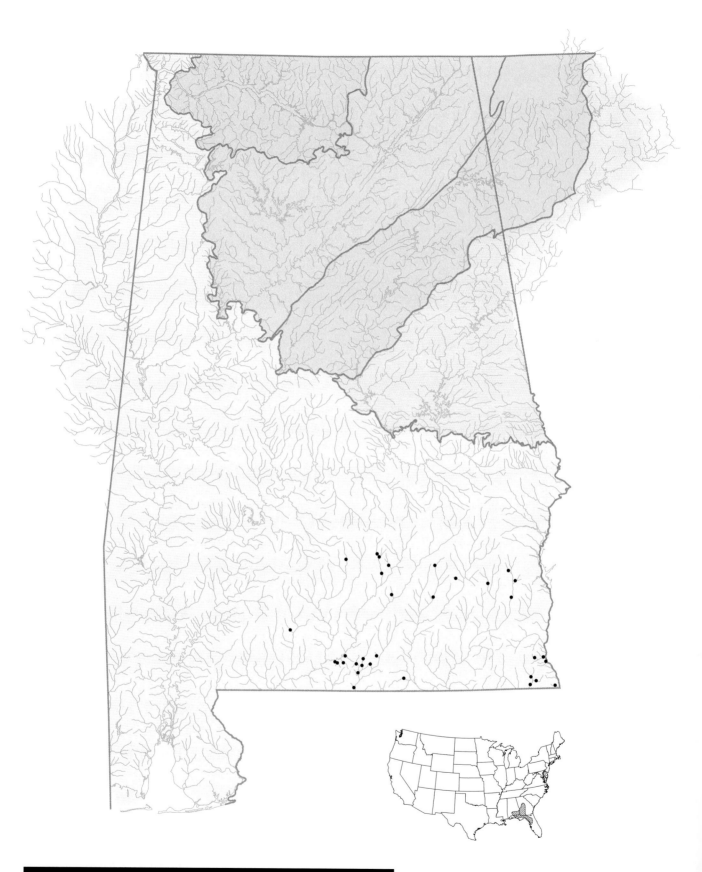

Notropis harperi
Fowler, 1941

ETYMOLOGY:

Notropis—keeled back

harperi—in honor of

Dr. Francis Harper, who in

1939–40 collected the type

specimens during field inves-

tigations along the routes of

John and William Bartram

Bazemores Mill Pond, Houston County, 17 March 1993, 1.2 in (31 mm) SL male, GSA 4378

CHARACTERISTICS: This distinctive species has a small barbel in each corner of the mouth and, as its name suggests, a bright red eye in live individuals. The body shape is slender and somewhat compressed, with a rounded, blunt snout containing a subterminal, some-what horizontal mouth. A dark lateral band encircles the snout and runs along both sides of the body from the snout to the caudal fin, terminating at a black cau-dal spot. A distinct light stripe borders the top of the lateral band.

ADULT SIZE: 1 to 2 in (25 to 50 mm)

DISTRIBUTION: *Notropis harperi* ranges from the Escambia River basin east to the St. Johns River in Florida and disjunctly north to the Altamaha drainage in Georgia. In Alabama the redeye chub is confined to the Southern Red Hills and Dougherty Plains, from the Conecuh River drainage east to the Chattahoochee drainage.

HABITAT AND BIOLOGY: The redeye chub is found almost exclusively in springs and spring runs, where it is usually quite abundant. The relatively constant temper-ature regime of springs fosters a protracted spawning

season for this species, and gravid individuals are found almost year-round. The diet of *N. harperi* consists of drifting insects, crustaceans, and small fish.

Blue Spring, Covington County, Conecuh National Forest

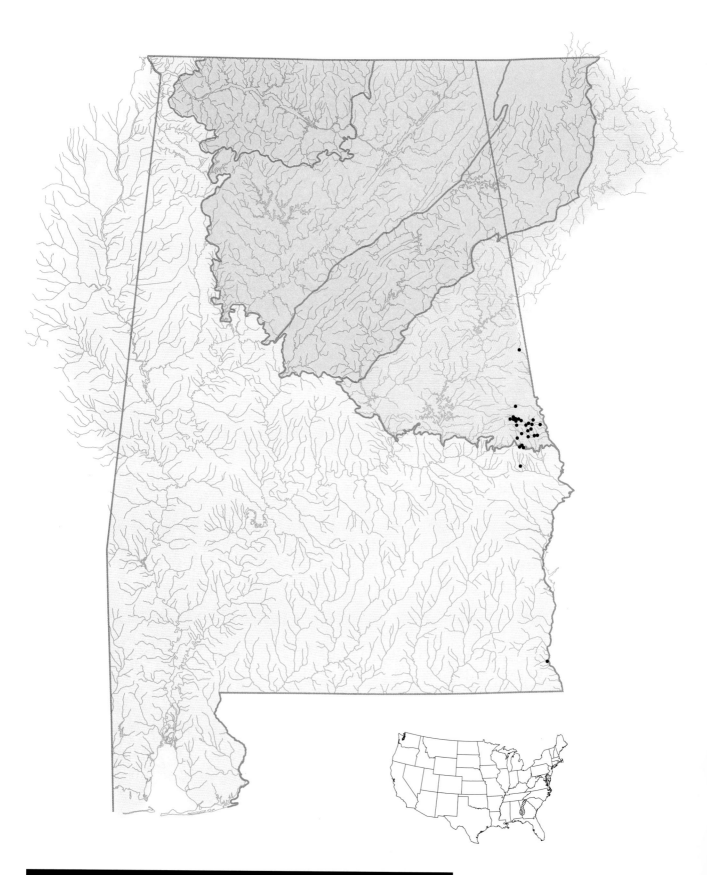

Little Uchee Creek, Lee County, 19 February 1993, 1.8 in (46 mm) SL male, GSA 4375

Notropis hypsilepis
Suttkus and Raney, 1955

ETYMOLOGY:
Notropis—keeled back
hypsilepis—high scale,
referring to this species'
elevated anterior lateral
line scales

CHARACTERISTICS: The highscale shiner is a small, fusiform, and somewhat pale species with a blunt snout that extends slightly beyond a small, inferior mouth. The lateral band is weakly developed, being more heavily pigmented on the peduncle, and a clean stripe occurs above the lateral band from the caudal fin to the gill opening. A small, wedge-shaped spot separate from the lateral band is found at the base of the caudal fin. Characteristic dark patches also occur at the bases of the anal and dorsal fins. The predorsal stripe is developed weakly, if at all, and the scales on the back are well outlined with pigment. *Notropis hypsilepis* most resembles the weed shiner, *N. texanus*, and the Coosa shiner, *N. xaenocephalus*. See Suttkus and Raney (1955c) for original description.

ADULT SIZE: 1.4 to 2 in (35 to 50 mm)

DISTRIBUTION: *Notropis hypsilepis* is limited to the Chattahoochee and Savannah river drainages. In

Alabama the species is generally confined to streams in the Halawakee and Uchee creek systems in the vicinity of the Fall Line. However, we have found a single record from the lower Chattahoochee River in Houston County.

HABITAT AND BIOLOGY: An upland species, the highscale shiner prefers small to medium-sized streams flowing over bedrock and sand substrates, as typified by streams in the southern edge of the Piedmont near the Fall Line. It is reported as occurring near the mouths of small tributaries, which is consistent with its preference for stream pools with flow. A large series of highscale shiners was collected in Little Uchee Creek at the foot of an extensive rock shoal, in a swift run approximately 2 to 3 feet deep flowing over sand and gravel substrate. Little is known about this species' life history, but as with many shiners, it probably consumes stream drift and spawns from May through June.

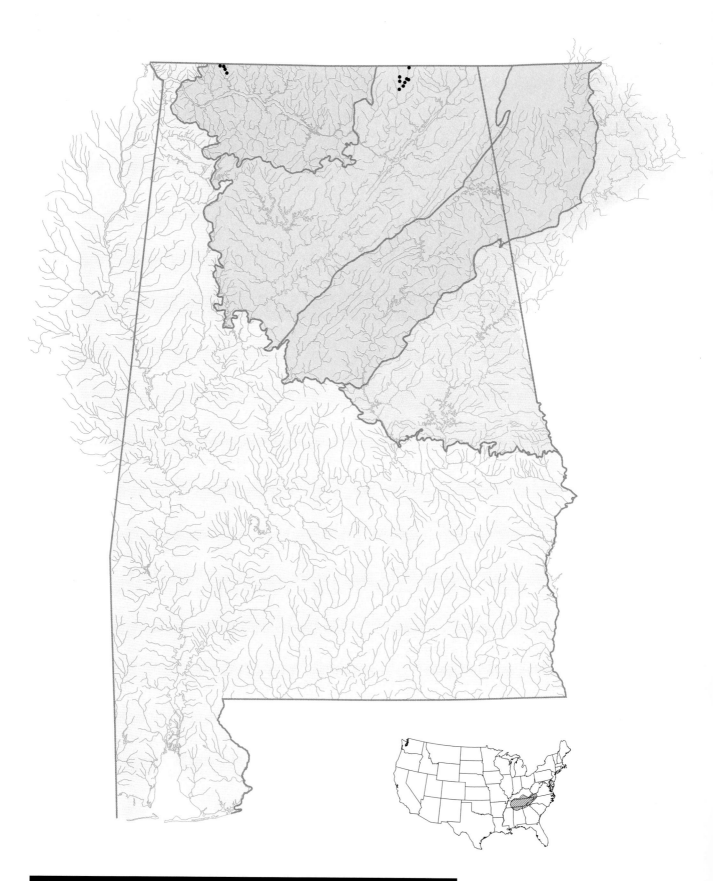

TENNESSEE SHINER *Notropis leuciodus* **12 STATIONS**

Notropis leuciodus

(Cope, 1868)

ETYMOLOGY:

Notropis—keeled back

leuciodus—white

appearance

Larkin Fork, Jackson County, 18 May 1993, 1.9 in (49 mm) SL male, GSA 4474

CHARACTERISTICS: The Tennessee shiner is a slender species, somewhat rounded in cross section, with a pointed snout, terminal mouth, and relatively large eyes. A dark lateral band extends from the gill opening to the tail base, narrowing on the peduncle. The caudal spot is rectangular and about the same width as, but separated from, the lateral band. A light stripe is found above the entire length of the lateral band. Pored lateral line scales dip below the lateral band anterior to the dorsal fin and are bounded above and below by small, dark bars. Scales on the back are heavily pigmented, and the venter is white. Breeding males are flushed with red-orange throughout the entire body. The Tennessee shiner is commonly found with the telescope shiner, *Notropis telescopus*, and the bigeye shiner, *N. boops*, with which it may be confused. Along with the colorful *N. baileyi*, *N. chrosomus*, *N. lutipinnis*, and *N. rubellus*, the Tennessee shiner is aligned in the subgenus *Hydrophlox* of *Notropis*. See Cope (1868a) for original description.

ADULT SIZE: 2 to 2.6 in (50 to 65 mm)

DISTRIBUTION: *Notropis leuciodus* occurs extensively throughout the Tennessee River drainage and parts of the Cumberland and Green river drainages. In Alabama the species is known only from the Shoal Creek system in Lauderdale County and the upper Paint Rock River system in Jackson County.

HABITAT AND BIOLOGY: This species typically prefers cool, clear upland streams with gravel and rubble substrates and often occurs in deeper flowing pools and scoured pools at the base of riffles. Individuals in breeding color have been collected in May and June. A spawning aggregation was observed in Larkin Fork of the Paint Rock River on 18 May 1993. More than a hundred bright orange males swarmed behind a large boulder in the middle of a long, flowing pool some 2 feet deep, with females briefly darting into the swarm to spawn. The aggregation looked like a small, pulsating orange ball which was continually changing shape. Outten (1962) reports *N. leuciodus* holding territories over a river chub nest, whereas Etnier and Starnes (1993) report spawning over stoneroller nests.

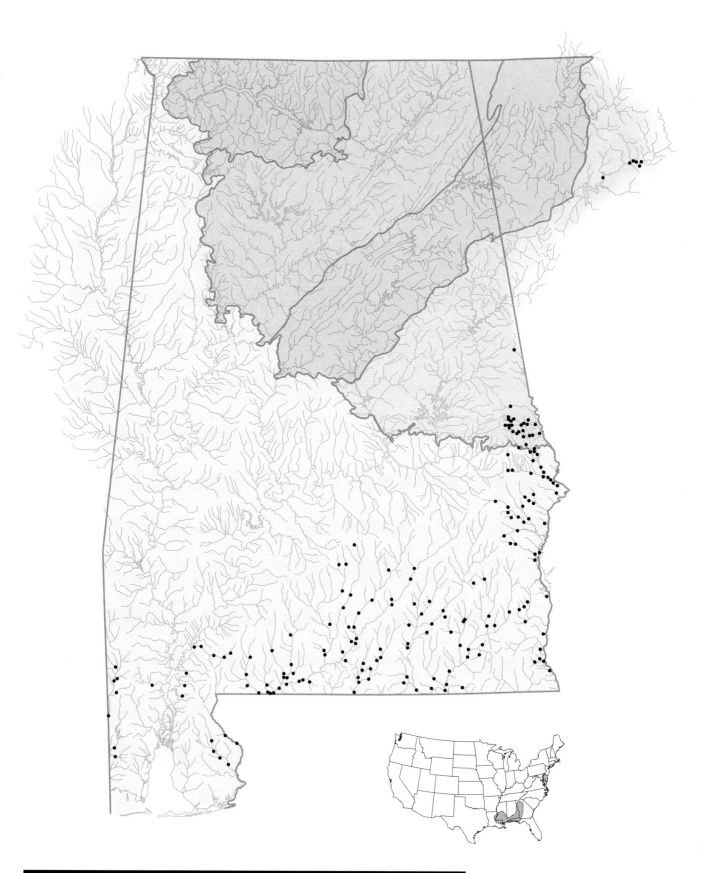

Notropis longirostris
(Hay, 1881)

ETYMOLOGY:
Notropis—keeled back
longirostris—long nose

Perdido River, Baldwin County, 19 August 1992, 2.3 in (58 mm) SL male, GSA 4466

CHARACTERISTICS: The longnose shiner is a pale species with a slender, somewhat compressed body that is flattened on the venter. The snout is long and rounded, with a subterminal mouth. Eyes are located toward the top of the head. The scales and lateral line are delicately outlined with pigment. Live individuals have straw yellow backs, silvery sides, and distinctly yellow fins. Breeding males have yellow to yellow-orange fins.

ADULT SIZE: 1.4 to 2.4 in (35 to 60 mm)

DISTRIBUTION: *Notropis longirostris* ranges from the lower Mississippi basin east to the Apalachicola basin and north to the Altamaha River drainage in Georgia. Isolated populations occur in the upper Coosa River system, presumably gaining access through headwater stream capture. The longnose shiner is absent from most of the Mobile basin, being replaced there by the similar orangefin shiner, *N. ammophilus*. The longnose

shiner is commonly found in the coastal drainages of south Alabama from the Escatawpa basin east to the Chattahoochee River drainage.

HABITAT AND BIOLOGY: This sand-loving species is most often found over shifting sand substrates of shallow shoals and quiet waters below riffle runs in coastal streams. Breeding individuals have been captured in May and June over sand and gravel shoals in coastal streams, and Hubbs and Walker (1942) report bottom spawning on sand and gravel bars with rapid current. Heins and Clemmer (1976) indicate a protracted spawning season from March through October, which is similar to that of *N. ammophilus*. Spawning occurs at the margins of pools that have some current and that are upstream of shoal areas. These shiners live for one to one and a half years, and their diet consists of dipteran immatures and lesser amounts of beetles, mayflies, dragonflies, terrestrial insects, and plant material (Heins and Clemmer, 1975).

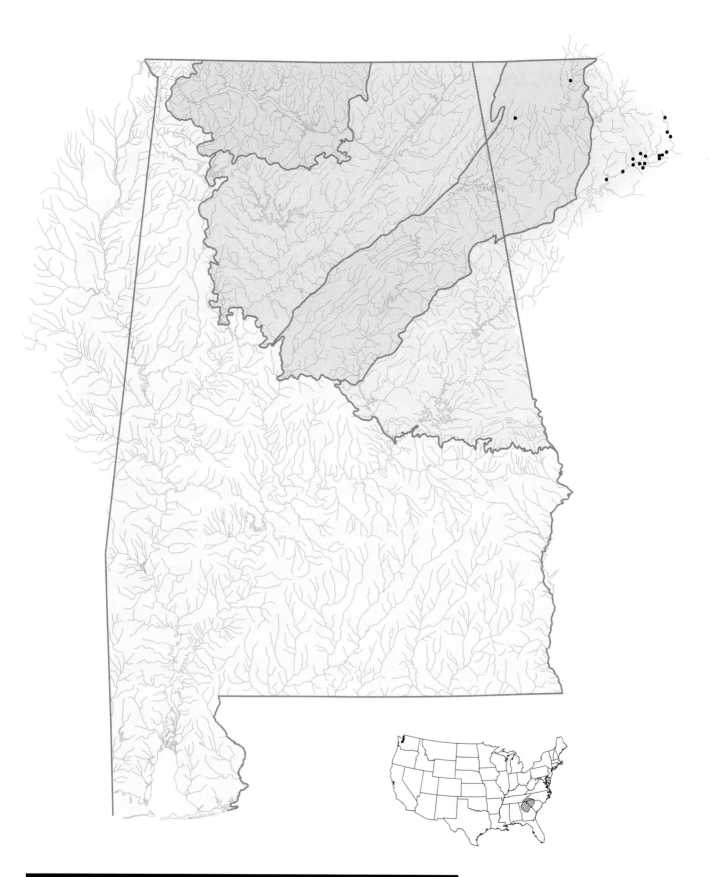

YELLOWFIN SHINER   *Notropis lutipinnis*   18 STATIONS

Notropis lutipinnis
(Jordan and Brayton, 1878)

ETYMOLOGY:

Notropis—keeled back
lutipinnis—yellow fin

Etowah River, Lumpkin County, Georgia, 8 July 1995, 2.3 in (58 mm) SL male, GSA 4654

CHARACTERISTICS: This species, which resembles the rough shiner, *Notropis baileyi*, has a rather stout, compressed body with a slight hump along the back between the dorsal fin and the back of the head. The eye is large (nearly the same size as the snout), while the mouth is large and oblique. Color in life is olive on the back with intense green lines. The lateral band is black, and the lower flanks are silvery. Breeding males have a berry red flush throughout the lower body. The fins are bright reddish yellow—a stark contrast to the reddish body. A member of the colorful subgenus *Hydrophlox,* this species is most similar phylogenetically to the rough shiner, *N. baileyi*, which occurs elsewhere in Alabama, and *N. chiliticus*, *N. chlorocephalus*, and *N. rubricroceus* (Swift, 1970), which are not found in the state. Within its range the yellowfin shiner may be confused with the rainbow shiner, *N. chrosomus*. However, on *lutipinnis* the lateral band is strongly developed, whereas on *chrosomus* it is weakly developed with scattered melanophores. Also, *chrosomus* has a well-developed oblique bar behind the opercle, whereas in *lutipinnis* this bar is weakly developed.

ADULT SIZE: 1.8 to 2.4 in (45 to 60 mm)

DISTRIBUTION: *Notropis lutipinnis* occurs in headwater tributaries from the Altamaha River drainage to the Santee River drainage in Georgia, North Carolina, and South Carolina. This species also inhabits extreme headwaters of the Chattahoochee River drainage in Georgia. Mobile basin records are from the Etowah River system upstream of Allatoona Reservoir and also from the Conasauga and Chattooga river systems in Georgia.

HABITAT AND BIOLOGY: The yellowfin shiner occurs most commonly in small, clear headwater creeks, where it may be very abundant. McAuliffe and Bennett (1981) report swarms of yellowfin shiners spawning over *Nocomis* nests in June, but they speculate that reproductive activity could extend from late May to late June or early July. McAuliffe and Bennett also describe *Notropis lutipinnis* repairing a disturbed *Nocomis* nest by moving small stones to restore the mound.

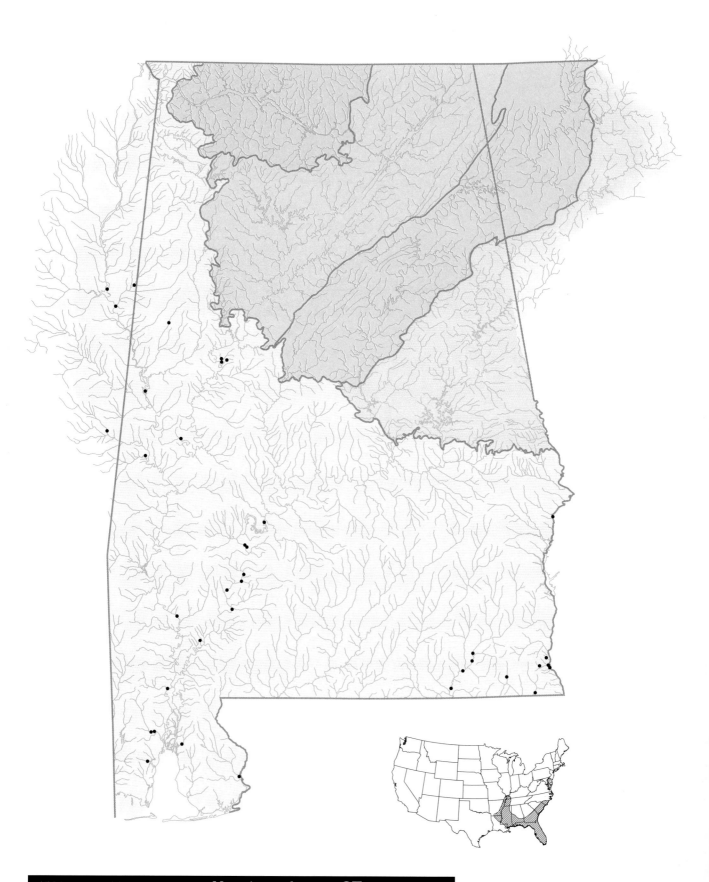

Notropis maculatus

(Hay, 1881)

ETYMOLOGY:

Notropis—keeled back

maculatus—spotted

Alamuchee Creek, Sumter County, 18 June 1992, 1.5 in (39 mm) SL male, GSA 4457

CHARACTERISTICS: The taillight shiner is a slender species with a rounded, blunt snout projecting slightly beyond the upper lip. The eyes are relatively large, and the small, oblique mouth is somewhat inferior. At the base of the tail occurs a characteristic round, darkly pigmented spot. The spot is separate from a narrow, dusky lateral band that extends from the gill opening to the tail. Scale edges are outlined with black, giving the species its distinctive diamond-shaped pattern along the sides. The body of breeding males is flushed with red or pink throughout, as are the outer third of the first few rays of the dorsal, anal, and pelvic fins and the edging along the caudal fin tips. The taillight shiner may be confused with the pugnose minnow, *Opsopoeodus emiliae*, but the latter can be recognized by its nearly vertical mouth.

ADULT SIZE: 1.8 to 2.4 in (45 to 60 mm)

DISTRIBUTION: *Notropis maculatus* inhabits Atlantic and Gulf slope drainages from the Cape Fear River in North Carolina north to Kentucky and west to the Red River in Texas. In Alabama it is occasionally seen in large rivers and tributaries of the Coastal Plain, including the Tombigbee, Alabama, Choctawhatchee, Chattahoochee, and Mobile river systems.

HABITAT AND BIOLOGY: This species' spotty distribution is likely a collecting artifact, since its preferred habitat—swampy, mud-bottomed backwaters with some aquatic vegetation or cover—is difficult to survey with conventional sampling methods. Spawning occurs from March through June in Alabama, although Cowell and Barnett (1974) report spawning from March to early October in central Florida. They also report a life span of over two years and a diet of algae, rotifers, microcrustaceans, and some insects and detritus.

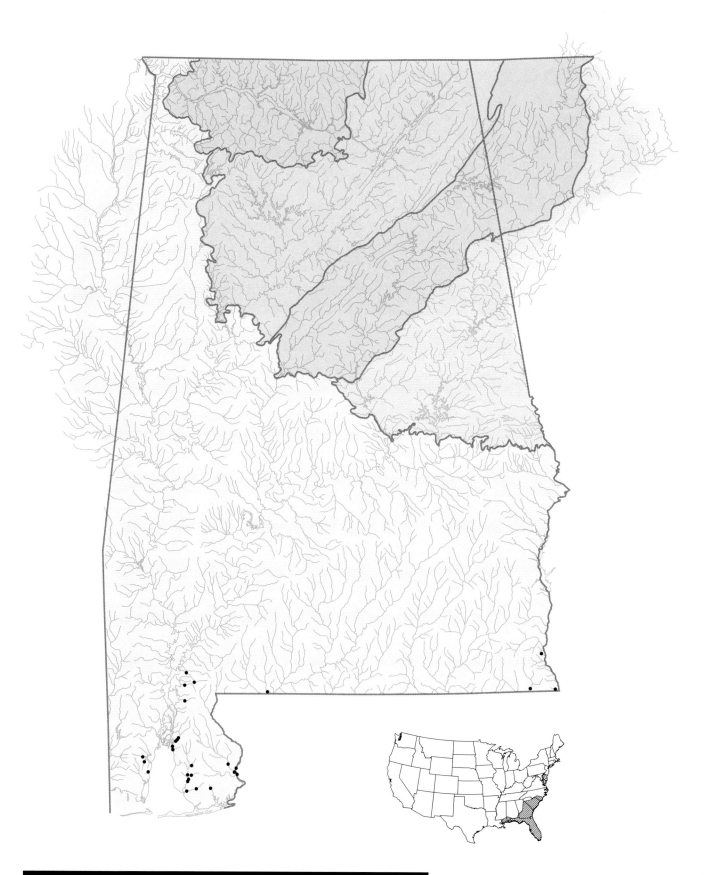

COASTAL SHINER *Notropis petersoni* **28 STATIONS**

Notropis petersoni
Fowler, 1942

ETYMOLOGY:
Notropis—keeled back
petersoni—in honor of
C. Bernard Peterson, who
assisted in collecting the
type specimens

Sandy Creek, Baldwin County, 19 August 1992, 2.2 in (55 mm) SL female, GSA 4469

CHARACTERISTICS: *Notropis petersoni* is a small minnow with a fairly compressed body, a blunt, overhanging snout, and a terminal mouth. The black lateral band is well developed, extending from the snout to the tail. The caudal spot is small, wedge-shaped, and narrower than the lateral band. Scales below the lateral band lack pigment, and all rays of the anal fin are lightly outlined with melanophores. In live individuals, the back is olive yellow, with an overall body color of light brown to olive yellow. Swift (1970) indicates that specimens from highly stained waters may be salmon in color with pinkish fins. The coastal shiner may be confused with the similarly colored weed shiner, *N. texanus*, but the two can be separated according to anal fin pigmentation: Melanophores outline all anal fin rays on the coastal shiner, but only the last four rays on the weed shiner.

ADULT SIZE: 1.6 to 2.6 in (40 to 65 mm)

DISTRIBUTION: The coastal shiner occurs in Atlantic and Gulf slope drainages from the Cape Fear River south to Lake Okeechobee and west to the Jordan River system in Mississippi. In Alabama the range is limited to scattered collections from eastern and western tributaries to Mobile Bay, the Mobile Delta, the lower Alabama River, and the Perdido, Conecuh, and Chattahoochee systems.

HABITAT AND BIOLOGY: Typically an inhabitant of slow backwaters, lakes, and impoundments near coastal areas, *N. petersoni* is also found in coastal tidewater areas and in small blackwater inland streams draining to coastal bays. Spawning occurs from April to June in Alabama. Davis and Louder (1971) report spawning from May to late August and a life span of more than three years in North Carolina. The coastal shiner is a midwater feeder, consuming drifting immature and adult insects, plant detritus, algae, and crustaceans.

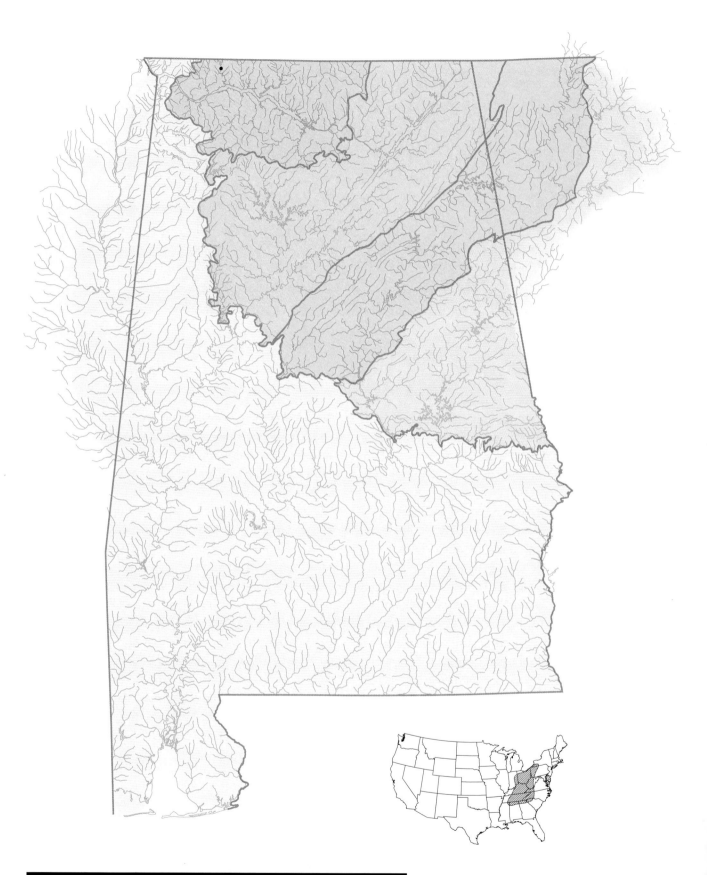

Notropis photogenis
(Cope, 1865)

ETYMOLOGY:

Notropis—keeled back
photogenis—light cheek

Holston River, North Fork, Washington County, Virginia, 6 June 1984, 2.8 in (70 mm) SL male. Photograph courtesy of Noel M. Burkhead.

CHARACTERISTICS: *Notropis photogenis* has a terete, slightly compressed body with a medium-sized head and a pointed snout. Its oblique mouth extends rearward almost to the front of the eye. A broad, black lateral band extends from the gill opening to the caudal fin and expands into a horizontal oval spot at the caudal fin base. The lateral band is more intense on the caudal peduncle and fades toward the head; in live individuals this band is obscured by a bright silvery band. The lateral line scales are bounded above and below by pigment. Life colors of this species are generally olive on the back and silvery on the sides, the scales on the back being well outlined with pigment. Similar species include the rosyface shiner, *N. rubellus*, and the emerald shiner, *N. atherinoides*, but both of these have a smooth dorsal edge to the anterior portion of the lateral band, whereas in *N. photogenis* this edge is bluntly saw-toothed. Additionally, a pair of large, dark crescents is present between the nostrils in *N. photogenis*. See Cope (1865b) for original description.

ADULT SIZE: 2.4 to 3.9 in (60 to 100 mm)

DISTRIBUTION: A predominantly northern species, the silver shiner is found throughout the upper Ohio basin south to the Tennessee River drainage and is also found in western tributaries to Lake Erie. This is a rare occupant of Alabama waters. The last known specimens were collected from Shoal Creek at Goose Shoal, Lauderdale County, in 1983 and from the Tennessee section of the Elk River near Alabama (Feeman, 1987).

HABITAT AND BIOLOGY: *Notropis photogenis* can be found in large creeks and small rivers with clear water flowing over rock substrates. Trautman (1981) states that these shiners are most abundant in streams with deep, swift riffles and eddies and in flowing pools immediately below such riffles and that they typically avoid muddy bottoms and rooted aquatic vegetation. Etnier and Starnes (1993) report tuberculate individuals from late April through May in Tennessee. Diet likely consists of stream drift made up of terrestrial and aquatic insects. We have not collected this species often enough to learn much about its life history in Alabama.

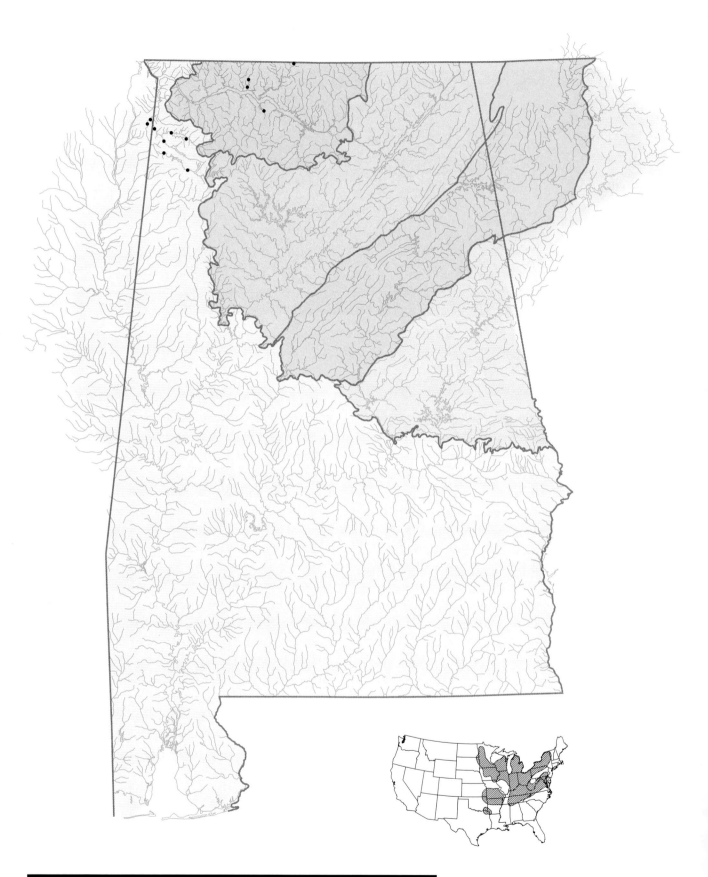

ROSYFACE SHINER   *Notropis rubellus*   **12 STATIONS**

Notropis rubellus
(Agassiz, 1850)

ETYMOLOGY:

Notropis—keeled back
rubellus—reddish

Bear Creek, Franklin County, 22 June 1995, 2.1 in (53 mm) SL female, GSA 4650

CHARACTERISTICS: The rosyface shiner is a slender, terete species with a pointed snout. The dusky lateral band extends from the gill opening to the caudal fin, expanding to form a distinct, quadrate caudal spot. The anterior lateral line scales are bounded above and below by weakly developed pigment spots. The lips are dark, but the chin is typically unpigmented. In life, *Notropis rubellus* has an olive back with silvery sides and a narrow emerald stripe similar to that of the emerald shiner, *N. atherinoides*, which the rosyface shiner also resembles in body form. The two can be distinguished by the anal fin margin, which is straight in *rubellus* and concave in *atherinoides*. Breeding male rosyface shiners acquire a red flush throughout the body and on the snout, lips, chin, and top of the head.

ADULT SIZE: 2.2 to 3 in (55 to 75 mm)

DISTRIBUTION: Two distinct populations are known for the rosyface shiner. One population is found throughout the upper Mississippi basin from the Tennessee River drainage north to the Great Lakes in Canada. The other population is found in the Ozark region in Arkansas and Missouri. In Alabama this species is uncommon and is confined to tributaries of the Tennessee River, including the Bear Creek system, a few streams in Lauderdale and Lawrence counties, and the Elk River system.

HABITAT AND BIOLOGY: *Notropis rubellus* inhabits small streams to relatively large rivers, preferring swift, clean waters flowing over hard substrates of bedrock, gravel, and cobble near riffles or in pools. It commonly occurs in large schools. Spawning is over gravel nests of other species from April to July, with peak activity in May and June. Pfeiffer (1955) reports spawning over gravel depressions and a life span of more than three years in New York. A sight feeder, this minnow consumes algae, immature stoneflies, mayflies, dipterans, and plant material.

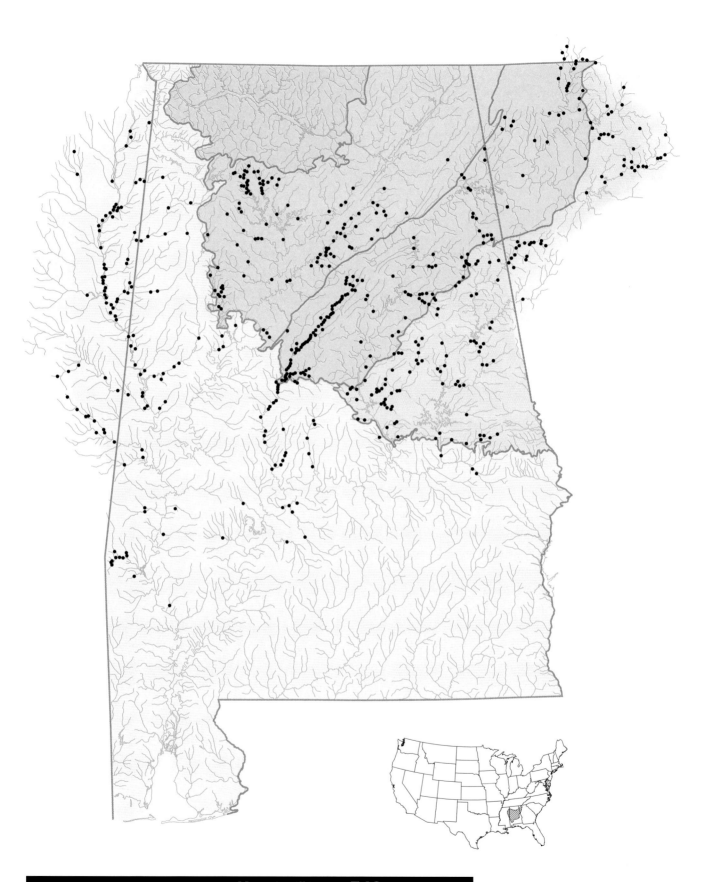

SILVERSTRIPE SHINER   *Notropis stilbius*   **543 STATIONS**

Notropis stilbius
(Jordan, 1877)

ETYMOLOGY:

Notropis—keeled back
stilbius—shining

Hatchet Creek, Coosa County, 24 June 1992, 2.0 in (50 mm) SL male, GSA 4320

CHARACTERISTICS: The silverstripe shiner has a terete, compressed body and a large head. Its pointed snout has a large, oblique mouth that extends rearward past the front of the eye. The lips are heavily pigmented. A broad silvery-black lateral band extends from the gill opening to the caudal fin and expands into a horizontal oval spot at the caudal fin base. The lateral band is more intense posteriorly and fades toward the head. Lateral line scales are bounded above and below by pigment. Life colors are generally olive on the back, becoming silvery on the sides. The scales on the back are well outlined with pigment. *Notropis stilbius* is grouped in the subgenus *Notropis* and resembles both the emerald shiner, *N. atherinoides*, and the silverside shiner, *N. candidus*. See Jordan (1877a) for original description.

ADULT SIZE: 2 to 3 in (50 to 75 mm)

DISTRIBUTION: This species is endemic to the Mobile basin and is more common above the Fall Line. It also inhabits large tributaries on the Coastal Plain. Specimens have been collected from the lower Bear Creek system in the Tennessee River drainage.

HABITAT AND BIOLOGY: Sometimes common when found, *Notropis stilbius* prefers moderate current in deep runs or eddies below riffles over sand, gravel, cobble, or boulders. Individuals in spawning condition have been found from April to August; peak activity is in May and June. Diet is likely stream drift consisting of plant material and adult and immature insects. Surprisingly, little else is known about this common forage species.

REMARKS: The type locality of the silverstripe shiner is tributaries to the Etowah, Oostanaula, and Coosa rivers near Rome, Floyd County, Georgia.

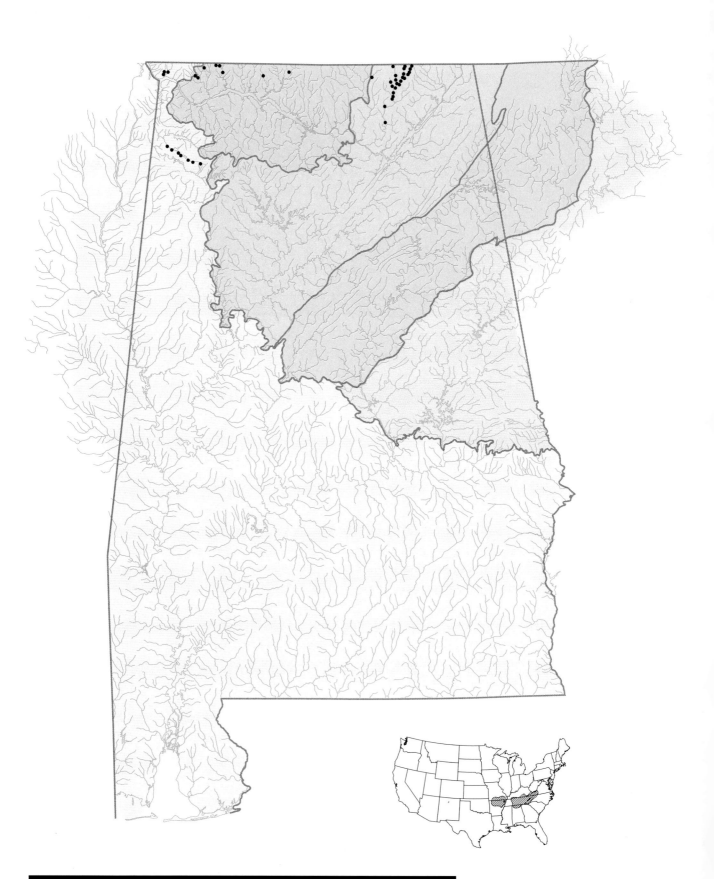

TELESCOPE SHINER   *Notropis telescopus*   **42 STATIONS**

Notropis telescopus

(Cope, 1868)

ETYMOLOGY:

Notropis—keeled back
telescopus—farsighted,
referring to this species'
large eyes

Sour Branch, Lauderdale County, 24 February 1993, 2.2 in (57 mm) SL female, GSA 4375

CHARACTERISTICS: The telescope shiner has a somewhat compressed body with large eyes that are longer than the short, pointed snout (though smaller than in the popeye shiner, *Notropis ariommus*). Viewed from above, the back has a dark predorsal stripe and two or three crooked, parallel stripes resulting from intense scale pigment. The lateral band extends along the entire body, becoming more intense on the peduncle and more diffuse toward the head. Lateral line scales are delicately outlined with melanophores above and below, while the venter is white. As mentioned above, *N. telescopus* is similar to *N. ariommus*, which has a larger eye, nine anal rays modally, no stripes on the back, and a weak predorsal stripe. See Günther (1868) for description.

ADULT SIZE: 2 to 4.1 in (50 to 105 mm)

DISTRIBUTION: Two *Notropis telescopus* populations are known. One occurs throughout the Tennessee and Cumberland river drainages of Tennessee, Kentucky, Alabama, and Virginia. The other inhabits the White and Black river systems in Arkansas and Missouri. This species was common in our samples from the Bear Creek, Paint Rock River, and Shoal Creek systems.

HABITAT AND BIOLOGY: The telescope shiner prefers small to medium-sized upland streams, favoring flowing water near riffles over gravel or rock substrates. Its biology in Alabama is unknown. Etnier and Starnes (1993) report spawning from mid-April through mid-June in Tennessee and a diet of about two-thirds terrestrial insects and one-third aquatic insect larvae (such as mayflies, stoneflies, and caddisflies).

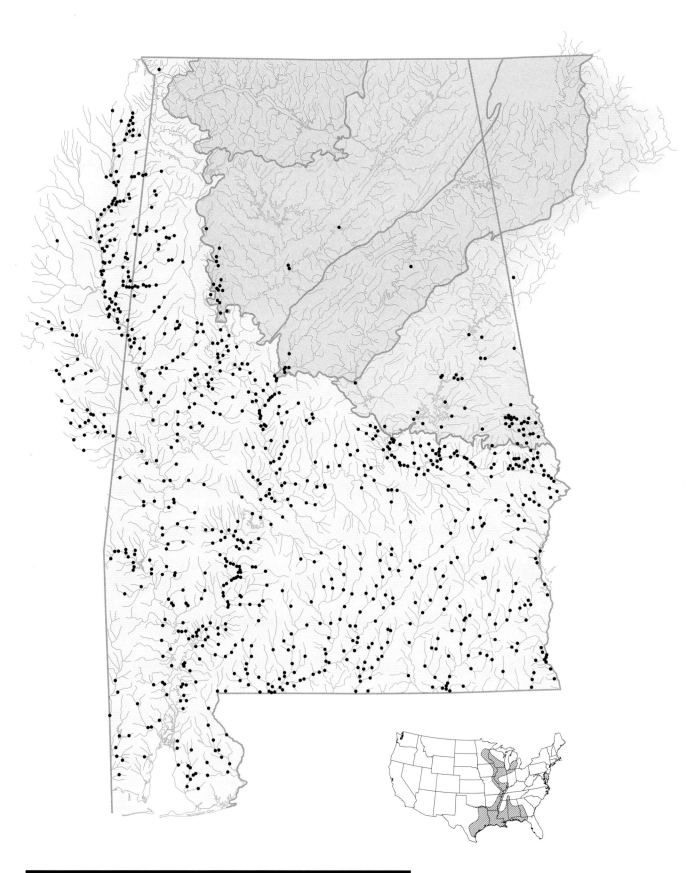

WEED SHINER *Notropis texanus* **892 STATIONS**

Notropis texanus

(Girard, 1856)

ETYMOLOGY:

Notropis—keeled back

texanus—pertaining to

Texas, the type locality

Hillabee Creek, Tallapoosa County, 24 June 1992, 2.1 in (54 mm) SL male, GSA 4321

CHARACTERISTICS: The weed shiner is a small min-now with a fairly compressed body, a blunt, overhanging snout, and a terminal mouth. The black lateral band is well developed, extending from around the snout to the tail. The tail spot is small, either square or rounded, and narrower than the lateral band. Scales below the lateral band are slightly pigmented, and the last four rays of the anal fin are delicately outlined with melanophores. The back is olive yellow in life, with an overall body color of light brown to olive yellow. *Notropis texanus* is easily confused with the similar coastal shiner, **N. petersoni**, but the latter can be distinguished by its anal rays, all of which are outlined with melanophores. Breeding males have reddish orange on the back, above and below the tail spot, and on the back edges of the dorsal and caudal fins (Swift, 1970), while the back third of the anal fin is orange on specimens from Florida and lower Coastal Plain streams in Alabama.

ADULT SIZE: 1.4 to 2.2 in (35 to 55 mm)

DISTRIBUTION: The weed shiner is found in Gulf slope drainages from the Suwanee River west to the Nueces River in Texas and north throughout the Mississippi basin to Minnesota. This species commonly inhabits the Alabama Coastal Plain, and it occurs in a few localities above the Fall Line. Our collection of weed shiners from Second Creek in Lauderdale County is the first reported Tennessee drainage record of this species in Alabama. The relative locations of this and another collection from Robinson Creek further down-stream in Tennessee (Etnier and Starnes, 1993) suggest that **N. texanus** has probably entered the Tennessee drainage via the Tennessee-Tombigbee Waterway.

HABITAT AND BIOLOGY: *Notropis texanus* is com-monly found in small to large, low-gradient streams with sand substrates. Often associated, as its name implies, with emergent vegetation in shoal areas, it can be quite abundant when found. Gravid females have been collected from March through June, with most spawning in April and May. Bresnick and Heins (1977) report that most individuals live for more than two years, with few surviving beyond three years. This con-trasts with the sand-dwelling cherryfin and longnose shiners, **Lythrurus roseipinnis** and **N. longirostris**, which live for little more than one year. Stream drift made up of insects and plant material composes the diet.

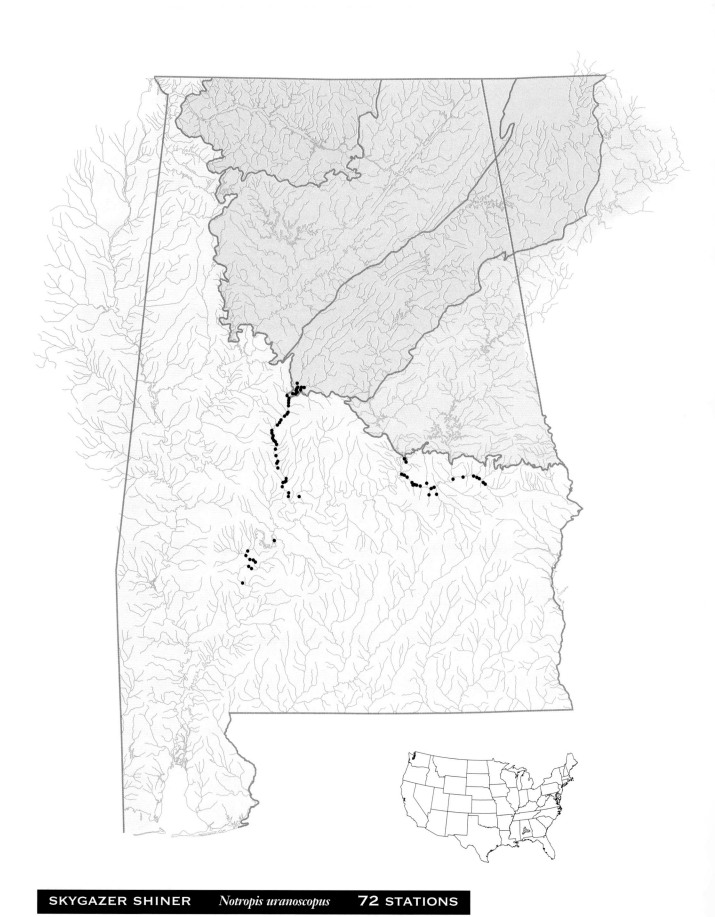

SKYGAZER SHINER   *Notropis uranoscopus*   **72 STATIONS**

Notropis uranoscopus

Suttkus, 1959

ETYMOLOGY:

Notropis—keeled back;
uranoscopus—sky watcher,
referring to this species'
upturned eyes

Tallapoosa River, Elmore County, 19 October 1992, 1.9 in (49 mm) SL male, GSA 4334

CHARACTERISTICS: This slender species has a long, pointed snout, a flattened head, and elliptical eyes shifted dorsally to the top of the head. A characteristic wedge-shaped, small spot marks the base of the caudal fin, and two dark crescents are between the nostrils. The lateral band is more heavily pigmented on the caudal peduncle and becomes diffuse and dusky anteriorly; each lateral line pore has paired spots. The species is straw colored along the back and upper sides, becoming silvery and white on the venter. Fins are colorless, and no vivid breeding colors develop. *Notropis uranoscopus* belongs to a closely related group that includes the palezone shiner, *N. albizonatus*; swallowtail shiner, *N. procne*; and chihuahua shiner, *N. chihuahua* (Warren et al., 1994).

ADULT SIZE: 1.8 to 2.2 in (45 to 55 mm)

DISTRIBUTION: *Notropis uranoscopus* is endemic to the Mobile River basin. It is found below the Fall Line in the Cahaba River, lower Alabama River, lower Tallapoosa River, and Uphapee Creek systems. A new record not depicted on the distribution map was recently collected in the Coosa River above the Fall Line near Wetumpka.

HABITAT AND BIOLOGY: This species is found along sand and gravel shoals in large rivers and streams having moderate to fast current. Indeed, it appears to require this habitat for its survival. Individuals are often encountered in moderate current over gravel shoals from 1 to 3 feet deep; they seem to avoid deeper habitats and areas of soft bottom. The skygazer shiner is one of the dominant cyprinids in the Tallapoosa River below the Fall Line. Spawning occurs from April to June.

REMARKS: The type locality of *N. uranoscopus* is the Cahaba River near Centreville, Bibb County, Alabama.

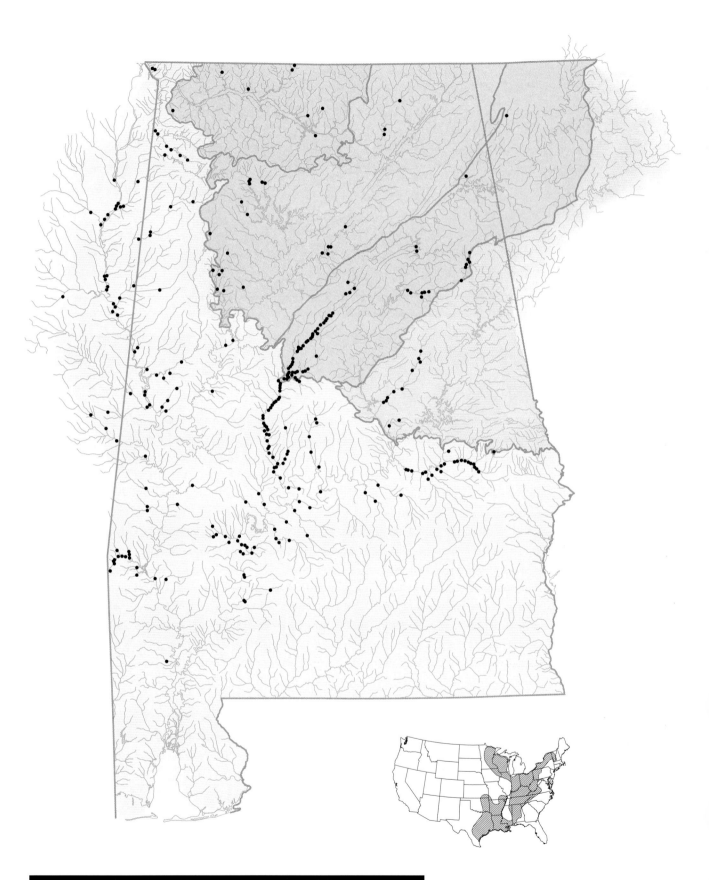

MIMIC SHINER   *Notropis volucellus*   **290 STATIONS**

Notropis volucellus

(Cope, 1865)

ETYMOLOGY:

Notropis—keeled back

volucellus—winged or swift

Little Cahaba River, Bibb County, 24 May 1994, 1.8 in (45 mm) SL female, GSA 4759

CHARACTERISTICS: *Notropis volucellus* is a slender species with a compressed body and a broad, rounded snout extending slightly beyond the mouth. At the front of the narrow lateral line, the pores look as though they have been stitched together by dark melanophores above and below each pore. On the peduncle, the lateral line is well developed, expanding ventrally into a lobed tail spot extending onto the caudal fin rays. The distinct predorsal stripe is heavily pigmented. Scales on the back are well outlined with pigment, and the caudal peduncle scales are more heavily pigmented posteriorly than anteriorly. Breeding colors do not develop. The mimic shiner is morphologically variable throughout its range. In the Tennessee River drainage, it occurs sympatrically with the channel shiner, *N. wickliffi*, which is distinguished by an indistinct predorsal stripe and uniformly pigmented caudal peduncle scales. An undescribed Mobile basin form of *N. volucellus* differs from the form described in this account by having different body proportions and an interrupted sensory canal under the eye (Mayden and Kuhajda, 1989). The Mobile basin form is pictured above. See Cope (1865b) for original description.

ADULT SIZE: 1.6 to 3 in (40 to 75 mm)

DISTRIBUTION: *Notropis volucellus* as currently recognized is found throughout Gulf slope drainages from the Guadalupe River east to the Mobile basin and north to the Red River of North in Canada. The undescribed "Mobile mimic shiner" is sympatric with **N. cahabae** in the Cahaba River (Mayden and Kuhajda, 1989).

HABITAT AND BIOLOGY: Schools of mimic shiners are most frequently encountered around concentrations of river weed over sand or sand and gravel substrates in large rivers and streams. The spawning season extends from May to August throughout Alabama, and females running with eggs occur from late April to July in the Cahaba River. Etnier and Starnes (1993), relying on their observations of breeding tubercle development, indicate an extended spawning season—from May through October—for Tennessee populations. Moyle (1973) reports that the diet of mimic shiners inhabiting a Minnesota lake consists of dipteran pupae, detritus, crustaceans, mayflies, and beetles.

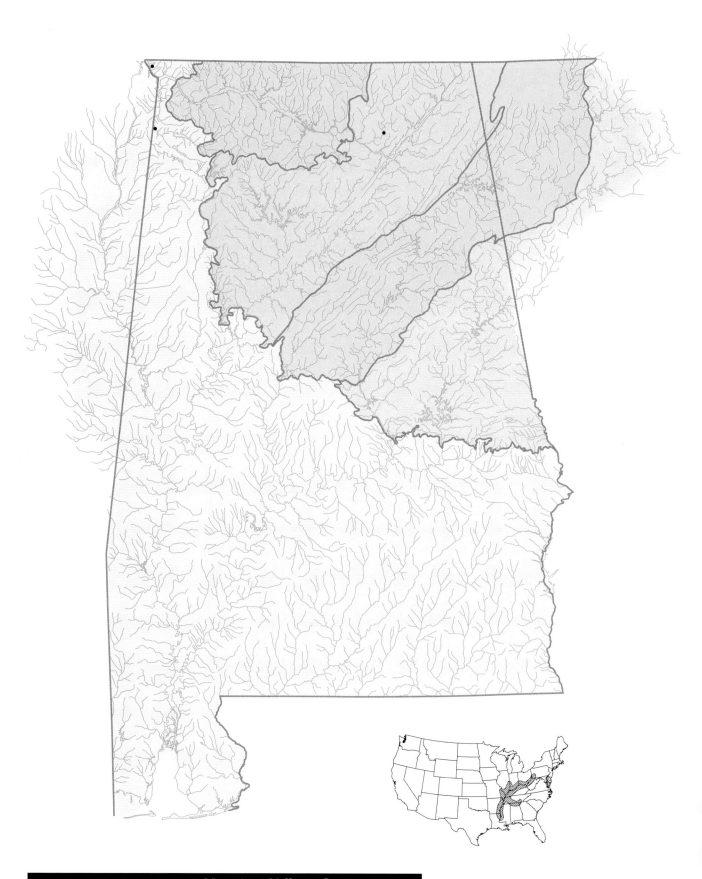

CHANNEL SHINER *Notropis wickliffi* **3 STATIONS**

Notropis wickliffi

Trautman, 1981

ETYMOLOGY:

Notropis—keeled back

wickliffi—in honor of

Edward L. Wickliff, a col-

league of Milton Trautman,

who described the species

Cedar Creek, Franklin County, 19 October 1993, 1.7 in (44 mm) SL male, GSA 4573

CHARACTERISTICS: The channel shiner, which resembles the mimic and Cahaba shiners, has a slender body form and a broad, rounded snout extending slightly beyond the mouth. At the front of the narrow lateral line, the pores look as though they have been stitched together by the dark melanophores located above and below each pore. On the peduncle, the lateral line is well developed, expanding ventrally into a lobed tail spot that extends onto the rays of the caudal fin. The predorsal stripe is nonexistent or only lightly pigmented. Scales on the back and caudal peduncle are well outlined with pigment. Breeding colors do not develop. *Notropis wickliffi* is similar to and occurs sympatrically with the mimic shiner, *N. volucellus*, in the Tennessee River; pigmentation of the scales on the dorsal peduncle distinguishes the two. In *N. wickliffi* these scales are uniformly pigmented, whereas in *N. volucellus* they are more heavily pigmented posteriorly than anteriorly (Mayden and Kuhajda, 1989). Mayden and Kuhajda (1989) assign *N. cahabae* as the closest relative to *N. wickliffi*. Trautman (1981) indicates that *N. wickliffi*, formerly a subspecies of *N. volucellus*, deserves species status. We concur with

Trautman, since Alabama populations of *wickliffi* are distinguishable from *volucellus*, and we follow his recommendation as recognized in Robins et al. (1991).

ADULT SIZE: 1.6 to 3 in (40 to 75 mm)

DISTRIBUTION: *Notropis wickliffi* is found throughout the lower Mississippi basin in main river channels. Our limited collections come from the main channels of the Tennessee River, Bear Creek, and the Paint Rock River. Additional sampling will likely reveal a greater range in Alabama.

HABITAT AND BIOLOGY: The channel shiner almost exclusively inhabits large rivers and streams, preferring backwaters and pools with little current. Trautman (1981) reports this species as also inhabiting swift currents below dams and being somewhat tolerant of turbid conditions. Little is known about its biology, but spawning is presumed to occur from late May to August in Alabama, as indicated for Tennessee populations (Etnier and Starnes, 1993).

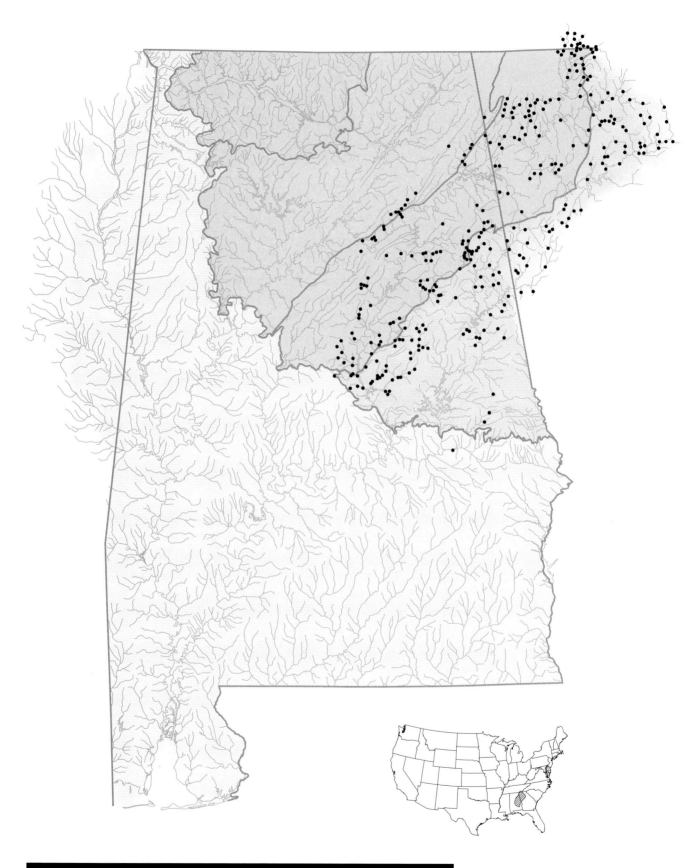

COOSA SHINER *Notropis xaenocephalus* **321 STATIONS**

Notropis xaenocephalus
(Jordan, 1877)

ETYMOLOGY:
Notropis—keeled back
xaenocephalus—scratch
head, referring to the head
tuberculation on males of
the species

Wash Creek, Chilton County, 21 April 1993, 2.0 in (50 mm) SL female, GSA 4437

CHARACTERISTICS: *Notropis xaenocephalus* has a compressed body form with a rounded snout slightly overhanging the mouth. The eye is large, generally exceeding snout length. A distinct lateral band extends from the snout to the tail, thinning along the caudal peduncle and expanding near the tail into a distinct, quadrate caudal spot. The clean, yellowish stripe above the lateral band extends from the gill opening to the tail, while the scales along the back are well pigmented. Throughout its range, the Coosa shiner often occurs with and may be confused with **N. chrosomus**, **N. asperifrons**, **Cyprinella caerulea**, and **Lythrurus lirus** (the rainbow, burrhead, blue, and mountain shiners, respectively). The Coosa shiner is placed in the **N. texanus** species group (Swift, 1970; Mayden, 1989). See Jordan (1877a) for original description.

ADULT SIZE: 1.6 to 2.6 in (40 to 65 mm)

DISTRIBUTION: This species is endemic to the Coosa and Tallapoosa river systems above the Fall Line and is known from the upper Chattahoochee River drainage in Georgia.

HABITAT AND BIOLOGY: This shiner prefers cool, clear upland streams flowing over bedrock and gravel occasionally mixed with sand—habitats typical of the Piedmont and the Alabama Valley and Ridge. Diet is stream drift of plant material and adult and immature insects. Ripe individuals have been collected from May to July. The field notes of R. D. Suttkus report ripe individuals from a tributary to Choccolocco Creek in April. Swift (1970) indicates a spawning season of June to July.

REMARKS: The type locality of this species is tributaries to the Etowah River near Rome, Floyd County, Georgia.

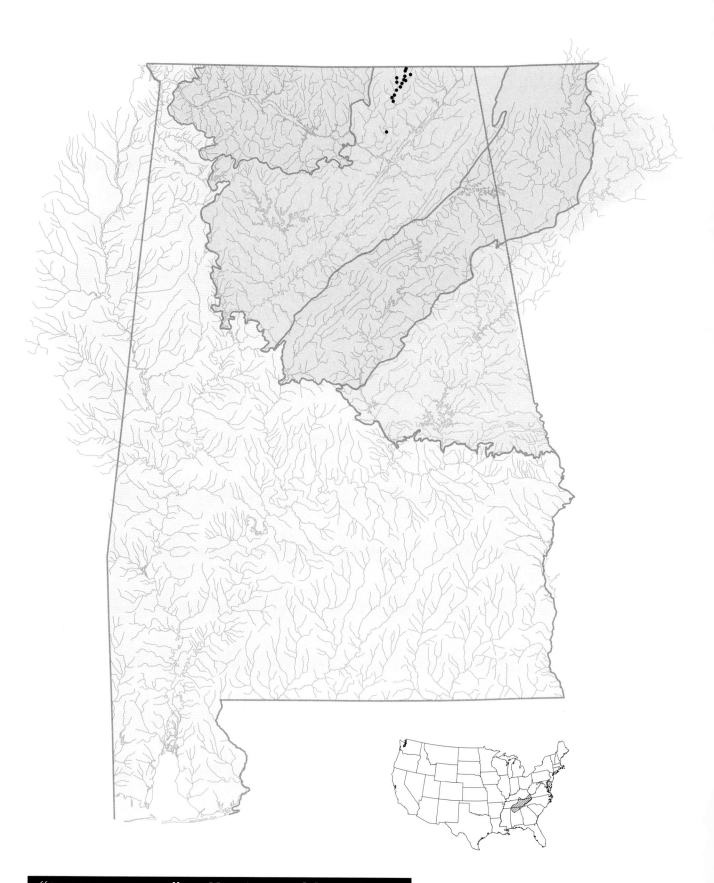

"SAWFIN SHINER"   *Notropis* sp.   **14 STATIONS**

Notropis sp.

ETYMOLOGY:

Notropis—keeled back

Larkin Fork, Jackson County, 18 May 1993, 1.9 in (49 mm) SL male, GSA 4474

CHARACTERISTICS: The undescribed "sawfin shiner" is a slender species with a blunt, rounded snout. The lateral band is weakly developed throughout, expanding slightly near the caudal fin to form a small, indistinct spot. A russet spot on the anterior half of the dorsal, anal, pectoral, and pelvic fins is characteristic of males. The upper and lower parts of the caudal fin base are lightly flushed with orange, and the scales along the back are well pigmented. Life colors are straw yellow and silver. The "sawfin shiner" is sometimes confused with the mimic shiner, *Notropis volucellus*, but examining the dorsal fin rays will prevent this mistake: In the "sawfin shiner," only the first four or five dorsal fin rays are outlined with melanophores, whereas in the mimic shiner, all of the rays are outlined with pigment. The "sawfin shiner" is aligned with the *N. volucellus* species group (Mayden, 1989) and most resembles *N. spectrunculus* and *N. ozarcanus*, species not known from Alabama.

ADULT SIZE: 1.4 to 2.6 in (35 to 65 mm)

DISTRIBUTION: This undescribed species is commonly found from the Tennessee River drainage in Alabama north to the Cumberland River drainage in Kentucky. Our collections were limited to the Paint Rock River system in Jackson County.

HABITAT AND BIOLOGY: The "sawfin shiner" occurs in clear, high-gradient streams flowing over rubble, cobble, gravel, bedrock, or clean sand. Individuals are most often found in flowing and eroded pools at the base of riffles or downstream of snags. Our collections indicate that spawning is probably from May through early July. Etnier and Starnes (1993) report tuberculate males from mid-May through July in Tennessee. Otherwise, little is known about the biology of this species.

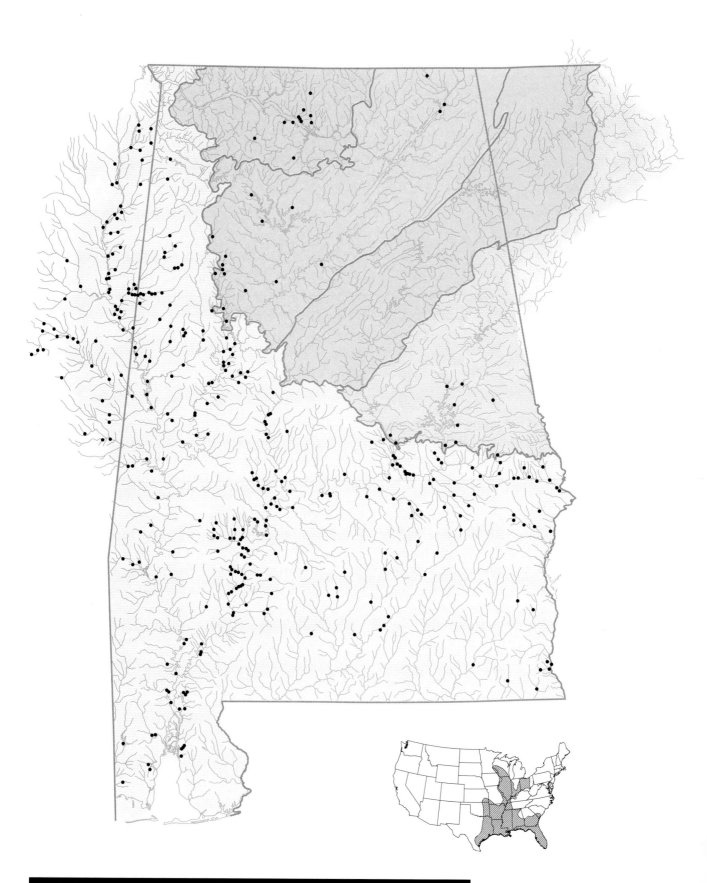

Opsopoeodus emiliae

Hay, 1881

ETYMOLOGY:

Opsopoeodus—broadly interpreted, "teeth for dainty feeding"

emiliae—in honor of Emily Hay, wife of Oliver P. Hay, describer of the species

Alabama River, Monroe County, 24 March 1993, 2.4 in (60 mm) SL male, GSA 4384

CHARACTERISTICS: This species has a moderately deep, compressed body, a small head, a blunt snout, and a small, almost vertical mouth. Body scales are heavily outlined with melanophores, giving them a diamond-shaped appearance. A slender, dark lateral band extends from the gill opening to the caudal fin base. The dorsal fin of breeding individuals is heavily pigmented except for a clear or white "window" in the middle. The caudal, anal, and paired fin membranes are pigmented and may be faintly shaded with pink or red. The tips of the paired fins and anal fin are usually white.

ADULT SIZE: 1.6 to 2.6 in (40 to 65 mm)

DISTRIBUTION: Gilbert and Bailey (1972) recognize two subspecies of pugnose minnows. *Opsopoeodus e. emiliae* occurs from Texas east to South Carolina and north through the Mississippi basin to Wisconsin, while *O. e. peninsularis* occurs from the St. Johns drainage south to the Okeechobee River in Florida. The pugnose minnow is widespread in the Mobile basin below the Fall Line, somewhat rare in coastal drainages, and only sporadically encountered in the Tennessee River drainage.

HABITAT AND BIOLOGY: *Opsopoeodus emiliae* is most often associated with sluggish, clear, vegetated waters over muddy or silty bottoms—habitats that occur in impoundments and some Coastal Plain streams. It reportedly feeds on midge larvae, microcrustaceans, filamentous algae, water mites, and fish eggs (McLane, 1955), although the position of its mouth suggests that it is a surface feeder. Spawning occurs from May to July and in warm southern waters may extend from late winter to early fall. Using a boat electrofisher, we have collected individuals in "high" spawning condition from aquatic vegetation beds in south Alabama, and the field notes of R. D. Suttkus report *O. emiliae* spawning low in the water column. In contrast, Page and Johnston (1990a) report spawning on the underside of rocks for aquarium-held individuals. Whatever their spawning condition, males apparently attract the attention of females by rapidly fluttering their dorsal fins.

REMARKS: The type locality of the pugnose minnow is Horsehunter Creek, a tributary of the Noxubee River near Macon, Noxubee County, Mississippi.

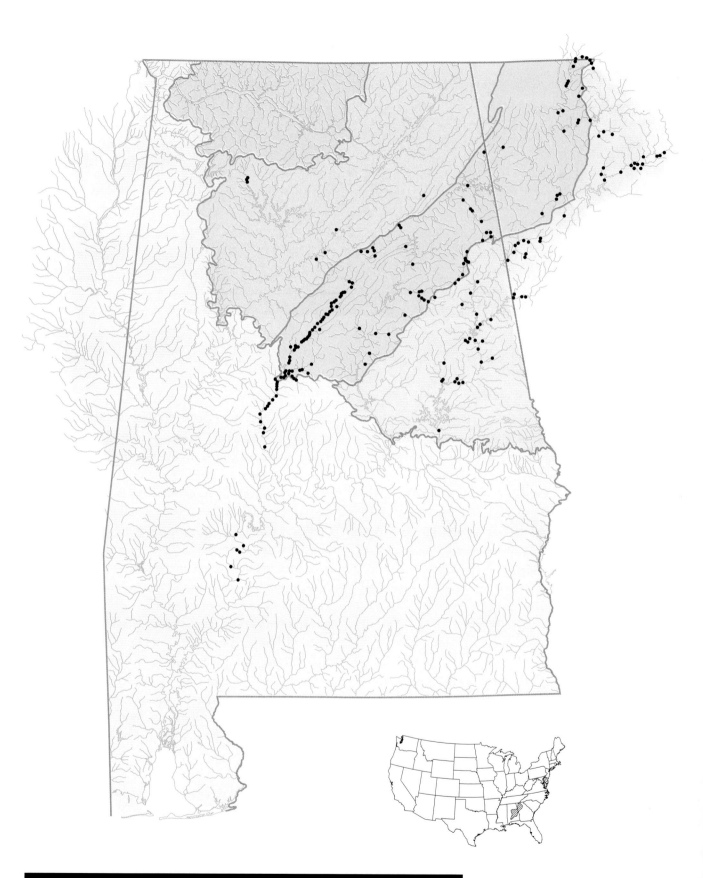

RIFFLE MINNOW   *Phenacobius catostomus*   **204 STATIONS**

Phenacobius catostomus
Jordan, 1877

ETYMOLOGY:

Phenacobius = deceptive life, because this species' bottom-feeding habits suggest that it, like the stoneroller, is herbivorous

catostomus = inferior mouth

Hillabee Creek, Tallapoosa County, 22 April 1993, 2.8 in (70 mm) SL male, GSA 4439

CHARACTERISTICS: The riffle minnow has a cigar-shaped body tapering to a slender peduncle toward the tail. The head is large, the snout blunt and rounded, and the mouth small, with thick lips expanded into corner lobes. The eye is small (about half the snout length), and the wide lateral band extends from the snout to the caudal fin. All the fins have rounded edges and lobes. In life, the snout and paired fins have some orange color. Scales are small all over the body, and life color is olive brown along the back, grading to white on the venter. See Jordan (1877a) for original description.

ADULT SIZE: 2.4 to 3.9 in (60 to 100 mm)

DISTRIBUTION: Although most collections of this Mobile basin endemic are from above the Fall Line, its range extends some distance downstream in the Cahaba River drainage. Another isolated population occurs in the lower Alabama River drainage, where it flows through the rugged Lime Hills physiographic district.

HABITAT AND BIOLOGY: *Phenacobius catostomus* is commonly found in swift riffles and runs of large rivers and tributaries with cobble and gravel bottoms. It often occurs in swift pool runs or deep erosional pools at the base of shallow riffles. The riffle minnow is adapted to life on the stream bottom. Its spindled body form and the placement of its fins are adapted to gathering insect immatures by foraging through the bottom gravel and sediments. While little is known about the reproductive behavior of this species, spawning occurs in gravel riffles and nearby swift, sandy shoals from April to June. Although the riffle minnow is typically considered a clean-water inhabitant, recent surveys in the Cahaba River reveal abundant populations in parts of the river receiving treated domestic wastes and nonpoint runoff of sediments.

REMARKS: The type locality of the riffle minnow is Silver Creek, a tributary of the Etowah River, Floyd County, Georgia.

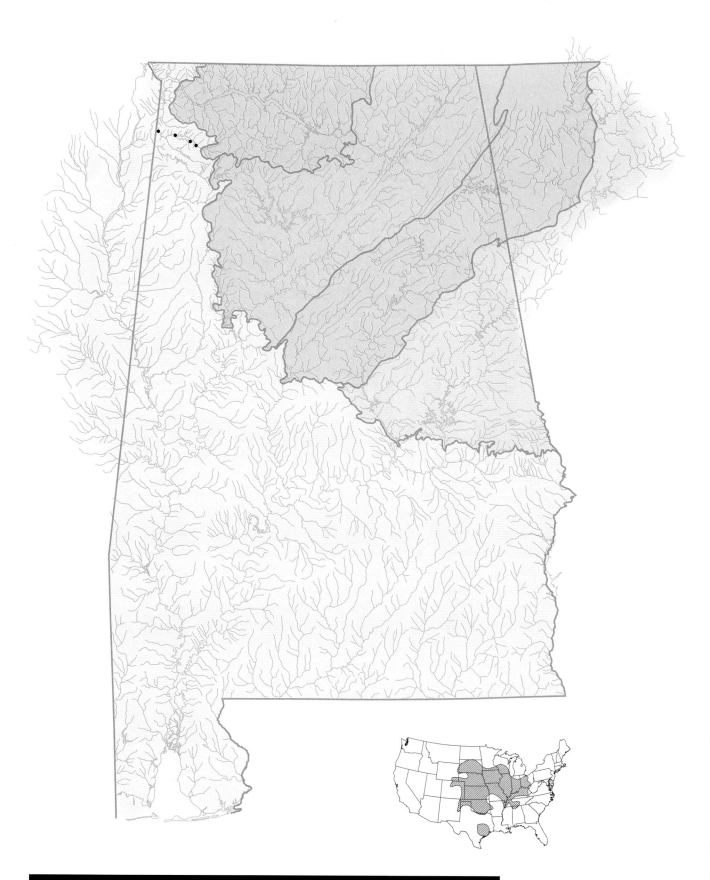

SUCKERMOUTH MINNOW   *Phenacobius mirabilis*   **4 STATIONS**

Phenacobius mirabilis

(Girard, 1856)

ETYMOLOGY:
Phenacobius—deceptive life, because this species' bottom-feeding habits suggest that it, like the stoneroller, is herbivorous
mirabilis—wonderful

Cedar Creek, Franklin County, 10 March 1993, 2.6 in (65 mm) SL female, GSA 4370

CHARACTERISTICS: The suckermouth minnow is a slender species with very small eyes and a horizontal mouth on the bottom of the head. It is similar in body form and shape to the riffle minnow, *Phenacobius catostomus*, differing primarily in having fewer lateral line scales—41 to 50 (59 to 69 for *catostomus*)—and a generally smaller, more robust body. The mouth has prominent lobes, the fins are rounded, and the snout is large and blunt. Body color is dark brown to straw above and silvery below, with a distinct spot at the base of the caudal fin.

ADULT SIZE: 2.6 to 3.5 in (65 to 90 mm)

DISTRIBUTION: *Phenacobius mirabilis* is commonly found throughout the upper Mississippi basin north and west of Alabama, and it occurs sporadically in western Gulf slope drainages. Alabama records are limited to the Bear Creek system, a tributary of the Tennessee River in northwestern Alabama (Wall, 1968), and recent collections are few. The single specimen we obtained while collecting at night in Cedar Creek in 1993 may represent the first record of this species from Alabama in nearly 30 years.

HABITAT AND BIOLOGY: Occurring in a variety of habitats, from small streams to large rivers and also pools, the suckermouth minnow prefers medium-sized streams with extensive riffle areas over gravel shoals. The individual shown above was taken in the middle of a large rubble riffle in swift current. Trautman (1981) reports that the suckermouth minnow in Ohio prefers turbid, moderate-gradient streams rich in organic matter and that it occurs in lower numbers in clear streams, streams of high gradient, and low-gradient, turbid streams. This is a bottom-dwelling species, consuming benthic insects and other invertebrates. Etnier and Starnes (1993) report tuberculate males from May through July in Tennessee, and spawning is presumably in gravel and sand shoals, as with the riffle minnow. Little is known about the biology of the suckermouth minnow in Alabama, because the periphery of its range captures only a small part of the Tennessee River drainage in the state.

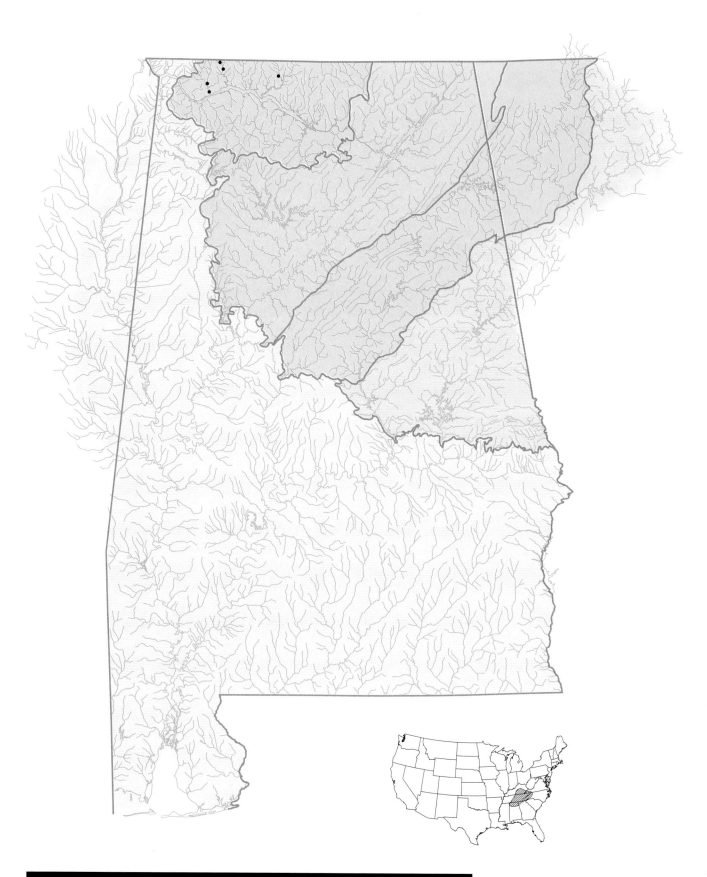

Phenacobius uranops

Cope, 1867

ETYMOLOGY:

Phenacobius—deceptive life, because this species' bottom-feeding habits suggest that it, like the stoneroller, is herbivorous

uranops—sky-gazing

Shoal Creek, Lauderdale County, 15 July 1992, 3.3 in (84 mm) SL male, GSA 4277

CHARACTERISTICS: The stargazing minnow's body is more slender and fusiform than those of the riffle and suckermouth minnows, *Phenacobius catostomus* and *P. mirabilis*. Its snout is very long and blunt, extending well past the upper lip. The fins are generally rounded, and a distinct lateral band extends from the snout to the caudal fin. The eyes are somewhat elliptical and rotated toward the top of the head. Body color is dark olive brown along the back and silvery below.

ADULT SIZE: 2.4 to 3.9 in (60 to 100 mm)

DISTRIBUTION: The stargazing minnow is found in the Green, Cumberland, and Tennessee river drainages. It is uncommon in Alabama, known from only a few localities in the Cypress Creek, Shoal Creek, and Elk River systems in the Tennessee River drainage. We have collected this species only from Shoal Creek in 1992.

HABITAT AND BIOLOGY: *Phenacobius uranops* prefers riffles and riffle-run habitats of clear, medium-sized streams and small rivers flowing over rubble and gravel. The individuals collected in 1992 in lower Shoal Creek were taken at the downstream end of large riffles and shoals where erosional pools had formed. The streamline

chub, *Erimystax dissimilis*, was taken syntopically in the same net haul with *P. uranops*. A bottom dweller, *P. uranops* consumes midges, immature caddisflies, and detritus by gleaning them from the substrate with its suckerlike lips (Jenkins and Burkhead, 1993). Jenkins and Burkhead also indicate that the spawning season in Virginia is from late April to June, and spawning in the streams of north Alabama probably occurs at the same time.

Shoal Creek at Goose Shoal, Lauderdale County

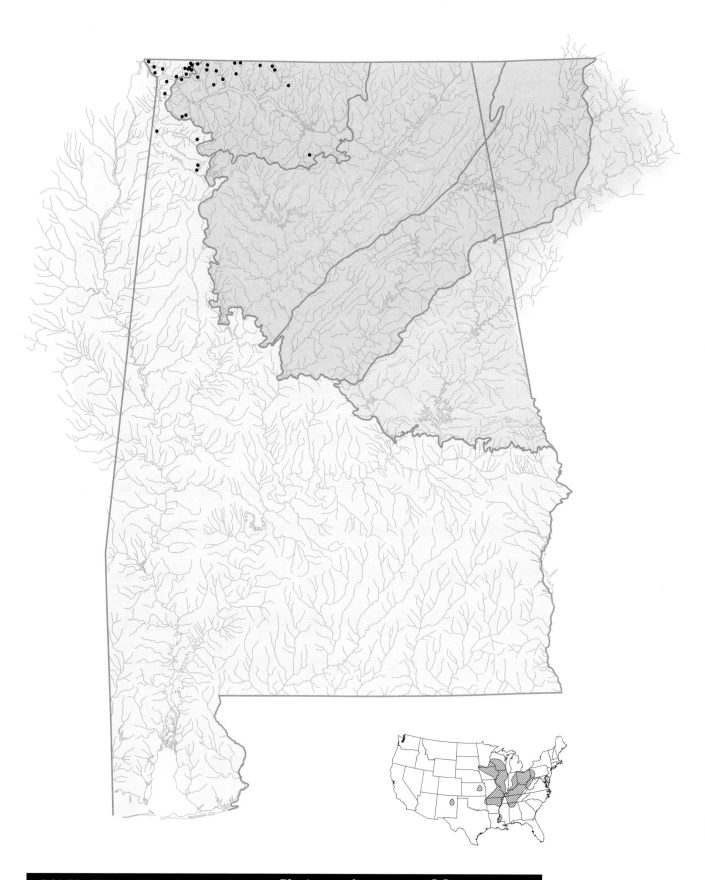

SOUTHERN REDBELLY DACE   *Phoxinus erythrogaster*   36 STATIONS

Phoxinus erythrogaster

(Rafinesque, 1820)

ETYMOLOGY:

Phoxinus—tapering, referring to this species' body shape *erythrogaster*—red belly

Lindsey Creek, Lauderdale County, 16 April 1993, 2.1 in (54 mm) SL male, GSA 4431

CHARACTERISTICS: The southern redbelly dace is one of Alabama's most beautiful minnows. The body is covered with tiny scales that number 70 to 95 in the lateral series and are so small as to be almost invisible to the unaided eye. The snout is pointed. Two lateral bands occur along either side of the body. The lower band is broad and dusky, extending from the eye to the caudal fin. The upper band is smaller, thinning to a series of small spots and extending from the gill opening to the caudal peduncle. A small, black, wedge-shaped spot marks the base of the caudal fin. In life, the back is olive brown with scattered black dots, and breeding males are bright red along the venter from the snout to the base of the tail. The dorsal fin base is red, and all the fins are bright yellow, with the paired fins developing a white base. A silver-white crescent borders the bottom of the eye. Females are similarly colored, with more subdued yellow in the fins and an absence of red along the venter.

ADULT SIZE: 2 to 3 in (50 to 75 mm)

DISTRIBUTION: *Phoxinus erythrogaster* is found in the upper Mississippi basin and Great Lakes drainages from Minnesota and Pennsylvania south to Arkansas and Alabama. In Alabama this species is known only from the Tennessee River drainage in the northwestern part of the state.

HABITAT AND BIOLOGY: The southern redbelly dace prefers cool, upland, spring-fed streams with gravel and hard sand substrates with little silt. It is frequently found in small pools 1 to 3 feet deep and is often associated with aquatic vegetation. The diet consists of plant material, algae, and invertebrates. Spawning occurs in gravel riffles or over the gravel nests of *Campostoma* or *Nocomis*. Reproduction is reported to occur from April through June in Kentucky (Settles and Hoyt, 1978), and individuals in nuptial color have been observed in April and May in the Cypress Creek system, Lauderdale County. Smith (1908) reports that eggs are released near the substrate and settle on the bottom or on nearby objects.

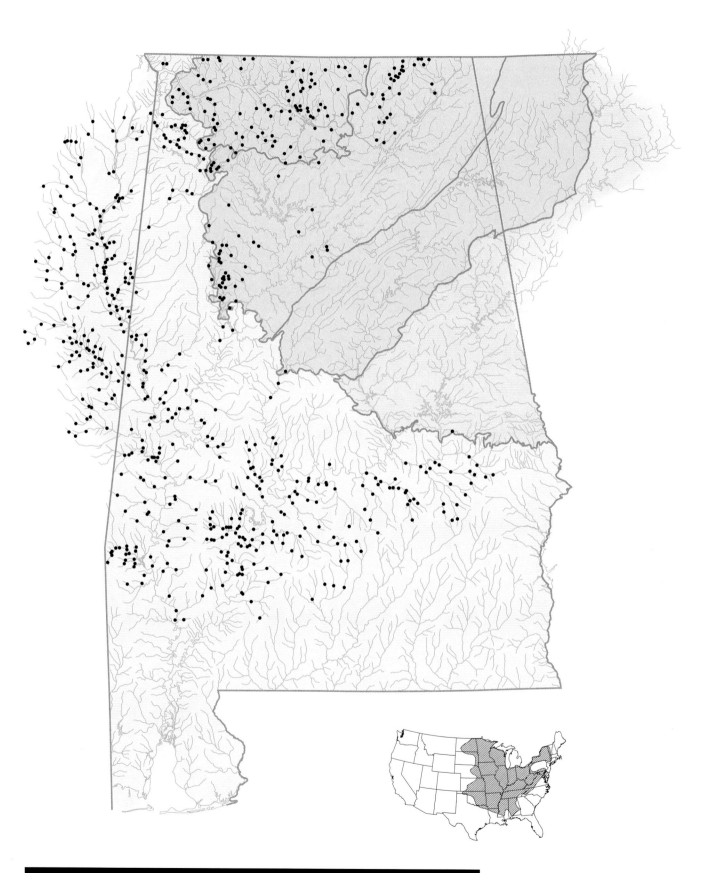

BLUNTNOSE MINNOW　*Pimephales notatus*　**639 STATIONS**

Pimephales notatus

(Rafinesque, 1820)

ETYMOLOGY:

Pimephales—fat head

notatus—marked or spotted

Chilatchee Creek, Dallas County, 14 April 1993, 2.7 in (68 mm) SL male, GSA 4422

CHARACTERISTICS: The bluntnose minnow is a stout species with a blunt, rounded snout and rounded fins. Body form is robust and round or squarish in cross section. The back is broad and flat, with small scales between the head and dorsal fin. A small spot is present at the base of the caudal fin. The dark lateral band extends from the eye to the caudal fin and is about the same width all along its length. Scales are edged with pigment along the entire back and sides to the venter. Breeding males are dark, have around 16 tubercles developed on the snout, and have milky white fins.

ADULT SIZE: 1.6 to 3.5 in (40 to 90 mm)

DISTRIBUTION: *Pimephales notatus* is common in the Mississippi and Mobile basins north to the Great Lakes and in Atlantic slope drainages from Virginia north. Although extremely widespread and often abundant below the Fall Line, this is one of a few widespread freshwater species in Alabama that is absent in streams draining the Fall Line Hills. Only scattered collections have been recorded above the Fall Line in the Black Warrior drainage, and none from the Tallapoosa or Coosa. We have also collected bluntnose minnows from

a few smaller, northern tributaries to the Conecuh River drainage. This species is common throughout the Tennessee River drainage in Alabama.

HABITAT AND BIOLOGY: Occurring in a variety of habitats, from small, upland streams to large rivers and impoundments, the bluntnose minnow generally prefers soft substrates of sand, mud, and silt, sometimes with aquatic vegetation. This bottom-dwelling species feeds on aquatic insects, algae, and crustaceans. The spawning season is long, extending from May to August. Breeding males excavate small cavities under flat, submerged objects. Over time, several females spawn with a single male, placing their eggs on the roof of the cavity. A male typically remains at a nest throughout the spawning season. The spawning behavior of *Pimephales* is the most intricate reported for the family Cyprinidae. Especially noteworthy is the observation that the inverted female apparently releases one egg at a time and rolls it with lateral undulations down her side, eventually pushing the egg with her tail and attaching the egg to the ceiling of the nest (Page and Ceas, 1989). This behavior is unique to *Pimephales*, distinguishing this genus as an advanced group of minnows.

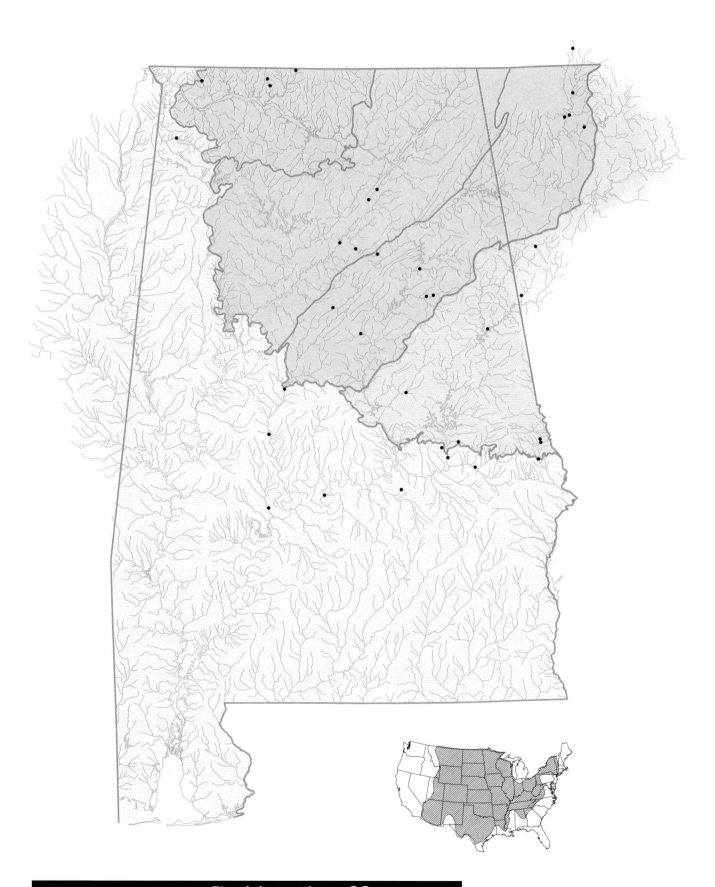

FATHEAD MINNOW *Pimephales promelas* **36 STATIONS**

Pimephales promelas
Rafinesque, 1820

ETYMOLOGY:

Pimephales—fat head
promelas—"forward" and
"black," referring to the
black head of breeding males

Marion Fish Hatchery, Perry County, 22 March 1995, 2.2 in (57 mm) SL male, GSA 4637

CHARACTERISTICS: *Pimephales promelas* is the most popular bait minnow in the country. Along with the golden shiner, *Notemigonus crysoleucas*, this minnow accounts for most of the live bait sold. Body form is stout and flat-sided, with a short, round snout and rounded fins. Like the bluntnose minnow, *P. notatus*, the fathead minnow has a broad, flat back with small scales. The tail spot is faint or often absent on a gray to silvery gray body. The mouth is more oblique and is the distinguishing character for separating this minnow from other *Pimephales* species. During the spawning season, the nape area behind the head of breeding males swells markedly.

ADULT SIZE: 1.6 to 3.9 in (40 to 100 mm)

DISTRIBUTION: Fathead minnows originally occurred throughout the Midwest and upper Mississippi River drainages, west to Utah, north to Great Slave Lake in Canada, and east to Maine. They have also been introduced extensively throughout North America. Because this species is not native to Alabama, all of the collection locations shown on the facing page are assignable either to bait-bucket introductions or to accidental losses from bait farms.

HABITAT AND BIOLOGY: In its native range, this species is reported to prefer pools of small, intermittent prairie streams and to tolerate high temperatures, turbidity, and low dissolved oxygen concentrations. Its diet consists of plant material, algae, microcrustaceans, and sometimes aquatic insects. Like the bluntnose minnow, *P. promelas* deposits eggs on the underside of submerged objects, with spawning occurring from May to August. Not only does the fathead minnow provide the bulk of bait minnows sold in the United States, but its young are also used as organisms for standardized testing in aquatic toxicology. Permits for wastewater discharge require that effluents not be toxic to aquatic life in the streams that will receive the waste. The aquatic toxicity test uses the sensitive young of this species to measure the levels of toxins, and the test has become a national standard followed by all municipalities and industries that use waterways for waste disposal.

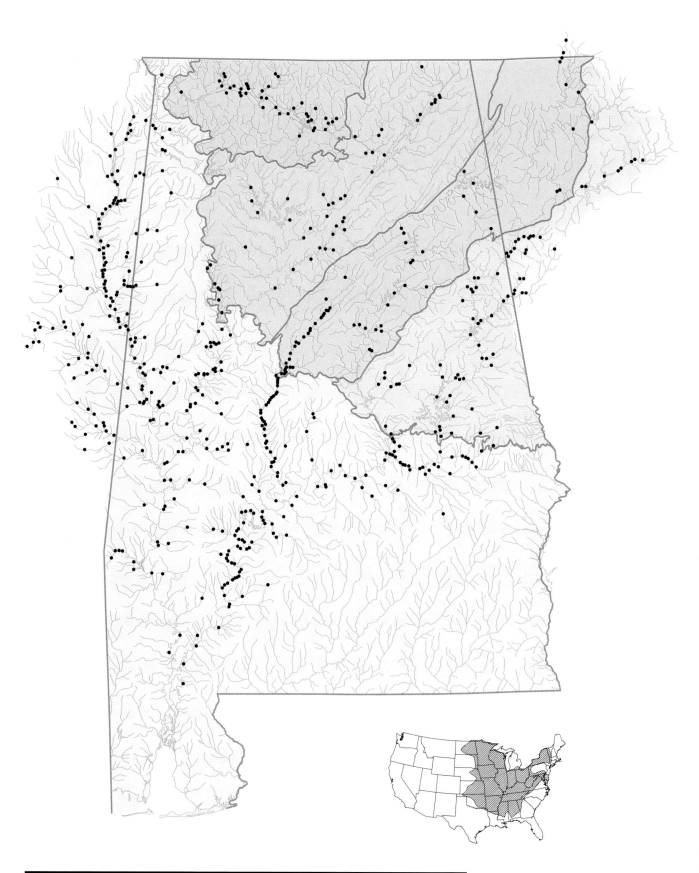

BULLHEAD MINNOW   *Pimephales vigilax*   **587 STATIONS**

Pimephales vigilax

(Baird and Girard, 1853)

ETYMOLOGY:

Pimephales—fat head

vigilax—watchful

Black Warrior River, Tuscaloosa County, 16 June 1992, 3.1 in (79 mm) SL male, GSA 4262

CHARACTERISTICS: *Pimephales vigilax* is a robust species with a blunt, rounded snout and rounded fins. The broad, flat back is covered with small scales. The caudal fin base has a small spot that is separated from the lateral stripe by a pale area, while the dorsal fin has a prominent, dusky blotch near the front. During the spawning season, breeding males darken and develop around nine large breeding tubercles on the snout. The milky white pectoral fins have a black leading edge. In contrast, the pectoral fins on a male bluntnose minnow, *P. notatus*, are milky white with no black leading edge. In life the back is pale yellowish olive, the sides silvery, and the venter white. The snout has a characteristic crescent mark on each side of the upper lip, while the subterminal mouth is somewhat inclined. The lateral line is bent dorsally near its anterior end, which distinguishes this species from the bluntnose minnow.

ADULT SIZE: 1.6 to 3.1 in (40 to 80 mm)

DISTRIBUTION: The bullhead minnow is distributed along the Gulf Coast from the Rio Grande basin in Texas east to the Mobile basin and north throughout the Mississippi basin. It occurs in all Mobile basin rivers and in many tributaries to the Tennessee River drainage.

HABITAT AND BIOLOGY: *Pimephales vigilax* is commonly found in small, slow streams, sluggish backwaters, and large streams and rivers, typically occurring over sand and mud substrates. It apparently tolerates the high turbidity that so often occurs in its riverine habitat. A bottom-living species, it feeds on aquatic insects, algae, and other organisms living in the mud. Spawning is similar to that of other species of *Pimephales* and in Alabama occurs from late spring to midsummer.

Cahaba River, Bibb County

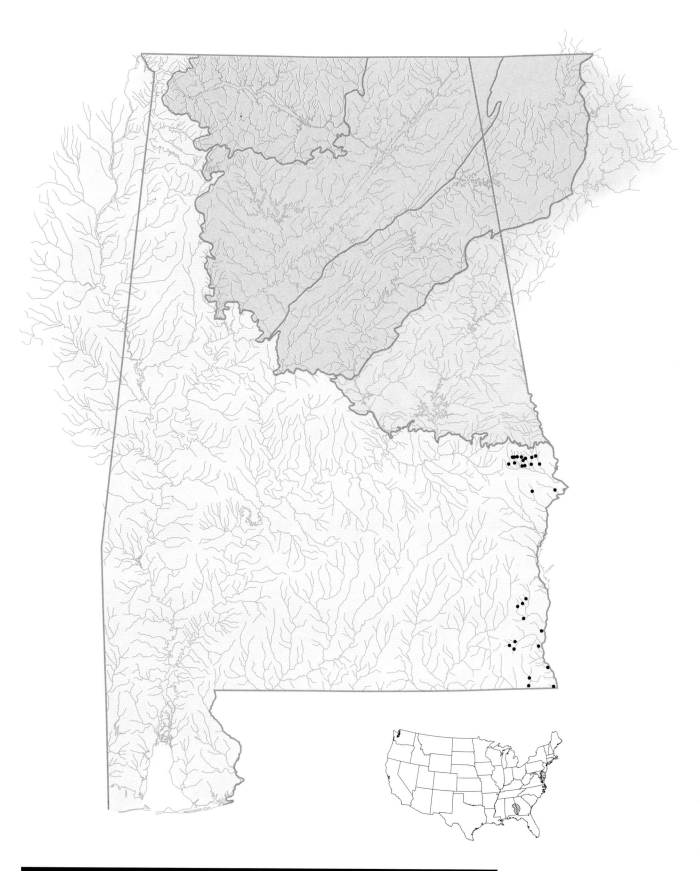

BROADSTRIPE SHINER   *Pteronotropis euryzonus*   **25 STATIONS**

Pteronotropis euryzonus
(Suttkus, 1955)

ETYMOLOGY:

Pteronotropis—winged, keeled back, referring to the enlarged dorsal fin of breeding males *euryzonus*—broad zone, referring to the broad lateral band

Maringo Creek, Russell County, 7 April 1993, 1.8 in (45 mm) SL female, GSA 4413

CHARACTERISTICS: The body of the broadstripe shiner is laterally compressed and deepest at the origin of the dorsal fin. Its head is small and somewhat triangular, with a blunt snout and a small, oblique mouth. A broad, dark lateral band extends from the tip of the snout to the base of the caudal fin. The lips and chin are dark. Breeding individuals have a bright orange caudal fin, as reported by Suttkus (1955). The lateral band is bluish gray and bordered above by a narrow orange stripe. The anterior tip of the dorsal fin is bright yellow-green, while the venter and lower flanks are pale. A clear "window" in the center of the caudal fin of large individuals is a distinguishing character and is not found in the similar sailfin shiner, *Pteronotropis hypselopterus*. Also, in breeding males of *P. euryzonus*, the outer margin of the extended dorsal fin is convex, with the anterior rays of the depressed dorsal fin equal to or slightly longer than the posterior rays. In *P. hypselopterus* this margin is concave or straight, with anterior rays shorter than posterior rays.

ADULT SIZE: 1.6 to 2 in (40 to 50 mm)

DISTRIBUTION: *Pteronotropis euryzonus* is endemic to the middle section of the Chattahoochee River drainage in Alabama and Georgia. Individuals have been collected from several western tributaries to the Chattahoochee in Alabama.

HABITAT AND BIOLOGY: The broadstripe shiner is typically found in small, clear streams (sometimes in blackwater streams) and is commonly associated with log snags or aquatic vegetation over substrates of sand, clay, silt, or exposed bedrock. It has not been collected sympatrically with the sailfin shiner. Spawning most likely occurs from May through July. It is presumably a drift feeder, consuming adult and larval insects and detritus.

REMARKS: The type locality of the broadstripe shiner is Uchee Creek near Marvyn, Lee County, Alabama.

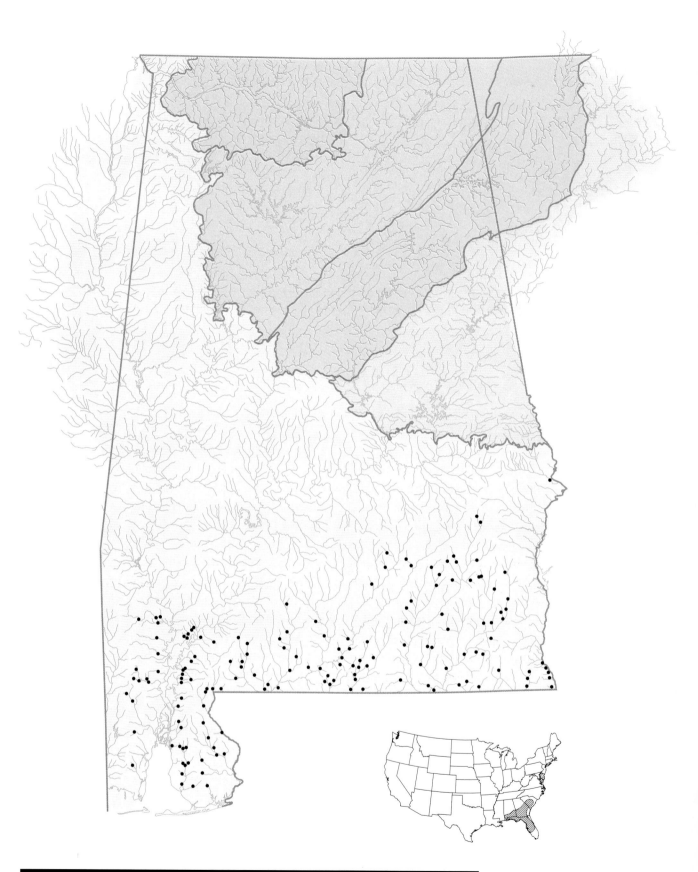

Pteronotropis hypselopterus

(Günther, 1868)

ETYMOLOGY:

Pteronotropis—winged, keeled back, referring to the enlarged dorsal fin of breeding males

hypselopterus—high fin

Sandy Creek, Baldwin County, 17 June 1993, 1.8 in (46 mm) SL male, GSA 4485

CHARACTERISTICS: The sailfin shiner has a small head and a deep, compressed body tapering to a narrow peduncle. Anal and dorsal fins are large and triangular, with the front rays of the dorsal fin much shorter than the rays at the back of the depressed fin. The outer margin of the dorsal fin is straight or somewhat concave. A broad, uniform, steel-blue lateral band extends from the head to the base of the tail. The dorsal fin is light near its base, dark in the middle, and white toward the outer edge, while the anal fin is uniformly olive yellow. Small red spots mark the base of the caudal fin. *Pteronotropis hypselopterus* is easily confused with the flagfin shiner, *P. signipinnis*, and the two frequently occur together. The flagfin shiner can be distinguished by its red fin color, yellow tail spots, and smaller tubercles. The sailfin shiner is also easily confused with the broadstripe shiner, *P. euryzonus*, which has a convex margin on the dorsal fin and anterior dorsal rays that are equal to or longer than the posterior rays.

ADULT SIZE: 1.6 to 2 in (40 to 50 mm)

DISTRIBUTION: The sailfin shiner is found below the Fall Line from the Peedee River drainage in South Carolina to western tributaries of Mobile Bay in Alabama. It is commonly found in the lower Mobile basin near the confluence of the Tombigbee and Alabama rivers and east to the Chattahoochee River drainage.

HABITAT AND BIOLOGY: *Pteronotropis hypselopterus* is commonly found in small, clear streams over sand and clay bottoms, often occurring in blackwater streams. It appears to prefer riffle runs and flowing pools, and individuals are often taken in eddies and deep runs immediately downstream of log and debris snags. Individuals in breeding condition have been collected in June. The sailfin shiner is most likely a drift feeder, consuming terrestrial insects, adult and immature aquatic insects, and plant material.

REMARKS: The precise type locality is unknown for this species; it was reported only as "Mobile, Alabama."

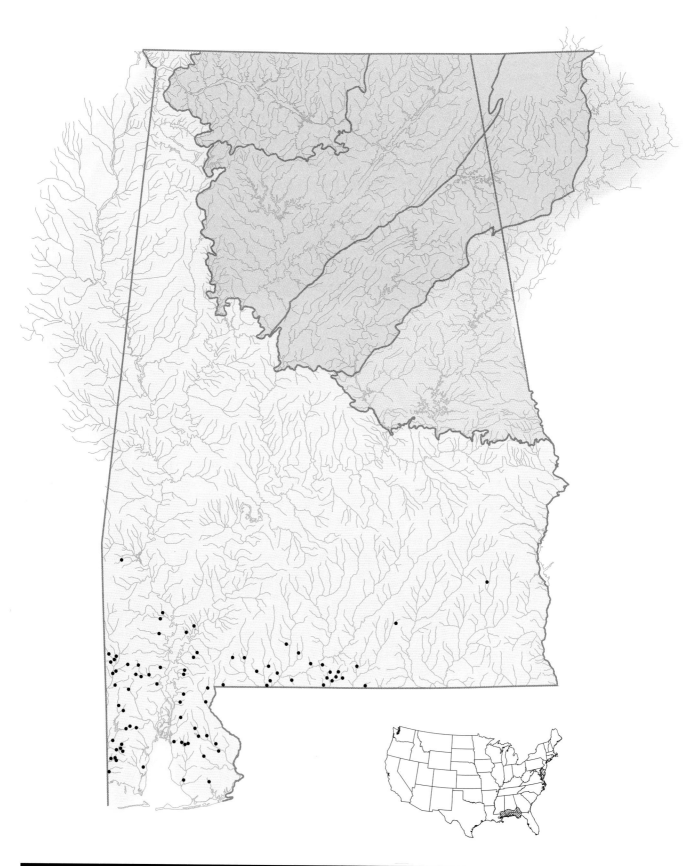

Pteronotropis signipinnis

(Bailey and Suttkus, 1952)

ETYMOLOGY:

Pteronotropis—winged, keeled back, referring to the enlarged dorsal fin of breeding males *signipinnis*—banner fin, denoting the striking color of the median fins

Wimpee Pond, Mobile County, 19 August 1992, 1.8 in (46 mm) SL male, GSA 4467

CHARACTERISTICS: The flagfin shiner has a deep, compressed body tapering to a narrow caudal peduncle. The broad, dark lateral band covers much of the sides. In life the dorsal, caudal, and anal fins are yellow or red-orange with black marginal rays, and the lateral band is deep blue-black, sharply delineated on the top and diffuse on the bottom. A narrow pink to pinkish red lateral stripe is present above the lateral band. Two bright sulfur yellow spots mark the caudal fin base, and the region between the spots is considerably darker. *Pteronotropis signipinnis* occurs syntopically with and is easily confused with the sailfin shiner, *P. hypselopterus*, but the former can be distinguished by its red fin color, yellow tail spots, and smaller tubercles.

ADULT SIZE: 1.6 to 2.2 in (40 to 55 mm)

DISTRIBUTION: This species is distributed in Gulf slope drainages from the Pearl River drainage east to the Apalachicola basin. Although the flagfin shiner is common from the Escatawpa to the Yellow river systems, collections of the species are inexplicably rare in the Alabama section of the Choctawhatchee drainage and are unknown in the Chattahoochee drainage.

HABITAT AND BIOLOGY: Flagfin shiners favor small, flowing blackwater streams draining forested wetland areas. They are often associated with aquatic vegetation and are sometimes found in the vegetation mat proper, but they appear to prefer deep areas of steady flow downstream of debris snags. Little is known about their life history, but spawning is presumably from May to June and the diet includes aquatic insects and plant material.

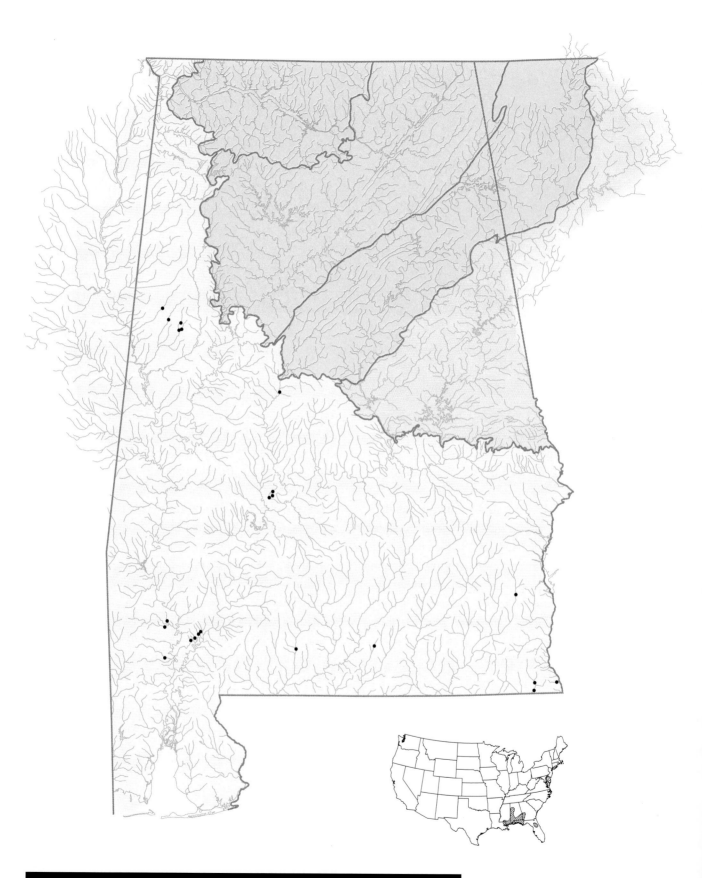

BLUENOSE SHINER *Pteronotropis welaka* **22 STATIONS**

Pteronotropis welaka
(Evermann and Kendall, 1898)

ETYMOLOGY:
Pteronotropis—winged, keeled back, referring to the enlarged dorsal fin of breeding males
welaka—the type locality, St. Johns River near Welaka, Florida

Lightsey Mill Pond, Bibb County, 27 April 1995, 1.8 in (47 mm) SL male, GSA 4639

CHARACTERISTICS: The spectacular colors exhibited by male bluenose shiners in breeding condition place them among the most beautiful minnows in North America. As the common name indicates, breeding males have bright blue snouts. The extremely enlarged dorsal, pelvic, and anal fins are also colorful. The dorsal fin is suffused with black pigment, while the pelvic and anal fins are yellow with a black diagonal band. A dark lateral band extends from the chin to the tail, where it expands into a large caudal spot extending to the tip of the caudal fin rays. A light yellow to amber stripe occurs above the lateral band. Life color is typically olive on the back (down to the lateral band) and whitish on the venter. Scales on the sides of breeding males are highlighted with bright, silvery pigment spots. In all adults, the body is slender, the head small, and the snout pointed.

ADULT SIZE: 1.6 to 2.2 in (40 to 55 mm)

DISTRIBUTION: The bluenose shiner is found in Gulf slope drainages from the Pearl River east to the Apalachicola basin, with isolated populations in the St. Johns basin in Florida. In Alabama its distribution is spotty, being limited to isolated localities throughout the Coastal Plain. This uneven distribution is most likely a collecting artifact arising from the fact that sampling in this species' preferred habitat is difficult.

HABITAT AND BIOLOGY: Bluenose shiners usually inhabit quiet backwaters and vegetated pools of streams and rivers. These pools generally have bottoms of mud or sand, with abundant growths of golden club and other aquatic vegetation. Cook (1959) describes this species' habitat as "weedy streams with beds of deep, dark, fetid mire, supporting such aquatics as broad leaf *Sagittaria*, submerged and floating *Potamogeton*, and *Uticularia*." We cannot improve on this description except to add that we have found breeding individuals to be more common deep within vegetation mats and small individuals to be more common on the periphery. Little is known about the life history of the bluenose shiner, but brightly colored males have been collected in April and June, and spawning presumably occurs from May to June. The diet is unknown, but it probably consists of small crustaceans, aquatic and terrestrial insects, and plant material.

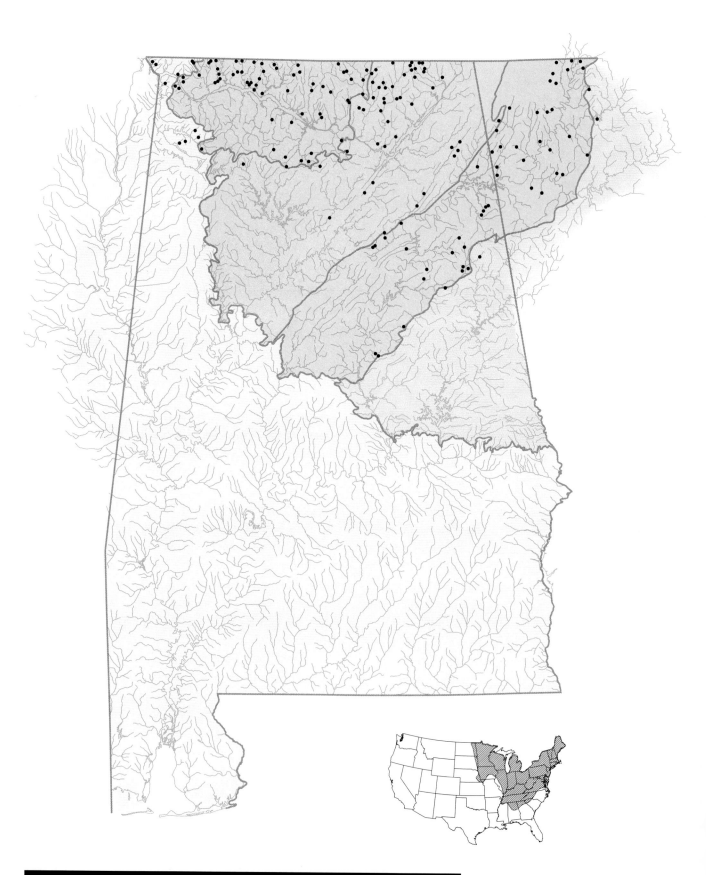

Rhinichthys atratulus

(Hermann, 1804)

ETYMOLOGY:
Rhinichthys—snout fish
atratulus—clothed in
black, referring to this
species' body color

Wilson Branch, Lauderdale County, 2 April 1993, 2.4 in (62 mm) SL male, GSA 4405

CHARACTERISTICS: The deep, rounded body of the blacknose dace is covered with small scales, tapers toward a deep caudal peduncle, and strongly arches downward from the dorsal fin to the tip of the snout. Numerous black-brown blotches of various sizes are scattered over the entire body. The dark lateral stripe extends from the snout to the tail, and a small dark spot is present at the base of the caudal fin. The pointed snout overhangs the mouth, which has a small barbel in each corner. A broad frenum connects the upper lip with the snout. Live breeding males have a deep golden yellow body color that is darker on the back and lighter on the lower sides and venter, with yellow-white paired fins and a yellow-orange stripe below the lateral band.

ADULT SIZE: 1.6 to 2.6 in (40 to 65 mm)

DISTRIBUTION: *Rhinichthys atratulus* is found throughout upper Mississippi River drainages from Minnesota to Pennsylvania and in Canada from Nova Scotia to Manitoba. It is also found in upland streams of Atlantic slope drainages from Georgia northward. In

the Mobile basin it occurs widely in the upper Coosa River system and has been reported from two locations in the Black Warrior River system. In Alabama it is commonly found throughout the Tennessee River drainage. Three subspecies are recognized (Hubbs, 1936): *R. a. atratulus* occurs along the Atlantic slope, *R. a. meleagris* in the central and northern interior, and *R. a. obtusus* from the lower Ohio to the Mobile basin.

HABITAT AND BIOLOGY: Blacknose dace prefer rocky riffles and riffle runs of small, upland headwater streams or spring-fed streams with clear water. Traver (1929) characterizes them as swift, active fishes that can easily elude would-be captors. Spawning occurs from April through June, with eggs deposited in sand or gravel substrates. Schwartz (1958) reports midwater spawning in pools for *R. a. obtusus*, whereas the other subspecies apparently spawn in riffles or pools, generally on the bottom in gravel or in bedrock cavities. Blacknose dace prefer to eat aquatic insects, but they will also consume algae and plant material.

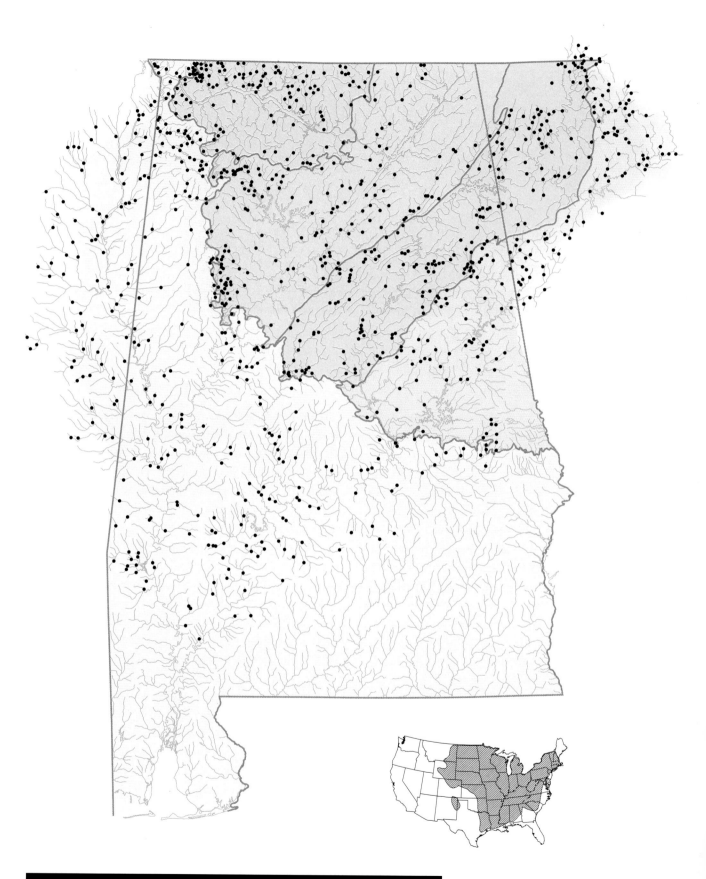

CREEK CHUB   *Semotilus atromaculatus*   **949 STATIONS**

316

Semotilus atromaculatus

(Mitchill, 1818)

ETYMOLOGY:

Semotilus—spotted banner, referring to the dorsal fin *atromaculatus*—black spotted

Tyro Creek, Fayette County, 3 June 1992, 4.0 in (102 mm) SL female, GSA 4449

CHARACTERISTICS: The creek chub is a rather robust, rounded minnow with a characteristic dark blotch at the base of its dorsal fin. The head is large, the mouth large and oblique. The upper lip is wider in the middle than at the sides, and a small barbel is usually present just forward from each corner of the mouth. The back is typically dusky olive. A broad, faint band extends along the sides and ends in a quadrate spot at the caudal fin base. Breeding males acquire red-orange color in the dorsal fin base and along the lower fins, with a pink flush along the lower head and sides. While *Semotilus atromaculatus* closely resembles the Dixie chub, *S. thoreauianus*, the two have differently configured caudal spots and head tubercle counts.

ADULT SIZE: 3.9 to 11 in (100 to 279 mm)

DISTRIBUTION: *Semotilus atromaculatus* is found throughout North America from Manitoba and New Mexico east to the Atlantic and Gulf slope drainages. It occurs extensively in the Mobile basin and Tennessee River drainage in Alabama.

HABITAT AND BIOLOGY: Although found in a variety of habitats, the creek chub prefers small headwater streams where there are few competitors. In late summer, this is often the only species found in intermittent pools of headwater streams. *Semotilus atromaculatus* is a generalized predator, consuming whatever food is available: plant material, insects, small fishes, worms, crayfishes, and mollusks. Its aggressive behavior undoubtedly helps it to survive in stressful environments. Spawning in Alabama occurs from April to June over gravel nests built by males. Creek chubs have a pit-ridge form of nest construction (Johnston and Page, 1992). Males construct depressions in the substrate by removing gravel with their mouths, and after spawning in the depressions, they cover the eggs with gravel from new pit construction. This formation of a single ridge is followed by successive excavation-spawning-burial episodes. Ross (1976, 1977) describes the creek chubs' mating behaviors, social interactions, and aggressive nature. Sexual maturity is reached by the second year (Shemske, 1974), and creek chubs may live to be five or more years old.

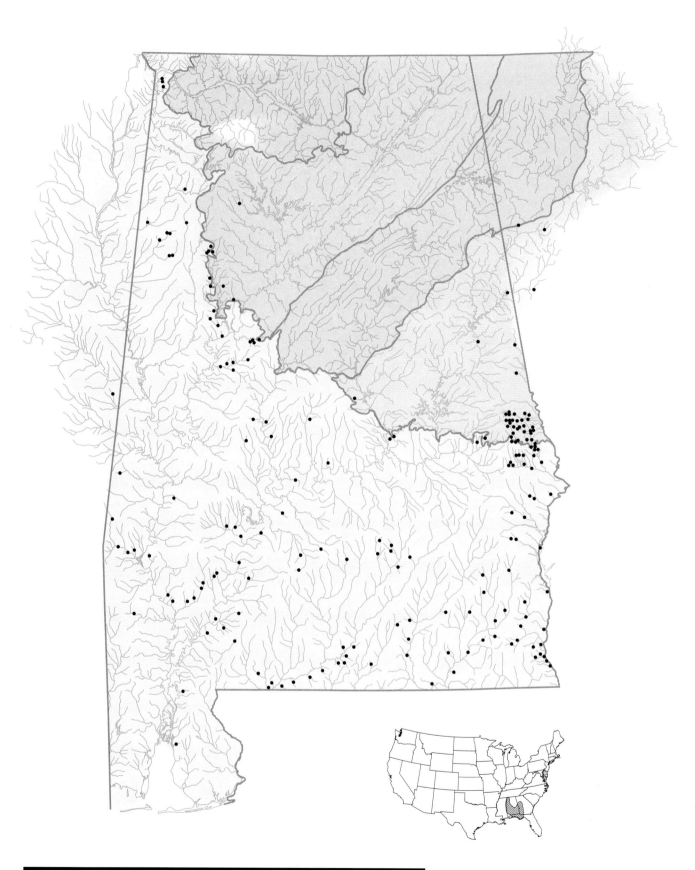

DIXIE CHUB *Semotilus thoreauianus* **190 STATIONS**

Semotilus thoreauianus

Jordan, 1877

ETYMOLOGY:

Semotilus—spotted banner, referring to the dorsal fin *thoreauianus*—in honor of Henry David Thoreau

Jernigan Mill Creek, Escambia County, 12 November 1980, 3.7 in (94 mm) SL male, GSA 6154

CHARACTERISTICS: The Dixie chub, whose body form resembles that of the creek chub, *Semotilus atromaculatus*, is generally shorter and more robust, with larger scales and less distinct dorsal and caudal spots. Breeding males have four large, hooked tubercles on each side of the head, with the tubercles nearest the nares often being fused. Body color is generally dark above, with orange to pink on the underside, and fins are yellow-orange. The Dixie chub is distinguishable from *S. atromaculatus* by having fewer head tubercles (eight), no tubercles on the gill covers and caudal fin, and a diffuse spot at the caudal fin base. This spot is typically wedge-shaped and separated from the lateral band, whereas the caudal spot in *S. atromaculatus* is quadrate-shaped and connected to the lateral band. See Jordan (1877b) for original description and Johnston and Ramsey (1990) for a recent redescription.

ADULT SIZE: 2.6 to 5.9 in (65 to 150 mm)

DISTRIBUTION: *Semotilus thoreauianus* is found in Gulf slope drainages from the Mobile basin east to the Ochlockonee River drainage in Georgia. It occurs sympatrically with *S. atromaculatus* throughout the Mobile basin, primarily below the Fall Line, and replaces it in coastal drainages from the Conecuh east to the Chattahoochee. Our collections of Dixie chubs from three Bear Creek tributaries in Colbert County represent the first records of this species in the Tennessee River drainage.

HABITAT AND BIOLOGY: The Dixie chub prefers headwater streams with riffles and flowing pools over sandy or soft substrates. Spawning aggregations were observed in April in a sandy tributary to Mahan Creek in the Cahaba River. R. D. Suttkus's field notes from March 1950 record the collection of a tuberculate male guarding a nest constructed of small, hard clay pieces and located in Omussee Creek, a Chattahoochee tributary in Houston County. Woolcott and Maurakis (1988) report nests located in the tails of pools with nearby cryptic refugia. A single male constructed each pit, and subsequent egg laying, burial, and new pit excavation created the ridge. The Dixie chub is an omnivore, consuming a variety of animal and plant foods, including insects, worms, fishes, mollusks, crayfishes, and plant material.

SUCKERS

Catostomidae

Commercial fishermen in Alabama have harvested buffalo and other sucker species for more than 100 years. In 1898, the U.S. Commission of Fish and Fisheries reported that two years earlier, fishermen took more than 1 million pounds of buffalo and 25,000 pounds of suckers. Nearly a century later, buffalo is still the most sought-after catostomid in Alabama, primarily as a food fish for northern U.S. markets. From December 1980 through November 1981, commercial fishermen harvested 374,850 pounds of smallmouth buffalo in the Mobile Delta and lower Tombigbee River (Malvestuto et al., 1983).

Suckers have cycloid scales and scaleless heads, and they can generally be distinguished from minnows of the family Cyprinidae by characteristics of the fins and mouth. On most suckers, the anal fin is located well behind the dorsal fin and close to the caudal fin. On most cyprinids, the dorsal and anal fins are vertically aligned near the center of the body. Suckers have 18 primary caudal fin rays, whereas minnows have 19. Suckers also have 10 or more dorsal rays, while minnows have nine or fewer.

As for mouth characteristics, on most species of suckers, the mouth is usually behind the tip of the snout, and the lips are either plicate or papillose. On most minnows, the mouth is usually slightly beneath the snout or sometimes at the tip of the snout; the lips are usually thin and well defined. Pharyngeal teeth in suckers number 20 or more and occur in one row on a moderately to strongly built pharyngeal arch. Pharyngeal teeth in minnows occur in one or two rows, and because their teeth are smaller and more delicate, teeth may be broken or missing.

Like minnows, suckers occupy a variety of habitats, including springs, small and large streams, lakes, reservoirs, and rivers. In the spring, most riverine suckers migrate into small streams to spawn, and older adults die shortly thereafter. After hatching, small suckers usually remain in tributary streams for several weeks before moving downstream.

During the spawning season, males and females of certain species become more brightly colored and develop tactile protuberances, known as tubercles, on their bodies or fins. Hundreds of small white tubercles develop over the entire body and fins of both sexes of the blue sucker, *Cycleptus elongatus*. Male and female spotted suckers, *Minytrema melanops*, have fewer but slightly larger and sharper tubercles on their bodies and fins. Some chubsuckers in the genus *Erimyzon* develop six to eight hooked tubercles up to a quarter-inch in length on top of the head. Well-defined bumps are restricted to the snout area on male river redhorses, *Moxostoma carinatum*, but are missing on females. Other sucker species—such as the undescribed "grayfin redhorse" of the Chattahoochee River drainage—develop fewer tubercles, which are usually restricted to the anal fin area.

The spawning behavior of the river redhorse is distinctive. Brightly colored males are constantly engaged in defending their territories over shallow gravel shoals in very swift water. The spawning act itself usually involves one female accompanied by two or three males. Once all are aligned facing upstream, the partners may quiver in unison for a few seconds and release the eggs and sperm (R. E. Jenkins, 1995, personal communication). Gravel disturbed by their thrashing tails covers some of the eggs from predation by other fishes or invertebrates. Shoal areas in the Cahaba and Coosa rivers in the Mobile basin and in Cypress and Shoal creeks in the Tennessee River drainage are some of the largest and best-known spawning areas in Alabama.

Anglers have used various means of catching suckers during their spring spawning migrations. Hackney et al. (1968) report that anglers have caught river redhorses in the upper Cahaba River by standing on a stepladder in a shallow shoal area and snaring fish with a stout pole bearing a slipwire loop. In southeastern Alabama, fishermen catch spotted suckers and blacktail redhorses by placing gill nets across the mouths of tributary streams in the Choctawhatchee and Pea rivers. Hackney et al. (1971) report that Flint Creek anglers in north Alabama

catch silver redhorses with worms and snag them with treble hooks. Although palatable, the sucker's flesh is interlaced with tiny bones and must be thoroughly cooked before being served.

Twenty-three species of suckers have been documented in Alabama. Eighteen species are known from the Tennessee River drainage. One of these, the harelip sucker, **Lagochila lacera**, is extinct; the single collection came from Cypress Creek, Lauderdale County, in 1889. Thirteen species inhabit the Mobile basin, and nine occur in coastal drainages. Two species of redhorses—the greater jumprock, **Moxostoma lachneri**, and the "grayfin redhorse," **Moxostoma** sp.—are restricted to the Chattahoochee River system in southeastern Alabama.

KEY TO THE SUCKERS

1a. Dorsal fin base long, containing more than 20 rays . . . . go to 2
1b. Dorsal fin base short, containing fewer than 20 rays . . . . go to 8

2a. Body long, cylindrical, and bluish, with small head; head length going 5 or more times into standard length; body cylindrical to slightly oval in cross section . . . . blue sucker, **Cycleptus elongatus**
2b. Body fairly stocky and brown or silver, with moderate to large head; head length going fewer than 5 times into standard length; body compressed and deeper than it is wide in cross section . . . . go to 3

3a. Body brown, almost black, or bronze; subopercular bone widest in middle . . . . go to 4, **Ictiobus**
3b. Body silvery; subopercular bone widest in its lower half . . . . go to 6, **Carpiodes**

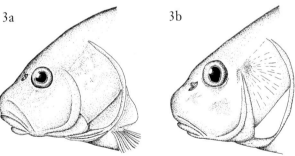

3a   3b

Subopercular bones of 3a, **Ictiobus,** and 3b, **Carpiodes**

4a. Mouth large, oblique, and positioned at front of snout; end of upper lip nearly level with lower margin of eye . . . . bigmouth buffalo, **I. cyprinellus**
4b. Mouth small, positioned slightly beneath front of snout, and nearly horizontal . . . . go to 5

5a. Mouth small, horizontal, and positioned distinctly beneath snout; back area between head and dorsal fin origin arched; eye and snout lengths about equal; body depth going 2.7 or fewer times into standard length . . . . smallmouth buffalo, *I. bubalus*

5b. Mouth large, slightly oblique, and positioned slightly beneath snout; back area not arched but with continuous upward slope from dorsal fin origin toward head; eye length shorter than snout length; body depth going 2.8 or more times into standard length . . . . black buffalo, *I. niger*

6a. Snout elongate; back edge of upper jaw usually not reaching front edge of eye; front edge of lower lip lacks nipple-shaped knob . . . . quillback, *C. cyprinus*

6b. Snout short, blunt; upper jaw extending to or beyond front edge of eye; front edge of lower lip with nipple-shaped knob . . . . go to 7

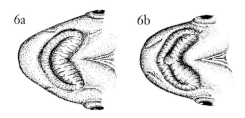

Lower lips of 6a, with knob absent, and 6b, with knob present

7a. Anterior dorsal fin rays, if unbroken, nearly as long as dorsal fin base (shorter in specimens from the Conecuh and Choctawhatchee rivers); body fairly deep, maximum depth going 2.6 or fewer times into standard length . . . . highfin carpsucker, *C. velifer*

7b. Anterior dorsal fin rays about half as long as dorsal fin base; body not as deep, maximum depth going more than 2.6 times into standard length; Tennessee River drainage . . . . river carpsucker, *C. carpio*

8a. Lateral line incomplete or missing . . . . go to 9

8b. Lateral line complete and generally well developed . . . . go to 12

9a. Body round, marked with several horizontal rows of small black or brown dots, 1 dot per scale; 43 or more lateral scales . . . . spotted sucker, *Minytrema melanops*

9b. Body deeper and slightly compressed; fewer than 43 lateral scales . . . . go to 10, *Erimyzon*

10a. Dorsal and anal fins sharply pointed . . . . sharpfin chubsucker, *E. tenuis*

10b. Dorsal and anal fins rounded; anal fin slightly to moderately bilobed . . . . go to 11

11a. Lateral scales 34 to 39 . . . . lake chubsucker, *E. sucetta*

11b. Lateral scales 39 to 45 . . . . creek chubsucker, *E. oblongus*

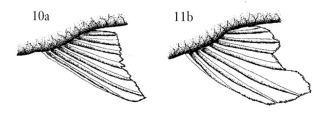

Anal fin shapes of 10a, *E. tenuis*, and 11b, *E. oblongus*

12a. Head depressed between eyes, forming concave area; body with several wide, black or brown vertical bars or blotches. . . . . go to 13, *Hypentelium*

12b. Head rounded between eyes, forming slightly convex curve; body color variable but without conspicuous | black bars . . . . go to 14

13a. Dorsal fin with 10 to 12, usually 11, rays; head strongly concave; lower fins generally yellowish to tan; Tennessee River drainage . . . . northern hog sucker, *H. nigricans*

13b. Dorsal fin with 9 to 11, usually 10, rays; head only slightly concave; lower fins are reddish orange; snout and lips usually orange . . . . Alabama hog sucker, *H. etowanum*

Front views of 13a, *H. nigricans*, and 13b, *H. etowanum*

14a. Lateral line scales more than 50 . . . . white sucker, **Catostomus commersoni**

14b. Lateral line scales fewer than 50 . . . . go to 15, *Moxostoma*

15a. Caudal peduncle scales usually 16 . . . . greater jumprock, *M. lachneri*

15b. Caudal peduncle scales usually 12 to 14 . . . . go to 16

16a. Dorsal fin rays usually 14 or more; halves of lower lip meeting at acute to right angle . . . . silver redhorse, *M. anisurum*

16b. Dorsal rays usually 13 or fewer; halves of lower lip meeting at obtuse angle . . . . go to 17

17a. Free margin of dorsal fin concave; head very short, usually 18 to 23 percent of standard length . . . . shorthead redhorse, *M. macrolepidotum*

17b. Free margin of dorsal fin straight or slightly convex; head moderate to large, usually 21 to 26 percent of standard length in adults, 18 to 21 percent in juveniles . . . . go to 18

Dorsal fin shapes of 17a, *M. macrolepidotum*, and 17b, *M. carinatum*

18a. Pharyngeal arch stout, lower teeth enlarged and molar-shaped; on live individuals, caudal and anal fins bright reddish orange . . . . river redhorse, *M. carinatum*

18b. Pharyngeal arch more delicate, lower teeth compressed and comblike; caudal and anal fins from gray to yellow or reddish orange . . . . go to 19

19a. Lateral line scales usually 44 to 47; pelvic fin rays 10. . . . . black redhorse, *M. duquesnei*
19b. Lateral line scales usually 43 or fewer; pelvic fin rays usually 8 or 9 . . . . go to 20

20a. Lower lobe of caudal fin with distinct dark stripe from base to free margin. . . . .
. . . . blacktail redhorse, *M. poecilurum*
20b. Lower lobe of caudal fin without distinct dark stripe . . . . go to 21

21a. Lateral line scales usually 42 to 44; caudal and dorsal fins usually gray, with no light orange or yellow; limited to the Chattahoochee River system. . . . . "grayfin redhorse," *M.* sp.
21b. Lateral line scales usually 39 to 42; caudal and dorsal fins light yellow, olive, or gray . . . .
. . . . golden redhorse, *M. erythrurum*

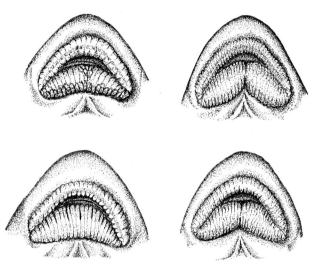

Mouth shapes of (top left) *M. macrolepidotum*, (top right) *M. carinatum*,
(bottom left) *M. duquesnei*, and (bottom right) *M. erythrurum*

CAHABA RIVER, SHELBY COUNTY

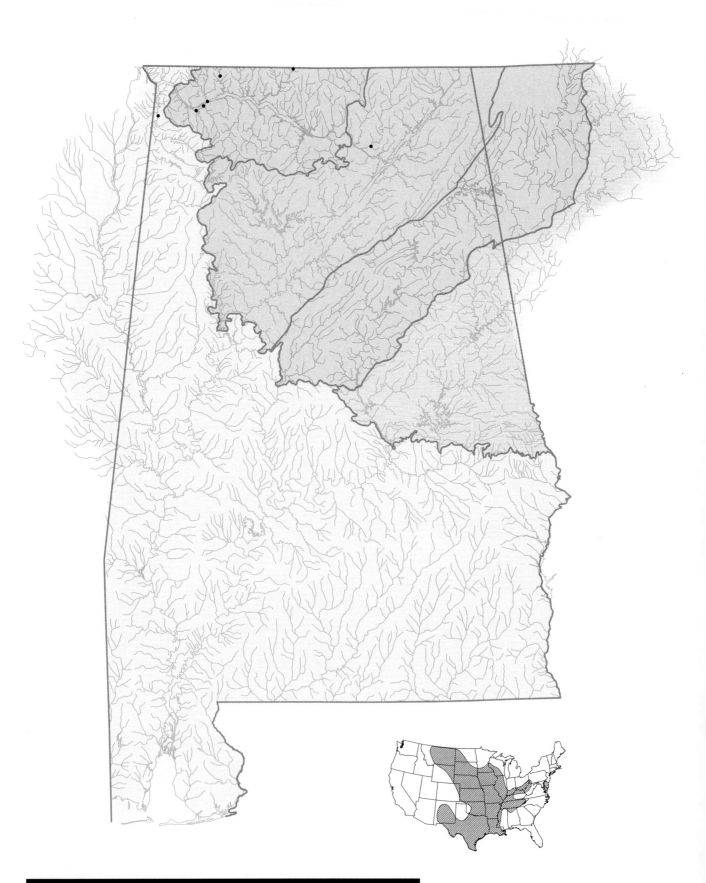

RIVER CARPSUCKER *Carpiodes carpio* **7 STATIONS**

Carpiodes carpio

(Rafinesque, 1820)

ETYMOLOGY:

Carpiodes—carplike

carpio—carp, or similar

to a carp

Bear Creek, Colbert County, 11 June 1993, 11.4 in (290 mm) SL male, GSA 4524

CHARACTERISTICS: The river carpsucker is the largest carpsucker species in Alabama. Older adults have a high arch on the back between the head and dorsal fin origin; on smaller individuals, this arch is absent. The dorsal fin is long, containing 23 to 30 rays. Length of anterior dorsal fin rays is an important character for separating river and highfin carpsuckers: On river carpsuckers, these rays are only about half as long as the dorsal fin base, whereas on highfin carpsuckers, they are longer than half the dorsal fin base. The rear edge of the upper jaw extends to or past the anterior edge of the eye. A distinctive nipple-shaped bulge occurs on the front edge of the lower lip. The body is silvery to very light green overall. The fins are clear to dusky.

ADULT SIZE: 16 to 24 in (406 to 610 mm)

DISTRIBUTION: River carpsuckers are fairly common in many rivers of the Mississippi basin, but their distribution and abundance are limited in the Tennessee and Ohio river drainages. Lee and Platania (1978a) include

records from both the upper and lower reaches of the Tennessee River drainage but none from Alabama. Boschung (1992) reports no specimens in the University of Alabama Ichthyological Collection. Our collections at seven stations in Alabama in 1992 and 1993 (three in the Tennessee River and one each in the Elk River and in Cypress, Shoal, and Bear creeks) may represent the first published records of this species from state waters.

HABITAT AND BIOLOGY: Reports on the fishes of Illinois (Smith, 1979) and Arkansas (Robison and Buchanan, 1988) indicate that river carpsuckers are abundant in quiet, silty or sand-bottomed pools of moderate or large streams, rivers, and reservoirs. Spawning occurs from May through July. We encountered this species in greatest abundance in Bear Creek, Colbert County. The sample collection area varied from 30 to 35 feet in width and 3 to 6 feet in depth. Streamflow ranged from slow to moderate, and substrates included clay, sand, and small gravel. Most individuals were found near trees and other submerged structures scattered along both banks.

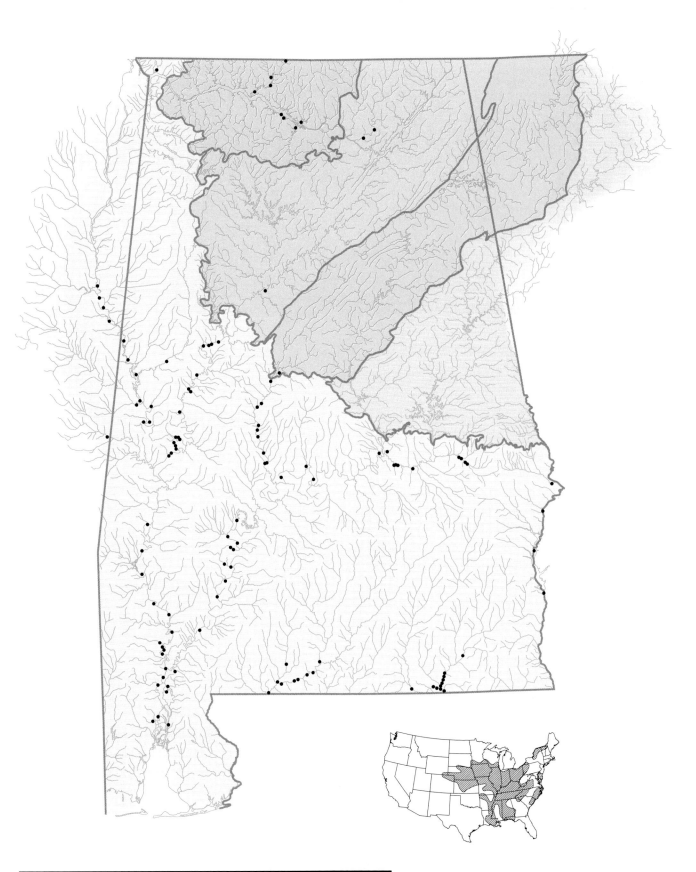

QUILLBACK *Carpiodes cyprinus* **118 STATIONS**

Carpiodes cyprinus
(Lesueur, 1817)

ETYMOLOGY:
Carpiodes—carplike
cyprinus—generic name
of common carp, which this
species resembles

Paint Rock River, Marshall County, 19 May 1993, 11.8 in (300 mm) SL male, GSA 4475

CHARACTERISTICS: The quillback lacks a nipple-shaped projection on the front of the lower lip, and the rear edge of the mouth fails to reach the anterior edge of the eye. The lateral line has 36 to 41 scales. Dorsal fin rays number 25 to 33, and the anterior rays, when depressed, extend to only one-half of the dorsal fin. Anal fin rays number seven or eight. Body color is generally silver to bronze, and all fins are essentially clear. See Lesueur (1817b) for original description.

ADULT SIZE: 12 to 20 in (300 to 508 mm)

DISTRIBUTION: Previous records from the Tennessee River drainage in Alabama were limited to samples collected in 1938 by the Tennessee Valley Authority (Platania and Jenkins, 1978; Boschung, 1992). We collected this species at four locations in the drainage in 1993. Royal D. Suttkus (1995, personal communication) reports that quillback populations in the Conecuh, Choctawhatchee, and Chattahoochee river drainages in southeastern Alabama and northwestern Florida may represent a new species.

HABITAT AND BIOLOGY: Quillbacks occur in large streams, rivers, and reservoirs. They are uncommon in the Tennessee and Chattahoochee river drainages and are widespread in the Mobile basin (but are not as abundant as highfin carpsuckers). We found the greatest densities of this species in the Conecuh and Choctawhatchee rivers in southeastern Alabama and in the tailwaters of most locks and dams in the Mobile basin. Collections of gravid, tuberculate adults and small young-of-the-year indicate that spawning occurs in April and May throughout Alabama. Growth is rapid, with one-year-old individuals reaching 4 or 5 inches in length.

Quillback from Choctawhatchee River, Geneva County, 6 May 1993, 12.8 in (325 mm) SL, GSA 4441

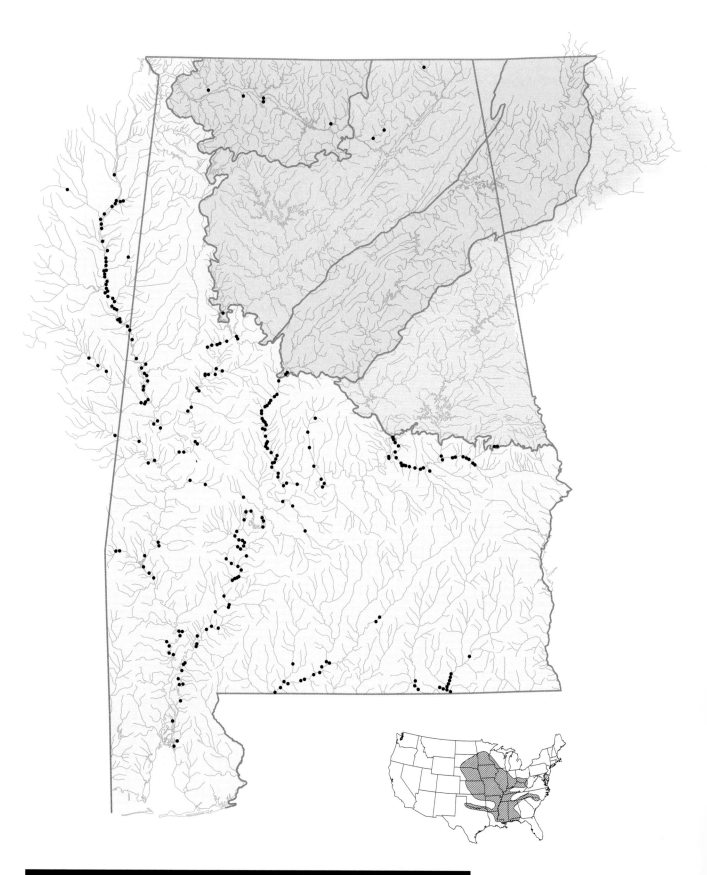

HIGHFIN CARPSUCKER *Carpiodes velifer* **250 STATIONS**

Carpiodes velifer

(Rafinesque, 1820)

ETYMOLOGY:

Carpiodes—carplike

velifer—sail bearer,

referring to this species'

elongate dorsal fin

Cypress Creek, Lauderdale County, 16 July 1992, 10.6 in (270 mm) SL male, GSA 4282

CHARACTERISTICS: The highfin carpsucker is named for its elongate anterior dorsal fin rays, which when depressed are almost as long as the dorsal fin base. The dorsal fin has 22 to 27 rays; the anal fin has seven or eight rays. The lateral line contains 36 to 38 scales. The snout is blunt and rounded. The upper jaw reaches the front edge of the eye, and a small, nipple-shaped projection appears on the front edge of the lower lip. Highfin carpsuckers have silvery to light bronze bodies and clear fins.

ADULT SIZE: 10 to 16 in (254 to 406 mm)

DISTRIBUTION: Page and Burr (1991) exclude Alabama on their range map for this species. Lee and Platania (1978b) have only one record from the Tennessee River drainage in eastern Tennessee. Boschung (1992) speculates that highfin carpsuckers have not been collected in the Alabama section of the Tennessee drainage since 1936 or 1938. In 1992 and 1993, we collected individuals at only three stations—two in Paint Rock River and one in Cypress Creek. Highfins are widespread and often abundant in the Mobile basin, particularly below the Fall Line and in the tailwaters of most locks and dams. Royal D. Suttkus (1995, personal communication) believes that a new species may be represented by populations found in the Conecuh and Choctawhatchee river drainages in southeastern Alabama and northwestern Florida.

HABITAT AND BIOLOGY: This schooling species occurs primarily in rivers and reservoirs and occasionally in moderate or large streams. Pflieger (1975) reports July spawnings in Missouri. We have encountered tuberculate adults running eggs and milt from April through June, indicating a protracted spawning season in Alabama. We have collected small, 1- to 3-inch highfins along sand and gravel bars in June and July as well as spent but still slightly tuberculate adults as late as August.

Highfin carpsucker from Choctawhatchee River, Geneva County, 6 May 1993, 10.2 in (260 mm) SL, GSA 4441

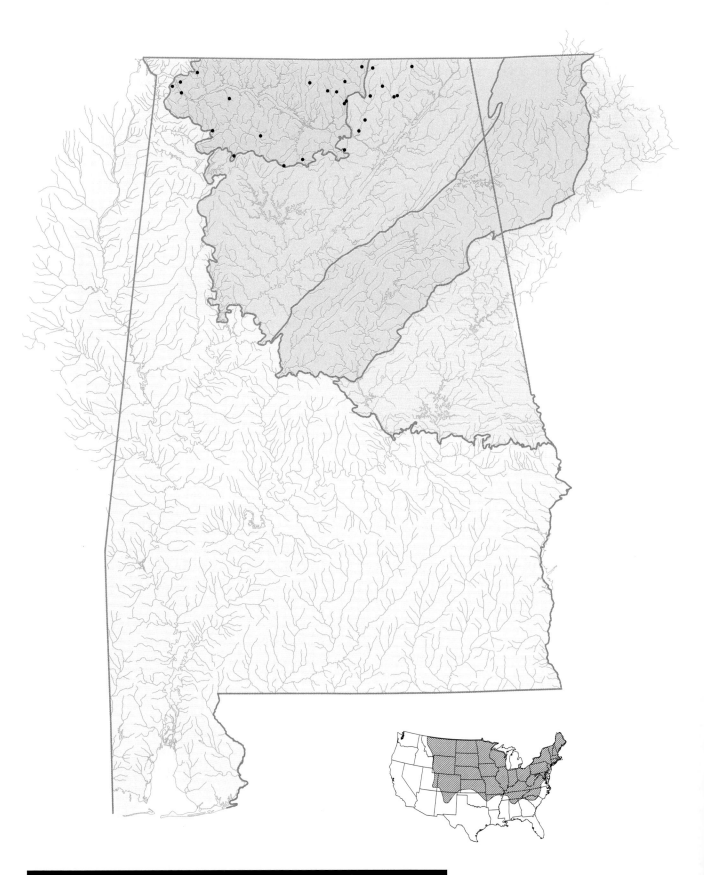

WHITE SUCKER   *Catostomus commersoni*   **26 STATIONS**

Catostomus commersoni
(Lacepède, 1803)

ETYMOLOGY:
Catostomus—inferior mouth
commersoni—in honor of
Phelebert Commerson, the
French naturalist

Glover Cave, Madison County, 16 September 1993, 11.3 in (287 mm) SL female, GSA 4611

CHARACTERISTICS: The white sucker has 55 to 85 lateral line scales—more than any other catostomid species in Alabama. Scale size and location are also distinctive. On the front of the body, scales are distinctly smaller and more crowded; behind the dorsal fin base, they are larger and less crowded. The eye is midway between the tip of the snout and the rear of the gill cover. The mouth is large, and the lips are papillose, with a bilobed lower lip that is nearly twice as thick as the upper lip. For most of the year, the body is gray to brown on the back, shading to cream on the venter. During the spawning season, however, it becomes purplish, with a dark, well-defined lateral band. The ventral fins are pale yellow, especially in spring. All other fins are generally clear to pale gray.

ADULT SIZE: 10 to 16 in (254 to 406 mm)

DISTRIBUTION: The Tennessee River drainage marks the southern limit of this species' range (Lee and Kucas, 1978). Collection records indicate that, although never abundant, it is widely distributed in northern Alabama. In 1991, we collected white suckers at eight stations.

HABITAT AND BIOLOGY: White suckers prefer springs and small streams. Like northern hog suckers and some redhorse species, white suckers usually occur in or just downstream of gravelly riffles, where they feed on aquatic insects and other invertebrates. On 6 November 1991, we collected two white suckers just inside the mouth of Glover Cave in Madison County. Since white suckers are not normally found in caves, these fishes probably became stranded there when stream levels in the area decreased. White suckers spawn over gravel shoals in March and April. Etnier and Starnes (1993) report that stomach contents of white suckers collected in Tennessee included 50 percent benthic invertebrates and 50 percent unidentified matter. Carlander (1969) reports that females grow faster than males. The life span may last from seven to 10 years, although errors in reading the annuli on scales of older individuals sometimes result in underestimates.

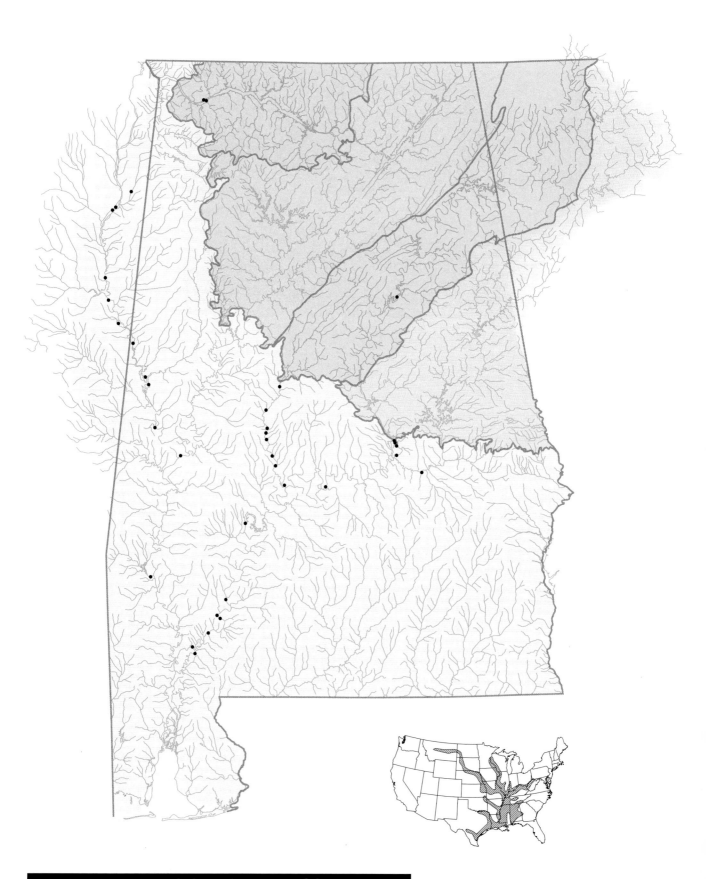

BLUE SUCKER *Cycleptus elongatus* **36 STATIONS**

Cycleptus elongatus
(Lesueur, 1817)

ETYMOLOGY:
Cycleptus—small,
round mouth
elongatus—elongate

Alabama River, Wilcox County, 27 February 1993, 16.5 in (420 mm) SL male, GSA 4372

CHARACTERISTICS: The blue sucker has an elongate, cylindrical body, a short head, and a small mouth covered with many small papillae. The dorsal fin contains 29 to 37 soft rays, and its free edge is sickle-shaped. The caudal fin is large and deeply forked. The ventral fins are bowed downward, with lower edges that are often calloused from rubbing on submerged structures. Individuals are pale to dark blue, with brown mottling on the back shading to light gray on the venter. On spawning adults, body colors intensify, and the body, head, and even fins become covered with hundreds of small, white breeding tubercles. According to Richard L. Mayden and Brooks M. Burr, blue suckers in the Mobile basin may represent a new species. See Lesueur (1817b) for original description.

ADULT SIZE: 24 to 35 in (610 to 890 mm)

DISTRIBUTION: The range of this species has expanded substantially since 1993 because of the collective efforts of the Alabama Game and Fish Division, the Geological Survey of Alabama, the U.S. Fish and Wildlife Service, and Alabama Power Company. The nine blue suckers we collected in 1993 at Alabama River mile 6.2 represent a new downstream range limit in the Mobile basin, except for a waif reported from Dauphin Island by Swingle (1971). The status of populations in the Tennessee River drainage is unclear, since individuals are recorded from only two locations, one in 1939 and the other in 1993.

HABITAT AND BIOLOGY: An excellent example of a habitat specialist, the blue sucker is limited in Alabama to large flowing rivers and tailwaters below dams. Data obtained from more than 125 blue suckers captured and released below Millers Ferry Lock and Dam on the Alabama River in 1995 indicate that the species spawns in early April. Females slightly outnumbered males in March and April and abandoned the area by May. Sonar tagging and tracking studies completed in 1996 indicate that, following spawning, individuals move over 100 miles downstream, well below Claiborne Lock and Dam. Yeager and Semmens (1987) artificially spawned ripe blue suckers collected from the Alabama River and subsequently described the species' early development from protolarva to juvenile. Knowledge of the early life history of this species in Alabama is incomplete. Rupprecht and Jahn (1980) report that blue suckers live 10 years in the Mississippi River and attain a maximum length of 32 inches.

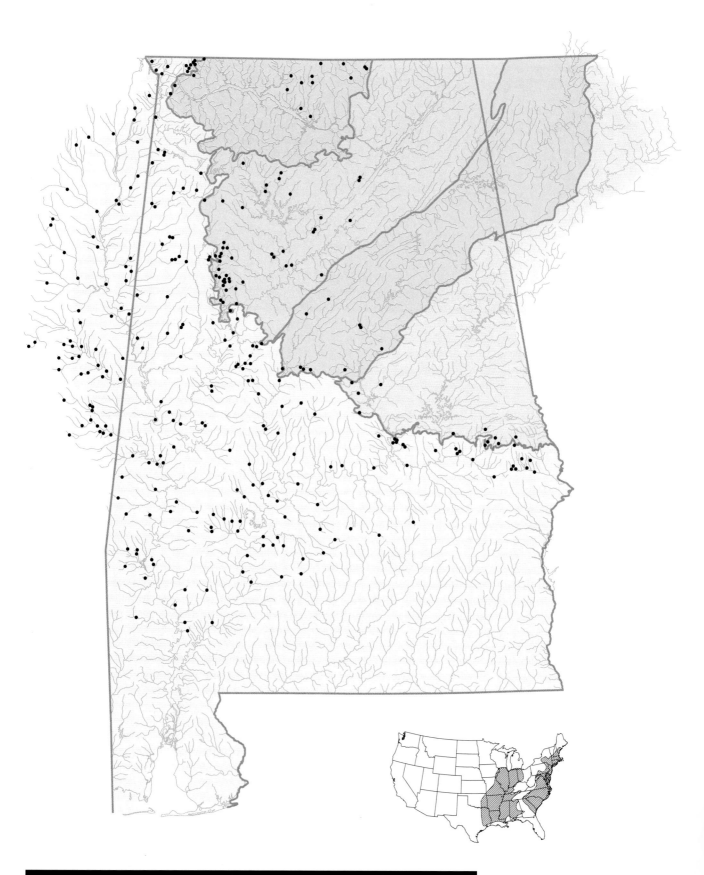

CREEK CHUBSUCKER   *Erimyzon oblongus*   305 STATIONS

Erimyzon oblongus
(Mitchill, 1814)

ETYMOLOGY:

Erimyzon—to suck
oblongus—oblong

Tyro Creek, Fayette County, 3 June 1992, 3.5 in (90 mm) SL male, GSA 4449

CHARACTERISTICS: The body of this small chub-sucker has 39 to 45 mid-lateral scales but no lateral line. The mouth is slightly subterminal, and the two halves of the lower lip meet almost at a right angle. The dorsal fin contains 10 to 12 soft rays, and its distal margin is convex. The anal fin is slightly to moderately bilobed, particularly on males. Body color on the back is light brown to gray, shading to cream on the venter. A lateral stripe containing six to eight dark blotches extends along the side of the body. Breeding males have three tubercles on each side of the head.

ADULT SIZE: 5 to 7 in (127 to 178 mm)

DISTRIBUTION: The most abundant chubsucker in Alabama, the creek chubsucker occurs in both the Tennessee River drainage and the Mobile basin, primarily below the Fall Line. Page and Burr (1991) indicate that the Gulf slope range of this species extends from the Chattahoochee River, Florida, west to the San Jacinto River, Texas. We have no records of its presence in the Escatawpa River system in southwestern Alabama or in any of the smaller coastal drainages in southeastern Alabama, although Wall and Gilbert (1980) report a single collection from the Escambia River system in Florida.

HABITAT AND BIOLOGY: Inhabitants of low-gradient, slow-moving, sandy-bottomed streams, creek chubsuckers usually occur around aquatic vegetation, leaf packs, or submerged tree roots. Small individuals form schools, while large adults are usually solitary. Based on collections of tuberculate, gravid adults, we believe this species spawns in March and early April throughout Alabama. Page and Johnston (1990b) note that males defend territories over gravel and near nests constructed by stonerollers, *Campostoma*, and creek chubs, *Semotilus atromaculatus*. The female indicates her readiness to spawn by burying her snout in gravel; then she spawns with a single male. Carlander (1969) reports that creek chubsuckers live for up to five years. The diet of small chubsuckers consists of copepods, cladocerans, and small aquatic insect larvae.

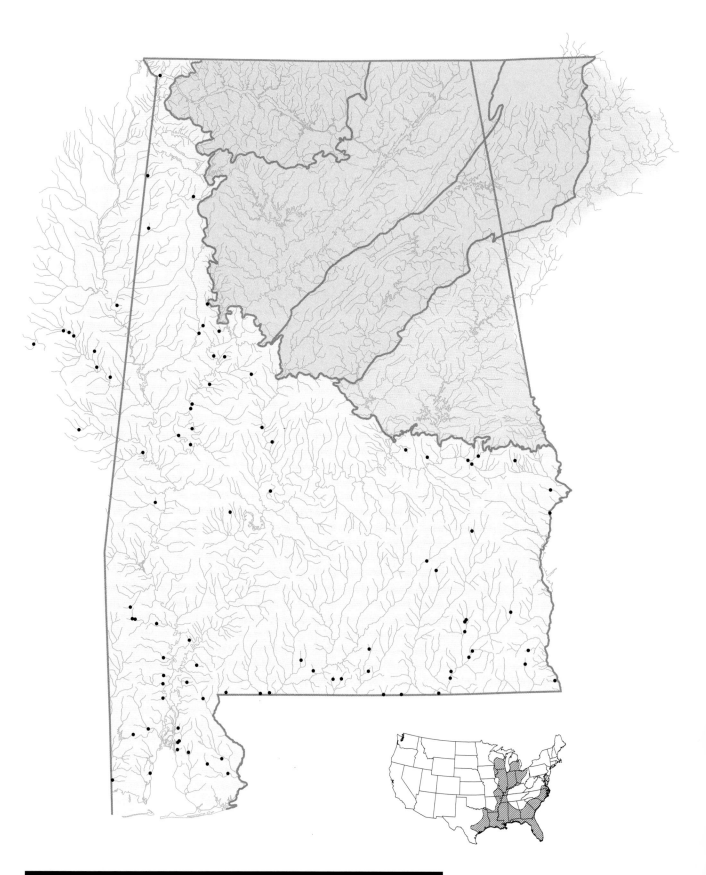

LAKE CHUBSUCKER *Erimyzon sucetta* **90 STATIONS**

Erimyzon sucetta
(Lacepède, 1803)

ETYMOLOGY:
Erimyzon—to suck
sucetta—a sucker or
sucking fish

Bay Minette Creek, Baldwin County, 15 June 1993, 8.9 in (225 mm) SL male, GSA 4481

CHARACTERISTICS: The lake chubsucker has a deeper body and reaches a larger adult size than the creek chubsucker, *Erimyzon oblongus*. Maximum body depth generally goes 3.2 or fewer times into standard length. Lake chubsuckers have 34 to 39 mid-lateral scales but no lateral line. The dorsal fin contains 11 or 12 soft rays, and its free edge is rounded. The anal fin is bilobed. The back is light brown in young fish to dark brown in adults. Young fish have a distinct, dark lateral band; older fish may have five or six broad, dark, vertical bars. The venter is tan or cream. Vertical fins are light tan, golden, or gray, with dark pigmentation near their bases. Paired fins are generally clear.

ADULT SIZE: 7.9 to 15 in (200 to 380 mm)

DISTRIBUTION: Lake chubsuckers occur in all Mobile basin drainages below the Fall Line. Individuals have also been collected from all coastal drainages between the Escatawpa and Chattahoochee drainages.

HABITAT AND BIOLOGY: This species is occasionally abundant in lakes, but because individuals generally will not bite a hook, they usually go unnoticed by anglers. Lake chubsuckers are most likely to be encountered in moderate or small streams with little or no current but with concentrations of aquatic vegetation over silty or sandy substrates. Large individuals flourish in lakes, river-overflow pools, and swamps. Our collections of tuberculate, gravid adults in both the Black Warrior and upper Tombigbee river systems indicate that spawning occurs from May to July. Little is known of this species' life history in Alabama. Carlander (1969) reports a life span of five or six years and a maximum size of 15 inches.

Bazemores Mill Pond, Houston County

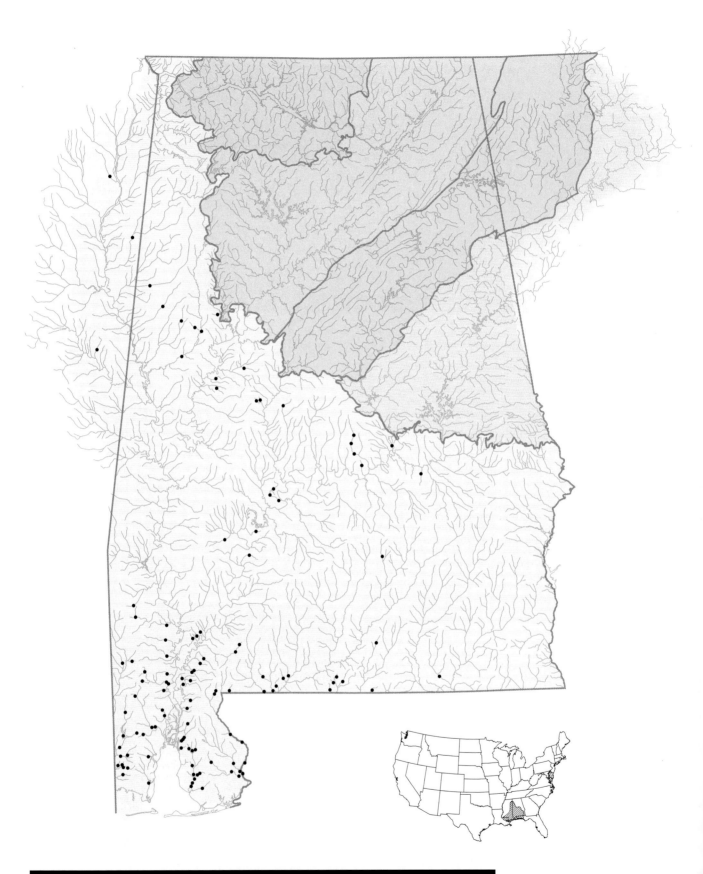

SHARPFIN CHUBSUCKER *Erimyzon tenuis* **116 STATIONS**

Erimyzon tenuis

(Agassiz, 1855)

ETYMOLOGY:
Erimyzon—to suck
tenuis—thin, presumably
referring to this species'
elongate anal fin

Bay Minette Creek, Baldwin County, 15 June 1993, 3.0 in (76 mm) SL male, GSA 4481

CHARACTERISTICS: The largest chubsucker in Alabama, the sharpfin chubsucker usually has a pointed dorsal fin, but the fin may become rounded on large individuals. The anal fin is almost always pointed, and when depressed, its longest rays extend beyond the caudal fin base. The body has 40 to 45 lateral scales but no lateral line. Large breeding males have four large, often hooked tubercles on each side of the head. Young sharpfins are brown on the back and cream on the venter, with a light yellow lateral band above a dark lateral stripe extending from the snout to the caudal fin base. As the fish ages, the lateral stripe disappears. Many scales are edged in black, giving them a diamond-shaped appearance. Fins are dusky overall, with rays outlined in black.

ADULT SIZE: 9.8 to 16 in (250 to 406 mm)

DISTRIBUTION: Most Alabama collections are from the Fall Line Hills and Southern Pine Hills of the East Gulf Coastal Plain. Sharpfins are particularly widespread and often abundant in the Escatawpa and Perdido drainages and freshwater tributaries to Mobile Bay.

HABITAT AND BIOLOGY: Sharpfin chubsuckers are most common in swamps, small or medium-sized streams, and coastal river backwaters with slow to moderate currents and sandy substrates often lightly covered with silt. Sharpfins congregate along undercut banks and around aquatic vegetation and submerged brush piles. Little is known about the species' life history in Alabama. Our collection of tuberculate, gravid individuals in the Styx River in 1991 indicates that spawning occurs in late March and April. Young sharpfins remain in schools until they are 4 or 5 inches long and probably consume zooplankton and small aquatic insect larvae. Adults eat larger aquatic larvae. Judging from the adult size of this and the two other *Erimyzon* species in Alabama, we believe that the sharpfin chubsucker lives for seven to eight years.

REMARKS: The type locality is given as "Mobile, Alabama."

341

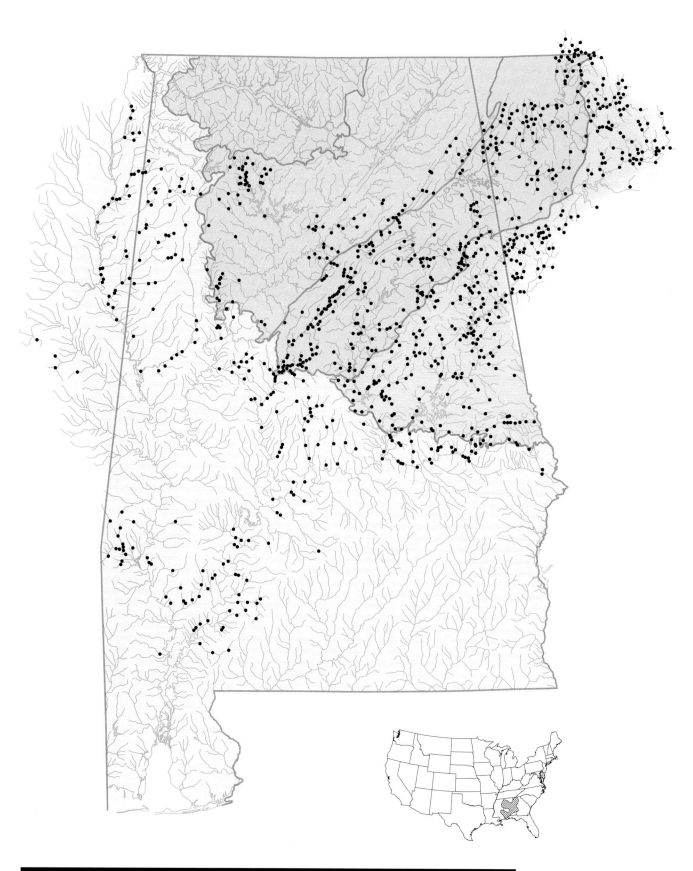

ALABAMA HOG SUCKER   *Hypentelium etowanum*   963 STATIONS

Hypentelium etowanum
(Jordan, 1877)

ETYMOLOGY:
Hypentelium—below "five-lobes," possibly referring to the form of the lower lip *etowanum*—Etowah, referring to the Etowah River, the type locality

Mill Creek, Blount County, 9 March 1993, 3.9 in (98 mm) SL male, GSA 4365

CHARACTERISTICS: The Alabama hog sucker has a large, rectangular head that is slightly concave between the eyes. The dorsal fin usually has 10 soft rays. A large mouth with many prominent papillae is located just beneath the snout. The back is light to dark charcoal, the venter cream, and the sides mottled charcoal and cream. Four or five dark, oblique bands extend forward along the side and are joined across the dorsal midline. The anterior band, which is broadest, is just behind the head. Two narrower bands occur beneath the dorsal fin and two behind it. All fins are light orange-red to cream mottled with charcoal brown. The snout and lips are also tinted with orange. See Jordan (1877a) for original description.

ADULT SIZE: 9.1 to 12 in (230 to 300 mm)

DISTRIBUTION: This species has an unusual distribution. It is extremely widespread and frequently abundant above the Fall Line and in the Fall Line Hills district of the East Gulf Coastal Plain below the Fall Line. But there are very few collections in streams draining the Black Belt and Southern Pine Hills districts of southwestern Alabama, a circumstance that is probably the result of physical and water-quality conditions in the

Black Belt and a lack of preferred substrates throughout. The influence of habitat on species distribution is indicated by the presence of hog suckers at Bilbo Creek, the southernmost gravel-bottomed tributary to the western side of the lower Tombigbee River in Washington County (Mettee et al., 1987). Alabama hog suckers are also present in the Chattahoochee River drainage, primarily above the Fall Line.

HABITAT AND BIOLOGY: Hog suckers are bottom-dwelling fishes that prefer moderate or fast currents over gravel, cobble, or sand substrates. Judging from our numerous collections of gravid adults, spawning occurs in April and early May in Alabama. R. D. Suttkus reports collections of males running milt from 58°F (14°C) water at Pace Creek, Clarke County, on 9 April 1988. Juvenile hog suckers are often common in slack or slow currents over sand and silt substrates. Etnier and Starnes (1993) report a life span of at least five years. Very little information is available on the life history of this species in Alabama.

REMARKS: The type locality given by Jordan (1877a) is the Etowah and Oostanaula rivers near Rome, Georgia.

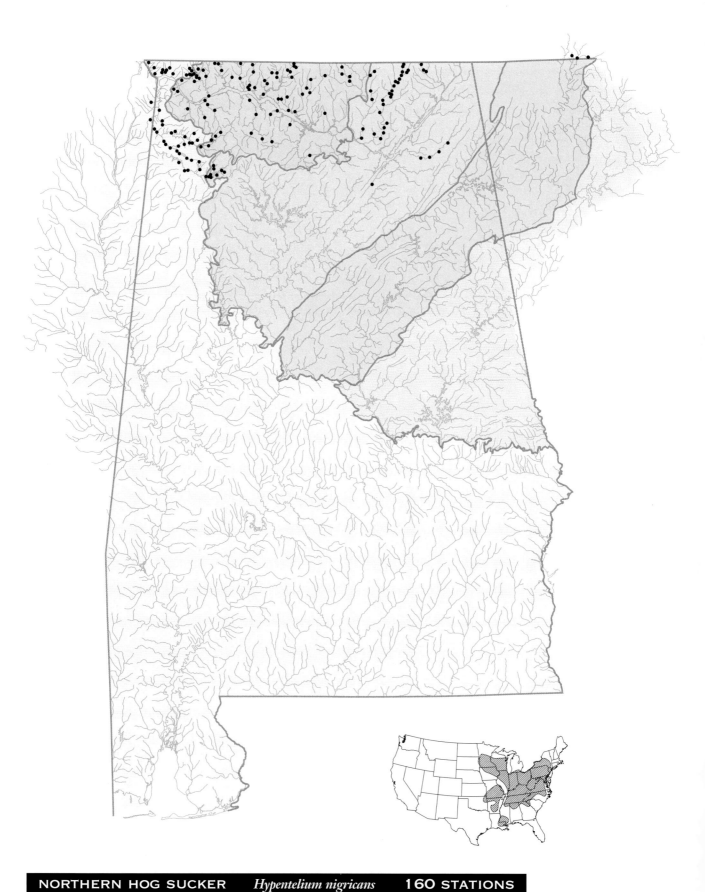

NORTHERN HOG SUCKER   *Hypentelium nigricans*   160 STATIONS

Hypentelium nigricans
(Lesueur, 1817)

ETYMOLOGY:

Hypentelium—below "five-lobes," possibly referring to the form of the lower lip
nigricans—blackish

Sour Branch, Lauderdale County, 24 February 1993, 5.5 in (139 mm) SL male, GSA 4357

CHARACTERISTICS: The northern hog sucker is distinguished from the Alabama hog sucker by its 10 to 12 (usually 11) dorsal rays, a distinctly concave area between the eyes, and a gray to brown body and yellowish fins. The Alabama hog sucker has nine to 11 (usually 10) dorsal rays, a flat or only slightly concave area between the eyes, and light to dark charcoal body colors with distinctly light to bright orange fins. The northern hog sucker's large mouth, with its many prominent papillae, is located on the underside of its snout. See Lesueur (1817b) for original description.

ADULT SIZE: 10 to 17 in (254 to 432 mm) in Alabama; up to 24 in (610 mm) in northern states

DISTRIBUTION: In Alabama, this species is limited to the Tennessee River drainage. A small population is also present in the upper Conasauga River, a tributary of the Coosa River drainage in southeastern Tennessee and northern Georgia (Etnier and Starnes, 1993).

HABITAT AND BIOLOGY: Northern hog suckers are widespread and often abundant in clear, high-gradient streams of small or moderate size. We collected our largest specimens in downstream reaches of several Tennessee River tributaries, including Second, Big Nance, and Limestone creeks and the Elk, Flint, and Paint Rock rivers. This species' preferred habitat includes gravel, rock, and cobble substrates and moderate to swift currents. Spawning occurs in March and April, and eggs are usually deposited directly on gravel or cobble substrates. After hatching, young individuals remain in the area for most of their lives. Northern hog suckers flip stones on the substrate to feed on aquatic insect larvae and small snails, an activity that frequently attracts minnows which forage on the smaller organisms that are also uncovered. Northern hog suckers live for eight to 10 years. We have infrequently observed both Alabama and northern hog suckers with swirled or reversed scale patterns on their backs and sides.

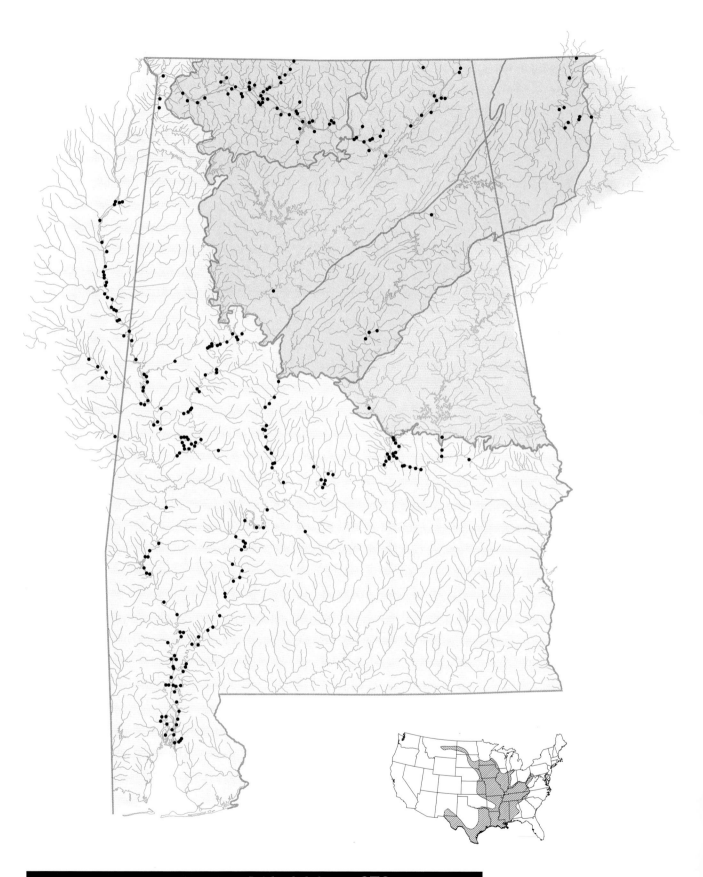

SMALLMOUTH BUFFALO   *Ictiobus bubalus*   270 STATIONS

Ictiobus bubalus

(Rafinesque, 1818)

ETYMOLOGY:

Ictiobus—bull fish

bubalus—buffalo

Paint Rock River, Marshall County, 19 May 1993, 14 in (355 mm) SL male, GSA 4475

CHARACTERISTICS: The smallmouth buffalo is a deep-bodied sucker; its maximum depth goes 2.7 or fewer times into its standard length. Its mouth is small and horizontal, with a distinctly grooved upper lip. The upper jaw is much shorter than the snout. A wide-based, falcate dorsal fin contains 25 to 31 soft rays. The complete lateral line has 35 to 37 pored scales. Body and fins are beige to slate gray for most of the year, turning darker during the spawning season. See Rafinesque (1818b) for original description.

ADULT SIZE: 24 to 35 in (610 to 890 mm)

DISTRIBUTION: The Tennessee drainage records included in Lee (1979) and Boschung (1992) are based mainly on specimens collected by the Tennessee Valley Authority in 1936 and 1938. Jandebeur (1972) reports three locations in the Elk River. From 1991 to 1993, we collected individuals at 34 stations in the Tennessee River drainage, where the species was abundant and seemed to be a favorite host for chestnut and Ohio lampreys. The species is widespread and abundant in the Mobile basin, primarily below the Fall Line.

HABITAT AND BIOLOGY: The smallmouth buffalo is a riverine species, although juveniles infrequently occur in small streams as well. This species is especially abundant along riverbanks and in open waters of reservoirs. Wrenn (1969) reports that smallmouth buffalo in Wheeler Reservoir on the Tennessee River spawn in early to middle spring, when water temperatures reach 59°–62°F (15°–16°C); his observation is supported by our collections of gravid, tuberculate adults in April and early May. Etnier and Starnes (1993) note upstream spawning migrations of this species in the Little Tennessee River before the construction of the Tellico Dam. On 14 May 1993, we collected a large number of tuberculate adults in very swift water below Lake Tuscaloosa Dam on the North River, near Tuscaloosa. Active spawning was occurring in the rapids, since most of the individuals we examined were running milt and eggs on light pressure. Smallmouth buffalo reach eight years of age and total lengths of approximately 22 inches (Wrenn, 1969). Individuals in the Tennessee drainage eat mostly bivalve mollusks (primarily **Corbicula**), copepods, and aquatic diptera.

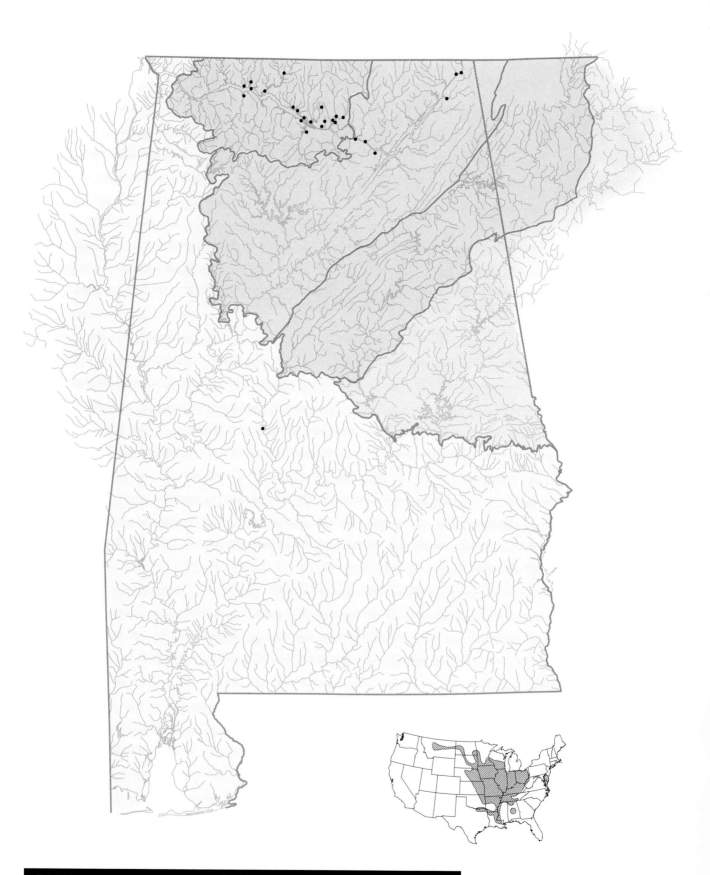

BIGMOUTH BUFFALO *Ictiobus cyprinellus* **26 STATIONS**

Ictiobus cyprinellus
(Valenciennes, 1844)

ETYMOLOGY:

Ictiobus—bull fish

cyprinellus—small carp

Town Creek, Lawrence County, 15 July 1992, 11.6 in (295 mm) SL male, GSA 4276

CHARACTERISTICS: The bigmouth buffalo has a large body and head and a terminal, oblique mouth. The front of the lightly grooved upper lip is nearly level with the lower margin of the eye. The dorsal fin contains 24 to 32 soft rays, and its free margin is falcate. The eye is small compared to that in other members of the genus *Ictiobus,* and it is located closer to the tip of the snout than to the rear of the operculum. The back is charcoal gray to olive brown, shading to light gray or cream on the venter. All fins are usually gray or black with white edges. See Cuvier and Valenciennes (1844) for original description.

ADULT SIZE: 24 to 35 in (610 to 890 mm). This species is the largest member of the sucker family in Alabama. A 50-pound specimen was landed in Lake Guntersville in 1982.

DISTRIBUTION: Biologists with the Tennessee Valley Authority collected bigmouth buffalo at 17 Tennessee River stations in Alabama from 1936 through 1941. Jandebeur (1972) mentions a previous TVA collection in the lower reaches of the Elk River. We collected bigmouth buffalo at seven stations during our 1991–93 surveys. Future gill-net sampling in the Tennessee River proper and in the mouths of its large tributaries will probably increase the species' known range. Moreover, individuals could eventually enter the upper Tombigbee River via the Tennessee-Tombigbee Waterway. The single record of bigmouth buffalo in Perry Lake, Perry County, resulted from purposeful introduction during studies at the federal fish hatchery near Marion (Phillip L. Kilpatrick, 1992, personal communication). A few large, possibly nonreproducing individuals still inhabited Perry Lake as late as 1992.

HABITAT AND BIOLOGY: This species occurs in large rivers and reservoirs, feeding on larval insects and other benthic invertebrates. Little is known of its life history in Alabama. Bigmouth buffalo may have been more common in previous years; because individuals live in deep water, it is a difficult species to collect. Minckley et al. (1970) report that bigmouth buffalo feed along the bottom, consuming algae, organic material, and aquatic insect larvae. Spawning probably occurs in shallow backwaters and tributaries of reservoirs.

349

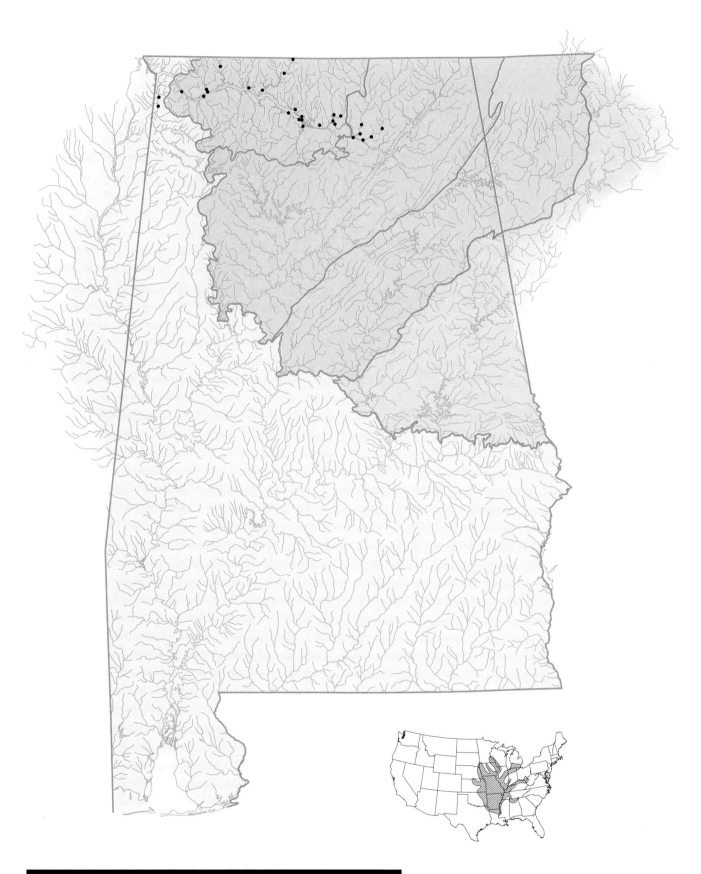

BLACK BUFFALO   *Ictiobus niger*   28 STATIONS

Ictiobus niger
(Rafinesque, 1819)

ETYMOLOGY:

Ictiobus—bull fish

niger—black

Paint Rock River, Marshall County, 19 May 1993, 19.9 in (505 mm) SL male, GSA 4475

CHARACTERISTICS: Adult black and smallmouth buffalo are easy to distinguish, but the task is more confusing with small individuals. The mouth on the black buffalo is located just beneath the front end of the snout, and it is slightly oblique; the mouth on the smallmouth buffalo is located in a more posterior position, and it is nearly horizontal. Body depth of the black buffalo goes 2.8 or more times into its standard length; for the smallmouth, the factor is 2.7 or fewer times. The black buffalo's nape region is rounded or only weakly keeled, and large breeding males develop a distinctive hump on the back near the dorsal fin origin. The lateral line contains 36 to 39 scales. The dorsal fin has from 27 to 31 soft rays. Overall body and fin color is dark gray or blue to bronze or olive.

ADULT SIZE: 20 to 34 in (508 to 863 mm)

DISTRIBUTION: Ichthyologists do not often encounter this species in Alabama because it is fairly uncommon and individuals are difficult to collect with standard sampling techniques. Tennessee Valley Authority biologists collected black buffalo at several stations in state waters from 1936 to 1941. Feeman (1987) notes individuals from the Elk River near Fayetteville, Tennessee. We collected black buffalo with electrofishing gear at seven stations in 1992 and 1993. Because most of the individuals had deep blue to black body colors, we suspect that they had entered Bear and Cypress creeks and the Flint and Paint Rock rivers to spawn. Black buffalo may eventually enter the upper Tombigbee River via the Tennessee-Tombigbee Waterway.

HABITAT AND BIOLOGY: The black buffalo inhabits the lower reaches of large streams, rivers, and reservoirs. Minckley et al. (1970) report that black buffalo feed on the Asian clam *Corbicula*, algae, and plankton. Our observations, which are supported by interviews with local anglers and commercial fishermen, indicate that spawning occurs in the shallow backwaters of major tributaries in April and May.

REMARKS: While sampling on the Tennessee River in August 1992, we met a commercial fisherman who referred to black buffalo as "blue rooters" because they turn blue during the spawning season and frequently kick up muddy plumes while rooting for food along the bottoms of shallow backwaters.

HARELIP SUCKER *Lagochila lacera* **1 STATION**

Lagochila lacera

Jordan and Brayton, 1877

ETYMOLOGY:

Lagochila—harelip

lacera—torn

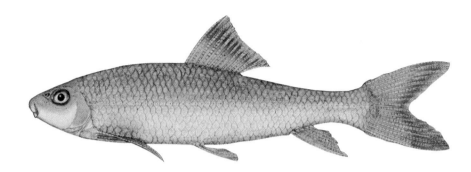

Drawing courtesy of Wayne C. Starnes. Based on specimens from the U.S. National Museum, USNM 36331 (5.2 in [131 mm] SL) and USNM 68853 (5.3 in [135 mm] SL).

CHARACTERISTICS: Two mouth characteristics separate the harelip sucker from all other catostomids: a nonprotractile upper lip and a lower lip that is divided into two distinct lobes. The head is short, accounting for only 20 to 22 percent of the standard length. The dorsal fin has 11 or 12 soft rays, and its free margin is slightly concave. The lateral line is complete and contains 42 to 46 scales. Body colors of freshly caught specimens are described by Jordan and Brayton (1877) and Jordan (1882). The back is olive to brownish, and the venter and sides are silver or white. The lower fins are slightly orange, while the remaining fins are cream to dusky. The dorsal fin is dusky and edged in black. Although of different genera, this species and the blacktail redhorse in the Mobile basin have similar body colors.

ADULT SIZE: Most museum specimens are small, averaging less than 7 inches (178 mm). Trautman (1981) relates that J. H. Klippart (1878) sent D. S. Jordan "a fine large specimen" collected in 1878 "at Columbus, just below the State dam" in the Scioto River. Jordan apparently refers to the specimen in reporting the maximum length of the species as "1 to 1.5 feet" in his 1882 report on Ohio fishes. Jordan later

donated the specimen to the Cincinnati Society of Natural History (Trautman, 1981), where it was lost.

DISTRIBUTION: The harelip sucker was first collected in 1859 and described in 1877. The last specimen was collected in 1893. By 1970, the species was believed to be extinct (Jenkins, 1970). The only known collection in Alabama came from Cypress Creek, Lauderdale County, in 1889. On the slight chance of collecting this species, we repeatedly sampled the lower flowing reaches of Cypress Creek in 1992 and 1993. Although we examined a total of 30 species, including six suckers, our efforts were unsuccessful. Jordan (1882) reports receiving a specimen from the Elk River, probably from Tennessee.

HABITAT AND BIOLOGY: Harelip sucker collections came from clear, gravel- or rock-bottomed streams with moderate to swift currents (Jenkins and Burkhead, 1993). Very little information exists on its precise habitat and life history, though Klippart (1878) relates that these fishes were called May suckers because they spawned in May. Ichthyologists speculate that harelip suckers may have become extinct when their habitats were modified by siltation.

353

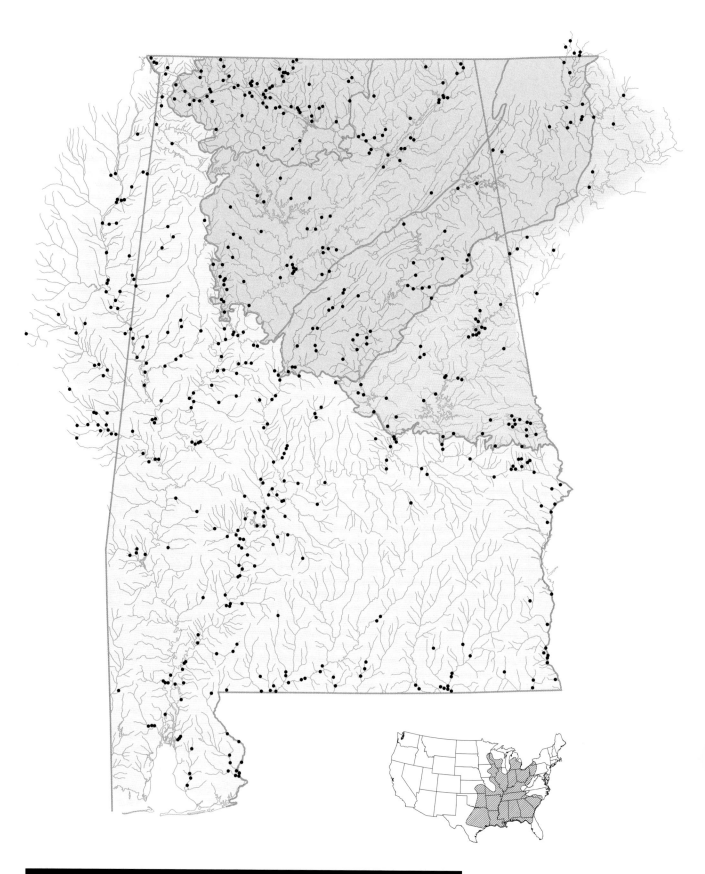

SPOTTED SUCKER   *Minytrema melanops*   536 STATIONS

354

Minytrema melanops
(Rafinesque, 1820)

ETYMOLOGY:
Minytrema—reduced
aperture, referring to the
reduced lateral line
melanops—black appearance

Bay Minette Creek, Baldwin County, 15 June 1993, 8.7 in (220 mm) SL male, GSA 4481

CHARACTERISTICS: Spotted suckers are easily distinguished from other catostomid species by several longitudinal rows of black or brown spots (one per scale) along the sides of the body. The dorsal fin contains 11 or 12 soft rays, is slightly concave, and may be edged in black along its free margin. The body has 43 or more lateral scales. The lateral line is poorly developed or absent. The back is light tan on small individuals to dark olive green on adults; the venter is usually cream to white.

ADULT SIZE: 12 to 18 in (300 to 460 mm)

DISTRIBUTION: A widespread species, the spotted sucker occurs from Texas through much of the Mississippi basin and east through the Gulf and Atlantic drainages to North Carolina. This species is distributed in every river system of Alabama.

HABITAT AND BIOLOGY: Spotted suckers inhabit a variety of habitats, including rivers, reservoirs, swamps, small and large streams, and springs. They flourish in little or no current over sand and mud substrates. Greatest densities occur in swamps, overflow pools, and the backwater sloughs of many rivers, especially in

the Mobile Delta. The spawning season is from late February into April, with males running milt for some time before and after spawning. We have collected males running milt on light pressure in the Black Warrior River, Tuscaloosa County, in late January and below Millers Ferry Lock and Dam, Wilcox County, in late February. Adult suckers also enter small stream tributaries of rivers and reservoirs to spawn. We observed a large number of spotted suckers about 12 to 16 inches in total length spawning in Hillabee Creek, a tributary to the Tallapoosa River, on 23 March 1988. Spawning was occurring in a long riffle containing gravel and cobble substrates and a moderate to swift current. Males were heavily tuberculate and had a pink-red lateral band; the area above was tinted with lavender or gray. We also observed dozens of heavily tuberculate spotted suckers in high spawning condition in the lower reaches of Uchee Creek, Russell County, on 6 April 1993. By late May and early June, we have occasionally found spotted suckers that have spawned and are near death. Most juveniles migrate downstream when they reach total lengths of 4 to 6 inches. Diet includes algae, organic bottom material, and associated aquatic invertebrates.

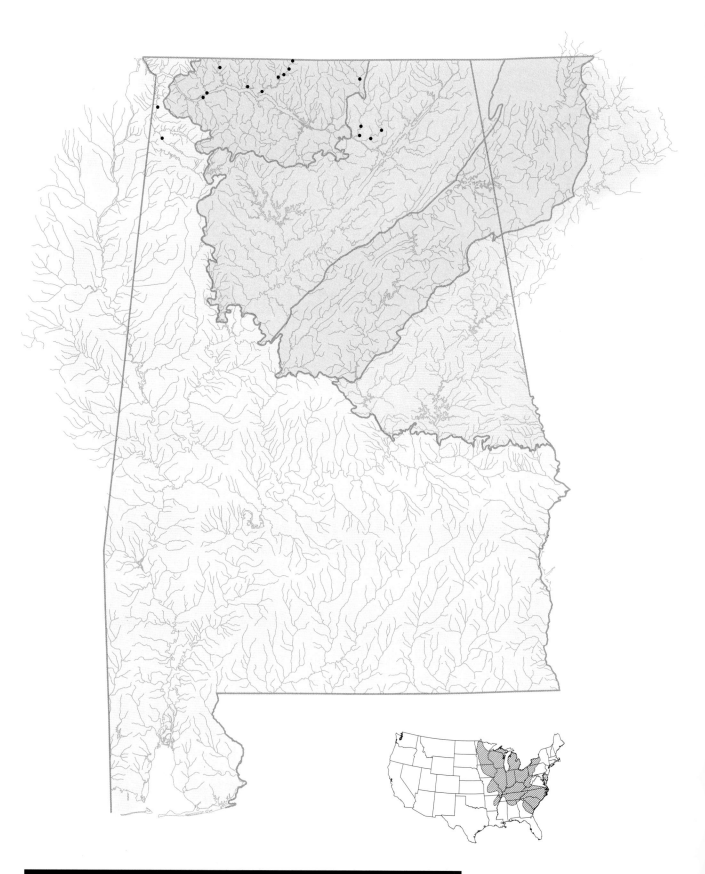

Moxostoma anisurum

(Rafinesque, 1820)

ETYMOLOGY:

Moxostoma—mouth to suck

anisurum—unequal tail

Paint Rock River, Marshall County, 19 May 1993, 11.4 in (290 mm) SL male, GSA 4475

CHARACTERISTICS: The silver redhorse and the river redhorse, *Moxostoma carinatum*, can be distinguished by fin color, lip shape, and number of dorsal fin rays. Silver redhorses have a light gray to tan dorsal fin, and the pectoral, pelvic, and anal fins are beige to orange. The halves of the silver redhorse's lower lip meet at an acute angle, and the dorsal fin contains 14 to 16 rays. The river redhorse, on the other hand, usually has bright red caudal and anal fins, lower lips that meet at an obtuse angle; and a dorsal fin that contains 12 or 13 rays.

ADULT SIZE: 12 to 28 in (300 to 711 mm). This species and the river redhorse are the two largest *Moxostoma* species in Alabama.

DISTRIBUTION: The southern bend of the Tennessee River drainage marks the southern extent of the silver redhorse's range in Alabama. Jenkins (1980a) and Boschung (1992) include records collected by Tennessee Valley Authority biologists in 1936 and 1938. None are reported from Bear Creek (Wall, 1968). Jandebeur (1972) includes one Elk River collection from Tennessee, and Feeman (1987) includes one

from the upper Paint Rock River. We collected silver redhorses at 10 new stations in the Tennessee River drainage from 1991 to 1993. Future sampling will undoubtedly expand the known range of this species in state waters.

HABITAT AND BIOLOGY: We have collected silver redhorses in the Tennessee River proper and in medium-sized and large streams having moderate to fast currents and silt, sand, gravel, and bedrock substrates. Interestingly, most of the individuals we examined during our electrofishing surveys ranged from 10 to 20 inches long; we found no small individuals. Hackney et al. (1971) report on spawning time, age, growth, and the sport fishery for this species in the Flint River, a tributary to Wheeler Reservoir in northern Alabama. Spawning occurs in March and April over gravel shoal areas in moderate to swift currents. Food items consist primarily of the Asian clam *Corbicula* and aquatic insect larvae. Silver redhorses live for up to eight years. This species is an excellent food fish (Hackney et al., 1971), but because its flesh contains small intermuscular bones it must be thoroughly cooked before being served.

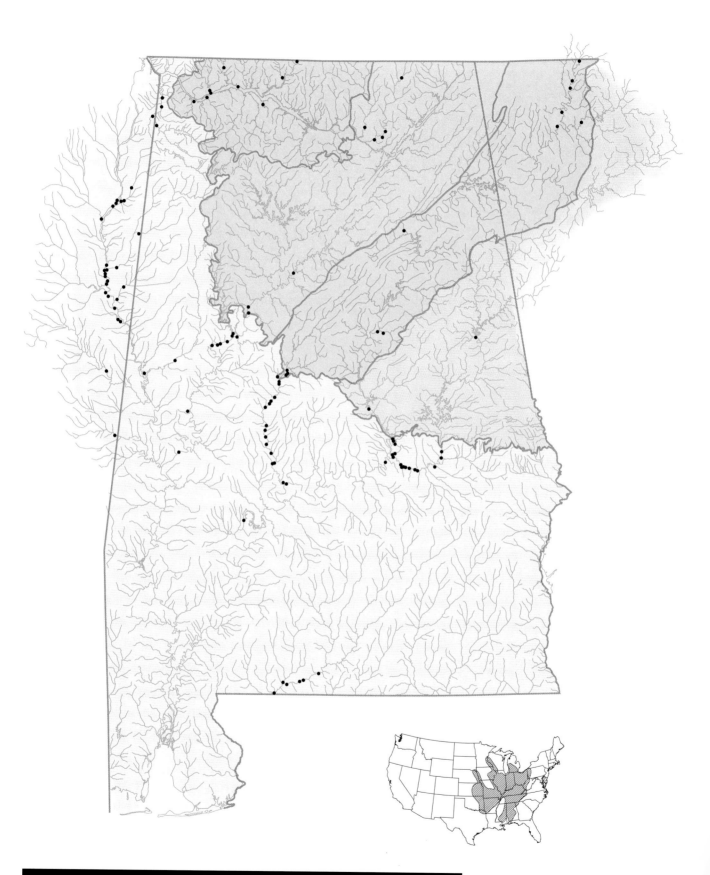

Moxostoma carinatum

(Cope, 1870)

ETYMOLOGY:

Moxostoma—mouth to suck

carinatum—keel

North River, Tuscaloosa County, 1 March 1993, 10.6 in (270 mm) SL male, GSA 4379

CHARACTERISTICS: Adults of this beautiful species attain a respectable size, weighing as much as 8 to 9 pounds (3.6 to 4.1 kg). The head is massive, its length going about four times into the standard length. The mouth is large, and upper and lower lips are strongly plicate. The dorsal fin usually contains 12 to 14 soft rays, and its free margin is straight or only slightly concave. The lateral line has 42 to 47 scales. Individual scales have dark, crescent-shaped bases. Body color is pale olive on the back and cream on the venter, but the entire fish usually has a brassy orange tinge. Fins are a moderate to bright orangish red, and the anal fin occasionally has bright yellow streaks. See Cope (1870a) for original description and the species account for the silver redhorse, *Moxostoma anisurum*, for information on distinguishing river from silver redhorses.

ADULT SIZE: 12 to 28 in (300 to 711 mm)

DISTRIBUTION: Our sampling efforts indicate that river redhorses are more widely distributed in Alabama than was previously believed. The Cahaba River is the species' stronghold. In recent years, however, we have collected and released numerous individuals in other locations, including a downstream range extension in the Alabama River system to below Millers Ferry Lock and Dam. Pierson et al. (1986) extended the upstream range in the Tallapoosa River system to below Harris Dam. We collected river redhorses at 10 new stations in the Tennessee drainage in 1992 and 1993. A small population exists in the Conecuh River and in Murder Creek in Escambia County. Lack of lower Tombigbee River records may be due to insufficient sampling.

HABITAT AND BIOLOGY: River redhorses occur in medium-sized and large streams having moderate to swift currents over sand, gravel, and cobble substrates. We have also collected them in rivers and reservoirs where currents are slow and substrates consist mainly of sand and silt. The Asian clam *Corbicula* and aquatic insect larvae are primary food items. River redhorses spawn in the Cahaba River in April when water temperatures reach 71° to 76°F (21° to 24.4°C) (Hackney et al. 1968). We observed spawning in the lower Coosa River in late April 1987 and collected tuberculate males and females running eggs below Millers Ferry Lock and Dam in April 1995.

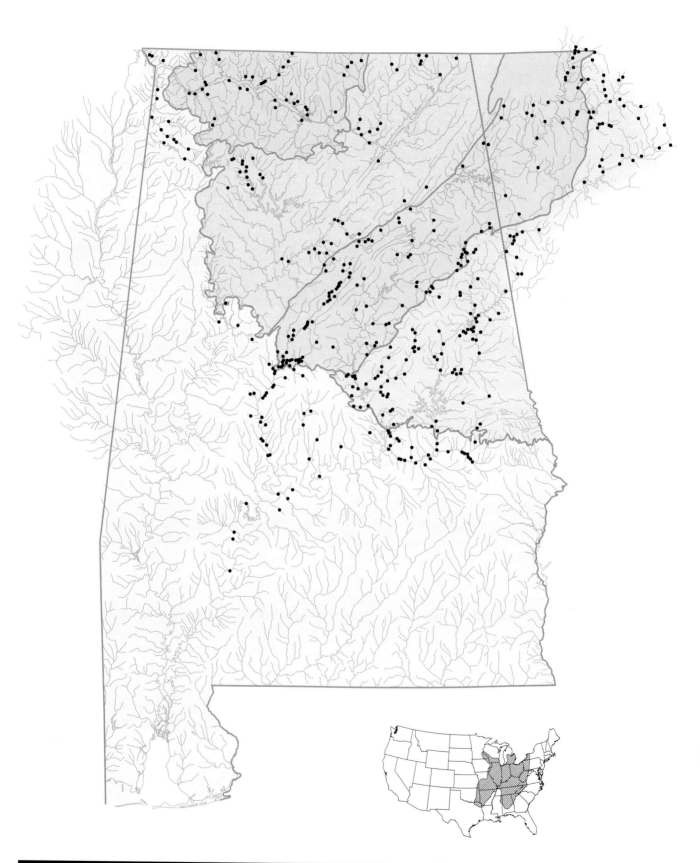

Moxostoma duquesnei

(Lesueur, 1817)

ETYMOLOGY:

Moxostoma—mouth to suck

duquesnei—named for Fort

Duquesne, Pennsylvania, the

type locality

Shoal Creek, Lauderdale County, 15 July 1992, 7.3 in (185 mm) SL male, GSA 4277

CHARACTERISTICS: The maximum depth of this slender-bodied redhorse goes 3.7 to 4.4 times into its standard length. The caudal peduncle is long and slender. The dorsal fin generally contains 12 or 13 rays, and its free margin is straight or slightly convex. The black redhorse is the only *Moxostoma* that has 10 pelvic fin rays; all other species have nine. The lateral line is complete, with 44 to 47 scales. Upper and lower lips are plicate, and their lobes meet at a very obtuse angle. The back is olive to brown, the sides silvery to light tan, and the venter cream. In adults, the lower fins are yellow to reddish orange, and the dorsal and caudal fins are olive or slate. Some fish have a pale reddish tail. See Lesueur (1817b) for original description. Jenkins (1970) notes that the Mobile basin population is distinct.

ADULT SIZE: 10 to 15 in (254 to 380 mm)

DISTRIBUTION: The black redhorse has an interesting distribution in Alabama. Collection locations occur above and below the Fall Line in the eastern Mobile basin but are lacking in the western portion. The species' occurrence in the headwater tributaries to the Sipsey Fork of the Black Warrior River system could be the result of faunal exchange with Bear Creek of the Tennessee River drainage. Populations in eastern tributaries to the Locust Fork seem to indicate an exchange with the Cahaba or Coosa river systems.

HABITAT AND BIOLOGY: Most collections are from medium-sized or small streams having moderate to swift currents and rock, gravel, and sand substrates. We have observed groups of black redhorses assembled for spawning in April and May. Males collected in a Coosa River tributary in Etowah County in early May were running milt on light pressure. R. D. Suttkus reports collecting males running milt and females running eggs in 57°F (14°C) water at a tributary of Souwilpa Creek, Choctaw County, on 9 April 1988. Bowman (1970) notes that male black redhorses select spawning habitats with precise concentrations of fine and coarse gravel and sand at depths of 12 to 24 inches. Two males usually spawn with a single female. Adults reach sexual maturity at three years of age and can live for up to 10 years. Black redhorses consume a variety of benthic invertebrates, especially crustaceans and aquatic insects.

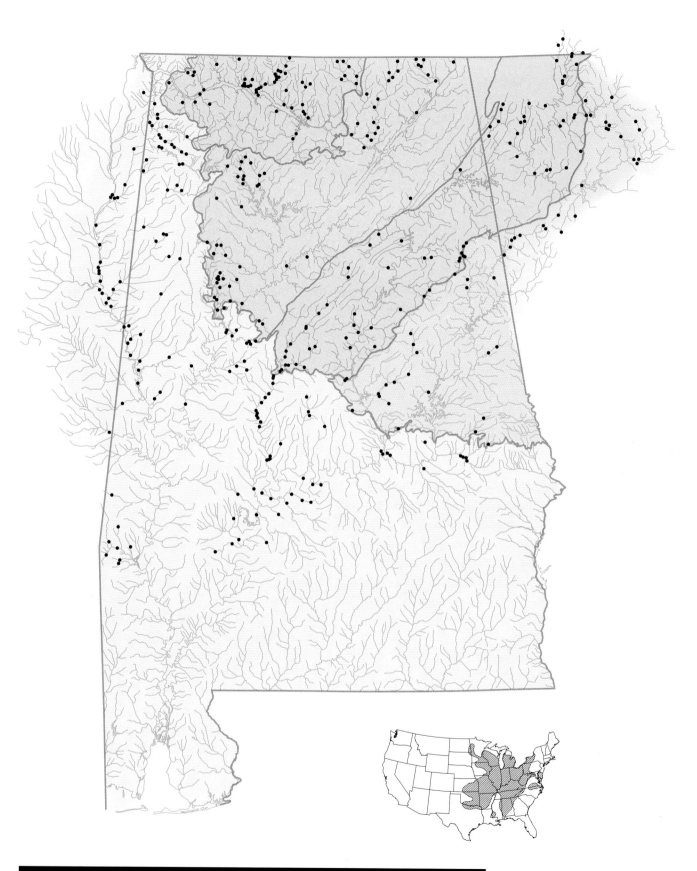

GOLDEN REDHORSE *Moxostoma erythrurum* **376 STATIONS**

Moxostoma erythrurum

(Rafinesque, 1818)

ETYMOLOGY:

Moxostoma—mouth to suck

erythrurum—red-tailed

Cedar Creek, Franklin County, 10 March 1993, 3.1 in (79 mm) SL male, GSA 4369

CHARACTERISTICS: This terete redhorse has a large head, with a length approximately 24 percent of the standard length. Upper and lower lips are plicate, and the rear edges of the lower lip meet in either a U or a V shape. The dorsal fin contains 12 or 13 soft rays, and its free margin is concave. The pelvic fin has eight or nine rays. The lateral line has 39 to 42 scales. The back varies from olive to light brown, the sides frequently have a dark lateral stripe, and the venter is cream. Fins are generally light gray to clear but may be tinged with yellow or orange during the spawning season. See Rafinesque (1818b) for original description.

ADULT SIZE: 12 to 20 in (300 to 508 mm). Slightly larger individuals are found in the Tennessee River proper.

DISTRIBUTION: The golden redhorse has been collected in all river systems of Alabama's Mobile basin, although its numbers diminish in the southern half of the state. Mettee et al. (1987) report a disjunct population of golden redhorses in Okatuppa Creek, a tributary of the lower Tombigbee drainage; the population was discovered there during a survey of streams that drain the Gilbertown oil field.

HABITAT AND BIOLOGY: Golden redhorses inhabit almost all aquatic environments in Alabama, including rivers, reservoirs, and small and large streams. In the Tennessee River drainage, they frequently occur with spotted suckers and black, silver, shorthead, and river redhorses. Like other members of this genus, golden redhorses migrate into moderate or small streams to spawn in April and early May, and they leave the area afterward. Etnier and Starnes (1993) report that golden redhorses generally spawn later than do black redhorses, depending on their latitude. As the young grow into juveniles, they progressively move downstream. Carlander (1969) reports that the golden redhorse's diet consists mainly of mayflies, caddisflies, and midge larvae. Age and growth data presented by Carlander (1969) suggest that in more northern states golden redhorses live from nine to 11 years. Data for populations in Alabama are not available.

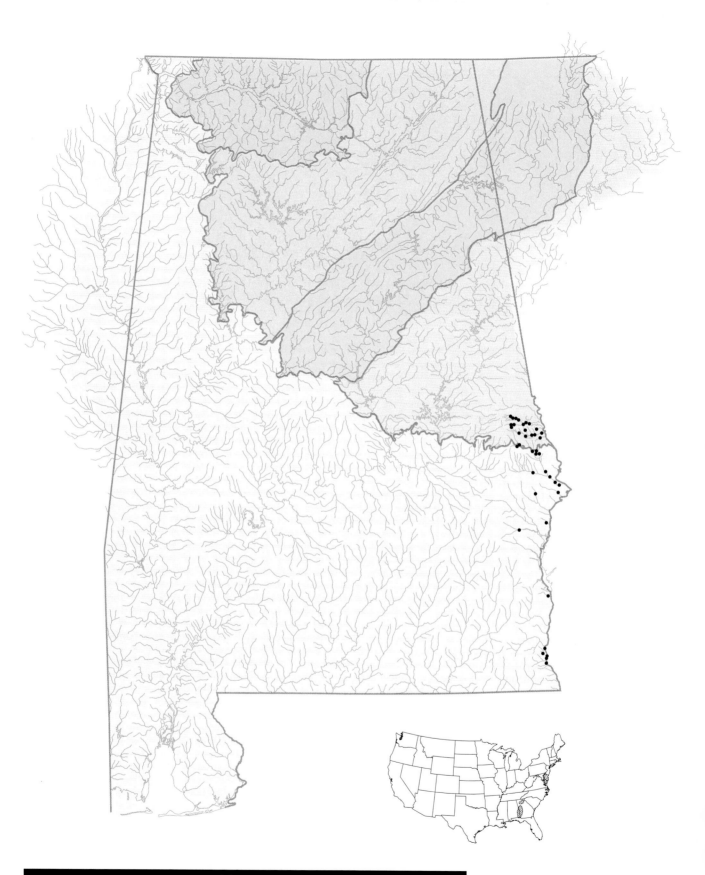

Moxostoma lachneri

Robins and Raney, 1956

ETYMOLOGY:

Moxostoma—mouth to suck *lachneri*—in honor of Ernest A. Lachner, noted North American ichthyologist

Uchee Creek, Russell County, 8 April 1993, 9.6 in (245 mm) SL male, GSA 4417

CHARACTERISTICS: The head of this species is long and rather pointed, and the body is cylindrical. The caudal peduncle is long and slender. The dorsal fin contains 12 soft rays, and its free margin is slightly concave. On the caudal fin, the upper lobe is distinctly pointed, while the lower lobe is slightly larger and distinctly rounded. The lower ray in the lower lobe of the caudal fin is usually white. Lateral line scales usually total 45 or 46. The greater jumprock is the only *Moxostoma* species in Alabama with 16 rows of scales surrounding its caudal peduncle; all other species have 12 to 14 rows. The lips are plicate; the posterior margin of the lower lips is broadly U-shaped. The back is light to dark olive, the venter is cream, and several dark, horizontal stripes, which may be either indistinct or obvious, may occur along the sides. The anal fin is usually blue-gray in adults, but all other fins are dusky gray. Burr (1979a) notes that on breeding adults the caudal and anal fins are a rich bluish gray; the back is an iridescent, silvery black, fading ventrally; and tubercles occur on the anal fin rays and rays of the lower caudal fin lobe of males only.

ADULT SIZE: 12 to 16 in (300 to 406 mm)

DISTRIBUTION: In Alabama, the greater jumprock is limited to the Chattahoochee River drainage.

HABITAT AND BIOLOGY: The primary habitat includes large and small streams having moderate to swift currents and gravel and rock substrates. Our collections of gravid females indicate that spawning occurs in May and June. Burr (1979a) observed spawning in the Chattahoochee River in White County, Georgia, on 10 and 11 June 1976. Water temperature was 67°F (19°C). In swift current over gravel, two males aligned themselves on either side of a female. With their bodies pressed tightly together, the three quivered as the eggs and sperm were released. Shortly thereafter, the trio separated and moved slightly downstream to join other members of the spawning aggregation.

REMARKS: The type locality is an unnamed tributary to Hatchechubbee Creek near Seale, Russell County, Alabama.

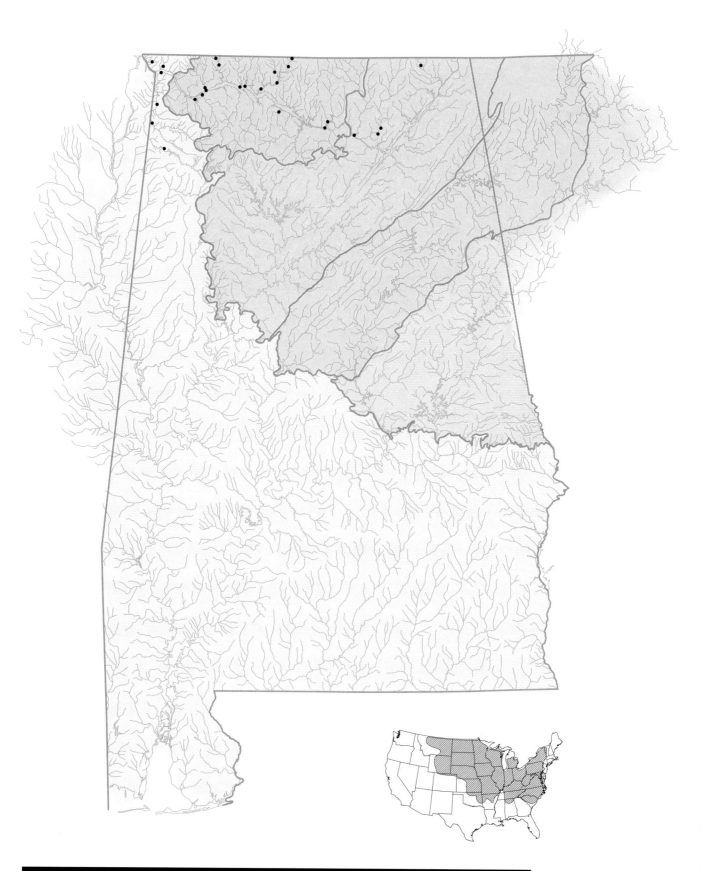

SHORTHEAD REDHORSE   *Moxostoma macrolepidotum*   **26 STATIONS**

Moxostoma macrolepidotum

(Lesueur, 1817)

ETYMOLOGY:

Moxostoma—mouth to suck
macrolepidotum—large-scaled

Shoal Creek, Lauderdale County, 15 July 1992, 11.6 in (295 mm) SL male, GSA 4277

CHARACTERISTICS: This slender redhorse has a short head, its length ranging from 18 to 23 percent of standard length. The lateral line is complete, with 38 to 45 scales. The dorsal fin usually has 12 rays, and its free margin is falcate. Lips on the small mouth are subplicate. In color, this beautiful fish strongly resembles the river redhorse, *Moxostoma carinatum*. The back is olive green, the venter is cream or white, and the entire body usually has a pale yellowish or brassy gold tinge. The river redhorse can be distinguished by its larger head (21 to 26 percent of standard length) and the straight or slightly convex outer margin of its dorsal fin. Most of the scales on the shorthead redhorse's body have reflective, crescent-shaped black spots near their bases. The dorsal and caudal fins are moderate to bright orange. Fins on the ventral side of the body are light to bright lemon yellow. See Lesueur (1817b) for original description. Jenkins (1970) recognizes three subspecies; one of them, *M. macrolepidotum breviceps*, occurs in the Ohio, Cumberland, and Tennessee river drainages.

ADULT SIZE: 16 to 18 in (406 to 460 mm)

DISTRIBUTION: The southern bend of the Tennessee River drainage is the southern limit of this species' range. Most locations cited in Jenkins (1980b) and Boschung (1992) were collected by Tennessee Valley Authority biologists in 1936 and 1938. From 1991 to 1993, we collected this species at 12 stations in the Tennessee River drainage. New locations include Panther, Bear, Cypress, and Shoal creeks and the Elk and Paint Rock rivers.

HABITAT AND BIOLOGY: Shorthead redhorses occur along the margins of the Tennessee River proper and in adjacent impounded creek mouths, but they are most abundant in flowing sections of the Paint Rock, Elk, and Flint rivers and just downstream of large shoals in Cypress and Shoal creeks—areas with gravel and bedrock substrates and moderate to swift currents. Burr and Morris (1977) report spawning, which usually involves a female and two males, in May in Illinois. Our collections of gravid, brightly colored adults indicate that spawning in Alabama occurs from late April into May. Etnier and Starnes (1993) report that adults in Tennessee become sexually mature at four years and that the life span can reach eight years.

367

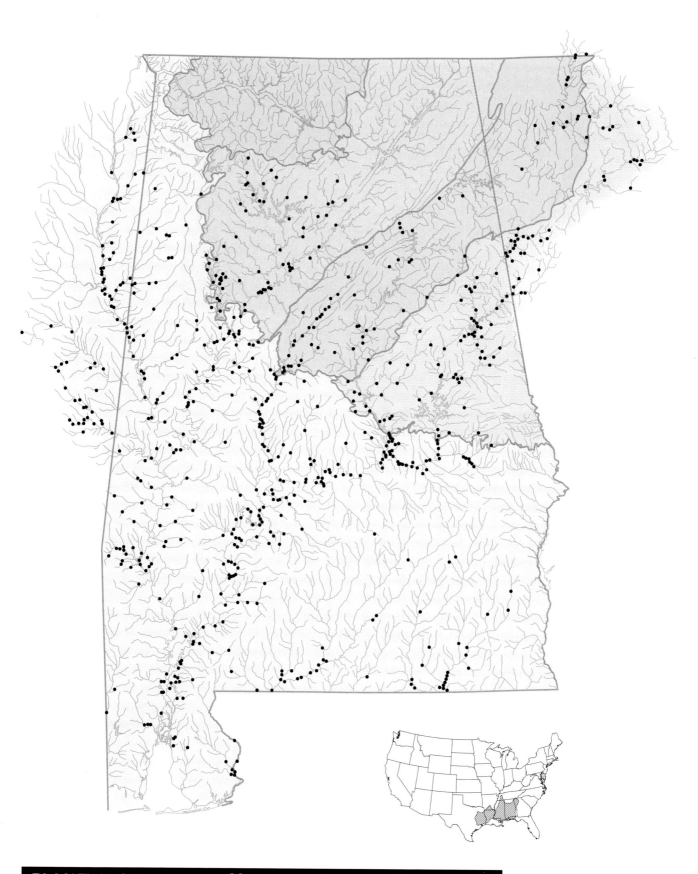

Moxostoma poecilurum

(Jordan, 1877)

ETYMOLOGY:

Moxostoma—mouth to suck

poecilurum—varicolored tail

North River, Tuscaloosa County, 1 March 1993, 9.4 in (240 mm) SL male, GSA 4379

CHARACTERISTICS: The blacktail redhorse is characterized by a prominent black or dusky stripe on the lower lobe of its tricolored caudal fin. The upper lobe and upper part of the lower lobe are bright orange, and the lower rays beneath the dark stripe are white. The dorsal fin has 12 or 13 soft rays and a black and straight or slightly convex free margin. The lips are plicate, the two halves of the lower lip joining at an obtuse angle. Lateral line scales number 41 to 44. The back is olive to light green, and the venter is white. A dark crescent occurs at each scale base, and dusky longitudinal stripes occur along the sides. Particularly during the spring spawning season, most fins are moderate to bright rust or orange. See Jordan (1877b) for original description.

ADULT SIZE: 10 to 16 in (254 to 406 mm)

DISTRIBUTION: The blacktail redhorse is distributed throughout the Mobile basin, where it is the most commonly encountered *Moxostoma* species, and in coastal systems from the Escatawpa to the Choctawhatchee drainage. It is replaced in the Chattahoochee drainage by the "grayfin redhorse" (see the following species account). We have never collected the blacktail redhorse in the Tennessee River drainage, but future sampling may reveal that it has entered there via the Tennessee-Tombigbee Waterway.

HABITAT AND BIOLOGY: Blacktail redhorses are widespread and often abundant in rivers, reservoirs, small to large streams, swamps, and the Mobile Delta. They occur in swift to standing water over sand, silt, rock, or gravel substrates and around aquatic vegetation. Spawning occurs in March and April. Adults frequently enter small streams to spawn and leave shortly thereafter. We collected substantial numbers of brightly colored, gravid adult blacktail redhorses below Millers Ferry Lock and Dam on the Alabama River in late March and early April 1995. Tailwaters below this and other locks and dams provide good spawning habitat. Kilken (1972) reports that pond-raised fingerlings feed on small crustaceans and aquatic insect larvae but also consume pelleted food.

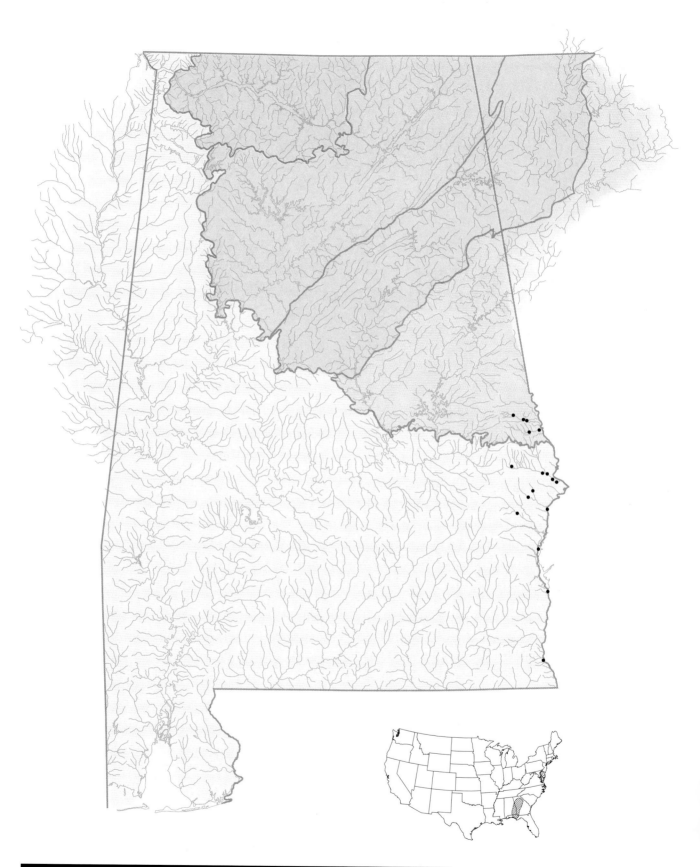

"GRAYFIN REDHORSE" *Moxostoma* sp. **17 STATIONS**

Moxostoma sp.

ETYMOLOGY:

Moxostoma—mouth to suck

Uchee Creek, Russell County, 6 April 1993, 13.2 in (335 mm) SL female, GSA 4411

CHARACTERISTICS: The "grayfin redhorse" has the same general body shape as the blacktail redhorse, but it lacks the distinctive black-and-white striping on the lower lobe of the caudal fin. Vertical and paired fins are gray rather than the light orange usually observed on blacktail redhorses. Live "grayfin redhorses" usually have a series of dusky stripes along the sides.

ADULT SIZE: 10 to 16 in (254 to 406 mm)

DISTRIBUTION: "Grayfin" and blacktail redhorses have allopatric (nonoverlapping) ranges in Alabama: The former is limited to the Chattahoochee River system, while the latter occurs only as far east as the Choctawhatchee River system, which lies immediately west of the Chattahoochee. Gilbert and Snelson (1992) report that dam construction has eliminated much of this species' riverine habitat along the Alabama-Georgia state line. During our boat electrofishing surveys from 1993 through 1995, we collected and released "grayfin red-horses" in the downstream sections of several large Chattahoochee tributaries near the Alabama-Georgia line.

HABITAT AND BIOLOGY: This species is often abundant in low-gradient streams characterized by moderate or slow currents and sand and silt substrates. Our observations indicate that spawning occurs in March and April. According to an unpublished study completed by McSwain and Pasch (1972) and reported by Gilbert and Snelson (1992), spawning occurs in moderate current over clean sand and gravel substrates from February through April. Principal food items include aquatic insect larvae, bivalve mollusks, and organic detritus. Maximum life span is around six years.

REMARKS: The taxonomic status of this species is being reviewed by R. E. Jenkins.

BULLHEAD CATFISHES

Ictaluridae

Members of the family Ictaluridae have hard, bony spines in the dorsal and pectoral fins, eight fleshy barbels around the mouth (four above and four below), a scaleless body, and a fleshy adipose fin between the dorsal and caudal fins. Thirty-eight species of ictalurid catfishes, which are native to North America, occur in the United States. In Alabama, anglers probably recognize many of the nine large catfish species, but few realize that 10 species collectively known as madtoms, most of which do not exceed eight inches as adults, also occur in the state.

Ictalurid catfishes can be separated into three groups according to differences in caudal and adipose fin structures. Blue and channel catfishes in the genus ***Ictalurus*** have a forked tail and a small, free adipose fin located on the back between the dorsal and caudal fins. Bullhead catfishes, including six species in the genus ***Ameiurus***, and the flathead catfish, ***Pylodictis olivaris***, have a free adipose fin, but the rear margin of the caudal fin is either rounded or straight. The madtoms, which are in the genus ***Noturus***, are distinctive because the adipose fin is fused to the leading edge of a rounded or straight caudal fin; the adipose fin looks more like a continuous fleshy ridge than a separate fin.

Blue, channel, and flathead catfishes are the largest members of the family in Alabama. In several rivers, we have collected individuals that weighed from 40 to 60 pounds. Anglers occasionally catch even larger individuals on trotlines and floating jug lines. Maximum weights of most bullhead catfishes rarely exceed 8 pounds, an exception being the white catfish, ***Ameiurus catus,*** which occasionally reaches 10 to 15 pounds. Madtoms generally weigh only a few ounces.

Catfishes are summer spawners that deposit their eggs in saucer-shaped depressions or nests they construct in natural cavities and crevices in streams and rivers. At catfish farms, brood catfish routinely spawn in five-gallon buckets or milk cans placed on the bottoms of shallow brood ponds. Male catfishes are extremely territorial after spawning and will aggressively defend their eggs.

Small catfishes, known as squealers, generally remain in schools until they become several inches long. We have encountered hundreds of squealers while seining at night along sand and gravel bars of large rivers. Although they have sharp dorsal and pectoral spines, young catfishes are not always protected from predation. During a trip along the Black Warrior River one night in 1991, we collected and released hundreds of squealer channel catfish that had congregated along some silt-covered sandbars. In the same net hauls, we caught some fairly large water snakes. To our dismay, the snakes were so intent on eating the young catfishes that they ignored our efforts to remove them from the seine.

Catfish aquaculture and processing are important industries in west and central Alabama. In 1995, farmers raised 75 million tons of catfish, which were sold for $57 million wholesale to processors and marketed as whole catfish, fillets, and nuggets (John Jensen, 1995, personal communication). While anglers enjoy catching and eating catfish, they do not like handling them, since some catfish can inflict painful wounds with their hard dorsal and pectoral spines and the toxins secreted from glands located at the base of these spines.

Because blue, white, and particularly channel catfishes have been widely introduced as game species into private lakes and ponds across Alabama and the United States, their current ranges are substantially greater than their original native ranges. For example, the native range of the white catfish, *Ameiurus catus,* is unclear. Glodek (1979a) reports that the white catfish is native to the southeastern portion of the Mobile basin and were later introduced elsewhere. Judging from our sampling data, we believe this

Atlantic Coast species is native to the entire Apalachicola basin and has probably been introduced in both the Mobile basin and the Tennessee River drainage in Alabama. The spotted bullhead, *A. serra-canthus*, is restricted to the Chattahoochee River drainage in Alabama. The snail bullhead, *A. brunneus*, occurs in the Chattahoochee River drainage and the upper Etowah River system in the Mobile basin.

KEY TO THE BULLHEAD CATFISHES

1a. Adipose fin free, not fused to caudal fin . . . . go to 2
1b. Adipose fin fused with caudal fin to form fleshy ridge . . . . go to 10, *Noturus*

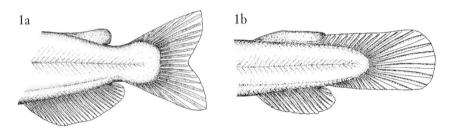

Adipose fin structures of 1a, *Ameiurus, Ictalurus,* and *Pylodictis,* and 1b, *Noturus*

2a. Caudal fin forked, with distinct upper and lower lobes . . . . go to 3
2b. Caudal fin margin rounded or emarginate . . . . go to 5

3a. Anal fin short, with 22 to 24 rays; caudal fin slightly forked. . . . . white catfish, *Ameiurus catus*
3b. Anal fin long, with 24 to 36 rays; caudal fin deeply forked . . . . go to 4, *Ictalurus*

4a. Anal fin with 24 to 29 rays and rounded free margin; body usually yellowish, with small, scattered black spots; young individuals distinctly yellowish . . . . channel catfish, *I. punctatus*
4b. Anal fin with 30 or more anal rays and usually straight margin; body very light blue, without black spots . . . . blue catfish, *I. furcatus*

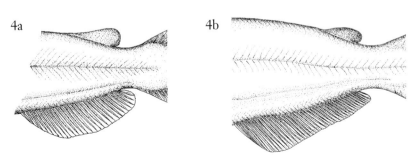

Anal fin structures of 4a, *I. punctatus,* and 4b, *I. furcatus*

5a. Head between eyes conspicuously flattened; lower jaw projects beyond upper jaw in all but youngest individuals; on each side of upper jaw, band of premaxillary teeth with a lateral extension that points to the rear; body with black-and-white mottling; upper edge of upper caudal fin lobe white in all but largest adults . . . . flathead catfish, *Pylodictis olivaris*

5b. Head between eyes rounded; lower jaw nearly equal to or slightly shorter than upper jaw; bands of premaxillary teeth without extensions; upper edge of caudal fin not white . . . . go to 6, *Ameiurus*

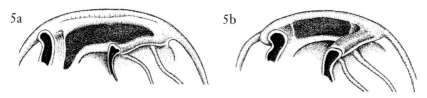

Bands of premaxillary teeth in upper jaws of 5a, *Pylodictis olivaris*, and 5b, *Ameiurus*

6a. Body with gray-white spots or black-and-brown mottling . . . . go to 7
6b. Body black, pale gray, yellow, or white, but never spotted or mottled . . . . go to 8

7a. Body dark gray or tan, with many small, gray-white spots; fins with narrow black edge; restricted to Chattahoochee River drainage . . . . spotted bullhead, *A. serracanthus*
7b. Body gray or tan, with black or brown mottling; no black margins on fins . . . brown bullhead, *A. nebulosus*

8a. Anal fin long, with 24 to 28 rays; chin barbels white to yellow . . . . yellow bullhead, *A. natalis*
8b. Anal fin short, with 17 to 23 rays; chin barbels black to dark gray . . . . go to 9

9a. Head between eyes flat; anal fin with 16 to 22, usually 17 to 20, rays; large, dark blotch at dorsal fin base; dorsal, anal, and caudal fins with distinct black band; chin barbels dusky; Chattahoochee River drainage . . . . snail bullhead, *A. brunneus*
9b. Head between eyes rounded; anal fin with 17 to 23 rays; no blotch at dorsal fin base; dorsal, anal, and caudal fins of various colors but without distinct black band; chin barbels black . . . . black bullhead, *A. melas*

10a. Light or dark saddles or bands across back; posterior edge of pectoral spines with conspicuous teeth . . . . go to 11
10b. No saddles or bands across back; posterior edge of pectoral spines with small, poorly developed, or no teeth . . . . go to 14

11a. Front edge of dorsal fin (including dorsal spine and first 3 or 4 dorsal rays) brown, with remainder yellow; usually 14 to 18 anal fin rays; Tennessee River drainage . . . . elegant madtom, *N. elegans*
11b. Front edge of dorsal fin not brown; 11 to 17 anal fin rays; body deepest at dorsal fin base . . . . . . go to 12

12a. Dorsal fin with dark spot extending across distal ends of first 4 or 5 rays; single black band near edge of caudal fin; 13 to 17 anal fin rays; venter essentially white; Tennessee River drainage . . . . brindled madtom, *N. miurus*
12b. Dorsal fin without dark spot; caudal fin possibly marked with 2 or 3 bands; generally 11 to 17 anal fin rays . . . . go to 13

13a. Anal fin with 12 to 15 rays; black or brown band marking middle of adipose fin; venter with dark specks or freckles; Mobile River basin . . . . frecklebelly madtom, *N. **munitus***

13b. Anal fin with 12 to 16 rays; dark band on adipose fin usually absent or not extending to edge of fin; venter white, without specks; Tennessee River drainage. . . . . mountain madtom, *N. **eleutherus***

14a. Upper and lower jaws equal in length . . . . go to 15

14b. Lower jaw shorter than upper jaw . . . . go to 16

15a. Dorsal, anal, and caudal fins with distinct, black marginal band; light yellow spot on nape behind head; pectoral fin usually with 9 rays; Tennessee River drainage . . . . slender madtom, *N. **exilis***

15b. Dorsal and caudal fins dusky, without distinct, black marginal band; anal fin with little if any black; no light blotches behind head or at dorsal fin base; pectoral fins with 7 or 8 rays; thin, dark line along side of body from near head to caudal fin base. . . . . tadpole madtom, *N. **gyrinus***

16a. Premaxillary tooth patch on upper jaw with lateral extensions that point to the rear; Tennessee River drainage . . . . stonecat, *N. **flavus***

16b. Premaxillary tooth patch on upper jaw without extensions . . . . go to 17

17a. Anal fin long, with 21 to 27 rays; body black or dark brown above, with small black or gray specks or mottling on sides and venter; chin barbels mottled. . . . . black madtom, *N. **funebris***

17b. Anal fin short, with fewer than 20 rays; back charcoal or gray; venter generally unpigmented; chin barbels cream . . . . go to 18

18a. Body slender, with black specks except on venter and underside of head; thin, dark line along side of body from head to caudal fin base; many dark specks in dorsal, anal, and caudal fins; anal fin with 14 to 19 rays . . . . speckled madtom, *N. **leptacanthus***

18b. Body robust with black and sides uniformly dark; venter unpigmented; no thin, dark line along side of body; anal fin with 15 to 18 rays . . . . freckled madtom, *N. **nocturnus***

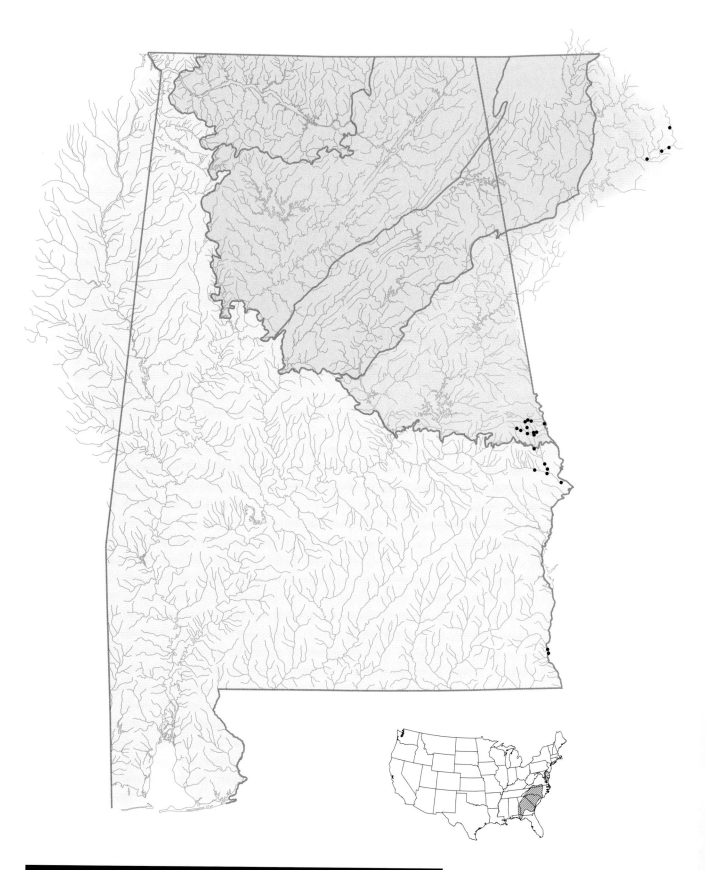

SNAIL BULLHEAD *Ameiurus brunneus* **23 STATIONS**

Ameiurus brunneus

(Jordan, 1877)

ETYMOLOGY:

Ameiurus—unforked caudal fin

brunneus—brown, the color pattern of young and juveniles, on which the species description is based

Uchee Creek, Russell County, 8 April 1993, 8.3 in (210 mm) SL male, GSA 4417

CHARACTERISTICS: When viewed from the side, the head of the snail bullhead is flattened and the snout is rounded. The short, rounded anal fin contains 16 to 22 (usually 17 to 20) rays. The pectoral spine has numerous small teeth on its anterior and posterior edges. Color on the back varies from light olive to black, grading to pale yellow on the sides and creamy white on the venter. The fins are dusky to brown, with a narrow black band along the margin. See Jordan (1877a) for original description.

ADULT SIZE: 10 to 12 in (254 to 300 mm)

DISTRIBUTION: Snail bullheads are limited to the Chattahoochee River drainage in Alabama and the upper Etowah (Coosa) River system in Georgia. Collection records in Lee and Russell counties are the result of several years of intensive sampling efforts by John S. Ramsey and fisheries students at Auburn University. The lack of additional records from the rest of this species' range is probably due to the scarcity of optimum habitats below the Fall Line and the likelihood that sampling was done without boat electrofishing gear and gill nets.

HABITAT AND BIOLOGY: Snail bullheads prefer deep, fast-flowing streams and rivers with sand and rock substrates. The life history of this species is not well known. Observations in Florida indicate that it has a protracted spawning season that may last from spring through mid-summer (Yerger and Relyea, 1968). Small fishes, aquatic vegetation, and snails of the genus *Elimia* make up the snail bullhead's diet.

REMARKS: Yerger and Relyea (1968) report that Chattahoochee fishermen prefer snail bullheads to either channel or white catfish, claiming that the flesh of snail bullheads has a better flavor.

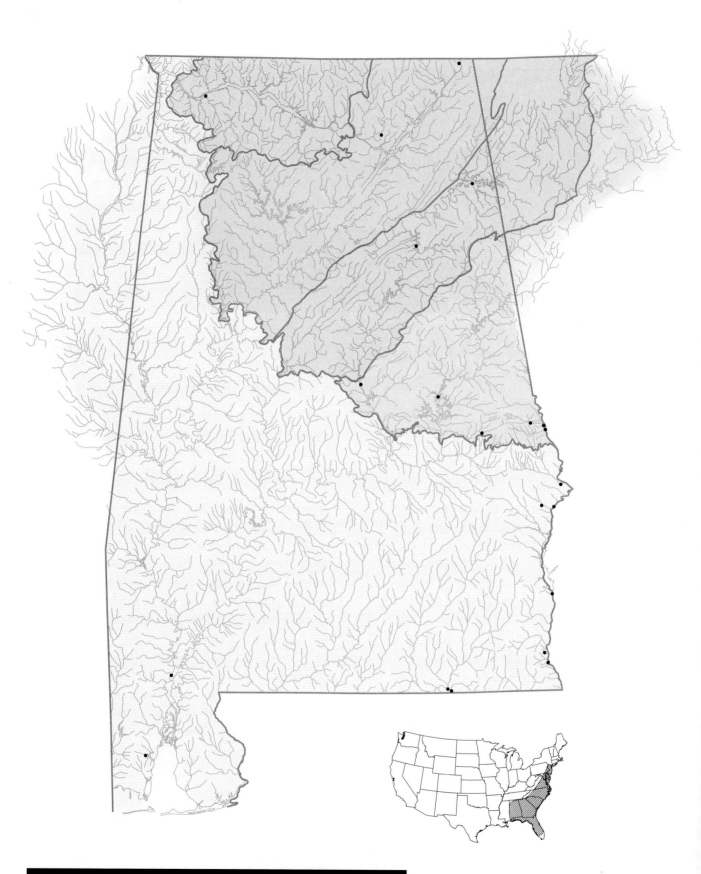

Ameiurus catus

(Linnaeus, 1758)

ETYMOLOGY:

Ameiurus—unforked

caudal fin

catus—cat

Hatchechubbee Creek, Russell County, 8 April 1993, 10.6 in (269 mm) SL female, GSA 4416

CHARACTERISTICS: The white catfish is distinguished from all other Alabama catfishes by its moderately forked caudal fin and short, large head, the width of which is usually greater than the anal fin length. The lower jaw is substantially shorter than the upper jaw. The anal fin is rounded and contains 22 to 24 rays. Burkhead et al. (1980) note that individuals always have a gap or depression in the "body ridge" running from the head to the dorsal fin origin. The back is generally dark to medium olive or gray, grading to white on the venter. Fins are light gray, often with a darker membrane between rays.

ADULT SIZE: 12 to 18 in (300 to 460 mm). The state angling record (10 lb, 5 oz) was caught in Chambers County Public Lake in 1981.

DISTRIBUTION: Glodek (1979a) maps the native range of white catfish along the Atlantic coast from New York southward through most of Florida and westward across the Mobile basin in Alabama. We found white catfish to be fairly widespread and occasionally abundant in the Chattahoochee drainage, which leads us to suspect that the species is native to the drainage. Its apparently introduced status elsewhere in Alabama is supported by collections of single individuals at only six widely scattered stations: two in the Choctawhatchee River, two in the Tennessee River drainage, and two in the Mobile Delta. Limited numbers of white catfish have also been collected in the Coosa and Tallapoosa river systems.

HABITAT AND BIOLOGY: We collected white catfish in streams and small rivers characterized by standing or slow-moving turbid water with sandy and silty substrates. White catfish spawn in South Carolina in June; small fishes and mayflies are primary food items (Stevens, 1959). Carlander (1969) estimates a maximum life span of about 11 years.

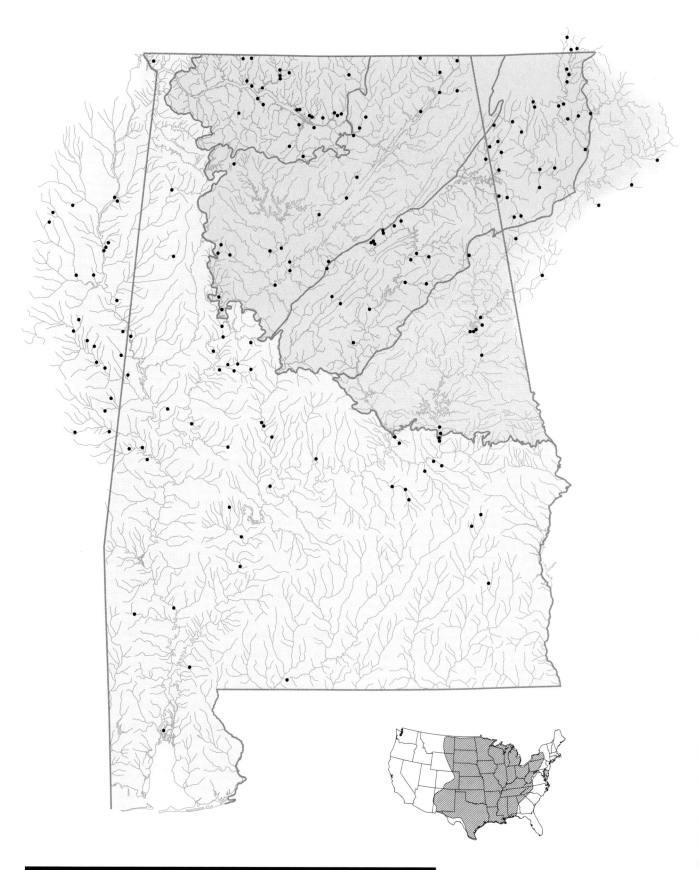

Ameiurus melas

(Rafinesque, 1820)

ETYMOLOGY:

Ameiurus—unforked
caudal fin
melas—black

Glover Cave, Madison County, 6 November 1991, 4.9 in (124 mm) SL male, GSA 4136

CHARACTERISTICS: This stocky catfish has a rounded anal fin containing 17 to 23 rays. The upper jaw is slightly longer than the lower jaw, and chin barbels are black to dark gray. (Dark chin barbels easily separate the young of this species from young of the yellow bullhead, *Ameiurus natalis*, which always have yellow or white barbels.) Teeth on the dorsal and pectoral spines are poorly developed. The back is uniformly dark gray to black, grading to pale yellow or white on the venter. Fins are dusky and occasionally darkened along their margins.

ADULT SIZE: 10 to 12 in (254 to 300 mm)

DISTRIBUTION: Black bullheads are widespread but generally not abundant in the Mobile basin and Tennessee River drainage. They are rarely encountered in coastal drainages, the Choctawhatchee River being the eastern limit of their Gulf Coast range. The black bullhead has been introduced in several western states.

HABITAT AND BIOLOGY: Black bullheads inhabit low-gradient streams, backwaters, and swamps with little or no streamflow, silt and sand substrates, and dense accumulations of aquatic vegetation. Wallace (1967) records spawning from mid-May into July. Multiple spawns, usually completed with the male and female lying side by side but facing opposite directions, occur over a single nest. The female initially guards the nest but is soon replaced by the male. Campbell and Branson (1978) report schools of young feeding on ostracods and amphipods. Adults feed after dark and consume aquatic insect larvae, snails, and small fish. Etnier and Starnes (1993) encountered "well-fed" individuals near the sewage outfall of a meat processing plant in Tennessee. Carlander (1969) reports a life span of five to six years.

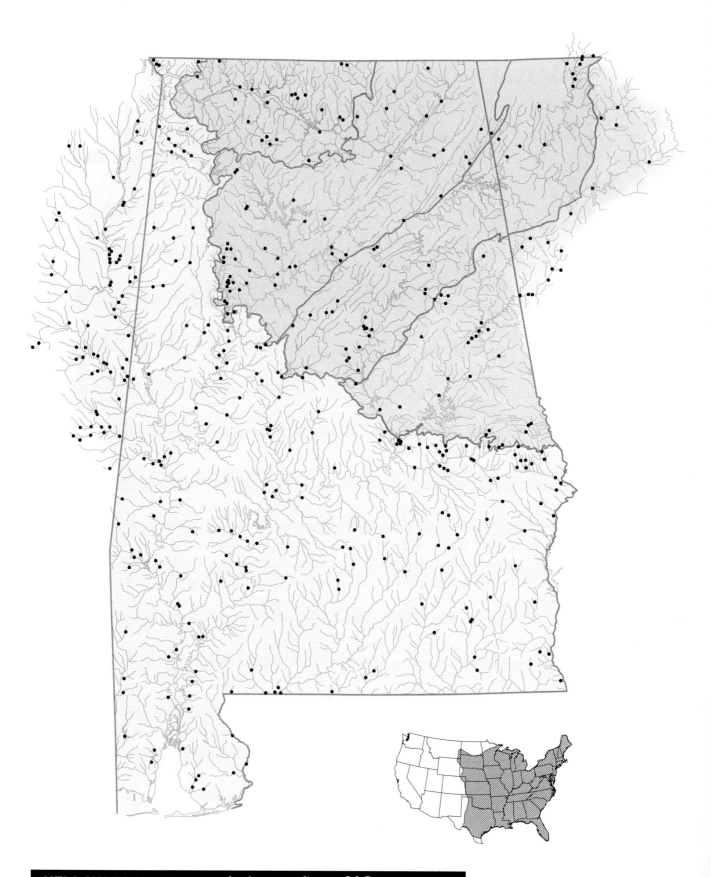

YELLOW BULLHEAD   *Ameiurus natalis*   **418 STATIONS**

Ameiurus natalis

(Lesueur, 1819)

ETYMOLOGY:

Ameiurus—unforked caudal fin

natalis—having large buttocks, referring to the large humps that develop between the head and dorsal fin origin on breeding males

Dry Creek, Jackson County, 10 June 1992, 3.7 in (93 mm) SL female, GSA 4315

CHARACTERISTICS: Locally known as yellow cat, the yellow bullhead is distinguished from the black bullhead, *Ameiurus melas*, by its white or yellow chin barbels, 24 to 28 rays in a straight-edged anal fin, and five to eight fairly large teeth on the posterior edge of each pectoral spine. The rear edge of the caudal fin is straight or slightly rounded. The back is yellow, olive, or dark gray, grading from light yellow to white on the venter. The fins are light to dark gray, and they may have light to darkened margins.

ADULT SIZE: 6 to 15 in (152 to 380 mm)

DISTRIBUTION: Yellow bullheads are widespread and occasionally abundant in all river systems of Alabama.

HABITAT AND BIOLOGY: This species prefers medium-sized to small streams, backwaters, and swamps characterized by slow-moving currents, sand and silt substrates, and varying amounts of aquatic vegetation. Yellow bullheads usually spawn in April and May, which is earlier than the spawning times of black and brown bullheads. Young remain close to the nest, congregating in schools, and are guarded by males (Etnier and Starnes, 1993). Food items include worms, crayfish, insects, small minnows, and quantities of aquatic vegetation and sediments. The life span is estimated to be seven years and the maximum adult size around 15 inches.

Locust Fork of Black Warrior River, Blount County

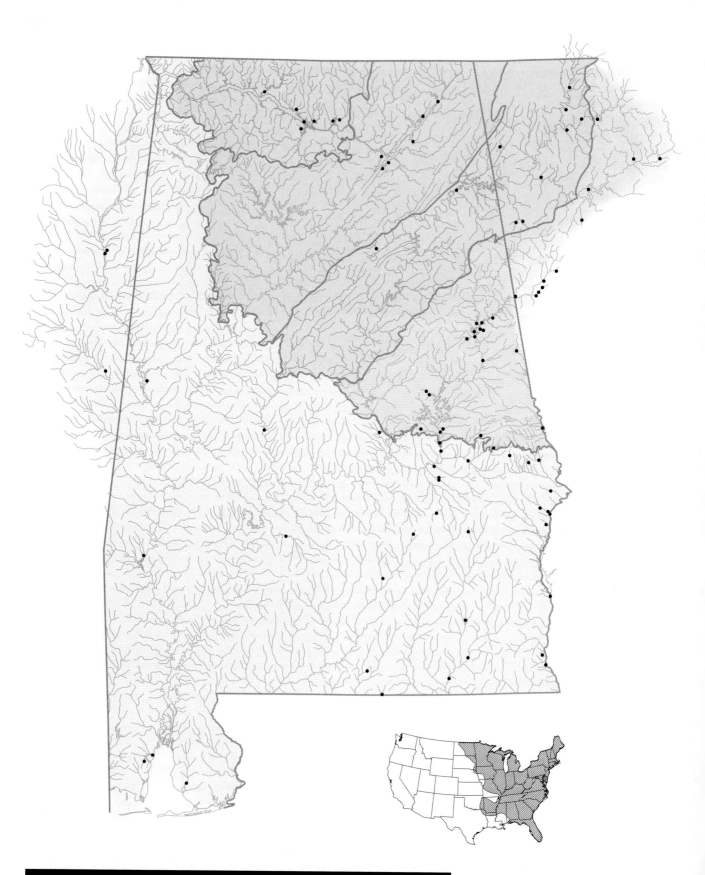

Ameiurus nebulosus

(Lesueur, 1819)

ETYMOLOGY:

Ameiurus—unforked caudal fin
nebulosus—clouded, referring to this species' mottled sides

Hatchechubbee Creek, Russell County, 8 April 1993, 11 in (280 mm) SL male, GSA 4416

CHARACTERISTICS: This species' attractive, well-defined black or brown mottling on its gray or tan body distinguishes it from most members of the bullhead family. (The spotted bullhead, *Ameiurus serracanthus,* also has a mottled or spotted body, but its dorsal, caudal, and anal fins have dark or black margins.) Other characters include pigmented chin barbels, 21 to 24 anal fin rays, pectoral spines with several well-developed teeth on their posterior margins, and a slightly notched caudal fin. All fins are dark to light gray; the dorsal and caudal fins are occasionally clear near their edge. Barbels surrounding the mouth are dark gray to black, a characteristic shared with the black bullhead, *A. melas,* and spotted bullhead, *A. serracanthus.*

ADULT SIZE: 12 to 18 in (300 to 460 mm)

DISTRIBUTION: Most brown bullhead records in Alabama are from the eastern part of the state, where rivers have not been dredged to maintain navigable channels. Glodek (1979b) concludes that populations throughout most of the Mobile basin are native, whereas those in the southern part of the Black Warrior drainage and the northern part of the lower Tombigbee drainage may be introduced. Boschung (1992) notes that brown bullheads are apparently absent in the Coosa drainage; most of our Mobile basin collections came from the Coosa River system in Georgia. We also collected specimens at several stations in the Conecuh, Choctawhatchee, and Chattahoochee river systems in southeastern Alabama and in the Tennessee River drainage in northeastern Alabama.

HABITAT AND BIOLOGY: We have collected this species in rivers and reservoirs, streams, oxbow lakes, and swamps characterized by clear to muddy water and low to moderate flow over sand and mud substrates. Like several other members of this group, brown bullheads usually occur near undercut stream banks and the edges of aquatic vegetation. Spawning begins in the spring or early summer when water temperatures reach 72° to 75°F (22° to 24°C). Food items include aquatic insect larvae, crayfish, freshwater shrimp, and minnows.

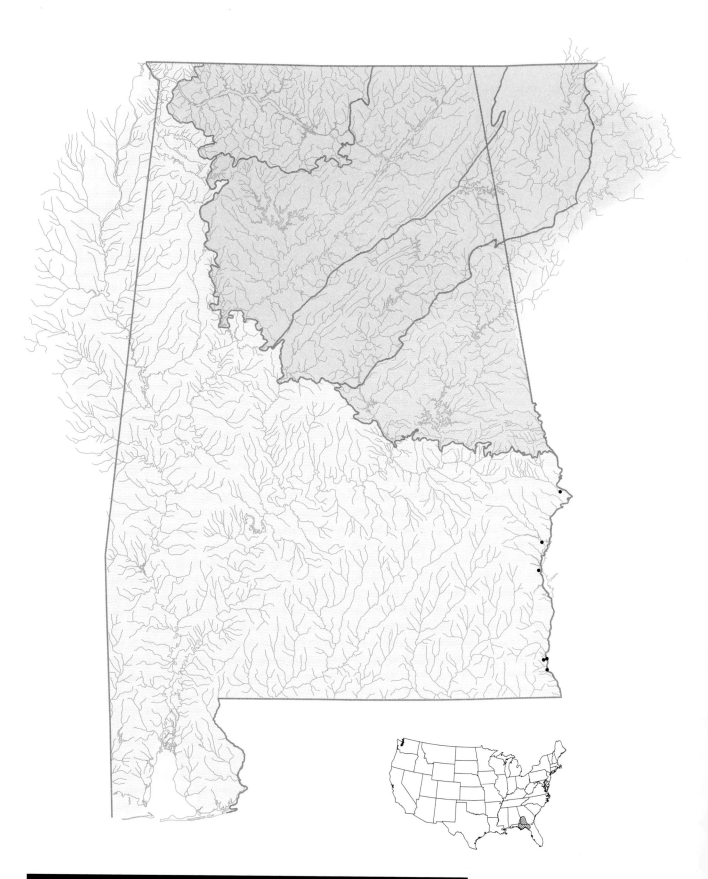

Ameiurus serracanthus

(Yerger and Relyea, 1968)

ETYMOLOGY:

Ameiurus—unforked caudal fin *serracanthus*—saw-edged spine

Uchee Creek, Russell County, 6 April 1993, 5.1 in (130 mm) SL female, GSA 4411

CHARACTERISTICS: The smallest of the *Ameiurus* species in Alabama, the spotted bullhead is the only one marked with small gray-white spots on a dark gray or tan body. Endemic to the Chattahoochee River system, the spotted bullhead and snail bullhead, *A. brunneus*, are the only two catfish species in Alabama that have prominent black margins along the edges of their lighter dorsal, anal, and caudal fins. The rounded anal fin on the spotted bullhead contains 19 to 23 rays. The caudal fin margin is essentially straight or slightly notched. Each pectoral spine has 15 to 18 large teeth along its posterior edge.

ADULT SIZE: 7 to 9 in (178 to 226 mm)

DISTRIBUTION: Spotted bullheads are limited to the Chattahoochee River drainage in Alabama. Although they appear to be rare in state waters, their limited distribution may be due to insufficient sampling of preferred habitats using large nets and boat electrofishing gear.

HABITAT AND BIOLOGY: Yerger and Relyea (1968) provide the description and most of the data on this species' habitat and reproduction. They collected spotted bullheads in slow to moderate currents over the sand and rock substrates of large streams and rivers. Because of the species' apparent preference for deep water, most of the individuals included in the report had been collected with large nets, slat boxes, and ichthyocides.Using boat electrofishing gear, we collected spotted bullheads around submerged treetops in the lower reaches of Uchee Creek in Russell County. Uchee Creek was approximately 50 feet wide there, the current was moderate, and substrates consisted mostly of sand and clay. In the main channel of the Chattahoochee River in Houston County, we collected specimens around logs and treetops and along sustaining walls below Columbia Lock and Dam. Our habitat observations were similar to those reported by Yerger and Relyea.

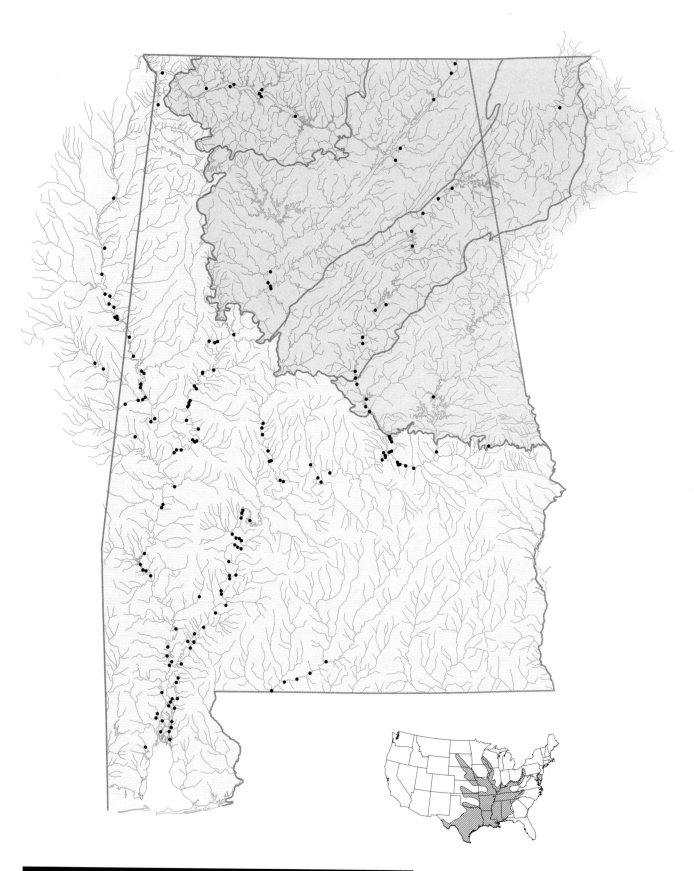

Ictalurus furcatus
(Lesueur, 1840)

ETYMOLOGY:
Ictalurus—fish cat
furcatus—forked, referring
to this species' deeply forked
caudal fin

Alabama River, Wilcox County, 18 April 1995, 13.8 in (350 mm) SL male, GSA 4638

CHARACTERISTICS: This pale blue catfish has a deeply forked tail and white chin barbels. The upper and lower jaws meet evenly, or the upper jaw may project slightly beyond the lower jaw. Distinguishing small blue catfish and channel catfish, *Ictalurus punctatus*, can be difficult, but the two species can usually be separated by anal fin shape and size. The anal fin on the blue catfish has 30 or more soft rays, and its free margin is straight. The anal fin on the channel catfish has 24 to 29 soft rays, and its free margin is rounded. In body color, the blue catfish is light blue, while the channel catfish is light yellow with small, scattered dark spots. See Cuvier and Valenciennes (1840) for the original description of blue catfish.

ADULT SIZE: 18 to 24 in (460 to 610 mm). The state angling record (104 lb) was caught in Wheeler Reservoir on the Tennessee River in 1994. During our river surveys, we infrequently collect and release blue catfish weighing 30 to 50 pounds; most specimens are 10 pounds or less.

DISTRIBUTION: Blue catfish are widespread and occasionally abundant in the Mobile basin and Tennessee River. The appearance of a limited range above the Fall Line could be due to insufficient and improperly

equipped sampling of large streams and rivers. Glodek (1979c) does not include the Conecuh River within the native range of this species, but our surveys confirmed its presence at five localities in the drainage. Blue catfish were accidentally introduced into the Choctawhatchee River in 1993, when heavy rains broke the dam of a private lake stocked with numerous brood fish. Most were caught by local anglers, but a few may persist in the area.

HABITAT AND BIOLOGY: As the distribution map illustrates, blue catfish prefer riverine and reservoir habitats. The largest individuals we have encountered were in tailwaters below dams, where currents were swift and substrates consisted of sand, gravel, and rock. Blue and flathead catfish also congregate around submerged treetops. Like many other species in the family, blue catfish are opportunistic feeders, consuming live and dead fish and benthic invertebrates.

REMARKS: Blue catfish are delicious, and they are therefore a target species for many sport and commercial fishermen. Malvestuto et al. (1983) report that anglers and commercial fishermen harvested approximately 250,000 pounds of blue catfish from the Mobile Delta and lower Tombigbee River in 1980 and 1981.

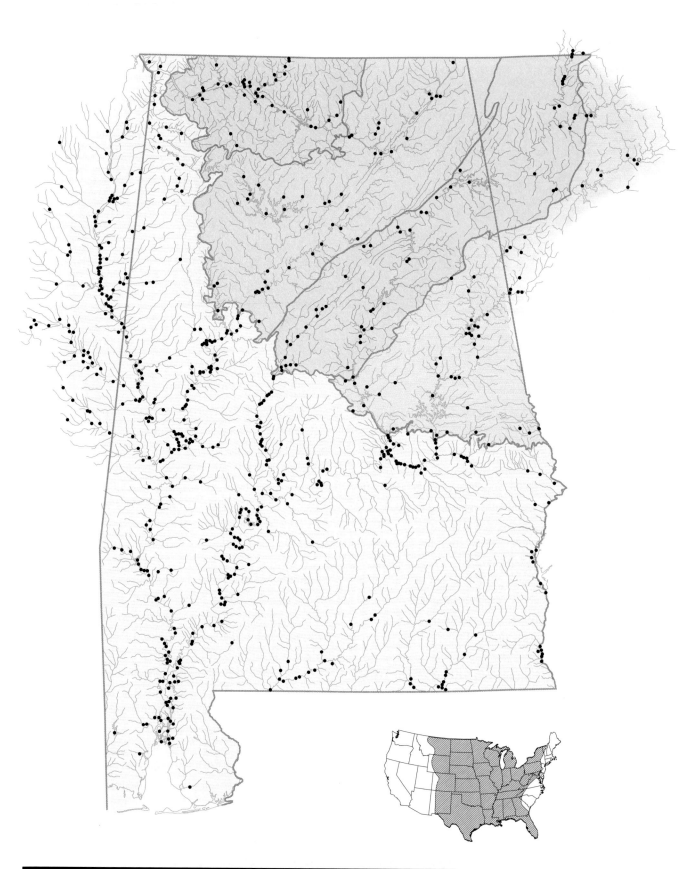

Ictalurus punctatus

(Rafinesque, 1818)

ETYMOLOGY:

Ictalurus—fish cat

punctatus—spotted

North River, Tuscaloosa County, 8 March 1994, 8.8 in (223 mm) SL male, GSA 4612

CHARACTERISTICS: This slender, elongate catfish has a deeply forked caudal fin and a protruding upper jaw. Adult channel cats are dark gray along the back, grading to light yellow or greenish yellow along the sides, and white on the venter. Juveniles are typically light gray on the back and silvery on the sides and venter. The sides of juveniles and adults have scattered dark spots. The head profile of the channel cat is curved from the dorsal fin to the snout. The same dimension in the blue cat is straight, giving the head of this similar species a wedge-shaped appearance. Small adult channel catfish are confused with blue catfish but are distinguishable by the above characteristics plus anal fin morphology. This fin on the channel catfish has a rounded margin and 24 to 29 soft rays, while on the blue catfish the free margin is straight and rays number 30 or more. The pectoral spine has well-developed serrae on the posterior edge.

ADULT SIZE: 15 to 24 in (380 to 610 mm). The state angling record (40 lb) was caught in Inland Lake, a tributary of Locust Fork in the Black Warrior River system, in 1967.

DISTRIBUTION: This species is native to Alabama, but its range has greatly expanded in the United States and Canada through its introduction into and sometimes escape from private and commercial fish ponds.

HABITAT AND BIOLOGY: Channel catfish inhabit rivers, reservoirs, small to large streams, backwaters, swamps, and oxbow lakes. We have collected species in conditions ranging from slow to moderate currents over sand, gravel, and silt and around submerged trees and aquatic vegetation. Spawning begins in May and continues for several months, for we have collected gravid females as late as August. Males guard the nest and schools of fry and small fish. Carlander (1969) reports fast growth in the first years of life, with eight-year-olds reaching 18 or 19 inches. Maximum age in northern climates is 24 years and in southern climates 15 years. Channel catfish feed on aquatic insect larvae, crayfish, mollusks, and small fish, along with baits such as cheese, chicken, dough balls, redworms, and cut bait.

REMARKS: This species is the most important food fish in Alabama (see 1995 harvest statistics in family introduction). In 1980 and 1981, anglers and commercial fishermen in southwest Alabama harvested more than 282,000 pounds of channel catfish in the Mobile Delta and lower Tombigbee River (Malvestuto et al., 1983).

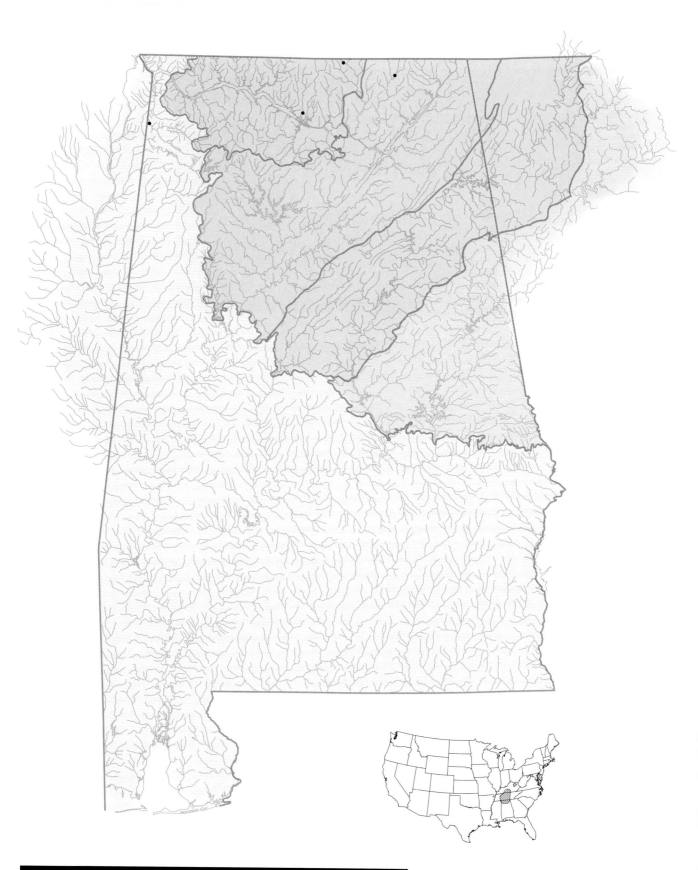

Noturus elegans
Taylor, 1969

ETYMOLOGY:

Noturus—back tail, referring to fusion of the adipose and caudal fins
elegans—elegant, referring to the species' handsomely colored body and fins

Cane Creek, Hickman County, Tennessee, 14 July 1964, 2.1 in (53 mm) SL female, TU 33085

CHARACTERISTICS: In his original description of this species, Taylor (1969) notes that specimens from several locations in Alabama and Tennessee are only tentatively identified as elegant madtoms because several characters differ from those of typical populations in Kentucky. Elegant madtoms in Alabama have a more robust body. A brown blotch at the front of the dorsal fin covers the dorsal spine and the lower half of the first three or four rays; the remainder is unpigmented. The pectoral spine is short and has five to nine prominent teeth on its posterior edge. Anal fin rays number 14 to 18. The back is yellowish gray to dark brown, with four light yellow saddles grading to creamy white on the venter. Two or three dark bands mark the caudal fin. J. M. Grady and B. M. Burr are investigating the taxonomic status of elegant madtoms in Alabama and Tennessee.

ADULT SIZE: 2.5 to 3.0 in (64 to 75 mm)

DISTRIBUTION: Specimens have been collected at four widely spaced locations in Alabama. The largest sample came from the west fork of the Flint River in 1969 (Tennessee Valley Authority, 1971). Feeman (1987) reported the last collections—from the upper Paint Rock River drainage—in 1981. Our repeated collection efforts there have been unfruitful, but our success with other species of marginal or historical occurrence leads us to believe that ***Noturus elegans*** still occurs in north Alabama.

HABITAT AND BIOLOGY: This species inhabits high-gradient streams with moderate to swift current flowing over boulders, bedrock, and clean sand and gravel substrates. Burr and Dimmick (1981) observed three nests, each one guarded by a male, under flat rocks in pools of a Kentucky stream in June; water temperature was 68°F (20°C). Elegant madtoms probably feed on small crustaceans and aquatic insect larvae.

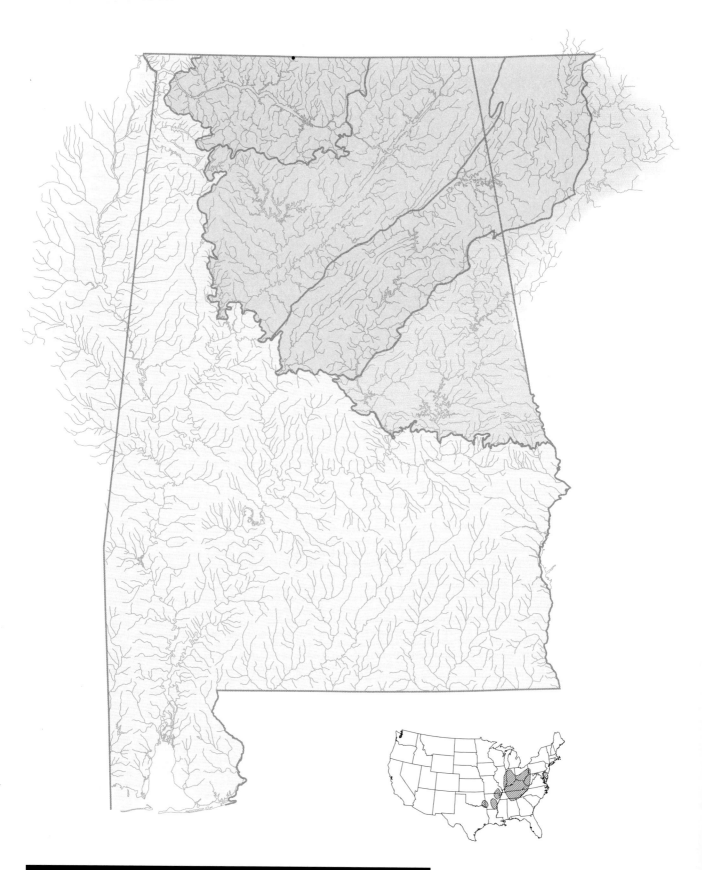

MOUNTAIN MADTOM   *Noturus eleutherus*   **1 STATION**

Noturus eleutherus

Jordan, 1877

ETYMOLOGY:

Noturus—back tail, referring to fusion of the adipose and caudal fins *eleutherus*—free, referring to the incomplete fusion of the posterior section of the adipose fin to the body

Elk River, Limestone County, 5 October 1993, 1.9 in (48 mm) SL male, GSA 4614

CHARACTERISTICS: This fairly small but robust madtom has a faint to dark vertical bar at the caudal fin base. The front edge of the first dorsal saddle usually crosses the back at the dorsal fin origin. An irregularly shaped band on the adipose fin is confined to the lower half of the fin. The caudal fin has two or three crescent-shaped bands, and its rear edge is slightly convex. The anal fin contains 12 to 17 rays. The body is light to dark mottled brown and has four light dorsal saddles, while the venter is white to pale yellow. See Jordan (1877a) for original description.

ADULT SIZE: 3 to 5 in (75 to 127 mm)

DISTRIBUTION: Mountain madtoms occur in rivers from Arkansas to western Pennsylvania (Rohde, 1978a; Page and Burr, 1991). Grady and LeGrande (1992) include northern Alabama as part of the species' range. Smith-Vaniz (1968) suspects that mountain madtoms may occur in the Tennessee River drainage, but Boschung (1992) excludes the species from his catalog of Alabama fishes. Our 1993 collection of several individuals in the Elk River just downstream of the Alabama-Tennessee line represents the first record of mountain madtoms in Alabama. Future sampling may expand its known range in state waters.

HABITAT AND BIOLOGY: Apparently a secretive species, the mountain madtom is not regularly encountered, even under ideal conditions. Using a backpack electrofishing unit and seines, we twice sampled one habitat in the Elk River in a three-week period. Each of the sampling periods lasted about two hours, but we did not find madtoms until the second visit. All individuals were collected in a swiftly flowing side channel about 20 feet wide and 10 to 20 inches deep. The substrate consisted of 4- to 8-inch pieces of flattened rubble with scattered pieces of larger flat rocks with attached clumps of matted algae. Starnes and Starnes (1985) found a mountain madtom guarding a nest in early July in Tennessee. We assume that spawning occurs in late June or early July in northern Alabama.

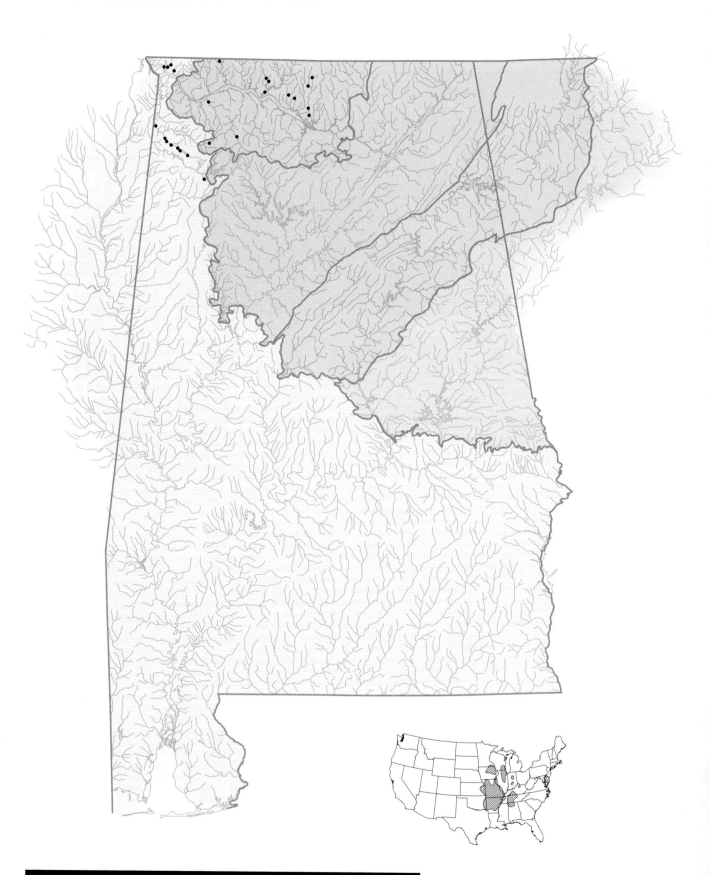

SLENDER MADTOM *Noturus exilis* **25 STATIONS**

Noturus exilis

Nelson, 1876

ETYMOLOGY:

Noturus—back tail, referring to fusion of the adipose and caudal fins

exilis—slender

Piney Creek, Limestone County, 20 May 1993, 3.0 in (75 mm) SL male, GSA 4477

CHARACTERISTICS: The slender madtom can be separated from other *Noturus* species in the Tennessee River drainage by the marginal black bands in its median fins and a yellow spot on its nape. Other characters include a strongly depressed head, jaws of equal size, and 17 to 22 anal fin rays. The back is yellowish to medium brown, grading to light yellow below. The caudal fin is short, usually rounded, and mostly black on small individuals. The proximal area becomes lighter with age. Slender madtoms resemble the stonecat, *Noturus flavus*, but the two can be separated by teeth on pectoral spines and vertical fin color. Stonecats lack well-developed teeth on the rear edge of the pectoral spines (slender madtoms have teeth), and their vertical fins lack a dark margin.

ADULT SIZE: 4 to 6 in (102 to 152 mm)

DISTRIBUTION: Alabama records are limited to the western half of the Tennessee River drainage. Boschung (1992) records a collection from Richland Creek, just across the Alabama-Tennessee line. We collected slender madtoms 13 times at 11 stations in Alabama from 1991 through 1993. Six stations were in Lauderdale County, one each in Lawrence and Marion counties, and three in Limestone County. Future sampling will likely expand the species' known range.

HABITAT AND BIOLOGY: Slender madtoms usually inhabit riffles in small or medium-sized streams having moderate to swift currents flowing over sand and gravel substrates. Mayden and Burr (1981) record that spawning occurs from mid-June through July in Illinois. Nests are excavated under rocks in pool areas and are guarded by males; females spawn more than once a year. Individuals probably live for five years. Diet consists primarily of immature aquatic insects and small crustaceans. This and most other madtom species feed at dusk and dawn.

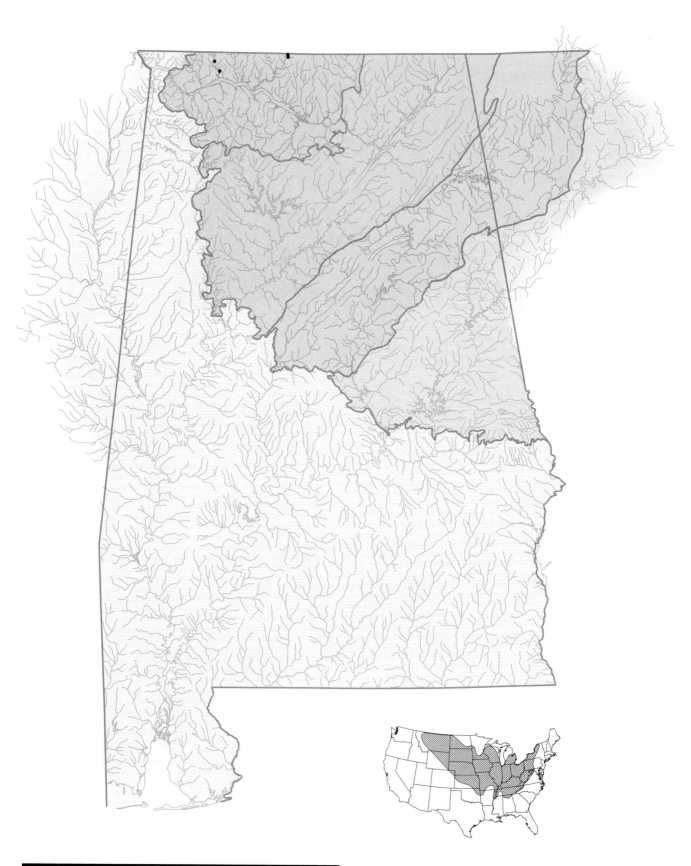

STONECAT   *Noturus flavus*   4 STATIONS

Noturus flavus
Rafinesque, 1818

ETYMOLOGY:

Noturus—back tail, referring to fusion of the adipose and caudal fins

flavus—yellow

Elk River, Limestone County, 5 October 1993, 5.1 in (130 mm) SL female, GSA 4614

CHARACTERISTICS: The stonecat is the only madtom in Alabama that possesses an extension reaching backward from each band of premaxillary teeth. Its flattened body allows it to wriggle beneath large, flat rocks to hide. Anal fin rays number from 15 to 18. The upper jaw protrudes in front of the lower jaw. The back is light brown, the venter usually white. Vertical fins are generally dark at their base and light at their edges. Stonecats can be distinguished from slender madtoms, ***Noturus exilis***, by the lack of well-developed teeth on the rear edge of their pectoral spines and the clear or pale margins on their dorsal, caudal, and anal fins. Page and Burr (1991) use pigment patterns on the nape and back to distinguish two forms of stonecats. An undescribed form in the Cumberland River has two light bars on the nape; all other members possess a light circular spot. Interestingly, the stonecats we collected in Alabama had a color pattern different from either form noted by Page and Burr, perhaps indicating the presence of yet another undescribed species in Alabama. See Rafinesque (1818c) for original description.

ADULT SIZE: 6 to 12 in (152 to 300 mm)

DISTRIBUTION: Gilbert (1891) reports stonecats in Shoal Creek, and Jandebeur (1972) collected one specimen from the Elk River in Tennessee. In 1993 we collected stonecats at two stations in the Elk River and in Goose Shoals on Shoal Creek. The largest population was in Goose Shoals, where we occasionally obtained two or three specimens, some reaching 6 to 9 inches, under a single rock.

HABITAT AND BIOLOGY: During the day, stonecats hide under large slabs of bedrock in riffles and rapids of medium-sized or large streams. Other preferred substrates include rubble, gravel, and scattered patches of aquatic vegetation. At night, stonecats emerge to feed on the many aquatic insects and crayfishes that also occupy these habitats. Walsh and Burr (1984) report spawning at 77°F (25°C) in Illinois and Missouri. Etnier and Starnes (1993) indicate that spawning in Tennessee occurs from April through July. Eggs deposited under flat rocks are guarded by males. Life span is about five years.

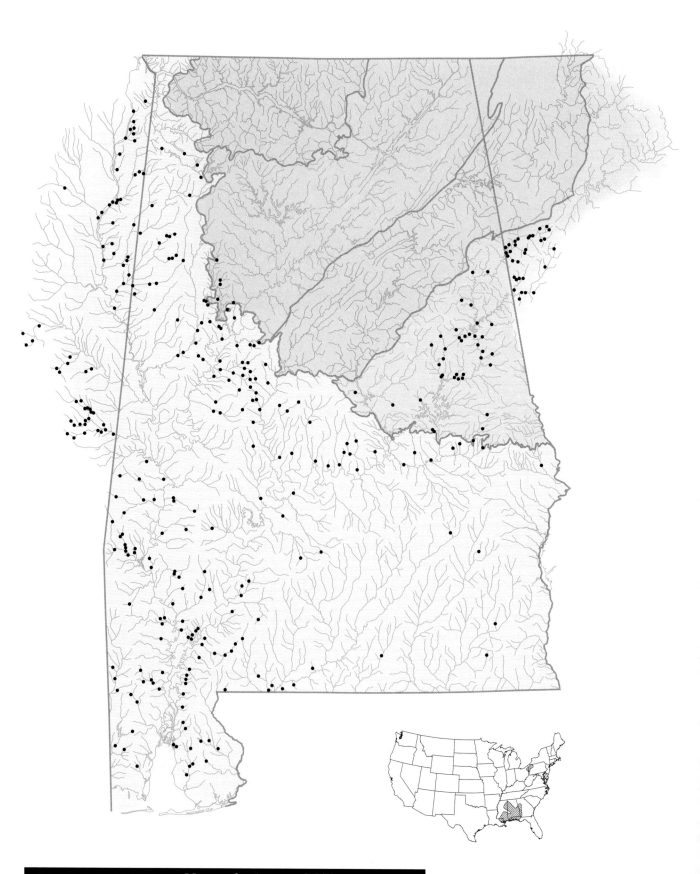

BLACK MADTOM   *Noturus funebris*   337 STATIONS

Noturus funebris

Gilbert and Swain, 1891

ETYMOLOGY:

Noturus—back tail, referring to fusion of the adipose and caudal fins *funebris*—pertaining to burial or funeral, in reference to dark colors

Yellow Creek, Tuscaloosa County, 15 May 1992, 4.1 in (105 mm) SL male, GSA 4448

CHARACTERISTICS: On this heavy-bodied madtom, the slightly rounded anal fin contains 21 to 27 rays, and because of the anal fin's length, the space between the anal fin and caudal fin base is short. The posterior edge of the pectoral fins is rough but lacks teeth. Body and fin color is dark brown to black; the venter is occasionally mottled. See Gilbert (1891) for original description.

ADULT SIZE: 4 to 7 in (102 to 178 mm)

DISTRIBUTION: Rohde (1978b) maps many collection locations in the Mobile basin and coastal drainages but includes no records from the Tennessee River system. Boschung (1992) reports that two collections from Mill Branch, a tributary of Bear Creek in Colbert County, represent the first collection of this species in the Tennessee River drainage. Actually, Wall (1968) collected the first specimen recorded in the drainage; it was taken in 1966 from Little Cripple Deer Creek, a tributary of Bear Creek in Tishomingo County, Mississippi.

Fisheries biologists at Auburn University collected more individuals in Little Bear and Bear creeks in 1973, and we collected the species in Rhinehart and Brush creeks in 1991. The occurrence of black madtoms and several other Mobile basin species in Bear Creek is probably due to faunal exchange between the Mobile basin and Tennessee River drainage. Only scattered collections have been recorded from coastal drainages east of the Mobile basin.

HABITAT AND BIOLOGY: Most of our black madtom collections came from small or medium-sized streams. Individuals usually occur around aquatic vegetation, near accumulations of leaf litter, and especially along undercut banks where current is slow and substrates consist of sand and silt. Spawning probably occurs in the spring. Little else is known of the species' life history in Alabama.

REMARKS: The type locality is a spring tributary to North River, Tuscaloosa County, Alabama.

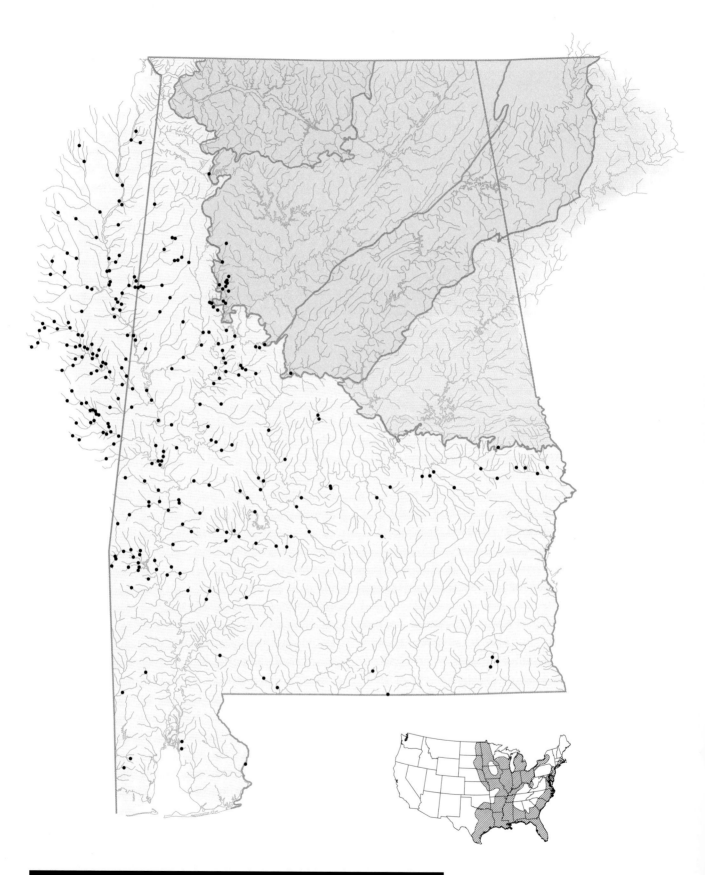

TADPOLE MADTOM *Noturus gyrinus* 276 STATIONS

Noturus gyrinus

(Mitchill, 1817)

ETYMOLOGY:

Noturus—back tail, referring to fusion of the adipose and caudal fins *gyrinus*—from the Greek for tadpole, which this species resembles in body shape

Chilatchee Creek, Dallas County, 23 July 1980, 1.9 in (48 mm) SL female, GSA 5899

CHARACTERISTICS: The body of this small but stocky madtom is angled downward near the dorsal fin base, giving it a bent appearance. The top of the head is somewhat depressed, and the upper and lower jaws are equal in length. Pectoral spines are grooved but lack teeth. The slightly rounded anal fin contains 14 to 17 rays, leaving little space between it and the caudal fin base. Elongate middle caudal rays give the caudal fin a rounded appearance. The back and sides are light to dark brown, grading from light brown to white on the venter. Fins are light to medium tan, sometimes with irregularly spaced black lines or spots. A conspicuous dark line extends along the side of the body from just behind the head to the caudal fin base.

ADULT SIZE: 3 to 4 in (75 to 102 mm)

DISTRIBUTION: Tadpole madtoms are widespread and often abundant in the Mobile basin below the Fall Line.

Unlike the black madtom, this species seems unaffected by the unique habitat and water-quality conditions of Black Belt streams. The only tadpole madtom record from the Tennessee River was collected from Bear Creek by Wall (1968). The small number of records from coastal drainages in Alabama could be due to inadequate sampling in this species' preferred habitats.

HABITAT AND BIOLOGY: We collected tadpole madtoms in small to large streams with slow currents and sandy and silty substrates. Individuals usually linger around aquatic vegetation, in leaf packs, and along undercut banks. Pflieger (1975) reports June and July spawning in Missouri. Etnier and Starnes (1993) note June as the peak spawning month in Tennessee. Food items in Arkansas include small crustaceans, small aquatic insect larvae, oligochaetes, snails, and selected plant material (Robison and Buchanan, 1988). Individuals live for three or four years.

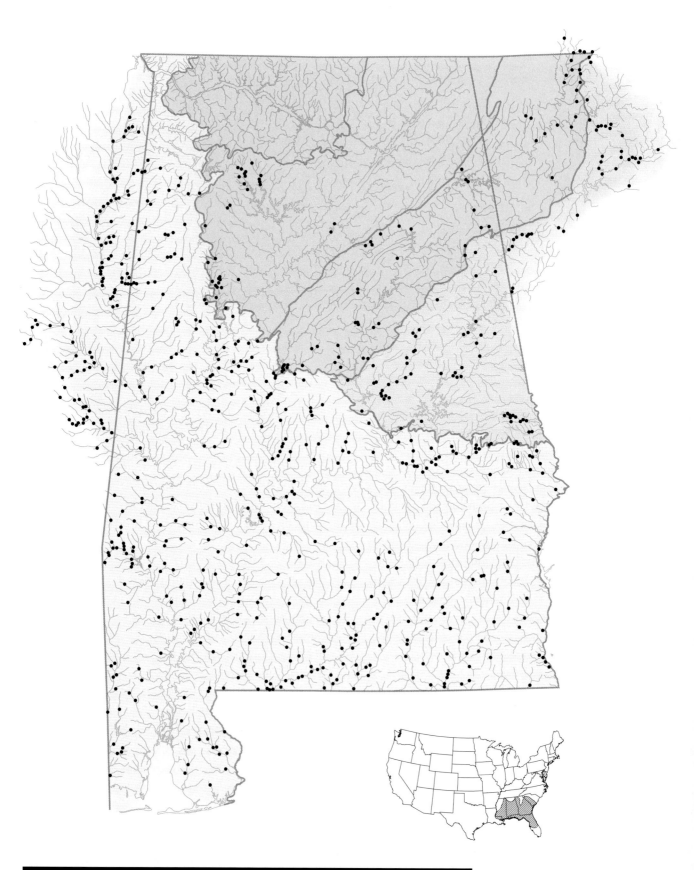

SPECKLED MADTOM   *Noturus leptacanthus*   **709 STATIONS**

Noturus leptacanthus
Jordan, 1877

ETYMOLOGY:

Noturus—back tail,
referring to fusion of the
adipose and caudal fins
leptacanthus—slender spine

Little Uchee Creek, Lee County, 19 February 1993, 2.2 in (57 mm) SL male, GSA 4375

CHARACTERISTICS: This slender, elongate species has small, distinct black spots scattered over the upper body and fins. The rounded anal fin contains 14 to 19 rays. The upper jaw protrudes slightly beyond the lower jaw. Pectoral spines are short and devoid of teeth. The back, sides, and fins are gray to medium brown with black spots. Chin barbels, underside of the head, and venter are white. See Jordan (1877a) for original description.

ADULT SIZE: 3.5 to 6 in (89 to 152 mm)

DISTRIBUTION: The widespread speckled madtom is possibly the most abundant madtom in Alabama. Like the black madtom, *Noturus funebris*, this Coastal Plain species avoids the alkaline water and physical stream conditions common to Black Belt streams in the upper Tombigbee, Black Warrior, and Alabama river systems.

HABITAT AND BIOLOGY: Individuals occur around submerged vegetation, near leaf packs, and along the margins of small to large streams having slow to moderate currents and sand, silt, rock, and gravel substrates. Speckled madtoms spawn in June and July. Mettee et al. (1987) observed spawning in Okatuppa Creek, a tributary to the lower Tombigbee drainage, in late June 1984. A male and female speckled madtom had deposited their spawn between the Masonite plates of a benthic invertebrate sampler. When the sampler was retrieved and disassembled, the male madtom and eggs were discovered. Madtoms often use crevices between rocks and logs as spawning sites.

REMARKS: The type locality for the speckled madtom is Silver Creek, a tributary to the Etowah River, Georgia.

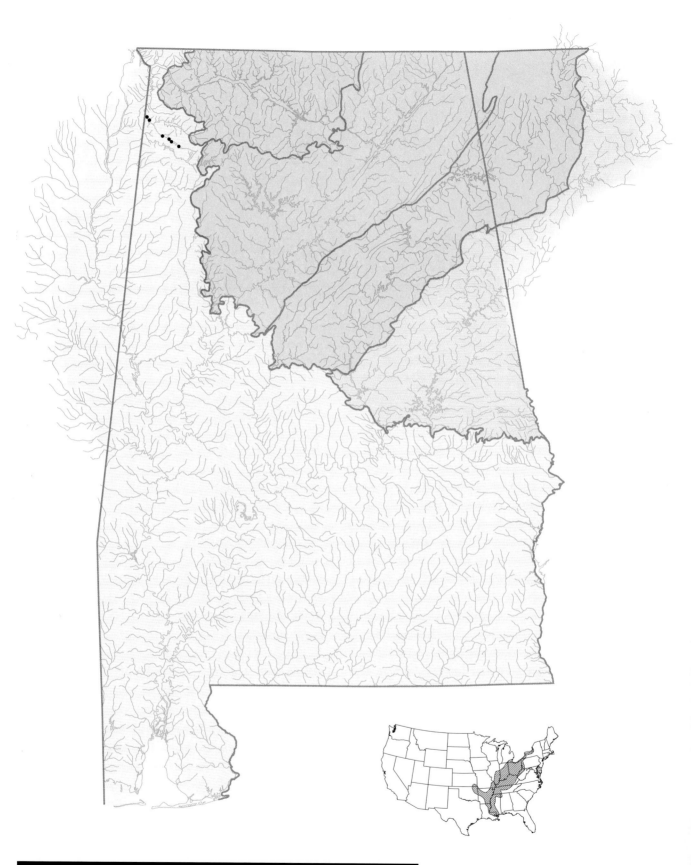

BRINDLED MADTOM *Noturus miurus* **6 STATIONS**

Noturus miurus

Jordan, 1877

ETYMOLOGY:

Noturus—back tail, referring to fusion of the adipose and caudal fins *miurus*—curtailed, possibly referring to the short, stocky build of this species

Cedar Creek, Franklin County, 10 March 1993, 1.7 in (42 mm) SL male, GSA 4370

CHARACTERISTICS: This small, robust madtom is mottled and has four dark saddles across the back. The anal fin is rounded and contains 13 to 17 rays. The rounded caudal fin has a single black band near its posterior margin. The posterior edge of each pectoral spine has five to eight prominent, recurved teeth, and the anterior edge is conspicuously serrated. Body color is light to medium yellowish brown with dusky mottling. A black blotch occurs on the distal one-third of the dorsal fin, and a black band extends to the edge of the adipose fin. See Jordan (1877a) for original description.

ADULT SIZE: 2.5 to 3.5 in (64 to 89 mm)

DISTRIBUTION: The known range in Alabama is limited to the Bear Creek system, a tributary of the Tennessee River in northwest Alabama. We collected the species only twice in 1993. There needs to be additional sampling in the Bear Creek system to assess the impact, if any, of recent strip mining and reservoir construction on the status of this marginally occurring species.

HABITAT AND BIOLOGY: The brindled madtom prefers low-gradient streams and rivers. It inhabits backwater areas and pools below riffles having a slow current over sand and gravel substrates topped with silt. Many of the individuals we collected occurred along stream margins and around accumulations of leaf litter. Judging from observations recorded for other states, we believe spawning occurs in May and June in Alabama and southern Tennessee. Etnier and Starnes (1993) note that individuals sometimes use soda or beer bottles and the undersides of rocks or pieces of wood as spawning receptacles. The diet of this species in Illinois includes aquatic insect larvae and isopods (Burr and Mayden, 1982b). Life span is estimated to be three years.

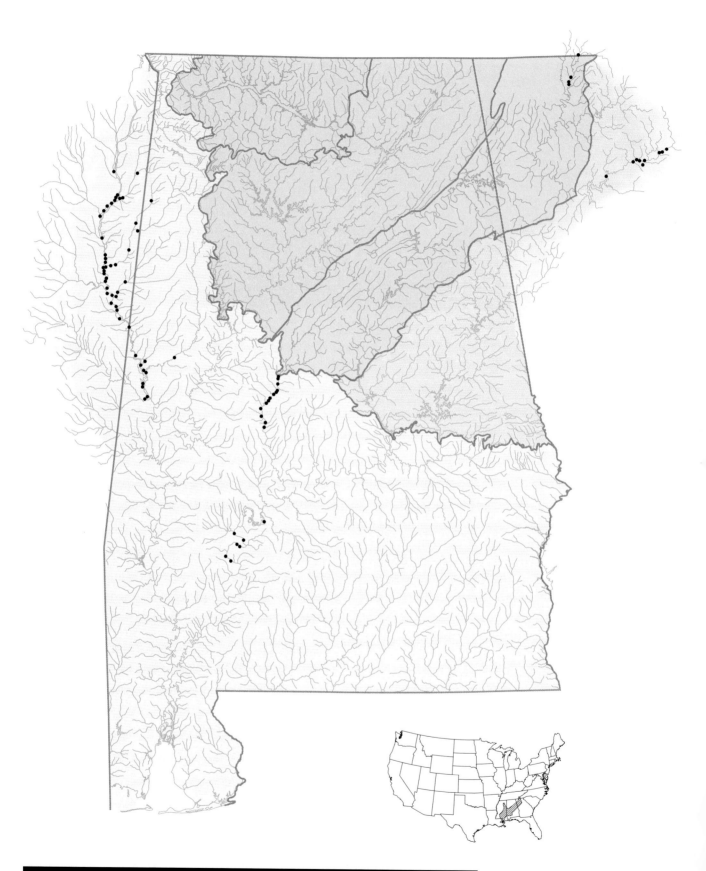

FRECKLEBELLY MADTOM *Noturus munitus* **81 STATIONS**

Noturus munitus

Suttkus and Taylor, 1965

ETYMOLOGY:

Noturus—back tail, referring to fusion of the adipose and caudal fins *munitus*—armed, referring to the extensive development of serrae on both sides of the pectoral spine

Sipsey River, Pickens County, 9 July 1993, 2.1 in (54 mm) SL female, GSA 4529

CHARACTERISTICS: In Alabama, the frecklebelly madtom is the only species that has four distinct, dark saddles across a yellow to golden back. Its common name derives from the many small, black specks that are scattered across the venter. Two dark, crescent-shaped bands occur on the slightly rounded caudal fin. Each well-developed pectoral spine has six to 10 prominent, recurved teeth on its posterior edge and some smaller but well-developed serrae on the anterior edge. The rounded anal fin contains only 12 to 15 rays, leaving a large space between the anal and caudal fin bases.

ADULT SIZE: 2 to 3 in (50 to 75 mm)

DISTRIBUTION: Several isolated but fairly abundant populations of frecklebelly madtoms previously occurred in the Mobile basin. Frecklebelly madtoms were also once common in sections of the upper Tombigbee and Alabama rivers. However, populations in both systems have dwindled in recent years, primarily because the construction and maintenance of inland waterways have destroyed most of the permanent gravel bars that the species inhabited. Our 1993-95 collections indicate this species still inhabits the Sipsey, Luxapallila and Butta-

hatchee tributaries of the upper Tombigbee River system. Pierson et al. (1989) note that the Cahaba River could also be a refuge for the species in Alabama. Isolated populations occur in the Etowah and Conasauga river systems in Georgia and Tennessee.

HABITAT AND BIOLOGY: This species prefers permanent gravel shoals and riffles of moderate or large flowing streams and rivers. Large and small individuals also occur in clumps of river weed and under large, flat rocks. In the upper Etowah and Conasauga main channels, frecklebelly madtoms have been collected in moderate to swift current over boulders, rubble, cobble, and coarse gravel and around concentrations of river weed (*Podostemon*). Trauth et al. (1981) report spawning in June and July in the Tombigbee River, Mississippi, and Miller (1984) remarks that individuals in the Tombigbee River consume aquatic insect larvae and mayfly nymphs. The life span of this species is estimated to be four or five years.

REMARKS: Ramsey (1986) lists **Noturus munitus** as a species of concern in Alabama. Its collection in state waters is restricted by the Alabama Game and Fish Division.

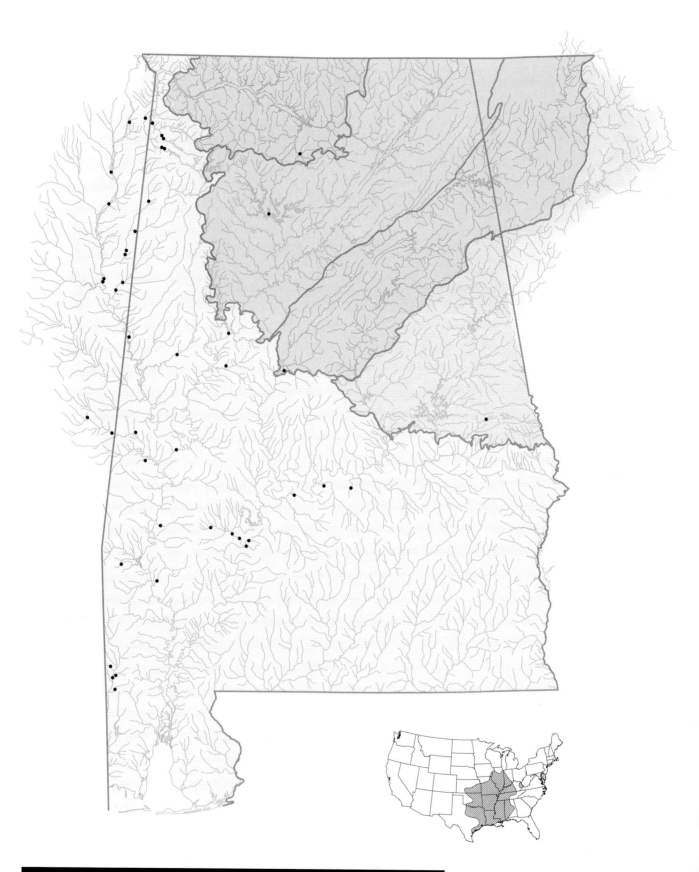

FRECKLED MADTOM *Noturus nocturnus* **45 STATIONS**

Noturus nocturnus

Jordan and Gilbert, 1886

ETYMOLOGY:

Noturus—back tail, referring to fusion of the adipose and caudal fins *nocturnus*—of the night, referring to this species' dark color

Puppy Creek, Mobile County, 3 May 1995, 4.6 in (118 mm) SL female, GSA 4642

CHARACTERISTICS: The body shapes and colors of the freckled madtom, *Noturus nocturnus,* and the black madtom, *N. funebris,* are similar, but the two can be distinguished by their anal fin rays: While the former has 15 to 18 anal fin rays, the latter has 21 to 27. The freckled madtom's pectoral fins lack posterior teeth and anterior serrae. The head is slightly depressed, and the upper jaw protrudes beyond the lower jaw. The back and sides are medium to dark gray, changing to pale yellow or creamy white on the venter. The fins are uniformly dark; median fins may be clear or edged in white.

ADULT SIZE: 2 to 5.5 in (50 to 135 mm)

DISTRIBUTION: Most locations in the Mobile basin are from below the Fall Line. The species has also been collected at a few locations in the Escatawpa River system and Tennessee River drainage. In our collections, freckled madtoms were never abundant or even common.

HABITAT AND BIOLOGY: This species usually occurs in moderate or slow current around aquatic vegetation, in leaf packs, and along undercut banks of medium-sized or large streams. In Puppy Creek, an Escatawpa River tributary, we found individuals behind rock and log snags in deep, moderate to swift waters. (This contrasts with our collection of the speckled madtom, *N. leptacanthus,* which occupied debris snags in waters less than 6 inches deep.) On 25 June 1993, we observed an adult guarding eggs under a flat rock in Bear Creek, a tributary to the Alabama River in Wilcox County. Burr and Mayden (1982c) note that freckled madtoms spawn in June and July in Illinois. Life span is probably four or five years. Diet consists of mayflies, caddisflies, and midges.

Puppy Creek, Escatawpa River drainage, Mobile County

411

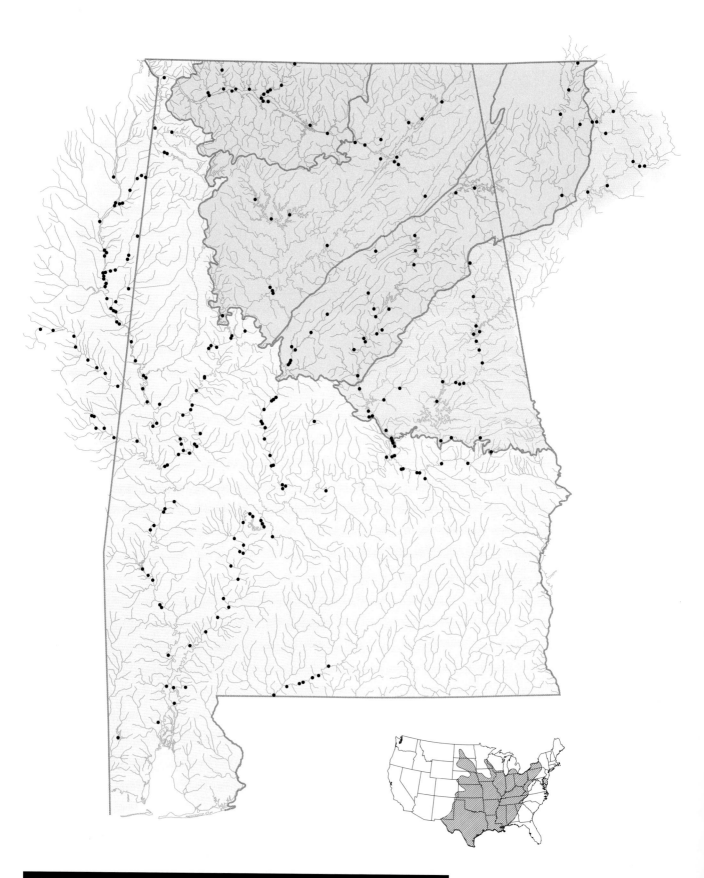

Pylodictis olivaris

(Rafinesque, 1818)

ETYMOLOGY:

Pylodictis—mud fish

olivaris—olive-colored

Short Creek, Marshall County, 9 June 1992, 5.8 in (147 mm) SL male, GSA 4246

CHARACTERISTICS: In Alabama, the flathead is the only large catfish with a head that is flattened between the eyes, a projecting lower jaw, and recurved tooth patches on either side of the upper jaw. The back and sides of the body and fins are mottled with black, white, olive, and even pale yellow, with the venter white or pale yellow. The short, rounded anal fin contains 14 to 18 rays. The caudal fin is slightly notched, and the top of the upper lobe is white on all but extremely large individuals. See Rafinesque (1818b) for original description.

ADULT SIZE: 18 to 24 in (460 to 610 mm). The state angling record (80 lb) was caught in the Alabama River near Selma in 1986. We have collected flatheads in the 30- to 50-pound class from the Tennessee River drainage south to the Alabama River and also in the tailwaters of several locks and dams.

DISTRIBUTION: *Pylodictis olivaris* is widespread and occasionally abundant in all rivers and reservoirs of the Mobile basin. It is common in the Tennessee River and many of its major tributaries. Flathead catfish have been introduced into the Conecuh and Escatawpa rivers in southern Alabama; they are fairly common in the former drainage and rare in the latter. Future sampling will probably expand the known range of this species in Alabama.

HABITAT AND BIOLOGY: We most frequently capture flathead catfish in flowing water over sand, gravel, and mud substrates. Individuals are usually associated with underwater structures such as fallen trees, stumps, rock ledges, and riprap. Flatheads are aggressive predators and opportunistic feeders. Young feed on aquatic insect larvae, crayfish, and small minnows. Adults eat crayfish and live or dead fish. Spawning over excavated pits occurs in June and July in Alabama and Tennessee (Etnier and Starnes, 1993). Young flatheads school, but they soon separate and become solitary after reaching lengths of several inches. Etnier and Starnes (1993) report a life span of 19 years.

REMARKS: The flathead catfish is a favorite food fish in Alabama. Malvestuto et al. (1983) report that 30,924 pounds of flathead catfish were harvested in the Mobile Delta and lower Tombigbee River in 1980 and 1981.

PIKES

E s o c i d a e

Two species in the family collectively known as pikes are native to Alabama, and one has been introduced. The native redfin pickerel, *Esox americanus*, and chain pickerel, *E. niger*, are widespread and are often abundant in their preferred habitats. The redfin pickerel inhabits small streams and swamps, and the chain pickerel prefers rivers, large streams, and oxbow lakes.

Muskellunge, *E. masquinongy*, have been introduced into both the Tennessee and Tallapoosa river drainages. Small, nonreproducing populations still inhabit both rivers, but they are not often encountered there. The state angling record (19 lb, 8 oz) was landed below Wilson Dam on the Tennessee River in 1972. (As many anglers know, pike make excellent table fare, but since the flesh contains many small intermuscular bones, it must be thoroughly cooked before being eaten.) The specimen in the photograph on the facing page was caught and released in 1993 by Auburn University graduate students who were studying paddlefish populations in the lower Tallapoosa River.

We should note that, while we have no confirmed records of northern pike in Alabama, they may have been introduced into the Tennessee River system. This species is distinguished by a fully scaled cheek and a gill cover that is scaled on the upper half.

Pikes and pickerels are long, slender fishes with duckbill snouts. The mouth is terminal, both jaws have many sharp teeth, and the lower jaw usually projects slightly beyond the upper jaw. Like muskellunge, pike have 10 or more sensory pores on the ventral side of the lower jaw. The dorsal and anal fins are closer to the forked caudal fin than to the snout, and the pelvic fins are situated about midway along the body. None of the fins has spines. The body is covered with small cycloid scales that are scalloped along the front margins.

Pike spawn in late winter and early spring, usually around aquatic vegetation. Eggs and young pike receive little, if any, parental care, and schools of young disband several months after hatching. Thereafter, the solitary individuals become highly efficient predators.

KEY TO THE PIKES

1a. Cheek and gill cover scaled on upper half only; 10 or more sensory pores on ventral side of lower jaw. . . . . muskellunge, *Esox masquinongy*
1b. Cheek and gill cover fully scaled; 8 or fewer sensory pores on ventral side of lower jaw. . . . . go to 2

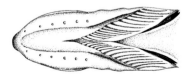  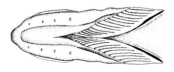

Heads: (left and center) ventral and lateral views of 1a, *E. masquinongy*, and (right) ventral view of 1b

2a. Distance from tip of snout to center of eye distinctly longer than from center of eye to rear margin of gill cover; pigmented bar beneath eye almost vertical in alignment. . . . . chain pickerel, *E. niger*

2b. Distance from tip of snout to center of eye equal to or slightly shorter than length from center of eye to rear margin of gill cover; pigmented bar beneath eye slanting slightly toward posterior . . . .
. . . . redfin pickerel, *E. americanus*

2a

2b

Lateral views of heads of 2a, *E. niger*, and 2b, *E. americanus*

INTRODUCED MUSKELLUNGE, TALLAPOOSA RIVER, ELMORE COUNTY

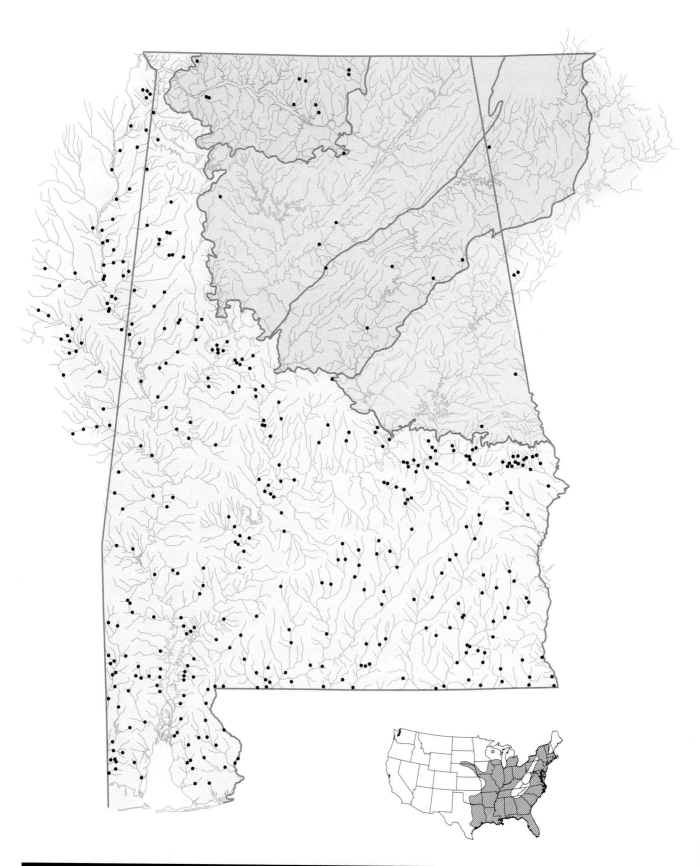

REDFIN PICKEREL *Esox americanus* **388 STATIONS**

Esox americanus

Gmelin, 1788

ETYMOLOGY:

Esox—pike

americanus—American

Pursley Creek, Wilcox County, 14 April 1993, 5.0 in (127 mm) SL female, GSA 4421

CHARACTERISTICS: The cheeks and gill covers on the redfin pickerel are fully scaled, while the top of the head has few if any scales. A darkened vertical bar beneath the eye slants slightly backward. In cross section, the body is oval or cigar-shaped. The back is dark green to brown. Color patterns on the sides are variable, from a green-and-white reticulate pattern resembling that of a brick wall to green, forward-slanting vertical bars. Along the lower sides, fingerlike green projections extend downward and forward onto a cream or yellow venter.

ADULT SIZE: 7 to 12 in (178 to 300 mm)

DISTRIBUTION: Crossman (1966) distinguishes two subspecies. The redfin pickerel, ***Esox americanus americanus***, is an Atlantic Coast form, its range extending from New York south to eastern drainages in Georgia. The grass pickerel, ***E. a. vermiculatus***, occurs throughout the Mississippi basin, including the Tennessee River in northern Alabama. Redfin pickerel inhabiting Gulf Coast drainages from the Mobile basin east into Florida and southwestern Georgia are intergrades between the two subspecies. Redfin pickerel are more widespread and abundant below the Fall Line. Few collections are available above the Fall Line or in the Tennessee River drainage.

HABITAT AND BIOLOGY: Redfin pickerel usually occur in clear streams having slow to moderate currents and abundant aquatic vegetation or undercut banks. We have also collected them in swamps and isolated overflow pools of rivers. The young occur in schools, but adults are solitary, aggressive predators. An individual will lie motionless along the edge of aquatic vegetation or an undercut bank for long periods. When unsuspecting prey appears, the fish darts out, grasps the prey, and swallows it head first. Large insect larvae, crayfishes, and fishes are staples of the adult diet. Redfin pickerel live to six years; grass pickerel reach seven years (Carlander, 1969).

REMARKS: Anglers are not likely to encounter this species, since it usually inhabits small streams.

417

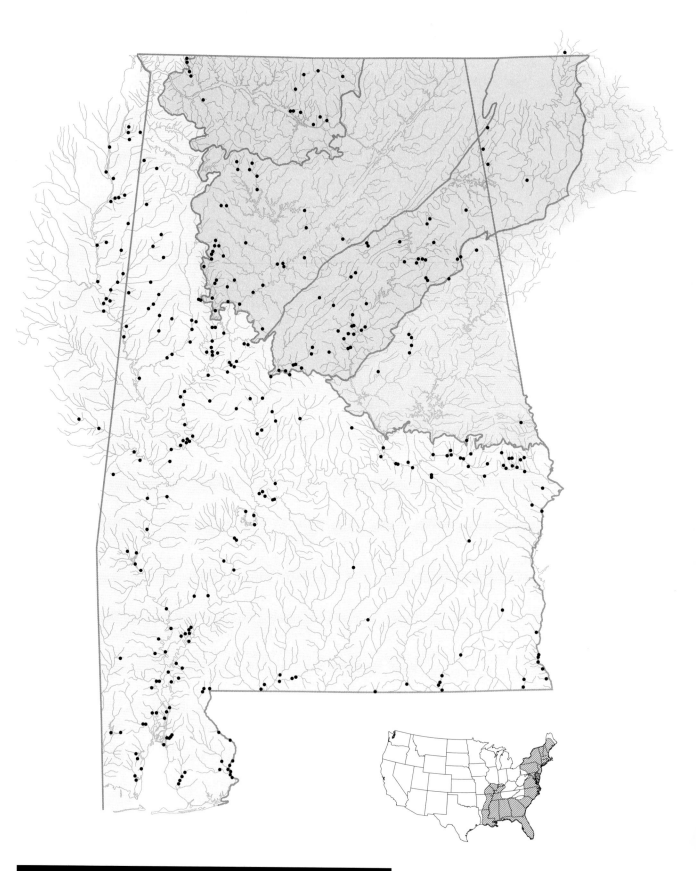

CHAIN PICKEREL *Esox niger* **332 STATIONS**

Esox niger
Lesueur, 1818

ETYMOLOGY:

Esox—pike

niger—black

Tombigbee River, Clarke County, 29 April 1992, 13 in (330 mm) SL male, GSA 4225

CHARACTERISTICS: Like the redfin, the chain pickerel has fully scaled cheeks and gill covers and few, if any, scales on top of the head. The pigmented bar beneath the eye is nearly vertical. The body in cross section is slightly deeper than it is wide. The back is dark green to brown. Sides are marked with greenish, rectangular-shaped patterns that resemble the links of a chain—hence the common name. The venter is either cream or pale yellow. See Lesueur (1818b) for original description.

ADULT SIZE: 15 to 30 in (380 to 762 mm). The state angling record (6 lb, 5.5 oz) was caught in Dyas Creek, a tributary of the Perdido River in Baldwin County, in 1976.

DISTRIBUTION: Chain pickerel have been collected in every river drainage except the Yellow and Blackwater rivers in south Alabama. Their apparent absence in headwaters of these drainages is probably due to either lack of preferred habitat or insufficient sampling.

HABITAT AND BIOLOGY: Chain pickerel prefer large streams, rivers, reservoirs, and swamps where there is minimal flow and substrates consist of silt and mud. This efficient predator lies motionless along the margins of aquatic vegetation or undercut banks. This species is a spring spawner. Young at first remain in schools; as they grow older, they become solitary hunters. As with the redfin pickerel, the adult diet consists of aquatic insect larvae, crayfishes, and sunfishes, especially bluegill. Crossman (1978) reports a maximum life span of nine years.

REMARKS: Anglers catch chain pickerel (locally known as "jack") in oxbow lakes, reservoirs, and swamps. It is an excellent game fish that jumps repeatedly when hooked.

TROUTS AND CHARS

Salmonidae

The family Salmonidae is native to the cool and cold waters of North America, Southeast Asia, Eurasia, and northern Africa. Thirty-nine species inhabit North America, including Canada, the western mountains and Pacific Coast, the Great Lakes and northern plains, and parts of the Appalachian Mountains. In recent years, private and government stocking programs have substantially expanded the ranges of several sport and commercial species. Although Alabama's warm water temperatures do not allow them to reproduce naturally, hatchery-raised stocks of rainbow trout, ***Oncorhynchus mykiss***, and brown trout, ***Salmo trutta***, have been introduced into northern Alabama and Georgia; brook trout, ***Salvelinus fontinalis*** (technically a char), occur as introduced in Georgia.

Most salmonids live in fresh water. Five Pacific and one Atlantic species are anadromous, meaning that the adults live in salt water and migrate into fresh water to spawn. The most dramatic example of this behavior is that of Pacific salmon, which may migrate several hundred miles to reach a home shoal in a particular stream. The adults die shortly after they spawn. The newly hatched fingerlings move downstream to the sea and mature into adults, which range in size from 6 inches to almost 5 feet for the chinook salmon. Several years after reaching maturity, adults return to the streams in which they hatched, spawn, and die, thus completing the cycle of life.

Breeding salmon and trout develop an enlarged, conspicuously hooked jaw known as a kype, which they use to defend their territory during spawning. After migrating to the spawning grounds, females prepare nests (known as redds) in gravel areas above or below riffles. Spawning activity usually covers the eggs with gravel. To survive, eggs require streams of exceptional water quality and cool to cold temperatures. If the spawning grounds become overly silted or if pollutants lower oxygen levels, many of the eggs will die.

Together, pollution and overfishing have already depleted populations of the Atlantic Coast anadromous species. However, recent information published by Etnier and Starnes (1993) indicates that some stocks may be rebounding as a result of improved fishery management and increased stocking of streams and rivers.

Trout are omnivorous sight feeders that prefer small fishes and large aquatic insect immatures. Their visual acuity and ability to adjust their diet to available prey—as well as their excellent taste when cooked—make trout the favorite of fly-fishermen worldwide. The adage "match the hatch" is based on these biological traits and refers to the angling practice of matching an artificial fly with the type of aquatic insect then emerging from the stream. Sport fishing for salmon and trout is a sizable industry, and it is absolutely dependent on the maintenance of clear, clean, and flowing streams and rivers.

KEY TO THE TROUTS AND CHARS

1a. Back with vermiculate or wormlike pattern; sides with pale spots; vomer bone shaft lacking teeth; lateral line scales 200 or more . . . . brook trout, *Salvelinus fontinalis*

1b. Back and sides with dark spots; shaft of vomer bone with 1 or 2 rows of teeth; lateral line scales 160 or fewer . . . . go to 2

2a. Caudal fin usually not spotted; medium-sized spots on head but not on area from tip of snout to nares; sides with red spots, but otherwise lacking color in life . . . . brown trout, *Salmo trutta*

2b. Caudal fin extensively spotted; numerous small spots on entire surface of head; sides usually lacking red spots, but with a dark pink lateral stripe . . . . rainbow trout, *Oncorhynchus mykiss*

LITTLE RIVER, DEKALB COUNTY, GEORGIA

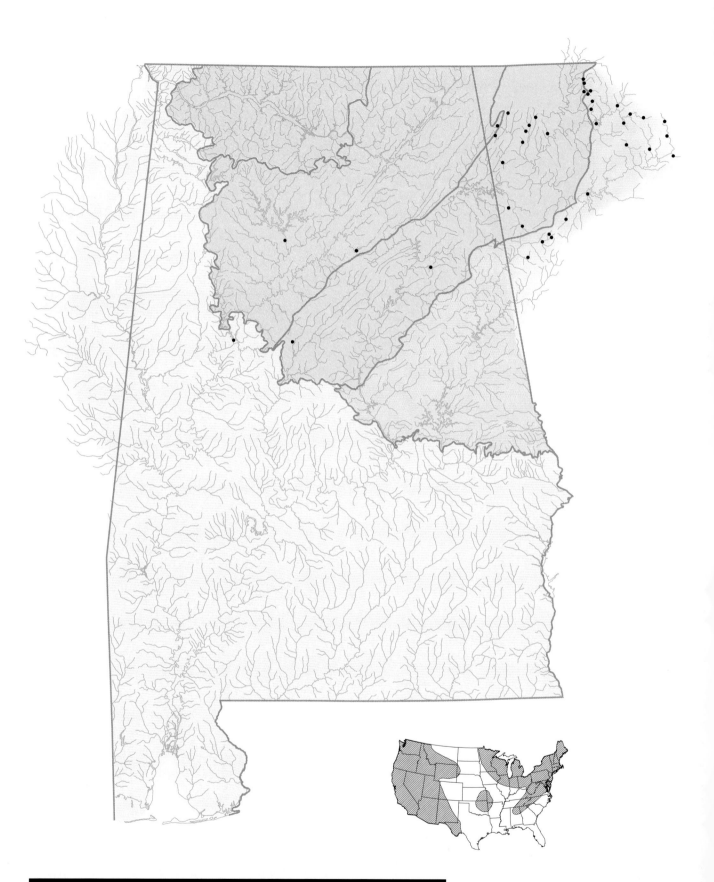

RAINBOW TROUT   *Oncorhynchus mykiss*   39 STATIONS

Oncorhynchus mykiss
(Walbaum, 1792)

ETYMOLOGY:
Oncorhynchus—hook snout, referring to the hooked jaw of a breeding male *mykiss*—presumably a derivative of *mikizha* or *mykyz*, the Kamchatkan word for trout

Bald River, Monroe County, Tennessee, 10 October 1995, 7.1 in (181 mm) SL male, GSA 4658

CHARACTERISTICS: The rainbow trout has many small spots scattered across its back, sides, head, and caudal fin. The back is brassy green flecked with iridescent purple and green; the venter is white or gray. A wide pink, purple, or red band marks the sides. The body form is spindle-shaped, and the mouth is terminal and large. No fins have spines. A fleshy adipose fin is present between the caudal and dorsal fins. Scales are cycloid, very small, and embedded under a thick mucus coat. Recent adjustments in the taxonomy of salmon and trout have placed Pacific salmon and trout in the genus ***Oncorhynchus***, while the Atlantic salmon, brown trout, and their Eurasian relatives are in the genus ***Salmo*** (reviewed by Smith and Stearley, 1989). The rainbow trout was previously known as ***Salmo gairdneri***.

ADULT SIZE: 9 to 29 in (226 to 737 mm)

DISTRIBUTION: This species occurs naturally in Pacific Coast drainages from Alaska to northwestern Mexico. It has been stocked extensively worldwide, and in North America it now occurs throughout Canada, the Great Lakes region, the Appalachians, the Ozarks, and central Mexico. In Alabama, rainbow trout are stocked in spring-fed Mud Creek in Tannehill State Park, and rainbows from the Dale Hollow National Fish Hatchery in Tennessee are stocked in cold tailwaters below Lake Lewis Smith Dam. In past years, they were stocked in some spring-fed ponds of Lauderdale and Limestone counties and in Inland Lake, which drains to the Black Warrior River. A downstream waif, most likely from the Smith tailrace or Inland Lake, was recently recorded at the mouth of North River near Tuscaloosa. Rainbows are also commonly stocked in headwaters of the Little Tallapoosa and Coosa rivers in Georgia.

HABITAT AND BIOLOGY: Rainbow trout can adapt to a variety of habitats, given proper temperature and water-quality conditions, and to flow regimes ranging from pools to calm eddies in riffles. A temperature range from 54° to 66°F (12° to 19°C) is optimal, and reproducing populations require a seasonal drop in temperature below 55°F (13°C). Rainbows feed on various organisms, including small crustaceans and juvenile insects; adults also feed on fishes. Brayton (1981) sets maturity at one year and longevity at three or four years in Virginia, while Carlander (1969) indicates that longevity is seven years. Wild populations spawn in the spring, with migrating males usually arriving at the spawning grounds before the females do.

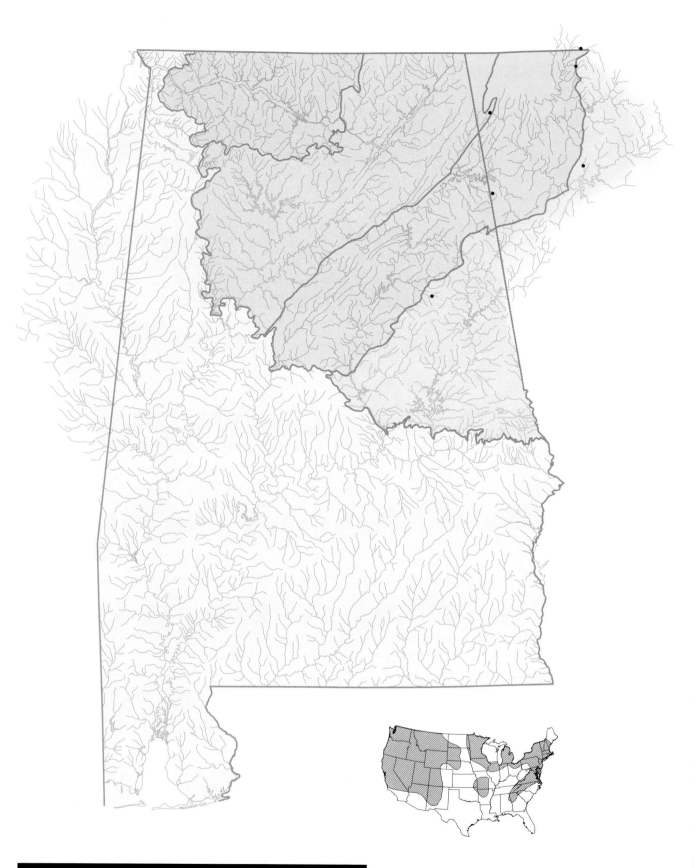

BROWN TROUT   *Salmo trutta*   **6 STATIONS**

424

Salmo trutta

Linnaeus, 1758

ETYMOLOGY:

Salmo—name for the
Atlantic salmon
trutta—Latin for trout

Bald River, Monroe County, Tennessee, 10 October 1995, 4.3 in (108 mm) SL male, GSA 4658

CHARACTERISTICS: The brown trout is distinguished by its silver venter and brown or tan back and sides. Large black spots mark the top and sides of the head, back, and dorsal fin, while large red or orange spots with pale haloes appear on the sides. (Individuals taken from lakes are silvery and may lack distinct spot patterns.) The leading edge of the anal fin is milky white. Large breeding males develop a prominent hook, called a kype, on the lower jaw. The body has small, embedded cycloid scales, a fleshy adipose fin, and no spines in the fins— resembling that of the brook trout, *Salvelinus fontinalis*, and the rainbow trout, *Oncorhynchus mykiss*. Browns hybridize with brookies, producing a form known as the tiger trout, named for the vermiculate patterns on its body and head.

ADULT SIZE: 7 to 31 in (178 to 787 mm)

DISTRIBUTION: The brown trout is native to Europe, Iceland, western Asia, and northwest Africa, and it was introduced to North America in 1883 from stocks in Germany and Scotland. It is now found throughout Canada, the western states, the upper plains, the Great

Lakes region, and the Appalachians. In the past, brown trout were stocked in cool streams in eastern Alabama, where single individuals are occasionally encountered. Records also exist for small streams in the upper Coosa River in Georgia.

HABITAT AND BIOLOGY: Brown trout prefer cool to cold streams, ponds, and lakes, tolerating substrates of hard rock or softer sediments. To survive, they appear to need cover and areas of low velocity for feeding. Compared to brook trout, brown trout are more tolerant of warmer stream temperatures: They prefer a range of 54° to 63°F (12° to 17°C), but they can survive at up to 75°F (24°C). Juvenile brown trout feed on a variety of prey, favoring aquatic insect immatures. Adults are opportunistic and seek bigger prey, including other fishes, salamanders, frogs, and crayfishes. Longevity is eight or more years (Carlander, 1969). Spawning of resident populations occurs during the late fall at temperatures of 45° to 48°F (7° to 9°C) in shallow gravel areas between pools and riffles, where the eggs are buried and abandoned. If not as athletic as the rainbow, the brown is still a strong fighter, and it is the most wary of all the trout.

BROOK TROUT *Salvelinus fontinalis* **2 STATIONS**

Salvelinus fontinalis

(Mitchill, 1814)

ETYMOLOGY:

Salvelinus—derivative of the old name for the char, a type of trout

fontinalis—of fountains or springs

Meadow Branch, Monroe County, Tennessee, 10 October 1995, 5.8 in (147 mm) SL male, GSA 4657

CHARACTERISTICS: Although the adult brook trout is smaller than the rainbow trout, *Oncorhynchus mykiss*, the bodies of the two are similar. The back of the brook trout has a pale vermiculate pattern that differentiates it from both the rainbow and brown trout, *Salmo trutta*. Breeding males are olive along the back and sides, while the lower sides and venter grade from yellow-red to brilliant orange. Pale yellow or olive spots occur along the sides, with some small red spots haloed in light blue. The male's dorsal fin is light yellow with dark spots or bars. The caudal fin is yellow-olive, grading to red in the middle with black markings along the outside of each lobe. Anal and paired fins are orange, with milky white leading edges contrasting with a thin black band. Females lack the brilliant red-orange color, but they retain the spots and vermiculate patterns on the back, sides, and fins. Teeth are lacking on the vomer bone shaft, located on the roof of the mouth.

ADULT SIZE: 7 to 15 in (178 to 380 mm)

DISTRIBUTION: This species' native distribution extends from the southern Appalachians north through the Great Lakes and much of eastern Canada, and it has been introduced to higher elevations throughout the western states. Although we have no records of brook trout from Alabama, we know of two localities from streams in the upper Coosa River in Georgia.

HABITAT AND BIOLOGY: Brook trout prefer small, rocky, clear mountain streams, such as the headwater areas of the Great Smoky Mountains National Park. Both anadromous and nonanadromous strains occur in northern states. Slow-flowing pools and riffle eddies are preferred habitats. Brookies, as these fish are sometimes called, are intolerant of habitat degradation, and they are the least competitive of the three salmonid species profiled here. Their preferred temperature range is from 52° to 55°F (11° to 13°C); maximum stream temperature is around 61°F (16°C). Southern Appalachian brook trout rarely exceed 12 inches, and they live to be three or four years old; northern populations in colder lakes and streams are generally larger and older. Adults feed on small forage fishes, insects, and other invertebrates and are even known to take field mice and snakes. Etnier and Starnes (1993) report spawning during the fall in Tennessee, with individuals from small streams reaching maturity at 4 or 5 inches. Despite their intolerant and somewhat docile nature, brookies are a favorite among fly-fishermen.

427

PIRATE PERCH

Aphredoderidae

The pirate perch and its nearest relatives in Alabama, the cavefishes, exhibit one of the most bizarre growth patterns among freshwater fishes in North America. The anal and urogenital openings on newly hatched individuals are located in the position considered normal—that is, just in front of the anal fin origin. But because the pirate perch grows disproportionately, its anal and urogenital openings gradually move forward through the pelvic fin area, eventually becoming displaced to the throat region on the underside of the head. This curious developmental process explains the Greek genus name ***Aphredoderus,*** which means "throat excrement."

The family Aphredoderidae contains only one species, ***Aphredoderus sayanus***, which is limited to the eastern United States. The pirate perch, together with the cavefishes in the family Amblyopsidae and the trout perch in the family Percopsidae, were originally grouped in the order Percopsiformes by Greenwood et al. (1966). A later study by Patterson and Rosen (1989) resolved that the pirate perch and cavefishes were not natural members of the Percopsiformes; they were placed instead in a separate group, the Aphredoderoidei, within the order Gadiformes.

Etnier and Starnes (1993) question the subordinal ranking proposed by Patterson and Rosen (1989) and place the pirate perch and cavefishes in the order Aphredoderiformes, a category that to us seems more appropriate until future study resolves this issue.

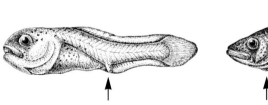 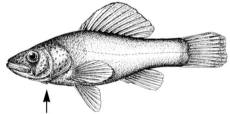

Anal and urogenital openings on (left) the immature pirate perch and (right) the adult pirate perch

BEAR CREEK, FRANKLIN COUNTY

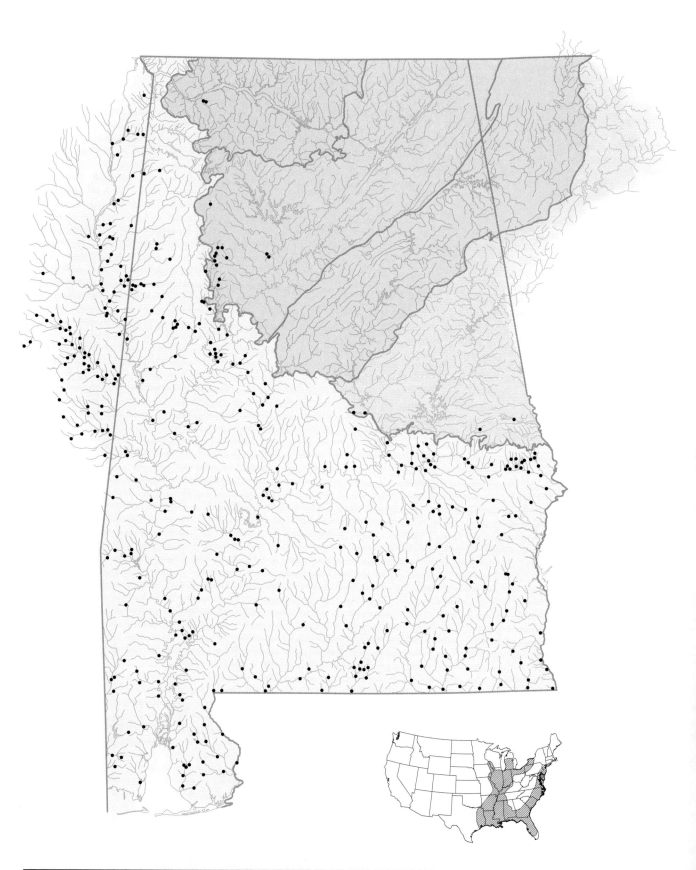

PIRATE PERCH *Aphredoderus sayanus* **395 STATIONS**

Aphredoderus sayanus
(Gilliams, 1824)

ETYMOLOGY:

Aphredoderus—excrement throat, from the Greek words *aphod* and *dere*, referring to the anal and urogenital openings on adult individuals' throats *sayanus*—in honor of entomologist Thomas Say

Dyas Creek, Baldwin County, 12 August 1994, 3.1 in (78 mm) SL male, GSA 4630

CHARACTERISTICS: Adult pirate perch have an elongate but stocky body; a single, rounded dorsal fin; dark gray body color; and a distinct bar below the eye. The head is relatively small, with a rounded snout and large mouth. The dorsal and anal fins are preceded by two or three weakly developed spines. The dark gray to purplish body is intensely speckled with small dusky spots, while the cheek and venter may appear blue in live individuals. Median fins have a dusky margin.

ADULT SIZE: 2.4 to 5.7 in (60 to 144 mm)

DISTRIBUTION: *Aphredoderus sayanus* is distributed in coastal streams from New York south through the Atlantic and Gulf coastal drainages to the Brazos River in Texas, and north through the Mississippi River basin to Michigan. Isolated populations are found in the Lake Ontario and Lake Erie drainages. In Alabama, the pirate perch occurs in all coastal drainages, the Mobile basin below the Fall Line, and Bear and Spring creeks, tributaries of the Tennessee

River drainage. Isolated populations are known from above the Fall Line in the Black Warrior River system.

HABITAT AND BIOLOGY: The pirate perch favors quiet backwaters in swamps, sloughs, ponds, lakes, and sheltered pools in creeks and streams. It prefers soft substrates, and it is commonly taken in dense cover over mud bottoms. Spawning throughout its range varies from January through May (Swift et al., 1977; Forbes and Richardson, 1920); ripe males have been found in March and April in Alabama. Martin and Hubbs (1973) propose that, like their relatives the cavefishes, pirate perch may be mouthbreeders. There is, however, little evidence that pirate perch carry their eggs in the mouth as a normal mode of incubation (Jenkins and Burkhead, 1993). Because of these fishes' nocturnal and secretive habits, not much is known about their reproduction. Shepard and Huish (1978) report that ***A. sayanus*** in North Carolina live for four or more years, and that their diet consists of crustaceans, dipteran larvae, and possibly small pirate perch.

CAVEFISHES

Amblyopsidae

The family Amblyopsidae is represented in North America by six small species restricted to limestone areas of Missouri, Arkansas and Alabama, and to swamp habitats in coastal rivers of Virginia, North Carolina, South Carolina, and Georgia. Two species occur in Alabama: the Alabama cavefish, ***Speoplatyrhinus poulsoni***, an endemic fish inhabiting only Key Cave in Lauderdale County, and the southern cavefish, ***Typhlichthys subterraneus***, found in many cave environments scattered across the Tennessee Valley area of northern Alabama. Localized ***T. subterraneus*** populations are rumored to inhabit headwater caves of the Black Warrior River system, though their presence there is unsubstantiated to date.

Like the pirate perch, the cavefish has anal and urogenital openings that are located in the throat region. A large mouth cavity is possibly adapted for mouth incubation of young. Eyes are either lacking or are substantially reduced in function. In most species, the nervous system is highly specialized for increased motion detection, which presumably aids feeding and locating of mates during spawning. Its tubular nostrils enable water to pass directly to the olfactory organs, which is believed to enhance the cavefish's sense of smell. The body, which is essentially white, is covered with embedded scales. Most species lack pelvic fins.

Cavefish species can be classified according to their habitats and level of cave adaptation. The swampfish, ***Chologaster cornuta***, inhabits swamps and quiet streams from Virginia to Georgia. The spring cavefish, ***Forbesichthys agassizi***, is adapted to cave environments in parts of Tennessee, Kentucky, Illinois, and Missouri (Cooper and Kuehne, 1974). The four remaining species are true cave-dwelling (troglobitic) forms: ***Amblyopsis rosae*** and ***A. spelaea***, the Ozark cavefish and northern cavefish, and the two species occurring in Alabama. The degree of eye and pigment degeneration appears to be positively correlated with the amount of time the species has been associated with cave environments (Poulson, 1963). Another indicator of the extent of cave adaptation is the exaggerated development of sensory receptors—notably, the numerous papillae scattered over the head, body, and caudal fin—which compensate for the cavefish's blindness.

The biology of these species also reflects their adaptation to cave environments (Poulson, 1963). Rate of growth is reduced, which is in turn related to the production of fewer yet larger eggs. As a result, the absolute population size of true troglobites is smaller, but longevity is greater, leading to an adult-dominated population that contrasts with the juvenile-dominated populations common among surface-dwelling species.

KEY TO THE CAVEFISHES

1a. Head extremely elongate and depressed anteriorly, with laterally constricted snout; mouth nearly terminal; no bifurcated fin rays and noticeably incised fin membranes . . . Alabama cavefish, ***Speoplatyrhinus poulsoni***

1b. Head rounded and more normally shaped anteriorly; mouth distinctly superior; fin rays bifurcated with smooth margins . . . . southern cavefish, ***Typhlichthys subterraneus***

IRON HOOP CAVE, JACKSON COUNTY

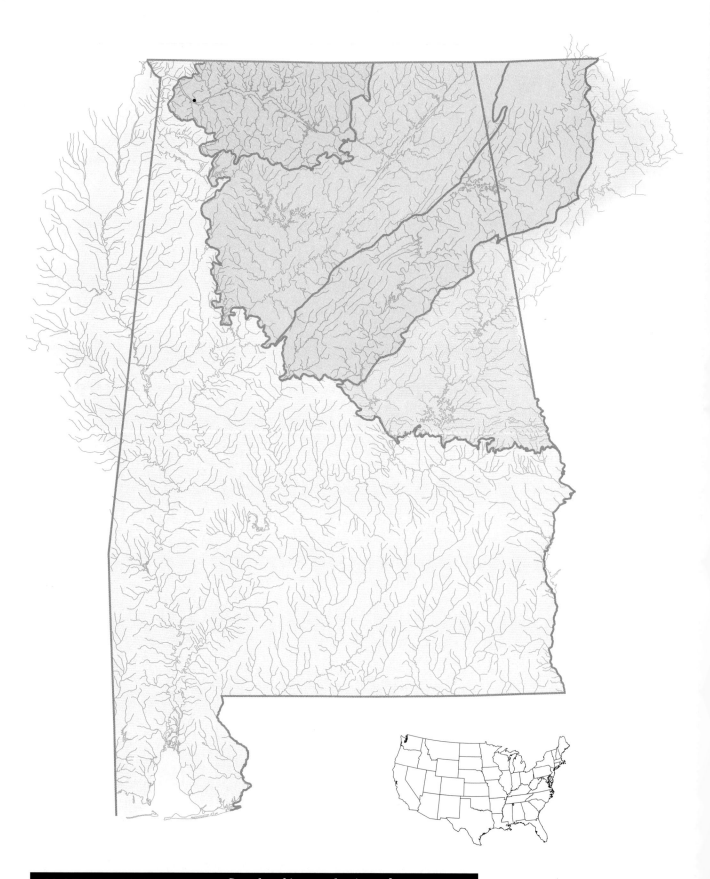

ALABAMA CAVEFISH *Speoplatyrhinus poulsoni* **1 STATION**

434

Speoplatyrhinus poulsoni
Cooper and Kuehne, 1974

ETYMOLOGY:

Speos—Greek word for cave, referring to this species' cave habitat

platyrhinus—flat nose

poulsoni—in honor of Thomas L. Poulson, for his work with amblyopsid fishes

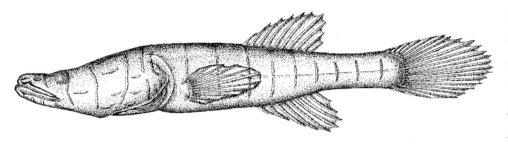

Key Cave, Lauderdale County. Composite drawing from photographs of a live individual.

CHARACTERISTICS: The Alabama cavefish is one of the rarest troglobitic fish species in North America. It is characterized by an extremely elongate, flattened head with a laterally constricted snout and a terminal mouth. It lacks pelvic fins, and fin rays are unbranched, with the fin membranes deeply incised between the rays. *Speoplatyrhinus poulsoni* has no eyes and practically no pigment. The elaborate system of sensory papillae, which are arranged in ridges on the head and sides, is apparently an adaptation to the dark environment these fishes inhabit. When this species was discovered in 1970, it was so unusual that a new genus had to be created for its description (Cooper and Kuehne, 1974).

ADULT SIZE: 1.2 to 2.3 in (30 to 58 mm)

DISTRIBUTION: *Speoplatyrhinus poulsoni* is known only from the type locality, Key Cave in Lauderdale County, Alabama.

HABITAT AND BIOLOGY: The type specimens of this species were netted near the surface of very clear,

10-foot-deep water below a bat roost (Cooper and Kuehne, 1974). Because the water contains nutrients supplied by bat guano, Key Cave supports an abundant and varied terrestrial invertebrate fauna, including mites, nematodes, dipterans, spiders, beetles, and millipedes. The troglobitic aquatic fauna is also diverse, consisting of two species of crayfishes, one species of amphipod, and one species of isopod. Cooper (1990) speculates that the Alabama cavefish, which is similar to the northern cavefish, *Amblyopsis spelaea*, uses its large mouth to incubate its eggs and protect its young. Population growth is speculated to be the lowest of all cave dwellers, and longevity is predicted to be between five and 10 years. Because its known range is limited to a single cave, the Alabama cavefish has an uncertain future, being threatened by changes in groundwater quality and level, changes in aquifer characteristics, diminished organic input, and perhaps competition with the syntopic southern cavefish, *Typhlichthys subterraneus.*

REMARKS: The Alabama cavefish is listed as endangered by the U.S. Fish and Wildlife Service.

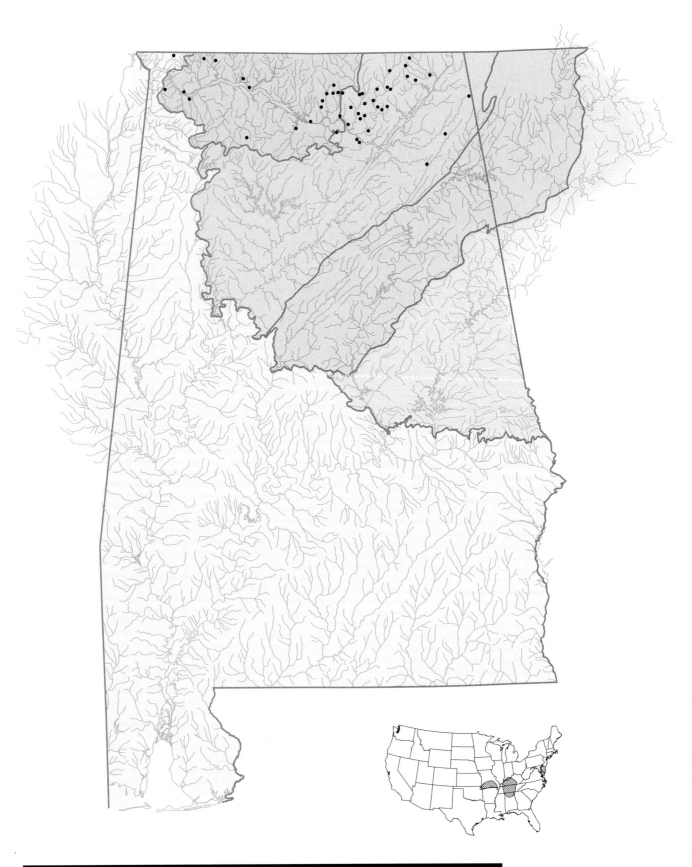

Typhlichthys
subterraneus
Girard, 1859

ETYMOLOGY:
Typhlichthys—blind fish
subterraneus—beneath the
earth, referring to the cave
environments in which the
species lives

Bobcat Cave, Madison County, 30 June 1993, 1.7 in (42 mm) SL female, GSA 4494

CHARACTERISTICS: Compared to the Alabama cavefish, *Speoplatyrhinus poulsoni*, which has a small head and terminal mouth, the southern cavefish has a larger, broader head and a distinctly superior mouth. The fin rays are bifurcated, and the fin margins are smooth. Like *S. poulsoni*, the southern cavefish has an elaborate system of sensory papillae along the head and sides and also in two rows down the caudal fin. It has little or no pigment, although live specimens are light pink where blood vessels are near the skin surface. It lacks eyes but does have vestigial eye tissue below the skin. Anal and urogenital openings lie underneath the throat.

ADULT SIZE: 1.4 to 2.6 in (35 to 65 mm)

DISTRIBUTION: The widely distributed southern cavefish occurs in the Ozark plateau of Missouri, Arkansas, and Oklahoma and in the Cumberland and interior low plateaus of north Alabama, northwest Georgia, and central Tennessee and Kentucky. In Alabama, *Typhlichthys subterraneus* is found in limestone cave environments in the Tennessee River drainage and in subterranean waters of the Coosa River system.

HABITAT AND BIOLOGY: Southern cavefishes occupy clear, mud-bottomed pools and flowing pools of limestone caves. Extensive field work in the Tennessee Valley indicates that distribution of these cavefishes may be partially limited by poor water quality and an inadequate food base. While the bulk of the southern cavefish's diet is made up of copepods, it also includes other microcrustaceans, crayfish, and trichopteran and dipteran larvae. Poulson (1963) reports that this species begins to reproduce at 24 months. Spawning usually occurs in the spring when water levels rise, and some individuals attain an age of four or more years.

REMARKS: This species is protected by rules and regulations of the Alabama Game and Fish Division.

NEEDLEFISH

Belonidae

Members of the family Belonidae are distributed worldwide. Most species occupy primarily marine and brackish water, but a few genera in South America and India are restricted to fresh water. The only belonid in Alabama freshwaters—the Atlantic needlefish, **Strongylura marina**—probably holds the state's distance record for inland occurrence of a primarily marine species.

The Atlantic needlefish is widespread and seasonally abundant throughout the Mobile basin except in the lower Coosa and Tallapoosa river systems, where it occurs only sporadically. Adults live and spawn in fresh water, as evidenced by our spring and summer collections of small, 2- to 4-inch individuals in the Alabama, Black Warrior, Coosa, and lower Tombigbee rivers.

Atlantic needlefish tend to congregate in tailwaters below locks and dams in the spring, and we observed hundreds of individuals below Millers Ferry and Claiborne locks and dams on the Alabama River in March and April 1995. This is apparently one of the first species to have entered the Tennessee River drainage via the Tennessee-Tombigbee Waterway. Specimens were observed in the Pickwick Pool in 1993, and it is possible that the species will increase in abundance there and expand its range. Although needlefish are quite common in the Conecuh and Choctawhatchee systems in south Alabama, we have not observed any in the Chattahoochee River above Woodruff Dam.

A family in the order Beloniformes, belonids have an elongate body covered with very small scales. The head is also elongate, and the beaklike jaws contain many sharp, pointed teeth that assist in capturing small fishes and other food items. The dorsal and anal fins are set close to the caudal fin. Live needlefishes are a translucent green, making them difficult to see in reservoirs and rivers. When frightened, they leap out of the water, and Munro (1967) reports that people in New Guinea have even been killed by belonids leaping at great speed.

CHOCTAWHATCHEE RIVER, GENEVA COUNTY

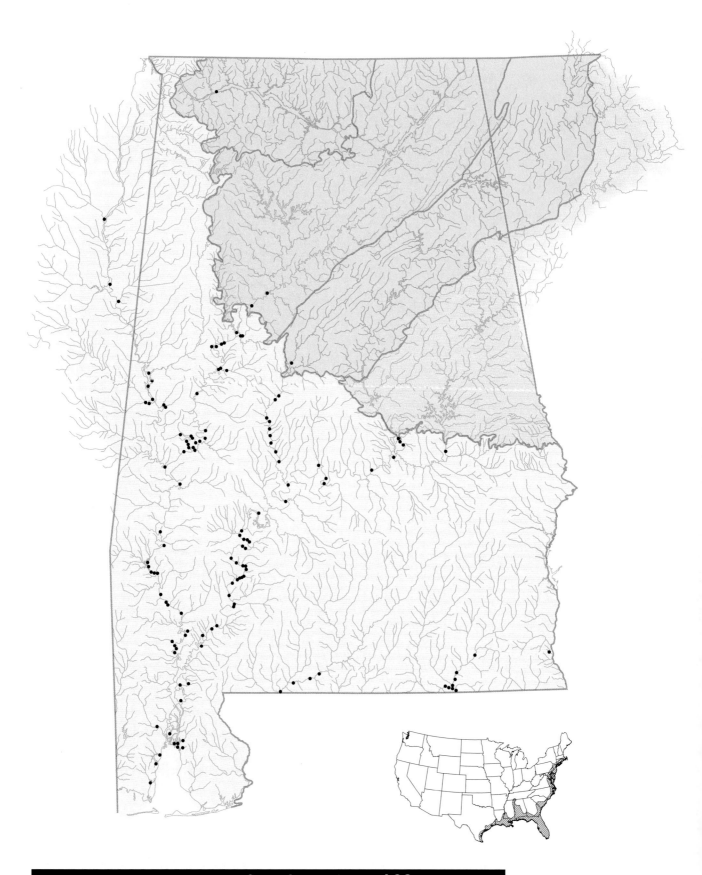

ATLANTIC NEEDLEFISH   *Strongylura marina*   **129 STATIONS**

440

Strongylura marina
(Walbaum, 1792)

ETYMOLOGY:

Strongylura—Greek for rounded, referring to the long, slender, rounded body of this species

marina—of the sea

Alabama River, Monroe County, 5 May 1994, 9.3 in (237 mm) SL male, GSA 4727

CHARACTERISTICS: The distinctive Atlantic needlefish has a long, slender body, elongated jaws with numerous sharp teeth, and dorsal and anal fins placed at the back of the body. The tip of the lower jaw extends slightly beyond the upper jaw. The body is generally translucent and light yellow to yellow-green above the lateral line, grading to silver below. A dark green stripe occurs on the midline of the back, and a narrow, bluish silver stripe runs along the sides. The fins are yellowish along the edges.

ADULT SIZE: 7.7 to 19 in (196 to 483 mm)

DISTRIBUTION: *Strongylura marina* is a common inhabitant of coastal waters from Maine to Brazil. In Alabama it has invaded fresh waters, occurring in coastal rivers and estuarine environments, in the Mobile basin upstream to the Fall Line, and in the Tennessee River drainage. Specimens of Atlantic needlefish from Alabama represent some of the farthest inland records known for this species.

HABITAT AND BIOLOGY: In Alabama, the Atlantic needlefish is usually found near the surface of large rivers and in the lower reaches of large tributaries, preferring open water. An efficient predator, this species is capable of sudden, short bursts of speed, which it uses to capture small fishes. Spawning occurs in late spring and summer, when females produce sinking, filamentous eggs that attach themselves to each other or to submerged objects. Inland populations apparently spawn in fresh water, although no studies have examined this. In coastal waters, the Atlantic needlefish feeds almost exclusively on fish, including silver mullet, killifish, silversides, and shrimp (Hildebrand and Schroeder, 1928). In Alabama rivers, it more than likely feeds on shiners, shad and brook silversides.

TOPMINNOWS

Fundulidae

As their name suggests, topminnows usually live near the water surface. They occupy a wide variety of freshwater and marine habitats, including quiet, shallow backwaters, sloughs, oxbows, and pools in flowing streams and freshwater springs. Vegetation and structure are critical features for the topminnow's habitat, providing cover, food, and a place for depositing eggs.

Several estuarine species are physiologically adapted to withstand salinities substantially greater than the 35 parts per thousand normally found in seawater. One example is the rainwater killifish, *Lucania parva*, collected in Texas by Simpson and Gunter (1956) at salinities varying from 1 to 48.2 parts per thousand. Another is the gulf killifish, *Fundulus grandis*, which occurs at salinities ranging from 1.8 to 76.1 parts per thousand.

Most topminnows have elongate, cylindrical bodies with rounded tails. The nape and top of the head are somewhat flattened. Adult sizes range from less than 1 inch for the pygmy killifish, *Leptolucania ommata*, to 6 inches in larger species such as the northern studfish, *Fundulus catenatus*. Small topminnows feed on terrestrial insects which fall into the water and on microcrustaceans near the surface. Large individuals also feed at the surface, but much of their diet consists of benthic (bottom-dwelling) forms, including insect larvae and mollusks.

Having adapted to life at the water's surface, topminnows have excellent vision and eyes that are oriented upward—characteristics that make it difficult to surprise and capture them with nets. We have improvised a strategy that may not be elegant but is certainly effective.

Two people stand in the water; each vigorously waves one hand while holding the net in the other hand. The topminnows are temporarily distracted by the movement and can be herded into the net by a third person thrashing toward the two net holders.

Species in the family Fundulidae are found only in North America. The taxonomic status of the topminnows and other members within the order Cyprinodontiformes has received considerable study by ichthyologists. We have elected to use Parenti's (1981) classification, which removes species in the genera *Adinia*, *Fundulus*, *Leptolucania*, and *Lucania* from the family Cyprinodontidae and places them in the topminnow family Fundulidae. The sheepshead minnow, *Cyprinodon variegatus*, remains in the family Cyprinodontidae. (Because of space limitations, the sheepshead minnow is not discussed in a species account, but it is listed in the drainage checklist that begins on page 28 and county checklist that begins on page 754.)

Alabama species of *Fundulus* include three of the four recognized subgenera (Wiley, 1986): *Fundulus*, *Xenisma*, and *Zygonectes*. Species assigned to *Xenisma* are generally large and robust and dwell in freshwater springs, streams, and rivers. Within Alabama, species in this subgenus include *Fundulus albolineatus* (presumed extinct), *F. bifax*, *F. catenatus*, and *F. stellifer*. Species assigned to *Zygonectes* are generally smaller fishes occurring in freshwater or brackish environments, including the *notti* species group (*F. blairae*, *F. dispar*, *F. escambiae*, and *F. notti*), the *notatus* species group (*F. notatus* and *F. olivaceus*), and the *chrysotus* species group (*F. auroguttatus* and *F. chrysotus*). *Fundulus grandis* is assigned to the subgenus *Fundulus*.

KEY TO THE TOPMINNOWS

1a. Dorsal fin origin closer to preopercle than caudal fin base. . . . . go to 2

1b. Dorsal fin origin closer to caudal fin base than preopercle . . . . go to 3

Dorsal fin origins of 1a, *Lucania*, and 1b, *Leptolucania*

2a. Dorsal fin rays 10 or 11; lateral stripe dark . . . . bluefin killifish, **L. goodei**

2b. Dorsal fin rays 12 or 13; lateral stripe faint or absent . . . . rainwater killifish, **L. parva**

3a. Dorsal fin rays 7 or 8; sides with vertical bars or large spot in front of anal fin; spot at caudal fin base . . . . .
. . . . pygmy killifish, ***Leptolucania ommata***

3b. Dorsal fin rays 9 or more; sides variably marked . . . . go to 4, ***Fundulus***

4a. Dorsal fin rays 10 to 15; dorsal fin origin directly over or in front of anal fin origin . . . . go to 5

4b. Dorsal fin rays 9 to 11; dorsal fin origin behind anal fin origin . . . . go to 8

5a. Anal fin rays 10 or 11 . . . . whiteline topminnow, **F. albolineatus**

5b. Anal fin rays 13 to 16 . . . . go to 6

6a. Anal fin rays usually 15 or 16; orange or dark flecks on sides arranged in parallel lines along scale rows; tail
fin of breeding male with pale yellow marginal band and black submarginal band; Tennessee River drainage
. . . . northern studfish, **F. catenatus**

6b. Anal fin rays usually 14 or 15; colored flecks scattered randomly or forming short, broken rows, producing
stippled appearance; tail fin with or without black marginal band; Mobile basin . . . . go to 7

7a. Side stippling of dark red or red-orange spots, evenly distributed from gill opening to caudal fin base, in interrupted rows (adult males typically with 50 to 75 percent of scales with spots); Tallapoosa and lower Coosa
river systems . . . . stippled studfish, **F. bifax**

7b. Side stippling of red spots, usually clustered around caudal peduncle or humeral region and not well organized into rows (adult males with up to 30 percent of scales with spots, occasionally more); Alabama, Coosa
and upper Chattahoochee river drainages . . . . southern studfish, **F. stellifer**

Side stippling on (left) **F. catenatus**, (center) **F. bifax,** and (right) **F. stellifer**

8a. Sides with obvious, dark lateral stripe . . . . go to 9

8b. No dark lateral stripe . . . . go to 10

9a. Distinct, dark, regular dorsolateral spots on light background . . . . . . blackspotted topminnow, *F. olivaceus*

9b. Dorsolateral spots absent or, if present, inconspicuous, diffuse, and brown on dark background; Tombigbee and lower Alabama river drainages . . . . blackstripe topminnow, *F. notatus*

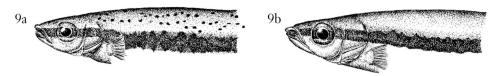

Lateral views of 9a, *F. olivaceus*, and 9b, *F. notatus*

10a. No dark blotch below eye . . . . go to 11

10b. Dark blotch below eye; females with 6 to 8 stripes on sides between scale rows . . . . go to 12

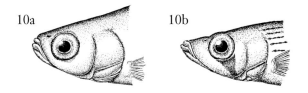

Subocular pigmentation of 10a, *F. chrysotus* group, and 10b, *F. notti* group

11a. Total mandibular pores 8; females with small "pearl" spots irregularly scattered along sides, males usually with fewer than 12 vertical bars . . . . golden topminnow, *F. chrysotus*

11b. Total mandibular pores 6; females lacking "pearl" spots, males and females generally with more than 12 vertical bars . . . . banded topminnow, *F. auroguttatus*

12a. Pores 4a and 4b of supraorbital sensory canal system fused; adult females with regular rows of dots (in addition to horizontal stripes) and/or with vertical bars along caudal peduncle; adult males with vertical bars or, if vertical bars absent, then without pigment blotches on caudal fin . . . . go to 13

12b. Pores 4a and 4b of supraorbital sensory canal system widely separated; adult females without vertical bars; adult males with thin vertical bars and with flank dots restricted to upper half of body, or vertical bars absent and with irregular rows of flank dots . . . . go to 14

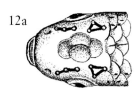 

Head pores of 12a, *F. notti*, and 12b, *F. dispar*

13a. Adult males with 9 to 15 vertical bars extending anteriorly toward pectoral fin base and below lowest row of flank dots; adult females with flank stripes interconnected with heavy melanophore concentrations and irregular flank dot pattern not forming rows . . . . bayou topminnow, *F. notti*

13b. Adult males with 10 to 14 shorter vertical bars ending between paired fins, not extending below lowest row of flank dots; adult females lack melanophore concentrations connecting flank stripes but flank dots, if present, are in 2 or more rows; Perdido River drainage eastward . . . . russetfin topminnow, *F. escambiae*

14a. Adult males with 3 to 13 thin vertical bars; adult females with little or no melanophore development between flank stripes; young of both sexes generally with vertical bars . . . .
. . . . .northern starhead topminnow, *F. dispar*
14b. Adult males lack vertical bars; adult females with many dashes, dots, and less discrete melanophore development between flank stripes; young of both sexes without vertical bars . . . .
. . . . .southern starhead topminnow, *F. blairae*

CANEY CREEK, BALDWIN COUNTY

WHITELINE TOPMINNOW *Fundulus albolineatus* **1 STATION**

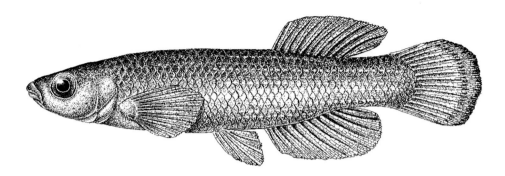

Fundulus albolineatus
Gilbert, 1891

ETYMOLOGY:
Fundulus—bottom
albolineatus—white line,
which runs along the sides of
live individuals

This composite drawing is based on the original description and the description of **Fundulus julisia**.

CHARACTERISTICS: The extinct whiteline topminnow is a member of the subgenus **Xenisma**. Information is limited, since few specimens were ever collected, but it indicates similarities to the Barrens topminnow, **Fundulus julisia** (Williams and Etnier, 1982). The following color description of the whiteline topminnow is from Gilbert (1891): "Males blackish brown, the sides plumbeous, the rows of scales with interrupted whitish streaks, most conspicuous on hinder half of body. A black streak along middle line of back. Vertical fins dusky, the caudal becoming translucent on distal half, its margin abruptly and narrowly black-edged. Females olivaceous, dusky on back, silvery below, the back and sides with narrow black lines following the rows of scales. Fins translucent, the dorsal sometimes with fine black specks at the base, the caudal black-edged."

ADULT SIZE: 3.3 in (84 mm)

DISTRIBUTION: *Fundulus albolineatus* was described from specimens collected at Spring Creek, Madison County, Alabama. The type locality is now in the middle of metropolitan Huntsville and, along with the surrounding area, has been developed into a recreational park. The downstream spring run has been extensively modified, leaving little chance that populations still exist there. The last individuals of the whiteline topminnow were collected in 1889.

HABITAT AND BIOLOGY: Nothing is known about the biology of this species, but it is presumed to be similar to that of *F. julisia* (Williams and Etnier, 1982). **Fundulus julisia** occurs in heavily vegetated springs and stream pools in the eastern Highland Rim of Tennessee. The peak reproductive period for this species is in May and June, and spawning occurs over clumps of filamentous algae. Its diet consists of aquatic invertebrates associated with spring habitats (including microcrustaceans, midges, mayflies, and snails).

REMARKS: The type locality is Spring Creek, Madison County, Alabama.

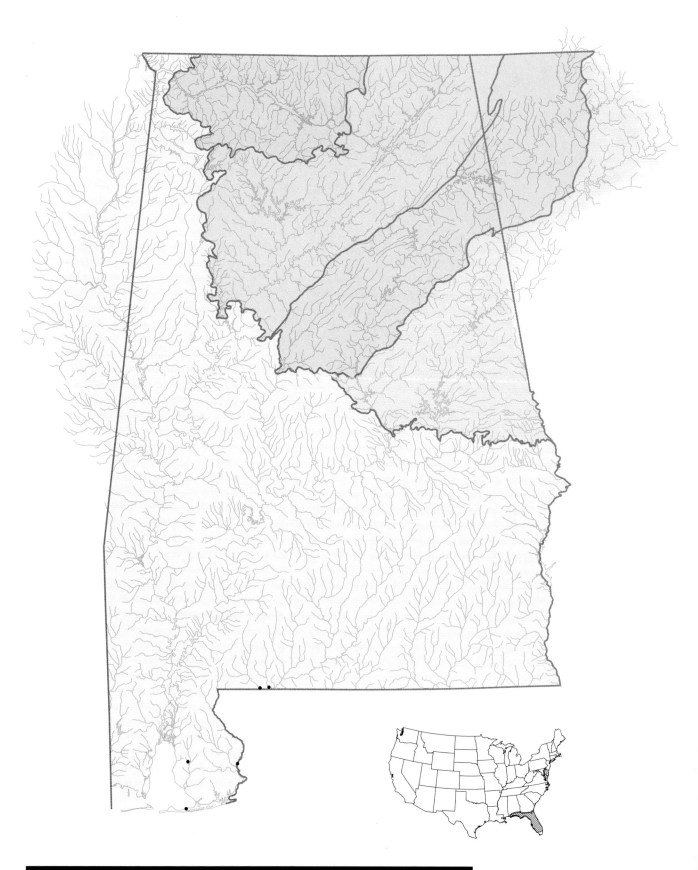

BANDED TOPMINNOW   *Fundulus auroguttatus*   5 STATIONS

Fundulus auroguttatus
(Hay, 1885)

ETYMOLOGY:

Fundulus—bottom
auroguttatus—speckled or
spotted gold

Fish River tributary, Baldwin County, 19 August 1992, 1.5 in (37 mm) SL male, GSA 4309

CHARACTERISTICS: The banded topminnow, now designated *Fundulus auroguttatus*, most resembles the golden topminnow, *F. chrysotus*. Male banded topminnows are olive green with orange highlighting the upper gill covers. From the pectoral fin to the caudal fin base, light orange dots along the sides produce subtle yet evident rows. The caudal fin is light orange, becoming translucent near its margin. Usually 12 or more vertical bars extend along the sides from the lower back to about halfway between the midline and the venter. Females are similar in color, except they lack bright orange on the gill covers; also, the orange dots along the sides produce more orderly rows. The systematics of the banded topminnow were revised by Gilbert et al. (1992) to correct Hay's misidentifications of the type series. *Fundulus cingulatus* was placed in synonymy because the holotype was actually a lined topminnow, *F. lineolatus*. *Fundulus auroguttatus* was suggested as the replacement name.

ADULT SIZE: 2 to 2.6 in (50 to 66 mm)

DISTRIBUTION: Gilbert et al. (1992) report that *F. auroguttatus* occurs continuously from the Perdido system on the Alabama-Florida state line east to the Ochlockonee system, with apparent isolated populations in the Suwannee and Waccasassa river drainages farther east. Our 1991–93 sampling efforts confirm banded topminnows in the Conecuh and Perdido systems in Alabama and extend their known range west to the Fish River system and Fort Morgan peninsula on the eastern side of Mobile Bay.

HABITAT AND BIOLOGY: Generally associated with aquatic vegetation, the banded topminnow is usually found in sluggish backwater areas of streams and rivers and in isolated flood pools disconnected from the main stream channel in drier months. This species probably spawns in April, as evidenced by our collection of more than 200 individuals in spawning condition from a small southern tributary to Choctawhatchee Bay in Walton County, Florida.

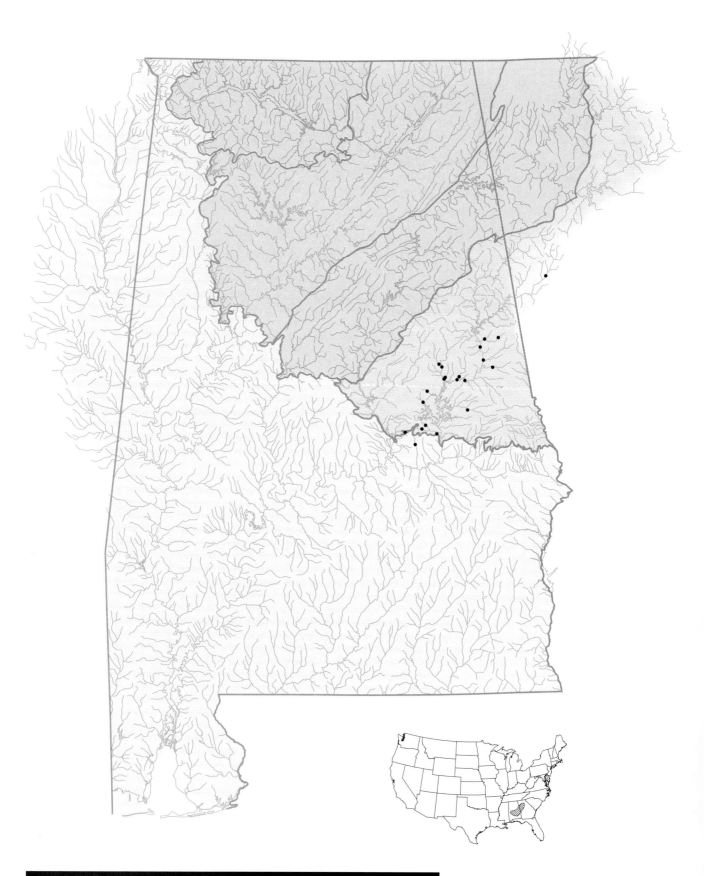

Fundulus bifax

Cashner and Rogers, 1988

ETYMOLOGY:

Fundulus—bottom

bifax—liar, referring to the fact that this species closely resembles both *F. catenatus* and *F. stellifer*

Josie Leg Creek, Tallapoosa County, 22 April 1993, 2.7 in (68 mm) SL female, GSA 4438

CHARACTERISTICS: This species is characterized by a series of darkened spots on individual scales that form a unique stippled pattern, which consists of short, broken bars extending along the sides of the body from the gill opening to the caudal fin base. Adult males have 50 to 75 percent of their scales marked with dark red to red-orange spots, and there are usually 8 to 10 rows along the sides and 5 to 7 rows along the peduncle. The sides of breeding *Fundulus bifax* are sky blue, changing to blue-brown dorsally and white ventrally. The caudal fin on males lacks a black band along its free margin. Paired fins are bluish gray. The stippled topminnow is a close relative of *F. stellifer* and *F. catenatus*, the southern and northern studfish, in the subgenus *Xenisma*. See Cashner et al. (1988) for original description.

ADULT SIZE: 3 to 3.7 in (75 to 95 mm)

DISTRIBUTION: *Fundulus bifax* is endemic to the Mobile basin. Individuals are limited in distribution to the Tallapoosa River system in Alabama and Georgia and to Sofkahatchee Creek, an eastern tributary to the lower Coosa River in Elmore County.

HABITAT AND BIOLOGY: The stippled topminnow is commonly found in small or medium-sized streams flowing over sand and gravel. This species is also common in the main channel of the Tallapoosa River above the Fall Line. The stippled topminnow's preferred habitat appears to be slow eddies along the margins of riffle runs. Neither the spawning season nor the life history of this newly described species has been studied, but the stippled studfish probably spawns in the late spring and the early summer, as does *F. stellifer*, a species with which *F. bifax* was previously confused.

REMARKS: The type locality for the stippled studfish is the Tallapoosa River near Daviston, Tallapoosa County, Alabama.

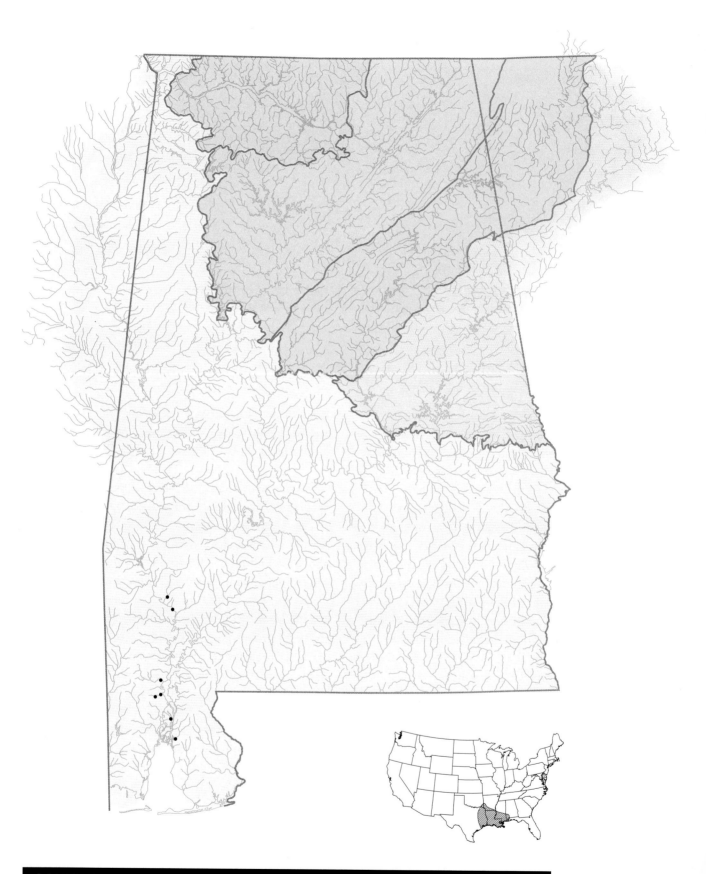

Fundulus blairae

Wiley and Hall, 1975

ETYMOLOGY:

Fundulus—bottom
blairae—in honor of Blair
Knies, whose extensive field
efforts yielded many
specimens for the description
of this species

Cahaba River overflow pool, Perry County, 20 June 1995, 1.7 in (44 mm) SL male, GSA 4649

CHARACTERISTICS: Despite the diverging views among ichthyologists, we have elected to recognize *Fundulus blairae* as a distinct species because individuals in Alabama are distinguishable from the bayou topminnow, *F. notti*, on the basis of body coloration. Male southern starhead topminnows lack vertical bars; females have more spots and other less discrete dashes between lateral stripes. (See Key to the Topminnows for more details on markings.) The systematics of the confusing *notti* species group, and especially its close relatives *F. blairae* and *F. dispar*, have been much investigated in recent years. Based upon his study of morphological characteristics, Wiley (1977) determined that the *F. notti* species group contained five species: *blairae*, *dispar*, *escambiae*, *lineolatus*, and *notti*. Later investigations by Cashner et al. (1992), however, found no significant genetic differences between *blairae* and *dispar*, leading them to eliminate *blairae* and reduce the number of species to four.

ADULT SIZE: 1.4 to 1.9 in (35 to 47 mm)

DISTRIBUTION: The southern starhead topminnow is found from the Brazos River drainage in Texas east through the Gulf Coastal Plain and the Mobile basin. In Alabama, this species is found in the lower Tombigbee and Alabama river drainages south to the Mobile River tributaries.

HABITAT AND BIOLOGY: Southern starhead topminnows occur in and around shoreline vegetation of clear lakes and ponds, backwaters, and overflow pools of large rivers. The population sampled for the above photograph was occupying a large overflow pool that had darkly stained water and that was isolated from the main river channel. The bottom was soft with deep accumulations of detritus, while the margins were heavily vegetated. In smaller streams, this species prefers quiet backwaters with slow or no current and shallow depths. Although little is known about its biology, the southern starhead topminnow is presumed to feed near the surface, where it consumes drifting organic matter, insects, and other animals associated with the water surface. As with other topminnows, this species probably has a spawning season that peaks in May or June; more protracted seasons may occur in some areas.

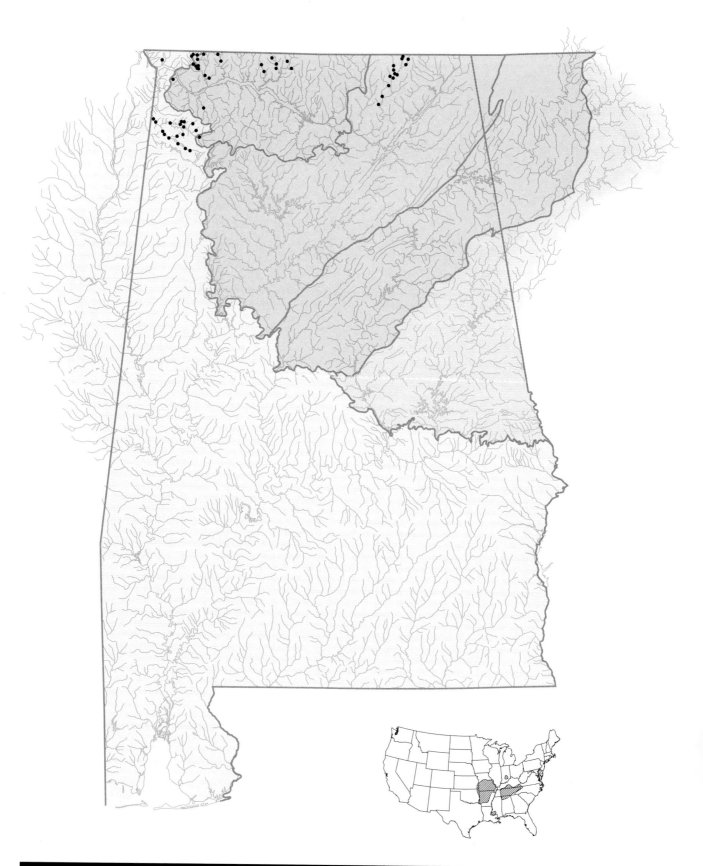

Fundulus catenatus

(Storer, 1846)

ETYMOLOGY:

Fundulus—bottom

catenatus—chained

Larkin Fork, Jackson County, 18 May 1993, 2.7 in (68 mm) SL male, GSA 4474

CHARACTERISTICS: The northern studfish is one of the most beautiful topminnows in Alabama. Breeding males have 8 to 10 continuous rows of orange to reddish orange dots along iridescent blue sides. Most of the upper half of the head is light blue-green, and the cheeks are punctuated with randomly scattered, bright orange dots. The lower half of the head and gill area are yellow or yellowish green. The anal fin, and particularly the dorsal fin on breeding males, are adorned with bright orange spots. The caudal fin has distinct black, then orange to yellow, bands near its free edge. Color development on females and juveniles is more subdued, with brown or olive spots or bars along the sides, little if any bright head color, and clear, usually unmarked fins. Small scales are lightly outlined with melanophores, although this pattern may not be visible on all individuals.

ADULT SIZE: 3 to 5.9 in (75 to 150 mm)

DISTRIBUTION: *Fundulus catenatus* occurs in the Ozark and Ouachita mountains, and upland regions of the Tennessee, Cumberland, and Green river drainages. Isolated populations occur in Indiana and Mississippi. In Alabama, the northern studfish is found throughout the Tennessee River drainage. Our recent collecting efforts confirmed this species in Bear, Cypress, and Shoal creeks and in the Elk and Paint Rock river systems.

HABITAT AND BIOLOGY: A lively inhabitant of clear streams and backwaters, the northern studfish often prefers shallow waters where food may be abundant. Reproduction probably occurs over gravel for an extended period but generally peaks from May through June. Pflieger (1975) reports that male northern studfish establish territories in shallow, quiet waters near shore. Fisher (1981) indicates longevity of three or more years for a Kentucky population. *Fundulus catenatus* feeds more on benthic organisms than on creatures floating at the water surface (McCaskill et al., 1972). Adults are predominantly insectivorous, consuming a wide variety of prey (including mayflies, caddisflies, and dipterans), but they also consume small snails and bivalves.

REMARKS: The type locality for the northern studfish is Florence, Lauderdale County, in either Cypress Creek or the Tennessee River proper.

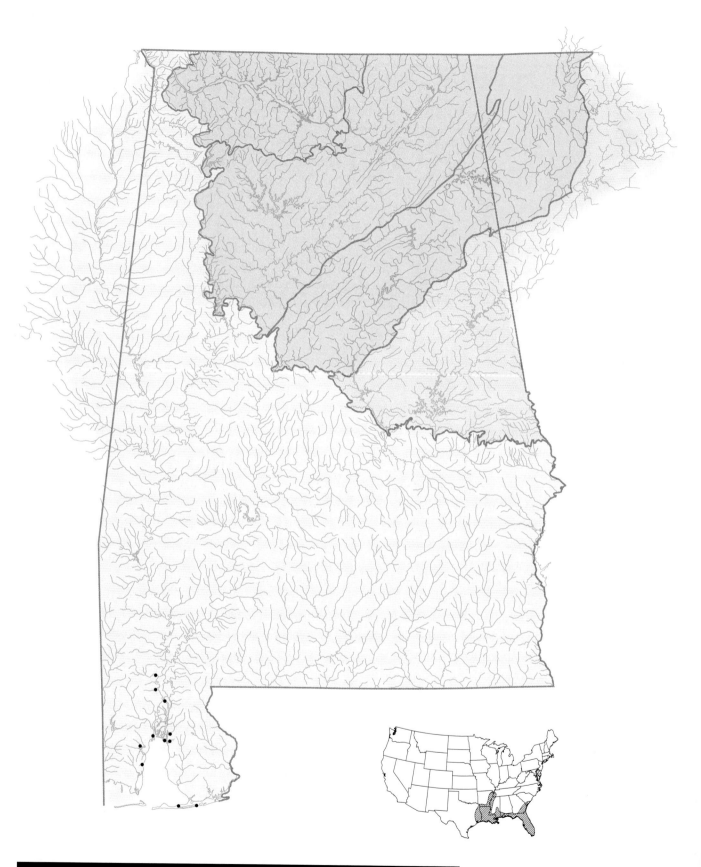

GOLDEN TOPMINNOW   *Fundulus chrysotus*   11 STATIONS

Fundulus chrysotus

(Gunther, 1866)

ETYMOLOGY:

Fundulus—bottom
chrysotus—golden ear,
referring to the golden
color of the gill covers

Fort Morgan peninsula, Baldwin County, 16 June 1993, 1.8 in (47 mm) SL female, GSA 4482

CHARACTERISTICS: The golden topminnow is a colorful species. On adult males, the caudal peduncle has many brown to brown-orange blotches and stipples, which become more numerous at the caudal fin base. The opercles are generally yellowish green, while the membranes of the dorsal, anal, and caudal fins have alternately light and dark brown stippling. The caudal fin has a faint tangerine color that fades near the margin. Twelve or fewer wavy, sometimes irregularly spaced vertical bars may mark the sides. On females, the body is greenish olive, and fins are translucent; they are otherwise not colored except for varying numbers of distinctly bright "pearl" spots scattered randomly along their sides. The golden topminnow is easily confused with the banded topminnow, *Fundulus auroguttatus*, but the banded topminnow has more vertical bars that are straighter, narrower, and more distinct; it also has a more rounded, shorter head shape and a mandibular pore formula of 3–3 (compared to 4–4 for the golden topminnow.

ADULT SIZE: 1.2 to 2.2 in (30 to 56 mm)

DISTRIBUTION: *Fundulus chrysotus* occurs throughout Florida, north along the coast of Georgia and South Carolina, and west along the Gulf Coast to Texas. It also occurs in the lower Mississippi River basin north to Tennessee and Arkansas. In Alabama, *F. chrysotus* is limited to tributaries and backwaters of the Mobile Delta, Mobile Bay, and coastal lowland systems.

HABITAT AND BIOLOGY: The golden topminnow prefers quiet ponds and backwaters with extensive accumulations of aquatic vegetation. Our most lucrative collections came from permanently vegetated ponds situated between old beach dune systems along Fort Morgan peninsula in Baldwin County. Golden topminnows feed on insects and aquatic invertebrates at or near the surface (Hunt, 1953). Spawning occurs in late spring through summer, with spawning pairs preferring roots of floating plants or the stems of plants such as *Myriophyllum*. Eggs are extruded and fertilized singly, with about 10 to 20 eggs produced on a daily basis for a week or more per spawning episode (Breder and Rosen, 1966).

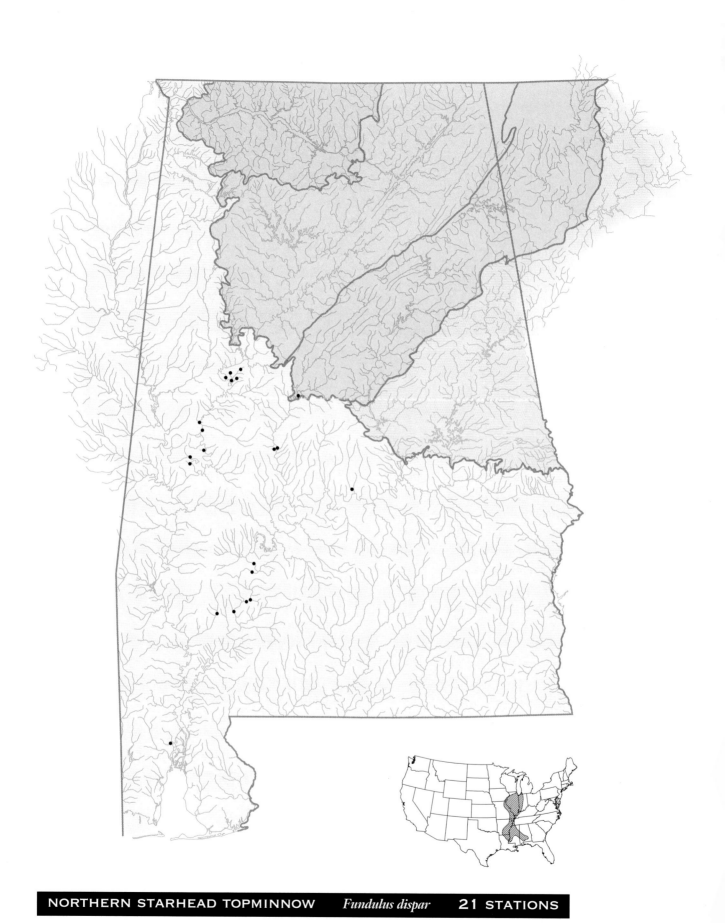

Fundulus dispar

(Agassiz, 1854)

ETYMOLOGY:

Fundulus—bottom

dispar—dissimilar

Alamuchee Creek, Sumter County, 10 June 1993, 1.9 in (48 mm) SL male, GSA 4479

CHARACTERISTICS: Adult males have 3 to 13 thin vertical bars, with the anterior bars restricted to the flanks and not extending onto the venter. Single spots on upper areas along the sides join along the lower areas to form generalized stripes. Adult females have longitudinal stripes, no vertical bars, and no spots along their sides. Paired fins of adult males are light yellow, while the median fins are speckled with light brown blotches. Male pigment spots are generally brown to rusty red, and the back is yellow-green, fading to white on the venter. Adult females are olive green to light brown on the back, fading to white on the venter, and all fins are translucent. Genetic data presented by Cashner et al. (1992) indicates that *Fundulus dispar* most resembles the lined topminnow, *F. lineolatus* (not occurring in Alabama), in the *F. notti* species group. "Starhead" refers to the star-shaped patch of light pigment on the top of the head.

ADULT SIZE: 1.2 to 3.2 in (30 to 81 mm)

DISTRIBUTION: The northern starhead topminnow is distributed from the Tombigbee River drainage of the Mobile basin westward to the Ouachita River drainage in Louisiana and northward through the Mississippi basin to Michigan. In Alabama it is generally found in northern counties, while the southern starhead topminnow, *F. blairae*, is found in southern counties.

HABITAT AND BIOLOGY: *Fundulus dispar* inhabits small streams and shallow, often vegetated backwaters of swamps and large streams. When encountered, individuals can usually be seen swimming at the water surface. The diet consists of terrestrial insects, snails, small crustaceans, and occasionally algae (Gunning and Lewis, 1955). Although little is known of this species' reproductive biology, Smith (1979) indicates spawning from late spring through early summer in dense beds of aquatic vegetation.

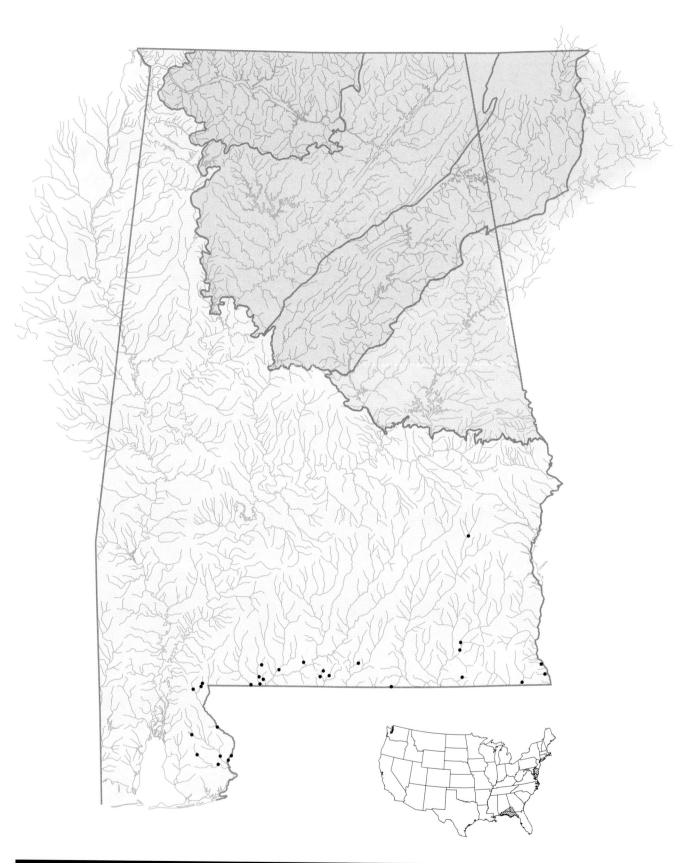

Fundulus escambiae
(Bollman, 1887)

ETYMOLOGY:
Fundulus—bottom
escambiae—referring to the
Escambia River, a coastal
river within this species'
range

Little Escambia Creek, Escambia County, 24 March 1992, 1.9 in (48 mm) SL male, GSA 4198

CHARACTERISTICS: Male and female russetfin top-minnows have several horizontal rows of brown or reddish brown spots extending along the sides of their bodies. Males may also have up to 14 vertical bars between the paired fins and the caudal peduncle; although not always present, these bars are of even width and extend ventrally no farther than the lowest row of spots. Females are characterized by stripes along the sides or, if the stripes are faint or missing, by regular rows of spots. Females may also have light vertical bars on the peduncle, but the bars rarely reach the origin of the anal fin. Red-orange pigment is common between the mouth and the eye. Both sexes have a dark, wedge-shaped spot beneath the eye. The russetfin topminnow and its phylogenetically similar relatives, the bayou top-minnow, *Fundulus notti*, and lined topminnow, *F. lineolatus*, are members of the *F. notti* species group (Wiley, 1977).

ADULT SIZE: 1.4 to 2.6 in (35 to 66 mm)

DISTRIBUTION: In Gulf coastal drainages, *Fundulus escambiae* is distributed from the Perdido River drainage eastward to the Santa Fe River in Florida. We have collected russetfin topminnows sporadically from the Perdido River drainage eastward to the Chattahoochee River drainage. We encountered them more frequently in streams and rivers near the Florida state line.

HABITAT AND BIOLOGY: Individuals of this species inhabit shallow, vegetated areas of slow-moving streams, quiet backwaters, and swamps. Examination of specimens in our collections indicates that spawning occurs in late spring and early summer. The diet, like that of many topminnows, consists of drifting insects (of either aquatic or terrestrial origin), surface-dwelling microcrustaceans, and plant material.

REMARKS: The type locality for the russetfin topminnow is a tributary of the Escambia River at Flomaton, Escambia County.

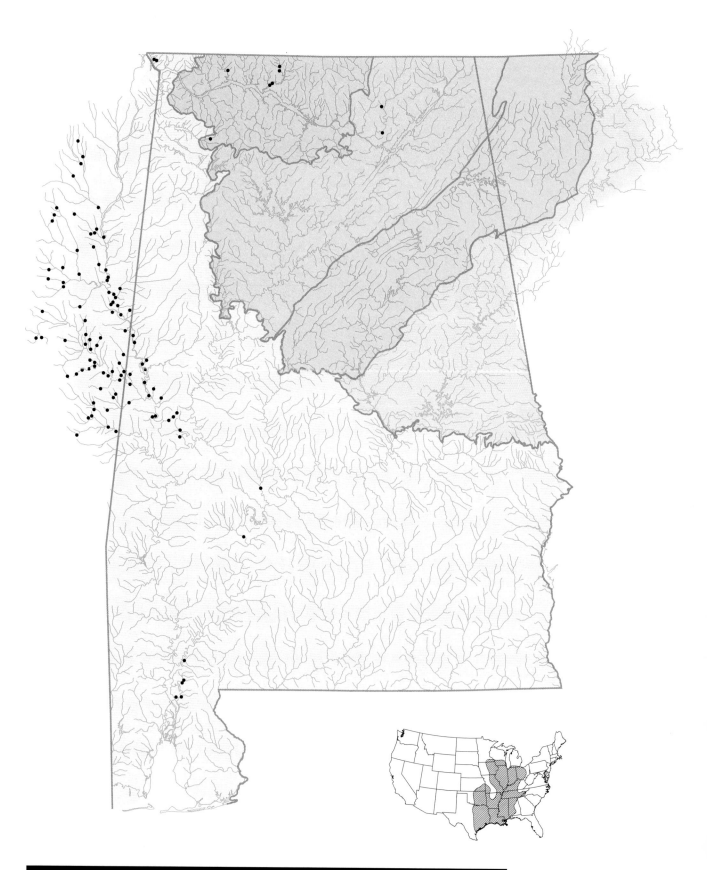

Fundulus notatus

(Rafinesque, 1820)

ETYMOLOGY:

Fundulus—bottom

notatus—spotted

Taylor Creek, Greene County, 10 June 1993, 1.9 in (48 mm) SL male, GSA 4480

CHARACTERISTICS: Individuals of this species are characterized by a dark lateral stripe extending from the mouth to the caudal fin base and a dark basicaudal spot that is separated from the lateral stripe. *Fundulus notatus* can usually be distinguished from the blackspotted topminnow, *F. olivaceus*, by the absence of small dark dots along the upper sides and back. The back is olive brown above the lateral stripe, and the venter is white. Breeding males have vague to prominent vertical spikes originating from the lateral stripe. The median fins of adult males have black blotching on their proximal halves, becoming translucent near their free margins. The paired fins and anal fin are light yellow near their margins. Adult females lack fin color and have little or only faint spotting in the fins. The blackstripe topminnow, together with *F. olivaceus* and *F. euryzonus* (the broadstripe topminnow, located in the Lake Pontchartrain system in Mississippi and Louisiana), are members of the *F. notatus* species group.

ADULT SIZE: 1.8 to 2.9 in (47 to 74 mm)

DISTRIBUTION: *Fundulus notatus* occurs along the Gulf Coast from the San Antonio Bay drainage in Texas east to the Tombigbee River drainage in Alabama and north through the Mississippi basin to Indiana and southern Wisconsin. It is also known to inhabit drainages of both Lake Michigan and Lake Erie. In Alabama, blackstripe topminnows are widespread in the upper Tombigbee River and its western tributaries, but they are absent from its eastern tributaries. We have also collected specimens from locations in the Alabama, Mobile, and Tennessee river drainages.

HABITAT AND BIOLOGY: Blackstripe topminnows prefer low-gradient, slow-moving, and slightly turbid streams. Food items include terrestrial insects, crustaceans, and algae. Breeding occurs in late spring and early summer, when individual eggs are laid in vegetation or debris patches. Thomerson and Wooldridge (1970) suggest that aggressive feeding behavior gives *F. notatus* a competitive advantage when it occurs with *F. olivaceus*, a rarely encountered circumstance since the two species occupy distinctly different habitats (Braasch and Smith, 1965). Nieman and Wallace (1974) report longevity of three or more years for a population in Michigan. Blackstripe topminnows in the Tombigbee River have a higher chromosome number than do other populations (Howell and Black, 1981).

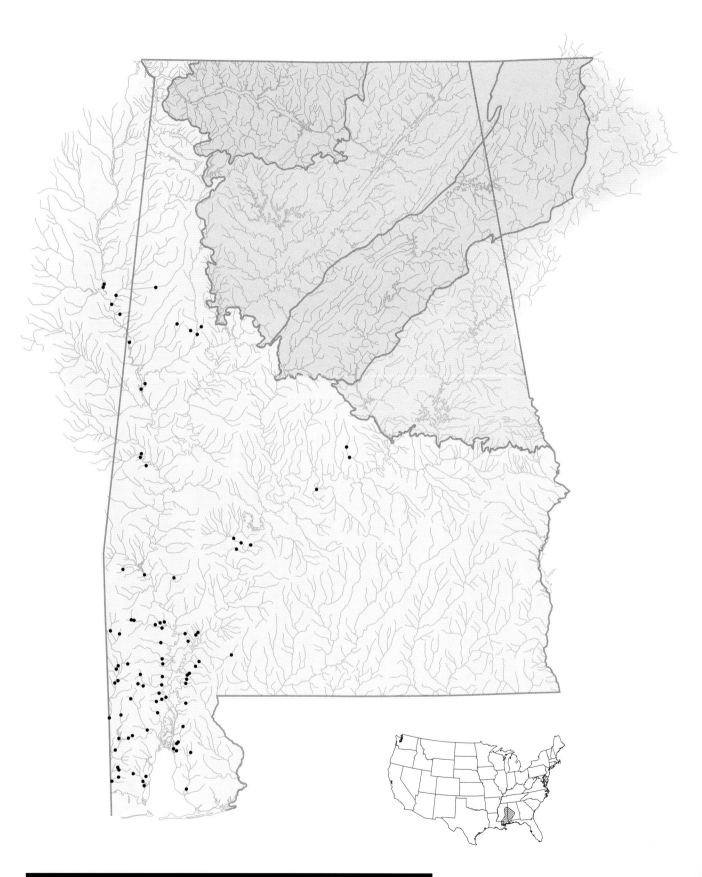

BAYOU TOPMINNOW *Fundulus notti* **87 STATIONS**

Fundulus notti

(Agassiz, 1854)

ETYMOLOGY:

Fundulus—bottom
notti—in honor of Dr.
Josiah Clark Nott, physician,
friend of Louis Agassiz, and
the discoverer of the species

Cold Creek, Mobile County, 18 August 1992, 2.1 in (53 mm) SL male, GSA 4461

CHARACTERISTICS: Adult bayou topminnow males have seven or eight rows of dots along the sides and nine to 15 dark vertical bars of even width, which extend below the lowest row of dots onto the venter and anteriorly to or nearly to the pectoral fin base. Adult females have six to eight side stripes interconnected by extensive dark pigmentation. The side dots of females are randomly distributed, and two to six thin, subdermal vertical bars frequently mark the caudal peduncle. Males are generally olive brown to green on the back, fading to white on the venter, with the dorsal, anal, and pelvic fins faint yellow near the margin. Females are generally darker brown along the back with colorless fins. *Fundulus notti* is a member of the subgenus *Zygonectes* and is closely related phylogenetically to *F. lineolatus* and *F. escambiae*, the lined and russetfin topminnows (Wiley, 1977).

ADULT SIZE: 1.2 to 2.6 in (30 to 65 mm)

DISTRIBUTION: The bayou topminnow has a limited distribution, ranging from the Mobile basin west to the Lake Pontchartrain drainage in Louisiana. In Alabama, the species occurs in the Alabama and Tombigbee river drainages, the Mobile Delta, the Escatawpa River drainage, and tributaries to Mobile Bay.

HABITAT AND BIOLOGY: *Fundulus notti* prefers swamps, sloughs, quiet backwaters of overflow pools, borrow pits near large streams, and slow-moving, shallow pools in streams. Though little is known about the bayou topminnow's biology, it presumably resembles other species in the *F. notti* species group, breeding in late spring and early summer and eating terrestrial insects, small crustaceans, and possibly plant material. Cook (1959) reports observing gravid individuals in mid-May in south Mississippi; they were in warm water full of water grass, green algae, bladderwort, and arrowheads.

REMARKS: The type locality for the bayou topminnow is reported to be in the vicinity of Mobile, Mobile County.

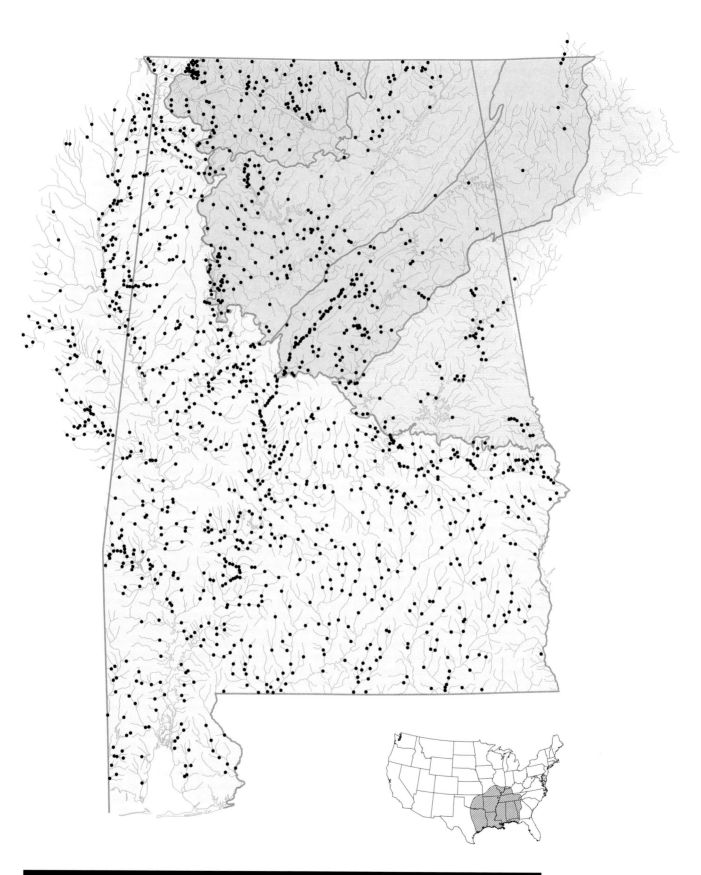

BLACKSPOTTED TOPMINNOW *Fundulus olivaceus* **1,410 STATIONS**

Fundulus olivaceus

(Storer, 1845)

ETYMOLOGY:

Fundulus—bottom

olivaceus—olive

Pea River, Bullock County, 12 April 1992, 2.2 in (56 mm) SL male, GSA 4213

CHARACTERISTICS: Blackspotted topminnows are characterized by a dark lateral stripe extending from the mouth to the caudal fin base and by small, distinct black spots along the back and upper sides (a useful characteristic for separating the blackspotted topminnow from the blackstripe topminnow, *Fundulus notatus)*. The back above the lateral stripe is olive brown, and the venter is white. Adult males have distinct spots on their median fins and a faint yellow tint on the dorsal, anal, and pelvic fins. On breeding males, the lateral stripe has vertical spikes that resemble those of *F. notatus*. On females, fins are colorless and translucent. A member of the subgenus *Zygonectes*, the blackspotted topminnow is most closely related to *F. euryzonus,* the broadstripe topminnow, and *F. notatus*, the blackstripe topminnow. See Storer (1845b) for original description.

ADULT SIZE: 2.2 to 3.8 in (56 to 97 mm)

DISTRIBUTION: *Fundulus olivaceus* is found in Gulf slope drainages from the Galveston Bay drainage east to the Choctawhatchee and middle Chattahoochee river drainages and north in the Mississippi basin to southern Illinois. In Alabama, it is widely distributed throughout the Tennessee River drainage, the Mobile basin, and all coastal drainages, including the Escatawpa River. It occurs with less frequency in the upper Coosa and upper Tallapoosa river systems.

HABITAT AND BIOLOGY: Successful inhabitants of most Alabama waters, blackspotted topminnows occur singly or in small schools in various habitats—small to large flowing streams, rivers, reservoirs, swamps, and isolated oxbow lakes. They prefer slow-moving, quiet waters. We regularly observe individuals near the water surface along stream margins and near vegetation or large woody debris. Reproduction occurs from late spring throughout the summer. Food items include terrestrial insects, small crustaceans, and aquatic insects (Thomerson and Wooldridge, 1970).

REMARKS: The type locality of the blackspotted topminnow is Florence, Lauderdale County; the exact stream location is unknown.

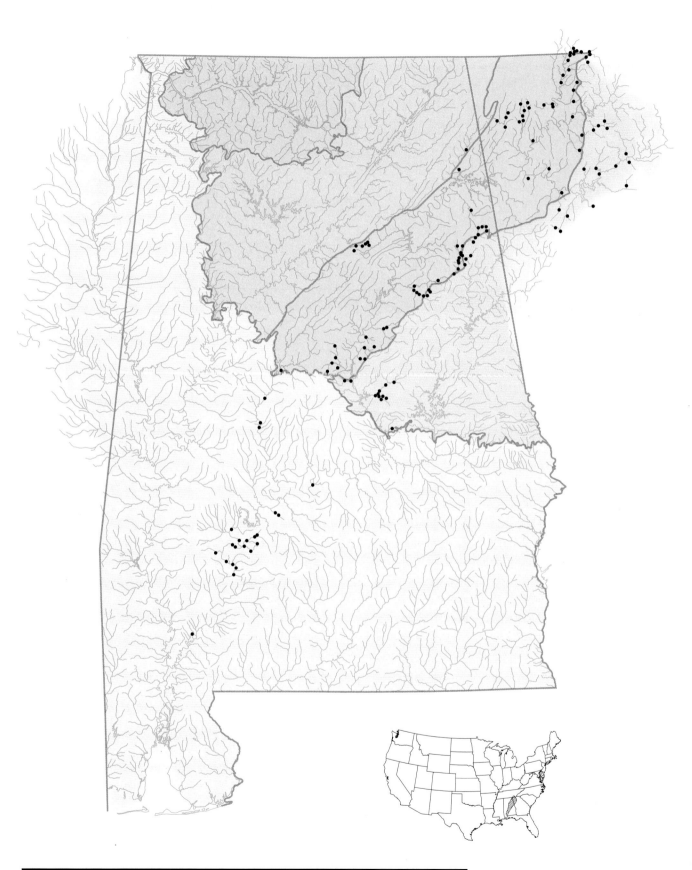

SOUTHERN STUDFISH   *Fundulus stellifer*   140 STATIONS

Fundulus stellifer

(Jordan, 1877)

ETYMOLOGY:

Fundulus—bottom

stellifer—star bearer

Wash Creek, Chilton County, 21 April 1993, 2.6 in (67 mm) SL male, GSA 4437

CHARACTERISTICS: Breeding males of the southern studfish are sky blue along the sides, white on the venter, and blue-brown on the back. Dark orange to orange-red spots are randomly scattered along the dorsolateral region and continue on the head, while spots on the peduncle may form primitive rows. The sides of *Fundulus stellifer* have a crosshatched appearance that extends to the base of the anal fin. The cheeks are white with flecks of blue, while the gill covers are flecked with gold. All fins are generally clear or yellow with rows of elongate orange spots in the dorsal fin and in the proximal halves of the caudal and anal fins. The caudal and dorsal fins may also have a black margin. A member of the subgenus *Xenisma,* the southern studfish is most closely related to *F. catenatus* and *F. bifax*, the northern studfish and stippled studfish. See Jordan (1877a) for original description.

ADULT SIZE: 2.2 to 3.9 in (56 to 100 mm)

DISTRIBUTION: Most collections of this species are from the Coosa River system above the Fall Line. An isolated population exists in the lower Alabama River drainage where the river divides the lower Southern Red Hills and Lime Hills regions. Our failure to collect additional specimens from previous sampling localities may indicate that this species has been extirpated from the Cahaba River system. *Fundulus stellifer* is replaced in the Tallapoosa River system by *F. bifax* (Cashner et al., 1988).

HABITAT AND BIOLOGY: This species is found in small or medium upland streams around pools and quiet shallow areas. It also occurs in pool areas of large streams and rivers. Nuptial individuals have been collected from undercut banks with extensive structure, and spawning occurs from late spring to early summer. Although no one has completed a study of the feeding biology of this species, its diet is believed to be similar to that of *F. catenatus*, consisting of terrestrial insects, crustaceans, snails, and bivalve mollusks. However, Thomerson (1969) reports that *F. stellifer* and *F. catenatus* have different pharyngeal bone and tooth structures; *F. stellifer's* larger crushing teeth are possibly correlated with its diet of mollusks and crustaceans.

REMARKS: The type locality for the southern studfish is tributaries to the Etowah, Oostanaula, and Coosa rivers in Georgia.

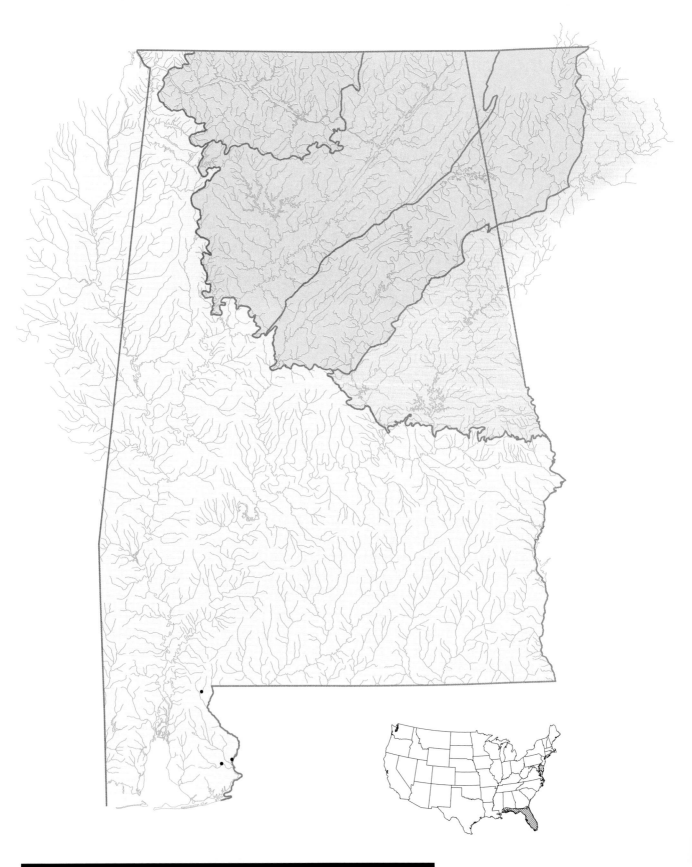

PYGMY KILLIFISH　　*Leptolucania ommata*　　**3 STATIONS**

Leptolucania ommata
(Jordan, 1884)

ETYMOLOGY:
Leptolucania—fine or slender fish like *Lucania*
ommata—eye, referring to the spot on the caudal peduncle

Perdido River, Baldwin County, 17 June 1993, 0.8 in (21 mm) SL male, GSA 4486

CHARACTERISTICS: Adult males of the pygmy killifish are generally uniform olive to yellow-olive, fading to light yellow or white on the venter. Five to seven wide but faint vertical bars mark the sides, being most conspicuous on the caudal peduncle and fading anteriorly. All median fins and the pelvic fins are yellow. A large black spot frequently haloed in creamy yellow is usually present at the caudal fin base. The dorsal and anal fins of breeding males are elongate and, when depressed, almost reach the caudal fin base. Females are slightly larger and have no vertical bars, shorter dorsal and anal fins, and a more intense lateral band. Females also have, in the middle of the lateral band, a large spot that is about the same size as the caudal spot. The body form is slender, and the mouth is small and upturned, presumably to facilitate feeding at the water's surface. See Jordan (1884a) for original description.

ADULT SIZE: 0.6 to 1.1 in (15 to 29 mm)

DISTRIBUTION: *Leptolucania ommata* is distributed from the Ogeechee River drainage in Georgia south to central Florida and west to the Escatawpa River drainage in Alabama and Mississippi. Our collections are limited to the Perdido River drainage, and the inferred presence of the species in the Escatawpa River system is based on a single record from Mississippi; we know of no specimens from the Alabama section of the system. The species had not been found in Mobile Bay tributaries until Boschung (1992) reported a collection from the Magnolia River in Baldwin County.

HABITAT AND BIOLOGY: This species prefers shallow, extensively vegetated overflow pools, sloughs, and blackwater swamps. We sampled dense populations in overflow pools of the Perdido River, netting 10 to 20 individuals per haul. Arndt (1971) reports spawning from late spring through summer and a life span of one or more years for Florida and Georgia populations. Foods include small insects and crustaceans found in vegetation.

BLUEFIN KILLIFISH *Lucania goodei* **1 STATION**

472

Lucania goodei

Jordan, 1880

ETYMOLOGY:

Lucania—a coined name that Jordan left undefined in the original description *goodei*—in honor of Professor George Brown Goode, who discovered this species in the Arlington River, Florida

Bazemores Mill Pond, Houston County, 6 May 1993, 0.9 in (23 mm) SL male, GSA 4442

CHARACTERISTICS: The bluefin killifish is a handsome species. Adult males have a bright blue, black-edged dorsal fin, the base of which is green at the front and deep orange to red at the rear. Interestingly, although Stoye (1935) and Page and Burr (1991) indicate that the dorsal and anal fins are bright blue, neither mentions the brilliant orange band in the anal fin, which is distinct in the above photograph. On males, the caudal fin is orange near the base fading to yellow, while the pelvic fins are orange edged in black. A dark lateral band extends from the snout to the caudal fin base. This species has a slender, compressed body and a strongly upturned mouth adapted for life at the water surface.

ADULT SIZE: 0.6 to 1.7 in (16 to 42 mm)

DISTRIBUTION: *Lucania goodei* occurs from the Ogeechee River drainage in Georgia southward along the Atlantic Coast throughout peninsular Florida and westward in Gulf slope drainages to the lower Choctawhatchee River drainage. This species is known in Alabama only from Bazemores Mill Pond in Houston County, a tributary of the Chipola River which eventually enters the Apalachicola River in Florida. This location is the northernmost point for the species in Gulf slope drainages.

HABITAT AND BIOLOGY: The bluefin killifish is frequently associated with spring habitats. It occurs in shallow, vegetated margins in association with extensive organic debris and cypress knees. Specimens collected in Bazemores Mill Pond were common, and the population appeared stable. Breeding occurs from spring through late summer. Over a period of several weeks, spawning pairs deposit up to 20 individually released eggs per day on vegetation or algae. The bluefin killifish feeds on small insects, crustaceans, and plant material.

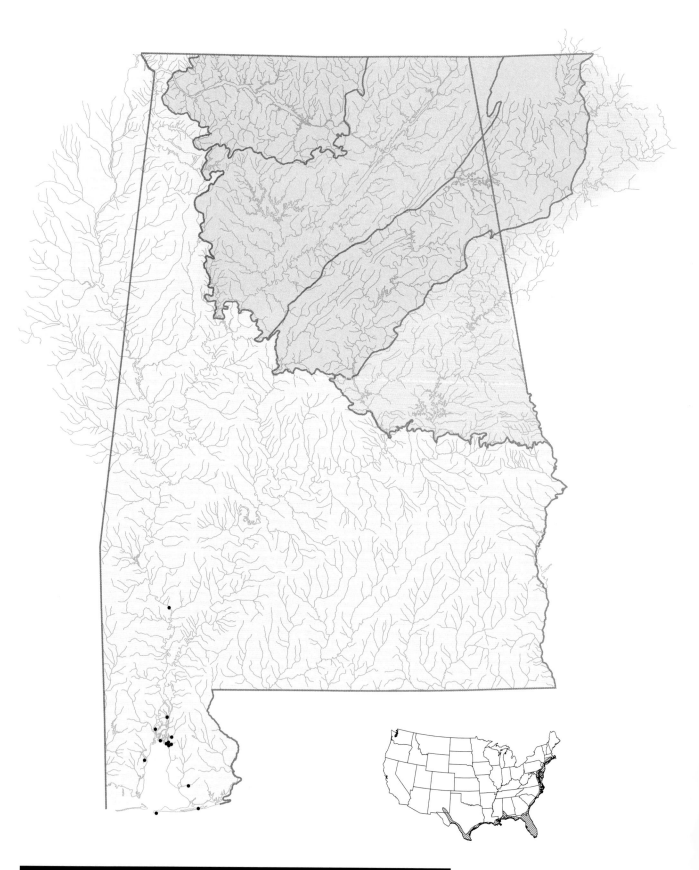

RAINWATER KILLIFISH   *Lucania parva*   **13 STATIONS**

Lucania parva

(Baird and Girard, 1855)

ETYMOLOGY:

Lucania—a coined name
that Jordan left undefined
in the original description
parva—small

Ducker Bay, Baldwin County, 17 August 1992, 1.2 in (31 mm) SL male, GSA 4459

CHARACTERISTICS: The rainwater killifish has a slightly compressed body, a small, upturned mouth, and a strongly compressed caudal peduncle. Most scales are edged in black, giving them a diamond-shaped appearance. The male's dorsal fin has a large black spot at the base, and the fin margin is orange. All other fins except the pectorals have thin black edges. The anal fin is light yellow. General body color is light yellow to straw on the back, fading to white on the venter. Small individuals are easily confused with species in the mosquitofish complex *Gambusia*. See Baird (1855) for original description.

ADULT SIZE: 0.8 to 2.4 in (20 to 60 mm)

DISTRIBUTION: *Lucania parva* is widespread from Cape Cod, Massachusetts, southward through the Atlantic and Gulf slopes to Tampico, Mexico. In Alabama, it is commonly found in fresh to brackish estuarine environments and in the Mobile Delta. Several individuals collected 92 miles upstream of Mobile Bay in an isolated overflow pool of the lower Tombigbee River at Jackson, Clarke County, represent a new inland record for the species in Alabama (R. D. Suttkus, 1995 personal communication).

HABITAT AND BIOLOGY: Although *L. parva* generally prefers brackish conditions, the species is tolerant of wide-ranging salinity and consequently can be found in a variety of shallow, quiet, vegetated habitats in coastal Alabama. Hildebrand and Schroeder (1928) report ripe females from early April through July in Chesapeake Bay and speculate that spawning occurs more than once during the reproductive season. These authors also report high densities of rainwater killifish in vegetation, based on totals of 18,300 individuals in seven net hauls and 14,600 individuals in 20 net hauls. The diet of this diminutive species consists of microcrustaceans and immature aquatic insects.

LIVEBEARERS

Poeciliidae

Members of the family Poeciliidae are the only viviparous (live-bearing) fishes in Alabama. Eggs are fertilized inside the female's body, where they develop for three to four weeks. At birth, livebearers are small, fully developed, free-swimming fishes that feed on microcrustaceans. All other fish species in Alabama are egg layers; their eggs are deposited and fertilized outside the female's body, either in the water column or on some submerged structure.

Male livebearers are generally smaller than females. As males mature, their anal fin rays grow into a long, movable structure known as a gonopodium. When mating, the male aligns himself beside the female and inserts his gonopodium inside her urogenital opening, into which he transfers small sperm bundles. The act lasts only a second or two, but it is repeated frequently throughout the spring and summer spawning season. Females are able to store the sperm and ration it for fertilizing individual eggs after mating.

Livebearers differ from topminnows in the family Fundulidae by having fewer scales, a gonopodium, and differently placed median fins. All Alabama species in the livebearer family—the (marine) sailfin molly, *Poecilia latipinna*; the least killifish, *Heterandria formosa*; and the mosquitofish, *Gambusia affinis* and *G. holbrooki*—are less than 2.5 inches long, with slightly compressed

Anal fin structure on (left) male and
(right) female livebearers

bodies, rounded caudal fins, and upturned mouths adapted for life at the water surface. Gravid females usually have distended abdomens and a darkened abdominal spot on each side near the anal fin origin.

Heterandria and *Poecilia* usually inhabit estuarine environments in coastal Alabama. *Gambusia*, the mosquitofish, thrive in fresh water but also occur in estuarine ditches, marshes, and streams. As their name suggests, mosquitofish feed primarily on mosquito larvae. Before the days of pesticide spraying, mosquitofish—which produce hundreds of offspring annually and can survive in low-oxygen habitats—were introduced throughout the United States as biological control agents for mosquitoes.

The systematics of the livebearer family have received extensive study (Rosen and Bailey, 1963; Rauchenberger, 1989). Hubbs (1955) regarded the eastern mosquitofish, *Gambusia holbrooki*, as a subspecies of the western mosquitofish, *G. affinis*. Genetic studies by Wooten et al. (1988) and morphological differences outlined in Rauchenberger (1989) indicate that *G. affinis* and *G. holbrooki* are distinct species. Black and Howell (1979) consider the Mobile basin form to be a semispecies, but Wooten et al. (1988) have observed little or no gene flow between the species, leading them to conclude that the Mobile basin form likely represents a contact zone. Angus and Howell (1996) mapped the distributions of *G. affinis* and *G. holbrooki* in the United States. Because our records are not separated by species, we therefore treat the genus *Gambusia* as a complex in the species account on the following pages. In the following key, the last two rays of both the dorsal and anal fins are counted as a single branched ray (Hubbs and Lagler, 1958).

KEY TO THE LIVEBEARERS

1a. Wide lateral stripe; black spot near base of male dorsal fin and female dorsal and anal fins; very small fishes in freshwater coastal drainages and upstream in lower Mobile basin . . . . least killifish, ***Heterandria formosa***

1b. No wide lateral stripe; no black spot on dorsal or anal fin; rows of small black dots on dorsal and caudal fins . . . . go to 2, ***Gambusia***

2a. On gonopodium, distal segments of modified anal ray 3 characteristically smooth; anal rays 9; dorsal rays usually 6 . . . . western mosquitofish, ***G. affinis***

2b. On gonopodium, distal segments of modified anal ray 3 serrate; anal rays 10; dorsal rays usually 8 . . . . eastern mosquitofish, ***G. holbrooki***

GRIFFIN CREEK, BALDWIN COUNTY

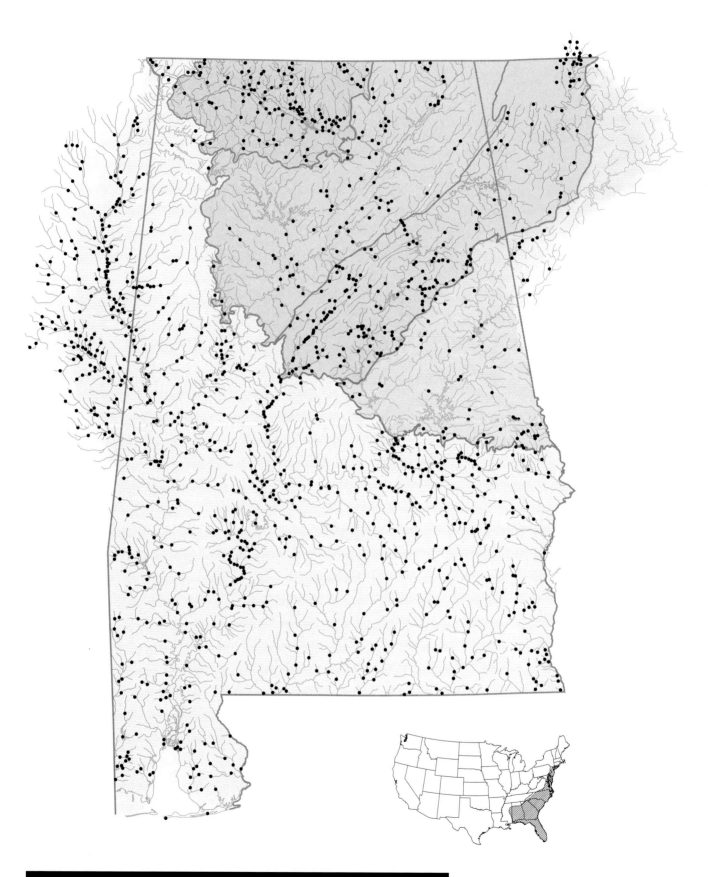

MOSQUITOFISH *Gambusia* complex   **1,259 STATIONS**

478

G. affinis and **G. holbrooki**, Magnolia River, Baldwin County, 19 August 1992, 1.5 in (37 mm) SL female, GSA 4468

Gambusia complex
G. affinis
(Baird and Girard, 1853)
G. holbrooki
Girard, 1859

ETYMOLOGY:

Gambusia—from the Cuban word *gambusino*, "nothing"
affinis—related
holbrooki—in honor of naturalist J. E. Holbrook

CHARACTERISTICS: The mosquitofish is known for the large, dusky teardrop shape below its eye and one to three rows of black dots on the dorsal and caudal fins. The scales appear to be diamond-shaped because their margins are well outlined with melanophores. Females are larger than males and, when pregnant, can be extremely potbellied. Females also have a distinct black anal spot that presumably serves as a target for the male gonopodium (see Livebearers family introduction). Individuals are generally olive green to yellow-brown on the back and upper sides, while the sides are an iridescent silver. The body shape is generally stout, with a small upturned mouth and rounded caudal fin. See Baird and Girard (1853b) for original description.

ADULT SIZE: Females: 1.2 to 2.2 in (30 to 55 mm)

DISTRIBUTION: The western mosquitofish, *Gambusia affinis*, occurs in Gulf coastal drainages from Alabama to Veracruz, Mexico, and northward in the Mississippi River basin to Illinois. *Gambusia holbrooki*, the eastern mosquitofish, is found in Atlantic coastal drainages from New Jersey to the Florida Keys and westward to the Mobile basin. In Alabama, **G.**
affinis occurs throughout the Tennessee River drainage and northern one-half to two-thirds of the Mobile basin, while **G. holbrooki** is known from Gulf coastal drainages eastward to the lower Mobile River. The lower Mobile basin contains both **G. affinis** x **holbrooki** intergrade populations and **G. holbrooki** populations (Angus and Howell, 1996). The mosquitofish's introduction as a control for mosquitoes has expanded its range throughout the United States.

HABITAT AND BIOLOGY: *Gambusia* are found in quiet pools and around the aquatic vegetation of springs, streams, rivers, ponds, swamps, large impoundments, isolated backwaters, and even waste treatment lagoons. Able to swallow atmospheric air, mosquitofish can live in poorly oxygenated environments that are marginal for many other fish species. As the mosquitofish's name indicates, mosquito larvae and pupae are particular favorites in its diet, but it also consumes fish larvae, small crustaceans, and various amounts of algae and aquatic plants. Krumholtz (1948) reports that, beginning in late spring through the summer, three to four broods of young may be produced in a season. The gestation period for each brood lasts for 21 to 28 days.

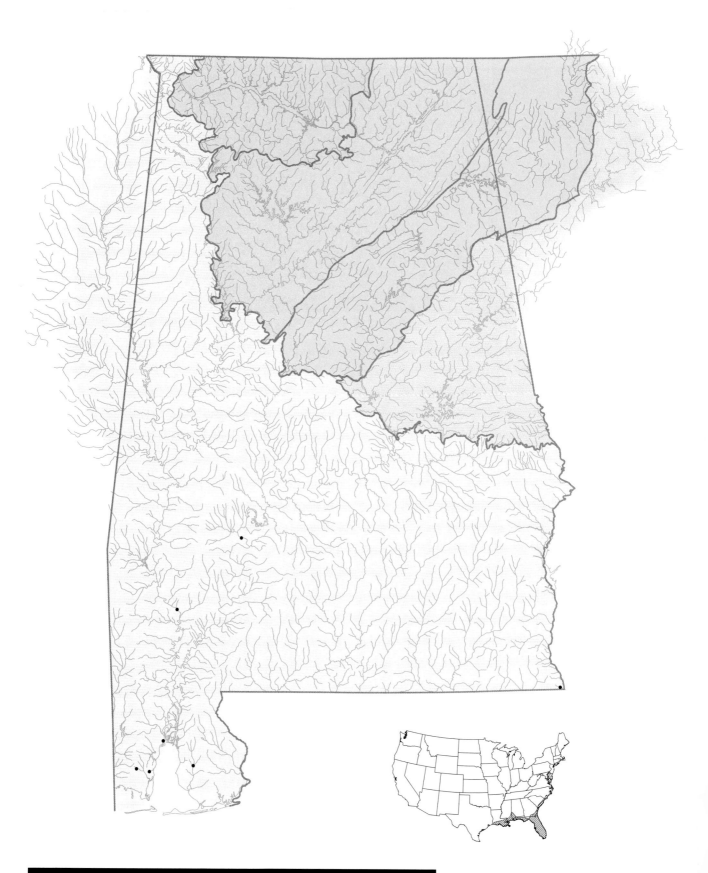

Heterandria formosa

Agassiz, 1855

ETYMOLOGY:

Heterandria—different male

formosa—beautiful or finely

formed

Fish River tributary, Baldwin County, 11 August 1994, 0.5 in (12 mm) SL male, GSA 4631

CHARACTERISTICS: One of the smallest fish species in the world, *Heterandria formosa* has a stout body, a small, upturned mouth, and a rounded caudal fin. A dark lateral stripe extends from the snout to the caudal fin. Faint bars project upward toward the back and occasionally downward toward the venter. Both sexes have a large black dot at the base of their dorsal fin, but only the female has a dot on her anal fin. The body is the color of straw, and the dorsal fin is light orange or yellow distal to the black dot.

ADULT SIZE: 0.5 to 1.2 in (12 to 30 mm)

DISTRIBUTION: The least killifish occurs sporadically across southern Alabama from the Chattahoochee River drainage in Houston County to Fowl River, a western tributary to Mobile Bay. Recent sampling efforts indicate that this species occurs considerably further inland in Alabama than was previously believed (Martin, 1978; Boschung, 1992). In 1990 and 1995, we collected least killifish 92 miles upstream of Mobile Bay in an overflow pool of the lower Tombigbee River near Jackson, Clarke County. This record was subsequently broken in 1994 when Royal D. Suttkus, a longtime collector of

Alabama fishes, took several specimens at Evans's lower bar on the Alabama River, Wilcox County, approximately 120 miles upstream of Mobile Bay. William Mike Howell recently reported to us his observation of *H. formosa* in ponds near the Choctawhatchee River, Geneva County.

HABITAT AND BIOLOGY: The least killifish occurs along weedy margins of deep, plant-filled blackwater habitats of the Southern Pine Hills and Coastal Lowlands of Alabama. *Heterandria formosa* is a daytime surface feeder, and its diet consists mainly of microcrustaceans and occasionally plant material (Reimer, 1970). Aquarists have cultured this species for its diminutive size and tolerant nature, including an ability to survive at temperatures ranging from 50° to 90°F (10° to 32°C) and the fact that it will readily sustain itself on water fleas (*Daphnia*). Axelrod and Schultz (1971) report that breeding females in aquariums drop two or three fry a day for 10 days and begin another reproductive cycle approximately four weeks afterward.

REMARKS: Agassiz (1855) listed the type locality as Mobile, Alabama.

SILVERSIDES

Atherinidae

Named for the silver stripe that runs along their sides, the silversides are diminutive, translucent fishes. They occur in small schools along the shores of lakes and impoundments, over deep, open waters, and around structures such as docks or piers. Along with the mullet family, Mugilidae, the family Atherinidae is characterized by a small, spiny dorsal finlet in front of the soft dorsal fin. Silversides are distinguishable from mullet, however, by their smaller size and relatively elongate jaws.

Silversides are worldwide in distribution and are represented by about 30 species. Most are marine species and occur in tropical and temperate regions, although many freshwater species have been described. Perhaps the best-known silverside in the United States is the marine California grunion, *Leuresthes tenuis*. At high tides during the spawning period, millions of individuals enter shallow surf areas along California beaches, and many are harvested for food. Two species of silversides occur in our area of study. The brook silverside, *Labidesthes sicculus*, is strictly a freshwater species, and the inland silverside, *Menidia beryllina*, occurs in estuarine to fresh waters penetrating to the lower Alabama River. These species are generally elongate, slender fishes with long jaws and a terminal mouth. High anal fin ray counts numbering 22 or more distinguish the brook silverside from most other freshwater species in Alabama.

Silversides constitute important forage for needlefishes, small striped basses, sunfishes, porgies, drums, and other freshwater and marine species. Live silversides are excellent bait for speckled trout, but they require a round live well and flowing water to stay alive and unbruised.

KEY TO THE SILVERSIDES

1a. Anal rays 22 to 25; more than 23 small predorsal scales; lateral line scales 74 to 87 . . . . brook silverside, *Labidesthes sicculus*

1b. Anal rays 16 to 18; from 14 to 16 large predorsal scales; lateral line scales 36 to 44 . . . . inland silverside, *Menidia beryllina*

PURSLEY CREEK, WILCOX COUNTY

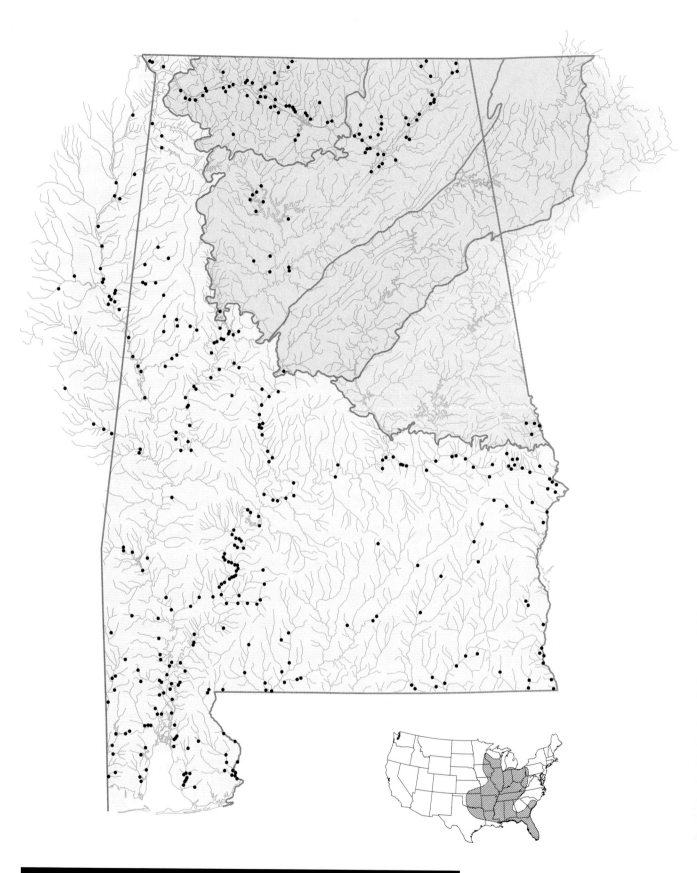

BROOK SILVERSIDE   *Labidesthes sicculus*   **398 STATIONS**

484

Labidesthes sicculus
(Cope, 1865)

ETYMOLOGY:
Labidesthes—forceps to eat, referring to the beaklike jaws on this species
sicculus—dried, possibly referring to the temporary pool environments in which this species was originally found

Snake Creek, Russell County, 7 April 1993, 2.5 in (64 mm) SL male, GSA 4410

CHARACTERISTICS: The brook silverside is a small, slender species with an elongate caudal peduncle. The top of the head and the anterior part of the back are somewhat flattened. A silver stripe extends from the front of the gill cover to the caudal fin and expands at the caudal fin base into a small silver spot. The jaws are long and adapted for feeding at the surface. Live *Labidesthes sicculus* are greenish yellow, and the outer edge of the sickle-shaped dorsal and anal fins are light lemon yellow. Scales are small, with 74 to 87 scales in the lateral series. The brook silverside's greater numbers of lateral scales, anal fin rays (22 to 25), and predorsal scales (greater than 23) separate it from the similar inland silverside, *Menidia beryllina*. See Cope (1865a) for original description.

ADULT SIZE: 2.4 to 3.9 in (60 to 100 mm)

DISTRIBUTION: Brook silversides are found in Atlantic and Gulf slope drainages from South Carolina to Texas and throughout the Mississippi River basin northward to the Great Lakes. The species is widespread and often abundant below the Fall Line in the Mobile basin. Future sampling of large streams and rivers will likely expand its apparently limited distribution in the Black Warrior River system above the Fall Line. Our collections indicate that brook silversides are widespread in the Tennessee River drainage and in the coastal drainages of Alabama. The lack of records in the Yellow and Blackwater river systems is likely due to inadequate sampling.

HABITAT AND BIOLOGY: *Labidesthes sicculus* is most common in large rivers, streams, and impoundments near the surface of open waters or quiet areas around piers and boat launches. Reproduction occurs from mid-spring to summer, and spawning takes place in the open water of shallow areas. Males establish loosely defined territories. Adhesive eggs are fertilized in open water and become attached to plants, sticks, or the substrate. Brook silversides consume microcrustaceans, flying insects, and insect larvae (Keast and Webb, 1966; Hubbs, 1921). Longevity is reported to be less than two years (Nelson, 1968).

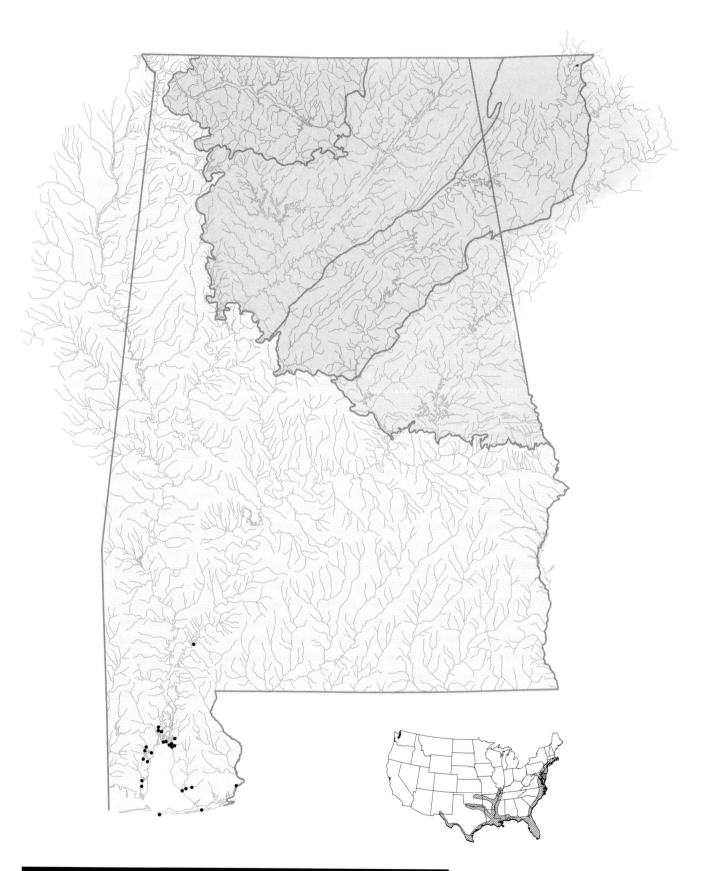

INLAND SILVERSIDE   *Menidia beryllina*   24 STATIONS

Menidia beryllina

(Cope, 1866)

ETYMOLOGY:

Menidia—Greek term for a small, silvery fish *beryllina*—emerald

Ducker Bay, Baldwin County, 17 August 1992, 2.1 in (53 mm) SL male, GSA 4459

CHARACTERISTICS: Although the inland silverside resembles the brook silverside, it has a stouter and more rounded body, fewer anal fin rays (16 to 18), fewer pre-dorsal scales (14 to 16), and fewer lateral scales (36 to 44). A silver stripe extends from the pectoral fin base to the caudal fin base, where it expands to form a small silver spot. The caudal fin is edged in light yellow, while color along the back and upper sides is pale yellow to translucent green. In 1866 Cope read his paper describing *Menidia beryllina* to the American Philosophical Society. See Cope (1869b) for the subsequent published account.

ADULT SIZE: 2 to 3.9 in (50 to 100 mm)

DISTRIBUTION: *Menidia beryllina* occurs in coastal drainages from Massachusetts south along the Atlantic and Gulf coasts to Veracruz, Mexico, and then north through the Mississippi River basin into large tributaries of southern Illinois. Our collections in Alabama are limited to tributaries of Mobile Bay and the Mobile Delta. We have one record from the lower Alabama River drainage, collected near the mouth of Little River. Increased netting and examination of smaller fishes with boat electrofishing gear will likely expand this species' known range in the lower reaches of the Tombigbee and Alabama river drainages.

HABITAT AND BIOLOGY: The habitat preferences of the inland and brook silversides are similar, including brackish and fresh waters of bayous, lagoons, and bays and quiet areas of inland rivers and streams. The inland silverside eats small crustaceans, mollusks, insects, worms, and occasionally algae (Hildebrand and Schroeder, 1928). The protracted spawning season, possibly with multiple spawnings, extends from April through August in Chesapeake Bay. Like *Labidesthes sicculus*, *M. beryllina* likely spawns in shallow areas of open water, and the adhesive, filamentous eggs attach to vegetation and other submerged objects.

SCULPINS

Cottidae

The sculpins are related to the marine scorpion fishes and sea robins in the order Scorpaeniformes. The family contains more than 300 described species, most of them in northern North America and Eurasia. In North America 122 species have been described. Only 28 are freshwater species, and they belong to the genera **Clinocottus**, **Cottus**, and **Myoxocephalus**. The greatest diversity of sculpins in the United States occurs in the Pacific Northwest.

Three species—**Cottus bairdi**, **C. carolinae**, and **C. pygmaeus**—are known from Alabama waters. The endemic pygmy sculpin, **C. pygmaeus**, is restricted to Coldwater Spring and its downstream spring run in Calhoun County. The mottled and banded sculpins, **C. bairdi** and **C. carolinae**, exhibit substantial physical variability and may eventually be redescribed as new species.

Sculpins have conspicuously large, broad heads armored with sharp spines and bony ridges, eyes placed almost directly on top of the head, and wide mouths. The head and nape of Sculpins are slightly depressed, and the body behind the first dorsal fin is progressively tapered, ending in a narrow caudal peduncle, behind which is a large caudal fin. Scales on this species are typically reduced to small prickles or are completely absent. The body is usually covered with a layer of mucus. The large pectoral fins are fan-shaped; the soft dorsal and anal fins are long. Along its anterior edge, the pelvic fin has a spine discernible only by dissection, noted in the key with a Roman numeral.

Sculpins are well adapted to their environments. Most have light to dark brown mottling resembling the rubble and gravel substrates on which they live, making them difficult for even the trained observer to see. Their flattened bodies, large fins, and lack of a swimbladder are adaptations to life on the bottoms of fast-flowing rivers and streams.

KEY TO THE SCULPINS

1a. Dorsal fins broadly connected; preopercular spines 2; pelvic fin ray count I, 3; rarely exceeding 1.5 inches (38 mm) SL . . . . pygmy sculpin, **Cottus pygmaeus**
1b. Dorsal fins separate or connected only at base; preopercular spines 3; pelvic fin ray count I, 4 . . . . . go to 2

2a. Body of breeding males dark with wide red to bright orange marginal band on spiny dorsal fin followed by wide black band extending to fin base; body shorter and more robust, generally no longer than 3.1 inches (80 mm) SL; dorsal saddles usually indistinct against dark body; chin generally uniformly pigmented; lateral line incomplete, ending before or near posterior end of soft dorsal fin . . . . mottled sculpin, **C. bairdi**
2b. Body of breeding males lighter, generally dark brown or tan, spiny dorsal fin without red, orange, or black bands; body generally longer and more slender, with distinct saddles which are darker near their edges; chin pigmentation blotchy; lateral line complete or nearly so . . . . banded sculpin, **C. carolinae**

CHEAHA CREEK, CLAY COUNTY

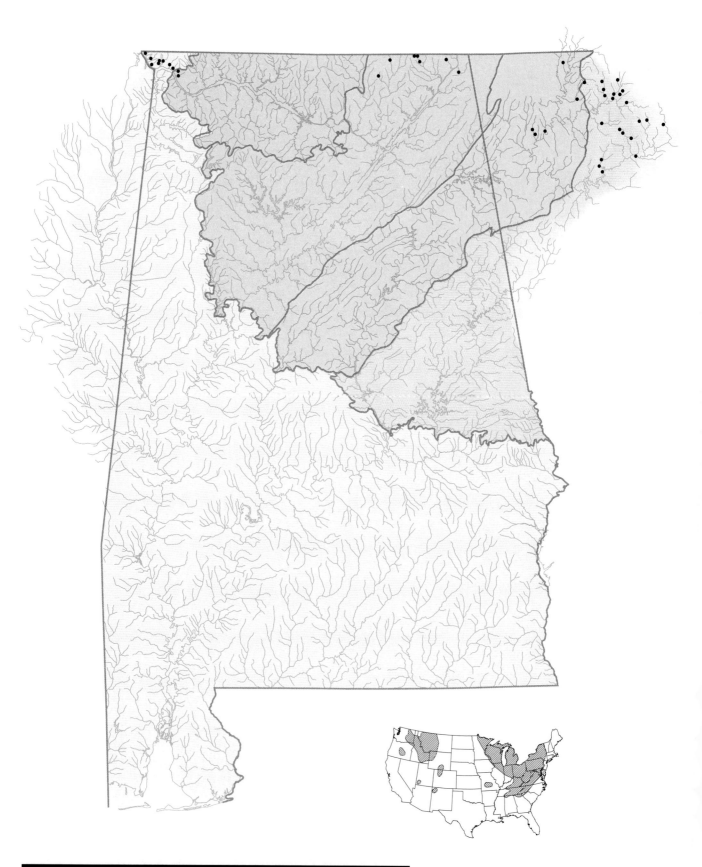

MOTTLED SCULPIN *Cottus bairdi* **43 STATIONS**

Cottus bairdi

Girard, 1850

ETYMOLOGY:

Cottus—an old name for a miller's-thumb

bairdi—in honor of Spencer F. Baird, the first United States fish commissioner and a prominent ichthyologist in the 1800s

Bumpass Creek, Lauderdale County, 25 February 1993, 2.6 in (65 mm) SL male, GSA 4359

CHARACTERISTICS: Although the pigmentation of *Cottus bairdi* is variable, nuptial males are usually dark or black with a conspicuous, bright red or orange band on the spiny dorsal fin margin. This banding pattern is also present on the female but is generally less intense, and the body color is more brown or golden. The saddle pattern across the back is more diffuse on *C. bairdi* than on the banded sculpin, *C. carolinae*, but *C. bairdi* has a distinct, narrow, vertical tail band at the caudal fin base. The soft dorsal and anal fins of breeding mottled sculpins are long, and when depressed, their rays extend to the caudal fin base. Male sculpins have short and stout heads. Females have longer heads and shorter rays in their dorsal and anal fins. Two distinct lines are visible along the sides of this species. The lateral line is incomplete, ending near the posterior end of the soft dorsal fin. A second line extends to the caudal base.

ADULT SIZE: 1.7 to 3.1 in (43 to 80 mm)

DISTRIBUTION: *Cottus bairdi* is distributed from eastern Canada southward through the Great Lakes and upper Mississippi basin to the Tennessee River drainage and upper Coosa River system in Alabama. Populations are also known from the Ozarks region in Missouri and Arkansas and from the upper Rocky Mountain and Pacific Northwest areas. Mottled sculpins occur in upland habitats in Jackson and extreme west Lauderdale counties in the Tennessee drainage. Populations also inhabit streams of the upper Coosa River system in Georgia and Tennessee.

HABITAT AND BIOLOGY: Mottled sculpins prefer clear, fast-flowing waters with substrates of boulders, broken rubble, and flat rocks. Spawning is earlier than that of most other sculpin species, with nuptial individuals found from February through April. In riffles around boulders or other protected zones, males establish and defend nesting areas; after spawning, they continue to guard the nests until the fry leave. Nagel (1980) reports that mottled sculpins may live for up to six years. *Cottus bairdi* consumes crayfishes, fishes (including other sculpins), and all sizes of aquatic insects.

491

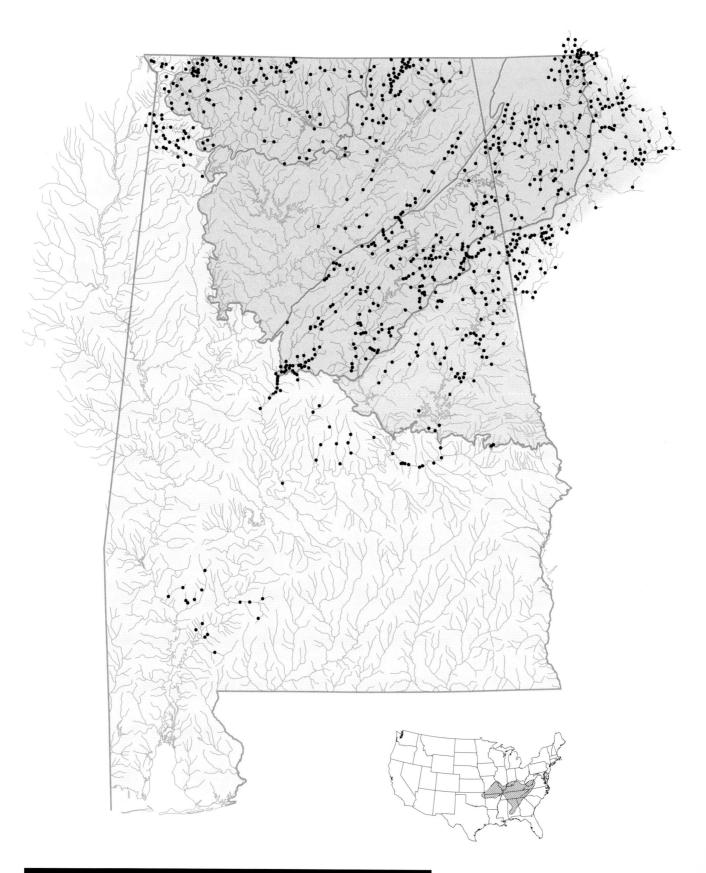

BANDED SCULPIN   *Cottus carolinae*   **784 STATIONS**

492

Cottus carolinae

(Gill, 1861)

ETYMOLOGY:
Cottus—an old name for a miller's-thumb *carolinae*—in honor of Caroline Henry, friend of Theodore Gill, the describer of this species

Butler Creek, Lauderdale County, 31 March 1992, 2.9 in (74 mm) SL male, GSA 4241

CHARACTERISTICS: The banded sculpin can be distinguished from the mottled sculpin by a less robust body, intense dorsal saddles with dark edges, and a somewhat longer snout. Dorsal saddles on mottled sculpins are less defined and more mottled, and the head is longer with a shorter snout. Banded sculpins lack banding in the spiny dorsal fin, but rays in the second dorsal and caudal fins have distinct light and dark banding that runs the length of the fins. The lateral line is generally complete.

ADULT SIZE: 2.8 to 5.8 in (70 to 147 mm)

DISTRIBUTION: *Cottus carolinae* occurs in upland habitats from the Alabama River drainage north to southern Indiana and Illinois, east to western Virginia and North Carolina, and west to the Ozarks. Subspecies of the banded sculpin include *C. c. zopherus* in the Coosa River system, *C. c. infernatus* in the Alabama and lower Tombigbee drainages below the Fall Line, and *C. c. carolinae* in the Tennessee River drainage. The systematic status of other Alabama populations is unknown. Because the distribution of *C. carolinae* group members

is so complex, we did not attempt to delineate their respective distributions on the accompanying map. Boschung (1992) postulates that a sculpin population found in the Tallapoosa River system above the Fall Line should be aligned with the mottled sculpin, *C. bairdi*, rather than with *C. carolinae*.

HABITAT AND BIOLOGY: Banded sculpins generally inhabit clear, cool upland streams flowing over cobble, rubble, and flat rocks, but they also occur in large flowing streams and upland rivers. Coastal Plain populations are restricted to hard-bottomed, cool streams, in upland areas. Spawning occurs from February through April. Spawning behavior is similar to that of *C. bairdi* in that eggs are deposited in nests guarded by males. Adult banded sculpins are known to eat salamanders, crayfishes, large aquatic insect immatures, and small benthic fishes, while juveniles have a typical riffle-dwelling diet of small insect immatures. Starnes (1977) reports night feeding, with the young consuming insect immatures such as caddisflies, mayflies, and midges, and adults eating larger prey such as stoneflies and fishes.

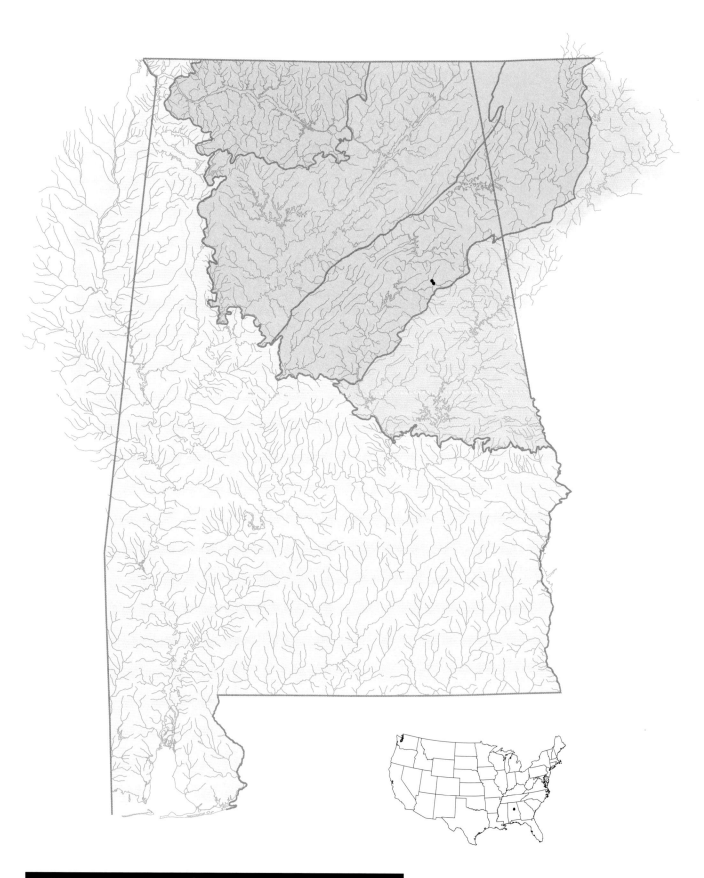

PYGMY SCULPIN   *Cottus pygmaeus*   **2 STATIONS**

Cottus pygmaeus

Williams, 1968

ETYMOLOGY:

Cottus—an old name for a miller's-thumb *pygmaeus*—dwarf, referring to the small adult size of this species

Coldwater Spring, Calhoun County, 30 August 1994, 1.1 in (28 mm) SL male, GSA 4633

CHARACTERISTICS: An Alabama endemic in the family Cottidae, the pygmy sculpin is distinguishable from the other species by its small adult size, broadly connected dorsal fins, two preopercular spines, and a I, 3 pelvic fin ray count. The body is moderately robust, being deepest at the spiny dorsal fin. Body color is somewhat variable, the dominant background colors being gray and black. The three light saddles extending across the back are creamy white to pinkish. The back is darkly mottled in males and evenly pigmented in females.

ADULT SIZE: 1.5 in (38 mm)

DISTRIBUTION: *Cottus pygmaeus* is known from Coldwater Spring and its adjacent downstream spring run (which is a tributary to Choccolocco Creek).

HABITAT AND BIOLOGY: Coldwater Spring maintains constant flow from the Jacksonville fault at an average rate of 31.4 million gallons per day (mgd). It is a public water supply for the city of Anniston, Alabama, which used approximately 11 mgd in 1993. The water is clear and colorless, has a constant temperature, and is extensively vegetated by several species of aquatic plants, including large mats of *Myriophyllum*, *Ceratophyllum*, watercress, and aquatic mosses. *Cottus pygmaeus* is most common in the gravel-bottomed spring run in moderate to swift flows. Williams (1968) reports on the life history and habitat requirements of this species. Known prey are small snails, microcrustaceans, and midge larvae. The fact that gravid females have been captured throughout the year could signify continuous spawning, but activity appears to intensify from April to August. Eggs are laid beneath cobble, and sexual maturity is reached when individuals grow to be 1 inch or longer.

REMARKS: The type locality is Coldwater Spring, Calhoun County. The U.S. Fish and Wildlife Service considers the pygmy sculpin to be threatened.

MORONIDAE

Striped Basses

Anglers have long recognized that the striped bass, **Morone saxatilis**, is an excellent food and game fish. In his book on North Carolina fishes, Smith (1907) reports that the striped bass was one of America's best and most valuable fishes. David Starr Jordan, the father of North American ichthyology, noted that the striped bass was one of the very best food and game fishes and a splendid candidate for artificial propagation by the U.S. government (Jordan and Evermann, 1908). The numbers and sizes of striped bass first encountered by settlers along the Atlantic Coast must have been phenomenal. Millions of pounds were landed in the nineteenth century. Smith (1907) reported that nearly 1.5 million pounds, valued at the time at $128,000, were landed in 1887. Individual fish weighing 60 to 75 pounds were not uncommon, and commercial fishermen and anglers occasionally landed striped bass weighing more than 100 pounds.

Members of this family are characterized by an elongate, strongly compressed, striped body covered with ctenoid scales; a moderate to large terminal mouth with a jutting lower jaw; a complete lateral line; and two dorsal fins. The first dorsal fin contains nine stout spines; the second dorsal has one anterior spine and 10 to 14 soft rays. The caudal fin is emarginate or forked, and the pectoral fins are positioned high on the sides—a definite advantage for speed in catching shad and other favorite prey.

The family Moronidae contains freshwater, anadromous, and euryhaline (salt water tolerant) species. Three species occur in Alabama: the freshwater white bass, **Morone chrysops**; yellow bass, **M. mississippiensis**; and the anadromous striped bass, **M. saxatilis**. All three live in rivers and reservoirs for most of the year, but in late summer they seek refuge in medium to small cool, flowing streams. The white bass is widely distributed in Alabama, but it is usually not abundant. Yellow bass inhabit the Tennessee River system and the Mobile Delta and have occasionally been stocked in private lakes.

Overfishing in the early twentieth century almost extirpated the Gulf Coast form of striped bass from Alabama. As a result, large numbers of Atlantic Coast juveniles were obtained from North Carolina hatcheries and stocked into many Alabama rivers. Subsequent natural interbreeding with native Gulf Coast fish and backcrossing with parental forms produced an array of intergrade fish that threatened to destroy the genetic integrity of native stocks in Alabama and other Gulf coastal drainages. Biologists with the Alabama Department of Conservation and Natural Resources successfully spawn and stock true Gulf Coast striped bass into most Mobile basin rivers and reservoirs and a few state lakes. Lake Lewis Smith on the Sipsey Fork of the Black Warrior River system contains a substantial population of Gulf Coast fish, where anglers annually land fish in the 15-to 30-pound class. Angling reports supported by fishery surveys have also substantiated the presence of naturally reproducing populations of striped bass in Weiss Reservoir on the Coosa River near the Alabama-Georgia state line.

Most of the hybrid striped bass stocked in Alabama are palmetto bass (Robins et al., 1991), which are hybrids of male white bass and female striped bass. Sunshine bass, hybrids of female white bass and male striped bass, have also been stocked in lesser numbers in previous years. The ADCNR and the Tennessee Valley Authority release most striped and hybrid bass fingerlings in public waters. Commercial hatcheries in Alabama and the southeastern United States also sell hybrid and striped bass fingerlings to private landholders for stocking ponds and to commercial producers who raise the fish for sale to fish markets and restaurants.

Striped and palmetto bass provide an excellent winter fishery in many Alabama rivers. These feisty fishes put forth a dramatic battle on artificial lures or cut bait, primarily shad and chicken livers. White and yellow bass seem to prefer cut shad and live minnows along river channels and in larger streams. Lake Lewis Smith

and tailwaters below dams of the Black Warrior, Coosa, and Tallapoosa rivers offer excellent habitat for both striped and palmetto bass. The largest individuals are usually taken on live adult gizzard shad.

The striped basses, together with the sea basses and several other freshwater European and South American genera, were previously grouped in the family Perci-chthyidae (Robins et al., 1991). Johnson (1984) removed members of the genus *Morone* from this family and placed them in the Moronidae because they lack features typical of other percichthyids. We concur with his recommendation.

KEY TO THE STRIPED BASSES

1a. Second anal spine longer than anal fin base, extending well beyond base of last anal fin ray when depressed; tip of lower jaw does not protrude beyond upper jaw . . . . yellow bass, ***Morone mississippiensis***
1b. Second anal spine shorter than anal fin base and it does not reach last anal fin ray base when fin is depressed; lower jaw protrudes past upper jaw except on very small individuals. . . . . go to 2

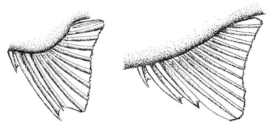

Anal fin spines on (left) ***M. mississippiensis*** and (right) other striped basses

2a. Center of tongue with two distinct tooth patches, their lengths being more than one-half the length of the lateral patches; body depth goes into standard length more than three times . . . . . striped bass, ***M. saxatilis***
2b. Center of tongue usually has one tooth patch; body depth goes into standard length less than three times . . . . white bass, ***M. chrysops***

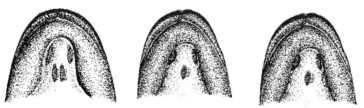

Tongue tooth patches on (left) ***M. saxatilis***, (center) ***M. chrysops***, and (right) palmetto bass

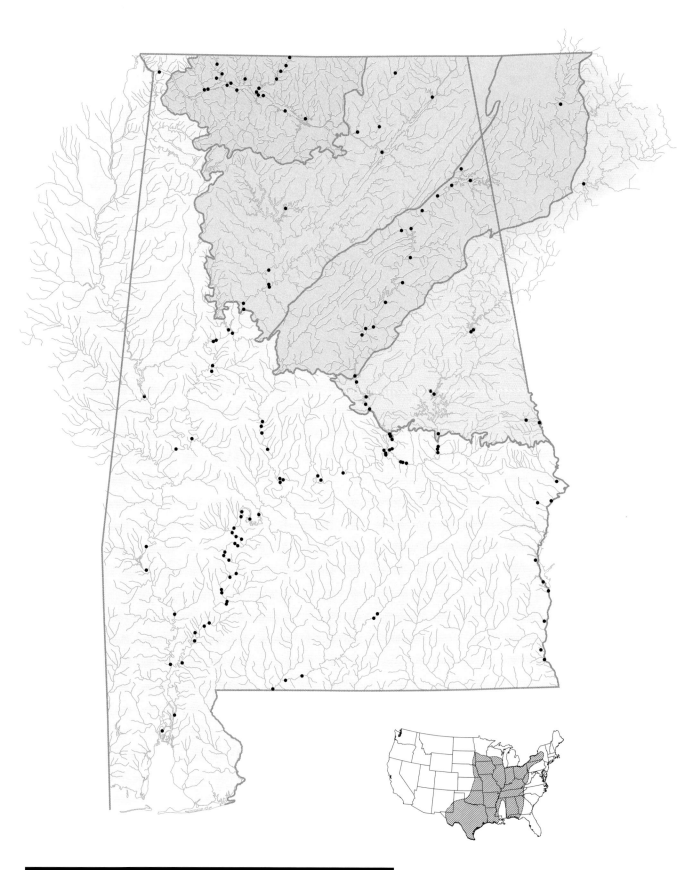

Morone chrysops

(Rafinesque, 1820)

ETYMOLOGY:

Morone—origin of this
genus name is unknown
chrysops—golden eye

Tombigbee River, Clarke County, 29 April 1992, 7.1 in (170 mm) SL male, GSA 4225

CHARACTERISTICS: At first glance, white bass resemble small striped bass with faint lateral stripes. But the two can be distinguished by tooth patches on the tonuge (one on white bass and two on striped bass). The head on the white bass is fairly small and pointed. The first and second dorsal fins are entirely separate. The first dorsal fin has nine spines, and the second has one spine and 13 to 15 soft rays. The anal fin has three progressively lengthening spines and 11 to 13 soft rays. The back is blue-gray, the sides are silver with six to 10 longitudinal (sometimes faint) stripes, and the venter is white to cream. The dorsal, caudal, and anal fins range from white to dusky. The pectoral and pelvic fins are usually clear, although the latter may have light iridescent blue margins.

ADULT SIZE: 10 to 15 in (254 to 380 mm). The state angling record (4 lb, 9 oz) was caught in the Black Warrior River below Selden Dam in 1987.

DISTRIBUTION: *Morone chrysops* is widely distributed in Alabama, but it is not generally abundant except in the Tennessee and Chattahoochee rivers. Duckett (1972) reports that white bass were introduced into Lake Lewis Smith from 1962 through 1965. The first Black Warrior

samples were collected in 1949, indicating that the species existed previously in the drainage. White bass are uncommon in the Conecuh River system, but we found none in more than 40 samples collected in the Alabama section of the Choctawhatchee River system from 1991 to 1994. Fishermen visiting from Illinois have told us that northern anglers like to fish for white bass in the Tennessee River near Florence in Lauderdale County.

HABITAT AND BIOLOGY: White bass inhabit the surface and pelagic (midwater) areas of rivers, reservoirs, and large streams. We have collected them along riprap, downed trees, and other structures below dams. White bass are aggressive predators that feed on gizzard and threadfin shad. Individuals migrate into the lower reaches of large flowing streams to spawn. Males usually precede females. Spawnings between one or more males and a single female usually occur at midwater depths in March and April. Once released and fertilized, eggs drift to the bottom and the larvae hatch in two or three days. Growth is fairly rapid. Etnier and Starnes (1993) report average total lengths of about 8 inches at age one, 14 inches at age two, 16 inches at age three, and 17 inches at age four in the Carter Hill Reservoir in Tennessee.

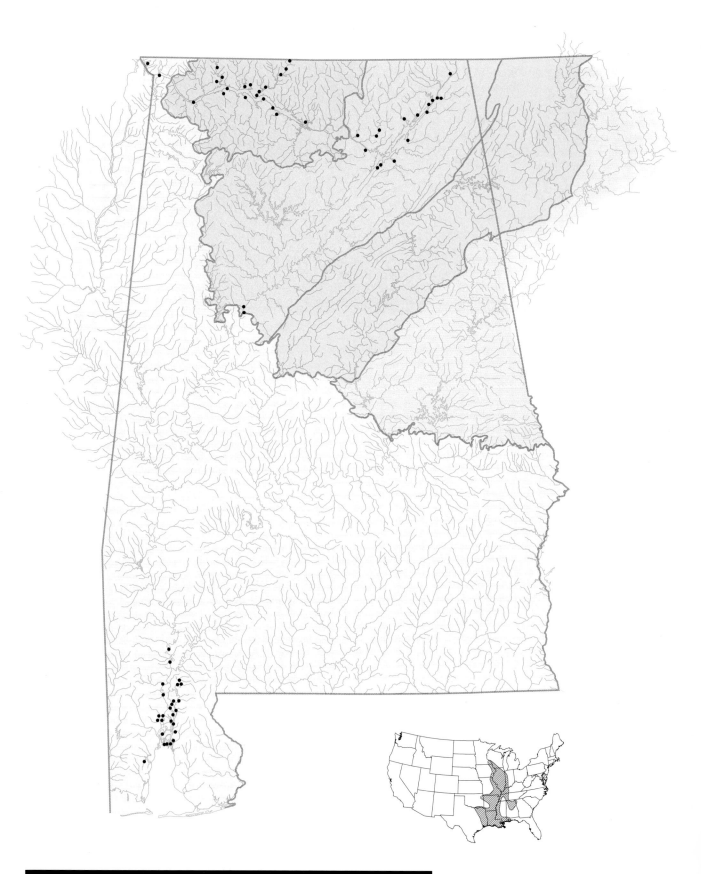

YELLOW BASS *Morone mississippiensis* **65 STATIONS**

Morone mississippiensis

Jordan and Eigenmann, 1887

ETYMOLOGY:

Morone—origin of this genus name is unknown

mississippiensis—of the Mississippi River

Short Creek, Marshall County, 9 June 1992, 4.3 in (110 mm) SL male, GSA 4246

CHARACTERISTICS: The yellow bass is named for its characteristic yellowish gold body and eye. Black longitudinal stripes occur as continuous lines along the back, but the lower three or four along the sides and venter are distinctly broken. The lateral line is complete with 50 to 55 scales. The tongue lacks the distinctive tooth patch found on other members of this group. See Eigenmann (1887) for original description.

ADULT SIZE: 8 to 11 in (203 to 279 mm). The state angling record (1 lb, 9.5 oz) was caught in Inland Lake, a tributary of the Locust Fork of the Black Warrior River system.

DISTRIBUTION: *Morone mississippiensis* is distributed from the Mobile basin west to the San Jacinto River, Texas. It is native to the lower Tombigbee and Tennessee rivers as well as the Mobile Delta. Dan Catchings of the Game and Fish Division confirmed that yellow bass have been introduced into select areas of the upper Cahaba River system, including Lake Purdy. Two specimens were collected in Lake Purdy in June 1982. Jim McHugh,

also of the Game and Fish Division, reported two collections from the Black Warrior River in 1989 and confirmed that individuals had been stocked in Inland Lake. We have no samples to date, but Walter Hubbard of the Mississippi Department of Wildlife reported that yellow bass, presumably from the Tennessee River, have entered the upper Tombigbee River via the Tennessee Tombigbee Waterway (Boschung, 1992).

HABITAT AND BIOLOGY: Populations of this schooling species occur more frequently in medium to large tributaries and backwater areas of reservoirs and rivers. In Missouri (Pflieger, 1975) and Tennessee (Etnier and Starnes, 1993), yellow bass migrate into large streams to spawn in April and May. Our collections of gravid males and females in the lower Tombigbee River system and the Tennessee River drainage in April support their observations. Spawning usually occurs between one to several males and a single female. Yellow bass feed mainly on insect larvae and small fishes, including minnows, silversides, and small threadfin shad. The maximum life span is estimated to be six years (Priegel, 1975).

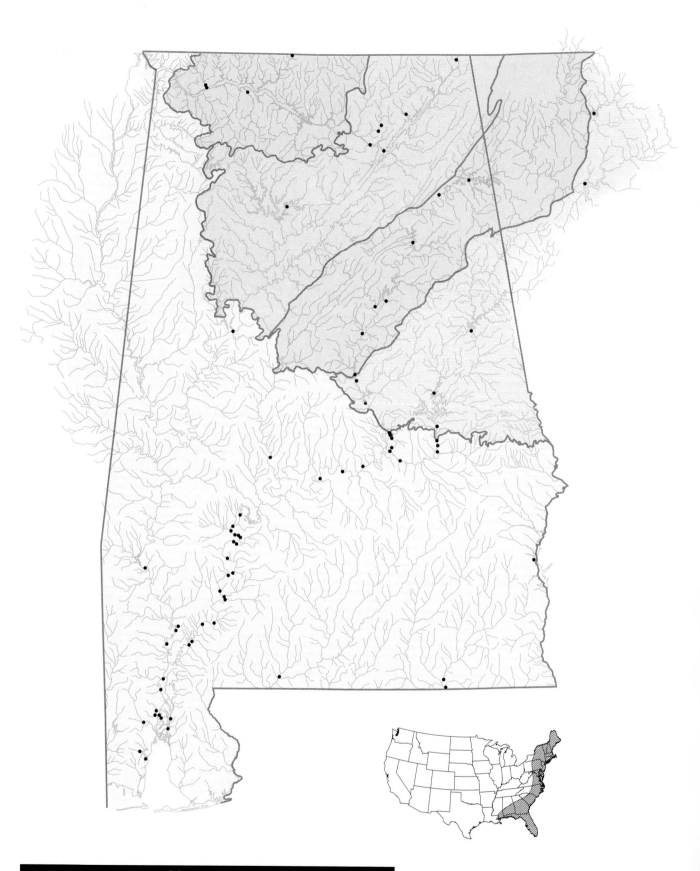

Morone saxatilis
(Walbaum, 1792)

ETYMOLOGY:
Morone—origin of this genus name is unknown
saxatilis—rock-dwelling

Cypress Creek, Lauderdale County, 16 July 1992, 10.8 in (275 mm) SL male, GSA 4282

CHARACTERISTICS: The striped bass has an elongate, compressed body and a relatively small head with an acute snout and a large, gaping mouth. Maximum body depth goes three or more times into standard length. The first dorsal fin has nine spines, the second fin has one spine and 12 soft rays. The front of the anal fin has three spines that are graduated in length. Two elongate median tooth patches are located on the back of the tongue. The lateral line is complete, with 57 to 68 scales. The back is dark gray to green; the sides are light green grading to silver with several continuous black stripes, and the venter is white to cream. Young striped bass have dusky vertical bars along the sides of the body.

ADULT SIZE: 20 to 24 in (508 to 610 mm). The state angling record (55 lb) was caught in the Tallapoosa River. The date is unknown but may have been in the mid-1960s.

DISTRIBUTION: Striped bass populations in Alabama are a mixture of Gulf Coast and Atlantic Coast fish. During the past five years, the Alabama Game and Fish Division has initiated an aggressive program to reestablish Gulf Coast populations in the Mobile basin, primarily below the Fall Line. Native populations probably still enter the Mobile Delta and lower Alabama and Tombigbee drainages. Landlocked populations of Gulf Coast fish occur in the Chattahoochee River above Jim Woodruff Dam and in Lake Lewis Smith. Most individuals in the Tennessee River are probably Atlantic Coast fish, although Gulf Coast fish were introduced into Wheeler Reservoir from 1992 to 1994.

HABITAT AND BIOLOGY: Schools of native and introduced populations of striped bass inhabit free-flowing rivers and reservoirs and feed primarily on gizzard and threadfin shad. Moss (1985) notes that spawning occurs from late March through April in Alabama. Using radio-tagged fish, he documented that individuals migrate from rivers into spring-fed tributaries in late May and early June in search of cooler water temperatures and higher oxygen levels. We observed similar behavior in 1992 and 1993 while sampling Big Nance, Cypress, and Shoal creeks and the Paint Rock River of the Tennessee River drainage.

REMARKS: In Alabama, striped bass angling is best during cool months and in tailwaters of locks and dams and also in Lake Lewis Smith. Favorite baits include live gizzard shad, white or yellow jigs, and spoon lures.

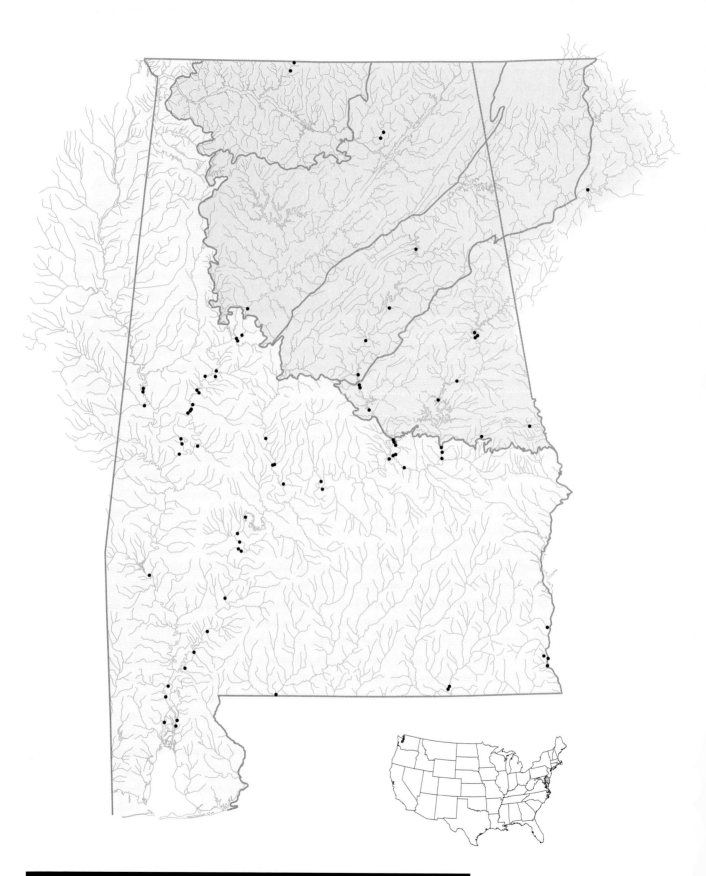

Morone chrysops x *saxatilis*

Alabama River, Wilcox County, 18 April 1995, 17.1 in (435 mm) SL, GSA 4638

CHARACTERISTICS: The palmetto bass, also called hybrid bass, is not a naturally occurring species. Individuals are produced by artifically spawning a male white bass with a female striped bass. Offspring usually exhibit a wide variety of color patterns which can be confusing when trying to separate them from the young of either parent species. A palmetto bass can usually be distinguished from a striped bass by its broken lateral stripes along the lower sides of the body (continuous on striped bass) and a distinctively shorter, thicker, and deeper body form. Palmetto bass can be distinguished from white bass by its two tooth patches on the tongue, as opposed to only one tooth patch on the white bass. As they grow older, palmetto bass become thicker and deeper-bodied, giving them a distinctive short and stocky appearance.

ADULT SIZE: 15 to 20 in (380 to 508 mm). The state angling record (23 lb, 2 oz) was caught at Lake Lewis Smith Dam in 1989.

DISTRIBUTION: The ADCNR has stocked more than 18 million palmetto bass in Alabama since 1974 (Nick Nichols, 1995 personal communication). The palmetto bass is probably the most wide ranging and abundant member of the striped bass family in state waters. We have collected individuals throughout the Mobile basin, in the Tennessee River and its larger tributaries, and in several coastal rivers.

HABITAT AND BIOLOGY: Each spring, biologists with the ADCNR collect white bass males and striped bass females and transport them to a state fish hatchery in Marion where they are spawned. Offspring are subsequently released into rivers, reservoirs, and public lakes. Palmetto bass feed heavily on shad and grow rapidly, often reaching total lengths of 18 inches or more in two years. Individuals migrate great distances in response to changing seasons and flow regimes and they congregate in tailwaters below dams in spring and during high discharge periods. The palmetto bass provides an excellent winter fishery in Alabama when many other game species are relatively inactive. Although they readily strike floating and sinking artificial lures, many fishes are taken with chicken livers and shad as cut bait. Palmetto bass rarely reproduce in nature, but they are known to occasionally back cross with white bass (Etnier and Starnes, 1993).

PYGMY SUNFISHES

Elassomatidae

In nature, pygmy sunfishes usually live among aquatic vegetation in silty, swampy habitats that are challenging to sample. Several species in the family are considered to be annuals, meaning that most individuals hatch from eggs, grow to adult size, spawn, and die within a year.

In captivity, these beautiful little creatures have gained a worldwide reputation as excellent aquarium fishes (Axelrod and Schultz, 1971). They reach only 1 to 1.5 inches in total length, readily consume commercially prepared foods, and will spawn repeatedly under the proper conditions (Mettee, 1974).

The family Elassomatidae includes six described and several undescribed species, all of which are native to the southeastern United States and middle Mississippi basin. Three species occur in Alabama. The banded pygmy sunfish, *Elassoma zonatum*, is the most widespread, found primarily below the Fall Line in the Mobile basin and coastal systems. The Everglades pygmy sunfish, *E. evergladei*, is known from eastern tributaries to Mobile Bay and western tributaries of the Perdido River system in Baldwin County.

The third species in Alabama is the spring pygmy sunfish, *E. alabamae*. It was previously known from collections at only two localities: Cave Spring in Lauderdale County in 1937 and Pryor Spring in Limestone County in 1941. For more than 30 years afterward, no other individuals were collected, leading most southeastern ichthyologists to conclude that the species had become extinct. But in 1973 a surviving population was discovered at Moss Spring, a tributary to Beaverdam Creek in Limestone County. Subsequent sampling

confirmed additional populations within the Beaverdam Creek system. On 17 February 1984, several gravid adults from the Beaverdam Creek system were introduced into the Pryor Spring system (Mettee and Pulliam, 1986). The introduction was successful, as evidenced by the collection of new offspring at two locations in Pryor Spring for several years. *Elassoma alabamae* is the first species of special concern in Alabama to be reintroduced into part of its original range. Local landowners and state and federal biologists cooperated in this effort, and their success should be applauded and used as an example for the recovery of other rare species in Alabama.

Although pygmy sunfishes were first described more than a century ago, their taxonomic status is still unsettled, particularly with regard to their phylogenetic relationship to the sunfishes in the family Centrarchidae. Hay (1881) and Jordan and Gilbert (1882) placed the banded pygmy sunfish, *E. zonatum*, in the family Elassomatidae because they believed pygmy sunfishes were intermediate between the pirate perch (family Aphredoderidae) and the sunfishes. Boulinger (1895) relegated the species to the Centrarchidae, assuming it was a dwarfed sunfish. Jordan and Evermann (1896) reaffirmed the belief that pygmy sunfishes were intermediate between the pirate perch and the sunfishes. They also introduced a new family name, the Elassomidae, and did not object to Boulinger's placing the pygmy sunfishes in the Centrarchidae. Bailey (1938) and Robins et al. (1991) retain the pygmy sunfishes in the family Centrarchidae.

To understand better the phylogenetic relationships between pygmy sunfishes and members of the family Centrarchidae, ichthyologists have thoroughly investigated the physical, chromosomal, and behavioral characteristics of these fishes. Eaton (1953, 1956), Branson and Moore (1962), Moore and Sisk (1963), Roberts (1964), Mettee (1974), and Johnson (1984) conclude that although pygmy sunfishes were undoubtedly derived from a primitive centrarchid stock (Branson and Moore, 1962), they differ enough to warrant placement in a separate family, the Elassomatidae. We support their conclusion, as have authors of works on the fishes of Kentucky (Burr and Warren, 1986), North Carolina (Menhinick, 1991), Alabama (Boschung, 1992), and Tennessee (Etnier and Starnes, 1993).

KEY TO THE PYGMY SUNFISHES

1a. On each side of body below dorsal fin origin, 1 or 2 black spots; dorsal fin with 4 or 5 spines; 8 to 12 wide, vertical black bars along sides of males, lighter bars on females . . . . banded pygmy sunfish, *Elassoma zonatum*
1b. No spots on sides below dorsal fin origin; dorsal fin with 3 or 4 spines; 5 to 8 thin yellow, blue or green bars along sides of males, females brown on back and brown and white mottled on sides and venter . . . . go to 2

2a. No scales on top of head; anterior part of lower jaw unpigmented; on males, last 2 or 3 dorsal and anal fin membranes with distinct clear window; females with darkened spot in last 1 or 2 dorsal fin rays; usually 3 dorsal spines; limited to springs and spring-fed tributaries to the Tennessee River drainage. . . . . spring pygmy sunfish, *E. alabamae*
2b. Embedded scales on top of head; anterior part of lower jaw distinctly pigmented; on breeding males, dorsal fin without clear window; on females dorsal fin usually clear with small brown spots but no large black spot; usually 4 dorsal spines; limited to coastal streams . . . . Everglades pygmy sunfish, *E. evergladei*

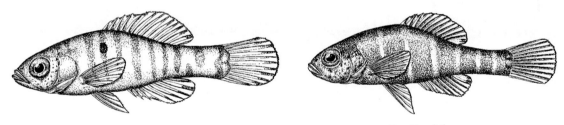

1a, *E. zonatum*   2a, *E. alabamae*

2b, *E. evergladei*

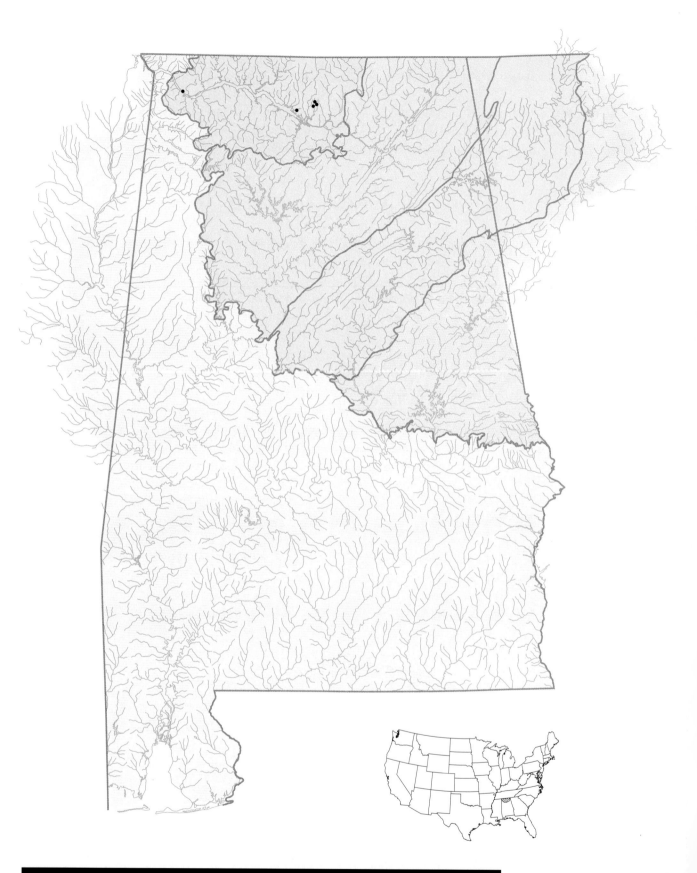

SPRING PYGMY SUNFISH   *Elassoma alabamae*   **5 STATIONS**

Elassoma alabamae
Mayden, 1993

ETYMOLOGY:

Elassoma—small body
alabamae—of Alabama, the
location of the species

Moss Spring, Limestone County, 23 March 1993, 0.7 in (18 mm) SL female, GSA 4385

CHARACTERISTICS: Males and females of this and most other pygmy sunfish species exhibit substantially different color patterns, a condition known as dichromatism. Breeding males are generally dark brown with five to seven narrow, silver or gold vertical bars along their sides. The venter is pale amber to white. The dorsal and anal fins have darkened bases, becoming lighter near their free margins. Clear areas in the last two or three membranes of the dorsal and anal fins form a distinctive window found in no other *Elassoma* species (Mettee, 1974). Females are brown on the back, mottled brown and white along the sides, and cream to white on the venter. Other identifying characteristics include a golden crescent beneath and behind the eye, 16 to 18 scales around the caudal peduncle, 28 to 30 lateral scales (no lateral line), and three dorsal spines.

ADULT SIZE: 0.75 to 1 in (19 to 25 mm)

DISTRIBUTION: The spring pygmy sunfish is endemic to the Tennessee River drainage in Alabama. Early collections recorded the species at Cave Spring, Lauderdale County, in 1937 and Pryor Spring, Limestone County, in 1941. The Cave Spring population appears to have been extirpated; however, a new population was successfully reestablished at Pryor Spring (Mettee and Pulliam, 1986) through the efforts of local landowners and state and federal biologists.

HABITAT AND BIOLOGY: Spring pygmy sunfish inhabit thick concentrations of *Myriophyllum*, coontail, and other aquatic vegetation along the margins of springs and spring runs. They are common in Moss Spring, an unshaded spring tributary of Beaverdam Creek and an area currently used for watering livestock. High densities occur in shallow, heavily vegetated margins of the spring run below a large lake on Beaverdam Creek proper. Recent sampling efforts extended the known range downstream in Beaverdam Creek to near its impounded reach within Wheeler Reservoir (P. W. Shute, 1994, personal communication). Smaller populations exist in several seepage areas and smaller tributaries to both sides of the creek. Spawning occurs from March into April, after which most adults die. Pygmy sunfishes in Alabama usually deposit their eggs in aquatic vegetation; centrarchids, on the other hand, lay eggs directly on the bottom in cleared nests. Spawning behavior, embryology, and larval development in aquariums were described by Mettee (1974).

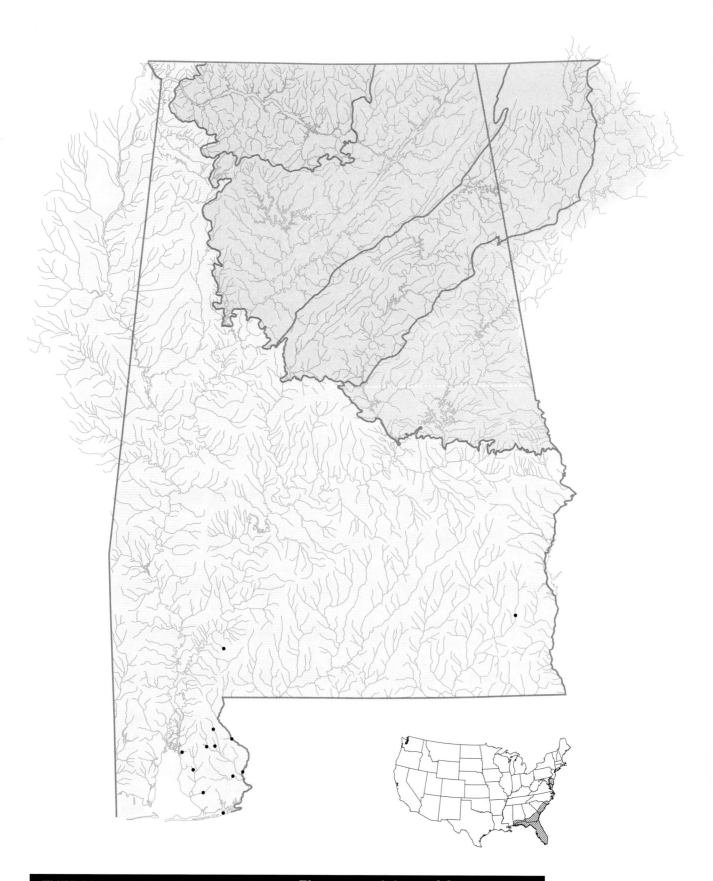

Elassoma evergladei

Jordan, 1884

ETYMOLOGY:

Elassoma—small body
evergladei—of the Ever-
glades, from which the type
specimens were collected

Fish River tributary, Baldwin County, 19 August 1992, 0.7 in (18 mm) SL male, GSA 4309

CHARACTERISTICS: The Everglades pygmy sunfish is distinguished from the other ***Elassoma*** species in Alabama by the embedded scales on the top of its head. Other characteristics include dark lips, four dorsal spines, and 23 to 32 lateral scales (no lateral line). The shoulder region lacks the two or three dark spots found on banded pygmy sunfish. Breeding males have a charcoal body with six to eight thin, iridescent blue vertical bars. Females are generally brown on the back, mottled brown and white along the sides, and cream to white on the venter; their fins are mostly clear with small, scattered brown spots. The crescent-shaped area behind and beneath the eye varies from gold to iridescent blue, depending on light reflection and possibly the mood of the fish. See Jordan (1884a) for original description.

ADULT SIZE: 1 to 1.25 in (25 to 32 mm)

DISTRIBUTION: *Elassoma evergladei* reaches its western range limit in tributaries to Mobile Bay and the Perdido River system. Its singular occurrence in the Choctawhatchee River drainage and apparent absence in Alabama sections of the Conecuh and Chattahoochee river drainages is probably due in part to inadequate sampling of its preferred habitats. The isolated record from Wallers Creek in Monroe County could be the result of a bait bucket introduction, but we doubt it. One or more Alabama-Conecuh interdrainage connections and faunal exchanges seem more plausible, given the fact that we have collected eight Mobile basin species (five cyprinids, one sucker, and two darters) in several Conecuh River tributaries scattered across Escambia, Conecuh, and Butler counties.

HABITAT AND BIOLOGY: Everglades pygmy sunfishes occur in aquatic vegetation along the margins of low-gradient streams, overflow pools, and swamps usually characterized by little or no current and soft silt and mud substrates. Spawning occurs in March and April. Pygmy sunfishes in Alabama usually deposit their eggs in aquatic vegetation, whereas centrarchids lay their eggs directly on the bottom of their habitat in cleared nests. Spawning behavior, embryology, and larval development in aquariums were described by Mettee (1974).

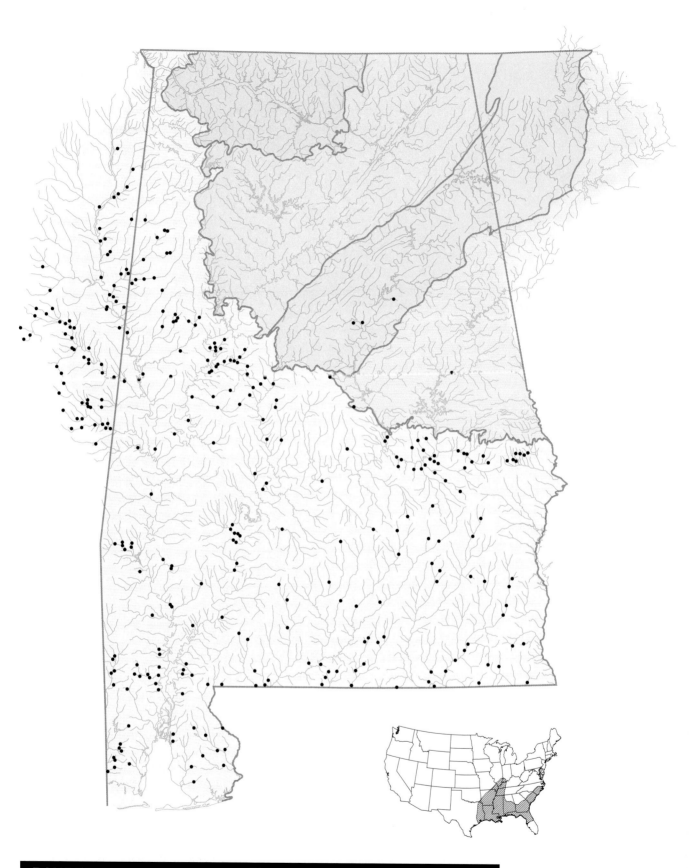

BANDED PYGMY SUNFISH *Elassoma zonatum* **311 STATIONS**

Elassoma zonatum

Jordan, 1877

ETYMOLOGY:

Elassoma—small body

zonatum—banded

Snake Creek, Russell County, 7 April 1993, 1.0 in (25 mm) SL male, GSA 4410

CHARACTERISTICS: *Elassoma zonatum* is the largest pygmy sunfish in Alabama. Males typically have nine to 11 dark vertical bars separated by narrow, pale yellow spaces along their sides. Fins are generally dark with scattered small light spots. Body colors on males intensify during the spawning season, when the fins and body exhibit flecks of iridescent blue. Females are generally brown on the back, mottled brown and cream on the sides, and cream to white on the venter. Their fins are clear, occasionally with scattered small brown spots. Males, and to a lesser extent females, have two or three prominent black spots in the shoulder region on either side of the body. The dorsal fin has four to five spines. Lateral scales number 31 to 36; a lateral line is absent. See Jordan (1877b) for original description.

ADULT SIZE: 1 to 1.5 in (25 to 38 mm)

DISTRIBUTION: Banded pygmy sunfish are more widespread in Alabama below the Fall Line, although a few scattered records do exist above the Fall Line in both the Coosa and Tallapoosa rivers.

HABITAT AND BIOLOGY: Like other members in the family Elassomatidae, this species inhabits swamps and backwater areas of moderate to small streams. These environments have little, if any, current; abundant concentrations of aquatic vegetation and mud, silt, and sand substrates. Spawning occurs in March and April. Spawning behavior, embryology, and larval development in aquariums are described by Mettee (1974) and Walsh and Burr (1984). Both studies note that banded pygmy sunfishes, like other *Elassoma* species, deposit their eggs in aquatic vegetation rather than in cleared nests on the bottom of their habitat, as the centrarchids do. Aquarium-kept individuals readily feed on commercially prepared foods. Small crustaceans, mollusks, and aquatic insect larvae comprise their natural diet (Walsh and Burr, 1984). Banded pygmy sunfishes live for one to two years. Most *Elassoma* species are solitary except in the spring, when they congregate to spawn in aquatic vegetation.

SUNFISHES

Centrarchidae

Centrarchids are the most popular warm-water game fishes in Alabama. The five bass species (genus **Micropterus**), 11 sunfish species (**Ambloplites** and **Lepomis**), and the black and white crappies (**Pomoxis**) provide food and recreation for thousands of residents and nonresidents each year. For many Alabamians, crappie fishing with live minnows or artificial lures when the dogwoods bloom in April is one of the year's most important rites. The protracted spawning seasons of several **Lepomis** species afford months of excellent angling, and all that is required to catch them is a fishing pole and a container of live redworms or crickets. In sportfishing, bass tournaments are widely followed events in which anglers compete for bragging rights, the reward of landing trophy fish, and prize money.

For Alabama the economic benefits of recreational and tournament fishing are considerable. Visiting and local anglers spend money at bait and tackle shops, motels, restaurants, gas stations, and other stores and businesses. Both recreational and tournament anglers spend millions of dollars on boats, motors, gasoline, and fishing gear. The state receives revenues from the sale of fishing licenses and from state and local taxes on fishing related products. Also, a portion of the federal taxes collected on the purchase of boats, motors, gasoline, and fishing gear is returned to the Alabama Department of Conservation and Natural Resources for its use on projects designated as Sport Fish Restoration. With these wide-ranging economic effects, sunfishes are among Alabama's most important natural resources.

Sunfishes are native to North America, and 21 of the 29 recognized species occur in the state. In recent years the distribution and abundance of at least 14 species—including the four basses, two crappies, six bream, and two rock bass—have been expanded substantially through private and governmental stocking programs. The Florida subspecies of largemouth bass, **Micropterus salmoides floridanus**, is the only non native black bass that has been widely introduced into Alabama. The rock bass and smallmouth bass are two whose native ranges are limited to the Tennessee River system in Alabama. Modest numbers of smallmouth bass have been introduced into the Black Warrior, upper Tombigbee, Cahaba, Coosa, and Tallapoosa river systems in past years, but efforts to establish naturally reproducing populations have been unsuccessful.

Sunfishes have deep, compressed bodies covered with ctenoid scales. The dorsal fin is composed of two parts, which are either continuous or separated by a slight to deep notch. The first dorsal fin contains five to 13 spines, depending upon the species; the second dorsal fin has soft, flexible rays. The anal fin always has three or more spines, followed by soft rays. Pectoral fins contain soft rays only. Located just beneath the pectoral fins, the pelvic fins have one spine and five soft rays. All centrarchids in Alabama have a complete lateral line.

Most members of this family are aggressive predators, a behavioral characteristic that explains their popularity among anglers. These fishes will lie in wait near submerged vegetation, an overhanging bank, or some other concealing structure, darting out to catch small fishes, crayfishes, or even terrestrial insects that come within their reach.

Most adult sunfishes are solitary creatures except in the spring, when they congregate to spawn. As the breeding season approaches, the males of most species become brightly colored to assist in attracting spawning partners. Some of the most beautiful color patterns found on fish in North America belong to the redbreast sunfish, *Lepomis auritus*; the orangespotted sunfish, *L. humilis*; the dollar sunfish, *L. marginatus*; and the longear sunfish, *L. megalotis*.

Spawning activities usually begin in March and April, when males of most species establish a defended territory and prepare a clean depression known as a nest or bed, fanning their fins and removing sticks and other debris with their mouths. Beds are located in shallow water, along weed beds, or around a submerged log or rock ledge. After preparing a bed, the male vigilantly keeps other males and predators at bay.

Some seasoned anglers claim that they can detect active beds of bluegill and other *Lepomis* species by smell. Male fish in high spawning condition apparently emit pheromones that evaporate into the air and create a musty odor. An angler encountering this odor knows that bedding fish, and thus exciting fishing, are close at hand. This association of a musty odor with spawning fish is not well documented in the scientific literature, but our sampling efforts in a few selected instances seem to support the idea that this relationship exists.

The actual spawning scenario is fairly similar for most sunfish species. The male entices the female into the nest with repeated displays of his brilliant colors and a series of elaborate swimming motions. When the female joins the male, they swim together for a few moments and then position themselves over the nest. The female usually lies on her side and extrudes eggs while the male remains in a vertical position alongside her and releases sperm. Once spawning is complete, the female leaves the territory. The male remains to guard the eggs and attract other potential spawning partners. Several spawns usually occur over a single nest.

Because the urge to spawn is so strong in some sunfish species, spawnings can involve a female and two males of the same species. Occasionally, males and females of different species will spawn and produce offspring possessing characteristics of one or both parents. Hybridization can occur anywhere, but it seems to be more prevalent in disturbed habitats and newly constructed lakes and reservoirs. Species that occur in Alabama and are known to hybridize include the redbreast sunfish, *Lepomis auritus*; green sunfish, *L. cyanellus*; warmouth, *L. gulosus*; orangespotted sunfish, *L. humilis*; bluegill, *L. macrochirus*; longear sunfish, *L. megalotis*; redear sunfish, *L. microlophus*; and redspotted sunfish, *L. miniatus* (Birdsong and Yerger, 1967; Childers, 1967).

1a. Anal fin with 5 or more spines . . . . go to 2
1b. Anal fin with 3 spines . . . . go to 6

2a. Dorsal spines 5 to 8 . . . . go to 3, ***Pomoxis***
2b. Dorsal spines 10 to 13 . . . . go to 4

3a. Dorsal spines usually 5 or 6; length of dorsal fin base usually less than distance from dorsal fin origin to
    posterior edge of eye . . . . white crappie, ***P. annularis***
3b. Dorsal spines usually 7 or 8; length of dorsal fin base equal to or greater than distance from dorsal fin origin
    to posterior edge of eye . . . . black crappie, ***P. nigromaculatus***

Dorsal spines of 3a, ***P. annularis***, and 3b, ***P. nigromaculatus***

4a. Anal fin with 7 to 9 spines and 14 to 16 rays . . . . flier, ***Centrarchus macropterus***
4b. Anal fin with 5 to 7 spines and 9 to 11 rays . . . . go to 5, ***Ambloplites***

5a. Dorsal fin usually with 11 or 12 rays; anal fin with 10 or 11 rays; usually 4 to 5 rows of scales on cheek below
    eye; sides with 2 to 4 dark brown vertical bands, no horizontal rows of spots; everywhere in Alabama except
    the Tennessee River drainage . . . . shadow bass, ***A. ariommus***
5b. Dorsal fin usually with 10 to 12 rays; anal fin with 9 to 11 rays; usually 7 to 8 rows of scales on cheek; dark
    spots form horizontal rows along sides, vertical bands usually absent; limited to the Tennessee River drainage
    in Alabama . . . . rock bass, ***A. rupestris***

6a. Lateral line scales 53 or more; body elongate; spiny and soft dorsal fins separated by notch . . . .
    . . . . go to 7, ***Micropterus***
6b. Lateral line scales 52 or fewer; body deep; dorsal fin continuous . . . . go to 11

Body shapes of 6a, basses (***Micropterus***), and 6b, other sunfishes

7a. Side of body colored with distinct, often wide black stripe or wide black blotches that are joined or nearly
    joined, forming a distinct lateral band . . . . go to 8
7b. Wide, distinct black stripe or blotches missing; sides may be uniformly dusky or with small, irregularly spaced
    black bars . . . . go to 9

8a. Area between spiny and soft dorsal fins deeply notched, fins barely connected; length of shortest posterior dorsal spine less than one-half length of longest spine; no tooth patch on tongue . . . .
. . . . largemouth bass, *M. salmoides*

8b. Area between spiny and soft dorsal fins not deeply notched, fins well connected; length of shortest posterior spine more than one-half length of longest spine; prominent tooth patch on tongue . . . .
. . . . spotted bass, *M. punctulatus*

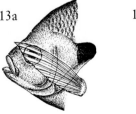

Dorsal fins of 8a, *M. salmoides,* and 8b, *M. punctulatus*

9a. Scale rows above lateral line 12 or 13; dorsal fin rays usually 13 to 15 . . . . . . smallmouth bass, *M. dolomieu*

9b. Scale rows above lateral line 9 or 10; dorsal fin rays usually 11 or 12 . . . . go to 10

10a. Upper and lower margins of caudal fin with white edges; lower sides of body with distinct rows of dark spots
. . . . redeye bass, *M. coosae*

10b. Upper and lower edges of caudal fin may be reddish brown but not white; sides of body with irregularly spaced vertical bars on greenish background . . . . "shoal bass," *M.* species

11a. Caudal fin rounded; 28 to 34 lateral line scales . . . . go to 12, *Enneacanthus*

11b. Caudal fin forked; usually 35 or more lateral line scales . . . . go to 13, *Lepomis*

12a. Scales around caudal peduncle 19 to 22; diameter of black spot on ear flap equal to or larger than eye; rows of purple or gold spots along sides . . . . banded sunfish, *E. obesus*

12b. Scales around caudal peduncle 16 to 18; diameter of black spot on ear flap smaller than eye (two-thirds or three-fourths of eye size); rows of blue or silver spots along sides . . . . bluespotted sunfish, *E. gloriosus*

13a. Pectoral fin long and pointed, with tip extending past front of eye when fin is bent forward and depressed against head . . . . go to 14

13b. Pectoral fin short and rounded, with tip not extending past front of eye . . . . go to 16

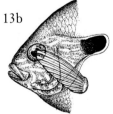

Pectoral fin shapes: 13a, pointed, and 13b, rounded

14a. Posterior portion of soft dorsal fin with black spot near base; ear flap at rear of operculum completely black
. . . . bluegill, *L. macrochirus*

14b. Soft dorsal fin lacks black spot; ear flap with light margin . . . . go to 15

15a. Gill rakers on first gill arch long, their length twice the width of base; 15 pectoral fin rays; ear flap completely black, red spot absent. . . . . orangespotted sunfish, *L. humilis*

15b. Gill rakers on first arch short and stubby; 13 or 14 pectoral fin rays; ear flap with prominent red or orange spot in life . . . . redear sunfish, *L. microlophus*

15a 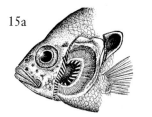 15b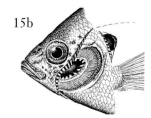

Gill rakers of 15a, *L. humilis*, and 15b, *L. microlophus*

16a. Median tooth patch on tongue; mouth large, usually extending to middle of eye; several dark lines radiating out from eye . . . . warmouth, *L. gulosus*

16b. No teeth on tongue; mouth small, barely extending to eye or only slightly beyond, but not behind it; no dark lines radiating out from eye . . . . go to 17

17a. Lateral line scales 43 or more; mouth large, its rear edge extending to beneath front of eye . . . . . go to 18

17b. Lateral line scales 42 or fewer; mouth small, its rear edge failing to reach front of eye. . . . . go to 19

18a. Gill rakers on first gill arch very long, 5 to 6 times longer than width of base; black ear flap small and bony, to near its rear margin; body elongate, maximum depth less than distance from tip of snout to dorsal fin origin; black spot at rear base of dorsal fin . . . . green sunfish, *L. cyanellus*

18b. Gill rakers on first gill arch relatively short, 1 to 2 times longer than width of base; black ear flap long and fleshy (can be bent without breaking); body deep, maximum depth equal to or greater than distance from tip of snout to dorsal fin origin; no black spot at rear of dorsal fin . . . . redbreast sunfish, *L. auritus*

18a 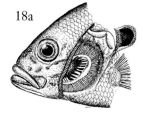 18b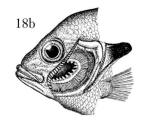

Gill rakers of 18a, *L. cyanellus,* and 18b, *L. auritus*

19a. Black ear flap bony to margin and generally inflexible; sides of body with horizontal rows of red spots. . . . . redspotted sunfish, *L. miniatus*

19b. Ear flap black and flexible, its rear margin with distinct light border; horizontal rows of black or red spots absent . . . . go to 20

20a. Pectoral fin usually with 12 rays; cheek with 3 or 4 rows of scales; ear flap with small green flecks on a black background and a light green border . . . . dollar sunfish, *L. marginatus*

20b. Pectoral fin usually with 13 or 14 rays; cheek with 5 or 6 rows of scales; ear flap with white margin and no green flecks . . . . longear sunfish, *L. megalotis*

TOMBIGBEE RIVER, CHOCTAW COUNTY

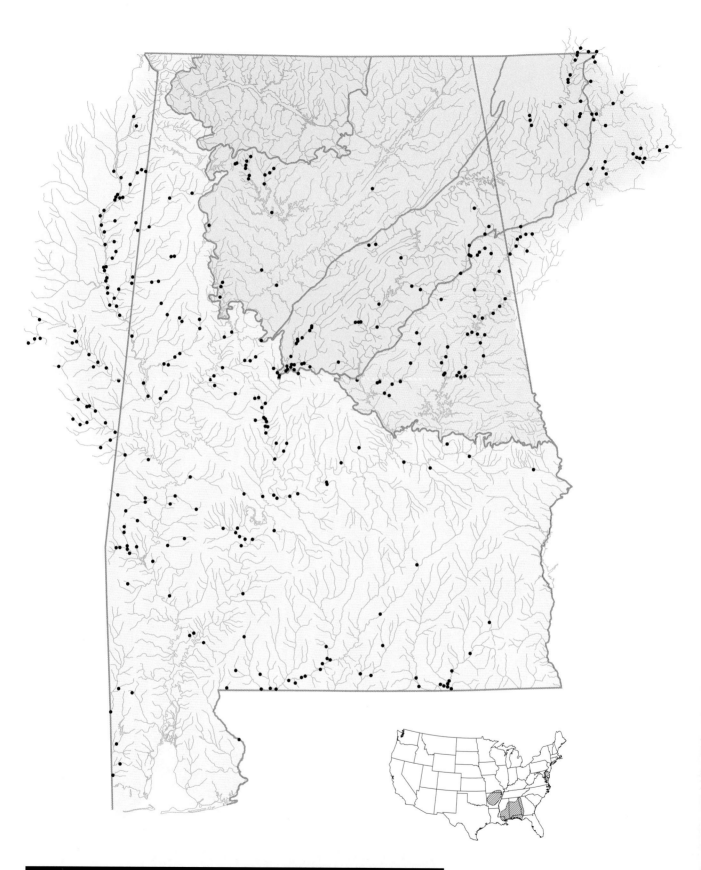

Ambloplites ariommus

Viosca, 1936

ETYMOLOGY:

Ambloplites—blunt armature

ariommus—big-eyed

Hillabee Creek, Tallapoosa County, 24 June 1992, 3.5 in (88 mm) SL male, GSA 4321

CHARACTERISTICS: The shadow bass, locally known as goggle-eye, was regarded as a subspecies of the rock bass until Cashner and Suttkus (1977) gave it full species status. Members of this species have from 36 to 42 lateral line scales. The dorsal fin has 11 spines and 11 or 12 rays; the anal fin has six to seven spines and 10 or 11 rays. The cheek has five to six rows of scales. The mouth is large, with the upper jaw extending to about the middle of the eye. Shadow bass in Alabama are usually olive to light brown, and their sides are frequently marked with two to four dark brown vertical bands and blotches. Vertical fins are clear to light yellow with black and gray mottling. The iris of the eye is red or reddish orange.

ADULT SIZE: 6 to 8 in (152 to 203 mm). Alabama has no state angling record for this species. The minimum weight limit is one pound.

DISTRIBUTION: Shadow bass have been collected in most drainages south of the Tennessee River. The lack of records from the Blackwater and Chattahoochee rivers in south Alabama is probably due to insufficient sampling of preferred habitats. Cashner (1979) includes records from both river systems in Florida. The apparent absence of shadow bass in Black Belt streams is probably the result of low streamflow and undesirable water-quality conditions during the late summer.

HABITAT AND BIOLOGY: The preferred habitat of this species includes weedbeds, undercut banks, and brush piles of medium to large slow-moving streams and rivers. Both members of the genus appear to be intolerant of increased siltation and degraded water quality. Food items include aquatic insects, crayfishes, and an occasional small fish. Our sampling efforts indicate that spawning occurs in late March and early April. Small individuals less than 2 inches (50 mm) long tend to congregate in aquatic vegetation; large individuals are solitary. Carlander (1977) reports a maximum life span of 12 to 13 years.

REMARKS: Shadow bass are excellent but often overlooked game fish because they prefer flowing streams and rivers over reservoirs. They are particularly exciting to catch with ultralight spinning gear or a fly rod.

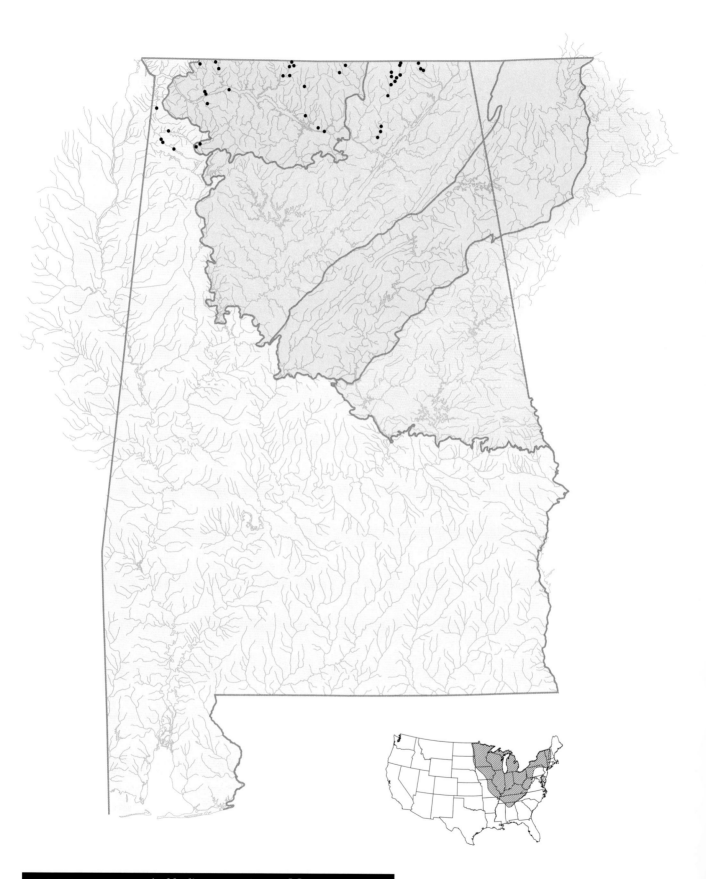

ROCK BASS   *Ambloplites rupestris*   40 STATIONS

Ambloplites rupestris

(Rafinesque, 1817)

ETYMOLOGY:

Ambloplites—blunt armature

rupestris—among the rocks

Paint Rock River, Marshall County, 19 May 1993, 6.1 in (155 mm) SL male, GSA 4475

CHARACTERISTICS: Rock bass, also called goggle-eye, can be easily distinguished from shadow bass by the well-defined rows of dark spots along the sides, particularly below the lateral line, which usually contains 37 to 46 scales. The dorsal fin has 10 to 13 spines and 10 to 12 rays. The anal fin has five to seven spines and nine to 11 rays. The mouth is large, and the upper jaw extends to below the middle of the eye. The back and sides of this species are olive to light brown with distinct horizontal rows of black spots. The vertical fins have a light yellowish background. The basal areas are mottled with brown or gray, and the distal portion has two to four dark bands. The anal fin on adult males has a distinct black margin. The iris is red to reddish orange. Venter color can vary from white to light brown or charcoal. See Rafinesque (1817b) for original description.

ADULT SIZE: 8 to 10 in (203 to 254 mm). Alabama has no state angling record for this species. The minimum weight limit is one pound.

DISTRIBUTION: Rock bass are limited to the Tennessee River system in Alabama, but they could eventually enter the upper Tombigbee River system through the Tennessee-Tombigbee Waterway.

HABITAT AND BIOLOGY: Most of our collections have come from small to medium streams with rubble and gravel substrates and slow to moderate current. Individuals linger around submerged vegetation or tree roots in pools. Pflieger (1975) reports that spawning occurs from April through June in Missouri. Although we have not observed spawning in Alabama, it probably occurs in March and April, when the shadow bass spawn. Primary food items include crayfishes, large aquatic insect larvae, and small fishes (Probst et al., 1984). Redmon and Krumholz (1978) report that rock bass have a maximum life span of eight years.

REMARKS: Rock bass are an excellent small-stream game fish, particularly when caught with ultralight spinning gear or a fly rod.

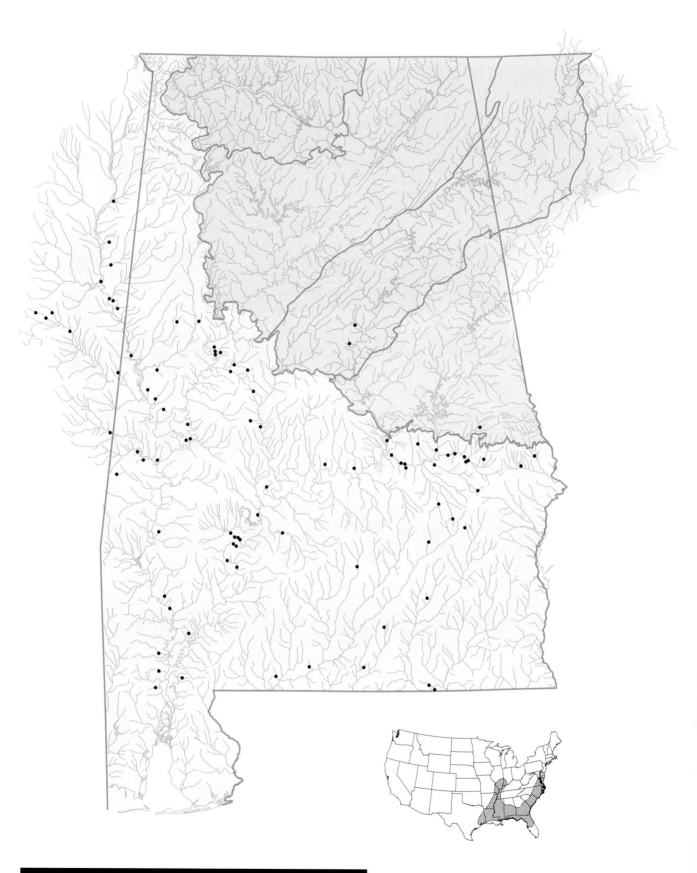

FLIER   *Centrarchus macropterus*   90 STATIONS

Centrarchus macropterus

(Lacepède, 1801)

ETYMOLOGY:

Centrarchus—anal-spined, referring to the long anal spines

macropterus—long fin

Little Escambia Creek, Escambia County, 24 March 1992, 2.6 in (66 mm) SL female, GSA 4198

CHARACTERISTICS: Fliers are small, deep-bodied, compressed sunfishes with large dorsal and anal fins that are nearly equal in size. The dorsal fin has 11 to 13 spines and 12 to 15 rays that are broadly connected to form one continuous fin. The anal fin has seven to nine spines and 14 to 16 rays. The upper jaw extends backward to the front of the eye, and the tongue has two tooth patches. Olive green on the back grades to pale yellow on the venter; the sides are marked with several rows of brown spots. In the posterior rays of the soft dorsal fin, small fliers have a prominent black spot surrounded by an orange circle. Resembling a large eye, this feature probably serves to confuse predators. The dorsal fin spot usually disappears with age. Most fins have light and dark brown bands.

ADULT SIZE: 5 to 7 in (127 to 178 mm)

DISTRIBUTION: This lowland species is distributed primarily in Coastal Plain areas on the Atlantic and Gulf coasts and in the lower Mississippi basin. Most Alabama collections are from below the Fall Line, with the exception of two collections from above the Fall Line in the Coosa River system.

HABITAT AND BIOLOGY: Fliers inhabit swamps, oxbow lakes, overflow pools, and slow-moving creeks, usually below the Fall Line. They occur only sporadically in Alabama and are rarely abundant, an observation that could be influenced by the fact that their preferred habitat is difficult to sample effectively. Fliers frequently seek cover in aquatic vegetation, around submerged tree roots, and in concentrations of rotting leaves and other plant matter. Our collections of brightly colored gravid adults indicate that spawning occurs in April in Alabama. Etnier and Starnes (1993) report similar spawning times in Tennessee and note that, since stomachs examined contained terrestrial insects, fliers appear to be surface feeders. Pflieger (1975) reports that fliers live approximately five years and become sexually mature at age one.

REMARKS: Because of their small size and sporadic occurrence, fliers have limited appeal for Alabama anglers, but they are beautiful aquarium fishes.

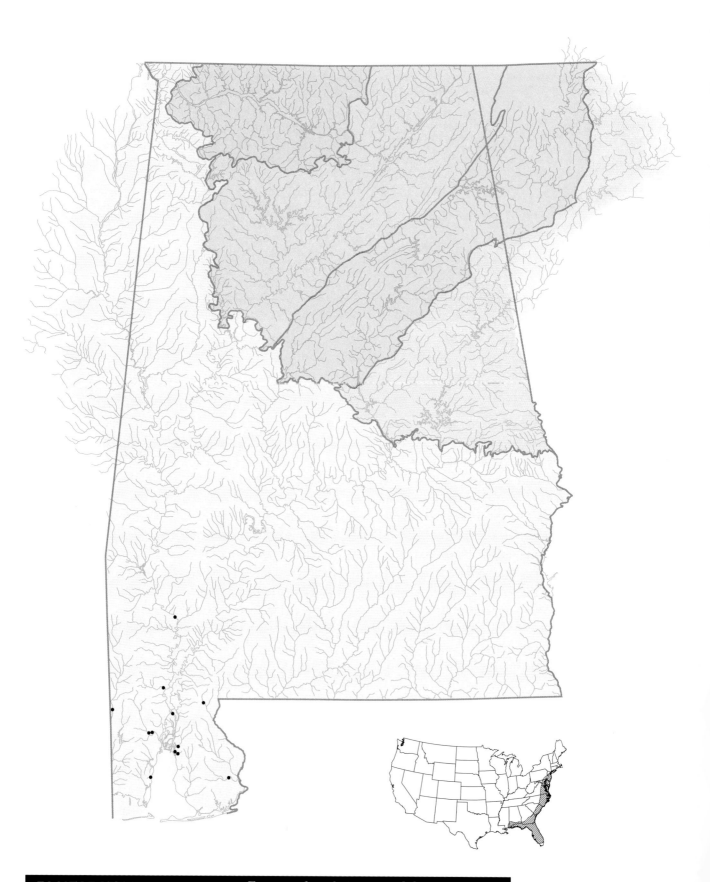

BLUESPOTTED SUNFISH *Enneacanthus gloriosus* **12 STATIONS**

Enneacanthus gloriosus
(Holbrook, 1855)

ETYMOLOGY:
Enneacanthus—nine-spined
gloriosus—handsome

Bay Minette Creek, Baldwin County, 15 June 1993, 1.4 in (36 mm) SL male, GSA 4483

CHARACTERISTICS: This small, dark sunfish is distinguished by nine or 10 dorsal spines and 10 to 13 rays. The anal fin has three spines and nine or 10 rays. Lateral line scales number from 30 to 32; 16 to 18 rows of scales surround the caudal peduncle. The maximum depth is equal to or less than half the total length. Males have rows of blue or silver spots along their dark sides; females have lighter sides with fewer spots. Small individuals have faint vertical bars that fade with age. Vertical fins exhibit scattered dark blue spots on a pale gray background. The black spot on the ear flap is about two-thirds to three-quarters the diameter of the eye. A dark bar extends downward from the eye. See Holbrook (1855a) for original description.

ADULT SIZE: 2 to 3 in (50 to 75 mm)

DISTRIBUTION: Bluespotted sunfish are not widely distributed in Alabama, but when found, they are usually abundant. Most records are from low-gradient tributaries to the Mobile Delta and Mobile Bay. The inland record for this species in Alabama is an overflow pool to the lower Tombigbee River in Washington County (Mettee et al., 1987). Bluespotted sunfish were not known from

the Escatawpa River system (Beckham, 1973) until June 1991 when Larry Johnson of the Alabama Game and Fish Division collected six individuals from an oxbow lake in western Mobile County.

HABITAT AND BIOLOGY: These beautiful little fishes occur around vegetation and submerged branches and roots in swamps, oxbow lakes, and small, slow-moving, soft-bottomed streams. These habitats are difficult to sample and do not allow underwater observation, so the life history of this species in Alabama is unknown. Breder and Redmond (1929) report that small crustaceans, aquatic insects, and small mollusks are primary food items. Spawning occurs when water temperatures reach 73°F (23°C). Eggs hatch in approximately 60 hours.

REMARKS: Beautiful body color and small size make these little sunfish an excellent candidate for the aquarium. They are somewhat hostile, so they are best kept in a single-species tank. They adapt well to both aged water and to aged water containing *Myriophyllum* or other natural vegetation, and they can be trained to eat dried or frozen foods, invertebrates, and small fishes.

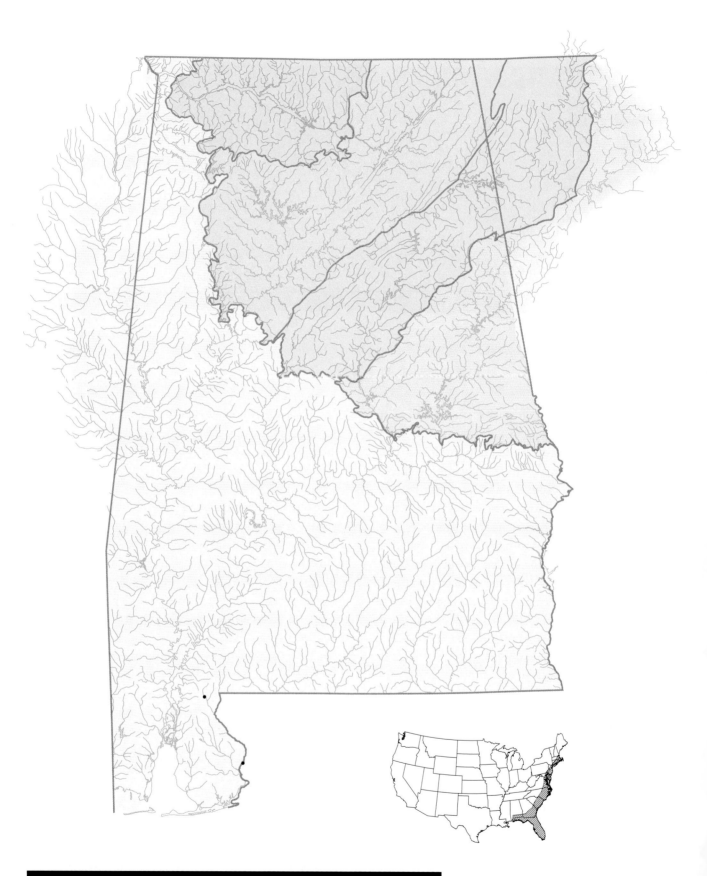

BANDED SUNFISH   *Enneacanthus obesus*   **2 STATIONS**

Enneacanthus obesus

(Girard, 1854)

ETYMOLOGY:

Enneacanthus—nine-spined

obesus—fat

Dyas Creek, Baldwin County, 12 August 1994, 1.3 in (34 mm) SL female, GSA 4630

CHARACTERISTICS: The banded sunfish has 29 to 35 lateral scales. The dorsal fin usually has eight to nine spines and 10 to 13 rays, the anal fin three spines and nine to 12 rays. The caudal peduncle has 19 to 22 rows of scales. Maximum depth is more than half the total length. The body is olive green with five to eight fairly dark vertical bars that do not disappear with age. Small, irregularly placed purple or golden spots occur on the body, fins, and head. The black spot on the ear flap is equal to or only slightly larger than eye diameter. A dark bar extends downward from the eye.

ADULT SIZE: 2 to 3 in (50 to 75 mm)

DISTRIBUTION: The banded sunfish reaches its western range limit at the Perdido River system. We have only two records in Alabama, one of which we collected from Dyas Creek, Baldwin County, in 1994. Additional sampling of swampy habitats could expand the known range of this species.

HABITAT AND BIOLOGY: When we sampled it, Dyas Creek had dark, tannin-stained water and no flow. The bottom was primarily sand overlaid with silt and detritus. Most of our specimens were collected along the margins in thick aquatic vegetation. Spawning activity has not been observed in nature, but Harrington (1956) notes that spawning can be induced if adults are maintained on 15 hours of daylight and a water temperature of around 71°F (22.7°C). Jordan and Evermann (1896) observe that bluespotted and banded sunfishes can coexist, but apparently do not interbreed.

REMARKS: The banded sunfish has a restricted range in Alabama. Individuals will adapt to aquarium life, but they perform best when maintained as a monoculture. Like the bluespotted sunfish, banded sunfish feed on small crustaceans, aquatic insects, and small mollusks.

Griffin Creek, Baldwin County

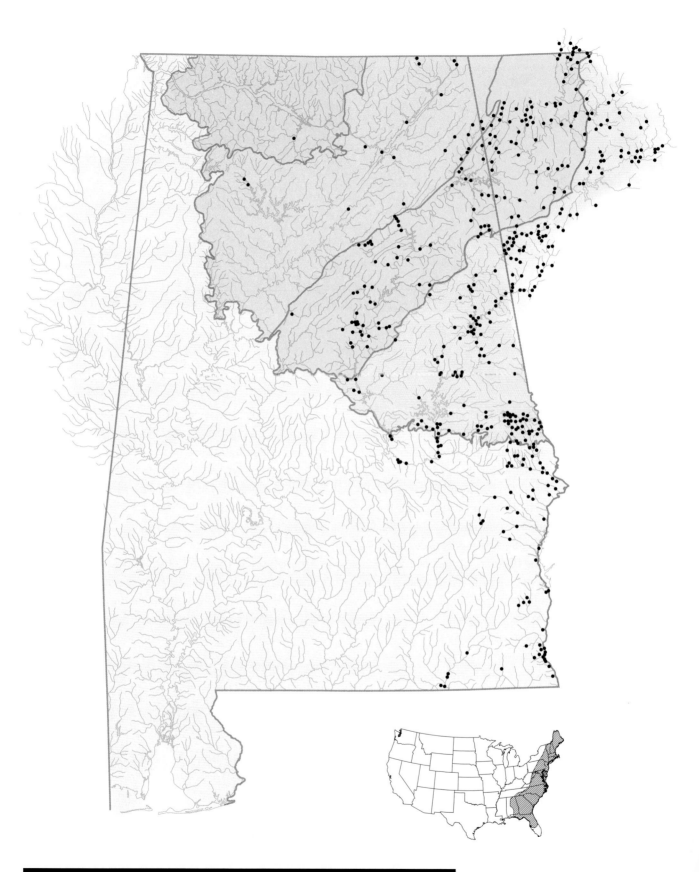

REDBREAST SUNFISH   *Lepomis auritus*   **443 STATIONS**

Lepomis auritus

(Linnaeus, 1758)

ETYMOLOGY:

Lepomis—scaled operculum

auritus—eared

Short Creek, Marshall County, 9 June 1992, 5.5 in (140 mm) SL male, GSA 4246

CHARACTERISTICS: The dorsal fin on this beautiful species contains 10 or 11 spines and 10 to 12 rays. The anal fin has three spines and nine or 10 rays. Lateral line scales number 41 to 52. Palatine teeth are present in the roof of the mouth. The cheek has six to eight rows of scales. The pectoral fin is short and does not reach the nostril when bent forward beside the head. Breeding males have a bright orangish red breast and venter. Membranes of the dorsal and anal fins have elongate, bright orange blotches. Margins of the soft dorsal and anal fins and much of the pelvic and pectoral fins are yellow. The back and head are olive green. Bright, bluish green stripes originate near the mouth and extend backward obliquely toward the base of the elongate, black ear flap. Females are less colorful, having a light orange to yellowish breast and venter.

ADULT SIZE: 6 to 8 in (152 to 203 mm). Alabama has no state angling record for this species. The minimum qualifying weight limit is 12 ounces.

DISTRIBUTION: Lee (1978c) notes that the redbreast sunfish occurs naturally along the Atlantic Coast and across southern Georgia and northern Florida to the Chattahoochee River. It may also be native to the Coosa and Tallapoosa river systems, based on its widespread and common to abundant distribution in both. Scattered collections of only a few individuals in the Black Warrior and Choctawhatchee river systems and in the Tennessee River drainage suggest an introduced status in these locations.

HABITAT AND BIOLOGY: Redbreast sunfish occur in a wide variety of habitats, from small streams to large rivers and reservoirs. Spawning occurs in North Carolina in June, when water temperatures reach 68°F (20°C) (Davis, 1972). Our collection of two brightly colored, gravid specimens in Halawakee Creek, Lee County, on 7 May 1993 indicates a slightly earlier spawning season in Alabama. Nests are constructed near flowing water and around aquatic vegetation or an underwater obstruction. Redbreast sunfish are one of only seven **Lepomis** species that do not produce sound during courtship (Gerald, 1971). Young grow to more than 2 inches at age one and live for five to six years. Sandon et al. (1975) report that young redbreasts feed on small aquatic larvae; adults consume large larvae, fishes, and mollusks.

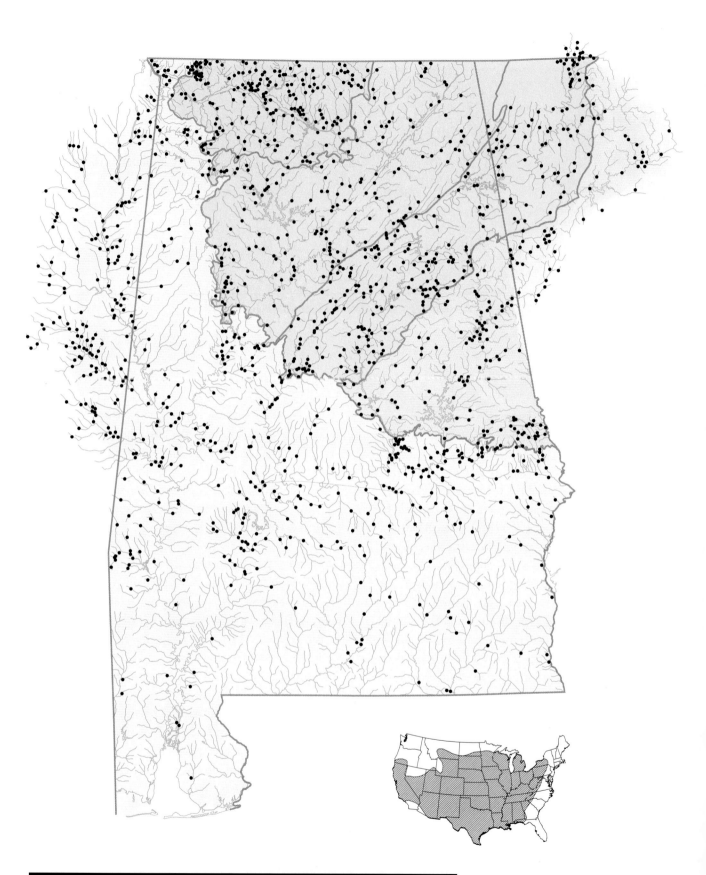

GREEN SUNFISH *Lepomis cyanellus* **1,313 STATIONS**

Lepomis cyanellus
Rafinesque, 1819

ETYMOLOGY:

Lepomis—scaled operculum

cyanellus—blue

North River, Tuscaloosa County, 3 June 1992, 3.2 in (81 mm) SL male, GSA 4452

CHARACTERISTICS: Green sunfish have 41 to 53 lateral line scales. The dorsal fin usually has 10 (rarely nine or 11) spines and 10 to 12 rays. The anal fin has three spines and eight to 11 rays. Palatine teeth are present in the roof of the mouth. The pectoral fin is short and does not reach the nostril when bent forward. The mouth is large, the upper jaw extending to near the middle of the eye. The ear flap is elongate, black, and usually inflexible to near its margin. Body color is brownish green on the back and sides with rows of small, metallic blue spots toward the head and irregularly spaced spots toward the tail. A large black spot occurs near the rear of the soft dorsal and anal fins. The edges of the pelvic, anal, caudal, and soft dorsal fins are yellow to orange, becoming much brighter during the spawning season.

ADULT SIZE: 4 to 8 in (102 to 203 mm). The state angling record (15 oz) was caught in Bayview Lake, Jefferson County, in 1985.

DISTRIBUTION: The green sunfish is native to the central United States from the Great Lakes south to the Gulf Coast. Its native range has been expanded in the United States and northern Mexico by stocking and sometimes accidental introduction into private ponds and public lakes. Limited habitat and competition with bluegill and redspotted sunfish may partly account for the sparse distribution of green sunfish across south Alabama.

HABITAT AND BIOLOGY: Green sunfishes tolerate a wide range of environmental conditions. They are widespread and often abundant in small to large streams, springs, swamps, and ponds, becoming less abundant in large rivers and reservoirs. Pflieger (1975) notes that the green sunfish is one of the first fish species to reinvade streams that go dry in late summer. Food items include insects, small fishes, and crayfishes. Spawning occurs from May through July, and sound production plays an important role in the spawning act (Gerald, 1971). Green sunfish are considered undesirable in small ponds and lakes because they grow much faster than bluegills and redear sunfish, can outcompete them for food and spawning space, and rarely reach suitable size for table fare. Redmond and Krumkolz (1978) report that four- to six-year-old green sunfish are rarely more than six inches long.

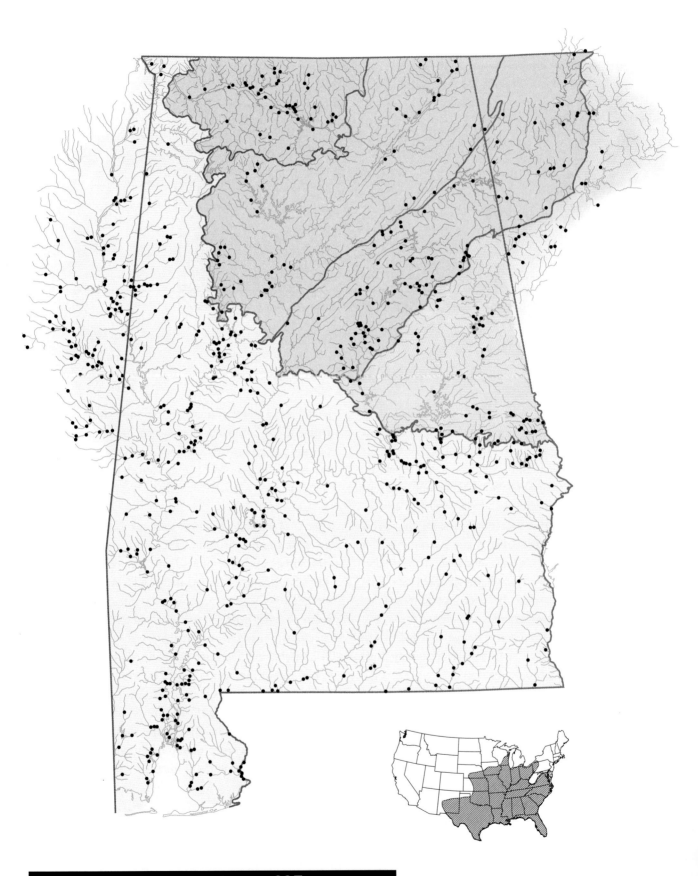

Lepomis gulosus
(Cuvier, 1829)

ETYMOLOGY:

Lepomis—scaled operculum
gulosus—large-mouthed

Panther Creek, Lauderdale County, 16 July 1992, 4.6 in (118 mm) SL female, GSA 4279

CHARACTERISTICS: The warmouth, like the shadow bass and rock bass, is known locally as goggle-eye. This species has 36 to 44 lateral line scales. The dorsal fin contains nine to 11 spines and usually 10 rays. The anal fin has three spines (rock and shadow bass have six) and nine or 10 rays. The mouth is large; the upper jaw reaches the middle of the eye or slightly beyond. A small patch of teeth on the tongue can be detected by rubbing its upper surface. One or two anterior and three or four posterior dark streaks radiate out from the eye. The back and sides are yellowish brown with dark blotches and mottling. The venter is light yellow to brown. Young individuals have a light horizontal stripe near the lateral line. Fins are light brown with mottling and banding, particularly near the rear of the soft dorsal and anal fins. See Cuvier and Valenciennes (1829) for original description.

ADULT SIZE: 6 to 8 in (152 to 203 mm). The state angling record (1 lb, 12 oz) was caught in a private pond in 1986.

DISTRIBUTION: Warmouth are found in every river system in Alabama but are abundant only in the Mobile Delta and lower sections of the Alabama and lower Tombigbee rivers.

HABITAT AND BIOLOGY: Warmouth usually occur around concentrations of aquatic vegetation and submerged roots and brush piles in medium to large streams, rivers, and reservoirs. We found them in greatest abundance in the Mobile Delta during late summer when lower river discharge and greater tidal intrusion elevated salinity values to one to 15 parts per thousand. Small freshwater shrimp of the genus *Palaemonetes* are an important food item for warmouth (Forbes, 1903) and were extremely abundant in our collections. Other prey include small crayfishes, aquatic insect larvae, and minnows. Malvestuto et al. (1983) report that anglers landed 16,666 pounds of warmouth in the Mobile Delta and the Alabama and lower Tombigbee river drainages in 1980 and 1981. A detailed study of warmouth life history in Illinois was completed by Larimore (1957). Spawning occurs in May and June near stumps or aquatic vegetation, but not over a clean, sandy bottom. Nests are guarded by males for several days until the fry hatch. Carlander (1977) finds that males of this species grow faster than females. Most individuals live six to seven years. Although they put forth a respectable fight on light tackle, warmouth are not a popular panfish because of their small size.

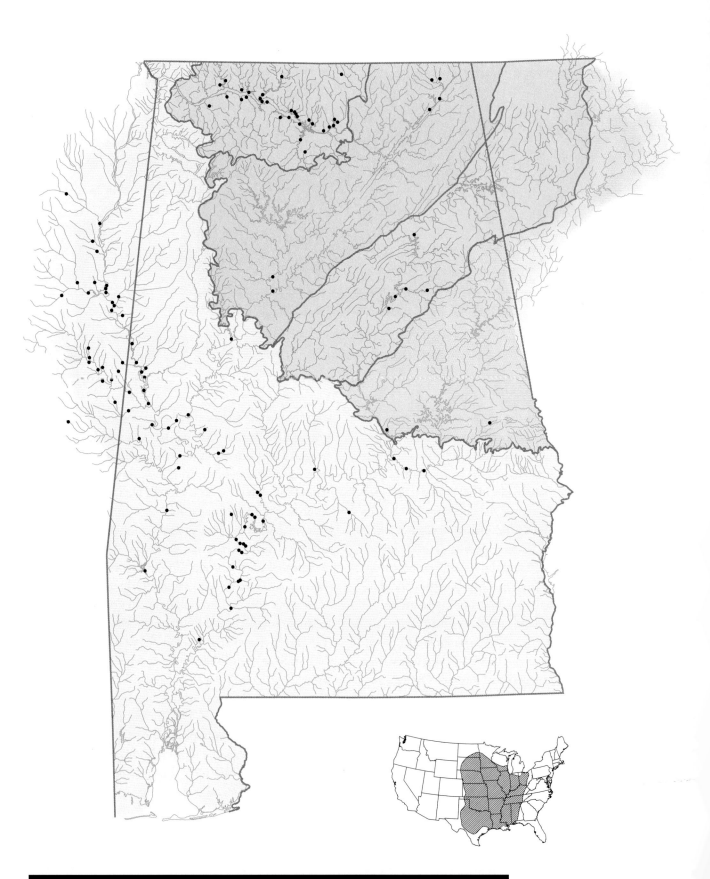

Lepomis humilis

(Girard, 1858)

ETYMOLOGY:

Lepomis—scaled operculum

humilis—humble, possibly referring to the small adult size of this species

Horsehunter Creek, Noxubee County, Mississippi, 12 May 1995, 2.0 in (50 mm) SL female, GSA 4645

CHARACTERISTICS: A relatively small but attractive species, the orangespotted sunfish has 32 to 41 lateral line scales. The dorsal fin contains nine to 11 spines and 10 or 11 rays. The anal fin has three spines and nine rays. The pectoral fin has 15 rays and it is long, its total length going fewer than 3.5 times into standard length. The mouth is fairly large, extending almost to the eye. Teeth are lacking on the tongue, but they are present on the palatine bone in the roof of the mouth. This is the only *Lepomis* species known to have a pair of sensory pores located in depressions between the eyes. The back and sides are greenish silver with scattered reddish orange spots. The venter is yellowish orange. The sides and caudal rays of breeding males assume an iridescent, bluish green color, and the vertical fins become bright yellowish orange. The black ear flap has a distinct, milky white border. See Girard (1858b) for original description.

ADULT SIZE: 3 to 4 in (75 to 102 mm)

DISTRIBUTION: Our records are predominantly from the Highland Rim region of the Tennessee River system and the Black Belt district of the Mobile basin. The apparent absence of this species from the Cahaba River system could be due to insufficient sampling of preferred habitats. This is the only sunfish species in Alabama not found in coastal rivers.

HABITAT AND BIOLOGY: *Lepomis humilis* inhabits medium to large streams and rivers characterized by little or no current and sand and silt substrates. Etnier and Starnes (1993) record this species from similar habitats in Tennessee. Our largest collections came from around concentrations of aquatic vegetation in backwater sloughs above and below Millers Ferry Lock and Dam in the Alabama River drainage. Spawning occurs over shallow nests from May to August in Alabama. Gerald (1971) indicates that sound production may be important to the spawning act. Barney and Anson (1922) note that this species feeds primarily on small crustaceans and aquatic insect larvae; Etnier and Starnes (1993) add terrestrial insects to the list. Orangespotted sunfish live for more than four years, but because of their small size, they receive little attention from anglers.

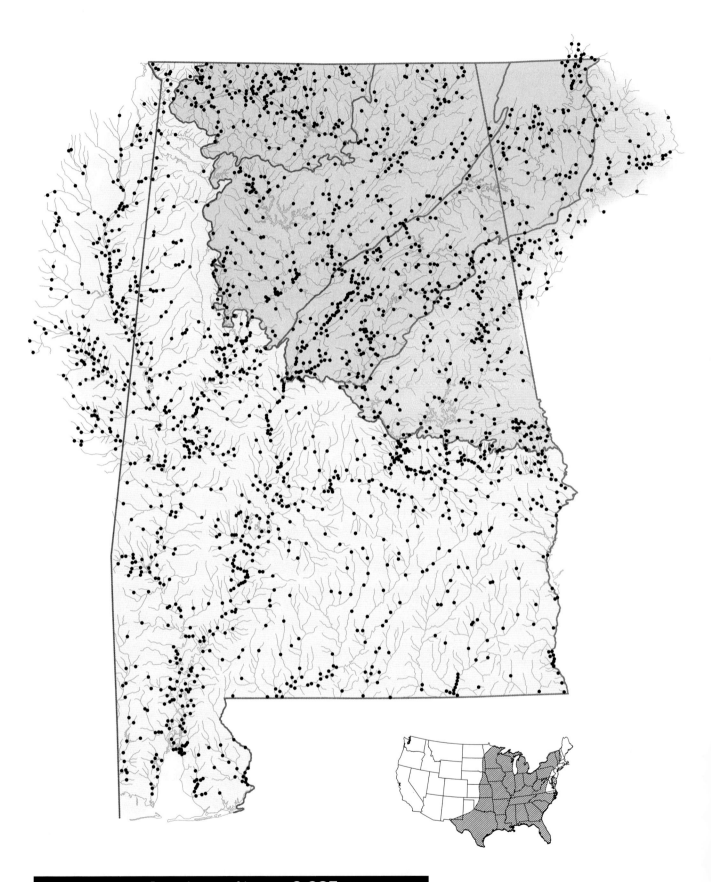

Lepomis macrochirus

Rafinesque, 1819

ETYMOLOGY:

Lepomis—scaled operculum *macrochirus*—large hand, referring to the large body size of this species

Bay Minette Creek, Baldwin County, 15 June 1993, 6.1 in (155 mm) SL male, GSA 4481

CHARACTERISTICS: The bluegill has 39 to 44 lateral line scales. Its dorsal fin contains nine to 11 spines and 10 to 12 soft rays, its anal fin three spines and 10 to 12 rays. The pectoral fin is long and pointed, extending past the eye when bent forward. The mouth is small; the upper jaw does not extend to the front of the eye. Always black, the flexible ear flap is small in juveniles, longer in adults. Juveniles and nonbreeding adults are light olive to gray on the back and sides with several evenly spaced, darker vertical bands. The venter varies from pale yellow to white. All but small individuals have a distinct black spot toward the rear of the soft dorsal fin. Breeding males darken, with the back and sides becoming purple.

ADULT SIZE: 6 to 10 in (152 to 254 mm). The state and world angling record for this species (4 lb, 12 oz) was caught at Ketona Lake, Jefferson County, in 1950.

DISTRIBUTION: Introductions into lakes and rivers have expanded this species' native range across the United States and into southern Canada and northern Mexico.

HABITAT AND BIOLOGY: Bluegills occur throughout Alabama in springs and small streams to large rivers, reservoirs, swamps, and private ponds. A protracted spawning season lasting from April into September produces millions of bluegill in Alabama each year. Nests are prepared on shallow sand and gravel bars in small to medium streams. Hundreds are constructed in shallow backwater areas of rivers and reservoirs, frequently near largemouth bass nests. Bluegill are routinely stocked in lakes and ponds as food for largemouth bass. They are an excellent game fish, especially for young anglers, and their white, flaky meat is quite tasty. Bluegills are density dependent, meaning that as their numbers increase (within limits), their relative sizes decrease. It is therefore imperative to catch and remove smaller fish to avoid overpopulation. Uncorrected overpopulation can adversely affect the age-class structure of largemouth bass populations and eventually take the lake out of balance. Bluegill live for five to six years in Alabama. The largest individuals usually come from well-managed lakes.

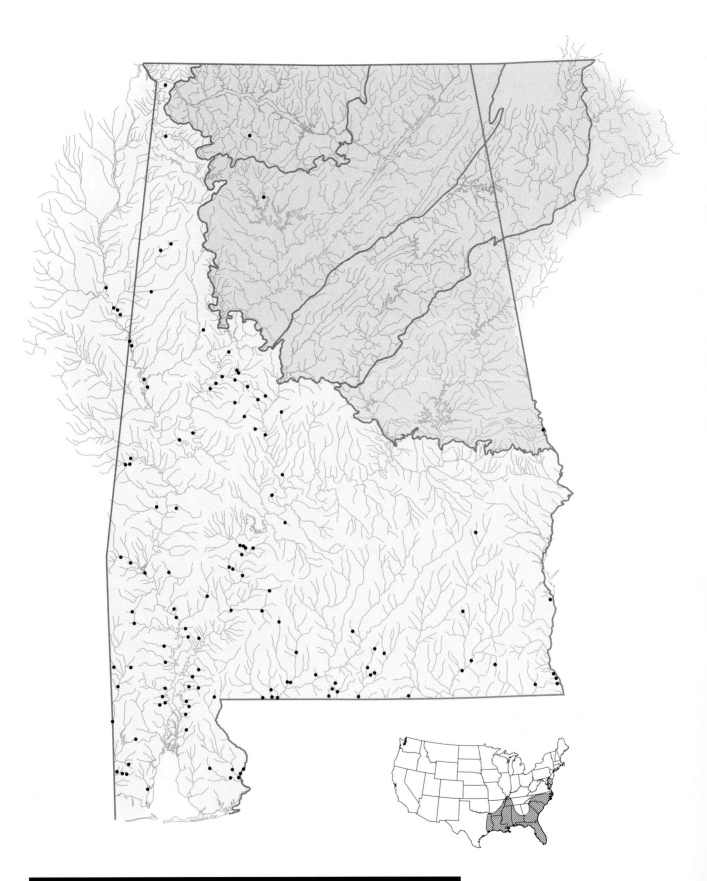

DOLLAR SUNFISH   *Lepomis marginatus*   **127 STATIONS**

Lepomis marginatus
(Holbrook, 1855)

ETYMOLOGY:

Lepomis—scaled operculum
marginatus—edged, probably referring to the marginal
banding on the ear flap

Cahaba River, Perry County, 20 June 1995, 2.8 in (71 mm) SL male, GSA 4649

CHARACTERISTICS: The dollar sunfish has a short, compressed body with 34 to 41 lateral line scales. The dorsal fin contains nine to 11 spines and 10 to 12 rays. The anal fin has three spines and nine or 10 rays. The mouth is small, barely reaching the front of the eye. The cheek has three or four rows of scales, and the short, rounded pectoral fin has 12 rays, two useful characteristics for separating this species from the longear sunfish, which typically has six rows of cheek scales and 13 or 14 pectoral rays. The black ear flap, which is elongate and angled upward, has a light green margin and is also adorned with bluish green spots and wavy stripes. Nonbreeding individuals are olive on the back with orange and brown flecks; the sides and venter are pale yellow to white. Vertical fins are light yellow to gray. Breeding males have a yellowish body and bright golden orange venter covered with iridescent blue scales. The head is covered with longitudinal bluish vermiculations. Vertical fins become much darker overall and develop a broad band of yel-

lowish orange at their bases. See Holbrook (1855b) for original description.

ADULT SIZE: 4 to 5 in (102 to 127 mm)

DISTRIBUTION: The dollar sunfish is distributed primarily below the Fall Line in Alabama. Scattered records occur in the Tennessee River drainage and the Black Warrior River system above the Fall Line.

HABITAT AND BIOLOGY: Collection sites for this lowland species include small to large streams, rivers, reservoirs, and swamps. Spawning occurs from April into August in Alabama. Growth is fairly slow. Individuals in North Carolina are sexually mature at age two and have a life span of six years (Lee and Burr, 1985). Food items of dollar sunfish in Tennessee (Etnier and Starnes, 1993) include detritus, filamentous algae, and terrestrial insects. Dollar sunfish are of little interest to anglers because of their sporadic distribution and relatively small adult size.

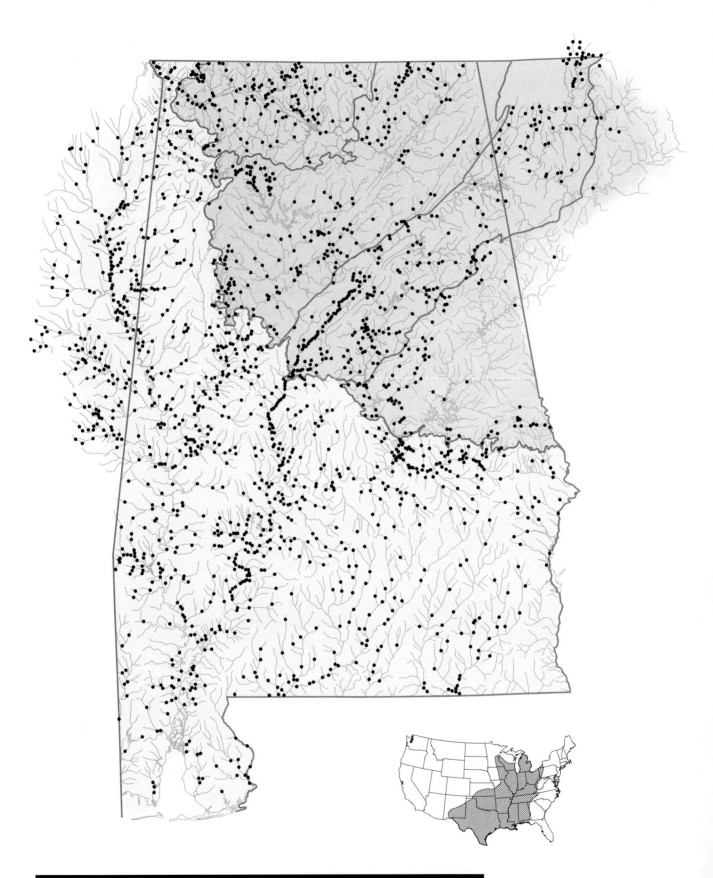

LONGEAR SUNFISH   *Lepomis megalotis*   1,766 STATIONS

Lepomis megalotis

(Rafinesque, 1820)

ETYMOLOGY:

Lepomis—scaled operculum
megalotis—large ear, referring to the long ear flap

North River, Tuscaloosa County, 3 June 1992, 4.7 in (120 mm) SL male, GSA 4452

CHARACTERISTICS: These beautiful small sunfishes have 36 to 43 lateral line scales. The dorsal fin contains 10 to 12 spines and 10 to 12 rays. The anal fin has three spines and nine or 10 rays. The mouth is small, with the upper jaw failing to reach the front of the eye. Teeth are lacking on the palatine bone. The short, rounded pectoral fin has 13 to 14 rays and does not reach the nostril when bent forward. The cheek has five to six rows of scales. The ear flap is elongate, especially on breeding males, and has a light margin. The back and sides are usually olive to brown, becoming yellowish orange on the venter. Breeding males have numerous metallic blue spots on the back and sides and wavy blue longitudinal lines on the head. The venter becomes brassy orange, as do the interradial membranes on all vertical fins.

ADULT SIZE: 5 to 7 in (127 to 178 mm). The state angling record (8 oz) was caught in the Yellow River in Covington County in 1990.

DISTRIBUTION: The longear sunfish is distributed throughout most of Alabama. Its apparent absence in the Blackwater River system is probably due to insufficient sampling. Fewer records in the Chattahoochee and upper Tallapoosa river systems could be the result of competition with the redbreast sunfish, **Lepomis auritus**.

HABITAT AND BIOLOGY: Longear sunfish are common in small to moderate flowing streams, rivers, reservoirs, and oxbow lakes. Spawning usually extends from March into August in Alabama. Berra and Gunning (1970) note that longears have a fairly small home range. Small groups of fish congregate and establish pods of nests on sand and gravel shoals and where streams enter reservoirs. Carlander (1977) reports that longear females may produce as many as 4,000 eggs. Males usually guard the nest and fan the eggs to remove silt and other debris until the larvae hatch. Applegate et al. (1967) have observed small longears feeding on aquatic insects, fish eggs, and bryozoans, while large fish consume terrestrial insects. Tennessee specimens grow faster in reservoirs than in streams and live for up to six years (Etnier and Starnes, 1993). The longear sunfish is an excellent game fish on light tackle in medium to large flowing streams.

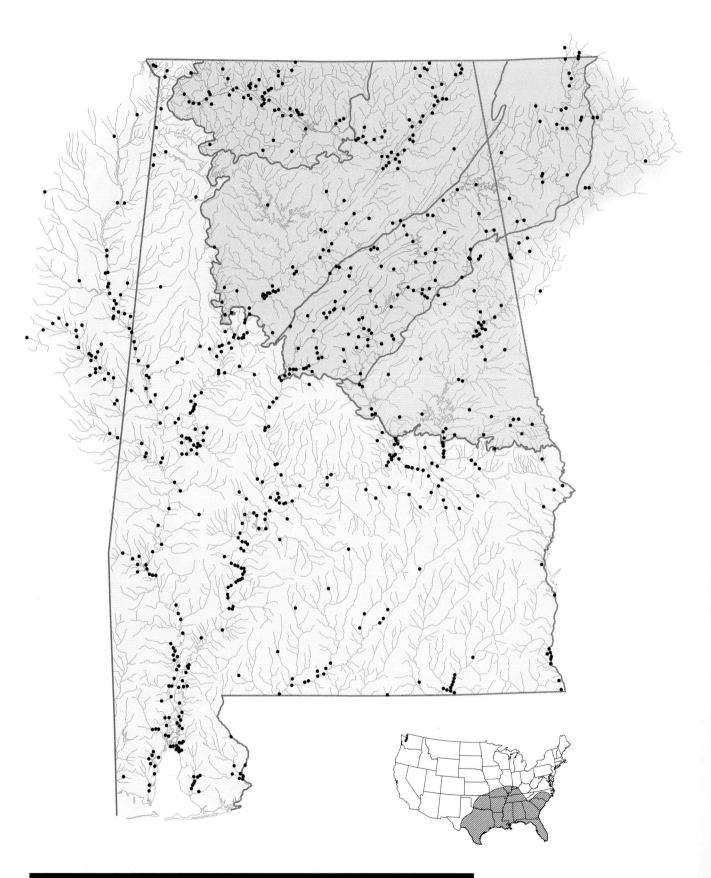

Lepomis microlophus

(Günther, 1859)

ETYMOLOGY:

Lepomis—scaled operculum

microlophus—small nape

Cypress Creek, Lauderdale County, 16 July 1992, 6.2 in (157 mm) SL male, GSA 4282

CHARACTERISTICS: Locally known as shellcracker, redear sunfishes are one of Alabama's least colorful but most sought after sunfishes. The back on this species is light green to brown with scattered darker spots. The light gray to silver sides have 34 to 43 lateral line scales. Lower surfaces of the head and venter are light yellow to white. Sides of the head are mottled with brown to dark orange spots. The dorsal fin is light gray with nine to 11 spines and 10 to 12 rays. The light yellow to white anal fin has three spines and 12 to 14 rays. The pectoral fin has 13 or 14 rays and it is long and pointed, its end reaching past the nostril when bent forward. The common name of this species is derived from the characteristic red or orange spot at the rear of the opercular flap.

ADULT SIZE: 8 to 11 in (203 to 279 mm). The state angling record (4 lb, 4 oz) was caught at Chattahoochee State Park in 1962.

DISTRIBUTION: Redear sunfish occur across all of Alabama, but they are much more abundant in the southern half of the state. They can apparently withstand salinities of up to 15 to 20 parts per thousand, which may account for the fact that they far outnumber bluegills in the lower reaches of the Mobile Delta and at the head of Mobile Bay.

HABITAT AND BIOLOGY: This species occurs in moderate to large streams, rivers, reservoirs, lakes, swamps, and other standing-water habitats. Spawning occurs from late April to early June. Males construct and defend nests during spawning and until the larvae hatch. Gerald (1971) notes that redear sunfish produce grunting noises during courtship. In his study of trophic specialization in sunfishes, Lauder (1983) describes the extensive molar surfaces on the pharyngeal arches of *Lepomis microlophus* and the associated musculature that enables the fish to crack mollusk shells (hence the local name shellcracker). Redear sunfish are usually stocked in small ponds and lakes with bluegills and largemouth bass. They grow quite well in these environments, and because they feed on mollusks and benthic aquatic insect larvae (Etnier and Starnes, 1993), they do not compete with bluegills. Bedding redear sunfish provide tremendous action on light tackle with live redworms or crickets. Carlander (1977) reports that individuals live for six years.

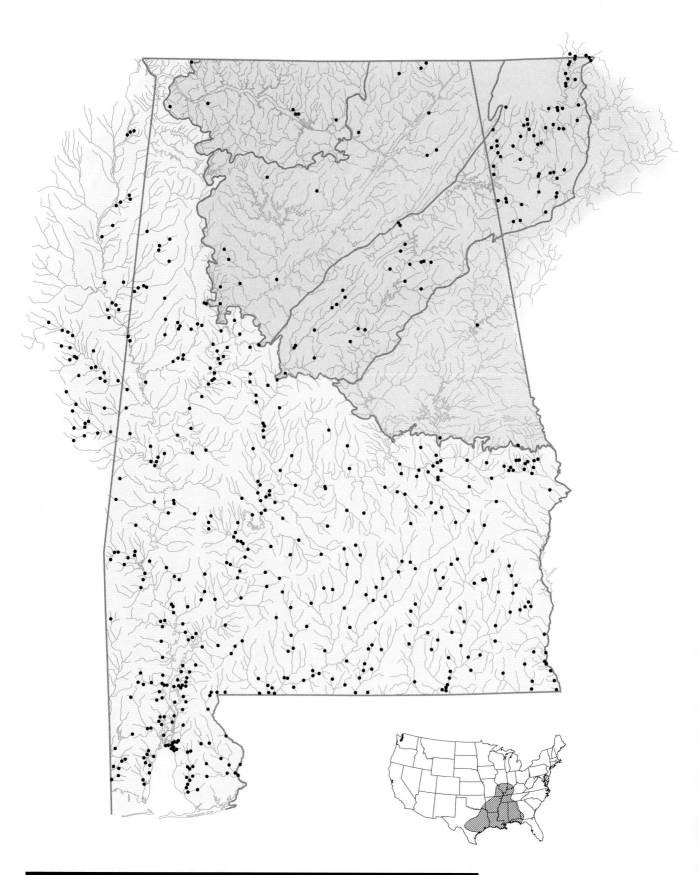

Lepomis miniatus
Jordan, 1877

ETYMOLOGY:
Lepomis—scaled operculum
miniatus—red

Little Cahaba River, Shelby County, 18 May 1994, 3.7 in (94 mm) SL male, GSA 4745

CHARACTERISTICS: Bailey et al., (1954) recognized two subspecies of spotted sunfishes (locally known as stumpknockers): an eastern form, ***Lepomis punctatus punctatus***, with black spots along its sides; and a western form, ***L. p. miniatus***, with orange spots. Intergrades between the two subspecies were noted to occur between the Perdido and Apalachicola systems and also in the upper Coosa River system in Georgia. As a result of his study on meristics, morphometrics, and distribution of the ***L. punctatus*** complex, Warren (1992) chose to elevate both subspecies to species. We accept his recommendation and include the following characteristics for the spotted sunfish. The body has 35 to 43 lateral line scales. The dorsal fin contains 10 or 11 spines and 10 to 12 rays. The anal fin has three spines and 10 or 11 rays. The short, rounded pectoral fin does not reach the nostril when bent forward along the head. The mouth is small, with the upper jaw not reaching the front of the eye. Palatine bones lack teeth. The back is olive to brown, the sides are pale olive with scattered bluish highlights, and the venter is light yellow. Breeding males develop beautiful orange spots along the sides and venter, and their vertical fins change from light gray to dark brown. Distal edges of the dorsal and anal fins become lemon yellow, and the caudal fin becomes a yellowish orange. See Jordan (1877b) for original description.

ADULT SIZE: 6 to 8 in (152 to 203 mm). No state angling record exists for this species.

DISTRIBUTION: Spotted sunfish occur throughout the Tennessee River drainage in Alabama and in most of the Mobile basin. Intergrades of ***L. miniatus*** and ***L. punctatus*** inhabit the upper Coosa River drainage in Georgia and coastal drainages from the Perdido eastward.

HABITAT AND BIOLOGY: Spotted sunfish live in rivers, reservoirs, lowland streams, swamps, and oxbow lakes, but they are most abundant in the Mobile Delta. Spawning occurs from May through July. Gerald (1971) notes that spotted sunfish produce grunting sounds as part of spawning behavior. Spotted sunfish may hybridize with bluegills (Childers, 1967). McLane (1950) reports that spotted sunfish feed almost exclusively on aquatic insect larvae, primarily midges.

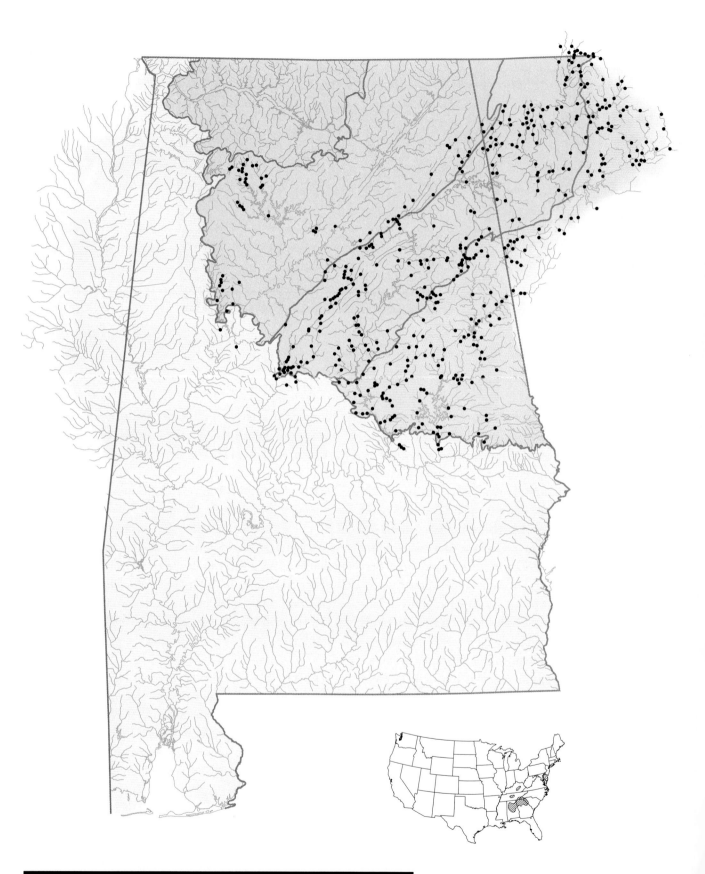

REDEYE BASS *Micropterus coosae* **482 STATIONS**

Micropterus coosae

Hubbs and Bailey, 1940

ETYMOLOGY:

Micropterus—small fin, name derived from an anomalous torn fin on the type specimen

coosae—Coosa River, the species' type locality

Turkey Creek, Jefferson County, 9 March 1993, 8.1 in (205 mm) SL male, GSA 4367

CHARACTERISTICS: The redeye or Coosa bass is an elongate, slender fish with a large mouth that extends to or slightly behind the rear margin of the eye. The dorsal fin contains nine to 11 (usually 10) spines and 11 to 13 (usually 12) rays, and the area between the two is only slightly notched. The anal fin contains three spines and nine to 11 (usually 10) rays. The complete lateral line has from 63 to 74 scales. Scales above the lateral line number 12 or 13. A small tooth patch is present on the tongue. The back and sides are generally olive to brown with darker brown mottling. Adults have several horizontal rows of dark spots on the lower sides and venter. Breeding males have a light bluish green color on the lower head and throat. On juveniles, the sides of the body usually have 10 to 12 dark blotches that do not join to form a lateral stripe. The upper and lower margins of the caudal fin are edged in white, a useful feature for separating redeye bass from both smallmouth bass and "shoal bass."

ADULT SIZE: 14 to 17 in (356 to 432 mm). The state angling record (2 lb, 11 oz) was caught in the upper Tallapoosa River in 1989.

DISTRIBUTION: Endemic to the Mobile basin, redeye bass are distributed above the Fall Line in the Coosa and Tallapoosa river systems. Lack of records from sections of the Sipsey, Mulberry, and Locust forks and upper Black Warrior River could be due to habitat disruption in the Birmingham area. Tennessee and Kentucky populations shown on the facing U.S. map are introduced.

HABITAT AND BIOLOGY: The redeye inhabits small to medium-sized upland streams and only rarely large rivers and impoundments. It is often found in water willow (*Justicia*) or other aquatic vegetation, near a submerged stump or boulder, or along an undercut bank. Juveniles occur in shallow runs and riffles over sand and gravel substrates. Spawning occurs from April to June. Etnier and Starnes (1993) note longevity of nine to 10 years. Diet includes aquatic and terrestrial insects, crayfishes, and small fishes.

REMARKS: The type locality is Fisher Creek, Etowah County, Alabama. The redeye bass is an excellent game fish, especially when taken on ultralight spinning tackle or a fly rod.

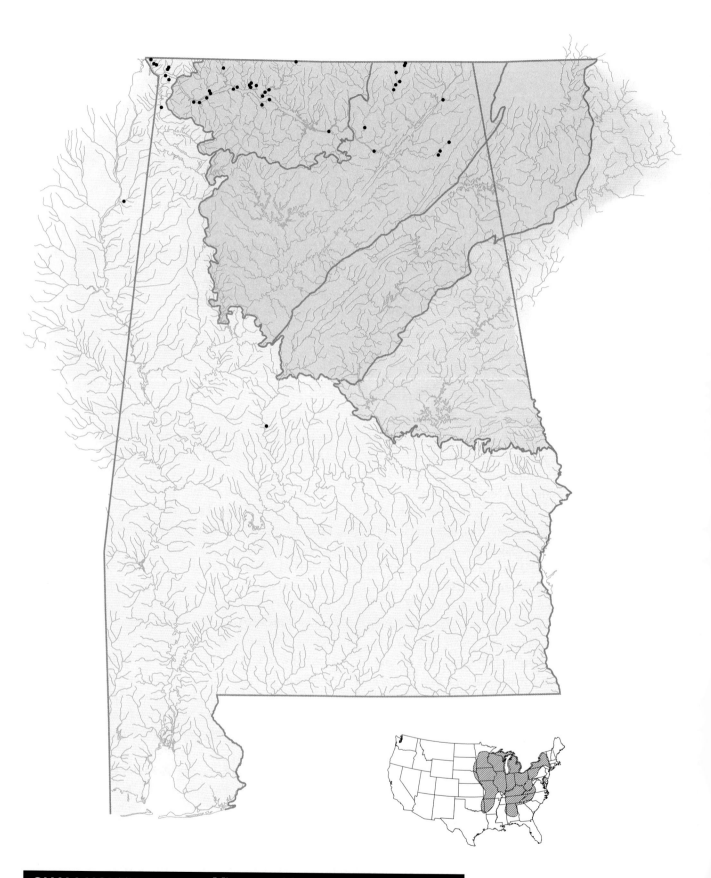

Micropterus dolomieu
Lacepède, 1802

ETYMOLOGY:
Micropterus—small fin, a name derived from an anomalous torn fin on the type specimen *dolomieu*—recognizing M. Dolomieu, a French mineralogist

Spring Creek, Lawrence County, 14 July 1992, 5.3 in (135 mm) SL male, GSA 4271

CHARACTERISTICS: The dorsal fin on the smallmouth bass is distinctly separated and contains nine to 11 spines and 13 to 15 rays. The anal fin has three spines and 10 or 11 rays. The bases of the soft dorsal and anal fins are covered with scales. The complete lateral line has 68 to 80 scales. The mouth is relatively large, with the upper jaw almost reaching the rear margin of the eye. The eye may have a reddish tint. Smallmouth bass lack the characteristic black stripe or jointed, lateral black blotches found on largemouth and spotted bass. Instead, the back and sides are bronze to olive green, with many irregularly spaced dark spots. The venter is generally white in small individuals, becoming dusky with age. Young smallmouth bass have several vertically oriented dark blotches along their sides that usually fade with age.

ADULT SIZE: 15 to 20 in (380 to 508 mm). The state angling record (10 lb, 8 oz) was caught in the Tennessee River below Wheeler Dam in 1950.

DISTRIBUTION: Smallmouth bass are native to the Tennessee River drainage. They have been unsuccessfully introduced into Lake Lewis Smith (Black Warrior River) and the Cahaba, Coosa, and upper Tombigbee rivers. The facing U.S. map shows only the native range of this species.

HABITAT AND BIOLOGY: Smallmouth bass inhabit clear, small to medium-sized streams, rivers, and reservoirs. They favor such underwater structures as rock outcrops, logs, treetops, and constructed riprap walls. Spawning usually occurs in April and May, when water temperatures reach 59° to 63°F (15° to 18°C) (Hubbs and Bailey, 1938). Smallmouth feed primarily on small fishes, crayfishes, and insects (Hubert, 1977). Carlander (1977) reports life spans of six to 14 years in southern and northern populations.

REMARKS: The smallmouth bass is a favorite game fish across much of the eastern United States. The tailwater area below Wheeler Lock and Dam is one of the premier smallmouth fishing areas in North America, and several world line-class records have been set there in recent years. Most anglers fishing the tailwaters either drift or anchor below the dam while using live bait or bouncing artificial jigs along the bottom.

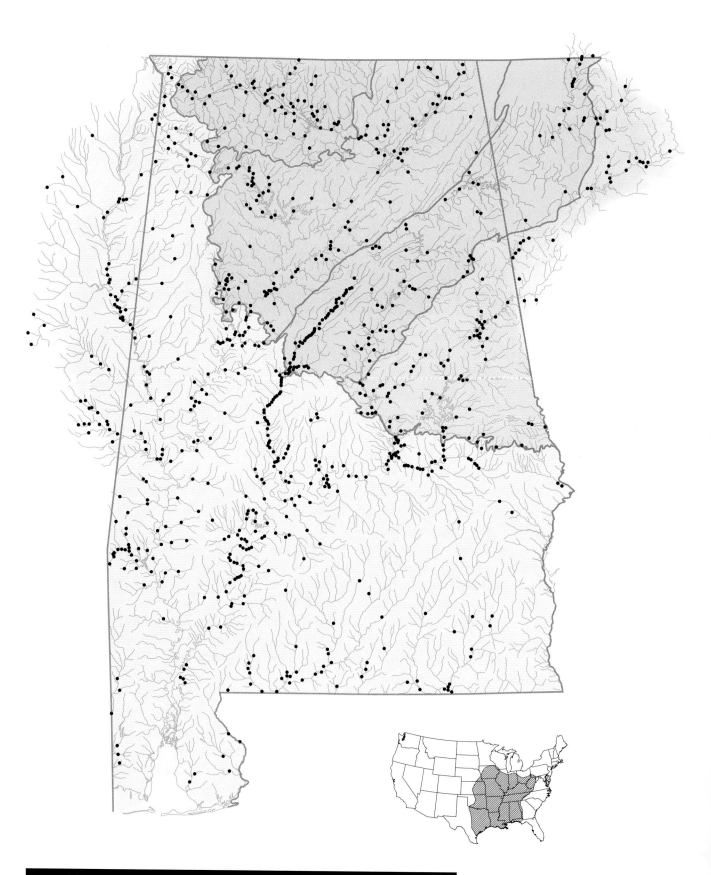

SPOTTED BASS   *Micropterus punctulatus*   **823 STATIONS**

Micropterus punctulatus
(Rafinesque, 1819)

ETYMOLOGY:

Micropterus—small fin, a name derived from an anomalous torn fin on the type specimen *punctulatus*—dotted, in reference to the spots along the lower sides of the body

Halawakee Creek, Lee County, 7 May 1993, 6.3 in (160 mm) SL, GSA 4444

CHARACTERISTICS: Also known as Kentucky bass, the spotted bass is a slender fish with black blotches along the middle of the body; with age, these join to form an irregular band. Hubbs and Bailey (1940) recognize two subspecies in Alabama. *Micropterus punctulatus punctulatus* occurs in the Tennessee River and has 58 to 71 lateral line scales and 22 to 27 scales around the caudal peduncle. *Micropterus p. henshalli* is limited to the upper Mobile basin and has 68 to 77 lateral line scales and 26 to 29 caudal peduncle scales. Intergrades are distributed below the Fall Line in the Mobile basin. Both subspecies and their intergrades have a large mouth, the upper jaw extending almost to the rear margin of the eye. A rectangular tooth patch on the tongue distinguishes this species from largemouth bass. The dorsal fin has nine to 11 (usually 10) spines and 11 to 13 rays that are broadly joined. The anal fin has three spines and nine to 11 rays. The bases of the soft dorsal and anal fins are scaled. The body is olive green on the back with scattered dark mottling. The sides below the lateral blotches are light gray; many scales have dark spots forming horizontal rows. The venter is white. Juveniles have a black spot in the middle of the caudal fin base bordered by bright orange areas. The eyes are usually reddish but not as bright as those of redeye bass.

ADULT SIZE: 12 to 17 in (300 to 432 mm). The state angling record (8 lb, 15 oz) was caught in Lake Lewis Smith in 1978.

DISTRIBUTION: Spotted bass are native throuhgout Alabama with the possible exception of the Apalachicola River Basin. The U.S. map on the facing page reflects the native and introduced range of the species, but excludes introductions on the Atlantic and Pacific coasts.

HABITAT AND BIOLOGY: Spotted bass usually occur around aquatic vegetation, submerged logs, and rock or riprap walls in small to large flowing streams, rivers, and reservoirs. Spawning occurs in April and May, often in the mouths of tributary streams. The male guards the nest until the fry have hatched. Food items include small fishes, crayfishes, and aquatic insects. Gilbert (1973) reports that *M. p. henshalli* grows faster than *M. p. punctulatus*. Life spans of southeastern populations vary from four to seven years.

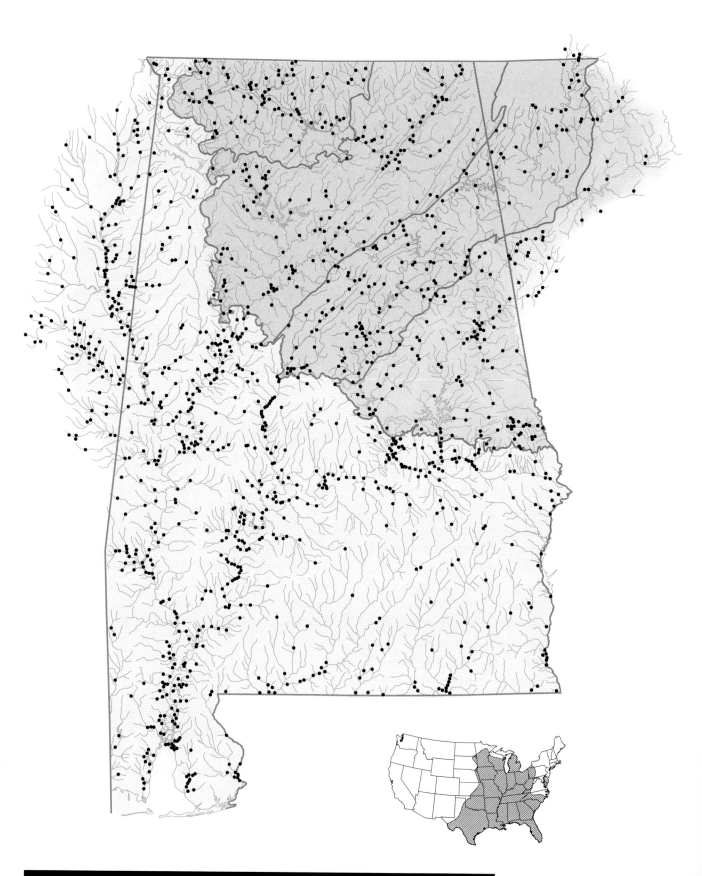

LARGEMOUTH BASS   *Micropterus salmoides*   1,284 STATIONS

Micropterus salmoides

(Lacepède, 1802)

ETYMOLOGY:

Micropterus—small fin, a name derived from an anomalous torn fin on the type specimen *salmoides*—from *salmo*, the name originally applied to this species

Bay Minette Creek, Baldwin County, 15 June 1993, 3.6 in (92 mm) SL male, GSA 4481

CHARACTERISTICS: The largemouth bass is a heavy-bodied fish with 56 to 70 lateral line scales and a large mouth, with the upper jaw usually extending past the rear margin of the eye. The area between the spiny and soft dorsal fin is deeply notched; the anterior part contains nine to 11 spines, the posterior part 12 to 14 rays. The anal fin has three spines and 10 to 12 rays. Dorsal and anal fin bases are usually scaleless or only marginally scaled. The tongue lacks teeth. The back is olive green to brown, and the greenish sides are marked with a broad black band composed of somewhat oval blotches connected by shorter blotches. The venter is white, and between it and the lateral stripe are several rows of scales with darkened centers, giving the fish a striped appearance. The dorsal, caudal, and pectoral fins are varying shades of green; pelvic and anal fins are clear to white.

ADULT SIZE: 12 to 30 in (300 to 762 mm). The state angling record (16 lb, 8 oz) was caught in Mountain View Lake, Shelby County, in 1987.

DISTRIBUTION: Native populations of *Micropterus salmoides* occur throughout the eastern United States. Extensive stockings of the Florida subspecies, *M. s. floridanus*, and the mainland subspecies, *M. s. salmoides*, have expanded the range of this species from the Atlantic to the Pacific coast and from southern Canada into Mexico. The Florida subspecies of largemouth bass has been selectively stocked in Alabama since 1971 and continues to be stocked by state and private fisheries biologists.

HABITAT AND BIOLOGY: Largemouth bass occupy almost all aquatic habitats in Alabama. Thriving in lakes, ponds, and reservoirs, they are more tolerant of turbidity and slack current than are other *Micropterus* species. Most of the large individuals landed in Alabama, including the state record, come from well-managed private lakes. Spawning occurs from April to late May, when water temperatures reach 63° to 68°F (17° to 20°C). Largemouth bass prey upon bluegills and redear sunfish in stocked ponds and upon shad, minnows, smaller sunfishes, crayfishes, and amphibians in natural habitats. Etnier and Starnes (1993) report an average life span of 10 to 12 years in Tennessee. Studies by biologists for the Alabama Game and Fish Division indicate similar ages in Alabama.

REMARKS: The largemouth bass is the primary target species of most recreational and tournament bass anglers in North America.

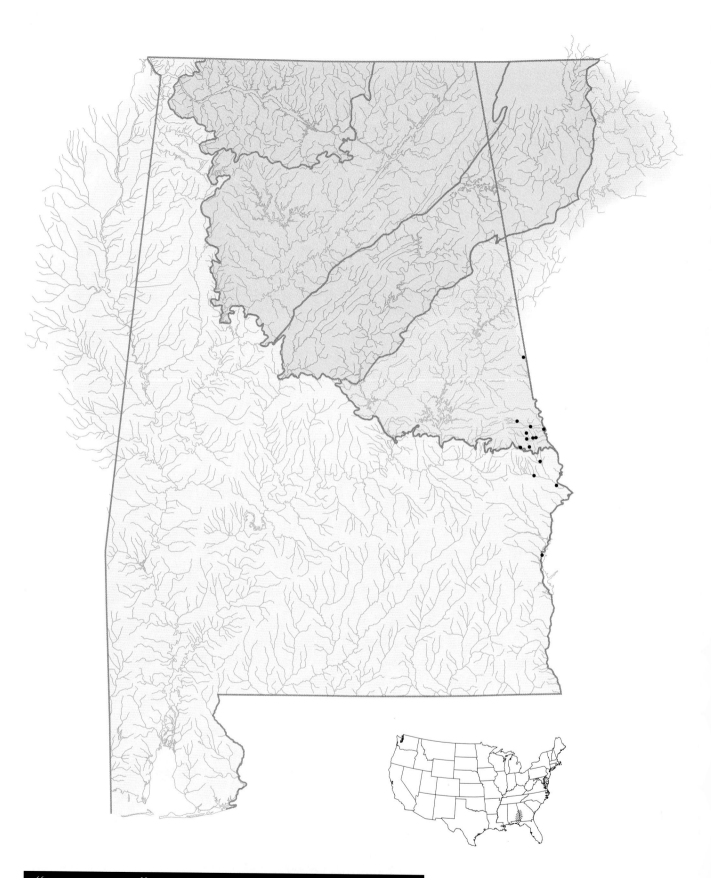

"SHOAL BASS" *Micropterus* species **14 STATIONS**

Micropterus species

ETYMOLOGY:
Micropterus—small fin, a name derived from an anomalous torn fin on the type specimen

Little Uchee Creek, Lee County, 11 July 1995, 3.3 in (85 mm) SL male, GSA 4655

CHARACTERISTICS: The undescribed "shoal bass" and the redeye bass are easily confused, even though the two have nonoverlapping ranges. Redeye bass have white margins on the upper and lower edges of the caudal fin; white fin margins are absent on "shoal bass." Whereas redeye bass have teeth on the tongue, "shoal bass" do not. Additionally, Page and Burr (1991) report that redeye bass have slightly larger scales, resulting in lower lateral line counts (64 to 73, compared to 70 to 79 in "shoal bass") and a lower number of scale rows around the caudal peduncle (26 to 30, compared to 29 to 34). Adult "shoal bass" are olive green on the back and white on the venter. Several rows of darkened scales form distinct parallel lines along the lower sides of the body. Small individuals have along their sides several vertical, dark blotches that fade somewhat with age.

ADULT SIZE: 12 to 18 in (305 to 460 mm). The state angling record (6 lb, 8 oz) was caught in Halawakee Creek, a tributary of the Chattahoochee River, in 1993.

DISTRIBUTION: "Shoal bass" are endemic to the Apalachicola River drainage in Alabama, Florida, and Georgia.

HABITAT AND BIOLOGY: "Shoal bass" inhabit shoals and riffles of small to moderate fast-flowing streams and apparently avoid reservoirs. Carlander (1977) reports a diet of aquatic insect larvae, crayfish, and small fishes. Spawning occurs from late April into May.

Flat Shoals Creek, Harris County, Georgia

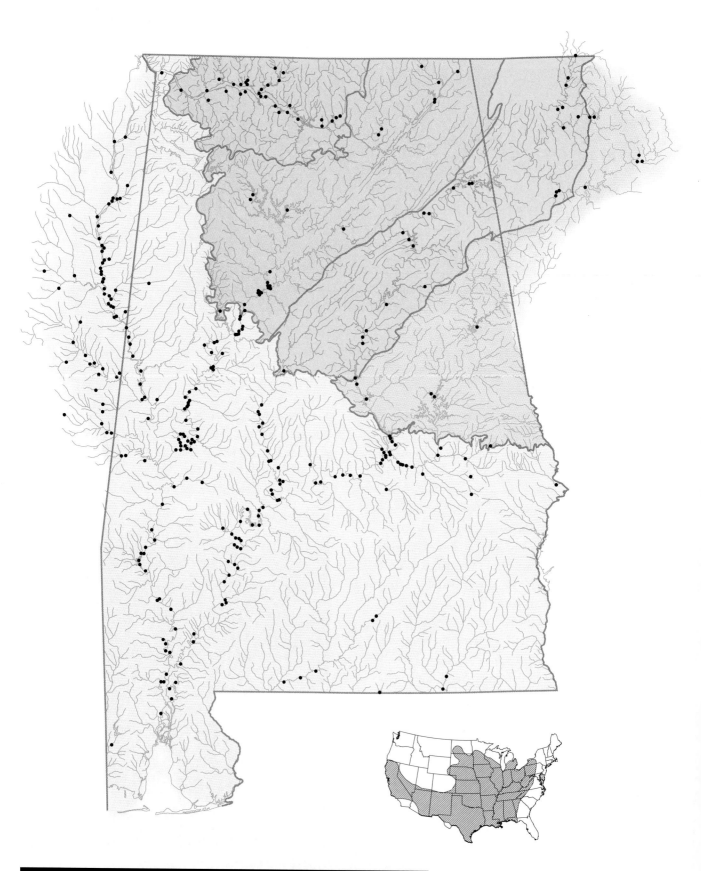

Pomoxis annularis
Rafinesque, 1818

ETYMOLOGY:

Pomoxis—sharp opercle
annularis—having rings,
probably referring to the
reticulated bars on the sides
of the body

Black Warrior River, Tuscaloosa County, 16 June 1992, 5.9 in (150 mm) SL, GSA 4262

CHARACTERISTICS: The white crappie or paper-mouth is a laterally compressed, deep-bodied fish with relatively large dorsal and anal fins. The completely joined dorsal fin contains five to six spines and 14 or 15 rays. The anal fin is slightly larger than the dorsal fin and has five to seven spines and 16 to 18 rays. The distance from the rear margin of the eye to the dorsal fin origin is usually longer than the length of the dorsal fin base. The back and upper sides are light gray to green, the lower sides are silvery, and the venter is white. Eight to 10 vertical, dark gray reticulated bars occur along the sides, with gray mottling on the venter and between the lateral bars. Dark margins occur on numerous scales in the nape and breast region, particularly during the spawning season. The dorsal, caudal, and anal fins contain several alternating light and dark bands. See Rafinesque (1818c) for original description.

ADULT SIZE: 12 to 20 in (300 to 508 mm). The state angling record (4 lb, 8 oz) was caught in Guntersville Reservoir on the Tennessee River in 1974.

DISTRIBUTION: White crappie occur naturally from the Mississippi Valley east to the Appalachian foothills and along the Gulf Coast from Florida to Texas. Individuals found east of the Mobile basin may have resulted from introductions (Smith-Vaniz, 1968). Introduction of the white crappie has expanded its native range to include most of the United States and parts of northern Mexico.

HABITAT AND BIOLOGY: White crappie live primarily in rivers and reservoirs, although small individuals occasionally enter small streams. This species seems to tolerate more turbidity than does the black crappie. Prior to spawning, adult crappie aggregate into schools, move into shallow water, and aggressively feed on threadfin shad and small minnows. During this time (usually when the dogwoods begin to bloom), anglers catch thousands of white and black crappie on live minnows and jigs around aquatic vegetation, submerged logs, and other structures. Spawning occurs from April into early June. White crappie live for nine years in Reelfoot Lake, Tennessee (Schoffman, 1965). Crappie will survive in lakes, but without proper management, populations become overcrowded, resulting in smaller fish and adversely affecting the sizes and recruitment of bluegill and largemouth bass (McHugh, 1990).

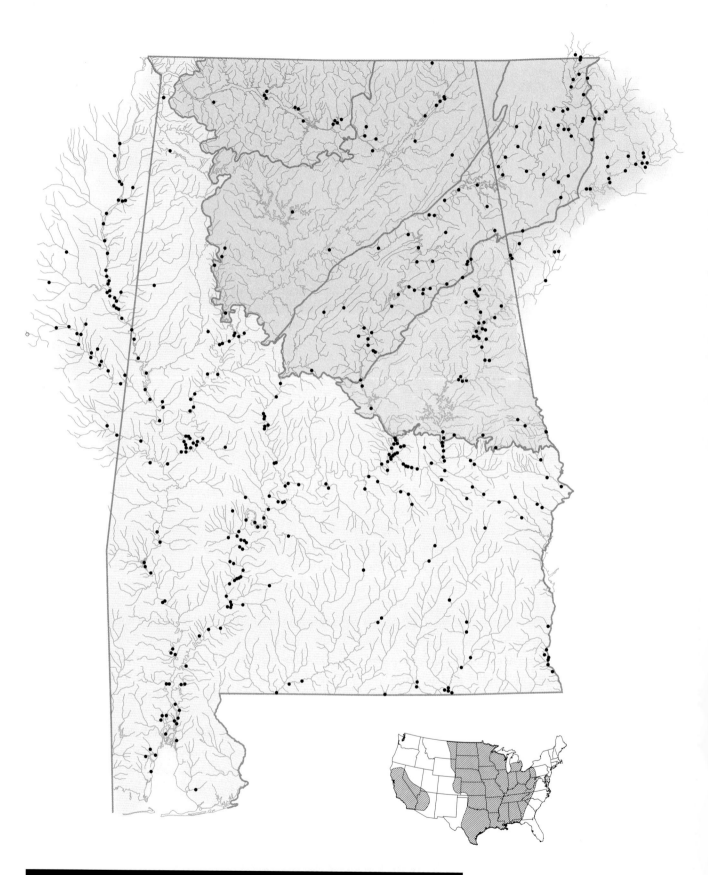

Pomoxis nigromaculatus

(Lesueur, 1829)

ETYMOLOGY:

Pomoxis—sharp opercle

nigromaculatus—black

spotted

Halawakee Creek, Lee County, 25 May 1995, 7.5 in (190 mm) SL female, GSA 4648

CHARACTERISTICS: Three characteristics easily distinguish black and white crappie. Black crappie have seven to eight dorsal spines; white crappie usually have six. The dorsal fin base on black crappie is equal to or slightly longer than the distance from the rear margin of the eye to the origin of the dorsal fin base; the dorsal fin base is shorter on white crappie. Finally, the sides of white crappie have eight to 10 vertical, dark gray reticulated bands that are lacking on black crappie. Other distinguishing characteristics of the black crappie include 35 to 41 lateral line scales, 14 to 16 dorsal rays, five to seven anal spines, and 16 to 19 rays. The back is usually light gray to light lime green. The sides and venter are lime green with a silvery sheen. Dark mottling is scattered across the body. The dorsal, caudal, and anal fins have several alternating light and dark wavy bands. See Cuvier and Valenciennes (1829) for original description.

ADULT SIZE: 12 to 18 in (300 to 460 mm). The state angling record (4 lb, 4 oz) was caught in Paint Creek on Lay Reservoir in the Coosa River system in 1984.

DISTRIBUTION: Black crappie occur naturally from the Mississippi Valley and Great Lakes southward to the Gulf Coast, including Alabama. Their apparent absence in the Escatawpa, Blackwater, and Yellow river systems could be due to insufficient sampling. Introductions have expanded the range of this species westward to the Pacific Coast and northward into Canada.

HABITAT AND BIOLOGY: *Pomoxis nigromaculatus* occurs in greatest abundance in rivers, reservoirs, and large lakes, although small individuals occasionally enter medium-sized to large streams. Black crappie seem to prefer clearer waters than do white crappie, which could account for the former species' wider distribution in the upper Coosa and Tallapoosa river systems. Before spawning, black crappie form schools and venture to feed into shallow water, where they are caught in large numbers by anglers using minnows and tiny jigs around heavy cover. Spawning occurs from April into May. Black crappie live for eight years in Reelfoot Lake, Tennessee (Schoffman, 1940).

PERCHES AND DARTERS

Percidae

The family Percidae contains about 160 species in nine genera worldwide, and is distributed from eastern North America through northern Asia and across Europe (Nelson, 1994). With over 150 species in North America, it is the second richest family of fishes on the continent, following the minnows in the family Cyprinidae (Berra, 1981). Ichthyologists collectively refer to them as darters, owing to their habit of darting along the bottoms of streams and lakes in quick wiggles and jolts. Some people call these fishes "crawly-bottoms" because they use their pelvic and caudal fins to rest on the bottom and move about in short, erratic bursts. Kuehne and Barbour (1983) term the group from Canada to Mexico American darters.

The best known members of the Percidae are the yellow perch, sauger, and walleye—all favorite game fishes. Yellow perch typically reach 1 pound with records in the range of 2 to 4 pounds. Sauger average 1 to 2 pounds and walleye usually grow to 6 to 10 pounds. All three species provide excellent sport and have firm white flesh with a delicate flavor. Good sauger and walleye fishing occurs in tailwaters below Pickwick and Wilson dams on the Tennessee River. Jigging along the bottom in winter and spring with live or artificial bait will usually yield respectable catches. Walleye occur in selected areas of the Mobile basin, but because their densities are fairly low, they are infrequently encountered by anglers.

The diet of perches and darters is varied. The yellow perch, walleye, and sauger are piscivorous as adults, consuming a variety of fish, crayfish, and larger invertebrates. Darters consume benthic organisms, primarily immature aquatic insects, microcrustaceans, arthropods, snails and small bivalves, and occasionally plant material. Many species are visual feeders that forage actively early and late in the day. The morphology of the mouth and snout allows similar species to utilize different food resources in a common habitat. Species with a blunt snout and subterminal mouth, as in the subgenus *Ulocentra*, graze the tops of stones, while those with pointed snouts and terminal mouths, as in the *Percina* subgenera *Alvordius* and *Swainia*, probe cracks and crevices in rocks and logs. Species of the subgenus *Catonotus*, with a supraterminal mouth, can feed on the undersides of rocks, while those of the subgenus *Imostoma* have larger mouths to consume large benthic invertebrates, including mollusks.

Midwater percid species are typically fusiform, tapering at both ends, with pointed snouts for feeding among gravel and rocks, and shorter fins. Benthic dwellers have a more flattened venter, a teardrop-shaped body thicker near the head, a blunt snout for grazing on the substrate, and rounded fins. Riffle species have deeper, compressed caudal peduncles, much longer fins, and pointed but short snouts. Body color and pigment patterns provide camouflage. Dark and variably intense lateral line and saddle patterns create a cryptic body outline, while tail spots mimic eyes, confusing predators. Sexual dimorphism is well developed in the darters with males generally larger and, at least in the genus *Etheostoma*, more colorful, which serves the purpose of mate recognition and selection. Kuehne and Barbour (1983) and Page (1983) document the diversity and beauty of darters in North America.

Darters and perches are characterized by an elongate body covered with ctenoid scales, a well-developed spiny first dorsal fin separated, or mostly so, from a soft second dorsal fin, and one or two anal fin spines. Darters, along with the sunfishes (family Centrarchidae), the temperate basses (family Moronidae), and the freshwater drum (family Sciaenidae), are members of the order Perciformes. Sunfishes and temperate basses have at least three anal spines compared to the darters' two. The freshwater drum has two anal spines, but the second is longer and more strongly constructed than the first. In addition, the body of the freshwater drum is extremely elevated near the head and tapers toward the tail. The body of most darters is essentially cylindrical.

There are two centers of high darter diversity in North America, one in northern Alabama and eastern Tennessee and the other in the Ouachita Mountains of western Arkansas and eastern Oklahoma. Page (1983) attributes the diversity of these centers to a specific combination of geologic and climatic factors.

The first factor concerns the geologic stability and age of the regions: both areas were beyond southern extensions of Pleistocene glaciation and northern invasions of the seas. Escaping these long-term, catastrophic events provided a favorable environment where species could diversify. The second factor is topographic diversity. Alabama, for example, is traversed by five physiographic provinces, each containing unique habitat types and hydrologic regimes providing optimum conditions for isolation and diversification of darter populations. The third factor concerns the temperate locale of both centers, enhancing their climatic stability.

Darters occupy a variety of habitats. Distributions of some species include multiple drainages, but some other species have become highly specialized, with restricted habitats such as springs or small stream systems. Some have adapted to survive in specific aquatic habitats such as stagnant, poorly oxygenated pools in coastal areas, or torrential streams in the Appalachian Mountains. Monitoring such isolated, rare, and/or specialized populations is a powerful tool for detecting change in environmental quality, especially in surface waters.

The life span of most darter species averages two to four years. Some reproduce in their first year and die soon thereafter. *Imostoma* species usually spawn from late fall through early spring, while those in the subgenus *Nothonotus* spawn from May through July. The spring-dwelling Tuscumbia darter, *Etheostoma tuscumbia,* and coldwater darter, *E. ditrema,* spawn at irregular times throughout the year.

Students of darter ecology recognize that similar spawning strategies have significant phylogenetic implications (Page, 1985). Egg buriers in the genera *Ammocrypta* and *Percina,* along with several species of *Etheostoma* in the subgenera *Etheostoma, Nothonotus, Oligocephalus,* and *Doration,* attempt to bury their adhesive eggs by making a furrow in the substrate during spawning. Egg clumpers in the subgenus *Nothonotus* usually deposit eggs between a stone and the bottom. The next most advanced group of darters are the attachers, which deposit single adhesive eggs onto rocks, logs, plants, or other substrate. Attachers include the subgenera *Ulocentra* (snubnose darters), *Ozarka,* some members of *Oligocephalus,* and *Hololepis* and *Microperca,* all of which exhibit little, if any, care of their eggs. Another reproductive behavior is egg clustering on the underside of stones, with limited male protection of the eggs as exhibited by species of *Boleosoma* and *Catonotus.* Breeding individuals are generally promiscuous, each female spawning with a host of males and generally selecting the largest and most colorful as mates.

The higher systematic relationships within the Percidae were summarized by Collette and Banarescu (1977) who propose a classification based on two major lineages: (1) the Percinae, consisting of the tribes Etheostomatini (*Ammocrypta, Etheostoma,* and *Percina*) and Percini (*Perca, Gymnocephalus,* and *Percarina*) and (2) the Luciopercinae, consisting of the tribes Luciopercini (*Stizostedion*) and Romanichthyini (*Zingel* and *Romanichthys*). Wiley (1992) recently proposed a preliminary conservative classification of the Percidae, using the techniques of phylogenetic systematics, also consisting of two subfamilies, the Percinae (*Perca*) and the Etheostomatinae (*Gymnocephalus, Stizostedion, Zingel, Romanichthys, Crystallaria, Percina,* and *Etheostoma*), agreeing with Simons' (1991) subsumation of *Ammocrypta* into *Etheostoma* and recognition of *Crystallaria.* Further, Page (1985) presents a phylogeny of North American Percidae based on reproductive behaviors, which agrees somewhat with that proposed by Wiley. As our knowledge accumulates and analytical techniques evolve, the higher phylogeny of this family will be refined.

Throughout the text we refer to subgenera within *Percina* and *Etheostoma*. The recognition of subgenera is a convenient label to attach to a group of related and similar species for discussion and analysis; it also indicates phylogenetic relationships. But such recognition is not without disagreement. Bailey and Gosline (1955) proposed the first modern classification of darter genera and subgenera, which was subsequently amended by Collette and Yerger (1962), Cole (1967), Page and Whitt (1973), Page (1974a), and Williams and Robison (1980), who diagnose additional subgenera. Page (1981) adopts a modification of the 1955 classification as amended, reorganizing some of the long-held relationships. Bailey and Etnier (1988) provide comments on the subgenera, rebut some of Page's conclusions, and refine the phylogeny according to their interpretation. We have elected to present subgeneric classifications within the key based on the historical literature, and on currently developing relationships using phylogenetic systematics.

KEY TO THE PERCHES AND DARTERS

1a. The back edge of the preopercle bone is very serrate; mouth large with the upper jaw extending to or past the anterior edge of the eye; larger fishes, adults generally more than 150 mm SL . . . . go to 2
1b. The back edge of the preopercle bone is not serrate or very weakly serrate; mouth is small with the upper jaw not extending past the anterior edge of the eye; smaller fishes, adults generally less than 150 mm SL . . . . go to 4

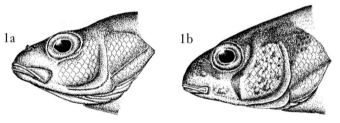

Head profile of 1a, *Perca flavescens,* and 1b, *Percina*

2a. Sides with 6 to 8 dark, vertical bars; color generally some shade of yellow; jaws and palatine bones without well-defined canine teeth; pelvic fins located very close to each other . . . . . . yellow perch, *Perca flavescens*
2b. Sides with blotches of irregular shape; color generally bronze or light gold; jaws and palatine bones with well-developed canine teeth; pelvic fins widely separated . . . . go to 3, *Stizostedion*

3a. Posterior end of the spiny dorsal fin with an obvious black blotch; membranes of spiny dorsal fin with dark streaks or blotches not formed into distinct rows . . . . walleye, *S. vitreum*
3b. Posterior end of the spiny dorsal fin without a black blotch; membranes of spiny dorsal fin with dark streaks or blotches formed into distinct, oblique rows . . . . sauger, *S. canadense*

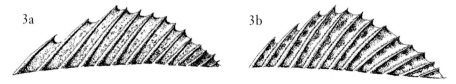

Dorsal fin pigmentation of 3a, *S. vitreum*, and 3b, *S. canadense*

4a. Breast of male (often venter of male and breast of female) with modified scales (enlarged with marginal spines); 2 anal spines; lateral line complete; head canals uninterrupted . . . . . *Percina,* go to key on page 566

4b. Breast of male without modified scales; 1 or 2 anal spines; lateral line incomplete or complete; head canals interrupted or uninterrupted . . . . go to 5

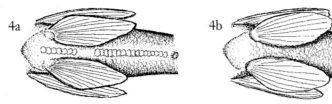

Mid-ventral scales of 4a, *Percina,* and 4b, *Etheostoma, Ammocrypta, Crystallaria*

5a. Body deeper, depth divides into standard length less than 7 times; body opaque; 1 or 2 anal spines; lateral line complete or incomplete; head canals interrupted or uninterrupted . . . . *Etheostoma,* go to key on page 569

5b. Body long and slender, depth divides into standard length at least 7 times; body clear or translucent in life with naked belly; one anal spine; lateral line complete; head canals uninterrupted . . . . go to 6

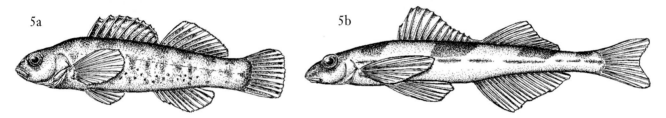

Body shape of 5a, *Etheostoma* and 5b, *Crystallaria*

6a. Caudal fin deeply forked; narrow premaxillary frenum present; dorsal rays usually 13 or 14; back with 4 large dark saddles . . . . crystal darter, *Crystallaria asprella*

6b. Caudal fin more rounded or only slightly forked; no premaxillary frenum; dorsal rays usually 10 or 11; back without dark saddles. . . . . go to 7, *Ammocrypta*

7a. Sides of body with a row of oval or rounded blotches; body scaled . . . . southern sand darter, *A. meridiana*

7b. Sides of body without a row of oval or rounded blotches; scales limited to lateral area. . . . . go to 8

8a. Dorsal and anal fins of males with a marginal and submarginal band; coastal drainages from the Perdido River east to the Choctawhatchee River. . . . . Florida sand darter, *A. bifascia*

8b. Dorsal and anal fins of males without marginal bands; submarginal band or blotches variously developed; Mobile basin and Escatawpa River drainage . . . . naked sand darter, *A. beani*

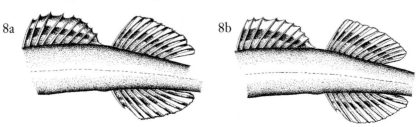

Dorsal and anal fin pigmentation of 8a, *A. bifascia,* and 8b, *A. beani*

KEY TO DARTERS OF THE GENUS *Percina*

1a. Snout conically shaped, projecting well past the upper lip; dorsal spines or dorsal rays usually 14 or more . . . . go to 2, subgenus ***Percina***

1b. Snout not projecting beyond upper lip; dorsal spines or dorsal rays usually fewer than 14 . . . . go to 7

2a. No colored bands in spiny dorsal fin . . . . go to 3

2b. Red or orange bands in spiny dorsal fin . . . . go to 4

3a. Nine whole-body bars with expanded lateral blotches on or below lateral line, 4 bars posterior to soft dorsal fin origin; lateral line scales large, less than 90; Tennessee River drainage . . . . logperch, ***P. caprodes***

3b. Eight whole-body bars with lateral blotches on or below lateral line, 3 bars posterior to soft dorsal fin origin; lateral line scales small, more than 90; upper Conasauga River system . . . .
. . . . Conasauga logperch, ***P. jenkinsi***

4a. Dorsal saddles grading to dorsolateral reticulations; lateral blotches centered on lateral line; nape partially naked; Tennessee River drainage . . . . blotchside logperch, ***P. burtoni***

4b. Dorsal saddles continue on sides as vertical bars extending to or below lateral line; lateral blotches below lateral line; nape completely scaled . . . . go to 5

5a. Bars on body wide, predominantly full and half-length bars, with full bars expanded at ventral base; wide red-orange band on spiny dorsal fin; Mobile basin above Fall Line . . . . "Mobile logperch," *P.* sp.

5b. Bars on body narrow, half-length and quarter-length bars often well developed; narrow red-orange band on spiny dorsal fin . . . . go to 6

6a. Scales large, diagonal sum 47 to 57 (diagonal sum = anal fin origin to spiny dorsal count + soft dorsal fin origin to anal fin count + scales above the lateral line); lateral line scales 88 or less; total pectoral rays usually 28 or less; Mobile basin below the Fall Line . . . . "Gulf logperch," *P.* sp.

6b. Scales smaller, diagonal sum 59 to 72; lateral line scales 88 or more; total pectoral rays usually 29 or more; Escambia and Choctawhatchee River drainages . . . . southern logperch, ***P. austroperca***

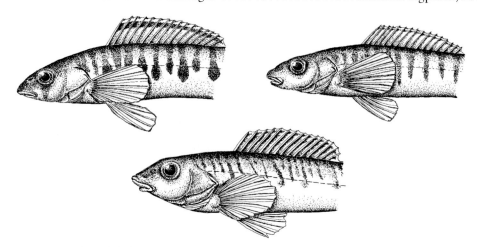

Body bar pigmentation of "Mobile logperch"(top left), "Gulf logperch" (top right), and ***P. austroperca*** (bottom)

7a. Gill membranes moderately joined across the isthmus . . . . go to 8

7b. Gill membranes separate or slightly joined across the isthmus (moderately to broadly connected in *P. shumardi*) . . . . go to 12

Gill membrane configuration 7a, moderately joined and 7b, separated

8a. Caudal fin base with single, distinct spot in the middle; spiny dorsal fin of males with an orange band; Tennessee River drainage . . . . slenderhead darter, ***P. (Swainia) phoxocephala***

8b. Caudal fin base with vertical row of 3 dark spots about equal in intensity; spiny dorsal fin without an orange band . . . . go to 9, subgenus ***Hadropterus***

9a. Lateral line scales 77 or more (usually 80 to 86); front of soft dorsal fin with a large black blotch near base . . . . freckled darter, ***P. lenticula***

9b. Lateral line scales 78 or fewer (usually 50 to 72); front of soft dorsal fin without a large blotch . . . . go to 10

10a. Side with 12 to 15 vertical bars; preopercle margin usually smooth; lateral line scales usually 50 to 62 . . . . blackbanded darter, ***P. nigrofasciata***

10b. Side of body with 7 to 12 oval and somewhat overlapping blotches; preopercle margin is serrate; lateral line scales usually 61 to 72 . . . . go to 11

11a. Upper side of body with a narrow, sometimes broken brown or amber stripe from head to caudal peduncle; Cahaba and upper Coosa river systems . . . . goldline darter, ***P. aurolineata***

11b. Upper side without brown or amber stripe. . . . . dusky darter, ***P. sciera***

12a. Premaxillary frenum is present and wide . . . . go to 13

12b. Premaxillary frenum absent, or if present it is narrow . . . . go to 16

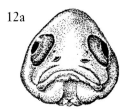 

12a, frenum present; 12b, frenum absent

13a. Sides with dark blotches confined to a center row; spiny dorsal fin without orange color; well-defined black spot present at base of caudal fin; spiny dorsal fin is dusky throughout or with black pigment at base and front . . . . go to 14, subgenus ***Alvordius***

13b. Sides with elongated dark blotches connected to dorsal saddles; spiny dorsal fin orange throughout or with an orange band . . . . go to 15, subgenus ***Ericosma***

14a. Nape typically with a naked median strip; soft dorsal fin rays 11 to 13, usually 12; lateral line scales usually 66 to 75 . . . . blackside darter, *P. maculata*

14b. Nape completely scaled; soft dorsal fin rays 9 to 11, usually 10; lateral line scales usually 56 to 65; Tallapoosa River system above Fall Line and Sipsey Fork of Black Warrior River system (a different form of this species occurs in the upper Conasauga River and Talking Rock Creek in Georgia) . . . .
. . . . "muscadine darter," *P.* sp.

15a. Cheeks partially to fully scaled; nape usually fully scaled; underside of head white to gray; Coosa and Tallapoosa river systems . . . . bronze darter, *P. palmaris*

15b. Cheeks usually unscaled; nape usually scaled in the center; underside of head and body red-orange; Tennessee River drainage . . . . gilt darter, *P. evides*

16a. Scales around caudal peduncle 18 or less; anal rays 7 to 10; anal fin of adult male not enlarged; upper Black Warrior, Cahaba, and Coosa river systems . . . . coal darter, *P. (Cottogaster) brevicauda*

16b. Scales around caudal peduncle 19 or more; anal rays usually 10 to 13; anal fin of adult male enlarged . . . .
. . . . go to 17, subgenus *Imostoma*

Anal fin of breeding male 16a, *P. brevicauda*, 16b, *P. (Imostoma) vigil*

17a. Spiny dorsal fin with small black spot in front and large black spot at rear; back without obvious dark saddles; lateral blotches become vertical, crowded bars toward head . . . . river darter, *P. shumardi*

17b. Spiny dorsal fin without spots; back with 4 or 5 obvious dark saddles . . . . go to 18

18a. First saddle anterior to spiny dorsal fin; anal rays 8 to 10; upper Coosa River system . . . .
. . . . amber darter, *P. antesella*

18b. First saddle under spiny dorsal fin; anal rays 10 to 13 . . . . go to 19

19a. Back yellow to olive with 5 saddles (fifth saddle is often small and sometimes indistinct near caudal fin) that generally do not extend and connect with lateral blotches; posterior margin of fourth saddle is anterior to dorsal insertion of caudal fin; anal rays modally 10 or 11 . . . . saddleback darter, *P. vigil*

19b. Back typically brown with 4 saddles connecting with lateral blotches; posterior margin of fourth saddle over dorsal insertion of caudal fin; anal rays modally 12; Tennessee River drainage. . . . . snail darter, *P. tanasi*

KEY TO DARTERS OF THE GENUS *Etheostoma*

1a. Lateral line arched upward at the front (always incomplete) or absent . . . . go to 2

1b. Lateral line not distinctly arched upward, complete or incomplete . . . . go to 6

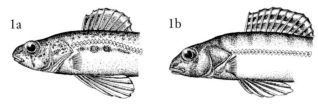

Lateral line configuration 1a, arched, and 1b, straight

2a. Pored lateral line scales modally 2 or 3; 7 or 8 dorsal spines . . . . . cypress darter, *E. (Microperca) proeliare*

2b. Pored lateral line scales 10 or more; 8 to 11 dorsal spines. . . . . go to 3

3a. Unpored lateral line scales less than 15; male with red dots scattered throughout body and in spiny dorsal fin
. . . . brown darter, *E. (Villora) edwini*

3b. Unpored lateral line scales 16 or more; male lacks red dots . . . . go to 4, subgenus *Hololepis*

4a. Infraorbital canal uninterrupted, with 6 to 8 pores; sides with green, vertical bars; upper Tombigbee River
drainage. . . . . slough darter, *E. gracile*

4b. Infraorbital canal interrupted, with 2 to 4 pores in the anterior unit and 0 to 2 (rarely 3) pores in the posterior unit; sides plain or colored . . . . go to 5

Infraorbital canal structure 4a, uninterrupted, and 4b, interrupted

5a. Breast fully scaled; 2 anal spines; no green vertical bars on sides . . . . swamp darter, *E. fusiforme*

5b. Breast unscaled or partly scaled; anal spines 1 or 2; green vertical bars on sides; Mobile basin below Fall
Line. . . . . backwater darter, *E. zonifer*

6a. Breeding males with fleshy knobs on tips of dorsal spines; base of pectoral fin typically enlarged and with
black humeral spot; Tennessee River drainage (key is to breeding males but distributions are highly restric-
tive, which will assist in identifying specimens) . . . . go to 7, subgenus *Catonotus*

6b. Breeding males without fleshy knobs on tips of dorsal spines; dark humeral spot may be present . . go to 12

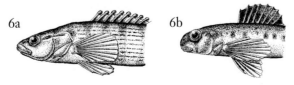

Spiny dorsal fin knobs 6a, present, and 6b, absent

7a. Breast fully scaled (often embedded); gill membranes separate or almost separate (may appear moderately connected on larger individuals). . . . . go to 8

7b. Breast naked; gill membranes broadly to moderately connected . . . . go to 11

Gill membrane structure (left) separated, (middle) moderately connected, and (right) broadly connected

8a. Soft dorsal fin with branch tips developed into fleshy knobs . . . . lollipop darter, *E. neopterum*

8b. Soft dorsal fin without fleshy knobs . . . . go to 9

9a. Soft dorsal fin rays with third branch greatly elongate; 6 to 7 rows of clear to light yellow crescents on soft dorsal fin; in Alabama, Shoal and Six Mile creek systems, Lauderdale County. . . . . fringed darter, *E. crossopterum*

9b. Soft dorsal fin rays with second and third branches about equal in length; 3 to 8 rows of rectangular clear to light yellow bars on soft dorsal fin . . . . go to 10

Soft dorsal fin morphology of 8a, *E. neopterum*, and 9a, *E. crossopterum*

10a. Soft dorsal fin with black margin, modally 13 rays; throughout Tennessee River drainage excluding Cypress and Shoal creek systems, Lauderdale County . . . . blackfin darter, *E. nigripinne*

10b. Soft dorsal fin with yellow margin, modally 14 to 15 rays; Cypress Creek system in Lauderdale County . . . . crown darter, *E. corona*

Soft dorsal fin morphology of 10a, *E. nigripinne*, and 10b, *E. corona*

11a. Soft dorsal rays 13 or 14; gill membranes broadly joined; lateral scale rows 42 to 56; sides with prominent vertical bars and longitudinal stripes . . . . fantail darter, *E. flabellare*

11b. Soft dorsal rays 11 or 12; gill membranes less broadly joined; lateral scale rows 38 to 48; sides without prominent vertical bars and longitudinal stripes . . . . stripetail darter, *E. kennicotti*

12a. Gill membranes separate (moderately connected in species of the subgenus *Nothonotus* and in *E. nigrum*, *E. stigmaeum*, and *E. davisoni*) . . . . go to 13

12b. Gill membranes broadly connected . . . . go to 32

13a. One anal spine (first ray may be thickened and mimic a spine) . . . . go to 14

13b. Two anal spines . . . . go to 17

14a. Frenum absent, premaxillae separated from snout by a complete groove. go to 15

14b. Frenum present, premaxillae connected anteriorly to snout at midline . . . . go to 16

15a. Lateral line complete; dark snout bridle interrupted . . . . johnny darter, *E. (Boleosoma) nigrum*

15b. Lateral line incomplete, ending near front of soft dorsal fin; dark bridle continuous on snout, touching upper lip; snout blunter than johnny darter. . . . . bluntnose darter, *E. (Vaillantia) chlorosomum*

15a   15b

Snout bridle of 15a, *E. nigrum*, and 15b, *E. chlorosomum*

16a. Lateral line incomplete; breast scaled; back with 5 or 6 blotches; Tennessee River drainage . . . .
. . . . Tuscumbia darter, *E. (Psychromaster) tuscumbia*

16b. Lateral line complete; breast naked; back with 3 blotches; Coosa River system . . . .
. . . . trispot darter, *E. (Ozarka) trisella*

17a. Lateral line complete or nearly so; nape usually naked or nearly so . . . . go to 18

17b. Lateral line incomplete (occasionally only 4 unpored scales in *E. swaini*); nape usually completely scaled, possibly embedded . . . . go to 25

18a. Cheeks completely scaled; palatine teeth absent; sides with 11 or 12 oblong dark blotches along lateral band that continues forward across opercle and through eye; distinct lateral blotches separate wavy dorsolateral lines from immaculate or lightly shaded ventrolateral area. . . . .
. . . . ashy darter, *E. (Allohistium) cinereum*

18b. Cheeks naked or a few scales associated with postorbital spot on upper cheek; palatine teeth present; sides without oblong dark blotches; pigmentation similar along sides . . . . . go to 19, subgenus *Nothonotus*

19a. Cheeks with horizontal black marks; lips orange in fresh specimens; pale spots present at base of caudal fin; Tennessee River drainage. . . . . redline darter, *E. rufilineatum*

19b. Cheeks unmarked; lips uncolored or reddish in fresh specimens, never orange . . . . go to 20

20a. Sides of body marked with dark horizontal lines, particularly on the posterior part of body; median fins with dark margins; Tennessee River drainage . . . . go to 21

20b. Sides of body marked but without dark horizontal lines; Mobile basin predominantly above the Fall Line . . . . go to 22

21a. Modal number of dorsal spines 13 or 14; snout produced . . . . boulder darter, *E. wapiti*

21b. Modal number of dorsal spines 11 or 12; snout blunt . . . . bluebreast darter, *E. camurum*

22a. Anal fin of breeding male with broad, median red band, lips red; Tallapoosa River system above the Fall Line . . . . lipstick darter, *E. **chuckwachatte***

22b. Anal fin of breeding male blue-turquoise in color without red band, lips olivaceous; Black Warrior, Cahaba, Coosa, and Alabama river drainages . . . . go to 23

23a. Red spots present on sides of breeding males; Cahaba and Coosa river systems, Tallapoosa River system below the Fall Line, and the upper Alabama river drainage . . . greenbreast darter, *E. **jordani***

23b. No red spots on sides of breeding males . . . . go to 24

24a. No scales on opercles; upper Black Warrior River system . . . . Tuskaloosa darter, *E. **douglasi***

24b. Opercles scaled; Etowah River system upstream of Lake Allatoona, Georgia. . Etowah darter, *E. **etowahae***

25a. Back with 3 prominent saddles; smaller saddles may be evident under dorsal fins; Tennessee River drainage . . . . slackwater darter, *E. (Ozarka) **boschungi***

25b. Back with more than 3 saddles . . . . go to 26

26a. Back with 6 or 7 dark blotches; blotches at origin of spiny dorsal fin and between spiny and soft dorsal fins distinctly wider than small blotches on peduncle; males with 10 or 11 dark blue to indigo bars along sides encircling the body posterior to pectoral fins; Tennessee River drainage. . . . . rainbow darter, *E. (Oligocephalus) **caeruleum***

26b. Dorsal blotches and body markings not as described above. . . . . go to 27

27a. Premaxillae protractile, separated from snout by a complete groove (partially protractile in *E. jessiae* which has a shallow groove above upper lip) . . . . go to 28

27b. Premaxillae not protractile, connected at front midline of snout by a narrow fleshy bridge . . . . go to 30, subgenus ***Oligocephalus***

28a. Nape completely scaled; dorsal blotches hourglass shaped; indistinct frenum is broad; Tennessee River drainage. . . . . blueside darter, *E. (Doration) **jessiae***

28b. Nape incompletely scaled, naked on anterior half; dorsal blotches not hourglass shaped; distinct groove separates upper lip from snout . . . . go to 29

29a. Nape scaled; breeding males with blue, blue-green, and red-orange . . . . speckled darter, *E. (Doration) **stigmaeum***

29b. Nape naked; breeding males without blue and red color; drainages east of the Mobile basin . . . . Choctawhatchee darter, *E. (Vaillantia) **davisoni***

30a. Unpored lateral line scales on caudal peduncle 4 to 12. . . . . gulf darter, *E. **swaini***

30b. Unpored lateral line scales on caudle peduncle 13 to 35. . . . . go to 31

30a, *E. **swaini*** unpored lateral line scales on peduncle

31a. Nape usually scaled; pored lateral line scales 19 to 35; Coosa River system. . . . .
. . . . coldwater darter, *E. ditrema*
31b. Nape naked; pored lateral line scales 12 to 24; Black Warrior system . . watercress darter, *E. nuchale*

32a. Back with 4 obvious dark saddles slanting slightly toward the head; Tennessee River drainage . . . .
. . . . blenny darter, *E. (Etheostoma) blennius*
32b. Back with six to 10 blotches or saddles (may be faint in *E. whipplei* and *E. parvipinne*) . . . . go to 33

33a. Anterior half of upper jaw fused to the preorbital bone; tip of upper lip in large individuals often
produced into a knob or nipple; lateral line scales 57 to 76; Tennessee River drainage . . . .
. . . . greenside darter, *E. (Etheostoma) blennioides*
33b. Anterior half of upper jaw not fused to the preorbital bone, but separated at sides by a groove; tip of
upper lip in large individuals without a knob or nipple; lateral line scales 36 to 57 . . . . go to 34

33a, *E. blennioides* upper jaw structure

34a. Bone at base of pectoral fin enlarged and underlaid with a concentration of pigment producing an
obvious black humeral spot; lateral line usually incomplete (3 to 16 unpored scales); body of males
with discrete red spots or blotches, females with yellow on body . . . .
. . . . redfin darter, *E. (Oligocephalus) whipplei*
34b. No dark humeral spot; lateral line complete . . . . go to 35

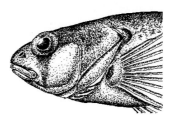

34a, *E. whipplei* pectoral fin with pigment concentration

35a. Lateral line scales without pigment producing a narrow, pale stripe contrasting against darker body;
breast completely scaled (may be embedded) . . . . goldstripe darter, *E. (Fuscatelum) parvipinne*
35b. No pale stripe along sides; breast naked or variously scaled (variously embedded) . . . . go to 36

36a. Back with 5 or 6 blotches (sometimes 7 in *E. zonale*) . . . . go to 37, subgenus *Etheostoma*
36b. Back with 8 or 9 blotches (key restricted to breeding males) . . . . go to 40, subgenus *Ulocentra*

37a. Cheeks completely scaled; Tennessee River drainage . . . . banded darter, *E. zonale*
37b. Cheeks almost or completely naked. . . . . go to 38

38a. Lateral line scales 36 to 44, usually 40; sides with 7 to 10 vertical bands which tend to encircle the body in the caudal peduncle area; Escatawpa River drainage. . . . . brighteye darter, *E. lynceum*
38b. Lateral line scales 45 to 60, usually 50 or more; vertical bands not encircling body . . . . go to 39

39a. Ventral surface of head with no dark pigment, or faintly marked; caudal fin base with a pair of small spots . . . . rock darter, *E. rupestre*
39b. Ventral surface of head obviously marked with spots and short bars; snout very blunt; prominent blotches at caudal fin base . . . . harlequin darter, *E. histrio*

40a. Soft dorsal fin with distinct brown to red-orange pigment streaking along length of interradial membranes . . . . go to 41
40b. Brown to red-orange pigment reduced in coverage, limited to proximal half or third of soft dorsal fin; band may extend entire length of fin, show only on posterior end, or occur as a series of ocelli. . . go to 44

41a. Frenum distinctly present; Tennessee River drainage . . . . snubnose darter, *E. simoterum*
41b. Frenum absent or reduced and hidden under lip flap . . . . go to 42

42a. Branchiostegal rays 5; spiny dorsal fin of breeding male with no distinct banding ventral to the red marginal band, black band near base of fin; saddle between dorsal fins appears fused with lateral band; Tennessee River drainage. . . . . black darter, *E. duryi*
42b. Branchiostegal rays 5 or 6; most populations of *E. coosae* have 6 rays, populations of *E. scotti* may have either 5 or 6; spiny dorsal fin with either well-developed bands or bands entirely absent; Coosa River system. . . . . go to 43

43a. Spiny dorsal fin of breeding male with distinct, alternating pigmented and clear, horizontal bands; outer band is black or blue, the next band is brown or red about one-fourth the height of the fin; small males have wide peduncle bars. . . . . Coosa darter, *E. coosae*
43b. Spiny dorsal fin of breeding male is entirely pigmented orange to brick red except for an irregular basal black band; peduncle bars on smaller males are narrow and more vertically produced; middle and upper Etowah River system, Georgia . . . . Cherokee darter, *E. scotti*

44a. Frenum reduced and poorly developed, hidden under lip flap . . . . go to 45
44b. Frenum distinctly absent . . . . go to 47

45a. Distinct red band present on anal fin of breeding male limited to the basal half of the posterior rays; Coosa River system . . . . holiday darter, *E. brevirostrum*
45b. No red band present in anal fin of breeding males; Black Warrior River system . . . . go to 46

46a. Distinct brown to cherry red submarginal band along entire length of spiny dorsal fin of breeding male; vermilion color limited to lower portions of sides and peduncle . . . . warrior darter, *E. bellator*
46b. Red band in spiny dorsal fin of breeding male more intense anteriorly, where it develops into a large cherry red ocellus, and posteriorly, with pigmentation in last 4 or so membranes, with red pigment weakly streaked between; vermilion color more extensive reaching dorsally to near lateral line . . . . vermilion darter, *E. chermocki*

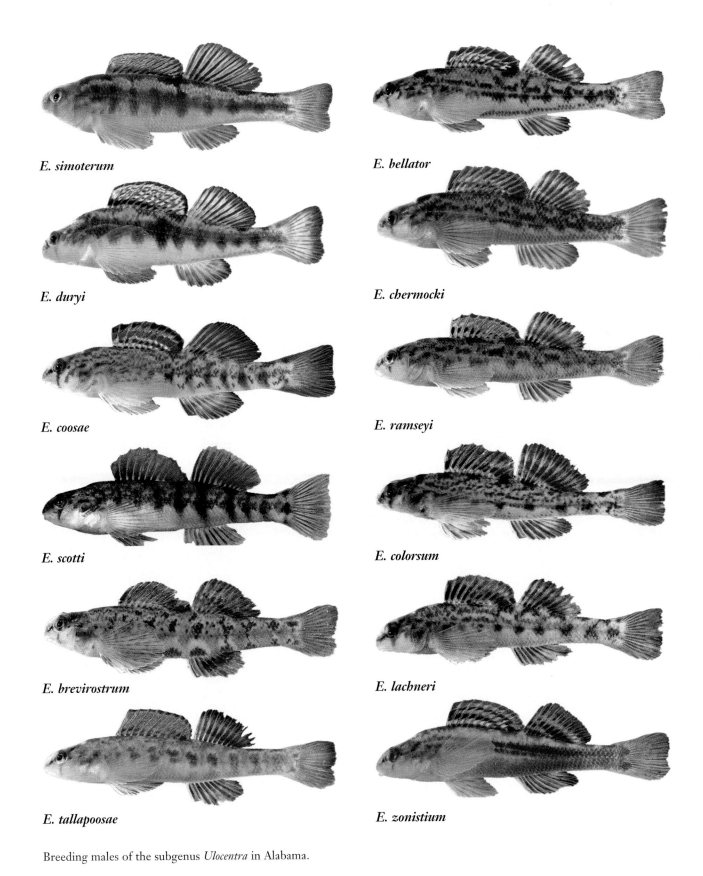

E. simoterum

E. bellator

E. duryi

E. chermocki

E. coosae

E. ramseyi

E. scotti

E. colorsum

E. brevirostrum

E. lachneri

E. tallapoosae

E. zonistium

Breeding males of the subgenus *Ulocentra* in Alabama.

47a. Spiny dorsal fin of breeding male with six distinct horizontal bands, alternating pigmented and light; outer band is black to dark blue, next colored band is dark brown to red in color; a well defined dark brown to brick red band from 1 to 3 scales wide is confined to the lateral line area; Tennessee River drainage and northwestern-most portion of the Sipsey Fork in the Black Warrior River system . . . . bandfin darter, *E. zonistium*

47b. Less distinct banding in spiny dorsal fin of breeding male; brown to reddish pigment confined to posterior part of spiny dorsal fin. . . . . go to 48

48a. Snout somewhat pointed, with junction of lips extending to or near anterior rim of orbit; brownish color in spiny dorsal fin of breeding male weakly developed, more intense posteriorly, forming 1 to 3 ocelli; brown to brick red bands well developed on peduncle; upper Tallapoosa River system . . . . Tallapoosa darter, *E. tallapoosae*

48b. Snout blunt, junction of lips extending well past anterior orbit of eye; reddish band in spiny dorsal fin of breeding male restricted to posterior end . . . . go to 49

49a. A series of small orange to red spots or punctulations present along the side of breeding males, extending from the base of the caudal fin to just above the pectoral fin base and found just above the lateral blotches; drainages from the Perdido River east to the Choctawhatchee River (this is the only *Ulocentra* found in these drainages) . . . . coastal darter, *E. colorosum*

49b. Sides lacking small distinct spots or punctulations; Mobile basin . . . . go to 50

50a. Breeding males with slightly oblique, dark green bars with bright orange interspaces on the side of the body and caudal peduncle; Tombigbee River system below the Fall Line . . . . Tombigbee darter, *E. lachneri*

50b. Breeding males with continuous orange along the entire lower body and caudal peduncle, extending dorsally to bottom of lateral blotches; series of orange to russet blotches occur dorsally to lateral blotches and the lateral blotches are interconnected with dorsal saddles; below the Fall Line in the Alabama River system and also common throughout Cahaba River system above the Fall Line. . . . . Alabama darter, *E. ramseyi*

WEST FORK SIPSEY RIVER, WINSTON COUNTY

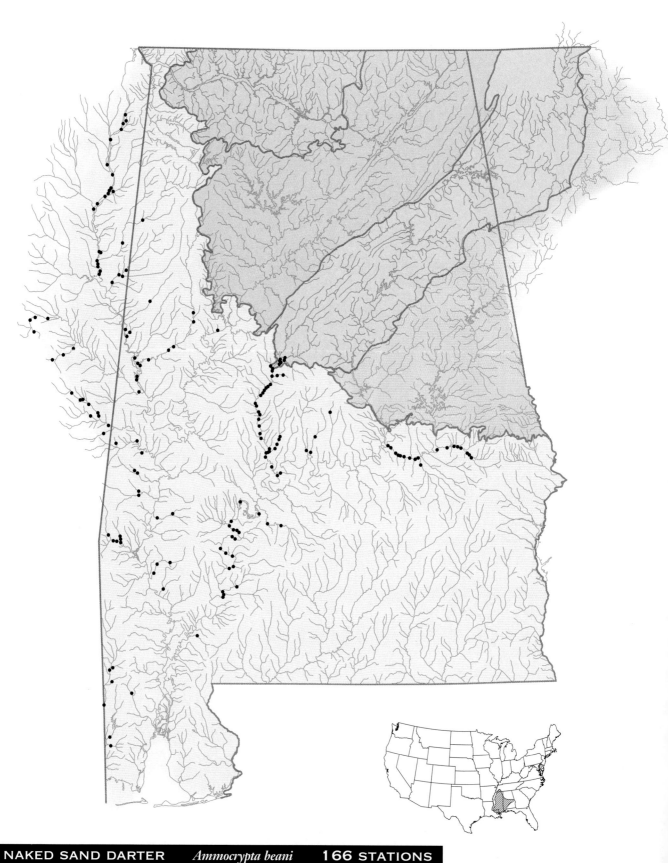

NAKED SAND DARTER   *Ammocrypta beani*   166 STATIONS

Ammocrypta beani
Jordan, 1877

ETYMOLOGY:
Ammocrypta—sand-concealed, referring to this species' habit of hiding in the sand with only their eyes exposed
beani—for T. H. Bean, the ichthyologist who first collected the species

Puppy Creek, Mobile County, 18 August 1992, 1.9 in (49 mm) SL male, GSA 4301

CHARACTERISTICS: The naked sand darter is characterized by a slender body with a pointed snout and a moderately large head and mouth. The body lacks pigmentation along the sides and the breast. The preopercle, opercle, cheek, nape, and venter are unscaled. A dark submarginal band is present on each dorsal fin. In life, *A. beani* is transparent, with a yellow to yellow-orange flush on the back. Dusky bands are present on the caudal and anal fins. Williams (1975) places *A. beani* in the **beani** species group along with *A. bifascia* and *A. clara*. See Jordan (1877b) for original description.

ADULT SIZE: 1.5 to 2.2 in (38 to 55 mm)

DISTRIBUTION: The naked sand darter is known from the Hatchie River system in Tennessee and Mississippi river drainages from the Big Black south to Lake Pontchartrain and east along the Gulf slope to the Mobile basin. It is also distributed below the Fall Line in the Mobile basin and in the Escatawpa River drainage in extreme southwest Alabama.

HABITAT AND BIOLOGY: This species prefers large streams and rivers with moderate current and shifting substrates of clean sand. It is frequently associated with other sand-loving species, including the silverjaw minnow, *Ericymba buccata*, and the orangefin and longnose shiners, *Notropis ammophilus* and *N. longirostris*. It is also known to occur sympatrically with the southern sand darter, *A. meridiana*, which prefers substrates with both sand and silt. Simon et al. (1992) report spawning in the Tallapoosa River from mid-May through early June, with adults congregating and spawning on sandy bars adjacent to large shoals. Protolarvae abundance peaks in June. Spawning likely extends through August in Alabama. Our examination of specimens from several different areas indicates that individuals feed almost exclusively on midges and other prey inhabiting sandy substrates.

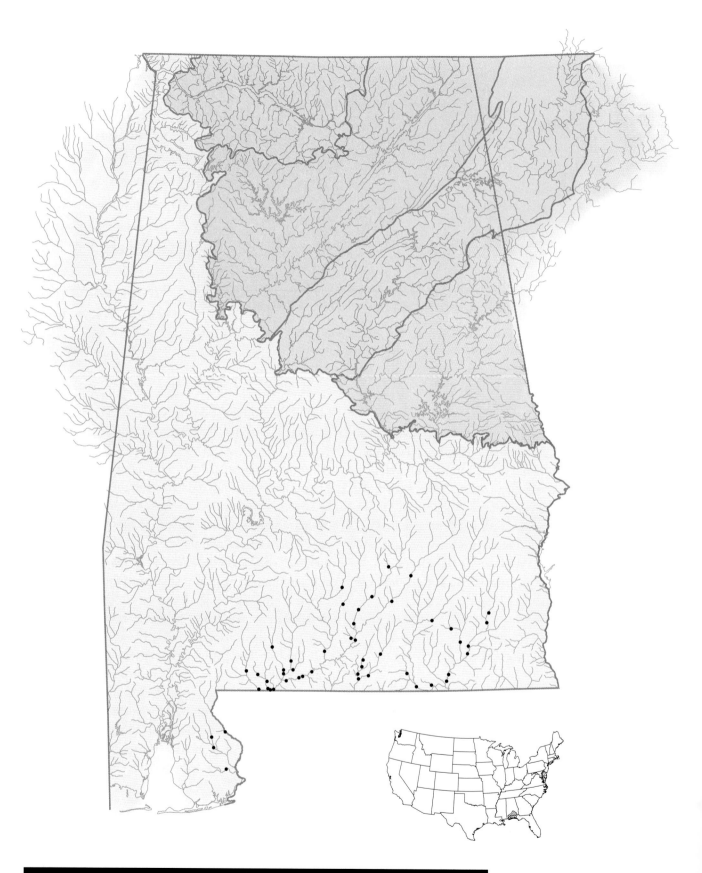

Ammocrypta bifascia
Williams, 1975

ETYMOLOGY:

Ammocrypta—sand-concealed, referring to this species' habit of hiding in the sand with only their eyes exposed
bifascia—two-banded, referring to the two bands in the dorsal and anal fins

Harris Mill Creek, Coffee County, 6 May 1993, 2.3 in (59 mm) SL male, GSA 4443

CHARACTERISTICS: The Florida sand darter is similar in character to the naked sand darter, *Ammocrypta beani*, but *A. bifascia* differs by having two dark bands, one marginal and one submarginal, in the spiny dorsal fin. The soft dorsal and anal fins each contain two bands that are lighter in color. Marginal pigmentation is much less developed in females. Breeding tubercle development and distribution over the body also distinguishes *A. bifascia* from *A. beani*. Individuals of *A. bifascia* have tubercles only on the ventral surface of the pelvic spine and rays, while tubercles cover both the dorsal and ventral surfaces of these fins in *A. beani*. The tubercles of *A. bifascia* are approximately half the size of those on *A. beani*. The Florida sand darter is the largest species of the *beani* species group. Live individuals generally have a soft yellow and orange flush on the body and a bluish green tint on the head. Fins may be somewhat yellow, particularly during the breeding season.

ADULT SIZE: 2 to 2.6 in (50 to 65 mm)

DISTRIBUTION: *Ammocrypta bifascia* is distributed in coastal drainages from the Perdido River east to the Choctawhatchee River proper, including the Escambia, Yellow, and Blackwater river systems.

HABITAT AND BIOLOGY: Like the naked sand darter, the Florida sand darter inhabits larger streams with shifting sand bottoms and moderate to swift currents. It is frequently associated with other sand-loving species, including the silverjaw minnow, *Ericymba buccata,* and the longnose shiner, *Notropis longirostris.* Spawning begins in April and extends through July, perhaps into August. Heins (1985) reports males are significantly larger than females and the maximum life span is about three years. Compared to *A. beani, A. bifacia* mature at a larger size, reproduce for a shorter period of time, and generally live longer. The diet of *A. bifascia* consists almost exclusively of midge larvae and microcrustaceans found in sand habitats.

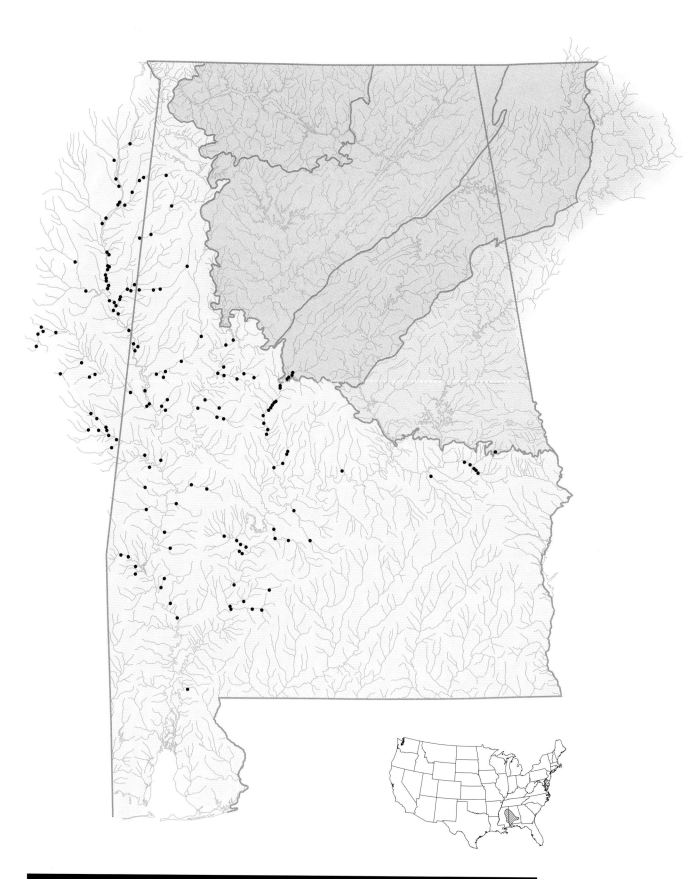

Ammocrypta meridiana
Williams, 1975

ETYMOLOGY:
Ammocrypta—sand-concealed, referring to this species' habit of hiding in the sand with only their eyes exposed
meridiana—a derivative of *meridionalis*, meaning southern

Big Brush Creek, Hale County, 14 May 1992, 2.1 in (53 mm) SL male, GSA 4447

CHARACTERISTICS: *Ammocrypta meridiana* is distinguished from other sand darter species by extensive body scalation, compared to the naked body of *A. beani* and *A. bifascia*. *A. meridiana's* cheeks and opercles are scaled while the venter is naked. The back has 10 to 15 small, irregular blotches of varying intensity that may be divided into pairs. Eight to 13 small, faint lateral blotches of varying size, intensity, and location are present along the sides. The median fins are clear, without the intense pigmentation of *A. beani* and *A. bifascia*. The body is flushed with pale yellow-orange to a more intense orange along the sides and back with a broad, iridescent, blue-green band along the lateral line. The cheeks and opercles are iridescent bluish green with the lower jaw iridescent blue. The snout is orange-yellow.

ADULT SIZE: 1.8 to 2.4 in (45 to 60 mm)

DISTRIBUTION: The southern sand darter is restricted to the Mobile basin below the Fall Line.

HABITAT AND BIOLOGY: The southern sand darter is found in rivers and large streams with a moderate current over sand and mixed sand-silt substrates. Species commonly taken with the southern sand darter are the silver-jaw minnow, *Ericymba buccata*, orangefin shiner, *Notropis ammophilus*, and the naked sand darter, *A. beani*. Simon et al. (1992) report spawning over clean sand and gravel riffles during the months of May and June in the lower portions of the Cahaba River, which coincides with our observations of spawning times for this species.

REMARKS: The type locality for *A. meridiana* is Cedar Creek near Sardis, Dallas County, Alabama.

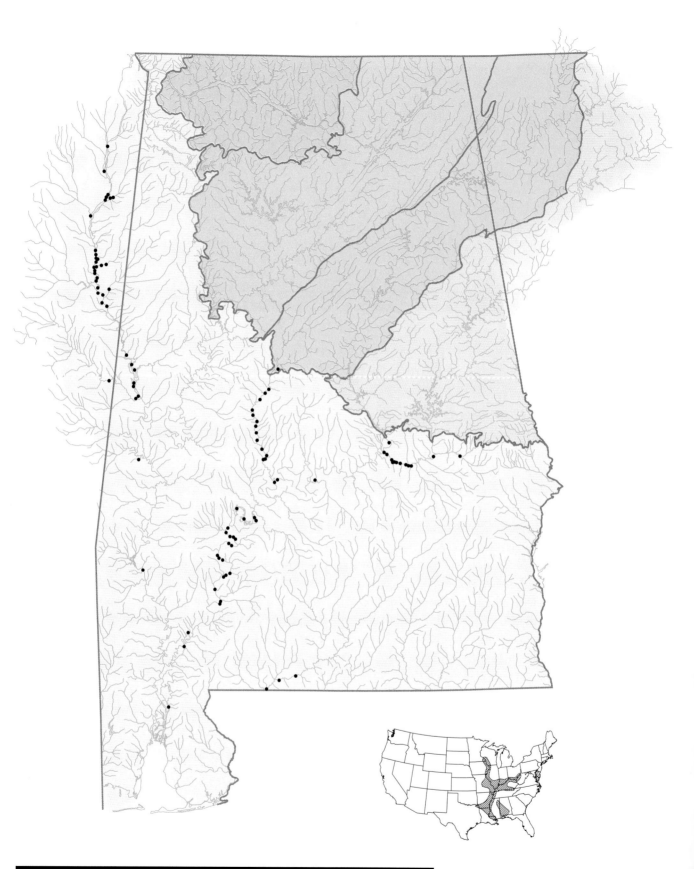

CRYSTAL DARTER   *Crystallaria asprella*   93 STATIONS

584

Crystallaria asprella
(Jordan, 1878)

ETYMOLOGY:
Crystallaria—crystallike, referring to the clear, translucent body *asprella*—diminutive form of *aspro*, meaning rough, in reference to scales

Conecuh River, Escambia County, 13 July 1993, 3.9 in (99 mm) SL male, GSA 4499

CHARACTERISTICS: *Crystallaria asprella* has a long, slender body with enlarged pectoral fins and a moderately long head and snout. Four to five dark saddles extend forward from the back to below the lateral line. The first saddle is entirely in front of the spiny dorsal fin. A small, narrow frenum is present on the upper lip. The body is fully scaled except on the venter and breast. Except for the dark saddles, live individuals are translucent. Simons (1991) places this species in the genus *Crystallaria* and the remaining *Ammocrypta* species in the genus *Etheostoma,* subgenus *Ammocrypta*. We elect to maintain *Ammocrypta* at the generic level, pending the results of further taxonomic studies of the group. See Jordan (1878b) for original description.

ADULT SIZE: 2 to 5.1 in (50 to 130 mm)

DISTRIBUTION: Crystal darters previously occurred throughout the upper Mississippi and Ohio river basins south to Louisiana, Mississippi, and Alabama, but today's isolated populations stem from the fact that many of their habitats have been drastically altered.

The species is possibly extirpated from Ohio, Indiana, and Illinois. Completion of the Tennessee-Tombigbee waterway greatly reduced or eliminated many populations in the western Mobile basin. Most Mobile basin records are from near or below the Fall Line. A small, isolated population inhabits the lower Conecuh River system.

HABITAT AND BIOLOGY: This species prefers sand and gravel bars in large flowing rivers and streams of the Coastal Plain. It has the interesting habit of burying itself in the sand, leaving only its eyes above exposed; this is presumably to minimize body movement, thus conserving energy, and to maintain its position in the swift waters of its preferred habitats. Most individuals remain in deep water during the day and move to shallow sand and gravel bars at dusk to search for aquatic insects. Spawning begins in late February (Simon et al., 1992) or early March through late April.

REMARKS: The crystal darter is protected by rules and regulations of the Alabama Game and Fish Division.

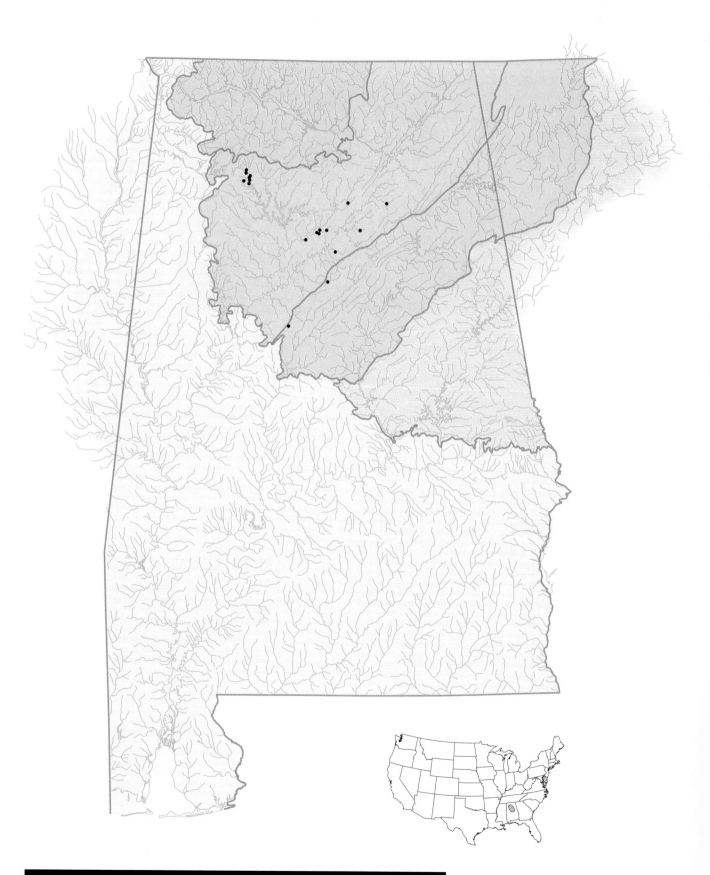

WARRIOR DARTER *Etheostoma bellator* **18 STATIONS**

Etheostoma bellator

Suttkus and Bailey, 1993

ETYMOLOGY:

Etheostoma—strain mouth, possibly referring to the small mouth

bellator—warrior, for the Black Warrior River system, the drainage inhabited by this species

Murphy Creek, Blount County, 9 March 1993, 2.2 in (56 mm) SL male, GSA 4365

CHARACTERISTICS: The Warrior darter is a member of the subgenus *Ulocentra*. Individuals have a reduced or poorly developed premaxillary frenum, but their vomerine teeth typical of individuals in *Etheostoma duryi*. Two series of elongated blotches separated by a pale area extend along the sides from the pectoral fins posteriorly to the caudal fin. Another characteristic pigment pattern is a narrow orange stripe along the lower side. Breeding males are brightly colored with turquoise on the head, breast, and pectoral fin area. The front two and back two dorsal saddles, along with the anal fin, pelvic fins, and margins of the caudal fin, are dark turquoise. The spiny dorsal fin has a bright red ocellus in the first membrane followed by less intense red blotches that form a submarginal band across the entire fin. The Warrior darter can be separated from its near relative, the vermilion darter, *E. chermocki*, by the narrow orange stripe along its lower side; in *E. chermocki*, this stripe is broad and red or vermilion. The body of *E. bellator* is more slender with a longer tail area and shorter dorsal fins.

ADULT SIZE: 1 to 2.3 in (25 to 58 mm)

DISTRIBUTION: *Etheostoma bellator* is endemic to the upper Black Warrior River system of the Mobile basin. Collection records exist from Valley Creek and the Locust, Mulberry, and Sipsey fork systems, all of which drain the Cumberland Plateau.

HABITAT AND BIOLOGY: Warrior darters occur in rubble pools and riffles, bedrock pools and raceways (generally over sandstone or shale substrates), and in flowing water over gravel-filled depressions in bedrock pools of small to medium-sized streams. Spawning for this species occurs from March through mid-May, with peak spawning in April. Prey consists of aquatic insect larvae.

REMARKS: The type locality for the Warrior darter is Murphy Creek near Blount Springs, Blount County, Alabama.

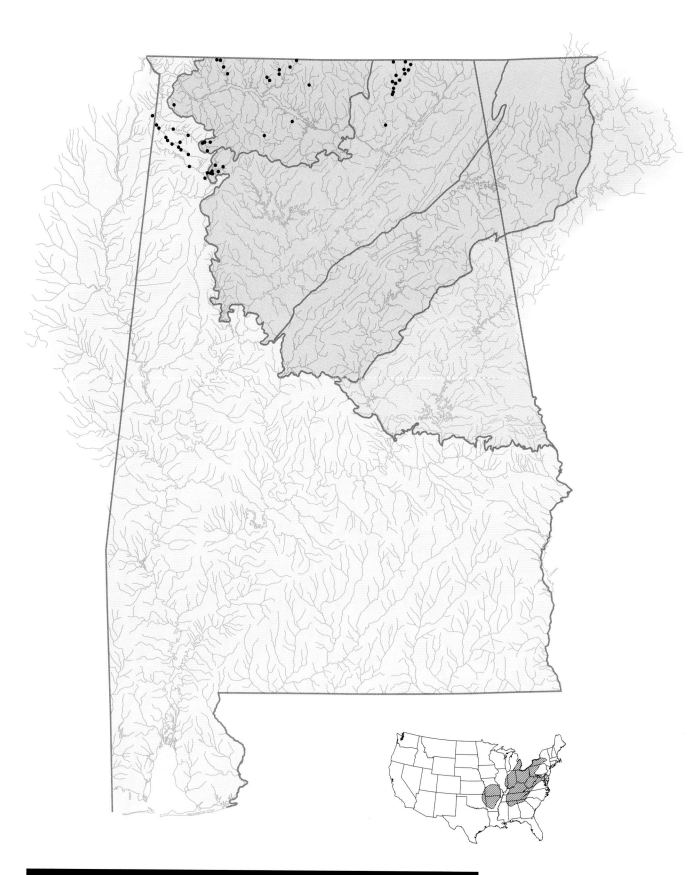

Etheostoma blennioides
Rafinesque, 1819

ETYMOLOGY:
Etheostoma—strain mouth,
possibly referring to the
small mouth
blennioides—blennylike, in
reference to the Mediter-
ranean blennies Rafinesque
knew from Europe

Little Butler Creek, Lauderdale County, 1 April 1993, 4.2 in (107 mm) SL male, GSA 4403

CHARACTERISTICS: The greenside darter is the largest species of **Etheostoma** in Alabama. It is readily distinguishable by a fusion of tissue over the upper jaw with the tissue on the snout and by very broadly connected gill membranes. Body color is generally yellow-green with five to eight dark green vertical bars or dark W- or U-shaped marks along the sides, and six to seven dark square saddles on the back. The dorsal fins are green with orange-red bands at the base; other fins are either green or clear with green bands. The pelvic, pectoral, and anal fin rays become thickened in both males and females during the breeding season. Four subspecies are recognized in this wide-ranging darter (Miller, 1968), with *E. b. newmanii* found in Alabama.

ADULT SIZE: 2.6 to 4.5 in (65 to 115 mm)

DISTRIBUTION: The greenside darter is distributed throughout the Ohio, Cumberland, and Tennessee river drainages, as well as western tributaries of the Mississippi River in Missouri and Arkansas. In Alabama it is restricted to the Tennessee River drainage and occurs most frequently in the Bear Creek, Paint Rock River, Elk River, and Shoal Creek systems.

HABITAT AND BIOLOGY: *Etheostoma blennioides* occupies a variety of habitats, but is most often found in large creeks and small rivers with gravel and rubble riffles and shoal areas. Individuals often retreat to deeper pools during winter months. This species is usually present in large numbers and frequently associated with algae and aquatic moss (Fahy, 1954). McCormick and Aspinwall (1983) found that greenside darters were attracted to aquatic vegetation and algae by distinct olfactory stimulation. Spawning occurs in these vegetated areas or sandy areas in riffles from April through June. Food of the greenside darter consists of snails and aquatic insect larvae including mayflies, blackflies, and caddisflies typical of a swift riffle habitat.

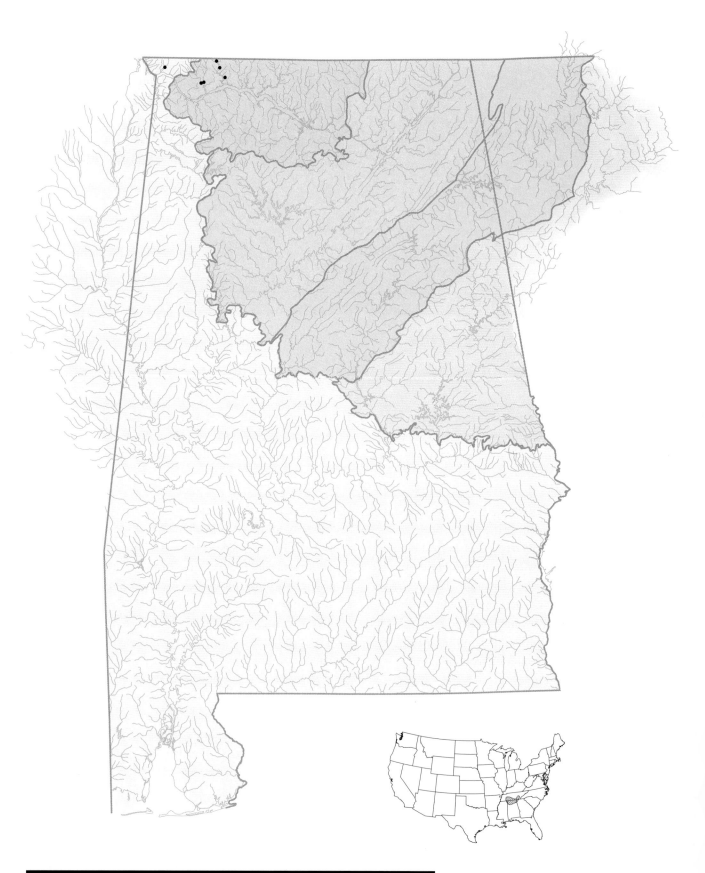

BLENNY DARTER *Etheostoma blennius* **6 STATIONS**

Etheostoma blennius

Gilbert and Swain, 1887

ETYMOLOGY:

Etheostoma—strain mouth, possibly referring to the small mouth

blennius—blennylike

Second Creek, Lauderdale County, 25 February 1993, 1.9 in (47 mm) SL female, GSA 4359

CHARACTERISTICS: The blenny darter is character- ized by four conspicuous blue-black saddles with light margins across the back and by broadly connected gill membranes. The breast and cheek are usually unscaled, the opercle is unscaled or partially scaled, and the ven- ter and nape are fully scaled. In life, the back and upper sides are olive brown, which usually extends below the lateral line as a serrated pattern. The venter is white or yellowish. Breeding males are brown- orange above the lateral line with a distinct small red dot in the center of each upper-body scale. The mouth and lip area is bright blue and the remainder of the head is green. Dorsal fins of breeding males are red- dish purple. The genital papilla of breeding females is characteristically a long extended tube. Breeding males usually have longer fins than females. See Gilbert (1887) for original description.

ADULT SIZE: 1.6 to 2.7 in (40 to 69 mm)

DISTRIBUTION: The blenny darter is distributed in the Highland Rim physiographic province and restricted to the middle and lower Tennessee River drainage in Tennessee and Alabama from the Sequatchie River system to the Duck River system. In Alabama, the blenny darter is known only from Lauderdale County in the Shoal, Cypress, and Second creek systems. Our collection efforts recently confirmed populations in Second and Cypress creeks.

HABITAT AND BIOLOGY: *Etheostoma blennius* lives in swift gravel riffles and shoals of clear streams. Our encounters with blenny darters in Second and Cypress creeks were in the swiftest parts of deep chutes with large gravel and small boulders, which are difficult habitats to sample. Longevity of this species is reported to be two to three years (Burr, 1979b), with sexual maturity attained by the first year. Spawning occurs in gravel riffles from March through April. Blenny darters feed on aquatic insect larvae, primarily mayflies and midges.

REMARKS: The type locality for the blenny darter is Cox Creek near Florence in the Cypress Creek system, Lauderdale County, Alabama.

Etheostoma boschungi
Wall and Williams, 1974

ETYMOLOGY:
Etheostoma—strain mouth, possibly referring to the small mouth
boschungi—in honor of Herbert T. Boschung, professor emeritus and former curator of the University of Alabama Ichthyological Collection

Middle Cypress Creek, Wayne County, Tennessee, 1 April 1993, 1.8 in (45 mm) SL male, GSA 4402

CHARACTERISTICS: A member of the subgenus *Ozarka,* the slackwater darter is characterized by dusky, irregularly spaced blotches on the underside of the head and body, separate or nearly separate gill membranes, and a terminal mouth with a broad frenum. Males have a large and conspicuous bar below the eye. The back is crossed by three distinct saddles; some individuals have one or two additional weakly developed saddles. Breeding males have deep orange to orange-gold on the breast, gill membranes, cheeks, and mouth, while the upper half of the body is uniformly dark. The breeding female is dark above and light below, developing no conspicuous orange color. Additional diagnostic characteristics are given in Wall and Williams (1974).

ADULT SIZE: 1.6 to 2.4 in (40 to 60 mm)

DISTRIBUTION: The slackwater darter is known from disjunct populations in the Cypress Creek, Swan Creek, upper Shoal Creek, and Flint River systems in north Alabama and south-central Tennessee and from the headwaters of the Buffalo River in Tennessee.

HABITAT AND BIOLOGY: *Etheostoma boschungi* exploits two distinct habitat types. For most of the year, individuals typically inhabit pool areas of small streams that contain organic debris. As streams swell from late winter and early spring rains, slackwater darters migrate into adjacent flooded lowland areas with spring seepage to spawn. Breeding populations have also been found in thick vegetation along the main channel of Swan Creek and Brier Fork of the Flint River (McGregor and Shepard, 1995). Spawning occurs from late January to March. Eggs are attached to vegetation. Nieland (1981) reports a diet of microcrustaceans and immature aquatic insects.

REMARKS: The type locality for the slackwater darter is Lindsey Creek in the Cypress Creek system, Lauderdale County, Alabama. The slackwater darter is listed as threatened by the U.S. Fish and Wildlife Service.

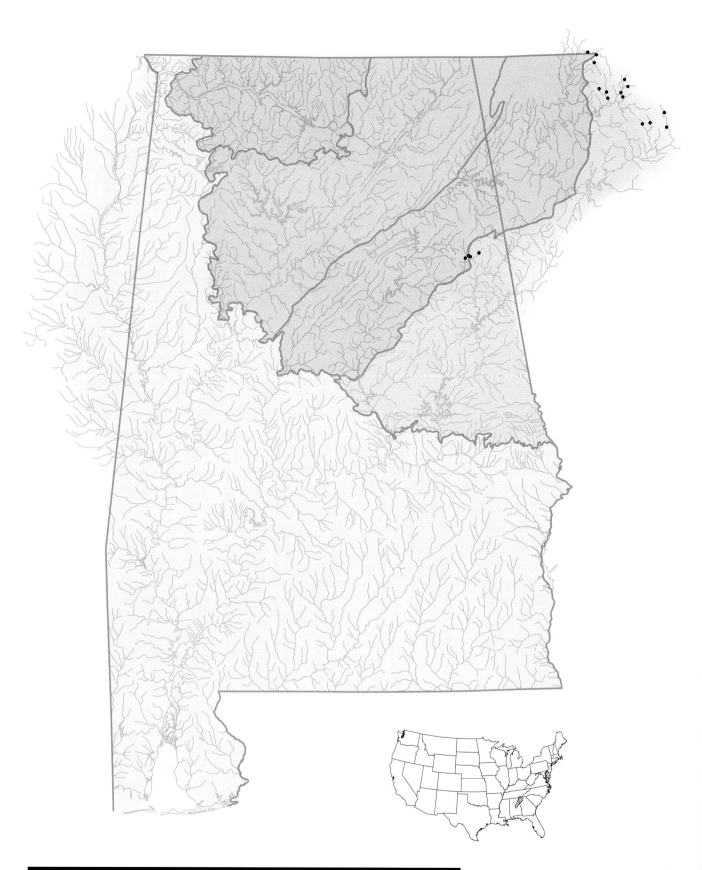

HOLIDAY DARTER   *Etheostoma brevirostrum*   **18 STATIONS**

Etheostoma brevirostrum

Suttkus and Etnier, 1991

ETYMOLOGY:
Etheostoma—strain mouth, possibly referring to the small mouth
brevirostrum—short beak, referring to this species' blunt snout

Shoal Creek, Cleburne County, 10 May 1993, 1.8 in (47 mm) SL male, GSA 4445

CHARACTERISTICS: Breeding holiday darter males exhibit the most distinctive coloration of all **Ulocentra** species in Alabama, including a median red band in the blue-green anal fin, a red ocellus in the first membrane of the spiny dorsal fin, and a narrow red band in the soft dorsal fin. Green pigmented areas darkened with black or dark brown occur on the lateral line. The lower sides have red blotches with white and/or bright yellow halos. The snout, breast, and entire back are green and the cheeks, opercles, and gill membranes are faint blue-green. The premaxillary frenum is absent or poorly developed. Exposed scales cover the venter, opercle, cheek, and nape, while the breast is without scales. Females are less colorful, developing a tint of green on the lateral blotches and dorsal saddles and, like males, a bright ocellus in the first membrane of the spiny dorsal fin.

ADULT SIZE: 1.5 to 2.1 in (38 to 53 mm)

DISTRIBUTION: The holiday darter is distributed in the Coosa River system in the Valley and Ridge, Piedmont, and Blue Ridge physiographic provinces (Suttkus and Etnier, 1991). Collection records in Alabama are limited to the Shoal Creek system. Disjunct populations occur in the upper Conasauga, the upper Coosawattee, and the upper Etowah river systems in Georgia and Tennessee.

HABITAT AND BIOLOGY: The holiday darter prefers medium to large, clear streams with moderate to fast current and mixed substrates consisting of boulders, rubble, gravel, sand, and river weed. Little is known about the biology of this species, but it is likely similar to other **Ulocentra**. Examination of available specimens indicates that spawning occurs during April and May. Diet of this interesting species consists of aquatic insect larvae and microcrustaceans. Populations in the upper Shoal Creek system appear relatively protected since they occur in the Talladega National Forest, whereas populations in the lower Shoal Creek drainage may have been locally extirpated due to development of small water-control impoundments.

REMARKS: The type locality of the holiday darter is Shoal Creek in the Talladega National Forest, Cleburne County, Alabama.

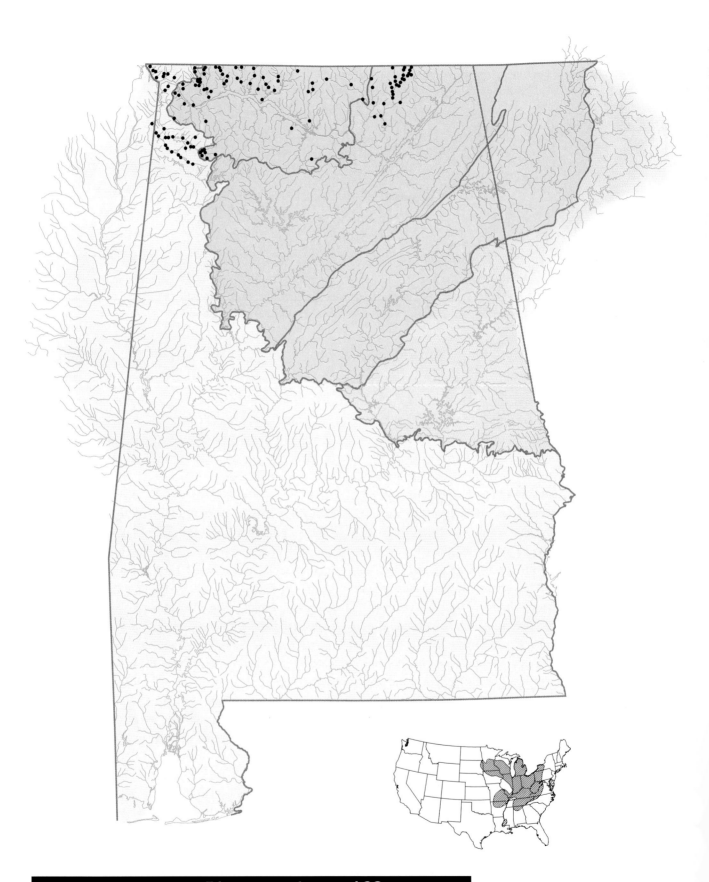

Etheostoma caeruleum
Storer, 1845

ETYMOLOGY:

Etheostoma—strain mouth,
possibly referring to the
small mouth
caeruleum—blue

Sour Branch, Lauderdale County, 24 February 1993, 2.1 in (53 mm) SL male, GSA 4357

CHARACTERISTICS: Rainbow darters are some of the most vividly colored darters found in Alabama. Breeding males have brilliant reds and blues on the sides of the body and head, while the gill membranes are typically orange. A blue marginal and a red submarginal band occur through the spiny dorsal fin. The anal fin is blue-green with a variously developed central red spot. The head is typically conical, a frenum is present in the upper lip, and the gill membranes are separate to slightly connected. Cheeks and breast are usually unscaled and the venter and opercles are scaled. The back has six to 10 dark brown, square saddles, the two most intense ones being located just in front of and behind the spiny dorsal fin. Approximately nine to 14 lateral blotches with narrow interspaces occur along the sides, with the posterior ones becoming more vertically elongated and occasionally encircling the caudal peduncle. See Storer (1845a) for original description.

ADULT SIZE: 1.6 to 2.6 in (40 to 65 mm)

DISTRIBUTION: *Etheostoma caeruleum* are widespread and often abundant in northern tributaries to the Tennessee River drainage in Alabama. Records are strangely absent in northeastern Alabama. The scarcity of observations from southern tributaries, except in Coastal Plain areas of the Bear Creek system, is likely attributable to the absence of suitable habitat.

HABITAT AND BIOLOGY: Adult rainbow darters inhabit fast, deep riffles over gravel, rubble, and cobble substrates while the young are typically encountered in quiet, shallow riffles and pools over sand and gravel substrates. Spawning occurs in Alabama from late April to July in shallow riffles. Winn (1958a, b) reports spawning from April to May in Michigan. Females deposit in the substrate three to seven eggs per spawning act, leaving the eggs unprotected. The diverse diet of rainbow darters consists of mayflies, midges, water mites, caddisflies, and blackflies. Variable feeding behaviors reported by Vogt and Coon (1990) may allow this species to remain common throughout its range in Alabama.

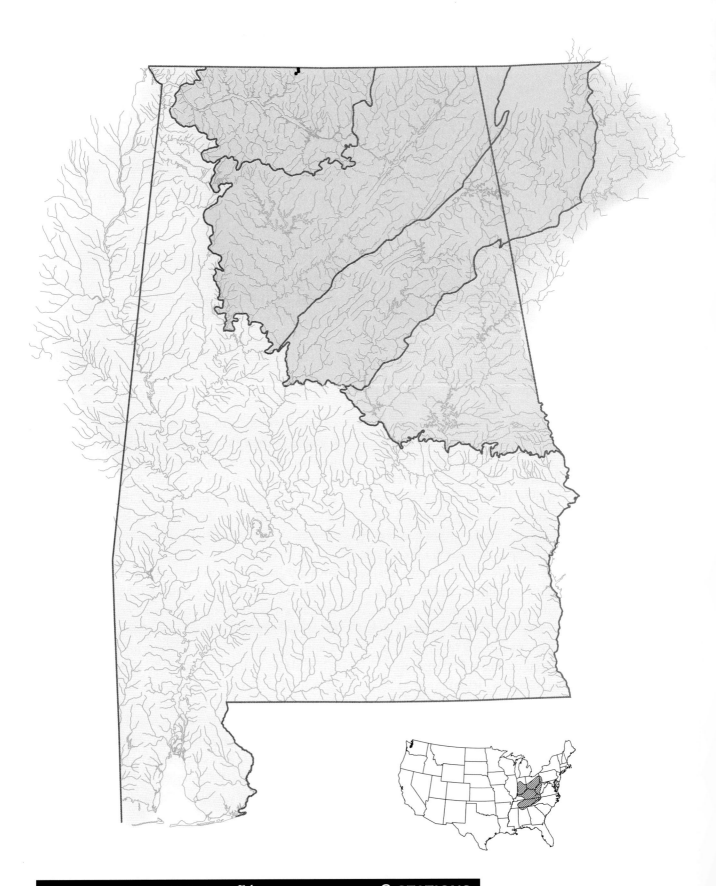

598

Etheostoma camurum

(Cope, 1870)

ETYMOLOGY:

Etheostoma—strain mouth, possibly referring to the small mouth

camurum—blunt-headed

Elk River, Limestone County, 5 October 1993, 2.0 in (51 mm) SL male, GSA 4614

CHARACTERISTICS: The bluebreast darter is distinguishable by a compressed body, deep caudal peduncle, and horizontal banding along the posterior two-thirds of the body. The snout is wide and rounded, while the lips are thick with a wide frenum on the upper lip. Gill membranes are separate to slightly connected. On the back are seven to 10 obscure saddles, and adult males have eight to 12 obscure but vertically elongated lateral spots along the sides. The body is olive green speckled with red or brown spots on the sides. On breeding adults the breast is green to bluish green, while the spiny dorsal fin is reddish gray with dark pigment anteriorly near the base. *Etheostoma camurum* is similar to the redline darter, *E. rufilineatum*, which has cheeks and gill covers marked with horizontal dashes, and to the boulder darter, *E. wapiti*, which is generally larger, lacks blue color on the breast, and has a more pointed snout. See Cope (1870b) for original description.

ADULT SIZE: 1.4 to 2.2 in (35 to 55 mm)

DISTRIBUTION: Etnier and Starnes (1993) report a population of bluebreast darters in the Elk River system just north of the Alabama-Tennessee state line. Chances of the species ocurring in Alabama appeared to be dim until 1993 when we discovered a fairly substantial population in the Elk River proper, approximately half a mile south of the state line. The same collection produced another fish species not previously known from Alabama, the mountain madtom, ***Noturus eleutherus***.

HABITAT AND BIOLOGY: We collected bluebreast darters around large boulders and over cobble in swift riffles and chutes. In addition, we collected and released substantial numbers of the redline darter and four individuals of the boulder darter. Spawning occurs from mid-May to mid-June; eggs are deposited in gravel and sand near large boulders (Mount, 1959). Stiles (1972) reports that areas behind boulders offer protected habitats for spawning adults. Midge larvae, baetid mayflies, blackflies, and caddisflies are primary food items (Bryant, 1979). Future sampling in the Elk River and other large streams near the Tennessee state line may yield additional localities for the bluebreast darter in Alabama.

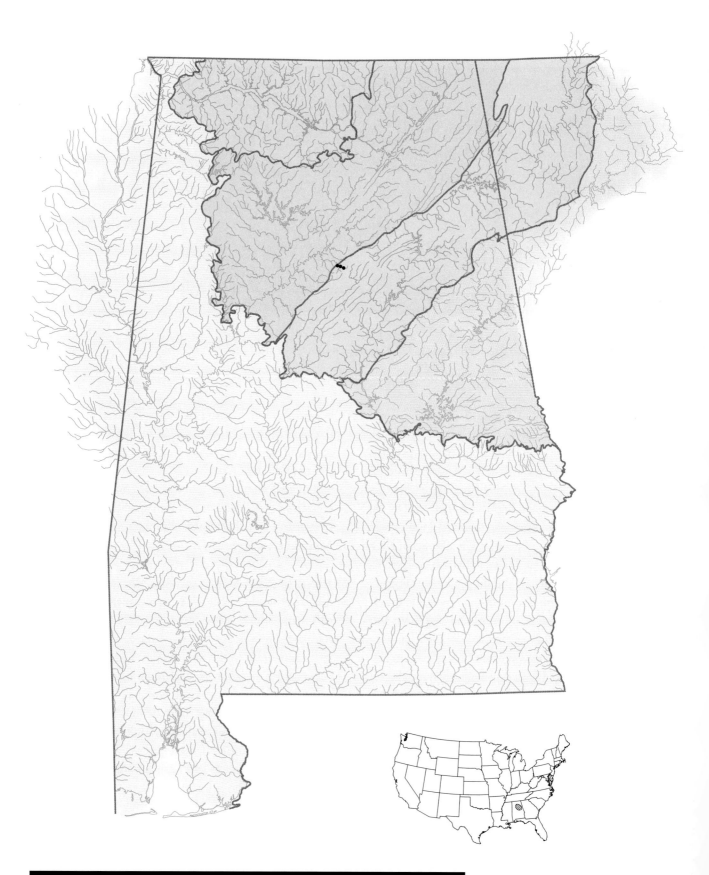

Turkey Creek, Jefferson County, 9 March 1993, 2.1 in (52 mm) SL male, GSA 4367

Etheostoma chermocki
Boschung and Mayden, 1992

ETYMOLOGY:
Etheostoma—strain mouth, possibly referring to the small mouth
chermocki—in honor of R. L. Chermock, former director of the Environmental Geology Division at the Geological Survey of Alabama

CHARACTERISTICS: The vermilion darter has a poorly developed frenum hidden under the upper lip flap and broadly connected gill membranes. Breeding males have a light olive to straw-colored body, and the back is crossed by eight dark olive saddles. Brick red spots and olive green blotches occur along the lateral line. The lower sides, venter, and lower caudal peduncle area are dark vermilion, which occasionally extends dorsally to the lateral line. The spiny dorsal fin has a cherry-red ocellus in the first membrane and a broad, brick red submarginal band in the remaining membranes. The soft dorsal fin has a submarginal red band along its entire length. *Etheostoma chermocki* is distinguished from the Warrior darter, *E. bellator,* by its stockier body, shorter caudal peduncle, taller dorsal fins, and more extensive vermilion along the venter. See Boschung et al. (1992) for original description and Suttkus and Bailey (1993) for additional diagnostic information.

ADULT SIZE: 1.8 to 2.4 in (45 to 60 mm)

DISTRIBUTION: *Etheostoma chermocki* is limited in distribution to upper Turkey Creek, a tributary to the Locust Fork of the Black Warrior River system in Jefferson County, Alabama. Existing populations appear isolated in the Birmingham–Big Canoe Valley section of the Alabama Valley and Ridge physiographic province.

HABITAT AND BIOLOGY: The vermilion darter occurs in moderate to swift currents in streams of alternating riffles and pools. Riffles contain small limestone rubble and shale cobble. Clean bedrock, occasionally covered with a layer of sand, occurs in pools. Breeding individuals have been captured during April in root mats of water willow in larger riffles and shoals. Near springs, we captured individuals in swift runs and chutes adjacent to watercress and pondweed. Sedimentation from urban expansion threatens the preferred habitat of this species.

REMARKS: The type locality of the vermilion darter is Turkey Creek, Jefferson County, Alabama.

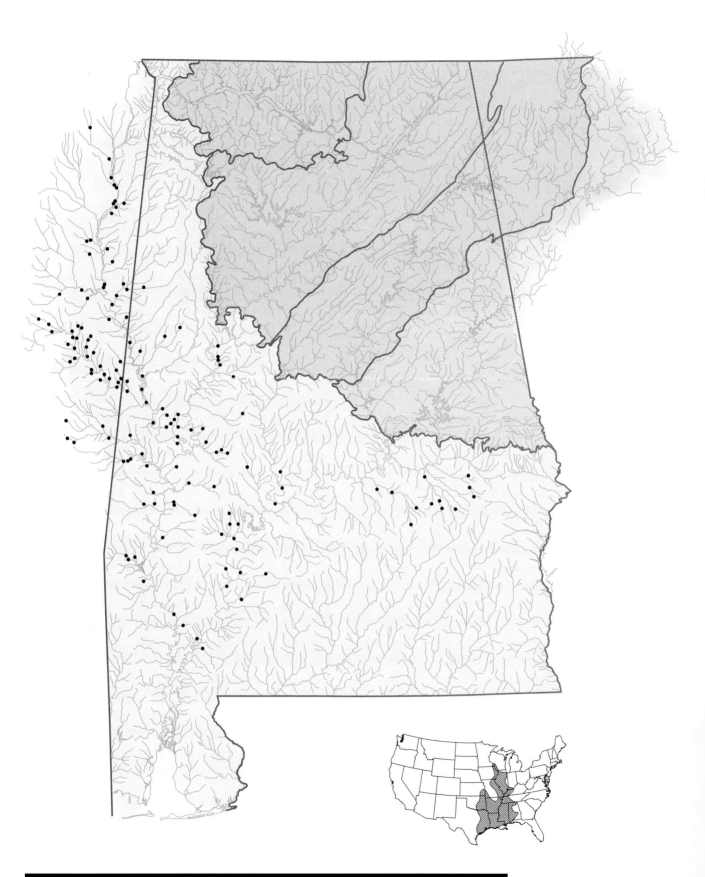

BLUNTNOSE DARTER *Etheostoma chlorosomum* 143 STATIONS

Etheostoma chlorosomum

(Hay, 1881)

ETYMOLOGY:

Etheostoma—strain mouth, possibly referring to the small mouth

chlorosomum—green body

Horsehunter Creek, Noxubee County, Mississippi, 12 May 1995, 1.7 in (43 mm) SL male, GSA 4645

CHARACTERISTICS: The bluntnose darter is a slender species with a blunt snout. Live individuals are often translucent. The body color is generally light yellow or olive with brown or black markings. The back has six to seven diffuse saddles and the sides have eight to 10 X-, V-, or W-shaped blotches. Thin black preorbital bars form a continuous bridle around the snout, extending slightly onto the upper lip. This continuous bridle distinguishes *Etheostoma chlorosomum* from the similar johnny darter, *E. nigrum*, which has an interrupted bridle. A small but clearly visible spot is present at the base of the caudal fin. Black bands develop in the spiny dorsal fin of breeding males. The enlarged genital papilla of the female is also characteristic of this species.

ADULT SIZE: 1.2 to 2 in (30 to 50 mm)

DISTRIBUTION: Widely distributed, the bluntnose darter occurs throughout the Mississippi basin from Minnesota to Louisiana and in Gulf coastal drainages from San Antonio Bay east to the Mobile basin. In the Mobile basin, *E. chlorosomum* is found below the Fall Line in the Tombigbee and Alabama river drainages.

HABITAT AND BIOLOGY: We have collected bluntnose darters in low-gradient streams, pools, oxbow lakes, ponds, and around the margins of lakes in the Coastal Plain, most of which are perceived as less than favorable habitats for most darter species. This species prefers muddy or sandy substrates. Individuals in obvious spawning condition have been collected in April. Page et al. (1982) report that eggs are placed on plants or plant debris. We have never taken bluntnose darters in large numbers, despite their wide distribution. Our largest series came from Horsehunter Creek, Noxubee County, Mississippi in May 1995. Etnier and Starnes (1993) report a diet of aquatic insects including caddisflies, beetles, and midge larvae.

LIPSTICK DARTER   *Etheostoma chuckwachatte*   31 STATIONS

Etheostoma chuckwachatte
Wood and Mayden, 1993

ETYMOLOGY:
Etheostoma—strain mouth, possibly referring to the small mouth *chuckwachatte*—anglacized version of the Creek words for mouth and red lips, referring to the red lips of breeding males

Hillabee Creek, Tallapoosa County, 24 June 1992, 2.1 in (53 mm) SL male, GSA 4321

CHARACTERISTICS: The lipstick, Tuskaloosa, and Etowah darters were considered a single species, the greenbreast darter, *Etheostoma jordani*, until recently (Wood and Mayden, 1993). Red lips, bright red spots along the sides, a broad red band in the anal fin of adult males, and scales on the opercles distinguish the lipstick darter from other members of the *E. jordani* species group. The lipstick darter is distinguishable from other species in the subgenus *Nothonotus* by the absence of dark horizontal lines between scale rows, by lack of dark mottling along the sides, and by absence of a broad red band in the caudal fin of males.

ADULT SIZE: 1.2 to 2.2 in (30 to 55 mm)

DISTRIBUTION: *Etheostoma chuckwachatte* is endemic to the Tallapoosa River system of the Mobile basin in Alabama and Georgia. Collection records are limited almost exclusively to the northern Piedmont Upland.

HABITAT AND BIOLOGY: Adult lipstick darters inhabit riffles of medium to large streams with a moderate to swift current and gravel, cobble, and boulder substrates. Orr and Ramsey (1990) report that populations in Hillabee Creek spawn from late April to late June, with peak activity in May. Adhesive eggs are buried in the sand. These authors speculate that individuals they examined had a life span of two or more years. Like many riffle-dwelling darters, the lipstick darter eats aquatic insect larvae.

REMARKS: The type locality of the lipstick darter is Hillabee Creek near Alexander City, Tallapoosa County, Alabama.

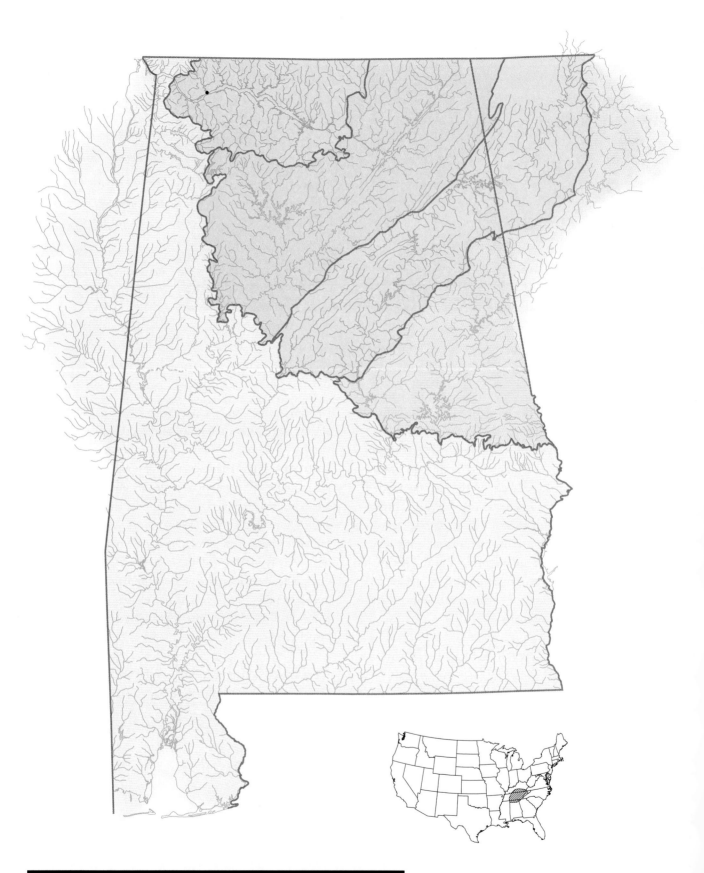

Etheostoma cinereum
Storer, 1845

ETYMOLOGY:
Etheostoma—strain mouth, possibly referring to the small mouth
cinereum—ashy, referring to the ashy gray color of the diagonal bands along the flanks

Little River, Blount County, Tennessee, 11 November 1981, 3.1 in (79 mm) SL male. Photograph courtesy of John R. and Peggy Shute

CHARACTERISTICS: The ashy darter is considered one of the more primitive species in the genus *Etheostoma* (Page, 1983). Individuals are characterized by a long snout, papillose lips, separate gill membranes, and a very long soft dorsal fin in breeding males. The sides have an obvious mid-lateral row of 12 small, dark gray-brown elongated blotches. Four to six longitudinal rows of small brown spots extend along the upper side of the body and back from the head to the caudal fin. General body color is dusky yellow. The spiny dorsal fin of breeding males has a margin with red markings throughout and a bright blue-green spot in the first membrane; the soft dorsal fin has bright red membranes. The chin, lower gill covers, breast, belly, and lower caudal peduncle are bright blue, as are the anal and pelvic fins. See Storer (1845b) for original description.

ADULT SIZE: 2.4 to 3.9 in (60 to 100 mm)

DISTRIBUTION: Although *E. cinereum* has not been collected in Alabama since 1845, a 1981 Elk River collection near Fayetteville, Tennessee, offers hope that the species may still inhabit state waters near the Alabama-Tennessee state line.

HABITAT AND BIOLOGY: Life history information about the ashy darter is from Shepard and Burr (1984). The ashy darter occurs in clear pools and eddies of medium to large upland streams characterized by a sluggish flow and silt-free sand or gravel substrates. It is usually found in low numbers and is associated with cover such as snags, boulders, or stands of water willow. This is a long-lived species, with a maximum life span of four years. Generally, only the large males and females spawn, from January to April, peaking in March. Small individuals feed on midge larvae, while large individuals feed on burrowing mayflies and worms. Etnier and Starnes (1993) report a considerable amount of detritus and sand grains in stomachs of fishes they examined.

REMARKS: Storer (1845) gave the type locality of the ashy darter as "near Florence."

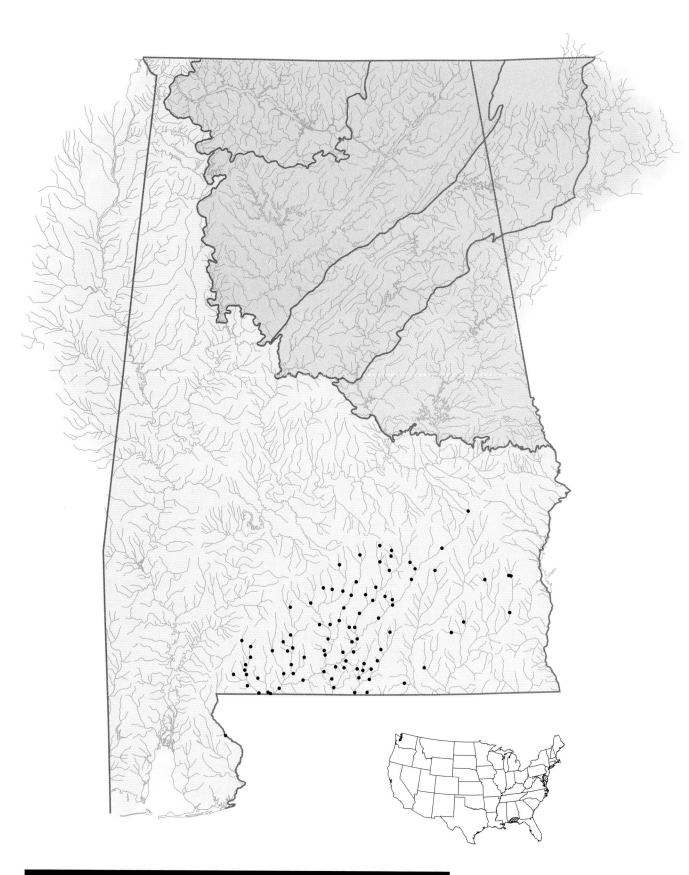

COASTAL DARTER *Etheostoma colorosum* **90 STATIONS**

608

Etheostoma colorosum
Suttkus and Bailey, 1993

ETYMOLOGY:
Etheostoma—strain mouth, possibly referring to the small mouth
colorosum—abundant color, referring to the exuberant colors on breeding males

Jordan Creek, Conecuh County, 4 May 1995, 1.9 in (48 mm) SL male, GSA 4643

CHARACTERISTICS: Breeding coastal darter males are distinguished by a series of small orange to red spots that extend along the side from the pectoral fin to the caudal fin base. Below these spots is a series of dark lateral blotches that are ovoid or quadrate and centered on the lateral line. Red in the spiny dorsal fin is limited to the posterior three to five membranes, resulting in an incomplete band from front to back. An incomplete black band extends posteriorly for six to eight membranes from the front of the fin. Breeding males have a weak orange stripe on the lower side, while the breast, gill membranes, lower gill covers, cheeks, and side of the snout are turquoise, as are the anal, pelvic, and caudal fins.

ADULT SIZE: 1.2 to 2.3 in (30 to 58 mm)

DISTRIBUTION: *Etheostoma colorosum* is distributed in Gulf coastal drainages from the Perdido River system east to the Choctawhatchee Bay basin. In Alabama the coastal darter occurs extensively throughout the Conecuh, Escambia, and Yellow river systems and less frequently in the Choctawhatchee River drainage.

HABITAT AND BIOLOGY: The coastal darter is commonly found in areas of moderate to swift flow where it is associated with log snags or other debris. Hard cobble and rubble riffles are typically absent in the Coastal Plain, replaced there by zones of swift flow through log and debris snags over a substrate of sand and occasionally gravel. A region of hard substrate does occur in the Dougherty Plain physiographic district, which provides suitable habitat and partially explains the frequent occurrence of this species in the region. We have examined numerous individuals running milt and eggs in April. Spawning probably occurs throughout the range from early March to late April. Little information exists about the life history of this long-known, but only recently described, species.

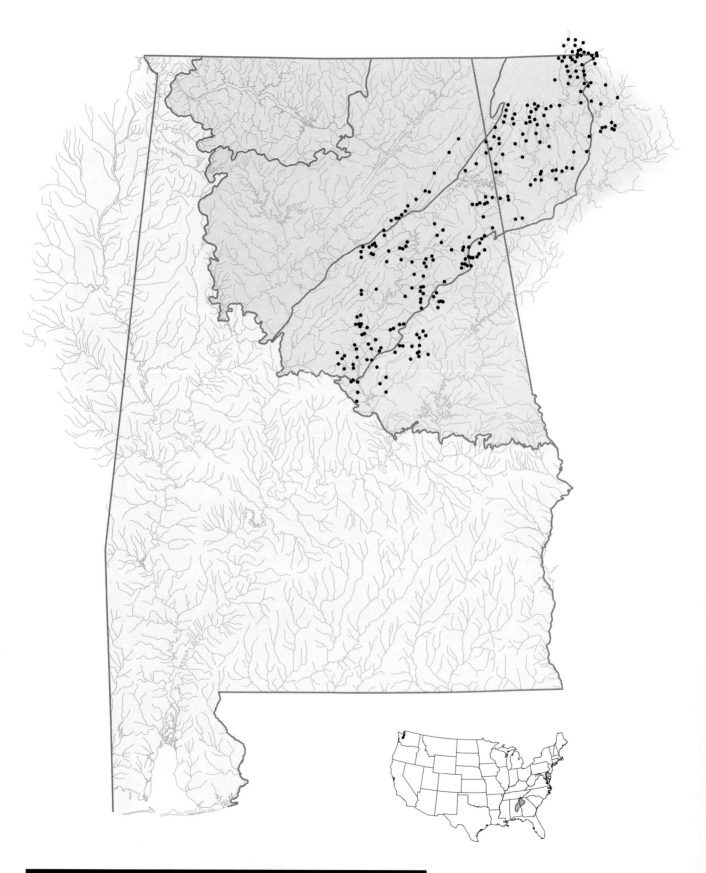

COOSA DARTER *Etheostoma coosae* 254 STATIONS

Etheostoma coosae
(Fowler, 1945)

ETYMOLOGY:
Etheostoma—strain mouth, possibly referring to the small mouth
coosae—in reference to its distributional range, the Coosa River

Blue Gut Creek, Chilton County, 21 April 1993, 1.9 in (49 mm) SL male, GSA 4433

CHARACTERISTICS: A robust species, the Coosa darter is characterized by a blunt snout, small mouth, and six rays in the broadly joined gill membranes, compared to five rays in most other *Ulocentra* species. *Etheostoma coosae* is most similar to the Cherokee darter, *E. scotti*, which also has six rays, sometimes five, in the gill membranes. The spiny dorsal fin of *E. coosae* is banded whereas in *E. scotti* the fin is entirely pigmented. The spiny dorsal fin has a medial red band through its entire length, but it lacks the front ocellus common to several other *Ulocentra*. Clear bands followed by dark bands occur above and below the red band. The medial portions of all soft dorsal fin membranes are red. Body color is yellow-olive, with eight to nine dark blotches both on the back and along the sides. The lower part of the snout and gular region are light green, while the anal fin and upper and lower parts of the caudal fin are turquoise. Lateral blotches have a slight green wash.

ADULT SIZE: 1.6 to 2.6 in (40 to 65 mm)

DISTRIBUTION: *Etheostoma coosae* is endemic to the Coosa River system in Alabama, Tennessee, and Georgia. It is replaced in the upper Etowah River system by *E. scotti*.

HABITAT AND BIOLOGY: The Coosa darter is widespread over rubble in raceways, around boulders, near sandbars, and occasionally in pool areas below riffles. O'Neil (1981) reports spawning from mid-March through mid-May for a central Coosa River population, with peak activity in April. Longevity in this population approaches three years. During spawning, the female places single eggs in small cracks and crevices in wood, rocks, or other similar structures, and the eggs are immediately fertilized by a male. Spawning position varies from upright to horizontal. The diet of *E. coosae* consists of midge larvae, microcrustaceans, mayfly larvae, and various other items including plant material, water mites, and mollusks. Dipterans are consumed in greater frequency during spring and summer, whereas crustaceans are a significant component in fall and winter.

REMARKS: The type locality of the Coosa darter is a small stream near Chesterfield, Cherokee County, Alabama.

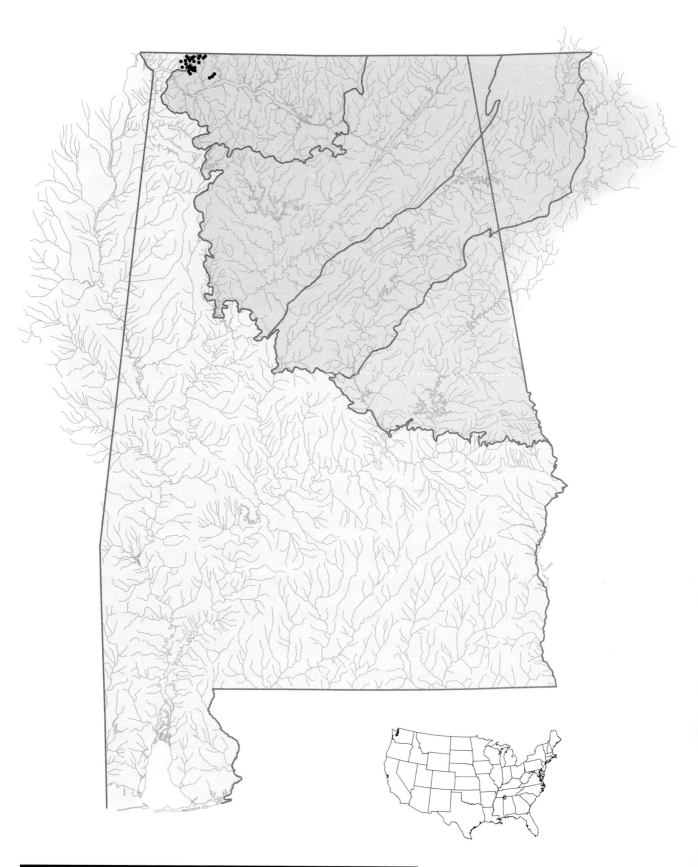

CROWN DARTER   *Etheostoma corona*   28 STATIONS

Etheostoma corona
Page and Ceas, 1992

ETYMOLOGY:
Etheostoma—strain mouth, possibly referring to the small mouth
corona—refers to the crown-like appearance of the soft dorsal fin on breeding males

Middle Cypress Creek, Wayne County, Tennessee, 24 March 1993, 2.7 in (68 mm) SL male, GSA 4419

CHARACTERISTICS: Breeding males of the crown darter have a dark soft dorsal fin with a bright egg yellow margin. The fin membranes extend almost to the tips of the rays. Each ray has three branches; the second and third rays, close together and of equal length, are distinctly separate from the first ray, giving the entire fin a frilled appearance. Six or seven rows of rectangular, clear to yellow bars are present on the dark fin rays in the soft dorsal fin. The caudal fin usually has 11 or 12 clear yellow and black alternating bands. The spiny dorsal fin is dusky black, with a small yellow or white knob on the tip of each spine. Body color in breeding males is dusky to black. Crown darters are similar in appearance to the fringed, blackfin, and lollipop darters, *Etheostoma crossopterum*, *E. nigripinne*, and *E. neopterum*, respectively. However, distributions of these three species generally do not overlap with the crown darter's limited range. See Page et al. (1992) for original description.

ADULT SIZE: 1.6 to 3 in (40 to 75 mm)

DISTRIBUTION: *Etheostoma corona* is known only from the Cypress Creek system in Tennessee and Alabama. Although its range is quite small, it is usually abundant within its preferred habitat.

HABITAT AND BIOLOGY: Crown darters occur in small headwater streams to medium-sized rivers, but are generally abundant in small streams. Although individuals have been taken in a variety of habitats, they are more common in pools and areas with reduced flow. Breeding individuals seek sheltered spawning sites, where the females deposit eggs on the underside of objects such as rocks and logs. Adults and larvae have been collected in spring seeps flowing through lowlands adjacent to headwater streams, and nuptial individuals have been found from late March to early June. Little else is known about the biology of this recently described species.

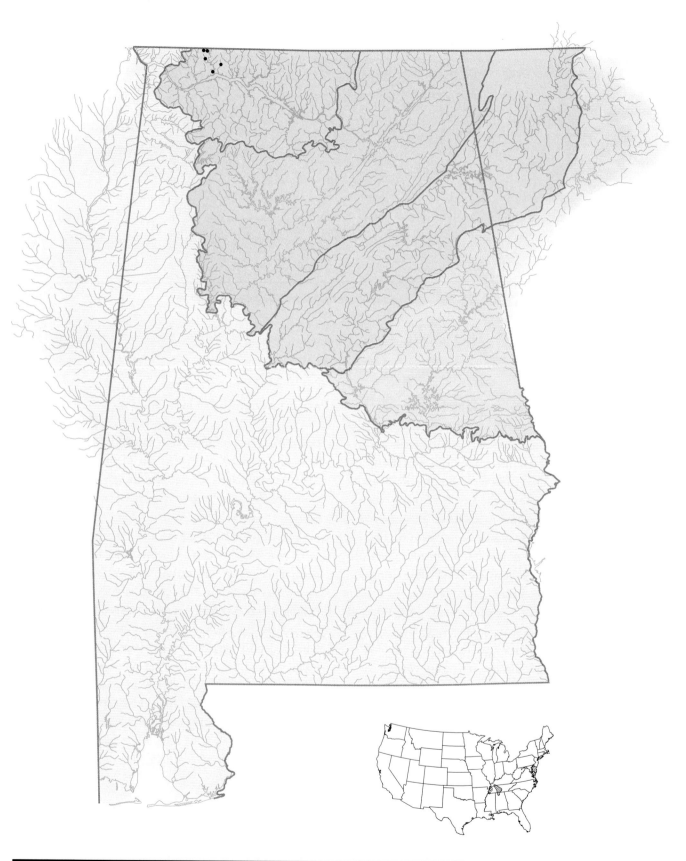

FRINGED DARTER   *Etheostoma crossopterum*   5 STATIONS

Etheostoma crossopterum
Braasch and Mayden, 1985

ETYMOLOGY:
Etheostoma—strain mouth, possibly referring to the small mouth
crossopterum—fringed fin, referring to the fringed soft dorsal fin on breeding males

Wilson Creek, Lauderdale County, 2 April 1993, 3.1 in (79 mm) SL male, GSA 4405

CHARACTERISTICS: The soft dorsal fin structure of breeding males for the fringed darter, *Etheostoma crossopterum*, and the crown darter, *E. corona*, is very similar. The soft dorsal fin of the fringed darter is dark with a white margin and three branches per ray. The third ray is elongated, and the second branch is much shorter than the third but slightly longer than the first. There are no knobs at the tips of the rays, which extend past the fin membranes. Six to seven horizontal rows of clear to light yellow crescents occur on the dorsal fin rays, sometimes connecting to form wavy lines. The caudal fin has five to nine clear to yellow and black alternating bands. The spiny dorsal fin is dusky with a small white knob on the tip of each spine. Fringed darters can be confused with crown, blackfin, and lollipop darters, *E. corona*, *E. nigripinne*, and *E. neopterum*, respectively, but occur syntopically only with *E. neopterum*, which has windows instead of crescents on the soft dorsal fin, large yellow knobs on the soft dorsal fin, and more light yellow bands (8–12) on the caudal fin (Page et al., 1992).

ADULT SIZE: 2 to 3.3 in (50 to 85 mm)

DISTRIBUTION: *Etheostoma crossopterum* occurs in the Cumberland, Duck, and Buffalo river systems and Shoal Creek system in Tennessee and Kentucky. Its range in Alabama is limited to Butler and Little Butler creeks of the Shoal Creek system, and to the Six Mile Creek system, which lies just east of Shoal Creek.

HABITAT AND BIOLOGY: Fringed darters occupy small headwater streams to medium-sized rivers. Although individuals have been taken in a variety of habitats, they are common around boulders in pool areas with reduced flow, in slabrock riffles, and in flowing pools with eroded depressions. Breeding individuals seek sheltered spawning sites, where eggs are clumped in a single layer on the underside of rocks or other objects. We have captured breeding adults from late March into early June. The diet, presumed to be similar to that of other members of the subgenus *Catonotus*, includes aquatic insect larvae, plant material, and possibly microcrustaceans.

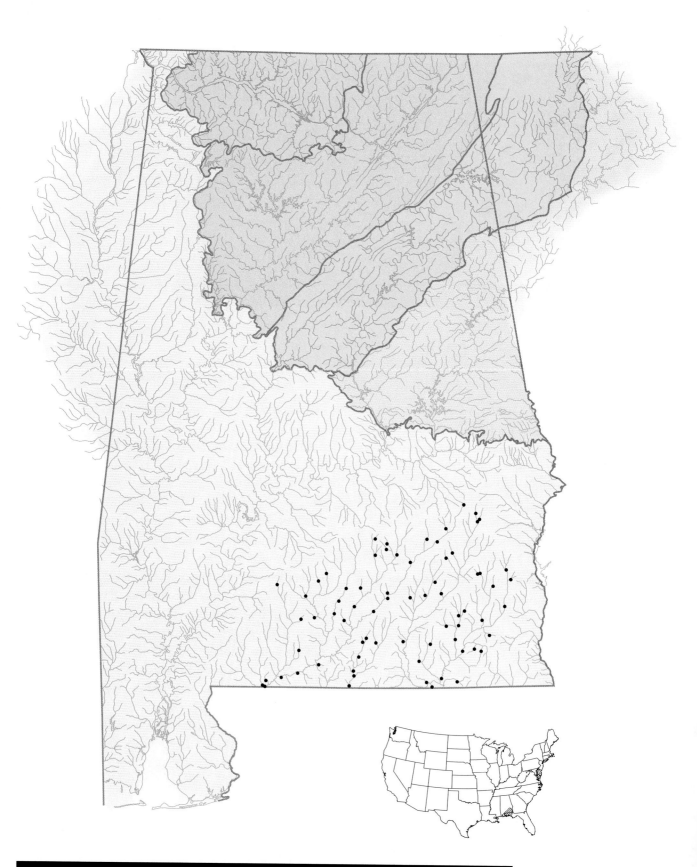

CHOCTAWHATCHEE DARTER   *Etheostoma davisoni*   71 STATIONS

Pea River, Bullock County, 7 April 1993, 1.4 in (35 mm) SL female, GSA 4412

CHARACTERISTICS: The Choctawhatchee darter is characterized by a body speckled with seven to 10 dark mid-lateral black and brown markings in W-, X- and M- shapes. Six narrow saddles cross the back and a bridle extends forward from the eyes, encircling the snout. *Etheostoma davisoni* is similar in appearance to the bluntnose darter, *E. chlorosomum,* from which it can be distinguished by the bridle of pigment extending over and around the snout. In *E. davisoni* the bridle is thinner and is confined almost entirely to the tip of the snout, while in *E. chlorosomum*, it is wider and extends slightly onto the upper lip. The body is the color of straw with an occasional light green wash along the back. The venter and breast are white. Dorsal and caudal fins are banded with light brown. Breeding males are generally dark with pigment spots over the body. Although also similar to *E. stigmaeum*, *E. davisoni* lacks nuptial coloration and breeding tubercles in males, and its cheek is completely covered with scales.

ADULT SIZE: 1.2 to 2 in (30 to 50 mm)

DISTRIBUTION: The Choctawhatchee darter is distributed in Alabama and Florida from the Escambia River drainage east to the Choctawhatchee River drainage.

HABITAT AND BIOLOGY: *Etheostoma davisoni* inhabits pools characterized by little or no flow. We have collected individuals on sand and gravel substrates and near the margins of flowing waters over sticks, aquatic plants, or root masses. Howell (1968) reports a habitat of sandbars in large rivers, the mouths of sloughs, and small to large streams, with individuals preferring slow pools over sand. Spawning occurs from mid-March to late May.

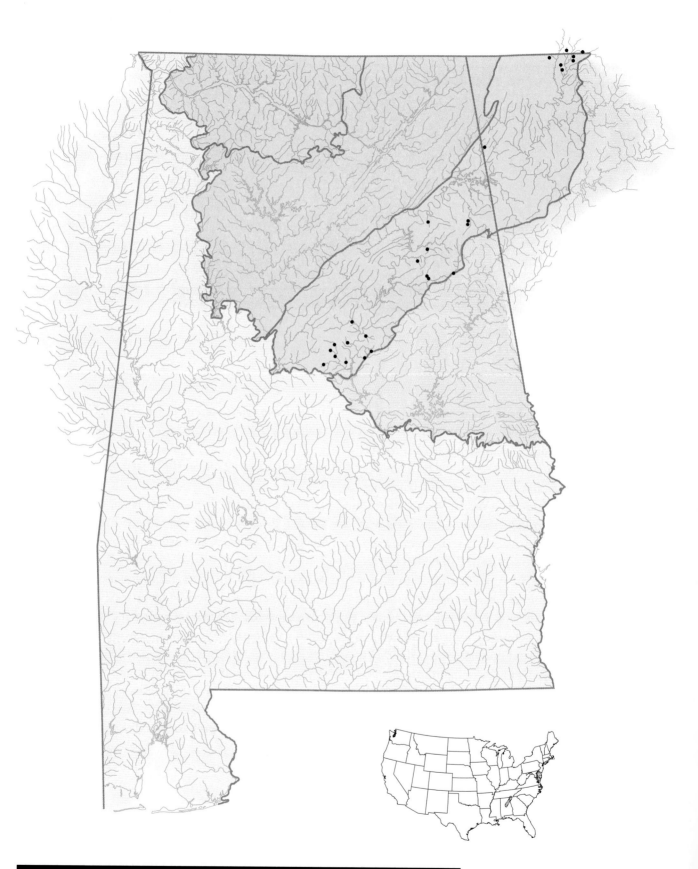

Etheostoma ditrema
Ramsey and Suttkus, 1965

ETYMOLOGY:
Etheostoma—strain mouth, possibly referring to the small mouth
ditrema—two-holed, referring to the two coronal pores present in the original populations discovered

Camp Branch, Shelby County, 21 April 1993, 1.7 in (43 mm) SL male, GSA 4434

CHARACTERISTICS: The coldwater darter is a small, somewhat slender species with a moderately arched and incompletely pored lateral line. The color of male *Etheostoma ditrema* is generally uniform brown on the back with faint longitudinal lines on the upper part of the sides. The venter and caudal peduncle are orange to red-orange, while the spiny dorsal fin is blue marginally and basally with a red-orange submarginal band. Other fins are generally light yellow with brown bands.

ADULT SIZE: 1 to 1.9 in (25 to 49 mm)

DISTRIBUTION: The coldwater darter is endemic to the Coosa River system of the Mobile basin, occurring intermittently from the Conasauga River downstream to Waxahatchee Creek in Chilton and Shelby counties.

HABITAT AND BIOLOGY: Preferred habitats of the coldwater darter include vegetated springs, spring runs, and small streams in areas of extensive spring development. Specimens collected in Beeswax Creek in Shelby County were found over aquatic moss and algae in a shoal area about 12 inches deep. In spring habitats, *Etheostoma ditrema* is associated with water milfoil and aquatic moss, with moss being the preferred substrate (Seesock, 1979). This species has an extended spawning season in spring habitat, lasting from March through September with peak activity between April and June. Seesock (1979) reports that adhesive eggs are deposited on leaves in beds of water milfoil and possibly on moss during vertical spawnings. Individuals may live to be two years old. Coldwater darters feed on crustaceans associated with spring habitats, including amphipods, isopods, and copepods as well as midge larvae and lesser amounts of other aquatic insect larvae.

REMARKS: The type locality for the coldwater darter is a spring tributary to Mills Creek near Lyerly, Chattooga County, Georgia. The species is protected by rules and regulations of the Alabama Game and Fish Department.

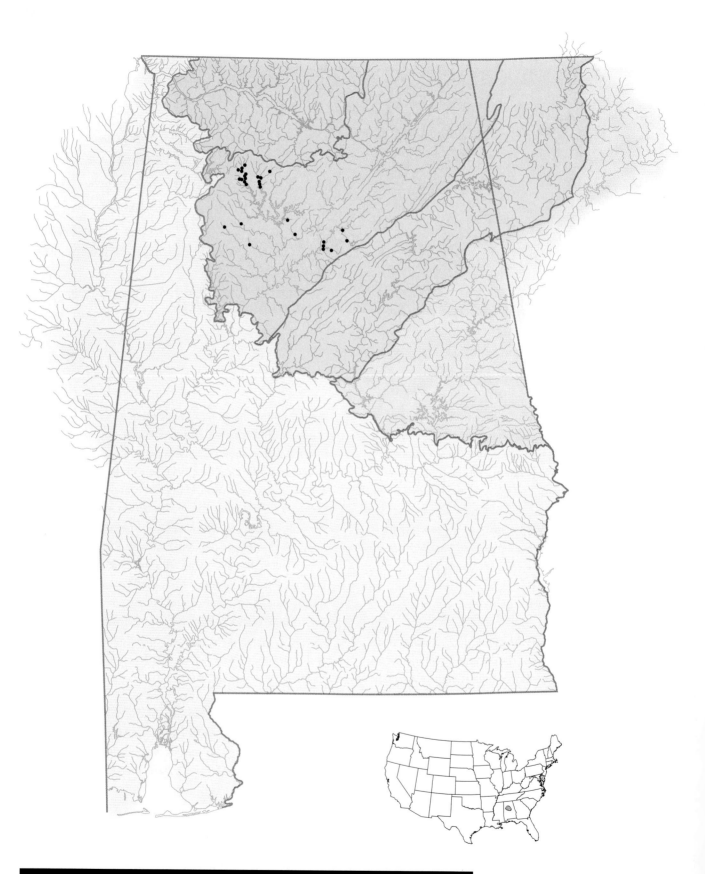

TUSKALOOSA DARTER   *Etheostoma douglasi*   **28 STATIONS**

Etheostoma douglasi
Wood and Mayden, 1993

ETYMOLOGY:
Etheostoma—strain mouth, possibly referring to the small mouth
douglasi—in honor of Neil H. Douglas, biology professor at Northwestern Louisiana State University and contributor to southeastern ichthyology

West Fork, Sipsey River, Winston County, 12 May 1994, 1.9 in (48 mm) SL male, GSA 4628

CHARACTERISTICS: The Tuskaloosa darter is distinguishable from other members of the *Etheostoma jordani* species group (see greenbreast darter species account) by the lack of red spots along the sides, absence of scales on the opercles, and by having no red pigment on the lips and anal fin. The body of breeding males is olive with a weakly formed pattern of three to 11 dark vertical bars along the sides. The back has eight or nine olive to brown blotches. Lower parts of the head, breast, and gill membranes are turquoise. The spiny dorsal fin has a clear to white margin with a submarginal red band most prominent on the front of the fin. The caudal fin has a narrow turquoise or black margin followed by a yellow band, which precedes a broad red band.

ADULT SIZE: 1.2 to 2 in (30 to 50 mm)

DISTRIBUTION: Collection records of *E. douglasi* are limited to disjunct populations in the Locust Fork sys-tem and upper Sipsey Fork system in the Bankhead Forest. Both systems lie above the Fall Line in the Cumberland Plateau physiographic province and are tributaries of the Black Warrior River system of the Mobile basin.

HABITAT AND BIOLOGY: Adults of this species occur in cobble, gravel, and slab riffles of moderate to swift flow. Spawning occurs from late April to early June, peaking in May. O'Neil (1980) reports females with mature ova ready for spawning in April and May. The diet of *E. douglasi* is presumably similar to that of *E. jordani*, which consumes midge larvae, mayflies, water mites, caddisflies, and occasionally some mol-lusks.

REMARKS: The type locality for the Tuskaloosa darter is the West Fork of the Sipsey River, Winston County, Alabama.

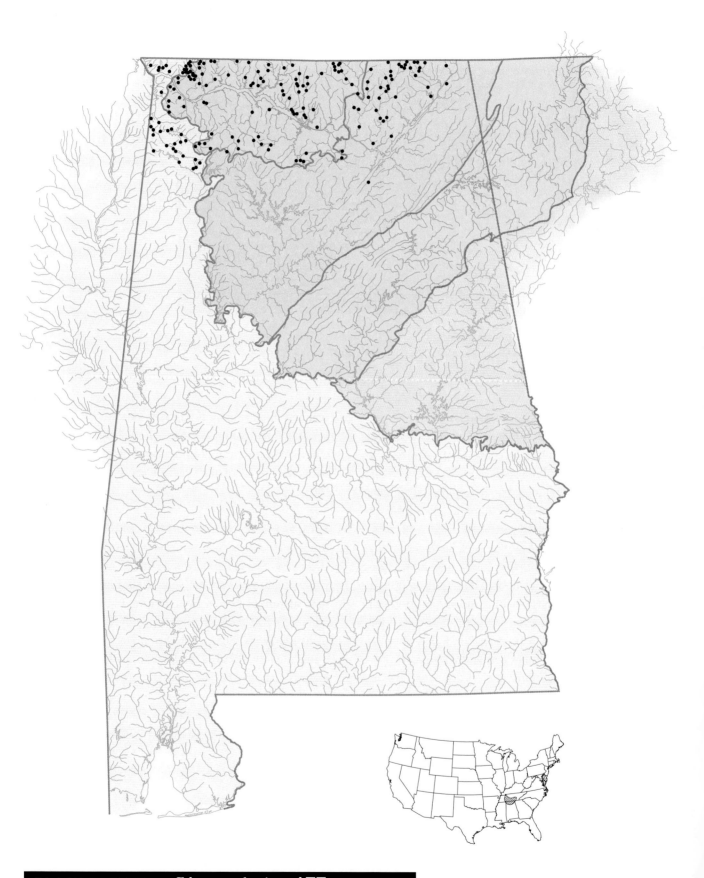

Etheostoma duryi

Henshall, 1889

ETYMOLOGY:

Etheostoma—strain mouth, possibly referring to the small mouth

duryi—in honor of Charles Dury, original collector of this species

Butler Creek, Lauderdale County, 24 February 1993, 1.9 in (47 mm) SL male, GSA 4358

CHARACTERISTICS: The black darter, a member of the subgenus *Ulocentra*, is easily recognized by its midlateral black blotches, which are fused, forming an irregular midlateral stripe. Similar to the snubnose darter, *Etheostoma simoterum*, the black darter is distinguishable by the absence of a frenum on the upper lip and by having a more pronounced snout; the snubnose darter has a frenum and a very blunt snout. The back of the black darter is usually brown or yellow, with eight dark saddles. The fourth saddle extends ventrally and often joins an expanded lateral blotch, a marking very characteristic of the species. Venter and breast are usually light yellow to orange while the snout, lower head, outer margin of the anal fin, and upper and lower margins of the caudal fin are turquoise. Soft dorsal fin membranes are red. The spiny dorsal fin has a red marginal band and a white submarginal band, followed by a poorly defined row composed of red, brown, and white blotches, as well as stippling. The base of the spiny dorsal fin is black.

ADULT SIZE: 1.6 to 2.4 in (40 to 60 mm)

DISTRIBUTION: *Etheostoma duryi* is restricted to the Tennessee River drainage and occurs most commonly in the southern bend of the river in Alabama and Tennessee. It is widely distributed in the Tennessee River Valley in Alabama and is often abundant in collections.

HABITAT AND BIOLOGY: Black darters inhabit pools and riffles of small to medium-sized, clear streams flowing over gravel, rubble, or slabrock substrates. Spawning occurs from late March to early May, peaking during April. Females usually lay single eggs in small depressions on the sides of rocks, logs, and other suitable hard surfaces (Page et al., 1982); the eggs are immediately fertilized by a nearby male. Etnier and Starnes (1993) report a longevity of three years. Aquatic larvae of midges, mayflies, caddisflies, and blackflies comprise the diet.

623

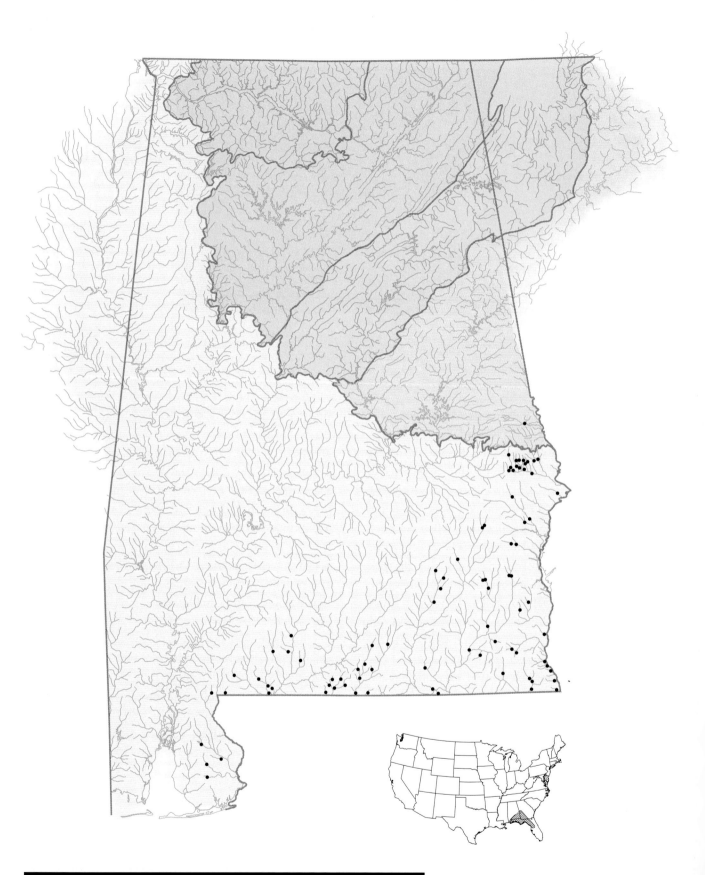

Etheostoma edwini
(Hubbs and Cannon, 1935)

ETYMOLOGY:
Etheostoma—strain mouth, possibly referring to the small mouth
edwini—in honor of Edwin P. Creaser, who provided the authors with specimens for description

Jernigan Mill Creek, Escambia County, 16 June 1993, 1.3 in (33 mm) SL male, GSA 4484

CHARACTERISTICS: The brown darter is a small species characterized by a lateral line arched well below the spiny dorsal fin. Individuals have embedded scales on their cheeks and opercles, a broad frenum, and three distinct spots at the base of the tail. The body color is tan or light yellow, with seven to 10 dark brown square blotches. Males usually have a number of bright red spots scattered along their sides. Bordering the spots are stipples of dark brown or black that are in various stages of development. The cheeks and opercles have large black spots and a black bar is present below the eye. The spiny dorsal fin of the male has two to four rows of bright red spots with a black spot at the posterior end.

ADULT SIZE: 1.2 to 1.7 in (30 to 43 mm)

DISTRIBUTION: *Etheostoma edwini* occurs in Gulf coastal drainages from the Perdido River system east to the St. Johns River system in northeast Florida. In Alabama the brown darter occurs in all coastal drainages including the Perdido River, lower Conecuh River, Blackwater and Yellow rivers, Choctawhatchee River, and the Chattahoochee River upstream to the Fall Line.

HABITAT AND BIOLOGY: The preferred habitat of the brown darter is aquatic vegetation or exposed root masses in small to moderate-sized, shallow, flowing streams. Population densities are generally greater where silt or coarse detritus have accumulated among the vegetation. Williams (1976) reports a protracted spawning season, lasting from winter to late summer. A single egg is usually deposited per spawning act on vegetation and is subsequently fertilized by the male. Food items of this species include copepods, cladocerans, mayflies, midges, water mites, and stoneflies.

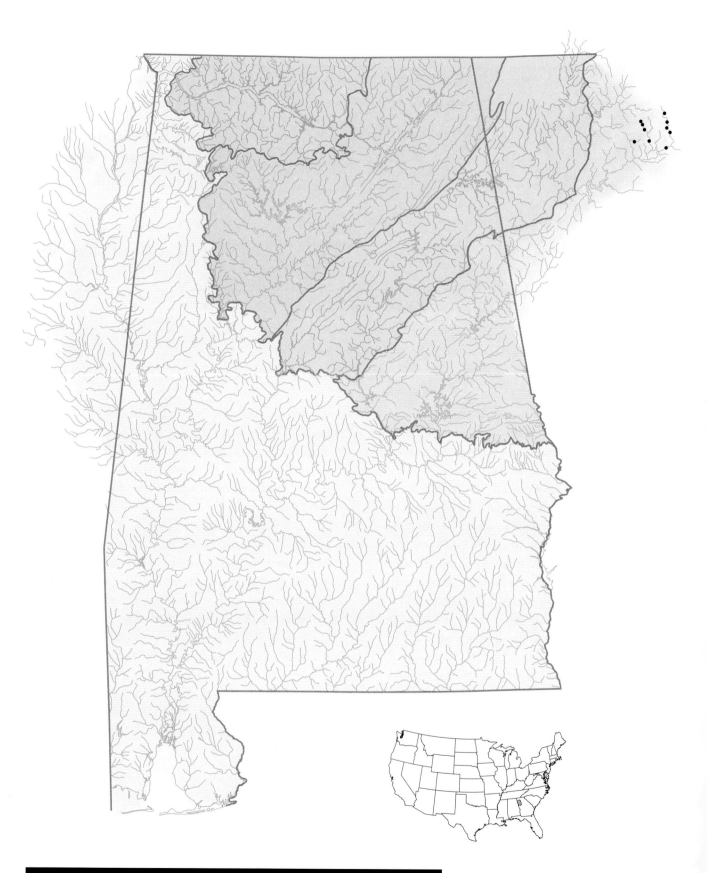

ETOWAH DARTER *Etheostoma etowahae* **10 STATIONS**

626

Etheostoma etowahae
Wood and Mayden, 1993

ETYMOLOGY:
Etheostoma—strain mouth, possibly referring to the small mouth
etowahae—in reference to its distributional range, the Etowah River in Georgia

Etowah River, Lumpkin County, Georgia, 2 May 1990, 1.8 in (47 mm) SL male, NMB 1171. Photograph courtesy of Noel M. Burkhead

CHARACTERISTICS: Breeding males of *Etheostoma etowahae* are dark olive with a weakly formed pattern of three to 11 dark vertical bars along their sides. The back has eight or nine olive to brown blotches. The lower portion of the head, breast, and gill membranes are all turquoise. The spiny dorsal fin of this species has a clear to white margin with a submarginal red band most prominent on the front of the fin. The caudal fin has a narrow turquoise or black margin followed by a yellow band, which is followed by a broad red band. The Etowah darter is distinguishable from other members of the *E. jordani* species group (see greenbreast darter species account) by the absence of red spots along the sides, no red banding in the anal fin, the absence of red pigment on the lips, and the presence of scales on the gill covers (Wood and Mayden, 1993).

ADULT SIZE: 1.6 to 2.2 in (40 to 55 mm)

DISTRIBUTION: The Etowah Darter is restricted to the Etowah River system of the upper Coosa River of Georgia, upstream of Lake Allatoona.

HABITAT AND BIOLOGY: Adults occur in small to medium-sized streams with cobble and gravel riffles and moderate to swift current. Because this species is newly described, little is known of its life history. Based on what is known of other species, spawning probably occurs from late April to early June, peaking in May. The diet of *E. etowahae* is presumably similar to that of the similar *E. jordani*, which consumes midge larvae, mayflies, water mites, caddisflies, and occasionally some mollusks.

REMARKS: The type locality for the Etowah darter is the Etowah River near Dawsonville, Lumpkin County, Georgia. The Etowah darter is listed as an endangered species by the U.S. Fish and Wildlife Service.

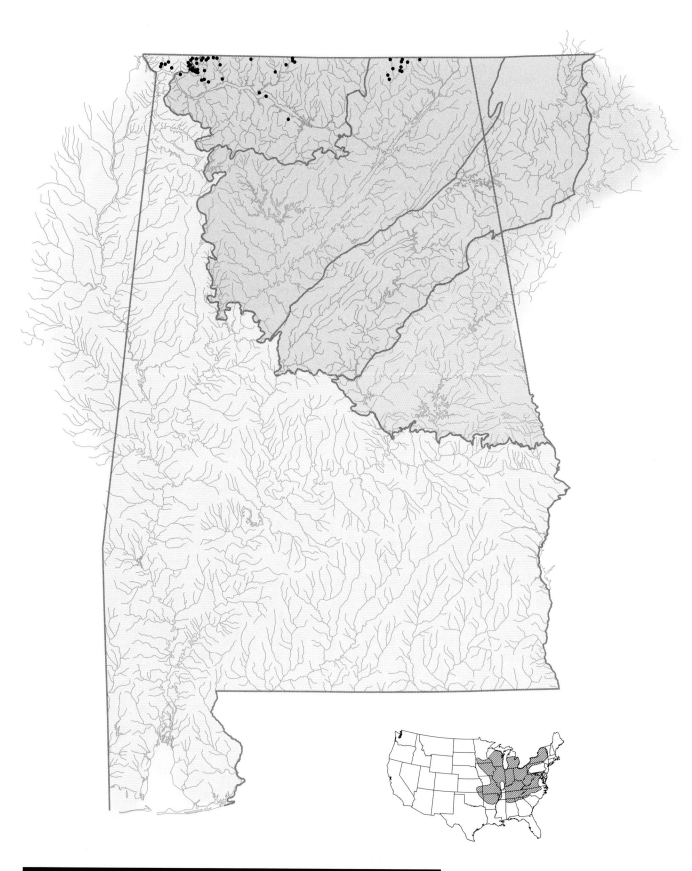

FANTAIL DARTER   *Etheostoma flabellare*   **53 STATIONS**

Etheostoma flabellare
Rafinesque, 1819

ETYMOLOGY:

Etheostoma—strain mouth, possibly referring to the small mouth

flabellare—fanlike, referring to the caudal fin

Cox Creek tributary, Lauderdale County, 24 February 1993, 1.8 in (45 mm) SL male, GSA 4428

CHARACTERISTICS: The fantail darter is characterized by a deep caudal peduncle, a protruding lower jaw, and broadly connected gill covers. Body color is brown to olive, with black stripes, 10 to 15 dark brown vertical bars, or both along the sides. The lateral bars are diffusely connected with about eight dark brown or black saddle blotches. The caudal fin and soft dorsal fin have black bands. The spiny dorsal fin is short, about half the height of the soft dorsal fin, and is typically black at the base, clear in the middle, and dusky at the margin with white, yellow, or gold knobs at the tip of each spine. *Etheostoma flabellare* is easily confused with the stripetail darter, *E. kennicotti*, which has a shorter spiny dorsal fin with smaller knobs on the tips, a prominent submarginal dark band below the knobs, and a more mottled pattern along its sides. Three subspecies of *E. flabellare* are presently recognized (McGeehan, 1995): *E. f. flabellare*, *E. f. brevispina*, and *E. f. humerale*.

ADULT SIZE: 1.3 to 3 in (33 to 75 mm)

DISTRIBUTION: *Etheostoma flabellare* is widely distributed throughout the upper Mississippi River basin and Great Lakes region with its southern extent reaching into Alabama. *Etheostoma f. flabellare* in Alabama is restricted to the Tennessee River drainage, commonly occurring in streams draining Lauderdale County, in upland tributaries of the Paint Rock River in Jackson County, and the Elk River in Limestone County.

HABITAT AND BIOLOGY: Adult fantail darters occur in shallow riffles of moderate to swift current over gravel and cobble substrate. Juveniles are often found in pools and slackwater areas downstream of riffles. Spawning occurs in April and May. Males establish territories in cavities beneath large rubble or small boulders. Females enter the nest, invert, and attach eggs in a single layer to the underside of a stone, after which eggs are fertilized by the male (Lake, 1936; Winn, 1958a, b). Bart and Page (1991) propose that the fleshy fin knobs on males function as egg mimics and stimulate female spawning activity. Individuals live to be four years old (Karr, 1964). The diet consists of midge larvae, mayflies, caddisflies, copepods, amphipods, and isopods.

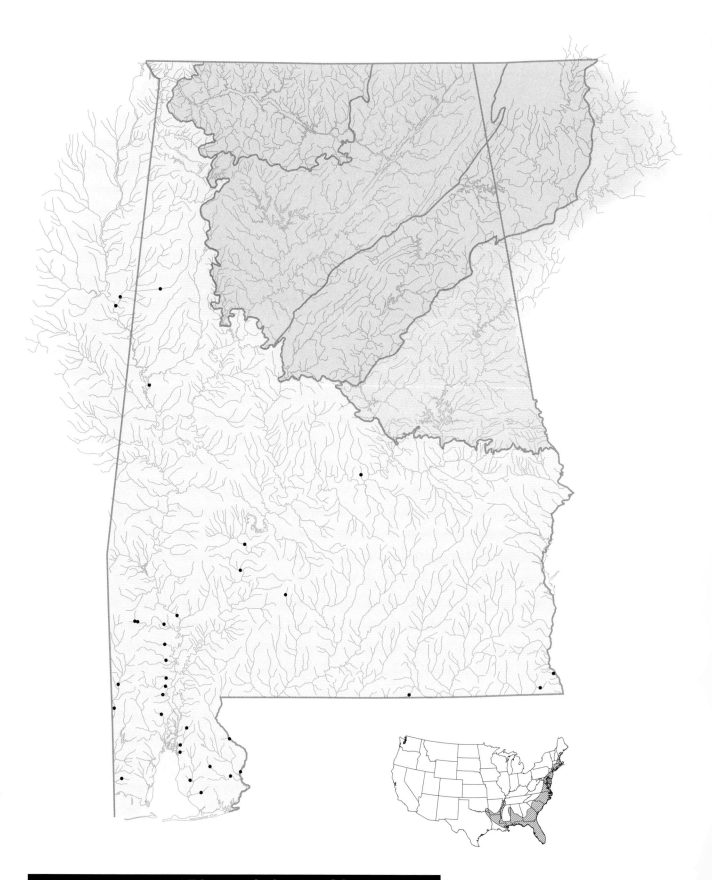

Etheostoma fusiforme
(Girard, 1854)

ETYMOLOGY:

Etheostoma—strain mouth, possibly referring to the small mouth *fusiforme*—long and cylindrical, referring to the fusiform body shape

Blackwater River, Baldwin County, 19 August 1992, 1.7 in (42 mm) SL male, GSA 4465

CHARACTERISTICS: Colors of both sexes of the swamp darter are rather subdued. The back is tan, light yellow, or green, and the venter is either white or light yellow with scattered dark pigment. The sides have about 10 to 12 brown, quadrate spots, and some individuals have a number of diffuse dorsal saddles. The fins are lightly banded or clear. Two prominent features of the swamp darter are a bar under the eye and one distinct spot at the base of the caudal fin. The lateral line is arched toward the spiny dorsal fin.

ADULT SIZE: 1.2 to 2 in (30 to 50 mm)

DISTRIBUTION: *Etheostoma fusiforme* is found in Atlantic and Gulf slope drainages from Maine to Louisiana. Collette (1962) recognizes two subspecies; *E. f. fusiforme* found from North Carolina north to Maine, and *E. f. barratti* found from South Carolina south to Florida and in Gulf slope drainages. Most collections of *E. f. barratti* in Alabama are from Baldwin, Mobile, and Washington counties in southwest Alabama. We also have scattered records from the Conecuh River system east to the Chattahoochee River system and the Alabama and Tombigbee river drainages below the Fall Line. Future sampling of preferred habitats will likely expand the known range of this lowland species.

HABITAT AND BIOLOGY: As its common name implies, *E. fusiforme* is a swamp-dwelling species, preferring still or slow-flowing waters over muddy and silty substrates mixed with detritus or aquatic vegetation. The tannin-stained swamps and backwaters of the Pine Hills district in southwest Alabama afford excellent habitats for swamp darters. Collette (1962) indicates a tolerance for stagnant, low-oxygenated, high-temperature waters, whereas Schmidt and Whitworth (1979) indicate a preference for vegetated ponds with detrital sediments. This latter study found that microcrustaceans were the main foods of the species, with lesser amounts of midges, mayflies, and caddisflies. Single eggs are deposited on aquatic vegetation during the months of March, April, and May. Collette (1962) reports that some populations of *E. fusiforme* live only one year.

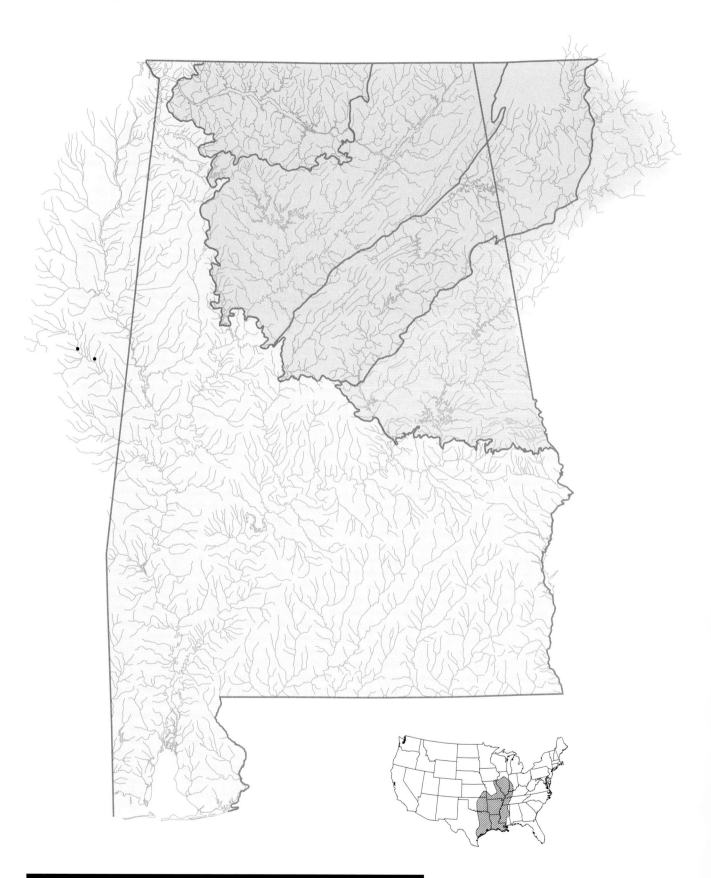

SLOUGH DARTER   *Etheostoma gracile*   2 STATIONS

Etheostoma gracile

(Girard, 1859)

ETYMOLOGY:

Etheostoma—strain mouth, possibly referring to the small mouth

gracile—slender

Red River, Rapides Parish, Louisiana, 3 June 1995, 1.1 in (29 mm) SL male, TU 175069

CHARACTERISTICS: Distinguishing characteristics of the slough darter are a small mouth and head and a lateral line that arches upward near the spiny dorsal fin. A broad frenum is present, and the gill membranes are slightly to moderately connected. *Etheostoma gracile* is typically yellow or olive with thin green reticulations and green saddles on the back. Males have a series of green bars along the sides, while female coloration is limited to small green squares along the sides. The spiny dorsal fin has a blue margin and base with a red band in the middle. A black spot is present at the caudal fin base. The slough darter is similar to the backwater darter, *E. zonifer*, but can be separated from this species by its uninterrupted infraorbital canal, usually with eight pores. The interrupted infraorbital canal of *E. zonifer* has only six pores.

ADULT SIZE: 1.2 to 2 in (30 to 50 mm)

DISTRIBUTION: *Etheostoma gracile* is found in the lower Mississippi River basin from Louisiana to Illinois, generally in western drainages. It is known from only two localities in the Mobile basin, both in the Noxubee River system, a tributary of the upper Tombigbee River in Mississippi and Alabama. We sampled these localities in 1995 and collected two juveniles.

HABITAT AND BIOLOGY: Slough darters inhabit quiet or slow-moving waters, usually over mud and silt substrate with vegetation and/or detritus. They may also occur in roadside ditches and sloughs, slow-moving streams, oxbows, and backwaters of large rivers. Male slough darters have chin tubercles that are used to stimulate the female's nape and head during courtship. Spawning occurs from April through June, peaking in late May and early June. Braasch and Smith (1967) report that eggs are fastened on small twigs or leaf stems with several eggs fastened on any one object. These authors indicate longevity of four years in an Illinois population. The diet of this species consists of midge larvae, copepods, mayflies, cladocerans, and other aquatic insects and crustaceans.

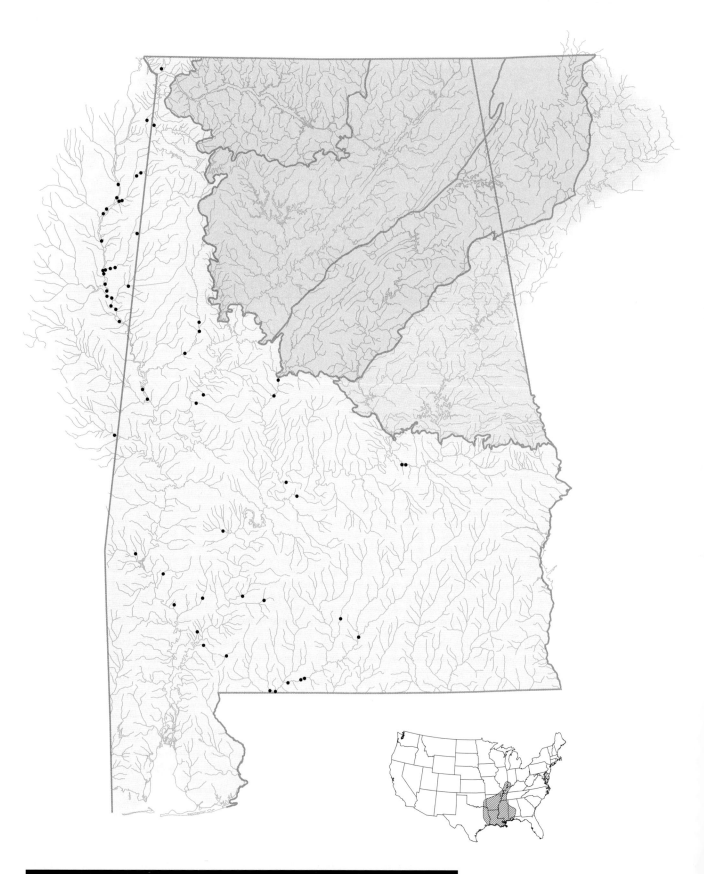

HARLEQUIN DARTER   *Etheostoma histrio*   **57** STATIONS

Etheostoma histrio

Jordan and Gilbert, 1887

ETYMOLOGY:

Etheostoma—strain mouth, possibly referring to the small mouth

histrio—harlequin, a pantomime character in traditional Italian comedy

Five Mile Creek, Hale County, 14 May 1992, 1.9 in (49 mm) SL male, GSA 4317

CHARACTERISTICS: The harlequin darter is distinguished by two large, tan to dark brown blotches near the caudal fin base and several large, dark spots on the side and ventral surface of the head and body. The gill membranes are broadly connected. On the back are six or seven dark saddles or blotches. The body color of *Etheostoma histrio* is light brown to tan with seven to 11 dark green or brown vertical bars on the sides of breeding males. The spiny dorsal fin has a red submarginal band. Very prominent dark preorbital and suborbital bars are characteristic for this species. See Gilbert (1887) for original description.

ADULT SIZE: 1.6 to 2.8 in (40 to 70 mm)

DISTRIBUTION: The harlequin darter is found in lower Mississippi River drainages north to the Embarras River in Illinois and in the Gulf slope drainages from the Escambia River west to the Neches and Sabine rivers in Texas. *Etheostoma histrio* occurs sporadically throughout the Mobile basin except in the Coosa River system. Wall (1968) and Boschung (1992) report single collections in Bear and Yellow creeks, both of which are tributaries to the Tennessee River drainage in Mississippi. Our collections at Cedar Creek in Franklin County and Bumpass Creek in Lauderdale County are the first records of the species in the Alabama section of the drainage. We have recently collected individuals at several locations in the Conecuh River system in south Alabama.

HABITAT AND BIOLOGY: Harlequin darters frequent a variety of habitats. We have collected them in upland streams with gravel and rubble riffles with swift flow and in lowland streams over sand in brush, debris, and log snags with moderate to swift current. We consistently find *E. histrio* on log snags in swift-flowing, deep waters of the Conecuh River and lower Tallapoosa River while boat electrofishing. Spawning occurs over gravel, rubble, or bedrock in fast current and individuals in breeding color have been observed from mid-March to May. Kuhajda and Warren (1989) report a maximum age of four years in Kentucky and a diet of midge larvae, blackflies, caddisflies, and mayflies. Little else is known about the life history of this colorful darter in Alabama. Five Mile Creek, a tributary of the lower Black Warrior River system in Hale County, and lower Bull Mountain Creek are two places where we have collected the harlequin darter and the similar rock darter together.

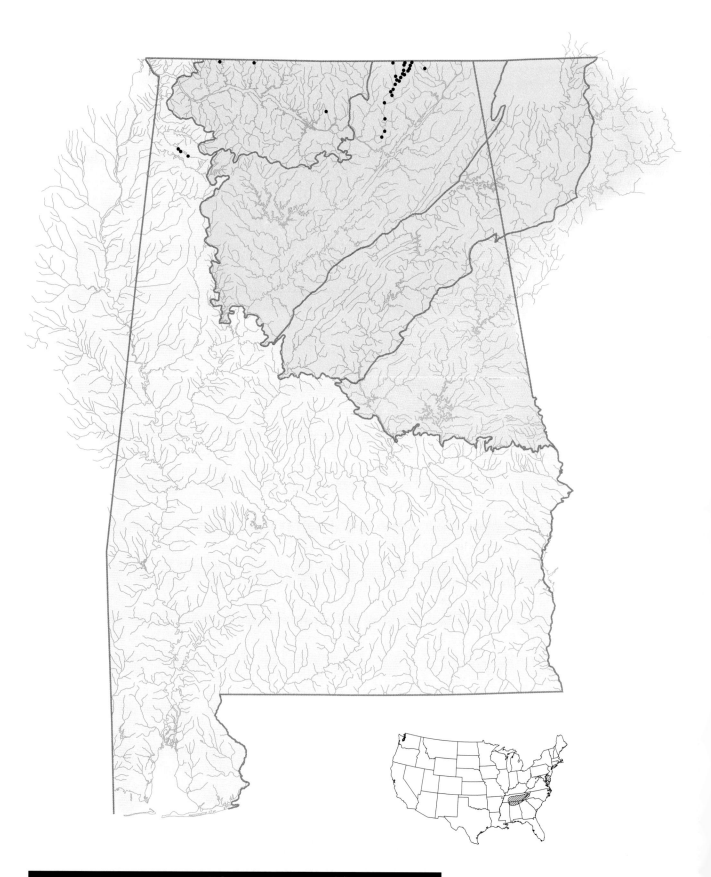

Etheostoma jessiae
(Jordan and Brayton, 1878)

ETYMOLOGY:
Etheostoma—strain mouth, possibly referring to the small mouth
jessiae—in honor of Jessie Brayton, wife of the junior author of the species

Little Butler Creek, Lauderdale County, 1 April 1993, 2.2 in (56 mm) SL male, GSA 4403

CHARACTERISTICS: Howell (1968) and Etnier and Starnes (1993) define the *Etheostoma stigmaeum* complex, of which the blueside darter is a member, as a series of highly variable subspecies. Along with Smith-Vaniz (1968), Page and Burr (1991), Boschung (1992), and Layman (1994), we consider these two taxa to be distinct species. The blueside darter, *Etheostoma jessiae,* and the speckled darter, *E. stigmaeum,* are different morphologically, as well as in coloration of breeding males. Specifically, individuals of the blueside darter have a moderately long and more pointed snout, generally with a narrow frenum on the upper lip (no frenum on *E. stigmaeum*), a larger mouth (compared to a smaller mouth), and a deep blue body (compared to turquoise-blue). Male blueside darters have nine or 10 V- or W-shaped blotches or bars along their sides, which appear as solid blue square blotches confined to the lateral area during the spawning season. The back has six hourglass-shaped saddles and is diffusely speckled. The spiny dorsal fin has a blue band and a wide orange band immediately dorsal to it. The soft dorsal, caudal, and pectoral fins are dusky, with distinct orange stippling in all rays. Iridescent blue is restricted to the preopercle and lower opercle. In contrast, the fins of

breeding males of *E. stigmaeum* lack orange stippling, the turquoise-blue bands on their sides are elongate and extend from the back to the venter, and most of the head region is colored. See Jordan (1878a) for original description.

ADULT SIZE: 1.4 to 2.4 in (35 to 60 mm)

DISTRIBUTION: *Etheostoma jessiae* is commonly found throughout the Tennessee River drainage in Tennessee, Alabama, North Carolina, and Virginia. It is widespread, though not necessarily abundant, in the Paint Rock River system in Alabama. It is also known from scattered collections in Bear, Barren Fork, Second, and Shoal creek systems, all of which are tributaries of the Tennessee River.

HABITAT AND BIOLOGY: *Etheostoma jessiae* inhabits gravel and rubble riffles and shoals, as well as sand- and gravel-bottomed pools and slow-moving areas of streams below riffles. We have collected gravid females and colorful males in early April. Spawning occurs in clean sand and gravel shoals from March to early May.

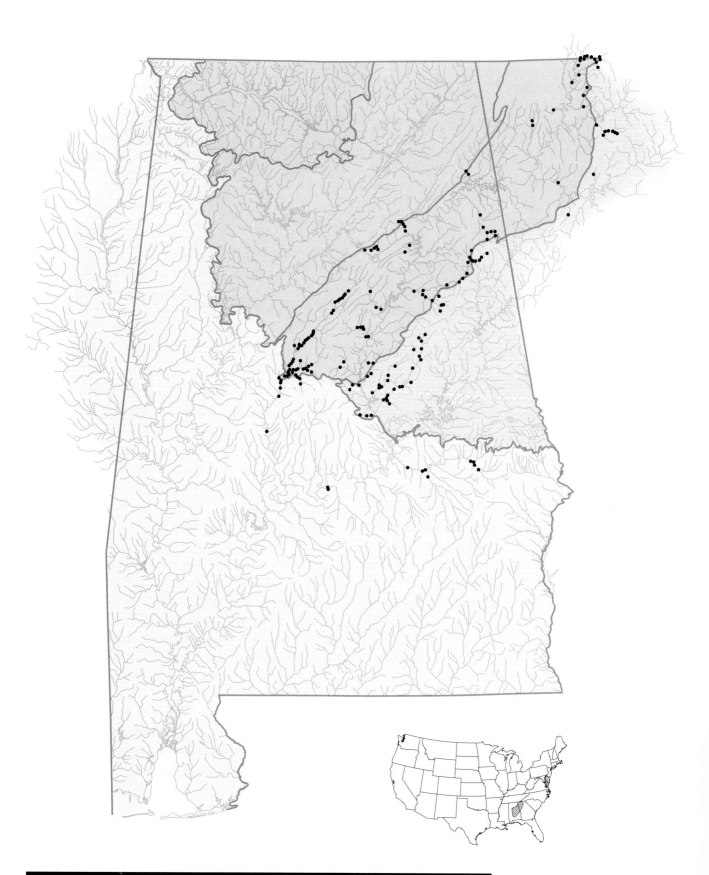

GREENBREAST DARTER *Etheostoma jordani* **181 STATIONS**

Etheostoma jordani

Gilbert, 1891

ETYMOLOGY:

Etheostoma—strain mouth,
possibly referring to the small
mouth

jordani—in honor of David
Starr Jordan, the father of
North American ichthyol-
ogy, for his vast contributions to the science

Blue Gut Creek, Chilton County, 21 April 1993, 1.9 in (49 mm) SL male, GSA 4433

CHARACTERISTICS: The greenbreast darter is distinguished from other members of the *Etheostoma jordani* species group, *E. chuckwachatte*, *E. douglasi*, and *E. etowahae*, by red spots without halos along the sides, olivaceous lips, a turquoise-blue anal fin, and exposed scales on the gill covers. Breeding males are olive with a weakly formed pattern of three to 11 dark vertical bars along the sides. The back has eight or nine olive to brown blotches. The lower part of the head, breast, and gill membranes are turquoise-blue. The spiny dorsal fin has a clear to white margin and a submarginal red band most prominent in the front section of the fin. The caudal fin margin has a narrow turquoise or black band distally, a median narrow yellow band, and a proximal broad red to orange band.

ADULT SIZE: 1.6 to 2.4 in (40 to 60 mm)

DISTRIBUTION: *Etheostoma jordani* is endemic to the Alabama River drainage of the eastern Mobile basin. Most of our collection records are confined to the

Cahaba and Coosa river systems above the Fall Line; however, scattered locations also exist in the Alabama, Cahaba, and Tallapoosa river systems below the Fall Line.

HABITAT AND BIOLOGY: A riffle-dwelling species, the greenbreast darter is found in cobble, gravel, and slab shoals with moderate to swift current. Peak reproductive activity occurs from late April to late June. Orr and Ramsey (1990) report that *E. jordani* males and females spawn in sand with only their heads and caudal fins exposed. O'Neil (1980) found that greenbreast darters live to be between two and three years of age, and feed on midge larvae, copepods, cladocerans, mayflies, water mites, caddisflies, and occasionally mollusks.

REMARKS: The description of the greenbreast darter was based on specimens from Choccolo (= Choccolocco) Creek in Calhoun County and Chestnut Creek in Chilton County. Later works designated Choccolocco Creek as the type locality.

STRIPETAIL DARTER   *Etheostoma kennicotti*   37 STATIONS

Etheostoma kennicotti
(Putnam, 1863)

ETYMOLOGY:
Etheostoma—strain mouth, possibly referring to the small mouth
kennicotti—in honor of Robert Kennicott, who first captured this species in Illinois

Larkin Fork, Jackson County, 18 May 1993, 1.9 in (48 mm) SL male, GSA 4474

CHARACTERISTICS: *Etheostoma kennicotti* is distinguished by its deep caudal peduncle, short spiny dorsal fin, and moderately connected gill membranes. Black bands are present on the caudal and soft dorsal fins. The stripetail darter is tan along the top and dusky-white on the ventral surface. Breeding males are golden orange. Six to seven poorly developed brown saddles are present along the back and nine to 11 vertical blotches along the sides. A black spot is evident over the pectoral fin. The spiny dorsal fin is black to brown submarginally with yellow or cream knobs at the tips of individual spines. As in other *Catonotus* species, the head and nape region of males become darker and swollen during the reproductive season. *Etheostoma kennicotti* can be distinguished from the similar *E. flabellare* by the submarginal dark band in the spiny dorsal fin and absence of longitudinal stripes on the sides.

ADULT SIZE: 1.2 to 2.8 in (30 to 70 mm). Individuals in the Cumberland drainage attain a maximum length of 2.8 inches (70 mm), while those in the Green and Tennessee drainages reach maximum lengths of 2 inches (50 mm).

DISTRIBUTION: Stripetail darters are found in tributaries of the lower Ohio River basin in Illinois and Kentucky and in the Tennessee and upper Cumberland river drainages. In Alabama, this species is most commonly found in the Paint Rock River system and less frequently throughout other stream systems in the Tennessee River drainage.

HABITAT AND BIOLOGY: *Etheostoma kennicotti* prefers shallow pools with slabrock substrate, as found in upland areas of small to moderate-sized streams. Slabrocks provide cover and serve as spawning sites for breeding males. Our observations in Alabama support reports of Page (1975), who indicates that spawning in southern Illinois occurs in slab pools from early April through May. Males select cavities under slabrocks as nesting sites, and eggs are laid on the underside of the slabs. The number of eggs per cluster ranges from 50 to 400 (Page, 1975). These fishes live to be a maximum of three years old. The diet of *E. kennicotti* consists of ostracods, copepods, cladocerans, isopods, stoneflies, mayflies, fishflies, and midge larvae.

641

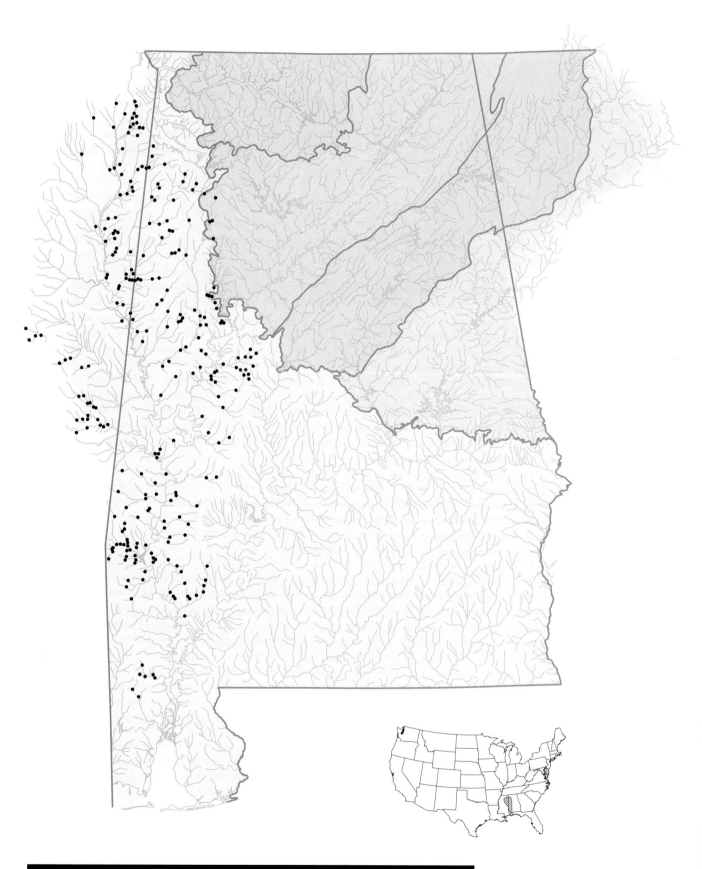

TOMBIGBEE DARTER *Etheostoma lachneri* **265 STATIONS**

Etheostoma lachneri

Suttkus and Bailey, 1994

ETYMOLOGY:

Etheostoma—strain mouth, possibly referring to the small mouth

lachneri—in honor of Ernest A. Lachner, of the Smithsonian Institute, a prolific contributor to North American ichthyology

Big Sandy Creek, Tuscaloosa County, 29 March 1993, 1.7 in (44 mm) SL male, GSA 4386

CHARACTERISTICS: Breeding males of the Tombigbee darter are distinguished from those of other *Ulocentra* species by having slightly oblique, dark green bars with bright orange interspaces along the sides and caudal peduncle. Color along the back and upper sides is variable, consisting of red-orange in a loose network pattern rather than discrete blotches. The snout, lips, gill membranes, lower gill covers, and breast are green or turquoise. The anal fin is generally deep turquoise, while the caudal fin has turquoise margins and a pale turquoise or nearly clear central portion. See Suttkus et al. (1994) for original description.

ADULT SIZE: 1.4 to 1.8 in (35 to 45 mm)

DISTRIBUTION: *Etheostoma lachneri* is distributed below the Fall Line in the Tombigbee River drainage of the Mobile basin. We also have collections above the Fall Line from a few selected localities in the Black Warrior River system and the Sipsey River system, a Tombigbee River tributary. This species is notably absent in the Black Belt region where physiography changes dramatically.

HABITAT AND BIOLOGY: The Tombigbee darter occurs in a variety of habitats, from small streams with sand and gravel substrates to large streams with mixtures of sand, gravel, and hard clay or bedrock. Although this is a Coastal Plain species, we routinely collect individuals in areas of hard, fractured substrate, around significant snag cover, and in bridge rubble and culverts with accumulated debris. Our observations indicate that spawning color becomes evident in February, and spawning occurs from early March through May. The diet of this species is presumably similar to that of other *Ulocentra*, composed predominantly of insect larvae.

REMARKS: The type locality for the Tombigbee darter is Wolf Creek, a tributary to Little Souwilpa Creek in Choctaw County, Alabama.

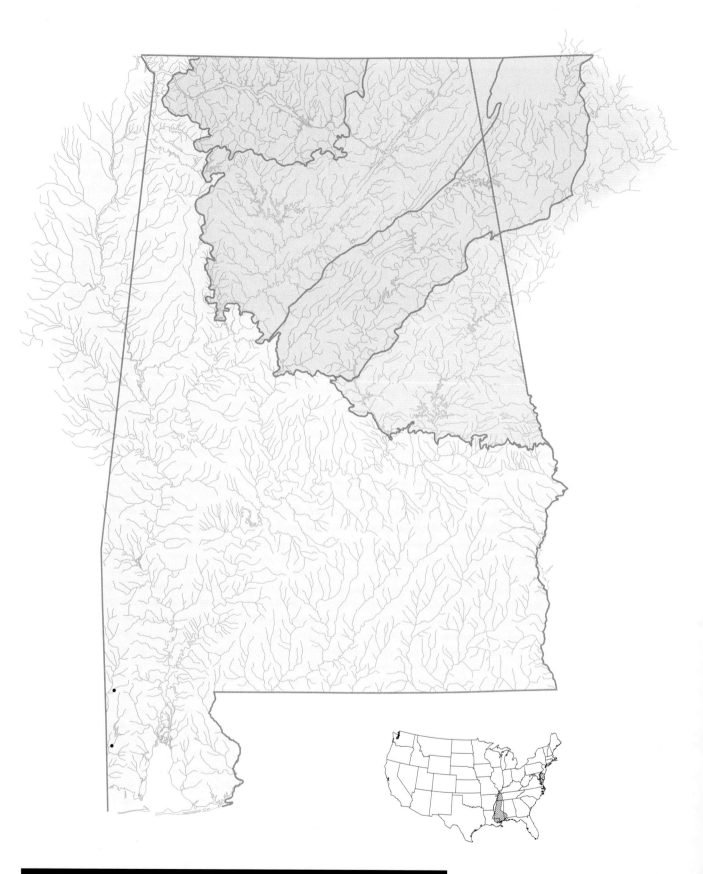

BRIGHTEYE DARTER   *Etheostoma lynceum*   **2 STATIONS**

Etheostoma lynceum
Hay, 1885

ETYMOLOGY:
Etheostoma—strain mouth, possibly referring to the small mouth
lynceum—referring to Lynceus, one of Jason's argonauts, to whom was attributed remarkable vision

Puppy Creek, Mobile County, 3 May 1995, 1.7 in (43 mm) SL male, GSA 4642

CHARACTERISTICS: Tsai and Raney (1974) considered the brighteye darter a subspecies of *Etheostoma zonale*; however, Etnier and Starnes (1986) present sufficient meristic, habitat, and distributional data to elevate it to species status. This short, robust species has a wide frenum on the upper lip, enlarged pectoral fins, and distinct pre-, sub-, and postorbital bars. The body is tan to light yellow; during the breeding season, the body of nuptial males takes on a greenish violet cast. Six dark dorsal saddles extend down the sides, becoming confluent with the six to nine yellowish green lateral blotches. A light blue-green wash is found on the breast region and anal fin. The pelvic, pectoral, and caudal fins are mottled with two light yellow to cream spots at the caudal fin base. The spiny dorsal fin has a black base, a submarginal light red-brown band, and a wide green band marginally. The soft dorsal fin also has a dark base with alternating light and dark bands. The brighteye darter is distinguishable from the banded darter, *E. zonale*, by fewer lateral line scales; 39 to 43 in the brighteye darter compared with 46 to 56 in the banded darter. See Jordan (1885a) for original description.

ADULT SIZE: 1.1 to 1.8 in (27 to 45 mm). Specimens collected from Puppy Creek in Mobile County are smaller than reported for other streams in its range.

DISTRIBUTION: The brighteye darter is distributed below the Fall Line in eastern tributaries of the Mississippi River from Louisiana north to western Tennessee and eastward along the Gulf Coast to the Escatawpa River system in Mobile County.

HABITAT AND BIOLOGY: *Etheostoma lynceum* occurs over sand and mud in sluggish pools, and over gravel and cobble substrates in swift riffles of small to medium-sized Coastal Plain streams. Alabama populations are consistently found in algae and vegetation rooted in swift-flowing runs and chutes with hard clay stone that has eroded into moderately deep and narrow channels. Our June collections of juveniles indicate spawning in late April and May, possibly into June. Bell and Timmons (1991) report that *E. lynceum* feeds primarily on aquatic insect larvae. The oldest individual they examined in a Kentucky population was between three and four years old.

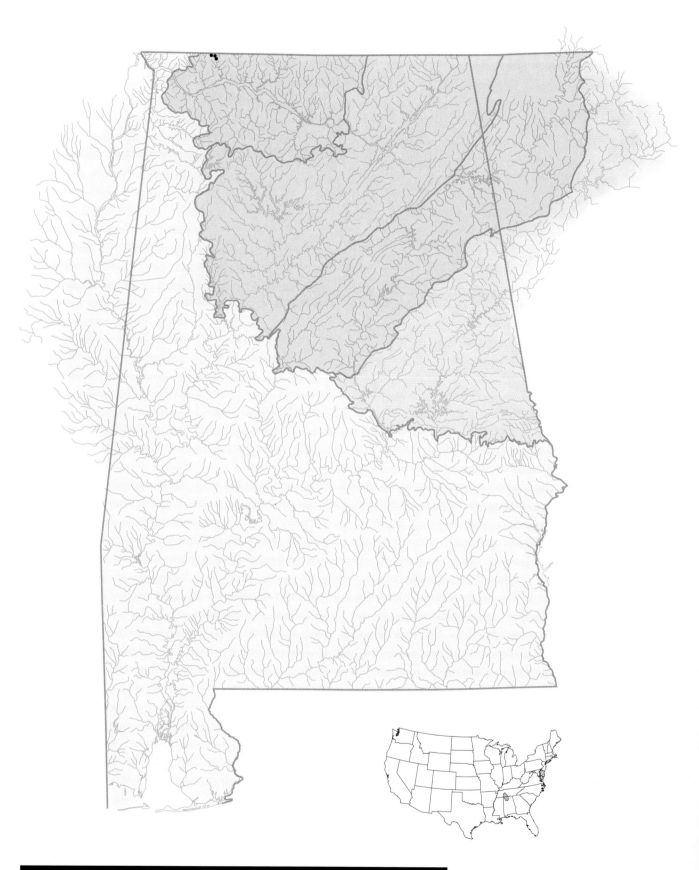

LOLLIPOP DARTER   *Etheostoma neopterum*   **3 STATIONS**

Etheostoma neopterum
Howell and Dingerkus, 1978

ETYMOLOGY:
Etheostoma—strain mouth, possibly referring to the small mouth
neopterum—new fin, referring to the newly observed morphology of the soft dorsal fin

Sour Branch, Lauderdale County, 31 March 1992, 2.1 in (52 mm) SL male, GSA 4305

CHARACTERISTICS: The lollipop darter is distinguishable from other members of the subgenus *Catonotus* in Alabama by the soft dorsal fin morphology of breeding males. In *Etheostoma neopterum*, each ray in this fin has two branches of equal length tipped with a large yellow knob characteristic of the species. Fin membranes extend only one-half to two-thirds the length of the rays. Two to four rows of small windows appear on each membrane. The caudal fin has eight to 12 yellow and black alternating bands. The spiny dorsal fin is black with a small yellow knob on the tip of each spine. *Etheostoma neopterum* is similar in appearance to *E. crossopterum*, *E. corona*, and *E. nigripinne*, and nonbreeding individuals are difficult to distinguish. However, *E. neopterum* does not occur sympatrically with either *E. corona* or *E. nigripinne*. The soft dorsal fin morphology of breeding males is sufficient to separate *E. neopterum* from *E. crossopterum*, which lacks knobs on the soft dorsal fin.

ADULT SIZE: 1.4 to 2.4 in (35 to 60 mm)

DISTRIBUTION: *Etheostoma neopterum* has a very restricted range, known only from the Shoal Creek system in northwestern Alabama and south-central Tennessee (Page et al., 1992). The lollipop darter occurs syntopically with the fringed darter, *E. crossopterum*, also of the subgenus *Catonotus*, in the Shoal Creek system in Alabama.

HABITAT AND BIOLOGY: The lollipop darter almost exclusively inhabits shallow undercut banks in slow-moving sections of cool, spring-fed, upland streams. Substrates in these areas usually consist of sand or chert covered with leaf litter and detritus. Spawning occurs from late March through April on the undersides of slabrocks, a similar behavior to that in other species of the subgenus *Catonotus*. Speculation is that the knobs on the spines of most *Catonotus* species, and the knobs on the soft dorsal rays of the *E. neopterum* species group in particular, function as egg mimics and stimulate spawning activity in females (Bart and Page, 1991).

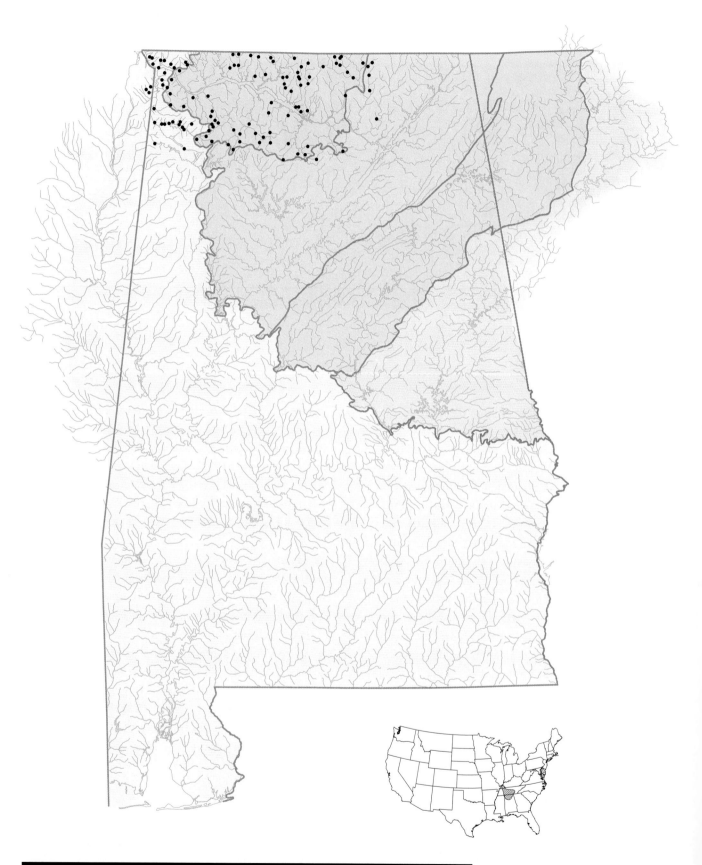

BLACKFIN DARTER   *Etheostoma nigripinne*   110 STATIONS

Etheostoma nigripinne
Braasch and Mayden, 1985

ETYMOLOGY:
Etheostoma—strain mouth, possibly referring to the small mouth
nigripinne—black fin, in reference to the dark fins of breeding males

Huckelteny Branch, Madison County, 9 March 1993, 2.6 in (67 mm) SL male, GSA 4426

CHARACTERISTICS: The blackfin darter is distinguished from other members of the *Etheostoma squamiceps* species group by morphology of the soft dorsal fin on breeding males (Page et al., 1992). The fin is dusky gray or black to its margin and has three branches per ray. The second and third branches are of equal length and separated from the first. The branches have no knobs on their tips, but the fin rays have four or five rows of rectangular, clear to light yellow bars. The caudal fin has eight to 12 clear to yellow and black alternating bands. The spiny dorsal fin has a small knob on the tip of each spine, with a small black spot on each membrane anterior to each knob. Anal and pelvic fins are dusky with a narrow clear margin.

ADULT SIZE: 1.4 to 2.8 in (35 to 70 mm)

DISTRIBUTION: *Etheostoma nigripinne* commonly occurs in Highland Rim tributaries of the middle and lower Tennessee River drainage of Tennessee and Alabama upstream to the Flint and Paint Rock river systems. This species is noticeably absent from the Cypress and Shoal creek systems in Alabama and Tennessee,

replaced there by *E. corona* and *E. crossopterum,* respectively. The blackfin darter does not occur sympatrically with any other species of the *E. squamiceps* species group found in Alabama, which includes the crown, fringed, and lollipop darters, *E. corona, E. crossopterum,* and *E. neopterum,* respectively (Page et al. 1992).

HABITAT AND BIOLOGY: *Etheostoma nigripinne* is the most common member of the *E. squamiceps* species group found in Alabama. Individuals usually inhabit areas characterized by a slow to moderate current over a slabrock substrate. They are infrequently found in other habitats, from spring runs to quiet areas on the margins of larger streams and small rivers. Spawning occurs from March through May, with males establishing territories under slabrocks as do other species of *Catonotus.* Spawning behavior is similar to *E. corona* and *E. crossopterum.* The diet of *E. nigripinne* has not been studied, but is speculated to be similar to other *Catonotus.* Page (1974b) examines the diet of *E. squamiceps* and reports consumption of microcrustaceans, mayflies, midges, and lesser amounts of aquatic beetles, worms, and caddisflies.

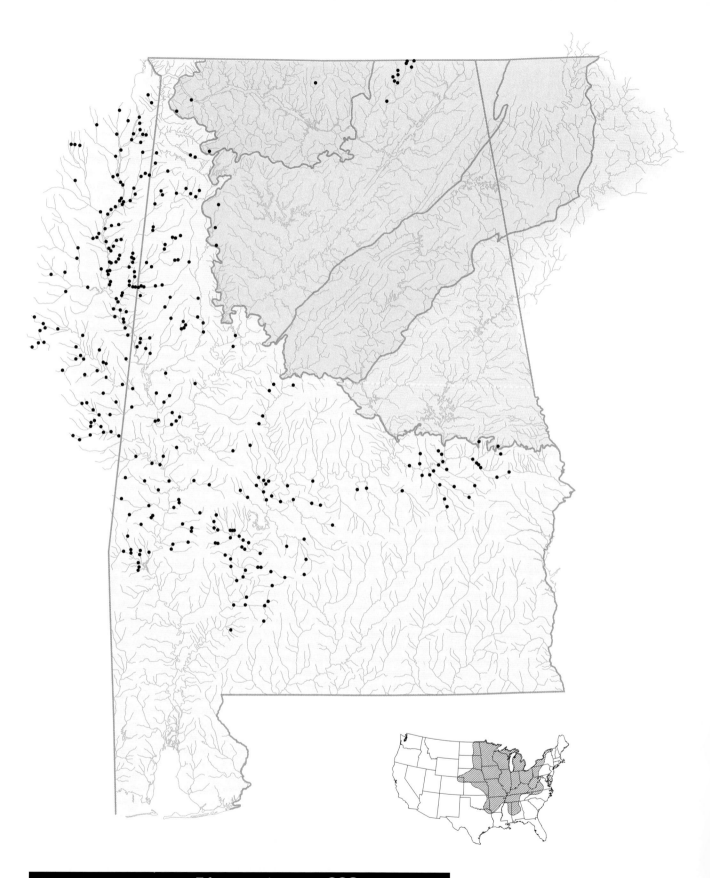

JOHNNY DARTER *Etheostoma nigrum* **338 STATIONS**

650

Etheostoma nigrum
Rafinesque, 1820

ETYMOLOGY:

Etheostoma—strain mouth, possibly referring to the small mouth

nigrum—referring to the dark head and body of breeding males

Chilatchee Creek, Dallas County, 14 April 1993, 1.8 in (46 mm) SL male, GSA 4422

CHARACTERISTICS: *Etheostoma nigrum* males typically darken during the breeding season or acquire dark stippling that develops into dark bands along the sides. Females have a slight yellowish cast. A frenum is absent on the upper lip and a black bridle extending across the somewhat blunt snout is interrupted above the upper lip, a feature which usually separates *E. nigrum* from the similar bluntnose darter, *E. chlorosomum*. Six to seven saddles are present on the back, and seven to 10 blotches are variously developed into W-, V-, or X-shaped markings along the side. A distinct spot is present at the base of the caudal fin and at the front of the spiny dorsal fin. Small spots occur on the spines and rays of both dorsal fins, presenting somewhat of a banding pattern. Krotzer (1990) examines variation and systematics of *E. nigrum* throughout its range.

ADULT SIZE: 1 to 2.8 in (25 to 70 mm)

DISTRIBUTION: *Etheostoma nigrum* occurs widely throughout the Mississippi River basin and Great Lakes area. Its southern range extent is reached in Alabama. Collection records of johnny darters are numerous in the Mobile basin, mainly below the Fall Line and usually not extending south beyond the Lime Hills. Known populations in the Tennessee River drainage are limited to collections in the Paint Rock River, Bear Creek, and Limestone Creek systems.

HABITAT AND BIOLOGY: The extensive range of the johnny darter indicates its ability to exploit a variety of habitats. Individuals are frequently taken in slow-flowing pools over sand, silt, and mud substrates with detritus or leaf litter, and also along the margins of lakes in northern states. The species occurs sparingly in moderate to swift-flowing riffles over gravel and cobble substrates. Spawning occurs from April through June. Winn (1958a, b) observed johnny darters spawning in an inverted position on the undersides of objects. Females deposit eggs singly into clusters of 30 to 200 eggs, with up to 1,150 eggs per nest. The maximum age of this species is four years, and its diet consists of midge larvae, small crustaceans, and mayflies.

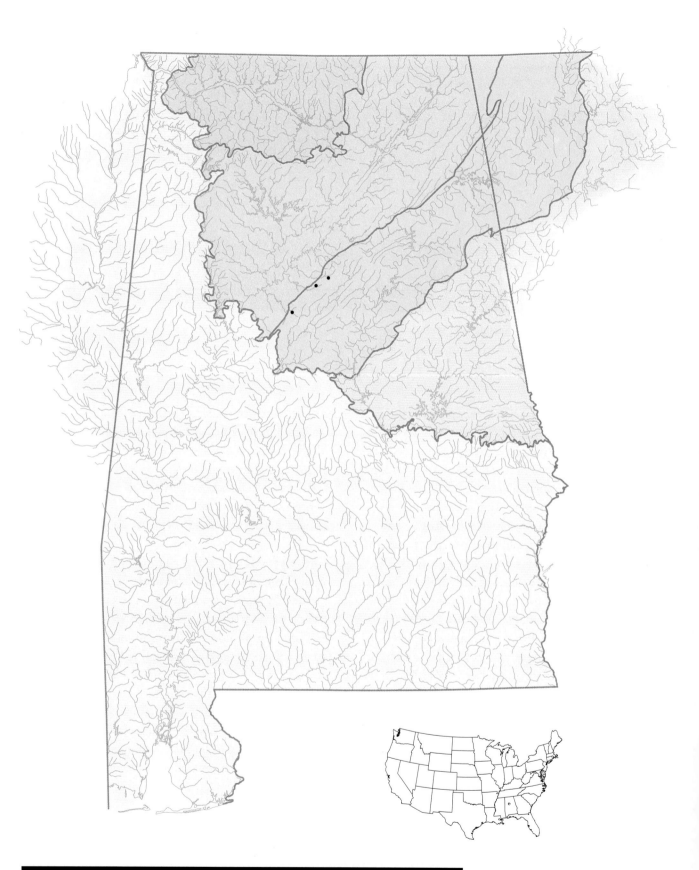

Etheostoma nuchale
Howell and Caldwell, 1965

ETYMOLOGY:
Etheostoma—strain mouth, possibly referring to the small mouth
nuchale—from *nucha*, meaning nape or back of the neck, in reference to the humped nape of breeding males

Roebuck Spring, Jefferson County, 23 March 1994, 1.5 in (39 mm) SL male, GSA 4619

CHARACTERISTICS: The watercress darter is distinguishable from the gulf darter, *Etheostoma swaini*, by having fewer pored scales in the lateral line and fewer dorsal spines and pectoral fin rays (Howell and Caldwell, 1965). Up to nine saddles cross the back and a pale stripe is usually present along the nape. Irregularly defined dark horizontal bands are formed by small spots in the center of scales along the sides. Breeding males have a reddish orange venter, fading anteriorly along the sides to a yellowish white. The caudal peduncle has up to six bluish brown vertical bars separated by poorly defined orange bars. Three distinct spots followed by large orange spots are present at the caudal fin base. The remainder of the caudal fin is blue around the spots and clear. The anal fin is bright blue, and the paired fins are lighter blue, fading to clear at their margins. Both the spiny and soft dorsal fins have four distinct color bands, from outside to inside: blue, reddish orange, blue, and red.

ADULT SIZE: 1 to 1.8 in (25 to 45 mm)

DISTRIBUTION: The watercress darter is restricted to three spring areas in the Black Warrior River system.

HABITAT AND BIOLOGY: Individuals of this species are found at mid-depths in dense accumulations of aquatic vegetation including watercress, *Chara*, and *Spirogyra* in deep, slow-moving backwaters of springs (Howell et al., 1980). Dense populations of aquatic insect larvae and microcrustaceans that thrive in these springs provide abundant food for watercress darters. The protracted spawning season, lasting from March through July, is likely related to the constant 62° to 65°F (16° to 18°C) water temperatures found in the springs. Surveys by Moss (1995) reveal that populations appear healthy, but that nonpoint urban runoff is a continuing threat to water quality of the springs.

REMARKS: The type locality for the watercress darter is a spring tributary to Valley Creek, Jefferson County, Alabama. The watercress darter is listed as an endangered species by the U.S. Fish and Wildlife Service.

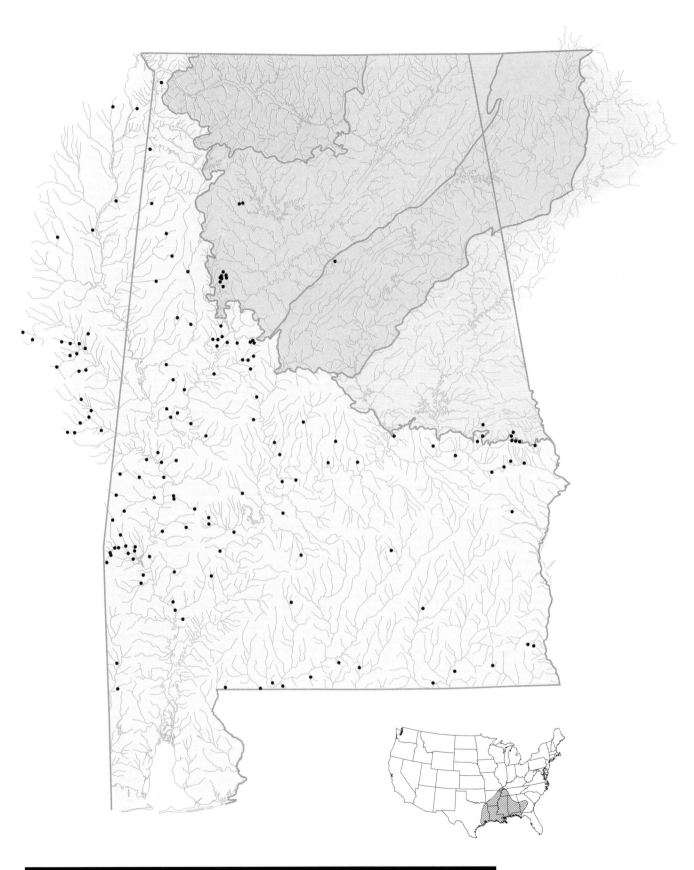

Etheostoma parvipinne
Gilbert and Swain, 1887

ETYMOLOGY:
Etheostoma—strain mouth, possibly referring to the small mouth *parvipinne*—small-finned, in reference to the small pectoral fins

Hogfoot Creek tributary, Covington County, 17 March 1993, 1.9 in (49 mm) SL male, GSA 4423

CHARACTERISTICS: The lateral line of the goldstripe darter in life appears as a thin golden stripe against a gray to brown body color. It may be interrupted by several dark brown distinct or mottled blotches along the side. *Etheostoma parvipinne* is a robust darter with a short, blunt snout and a deep caudal peduncle. Dark bars are present around the eye. Up to four vertically aligned spots are located at the caudal fin base. Vivid breeding colors are generally absent in this species, although males turn slightly golden brown and may be blotched or plain during the spawning season. See Gilbert (1887) for original description.

ADULT SIZE: 1.4 to 2.2 in (35 to 55 mm)

DISTRIBUTION: *Etheostoma parvipinne* is found in Gulf slope drainages from Texas to Florida and north in the lower Mississippi River basin to Illinois. It is distributed throughout the Mobile basin below the Fall Line and sporadically above the Fall Line. We have widely scattered records from the Escatawpa east to the Chatta-hoochee River system. A distinct form of *E. parvipinne*

was discovered in the Turkey Creek system, Jefferson County, and should be described in the near future.

HABITAT AND BIOLOGY: Goldstripe darters inhabit small sluggish streams, spring seepage areas, and small woodland tributaries adjacent to larger streams. Patches of woody debris, leaf material, mud, silt, and sand appear to be favored microhabitats. Success in collecting this species is unpredictable because of its spotty occurrence and migratory habits. We have collected individuals in spawning condition around root masses, aquatic vegeta-tion, and snags in swift chutes of Coastal Plain streams. The life history of the goldstripe darter in Alabama is not completely known. Spawning most likely occurs from mid-March through June, based on our collections of gravid specimens. Preferred food items include midges, mayflies, blackflies, beetles, and microcrustaceans. The life span is two to three years.

REMARKS: The type locality for the goldstripe darter is a small spring tributary to the Black Warrior River near Tuscaloosa, Tuscaloosa County, Alabama.

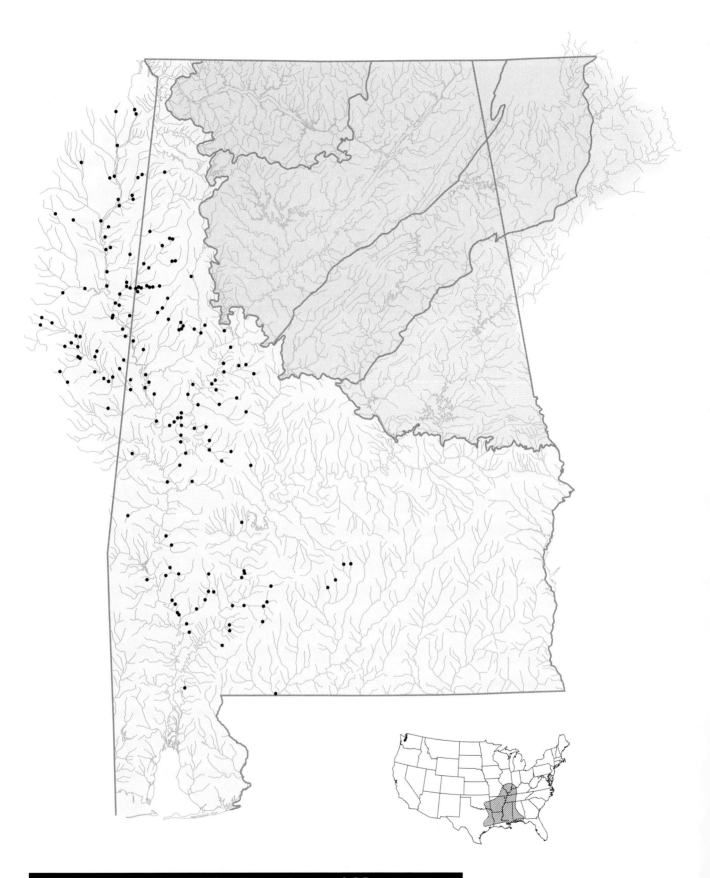

CYPRESS DARTER   *Etheostoma proeliare*   168 STATIONS

Etheostoma proeliare
(Hay, 1881)

ETYMOLOGY:
Etheostoma—strain mouth, possibly referring to the small mouth
proeliare—pertaining to battle, referring to a battlefield near the Tuscumbia River, where this species was discovered

Big Sandy Creek, Tuscaloosa County, 29 March 1993, 1.3 in (32 mm) SL male, GSA 4387

CHARACTERISTICS: The cypress darter has six to nine dusky brown dorsal saddles and seven to 12 dark brown lateral blotches. Irregularly arranged dark brown spots appear as rows above and below the lateral line. Body color is olive brown on the back and sides and white on the venter and breast. Orbital bars are present on the head. The spiny dorsal fin has a black base and reddish orange blotches in the middle. The soft dorsal and caudal fins have orange or amber bands. Burr (1978) notes that this species and other species of the subgenus *Microperca* have cuplike webs of skin on their long pelvic fins.

ADULT SIZE: 1.1 to 1.5 in (29 to 38 mm)

DISTRIBUTION: *Etheostoma proeliare* occurs in Gulf slope drainages from east Texas to the Choctawhatchee River and north in the Mississippi River basin to Illinois. The cypress darter is broadly distributed throughout the Tombigbee River drainage and the extreme lower Alabama River drainage. Collection records are notably absent in streams draining the Fall Line Hills and Lime Hills sections of the Alabama River drainage. Scattered records of the cypress darter in the Conecuh River drainage may be due to insufficient sampling of its preferred habitat in this drainage. Collection records are lacking in all other coastal drainages.

HABITAT AND BIOLOGY: *Etheostoma proeliare* commonly occurs around accumulations of woody debris, leaves, and aquatic vegetation in backwater pools of sluggish streams and swamps. Spawning occurs from late March to early June. Males exhibit chin-bobbing behavior to attract females to spawn (Burr and Page, 1978). Up to three eggs are deposited on a single substrate, usually dead leaves, twigs, and the sides and undersides of rocks. These authors report that cypress darters are relatively short-lived, surviving up to 18 months. Foods include midge larvae, cladocerans, copepods, isopods, mayflies, and an occasional springtail.

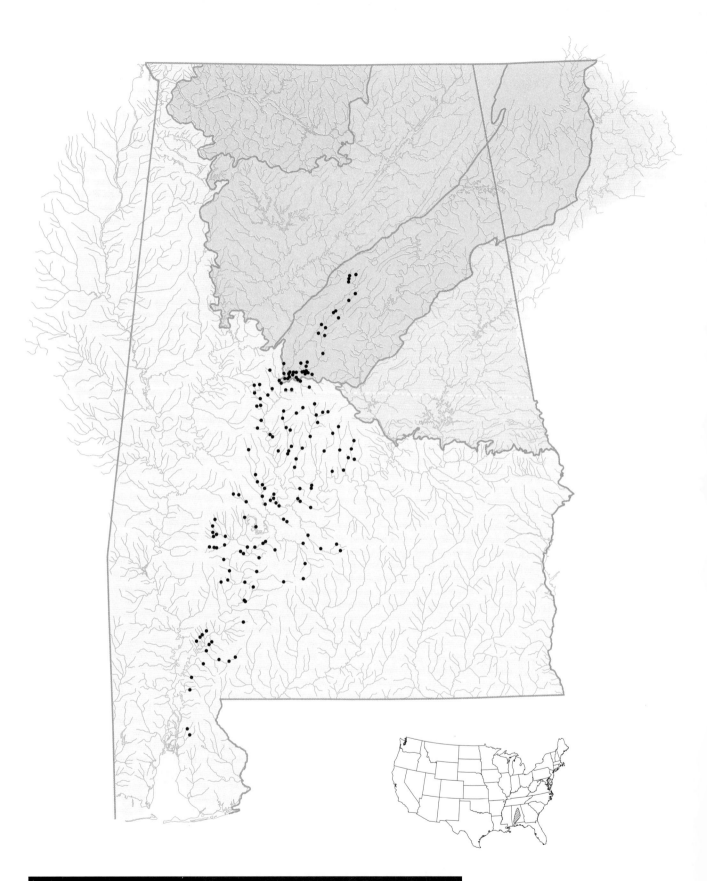

ALABAMA DARTER   *Etheostoma ramseyi*   **159 STATIONS**

Chilatchee Creek, Dallas County, 14 April 1993, 1.9 in (49 mm) SL male, GSA 4420

Etheostoma ramseyi
Suttkus and Bailey, 1994

ETYMOLOGY:
Etheostoma—strain mouth, possibly referring to the small mouth *ramseyi*—in honor of John S. Ramsey, formerly of Auburn University, who contributed extensively to knowledge of Alabama's fishes

CHARACTERISTICS: Breeding males of *Etheostoma ramseyi* have orange along the lower sides and caudal peduncle, extending dorsally to the bottom of brown lateral blotches that are sporadically overlaid with green. A series of distinct, oblong blotches occurs on the upper sides, just above the lateral line and between the diagonal brownish green bars. The blotches are bright red or red-orange near the caudal base to russet anteriorly. Breast, gill membranes, lower gill covers, cheeks, and lower snout are light to dark turquoise. See Suttkus et al. (1994) for original description.

ADULT SIZE: 1.4 to 2 in (35 to 50 mm)

DISTRIBUTION: The Alabama darter is distributed below the Fall Line in the Alabama River drainage and above the Fall Line throughout the Cahaba River system to its headwaters. Absence of this species in tributaries upstream of the Autauga Creek system is perhaps related to the large areal extent of the Black Belt in this region. The Alabama darter is replaced in the Coosa River system by the Coosa darter, *E. coosae*, and in the Tallapoosa River system by the Tallapoosa darter, *E. tallapoosae*.

HABITAT AND BIOLOGY: *Etheostoma ramseyi* occurs in a variety of habitats, from small stream pools with sand and gravel substrates to stream riffles containing sand, gravel, clay, rubble, bedrock, and cobble. The occurrence of structure—cobble, rubble, broken bedrock, or log snags—is a prerequisite for finding this species in numbers. Spawning occurs from early March to late April or May at temperatures less than 68°F (20°C) (Suttkus, Bailey, and Bart, 1994).

REMARKS: The type locality of the Alabama darter is Beaver Creek near Sunny South, Wilcox County, Alabama.

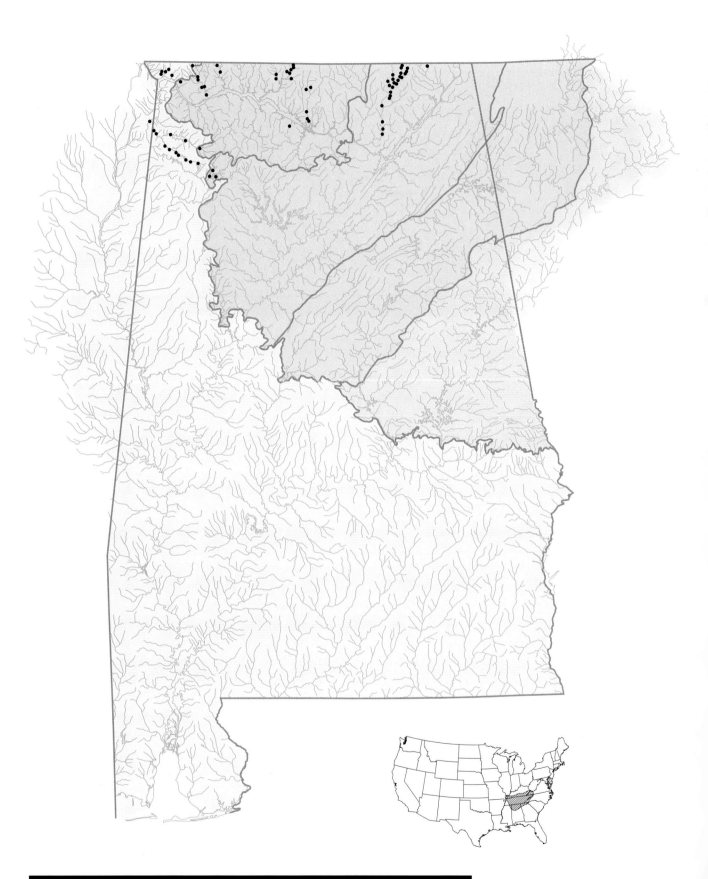

REDLINE DARTER *Etheostoma rufilineatum* **68 STATIONS**

Etheostoma rufilineatum
(Cope, 1870)

ETYMOLOGY:
Etheostoma—strain mouth, possibly referring to the small mouth
rufilineatum—red-lined, in reference to the horizontal side stripes

Butler Creek, Lauderdale County, 24 February 1993, 2.3 in (59 mm) SL male, GSA 4358

CHARACTERISTICS: The redline darter is distinctive in appearance, characterized by a compressed body, pointed snout, deep caudal peduncle, horizontal banding down the sides, and evident dark markings and bars on the cheeks and gill covers. Numerous small red or orange spots occur along the sides of the body between the horizontal lines. Body color is generally tan with variously developed quadrate spots and vertical bars on the sides and nine or 10 dorsal saddles. The breast of males is a deep blue, while the median fins have dark blue margins, white and orange submarginal bands, and gray bands at their bases. All paired fins are orange, and two large yellow spots are present at the base of the caudal fin. See Cope (1870b) for original description.

ADULT SIZE: 1.8 to 3 in (45 to 76 mm)

DISTRIBUTION: *Etheostoma rufilineatum* is found throughout the Tennessee River drainage and in the Cumberland River drainage downstream of the Rockcastle River. Areas of greatest occurrence and abundance in Alabama are the Paint Rock and Elk river systems, and Shoal, Cypress, Second, and Bear creek systems.

HABITAT AND BIOLOGY: Redline darters are found in swift to very swift riffles and shoals beneath and behind boulders and large rocks in small to large streams. In shallower areas, they occur over gravel and cobble shoals and exposed bedrock with scattered gravel or rubble. The redline darter and the rainbow darter, *E. caeruleum*, are two of the most abundant darter species occurring in the Tennessee River drainage in Alabama. Widlak and Neves (1985) report May through August spawning for a population in Virginia. Our observations indicate spawning from May through June in Alabama. Eggs are buried in sand and gravel (Stiles, 1972). The diet includes midges, blackflies, mayflies, caddisflies, and water mites, which are abundant in its preferred habitat (Bryant, 1979; Widlak and Neves, 1985). Males live three or more years and females live two or more years in Virginia.

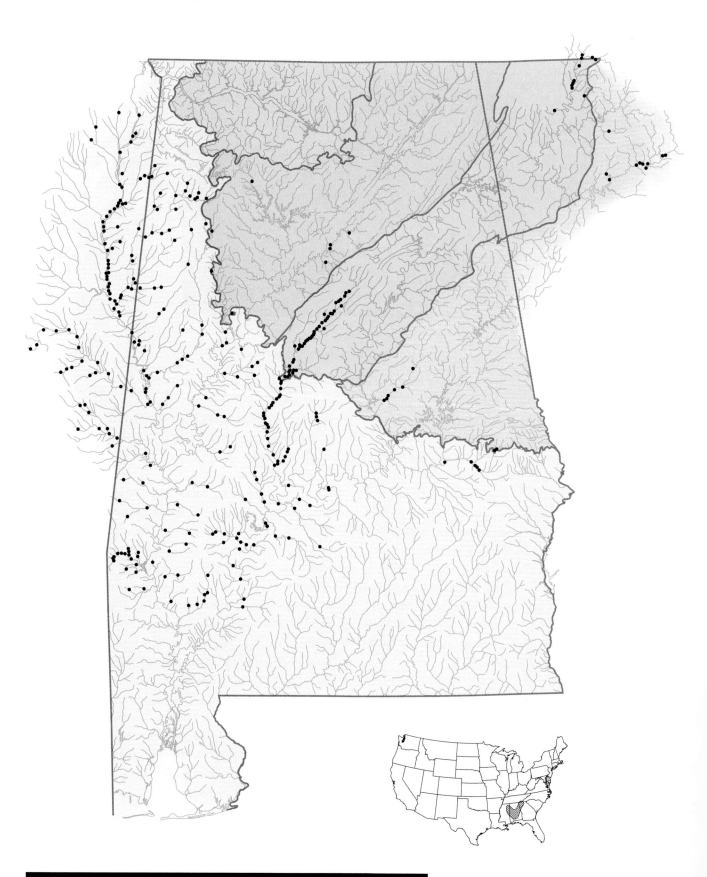

ROCK DARTER *Etheostoma rupestre* **336 STATIONS**

Etheostoma rupestre
Gilbert and Swain, 1887

ETYMOLOGY:

Etheostoma—strain mouth, possibly referring to the small mouth
rupestre—living among the rocks

Chilatchee Creek, Dallas County, 14 April 1993, 2.4 in (60 mm) SL male, GSA 4429

CHARACTERISTICS: The rock darter has large pectoral fins, broadly joined gill membranes that form a shallow V, a moderately blunt snout, a slightly inferior mouth, and a frenum. The back and upper sides are brownish green with six brown blotches on the back and six to nine variously developed green V- or W-shaped blotches or vertical bars with brown edging along the sides. The most posterior bars are green and may encircle the caudal peduncle. Orbital bars are well developed. Breeding males are dark green with a base body color of tan to light brown. Both dorsal fins have green margins, clear median bands, and brown basal bands. The head is entirely green, and the back is green around slightly diffused saddles. Pelvic, anal, and pectoral fins are green, fading to clear at their tips. The caudal fin is green with two to four light tan medial spots at its base. See Gilbert (1887) for original description.

ADULT SIZE: 1.8 to 2.8 in (45 to 70 mm)

DISTRIBUTION: Most collection records of this Mobile basin endemic are from below the Fall Line in the Tombigbee and lower Alabama river drainages. Rock darters are particularly abundant above and below the Fall Line in the Cahaba River system. Isolated populations are known in the upper Coosa River system in Georgia and Tennessee, Hatchet Creek in the lower Coosa, and Uphapee Creek in the lower Tallapoosa.

HABITAT AND BIOLOGY: *Etheostoma rupestre* is generally confined to riffle habitats containing gravel, cobble, and rubble in moderate to large rivers and streams. It is generally absent when these habitats are unavailable. Artificial rubble and riprap occasionally left in streams during bridge construction provide excellent habitat for rock darters. Individuals are usually uncommon in small woodland streams. Spawning occurs from March to early May. The diet of this and many other riffle-dwelling darters is composed of aquatic insect larvae.

REMARKS: The type locality for the rock darter is the North River near Tuscaloosa, Tuscaloosa County, Alabama.

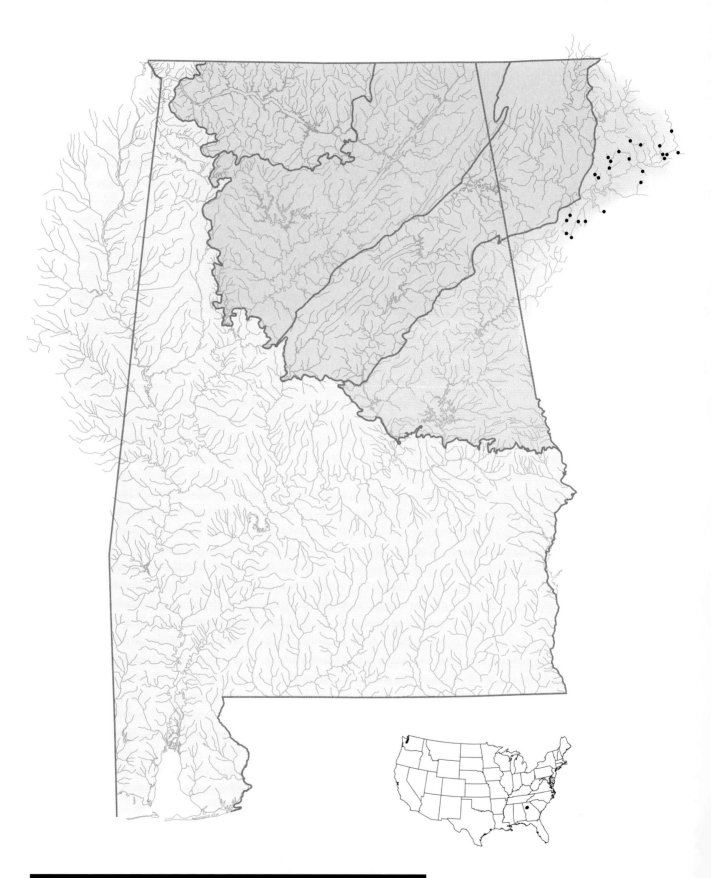

Etheostoma scotti
(Bauer, Etnier and
Burkhead, 1995)

ETYMOLOGY:
Etheostoma—strain mouth,
possibly referring to the
small mouth
scotti—in honor of Donald
C. Scott, who established the
University of Georgia
ichthyological collection

Shoal Creek, Dawson County, Georgia, 4 April 1995, 2.2 in (56 mm) SL male, NMB 1480. Photograph courtesy of Noel M. Burkhead

CHARACTERISTICS: The Cherokee darter is very similar in appearance to the Coosa darter, distinguishable by the color pattern of the breeding male spiny dorsal fin. *Etheostoma coosae* has distinct banding in the fin with a black to dark blue marginal band and a red middle band about one-fourth the height of the fin. In breeding *E. scotti* the entire fin is pigmented brick red except for a black band at the base. Smaller and nonnuptial males may exhibit some banding, but dark bars are usually visible in the clear bands. The soft dorsal fin is brick red, often of less intensity than the spiny dorsal fin. The caudal fin is turquoise to blue-green, while the anal fin is turquoise. The back is crossed by eight dark saddles which connect with dark lateral blotches. Bauer et al. (1995) also report that populations of *E. scotti* are variable with respect to the number of branchiostegal rays. Approximately 64% of the specimens examined had 6 rays (36% had 5 rays), whereas nearly 88% of the specimens examined for *E. coosae* had 6 rays.

ADULT SIZE: 1.4 to 2.2 in (35 to 56 mm)

DISTRIBUTION: *Etheostoma scotti* is endemic to the upland portions of the middle Etowah River system in Georgia upstream of Lake Allatoona. Cherokee darters are found in the Blue Ridge and Piedmont physiographic sections in this area with most populations occurring in the Northern Piedmont Upland. *Etheostoma coosae* also occurs in the range of *E. scotti* downstream of Lake Allatoona, but appears allopatric.

HABITAT AND BIOLOGY: The Cherokee darter inhabits small to medium-sized creeks with moderate gradient and rocky substrates. It occurs in runs above and below riffles, typically in waters one to two feet deep over large gravel, cobble, and small boulders (Bauer et al., 1995). Little is known about the life history of this species, although it is assumed to be similar to the Coosa darter, which eats aquatic insect larvae and spawns in late spring. Bauer et al. (1995) report vertical or near vertical spawning on cobble and small boulders with one egg deposited per spawning episode.

REMARKS: The type locality for the Cherokee darter is McCannless Creek, Cherokee County, Georgia. This species is listed as threatened by the U.S. Fish and Wildlife Service.

665

Etheostoma simoterum

(Cope, 1868)

ETYMOLOGY:

Etheostoma—strain mouth, possibly referring to the small mouth

simoterum—generally means flat- or blunt-nosed

Butler Creek, Lauderdale County, 24 February 1993, 2.3 in (58 mm) SL male, GSA 4358

CHARACTERISTICS: A member of the subgenus *Ulocentra*, the snubnose darter is distinguished from the similar black darter, *Etheostoma duryi*, by having a blunter snout, separate lateral blotches, and a frenum. Eight quadrate dorsal saddles are present on the back; the fourth saddle occasionally extends downward to the lateral line and fuses with one of the lateral blotches. Eight or nine vertically elongated, lateral blotches are present on the sides, above which are numerous, moderate-sized red dots that form irregular longitudinal lines. The breast, venter, and lower peduncle are orange. The pelvic and anal fins and the lower head region are blue-green. The spiny dorsal fin has a red ocellus in the first membrane, a yellow basal band, and a red distal band. Several elongate red spots in each membrane form a somewhat wavy banding pattern. The soft dorsal fin has red pigment throughout the membranes. Etnier and Starnes (1993) recognize two subspecies of *E. simoterum*; *E. s. atripinne* occurs in the Cumberland, Duck, and Buffalo river systems, while *E. s. simoterum* occurs from the Paint Rock River upstream. A broad zone of intergradation occurs between the Duck and Elk rivers.

ADULT SIZE: 1.6 to 2.4 in (40 to 60 mm)

DISTRIBUTION: The snubnose darter is widely distributed throughout the Tennessee River drainage in upland streams downstream to the Duck River system and in the Cumberland River drainage upstream to Cumberland Falls. Most collection locations in Alabama are from northern tributaries of the Tennessee River and from the Bear Creek system.

HABITAT AND BIOLOGY: This species is found in small, clear streams and medium-sized rivers with moderate current over gravel or bedrock-strewn substrates. Our observations indicate that spawning occurs from March to early May, peaking in April, as in other species of *Ulocentra* in Alabama. These times are similar to the spawning season Page and Mayden (1981) report. Single eggs are deposited on the sides of large stones or sticks from a horizontal to inverted position. Page and Mayden (1981) report that snubnose darters live for a maximum of 18 to 24 months, varying with geographic location. The diet of *E. simoterum* consists of midge larvae, mayflies, caddisflies, and microcrustaceans.

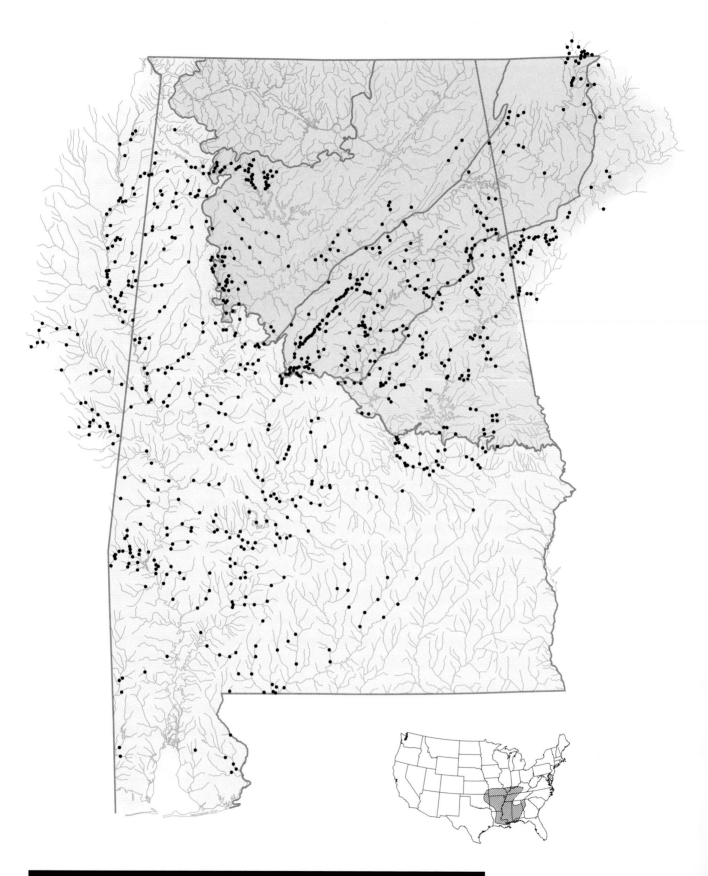

SPECKLED DARTER *Etheostoma stigmaeum* **825 STATIONS**

668

Etheostoma stigmaeum
(Jordan, 1877)

ETYMOLOGY:
Etheostoma—strain mouth, possibly referring to the small mouth
stigmaeum—speckled or spotted

Carrolls Creek, Tuscaloosa County, 15 May 1992, 1.7 in (44 mm) SL male, GSA 4313

CHARACTERISTICS: The speckled darter has a blunt snout but no frenum and slightly joined gill membranes. The body is light brown to straw-colored along the back and sides, grading to light yellow and white on the venter. The back is marked by six dark brown saddles and many large specks; the lateral band is marked with seven to 11 W- or V-shaped blotches. Breeding males have around eight large turquoise bars along their sides. The bases of the pelvic and anal fins are turquoise, while their margins and all other fins are generally clear. The spiny dorsal fin has a deep blue margin, a white band followed by a rusty red band, another blue band, and a basal black band. The cheeks, gill covers, gular region, and lips are brilliant turquoise. *Etheostoma stigmaeum* is similar to the blueside darter, *E. jessiae*, which exhibits dark blue, well-defined blotches along its sides rather than elongate turquoise bars, and has a more pointed snout and distinct frenum. Layman (1994) recently completed a detailed review of the subgenus *Doration*, settling many unresolved systematic questions. See the blueside darter account for further information and Jordan (1877a) for original description.

ADULT SIZE: 1.2 to 2 in (30 to 50 mm)

DISTRIBUTION: Above and below the Fall Line in the Mobile basin this species is widespread and abundant. It occurs in low numbers in the Escatawpa and Perdido river systems and reaches its eastern range limit along the Gulf Coast in the Escambia River drainage in Alabama and Florida. Speckled darters occur in the upper reaches of the Bear Creek system, but are absent in the remainder of the Tennessee River drainage in Alabama.

HABITAT AND BIOLOGY: *Etheostoma stigmaeum* occupies shallow to deep pools of small to large streams having slow to moderate flow and coarse detritus mixed with gravel, small cobble, and sand. It occurs in shallow riffles and shoals, but rarely in swift deep riffles. Spawning is from late March through early May. Eggs are deposited in shallow, sandy pools at the base or head of riffles (O'Neil, 1980). Longevity of this species approaches three years. Its diet consists largely of midge larvae and microcrustaceans supplemented by mayflies and caddisflies.

REMARKS: The type locality of the speckled darter is tributaries to the Etowah and Oostanaula Rivers, Floyd County, Georgia.

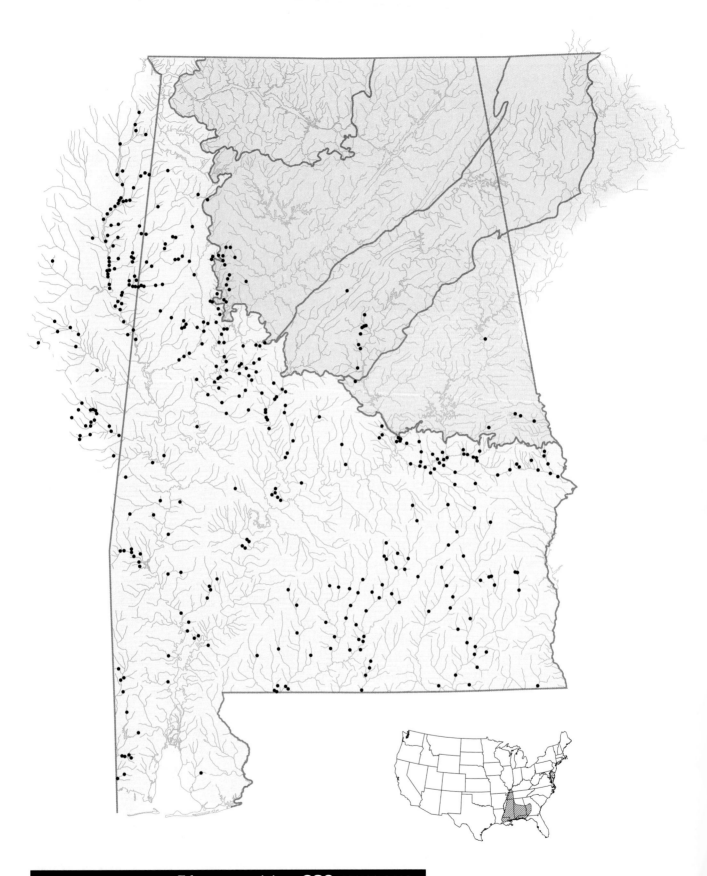

GULF DARTER *Etheostoma swaini* **389 STATIONS**

Etheostoma swaini
(Jordan, 1884)

ETYMOLOGY:
Etheostoma—strain mouth, possibly referring to the small mouth
swaini—in honor of Joseph Swain, a 19th-century ichthyologist

Carrolls Creek, Tuscaloosa County, 15 May 1992, 2.0 (50 mm) SL male, GSA 4313

CHARACTERISTICS: The gulf darter is known for its laterally compressed, robust body with small conical head, slightly joined gill membranes, and a wide frenum on its upper lip. The back has seven to nine diffuse, square saddles and a distinctive light predorsal stripe. Horizontal light and dark banding is evident along the sides. Along their sides breeding males have alternating red-orange and blue-green vertical bars that are developed best near the caudal fin. The venter is orange. The spiny dorsal fin has a red band near its base, above which is a blue band, then another red band, and finally a light blue to clear band at its free margin. The anal fin and base of the pelvic fins are blue; other fins are generally clear. A large, black spot is present at the base of the pectoral fin and three diffuse spots occur at the caudal fin base. The caudal fin has diffuse, wavy black bands. *Etheostoma swaini* is most similar to the watercress darter, *E. nuchale,* and coldwater darter, *E. ditrema*, both of which have fewer pored lateral line scales. See Jordan (1884b) for original description.

ADULT SIZE: 1.8 to 2.4 in (45 to 60 mm)

DISTRIBUTION: *Etheostoma swaini* is predominantly a lowland species. Most of our collection records in the Mobile basin are from either below or short distances above the Fall Line. Northward extensions occur in western tributaries to the Coosa River system in Chilton and Shelby counties, and a single record exists for the Cahaba River in Jefferson County. This species is also found in coastal drainages of Alabama from the Escatawpa River east to the Chipola River, a tributary to the Apalachicola River.

HABITAT AND BIOLOGY: Gulf darters are found in riffles, fast-flowing areas of clear streams, and small rivers over gravel, cobble, debris snags, clay stone, and rubble at bridge crossings. Almost any material that provides cover in suitable current serves as a preferred habitat for this species. The gulf darter is often associated with vegetation. Spawning occurs from mid-March to late April or early May.

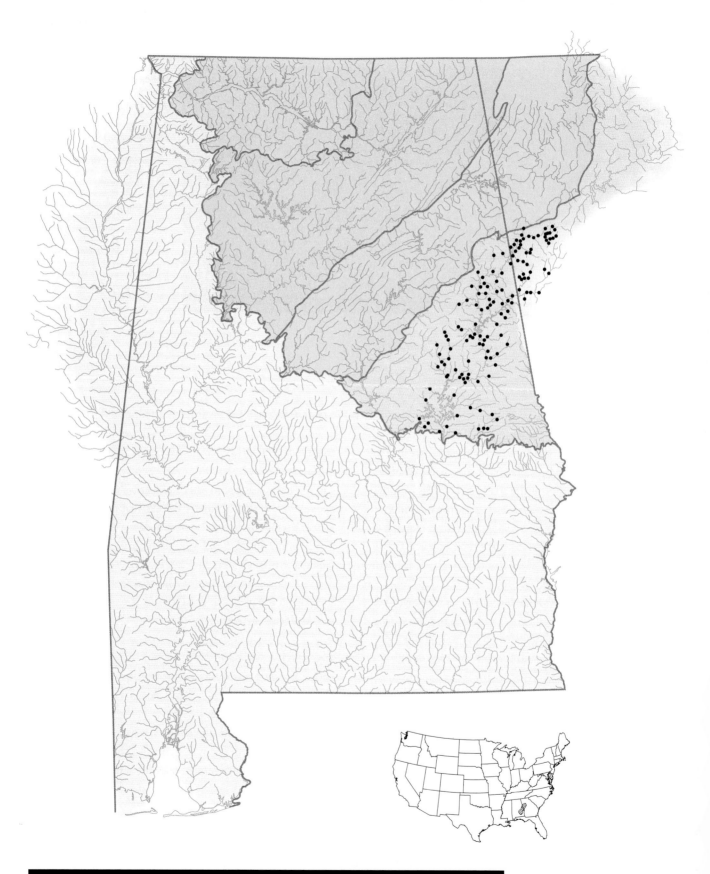

TALLAPOOSA DARTER   *Etheostoma tallapoosae*   135 STATIONS

Etheostoma tallapoosae
Suttkus and Etnier, 1991

ETYMOLOGY:
Etheostoma—strain mouth, possibly referring to the small mouth
tallapoosae—in reference to its distributional range, the Tallapoosa River

Channahatchee Creek, Elmore County, 8 April 1993, 2.2 in (57 mm) SL male, GSA 4415

CHARACTERISTICS: The Tallapoosa darter has seven to 10 vertically oval to quadrate, chocolate brown blotches along the lateral line, darkest near the head and fading to brownish orange or orange near the caudal base. Breeding males occasionally have blue-green between the blotches. *Etheostoma tallapoosae* does not have the red ocellus in the spiny dorsal fin present in several Alabama *Ulocentra*. The lower part of the head, cheeks, and gill covers are bright blue-green. The spiny dorsal fin has a blue margin followed by a thin white submarginal band. Various bands of brown and black then follow to the fin base. The soft dorsal fin has a prominent central red band throughout its length. Two distinct light brown spots surrounded by yellow are found at the base of the caudal fin.

ADULT SIZE: 1.4 to 2.6 in (35 to 65 mm)

DISTRIBUTION: *Etheostoma tallapoosae* is endemic to the Tallapoosa River system of the Mobile basin. All our collection records are from above the Fall Line in the Piedmont Upland.

HABITAT AND BIOLOGY: Tallapoosa darters inhabit small to moderate-sized streams over boulders, rubble, gravel, and/or sand. Breeding individuals have been taken in rubble shoals behind large boulders or logs that create a less turbulent environment. Suttkus and Etnier (1991) report spawning from March through April. Like other *Ulocentra*, the Tallapoosa darter may spawn in a variety of positions on rocks or logs. The diet of this darter is composed of aquatic insect larvae and possibly microcrustaceans common in its preferred habitat.

REMARKS: The type locality of the Tallapoosa darter is Gold Branch near Eclectic, Elmore County, Alabama.

Etheostoma trisella
Bailey and Richards, 1963

ETYMOLOGY:

Etheostoma—strain mouth, possibly referring to the small mouth

trisella—three-saddled, in reference to the three dorsal saddles

Mill Creek tributary, Bradley County, Tennessee, 10 March 1979, 1.5 in (38 mm) SL male. Photograph courtesy of Bruce H. Bauer.

CHARACTERISTICS: *Etheostoma trisella* is distinguished from other members of the subgenus *Ozarka* by a complete lateral line, uninterrupted supratemporal canal, and single anal spine. The back of this small species is yellow-brown crossed by three dark brown saddles. The venter and breast are yellow or white. A thin bar is present below the eye. Breeding males are bright orange, with dusky fins and about four green blotches along the sides. The spiny dorsal fin develops a median band of red spots. Etnier and Starnes (1993) provide additional meristic data for this uncommon species.

ADULT SIZE: 1.3 to 1.6 in (33 to 40 mm)

DISTRIBUTION: The trispot darter is endemic to the Conasauga and Coosawattee river drainages in the upper Coosa River system of Tennessee and Georgia. This species was described from a single specimen collected in 1947 from Cowens Creek, Cherokee County, Alabama. When the type locality was inundated in 1960 by Weiss Reservoir, the species was believed extinct until Howell and Caldwell (1967) discovered several misidentified specimens collected in 1954.

HABITAT AND BIOLOGY: Life history and habitat are summarized from Ryon (1981). The trispot darter has two distinct habitat types. The nonbreeding habitat consists of slow, clear backwaters or eddies of streams with small cobble, pebble, and gravel substrates, often covered with a thin layer of silt. Breeding habitat consists of spring seepage over marsh grasses in lowland areas adjacent to the nonbreeding habitat. Trispot darters spawn from January through March. Following courtship, the pair apparently swim upward through the water column in unison, the female releasing adhesive eggs that are fertilized and, upon falling, adhere to plants, rocks, or the substrate. Adults survive for two to three years. The diet consists of midge larvae, mayflies, microcrustaceans, and lesser amounts of other aquatic insect taxa.

REMARKS: The type locality of the trispot darter is Cowens Creek, Cherokee County, Alabama.

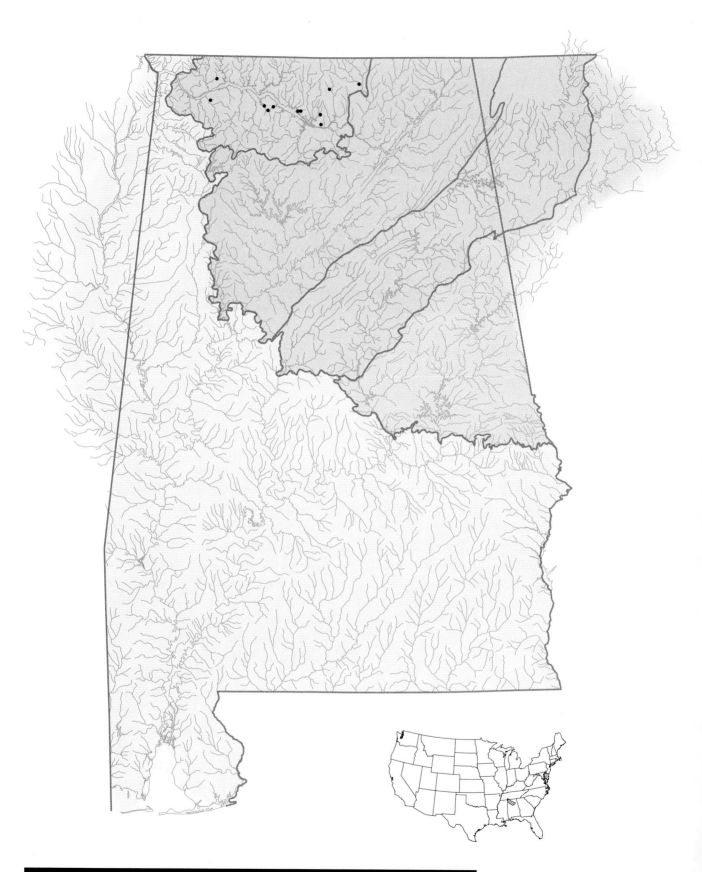

Etheostoma tuscumbia

Gilbert and Swain, 1887

ETYMOLOGY:

Etheostoma—strain mouth, possibly referring to the small mouth

tuscumbia—from the type locality, Tuscumbia Spring, which in turn is named for the Cherokee Indian chief Tuscumbia

Buffler Spring, Lauderdale County, 23 February 1993, 1.4 in (35 mm) SL male, GSA 4356

CHARACTERISTICS: The Tuscumbia darter is characterized by heavy scalation on top of the head, a short snout, small mouth, and a well-developed frenum. The back has five to seven variously developed saddles, and the sides have small blotches along the midline. Both sexes are olive with gold or gold-brown spots. Orbital bars are present, as is a distinct bar or spot at the base of the caudal fin. The fins are for the most part clear, with weak banding due to scattered pigment in the rays. See Gilbert (1887) for original description.

ADULT SIZE: 1.4 to 2.5 in (35 to 64 mm)

DISTRIBUTION: Endemic to the Tennessee River drainage, the Tuscumbia darter is represented by several widely scattered populations restricted to vegetated limestone springs of the Highland Rim. Etnier and Starnes (1993) report several collection sites in southern Tennessee that are now inundated by Pickwick Reservoir. The Tuscumbia darter is not common throughout its range but, when found, local population densities may be high for the available habitat.

HABITAT AND BIOLOGY: *Etheostoma tuscumbia* lives among aquatic vegetation in ponded areas of limestone springs with exceptionally good water quality. Koch (1978) reports no sharp, well-defined spawning peak, finding gravid females year-round in Buffler Spring in Lauderdale County. Increased spawning activity was noted from January through March over clean gravel and sand substrate. Longevity is two or more years in Buffler Spring. Food items consist of amphipods, snails, and midge larvae, all of which are abundant in limestone springs in north Alabama.

REMARKS: The type locality for this species is Tuscumbia Spring in the town of Tuscumbia, Colbert County, Alabama. The Tuscumbia darter is protected by rules and regulations of the Alabama Game and Fish Division.

677

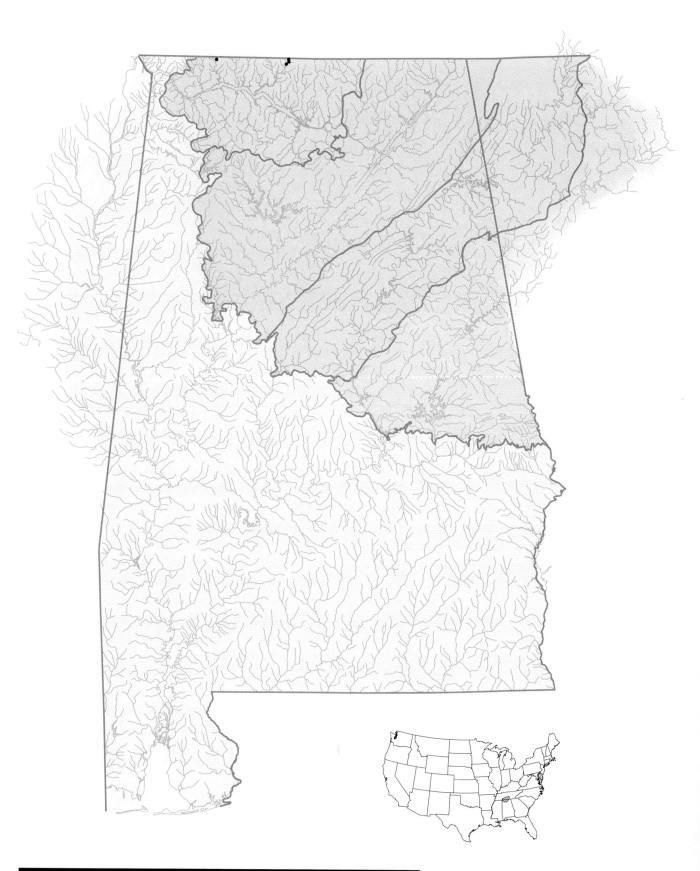

BOULDER DARTER *Etheostoma wapiti* **4 STATIONS**

678

Etheostoma wapiti

Etnier and Williams, 1989

ETYMOLOGY:

Etheostoma—strain mouth, possibly referring to the small mouth

wapiti—from the Cherokee word for elk, in reference to the Elk River

Elk River, Limestone County, 5 October 1993, 2.6 in (65 mm) SL female, GSA 4614

CHARACTERISTICS: The body of breeding males is olive to gray; the posterior half has 10 to 14 distinctive horizontal stripes between scale rows. The head, venter, breast, and prepectoral areas are also grayish, while the throat area is blue. The spiny and soft dorsal fins and caudal fin are dark gray with a thin black margin and pale yellow submarginal band. *Etheostoma wapiti* can be confused with the redline darter, *E. rufilineatum*, and the bluebreast darter, *E. camurum*. The boulder darter lacks the distinctive bars associated with the eye and cheek of *E. rufilineatum*, and it has 13 to 14 dorsal fin spines compared to the 11 to 12 of *E. camurum*. The spiny dorsal fin of *E. wapiti* is longer than but not as high as that in *E. camurum*.

ADULT SIZE: 1.7 to 2.8 in (43 to 70 mm)

DISTRIBUTION: Extant populations of this species are known from a small mainstem section of the Elk River along the Alabama-Tennessee state line and from two large Elk River tributaries in Tennessee. In 1993 we collected and released boulder darters at three locations in the Elk River, all upstream of Alabama Highway 127 in Limestone County. The type locality of the species is Shoal Creek in Lauderdale County; however, no specimens have been observed there since 1884.

HABITAT AND BIOLOGY: Boulder darters appear restricted to swift riffles over fractured limestone cobble and to fast chutes with gravel and small cobble substrates. We collected individuals in the same net haul with *E. camurum* and *E. rufilineatum*. Little is known of boulder darter life history; however, as in other *Nothonotus*, spawning likely occurs in late April and May. Food items include aquatic insect larvae and other riffle-dwelling invertebrates.

REMARKS: The type locality for the boulder darter is Shoal Creek (exact location unknown), Lauderdale County, Alabama. The boulder darter is listed as an endangered species by the U.S. Fish and Wildlife Service.

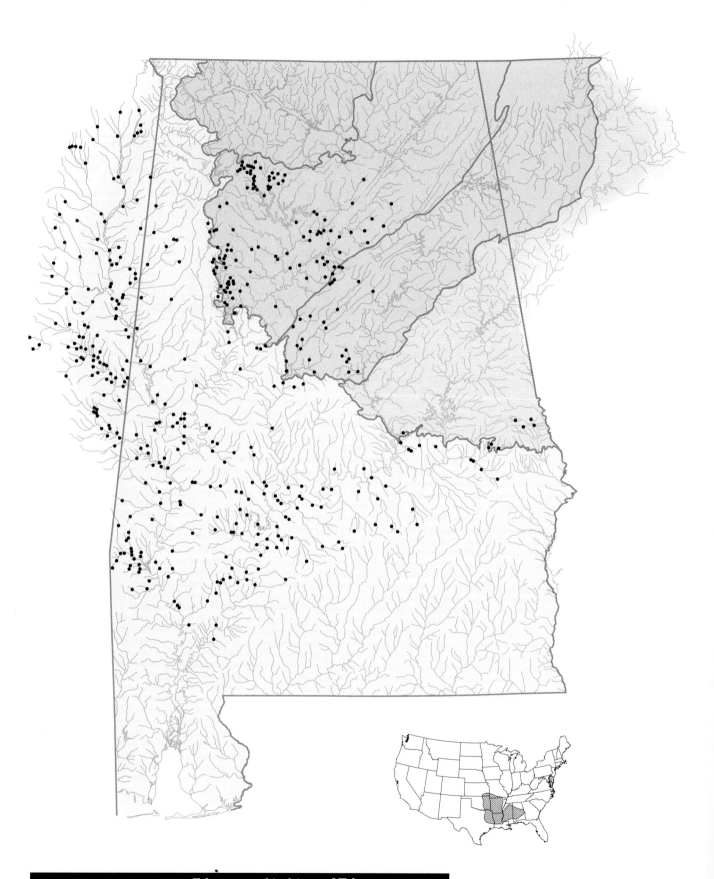

REDFIN DARTER *Etheostoma whipplei* **451 STATIONS**

Etheostoma whipplei
(Girard, 1859)

ETYMOLOGY:

Etheostoma—strain mouth, possibly referring to the small mouth

whipplei—in honor of A. W. Whipple, leader of the survey party that first collected this species

Slater Branch, Wilcox County, 16 March 1993, 1.9 in (47 mm) SL male, GSA 4425

CHARACTERISTICS: The redfin darter is one of the largest *Etheostoma* species in Alabama. Individuals have a broad frenum on the upper lip and a small pointed head. The back and sides of the body are a mottled light olive; the lower head, breast, and gill membrane areas are white. The sides of breeding males are adorned with various sizes of distinctive large red dots. The venter is red-orange in breeding males, the pelvic fins are blue, and the pectoral fins are clear. Both dorsal fins are quite colorful, with a blue margin followed by thin white, red, clear, and red bands, and ending in a white band at the fin base. The caudal and anal fins are similar with blue margins, a thin white band, followed by red then white bands. The caudal fin has a light blue base.

ADULT SIZE: 1.8 to 3.7 in (45 to 95 mm)

DISTRIBUTION: *Etheostoma whipplei* occurs in western tributaries to the lower Mississippi River and in Gulf slope drainages from the Sabine to the Mobile basin. The redfin darter is common throughout the Tombigbee and Alabama river drainages, including the Black Warrior and Cahaba river systems. It is absent from the upper Coosa and upper Tallapoosa river systems and from streams draining the Fall Line Hills, except in localized preferred habitats. Several isolated populations are known from Halawakee Creek in the Chattahoochee River drainage.

HABITAT AND BIOLOGY: *Etheostoma whipplei* inhabits riffles and pools in small to medium-sized streams, over a variety of substrates including slabrock, cobble, rubble, gravel, sand, and silt. When these habitat components are missing, such as in the Coastal Plain, individuals gather around log and debris snags and rooted aquatic vegetation. Our observations indicate spawning from late March to early April. Suttkus' field notes report March 1992 collections of female redfin darters running eggs at Salt Creek in Clarke County. Heins and Machado (1993) report spawning from late February to mid-May in Alabama. The diet includes insect larvae and small crustaceans (Miller and Robison, 1973).

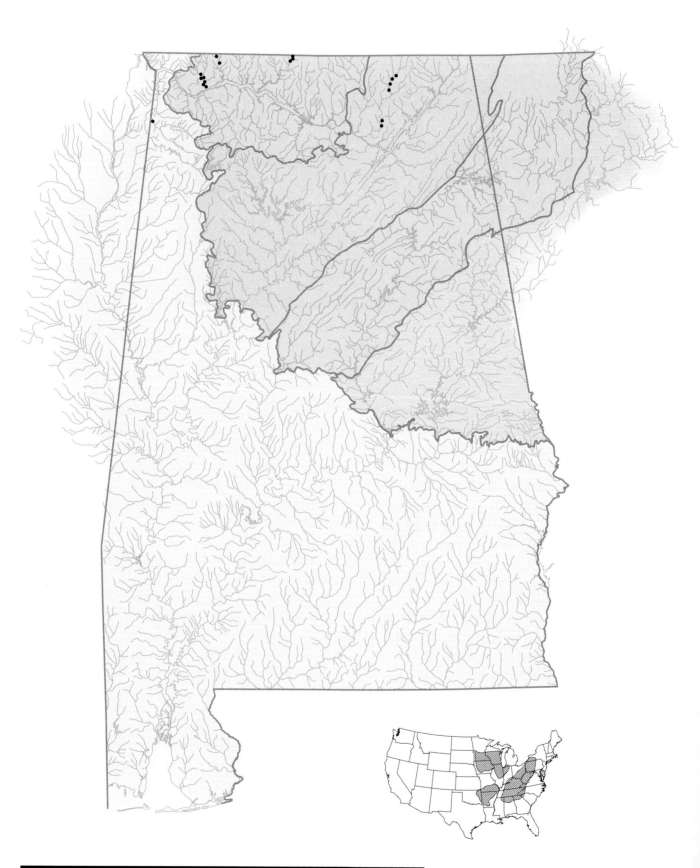

BANDED DARTER   *Etheostoma zonale*   **18 STATIONS**

Etheostoma zonale

(Cope, 1868)

ETYMOLOGY:

Etheostoma—strain mouth, possibly referring to the small mouth

zonale—banded

Butler Creek, Lauderdale County, 24 February 1993, 2.4 in (60 mm) SL male, GSA 4358

CHARACTERISTICS: Banded darters acquire a beautiful emerald green tint during the breeding season. The back is yellow-green; the sides have nine to 13 dark green vertical bars that often encircle the ventral side. Six to eight dark greenish brown saddles traverse the back. Three vertically aligned black spots appear at the caudal fin base. The dorsal fins have a green margin, a dusky midsection, and a red base. The banded darter is distinguishable from the brighteye darter, *E. lynceum*, by having 46 to 56 lateral line scales compared with 39 to 43 for *E. lynceum*. See Cope (1868b) for original description.

ADULT SIZE: 1.8 to 2.4 in (45 to 60 mm).

DISTRIBUTION: Widely distributed, the banded darter occurs from the upper Mississippi River basin in Minnesota east to Pennsylvania, south to Alabama, and west to eastern Oklahoma. Our collections of this species were limited to Shoal and Cypress creeks, the Paint Rock and Elk river systems on the northern side of the Tennessee River, and a single collection in the Bear Creek system in Franklin County.

HABITAT AND BIOLOGY: *Etheostoma zonale* prefers swift riffles of moderately large to large cobble or gravel, slabs, and small boulders in moderate-sized streams and rivers. Our best collections came from larger shoals with extensive mats of aquatic vegetation, particularly *Podostemum*, and attached mosses. Etnier and Starnes (1993) report that breeding color intensifies in males in late February and spawning occurs in April and May in Tennessee. Eggs are attached to aquatic vegetation. Lachner et al. (1950) report longevity of three or more years for a Pennsylvania population. Bryant (1979) and Cordes and Page (1980) found banded darters consuming a mixed diet of midge and mayfly larvae, with lesser amounts of blackflies and trichopteran larvae.

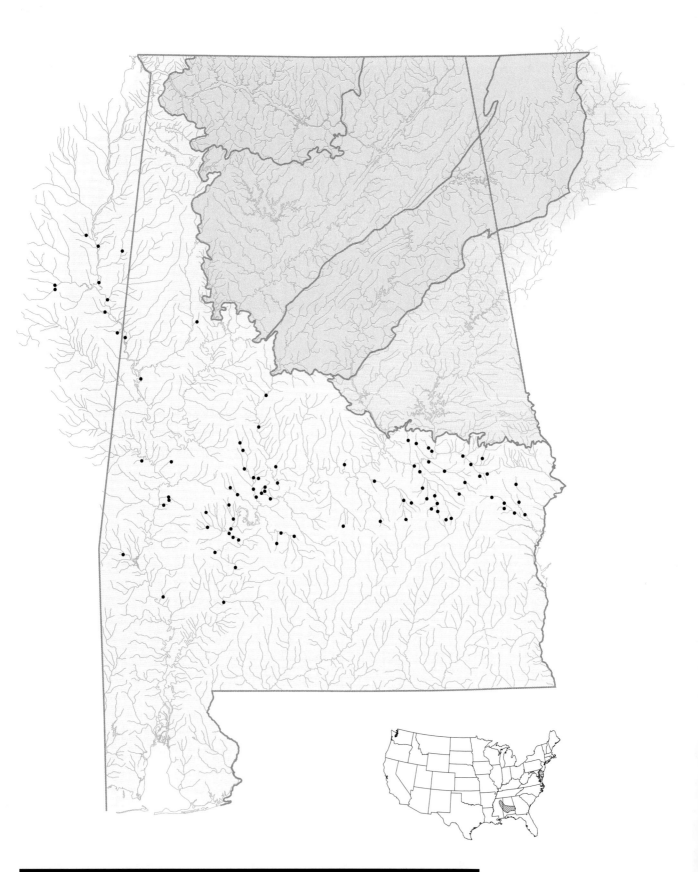

Etheostoma zonifer

(Hubbs and Cannon, 1935)

ETYMOLOGY:

Etheostoma—strain mouth, possibly referring to the small mouth

zonifer—banded, in reference to the caudal peduncle bands

Panther Creek, Bullock County, 19 March 1993, 1.7 in (42 mm) SL male, GSA 4400

CHARACTERISTICS: Like the slough darter, the backwater darter is noted for having a small mouth and head, and a lateral line that arches upward anteriorly. A broad frenum is present and the gill membranes are sightly to moderately connected. *Etheostoma zonifer* is typically yellow or olive with thin green reticulations and green saddles on the back. Males have a series of green bars along their sides; female coloration is limited to small green squares along the sides. The spiny dorsal fin has a blue margin and base with a red median band. A black spot is present at the base of the caudal fin. The backwater darter is similar to the slough darter, *E. gracile*, but can be distinguished by its interrupted infraorbital canal with six pores. *Etheostoma gracile* has an uninterrupted infraorbital, canal usually with eight pores.

ADULT SIZE: 1 to 1.8 in (25 to 45 mm)

DISTRIBUTION: The backwater darter is found below the Fall Line in both the Alabama and Tombigbee river drainages of the Mobile basin and also in the Cowikee Creek system of the Chattahoochee River drainage.

Etheostoma zonifer is one of the few darter species in Alabama that prefers sluggish, marl-laden streams draining the Black Belt across the central part of the state. Backwater darters are usually rare to uncommon even in preferred habitats.

HABITAT AND BIOLOGY: Backwater darters inhabit small turbid streams and adjacent pools with sandy or muddy substrates and little or no flow. The species occasionally occurs in patches of vegetation and along stream margins. Peterson (1993) reports habitats characterized by high turbidity, slow currents, high conductivity, and little to no vegetation. Spawning occurs from late March through June, peaking in late May and early June. Single eggs are laid on small submerged twigs and roots. The diet consists of midge larvae, copepods, mayflies, cladocerans, and smaller aquatic organisms.

REMARKS: The type locality of the backwater darter is Catoma Creek near Montgomery, Montgomery County, Alabama.

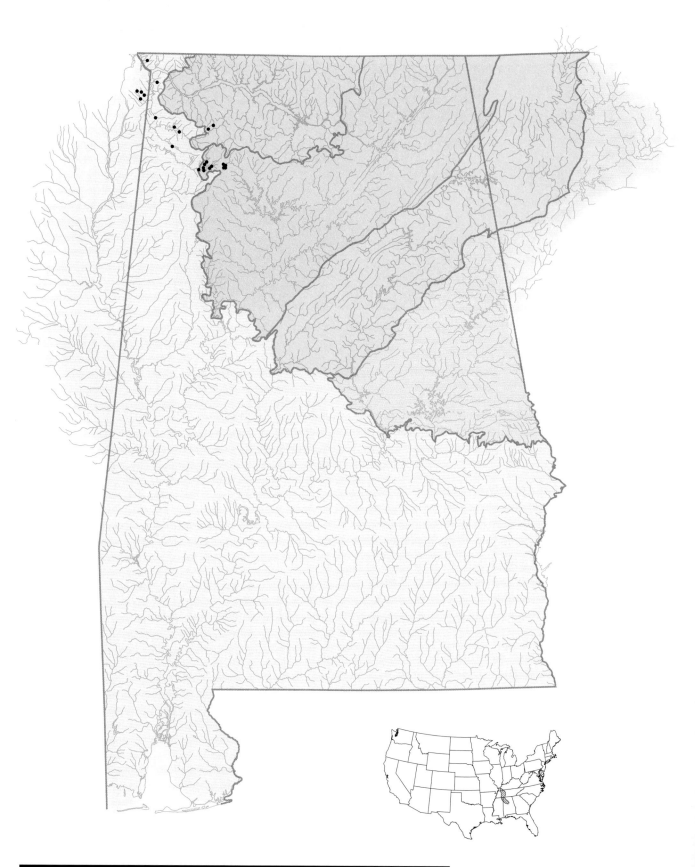

Etheostoma zonistium
Bailey and Etnier, 1988

ETYMOLOGY:
Etheostoma—strain mouth, possibly referring to the small mouth
zonistium—band fin, referring to the banding pattern in the spiny dorsal fin of male

Pennywinkle Creek, Colbert County, 3 May 1996, 2.1 in (54 mm) SL male, GSA 4672

CHARACTERISTICS: The bandfin darter has an olive to tan back and a cream to white venter. The sides have nine or so lateral dark blotches extending to just above and below the lateral line. The lower head, throat, and breast of breeding males are light blue-green. Males acquire an intense orange to red-orange wash throughout the venter extending dorsally to the lateral band. The anal and pelvic fins are turquoise with a clear base. The alternating dark and light spiny dorsal fin coloration is characteristic for this species with the following order of colors beginning at the margin: dark blue, light, brick red, light, black, light, and a faint dark basal band. The soft dorsal fin has a distinct red medial band on the posterior two-thirds of the fin. The bandfin darter is distinguishable from the Coosa darter, *Etheostoma coosae*, by having five rather than six rays in the gill membranes, ovoid lateral blotches confined to the lateral line area, and orange to yellow on the lower sides and venter.

ADULT SIZE: 1.4 to 2.2 in (35 to 56 mm)

DISTRIBUTION: *Etheostoma zonistium* was described from populations in the Bear Creek system, small tributaries to the Tennessee River in extreme western Lauderdale County, and in Hubbard Creek, a tributary of the Sipsey Fork and upper Black Warrior River system. Populations in Hubbard Creek and the upper reaches of Bear Creek lack the distinctive red ocellus in the front of the spiny dorsal fin; they have been tentatively recognized as a new species awaiting description.

HABITAT AND BIOLOGY: Bandfin darters usually inhabit the margins of small streams having either fine gravel substrates and little flow or a moderate flow over slab and bedrock substrates (Carney and Burr, 1989). These authors report peak spawning activity from March through May. Single eggs are deposited on cobble, rubble, submerged logs, and snags. Bailey and Etnier (1988) indicate spawning in April and May and suggest a longevity of three years. Aquatic insect larvae and microcrustaceans comprise the diet.

YELLOW PERCH   *Perca flavescens*   60 STATIONS

Perca flavescens
(Mitchill, 1814)

ETYMOLOGY:

Perca—perch
flavescens—yellow

Bay Minette Creek, Baldwin County, 15 June 1993, 7.9 in (200 mm) SL male, GSA 4481

CHARACTERISTICS: This moderately large, yellow percid is distinguished by a serrated preopercle and a large black spot at the posterior base of the spiny dorsal fin. Most individuals have six to nine black saddles across the back, continuing down the sides to below the mid-lateral area. The body has yellowish green or golden yellow color on the back, lighter yellow on the sides, and a white venter and breast. Dorsal and caudal fins are olive yellow; pectoral fins silvery orange or yellow. The pelvic and anal fins are yellowish orange on individuals in the Tennessee River drainage and Chattahoochee River system and bright red on individuals from tributaries of the Mobile Delta.

ADULT SIZE: 3 to 12 in (75 to 300 mm)

DISTRIBUTION: The range of this northern species has expanded through introduction into western and selected southern states (see inset map). Populations in the Tennessee River drainage and Chattahoochee River system are introduced. A single 1964 Choctawhatchee system specimen housed at the University of Michigan Museum of Zoology is puzzling; no other individuals of yellow perch have been collected from that drainage.

Populations in the Mobile Delta are native, based on collections made in 1851 housed at Harvard University (Smith-Vaniz, 1968). Yellow perch bones were also recovered from an archaeological excavation in Mobile dating to French occupation in 1702-20 (Sheldon and Cottier, 1983). Our samples from four delta tributaries confirm that the species still exists in the area. The single observation in the upper Tombigbee River system probably resulted from migration through the Tennessee-Tombigbee Waterway.

HABITAT AND BIOLOGY: We have collected yellow perch in a variety of habitats, including moderate to large flowing streams and rivers, tannin-stained tributaries of the Mobile Delta, and reservoirs. Most fish remain in deep water during the day and move closer to shore to feed during the evening hours. Spawning occurs from March to May, when gelatinous strands of eggs are scattered over sand and gravel substrates or draped over vegetation or submerged snags. Small yellow perch eat microcrustaceans and insect larvae. Large adults consume small fishes, large crustaceans, and are occasionally caught by anglers fishing for crappie with live minnows. The flesh of this small fish is delicious.

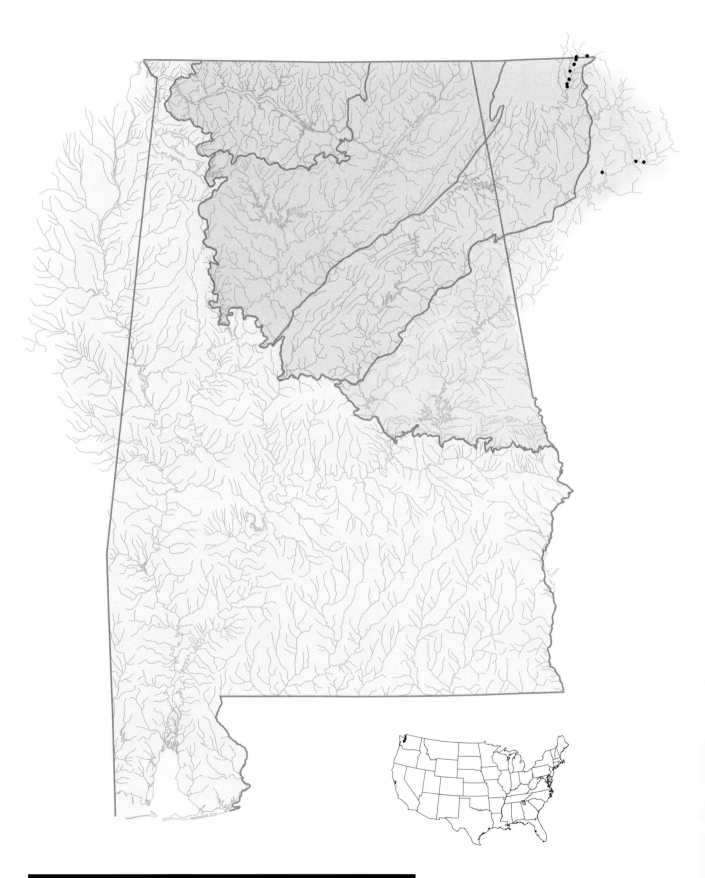

AMBER DARTER *Percina antesella* **11 STATIONS**

Percina antesella

Williams and Etnier, 1977

ETYMOLOGY:

Percina—a diminutive of *Perca*, meaning perch

antesella—anterior saddle, referring to the distinct position of the first dorsal saddle

Etowah River, Cherokee County, Georgia, 25 August 1990, 2.2 in (57 mm) SL male. Photograph courtesy of Richard T. Bryant and Wayne C. Starnes

CHARACTERISTICS: The amber darter, a member of the subgenus *Imostoma*, is distinguished by the placement of its first dorsal saddle, which is located well anterior to the spiny dorsal fin. The body is slender, the snout is moderately long and pointed, and the eyes are located high on top of the head. The throat area of breeding males in this species is blue. Four dark brown saddles cross the yellow-brown back and extend down to the lateral line. The venter generally is yellow or white, and a distinct bar is present below the eye. The fins are generally clear, with faint dusky markings in the dorsal, caudal, and pectoral fins. The elongate anal fin of breeding males is characteristic of this subgenus.

ADULT SIZE: 1.8 to 3 in (45 to 75 mm)

DISTRIBUTION: *Percina antesella* is endemic to the Conasauga and Etowah river systems in the upper Coosa River system. Individuals were observed in the Etowah River and Sharp Mountain Creek in 1990, and this species was recently rediscovered in Shoal Creek,

Cherokee County, Georgia. The Conasauga population is limited to about 33 miles of the river in north Georgia and southeast Tennessee.

HABITAT AND BIOLOGY: The amber darter inhabits cool, clear, small rivers with moderate to swift currents over gravel and cobble substrates. Most individuals live in deep riffles with moderate current. Freeman (1983) reports as preferred habitat the midsection or upstream end of low-gradient riffles, either over sand and gravel or among clumps of river weed in midsummer. Spawning occurs early, as with all *Imostoma*, from late fall to early spring. Eggs are deposited in sand and gravel areas of riffles and shoals (Freeman, 1983). The diet of *P. antesella* includes snails, limpets, and insect larvae. Etnier and Starnes (1993) report longevity of three or more years.

REMARKS: The type locality of the amber darter is the Conasauga River, Bradley County, Tennessee. This darter is listed as an endangered species by the U.S. Fish and Wildlife Service.

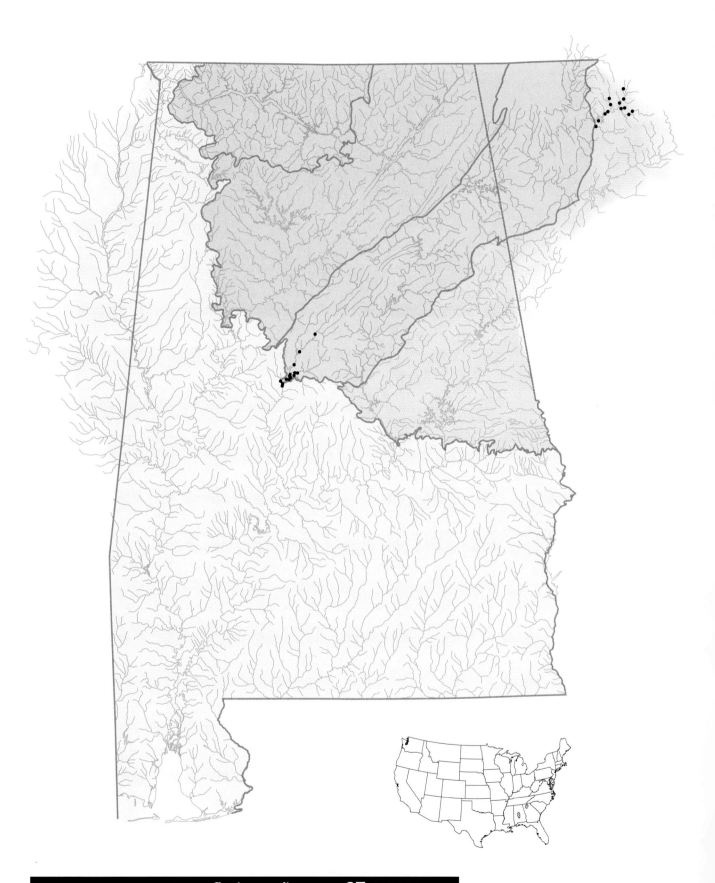

GOLDLINE DARTER *Percina aurolineata* **27 STATIONS**

Percina aurolineata

Suttkus and Ramsey, 1967

ETYMOLOGY:

Percina—a diminutive of *Perca*, meaning perch
aurolineata—gold-lined, referring to the gold stripe on the upper sides

Little Cahaba River, Bibb County, 29 September 1993, 2.4 in (60 mm) SL male, GSA 4613

CHARACTERISTICS: The goldline darter has broadly joined gill membranes, three vertically placed dark spots at the base of the caudal fin, no breeding tubercles, and a complete row of enlarged scales on the midline of the venter. It is distinguished from other members of the subgenus *Hadropterus* in Alabama by the presence of a continuous or slightly interrupted bright amber or russet stripe extending from the head to the end of the soft dorsal fin between the eight or nine dark lateral blotches and two dorsal fins. The fins are generally dusky and lightly banded, with breeding males developing bright yellow submarginal bands and yellow around the caudal spots.

ADULT SIZE: 1.6 to 2.9 in (40 to 74 mm)

DISTRIBUTION: *Percina aurolineata* is endemic to the Mobile basin and is represented by two disjunct populations in the Alabama River basin. One is found in the middle Cahaba River system and the other occurs in the

Coosawattee River system in Georgia. Stiles (1990) indicates that decreasing densities in the Little Cahaba River population over the last 12 years could be due to increased turbidity and sedimentation in upper reaches of the watershed.

HABITAT AND BIOLOGY: The preferred habitat of this species is moderate to swift-flowing shallow riffles in main channels of free-flowing rivers, characterized by cobble, small boulders, or bedrock substrates and extensive patches of water willow, *Justicia*, or river weed, *Podostemum*. As in other *Hadropterus*, spawning occurs early in the year, extending from March through May or June. Individuals in peak nuptial condition can be found in the Cahaba River from late May to early June.

REMARKS: The type locality for *P. aurolineata* is the Coosawattee River near Ellijay, Gilmer County, Georgia. The goldline darter is listed as a threatened species by the U.S. Fish and Wildlife Service.

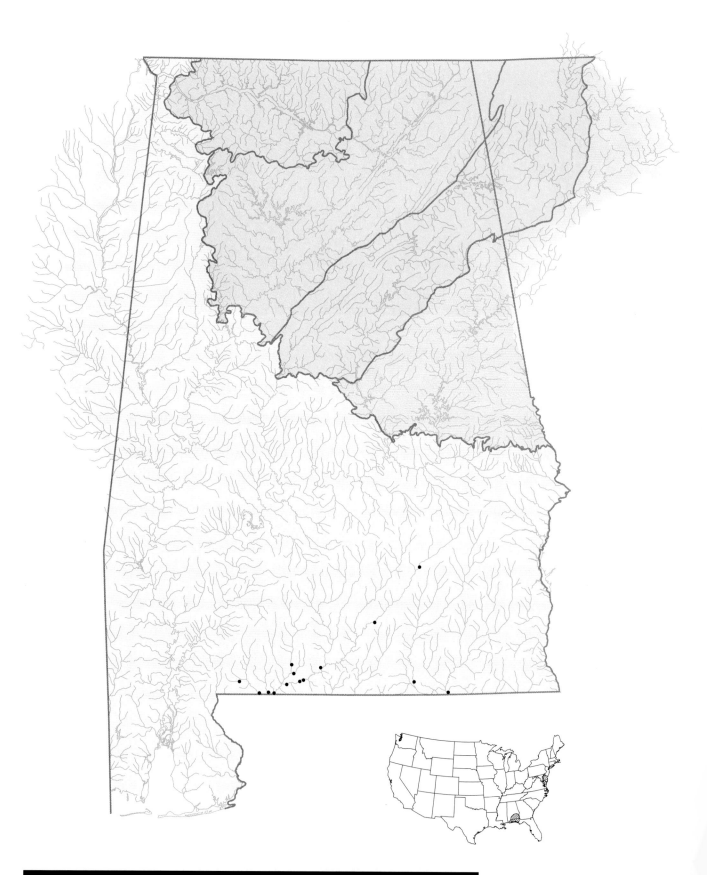

Percina austroperca

Thompson, 1995

ETYMOLOGY:

Percina—a diminutive of *Perca*, meaning perch *austroperca*—southern perch, referring to the southern extent of its distribution

Murder Creek, Escambia County, 29 June 1995, 4.5 in (115 mm) SL male, GSA 4653

CHARACTERISTICS: The southern logperch, one of Alabama's most recently described darter species (Thompson, 1995), closely resembles two other undescribed logperch species in the state, the "Mobile logperch" and the "Gulf logperch" (Thompson, 1985). *Percina austroperca* is distinguished from other logperch by a thin red submarginal band in the spiny dorsal fin, an entirely scaled nape, by absence of scales on top of the head and the anterior part of the breast, and by having no preopercle blotch on adults. Its lateral banding pattern consists of nine vertically elongated bars, separated by a series of thin, short vertical bars. The anterior elongate bars are slightly widened into blotches. *Percina austroperca* has higher anal ray and pored lateral line counts than the "Gulf logperch," which it most closely resembles. In contrast to the southern logperch, vertically elongated bars along the sides of the "Mobile logperch" are expanded into blotches below the lateral line, and are individually separated by shorter bars that are not expanded at the lower ends.

ADULT SIZE: 3.1 to 5.3 in (80 to 135 mm)

DISTRIBUTION: The southern logperch is known from the Choctawhatchee and Conecuh river drainages in Alabama and Florida. We collected the only two records from the lower Choctawhatchee River system in Alabama and most of the records in the Conecuh River system, where the species is more widespread. This logperch is known only from these two drainages and is allopatric with all other logperch.

HABITAT AND BIOLOGY: The southern logperch prefers large rivers and streams with shifting sand and gravel substrates. Large numbers have been observed in the main channel of the Conecuh River over shoals two to three feet deep. Little else is known about the biology of this species, although its diet is presumably similar to that of other logperches, consisting of aquatic insect larvae. Our observations indicate that southern logperch spawn early in the year, as do other logperch in the subgenus *Percina*. This and other logperch species are known to flip stones or similar objects scattered along the bottom in search of food. With age, their snouts often become blunt and somewhat calloused.

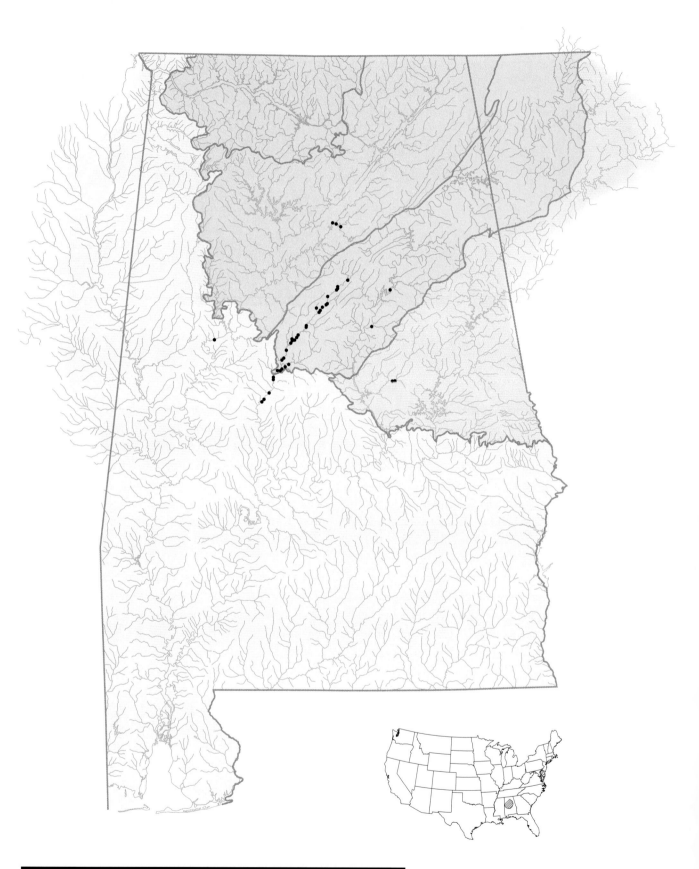

COAL DARTER   *Percina brevicauda*   40 STATIONS

Percina brevicauda
Suttkus and Bart, 1994

ETYMOLOGY:
Percina—a diminutive of *Perca*, meaning perch *brevicauda*—descriptive of the short caudal fin; the common name, coal darter, is in reference to the dark pigmentation of nuptial males

Hatchet Creek, Coosa County, 24 June 1992, 1.5 in (39 mm) SL male, GSA 4320

CHARACTERISTICS: One of the smallest *Percina* species in Alabama, the coal darter has a cylindrical body, a blunt snout, and an inferior mouth. A dusky vertical bar is present below the eye and the gill cover has a distinct spot near the top. About eight to 12 somewhat oval blotches extend along the sides from the gill covers to the caudal fin. Pigmentation on the back is variously developed into unorganized saddles. Scales on the body are small and outlined with pigment above the lateral line, giving them a diamond-shaped appearance. The pelvic, anal, and caudal fins are dusky. The spiny dorsal fin has a dusky marginal band followed by a light band, then a wide dusky band near the base. Membranes in the soft dorsal fin are darkly pigmented in the center, becoming dusky near the margin. Nuptial males are heavily pigmented on the ventral surface of the head and body. See Suttkus, Thompson, and Bart (1994) for original description.

ADULT SIZE: 1.2 to 1.8 in (30 to 45 mm)

DISTRIBUTION: *Percina brevicauda* is endemic to the Mobile basin in Alabama. It is uncommon in Blackburn and Locust forks of the Black Warrior River system and in Hatchet Creek and limited areas of the Coosa River system. The coal darter is widespread in the main channel of the Cahaba River ranging from near Leeds to below the Fall Line near Centreville.

HABITAT AND BIOLOGY: *Percina brevicauda* prefers shoal areas of flowing rivers and larger streams characterized by gravel, cobble, and sand substrates and a swift current. We have collected reproductively mature males and females in the Cahaba River in May and June. Little else is known about the species' life history; but preferred prey likely include insect larvae, microcrustaceans, and aquatic worms.

REMARKS: The type locality for *P. brevicauda* is the Cahaba River at County Highway 52 near Helena, Shelby County, Alabama.

Percina burtoni

Fowler, 1945

ETYMOLOGY:

Percina—a diminutive of *Perca*, meaning perch

burtoni—in honor of E. Milby Burton, who first collected the species

Larkin Fork, Jackson County, 29 November 1994, 2.1 in (54 mm) SL juvenile, GSA 4634

CHARACTERISTICS: A member of the subgenus *Percina*, the blotchside logperch is characterized by a naked or mostly unscaled nape, and along the lateral line, a series of large blotches that are usually present in juvenile specimens. An orange submarginal band in the anterior part of the spiny dorsal fin distinguishes the blotchside logperch from the similar *Percina caprodes*, which has an uncolored spiny dorsal fin. *Percina burtoni* is olive on the back, fading to yellow and white along the lower sides and venter. Lateral pigmentation consists of eight to 10 dark green to black oval or round blotches that are partially connected along their width by the lateral band. In older individuals the back has nine to 11 dark saddles and numerous dark stripes extending ventrally along the upper sides. A distinct caudal spot is typically present.

ADULT SIZE: 3.5 to 5.9 in (90 to 150 mm)

DISTRIBUTION: Although not common, *Percina burtoni* is widely distributed in upland streams of the Tennessee River and upland streams of the middle Cumberland River. It is quite rare in Alabama, restricted to Estill and Larkin forks of the Paint Rock River system. This species may also occur in the Shoal Creek system, as Etnier and Starnes (1993) report specimens from Little Butler Creek just north of the Alabama-Tennessee state line.

HABITAT AND BIOLOGY: *Percina burtoni* inhabits swift riffles and flowing pools over gravel and small cobble substrates in clear, moderately large streams and smaller rivers that have exceptionally good water quality. Spawning is reported to occur from April to May (Etnier and Starnes, 1993). Reproductive behavior is unknown but is assumed to be similar to that of other logperch. The diet consists of aquatic insect larvae including mayflies, caddisflies, midges, blackflies, and riffle beetles.

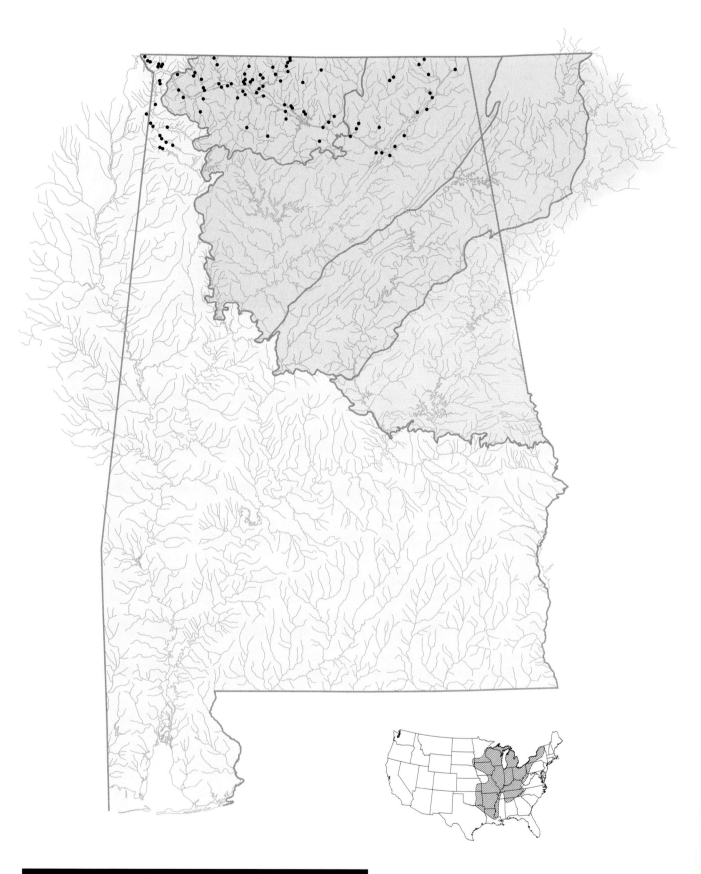

LOGPERCH   *Percina caprodes*   94 STATIONS

Percina caprodes

(Rafinesque, 1818)

ETYMOLOGY:

Percina—a diminutive of *Perca*, meaning perch *caprodes*—piglike, in reference to the distinctive snout of this species

Cedar Creek, Franklin County, 25 February 1993, 3.9 in (100 mm) SL male, GSA 4362

CHARACTERISTICS: The logperch, of the subgenus *Percina*, is one of the largest and most distinctive darters. Individuals have a conical snout that projects well beyond the upper jaw, a wide frenum, obvious tiger-like vertical banding along the sides, and a single black spot at the base of the caudal fin. The back has 16 to 22 narrow bands that vary in intensity and width; some resemble saddles and continue downward toward the venter. The body is yellowish brown to yellow-green along the back and sides, changing to light green to white on the venter. The uncolored caudal and dorsal fins contain light basal and marginal black bands while breeding males have dusky membranes on the dorsal fins. *Percina caprodes* is similar to *P. burtoni*, *P. austroperca*, the "Mobile logperch," and the "Gulf logperch" and is distinguished from these species by its spiny dorsal fin with no orange or red banding. See Rafinesque (1818b) for original description.

ADULT SIZE: 3.9 to 5.9 in (100 to 150 mm)

DISTRIBUTION: *Percina caprodes* is distributed from Hudson Bay southward to western tributaries of the lower Mississippi River basin and eastward to the Tennessee River drainage in Alabama. The subspecies *Percina c. caprodes* occurs throughout the Tennessee River drainage in Alabama, where it is widespread and occasionally abundant (Morris and Page, 1981).

HABITAT AND BIOLOGY: We have collected this species in a variety of habitats, ranging from small tributaries to large rivers and impoundments. Individuals usually occur over sand and gravel in streams with a moderate current or over sand and mud substrates in lakes, sometimes at great depths. Spawning occurs from March to May. Females bury from 10 to 20 eggs per spawn in sand or gravel substrates of riffles or shoals (Winn, 1958a, b). We have observed large spawning aggregations of logperch in the free-flowing reaches of large streams upstream of reservoirs. Logperch live three to four years (Thomas, 1970) and young logperch feed on small crustaceans, while adults consume midge larvae, mayflies, and caddisflies. This and other logperch species flip stones scattered along the bottom in search of food. With age, their snouts often become blunt and calloused.

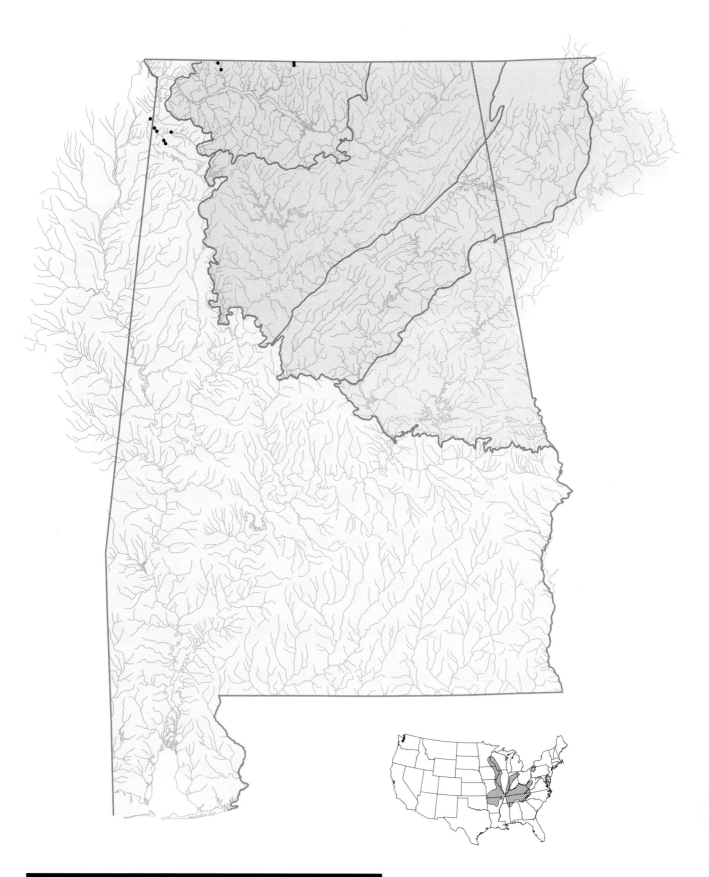

Percina evides

(Jordan and Copeland, 1877)

ETYMOLOGY:

Percina—a diminutive of *Perca*, meaning perch *evides*—comely or attractive, referring to the gilded lower head and body of breeding males

Cedar Creek, Franklin County, 25 February 1993, 2.8 in (70 mm) SL male, GSA 4362

CHARACTERISTICS: The gilt darter, one of Alabama's most colorful *Percina* species, is known for the brilliant reddish orange on the underside of the head. The body color of breeding males is olive with seven to nine blue-black or blue-green saddles and eight or nine lateral blotches that are often connected to form a continuous bar along the sides. The base of the caudal fin has two oval white or yellow spots. A distinct dark bar is present below the eye, and the cheeks are usually unscaled. The spiny dorsal fin has a blackish orange to amber base with a yellowish orange submarginal band. The pelvic and anal fins are blue-black. The gilt darter is similar in appearance to the bronze darter, *Percina palmaris*, which lacks reddish orange coloration on the head and has partly to fully scaled cheeks. See Jordan (1877c) for original description.

ADULT SIZE: 1.8 to 3 in (45 to 75 mm)

DISTRIBUTION: *Percina evides* occurs in tributaries of the Ohio River basin and in western tributaries of the Mississippi River in Missouri and Arkansas. We collected gilt darters on several occasions in both the Bear Creek and Shoal Creek systems. Our collections at two sites in the upper Elk River are the first records of gilt darters in the Alabama section of this river system.

HABITAT AND BIOLOGY: Gilt darters inhabit gravel to small cobble shoals, large streams, and small rivers with moderate current. Individuals are most often taken in deep chutes and runs and at the head of riffles. We collected individuals in breeding condition during March and the spawning season may extend until May. Page et al. (1982) report that *P. evides* is an egg burier that spawns over sand and gravel interspersed with cobble and boulders in the upstream reaches of riffles. These fishes feed on midge larvae, blackflies, caddisflies, mayflies, and occasionally on snails (Starnes, 1977). Tudor (1982) indicates a longevity of three years and marked change in diet with age and season for a Minnesota population.

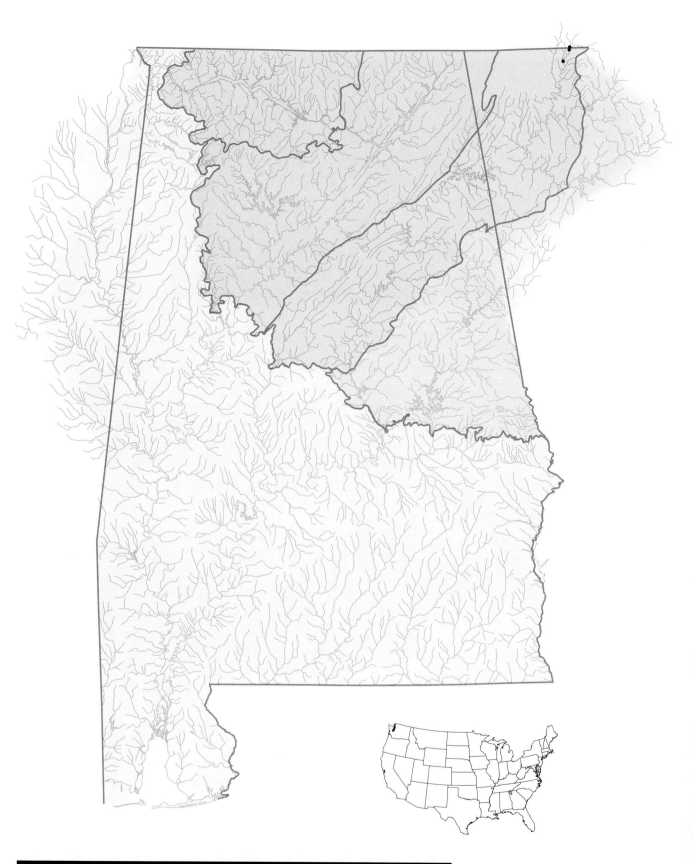

Percina jenkinsi

Thompson, 1985

ETYMOLOGY:

Percina—a diminutive of *Perca*, meaning perch
jenkinsi—in honor of R. E. Jenkins, noted ichthyologist at Roanoke College in Salem, Virginia

Conasauga River, Polk County, Tennessee, May 1980, 3.5 in (88 mm) SL. Photograph courtesy of Richard T. Bryant and Wayne C. Starnes

CHARACTERISTICS: The Conasauga logperch has a long, pointed snout with a blunt tip extending beyond the upper jaw. Numerous dark brown vertical bars are present along the sides against a yellowish tan body; the venter is white. The eight whole-body bars expand into diffuse blotches below the lateral line. The half and quarter bars between the whole-body bars are thin. A prominent bar is present below the eye in addition to irregular markings on the cheeks and opercles. The Conasauga logperch is distinguished from other logperches in the Mobile basin by its 90 or more lateral line scales, three whole-body bars posterior to the origin of the soft dorsal fin, and the absence of a red, orange, or yellow band in the spiny dorsal fin.

ADULT SIZE: 3.1 to 4.6 in (80 to 116 mm).

DISTRIBUTION: This is one of the rarest darters in North America. *Percina jenkinsi* is endemic to the Mobile basin, its entire range limited to approximately 11 miles of the upper Conasauga River of the Coosa River system in Tennessee and Georgia.

HABITAT AND BIOLOGY: This rare and seldom encountered species occurs in flowing pools over silt-free substrates of gravel and rubble and in swift riffles and deeper chutes with gravel and small rubble (Thompson, 1985). Little is known of the Conasuga logperch's life history, although it is assumed to be similar to that of other logperches. Spawning probably extends from late March to May. Thompson (1985) speculates that spawning occurs during April, based on examination of tuberculate males. The diet consists of aquatic insect larvae.

REMARKS: The type locality of the Conasauga logperch is the Conasauga River, Bradley County, Tennessee. The species is listed as endangered by the U.S. Fish and Wildlife Service.

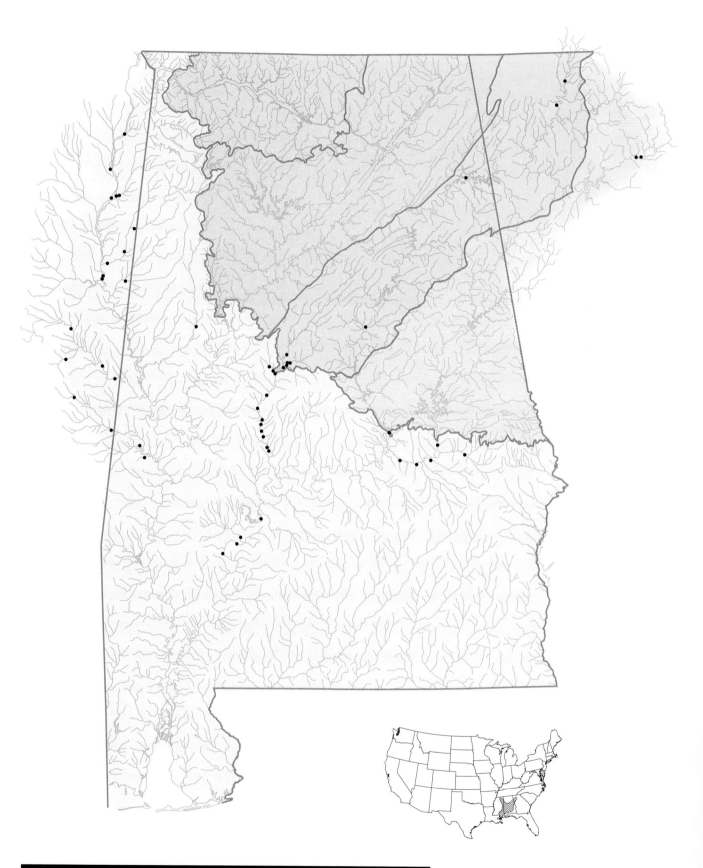

FRECKLED DARTER   *Percina lenticula*   52 STATIONS

706

Percina lenticula

Richards and Knapp, 1964

ETYMOLOGY:

Percina—a diminutive of *Perca*, meaning perch *lenticula*—freckled, referring to the frecklelike spots on the pectoral fin base

Tallapoosa River, Elmore County, 19 October 1992, 5.3 in (135 mm) SL male, GSA 4334

CHARACTERISTICS: The freckled darter, a member of the subgenus *Hadropterus*, is considered by taxonomists to be one of the more primitive darters in the family Percidae. *Percina lenticula* is distinguished by high lateral line scale counts (modally 80 to 86 scales) and a large maximum body size in comparison to other darters. The back has eight dark dorsal saddles and the sides have around eight dark vertical blotches. The venter and breast are light or dusky, while the head is mottled above and light below. A large black blotch occurs at the origin of the soft dorsal fin, which has more rays (modally 13) than in other species of *Hadropterus*. Three vertically aligned spots at the base of the caudal fin are often fused. The dorsal, anal, and caudal fins usually contain light and dark banding. Neither sex develops bright nuptial color. Freckled darter males develop a double row of enlarged mid-ventral scales, a feature rarely observed in other *Percina* species. See Suttkus and Ramsey (1967) for comparisions with *P. aurolineata*, *P. nigrofasciata*, and *P. sciera*.

ADULT SIZE: 3.9 to 6.6 in (100 to 168 mm). This is the largest darter in North America (Page and Burr, 1979).

DISTRIBUTION: *Percina lenticula* is found from the Pearl River system in Mississippi east to the Mobile basin. Most records of freckled darters in the Mobile basin are below the Fall Line, although scattered records exist just above this line in the Cahaba and Coosa river systems and in the upper Coosa River system in Georgia.

HABITAT AND BIOLOGY: Individuals usually live in deep, swift areas of flowing rivers and large streams. Pierson et al. (1989) report a preferred habitat of deep runs and rapids with moderate to fast current with juveniles occurring in *Justicia* beds of shallow riffles. Little is known about the life history of this species; however, it presumably spawns in the spring, late March to early May, and eats aquatic insects and crustaceans. Suttkus' field notes indicate 12 young *P. lenticula* (18–23 mm SL) were found on a flooded, vegetated sandbar of the Pearl River in Louisiana during April 1995. Twenty-three young *Etheostoma histrio* (15–23 mm SL) and 18 young *Percina vigil* (18–26 mm SL) were also taken with the *P. lenticula*.

REMARKS: The type locality of the freckled darter is the Cahaba River, Bibb County, Alabama.

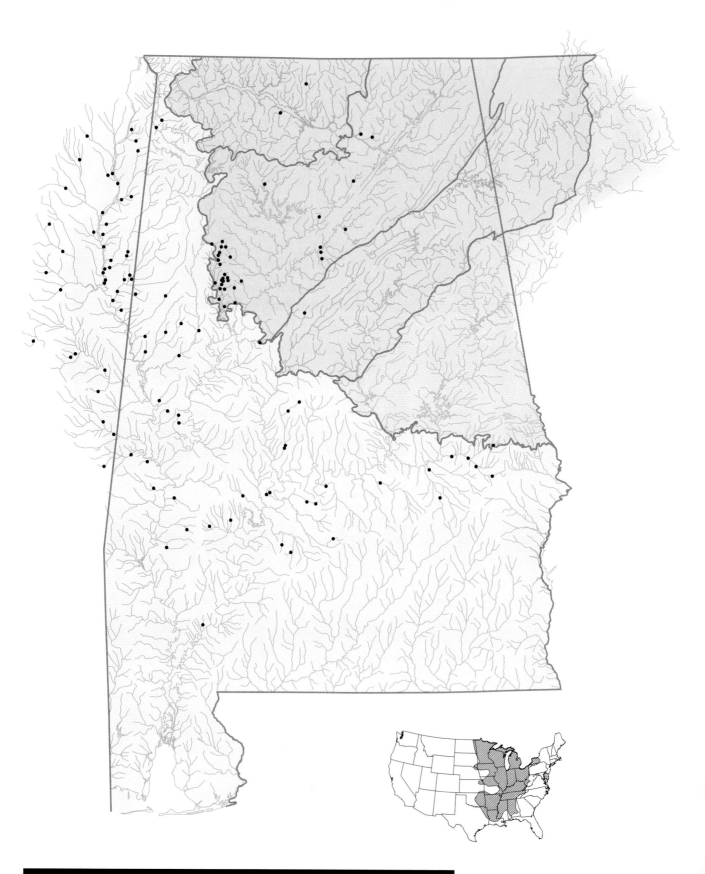

BLACKSIDE DARTER *Percina maculata* **123 STATIONS**

Percina maculata

(Girard, 1859)

ETYMOLOGY:

Percina—a diminutive of *Perca*, meaning perch

maculata—spotted, referring to the lateral blotches

Red Creek, Wilcox County, 12 April 1983, 2.9 in (74 mm) SL male, GSA 6891

CHARACTERISTICS: A member of the subgenus *Alvordius*, the blackside darter has separate gill membranes and a wide frenum on the upper lip. The back is olive to yellow-olive with black vermiculations and eight or nine saddles. The venter is light yellow to white. Six to nine black blotches occur along the sides, and a distinct spot is present at the caudal fin base. Breeding males are dusky with very dark blotches. Individuals can be distinguished from their nearest relative, the undescribed "muscadine darter," by having modally 12 soft dorsal fin rays and 66 to 75 lateral line scales; the "muscadine darter" has modally 10 soft dorsal rays and 56 to 65 lateral line scales.

ADULT SIZE: 1.5 to 3.3 in (38 to 85 mm)

DISTRIBUTION: *Percina maculata* is widely distributed in the Mississippi River basin from Minnesota to Louisiana and east to the Mobile basin and Tennessee River drainage. Most records in Alabama are from below the Fall Line; however, some scattered collections are available from above the Fall Line in the Cahaba and Black Warrior river systems. We encountered this species infrequently in the Tennessee River drainage.

HABITAT AND BIOLOGY: Blackside darters inhabit creeks and small to medium-sized streams, generally of moderate gradient, in a variety of habitats including gravel riffles, pools, and swift chutes. Spawning occurs from March through April in Alabama. Petravicz (1938) reports that females deposit eggs in sand or gravel substrates. Karr (1963) and Thomas (1970) both report longevity of four to five years in Iowa and Illinois. Karr reports a diverse diet of midges, blackflies, mayflies, caddisflies, and microcrustaceans.

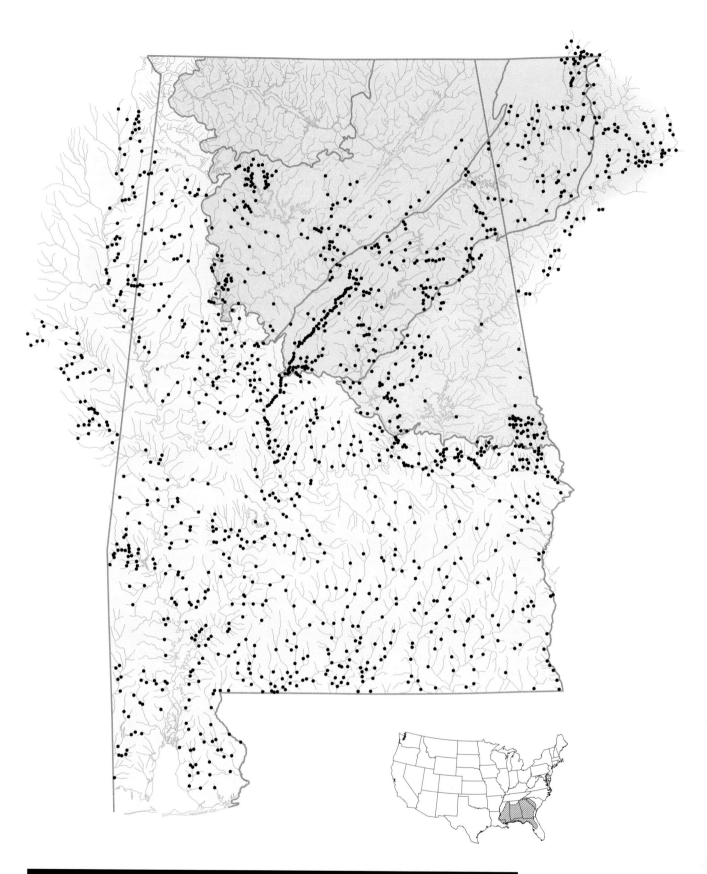

BLACKBANDED DARTER   *Percina nigrofasciata*   **1,416 STATIONS**

Percina nigrofasciata

(Agassiz, 1854)

ETYMOLOGY:

Percina—a diminutive of *Perca*, meaning perch

nigrofasciata—blackbanded

Turkey Creek, Tuscaloosa County, 23 April 1992, 2.6 in (65 mm) SL male, GSA 4451

CHARACTERISTICS: Our field observations suggest the body color of blackbanded darters is extremely variable and appears to be strongly influenced by the surrounding habitat. Individuals collected over clean, sandy substrates are lightly colored. Those taken around sticks, leaf detritus, accumulations of aquatic vegetation, or dark gravel are darker overall, with accentuated banding and barring patterns. Most individuals have 12 to 15 light to dark, elliptical bars along light green or brown to tan sides. The back has six to eight dark saddles. All fins are normally clear, but become dusky, stippled, and even lightly banded during the spawning season. Breeding males develop a greenish blue wash over the body and a brownish gold color in the head region. Blackbanded darters and dusky darters, *P. sciera*, can be confused; however, comparing the vertically elongated blotches in *P. nigrofasciata* with the laterally oval blotches on *P. sciera* will usually separate the two.

ADULT SIZE: 1.6 to 3.5 in (40 to 90 mm)

DISTRIBUTION: The blackbanded darter is found in Gulf and Atlantic slope drainages from Louisiana to South Carolina. It occurs throughout the Mobile basin and coastal drainages in Alabama. It is notably absent in the Tennessee River drainage and the middle reaches of the Tallapoosa River system above the Fall Line in Alabama.

HABITAT AND BIOLOGY: The blackbanded darter is the most widespread and abundant percid species in Alabama. We have collected individuals in all types of flowing streams and rivers outside the Tennessee River drainage. *Percina nigrofasciata* is an early spawner, as evidenced by our collections of males running milt from February through June. Suttkus' field notes from 1992 report several collections of individuals running milt and eggs at a water temperature of 61°F (16°C) in April in the upper Black Warrior River system. Mathur (1973a) indicates May and June spawnings of individuals in Halawakee Creek in east-central Alabama. Mathur (1973b) also reports late afternoon feeding on dipterans, mayflies, caddisflies, and microcrustaceans.

REMARKS: The type locality for the blackbanded darter was reported as near Mobile, Mobile County, Alabama.

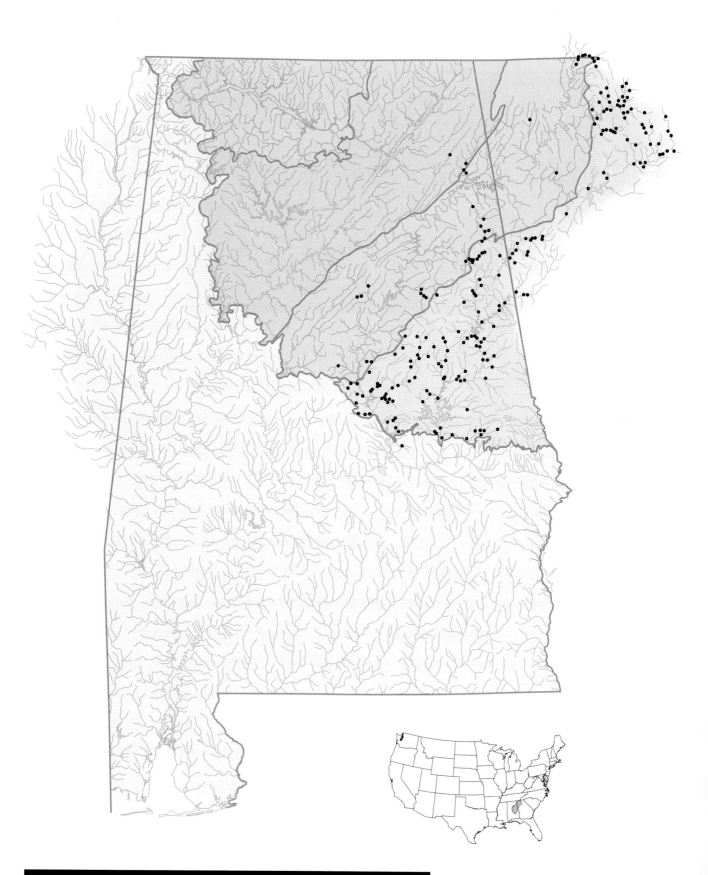

BRONZE DARTER *Percina palmaris* **218 STATIONS**

Percina palmaris

(Bailey, 1940)

ETYMOLOGY:

Percina—a diminutive of *Perca*, meaning perch

palmaris—prize, which R. M. Bailey left undefined in the original description

Channahatchee Creek, Elmore County, 8 April 1993, 2.9 in (73 mm) SL male, GSA 4415

CHARACTERISTICS: *Percina palmaris* has eight to 10 broad saddles on the back that extend downward through the lateral band onto the venter. Bronze darters are brown to yellow along the back, grading to light tan along the sides, venter, and breast. Breeding males acquire a deep bronze color tinted with green at the height of nuptial activity. Three distinct dark spots and two larger lighter patches are present at the caudal fin base. The spiny dorsal fin of breeding males has a white margin and light orange base; all other fins are light yellow or clear. Denoncourt (1976) reports marked sexual dimorphism, with males having significantly higher fin ray counts and longer dorsal and anal fins than do females. *Percina palmaris* is distinguished from the gilt darter, *P. evides*, by the absence of the distinct suborbital bar and the orange-gold color in the head region.

ADULT SIZE: 2.2 to 3.9 in (55 to 100 mm)

DISTRIBUTION: The bronze darter is endemic to the Mobile basin. Most collection records are from above the Fall Line in the Tallapoosa and Coosa river systems. This is one of the more common darter species in the Tallapoosa River main channel between R. L. Harris and Martin lakes.

HABITAT AND BIOLOGY: *Percina palmaris* is found in moderate to swift riffles over gravel, cobble, or small boulders in streams and rivers, and it is frequently associated with water willow or river weed. Our observations indicate spawning from late March through late May. Wieland (1983) reports a life span of three to four years and a diet of midge larvae, mayflies, blackflies, caddisflies, stoneflies, and snails.

REMARKS: The type locality for the bronze darter is the Etowah River near Dahlonega, Lumpkin County, Georgia.

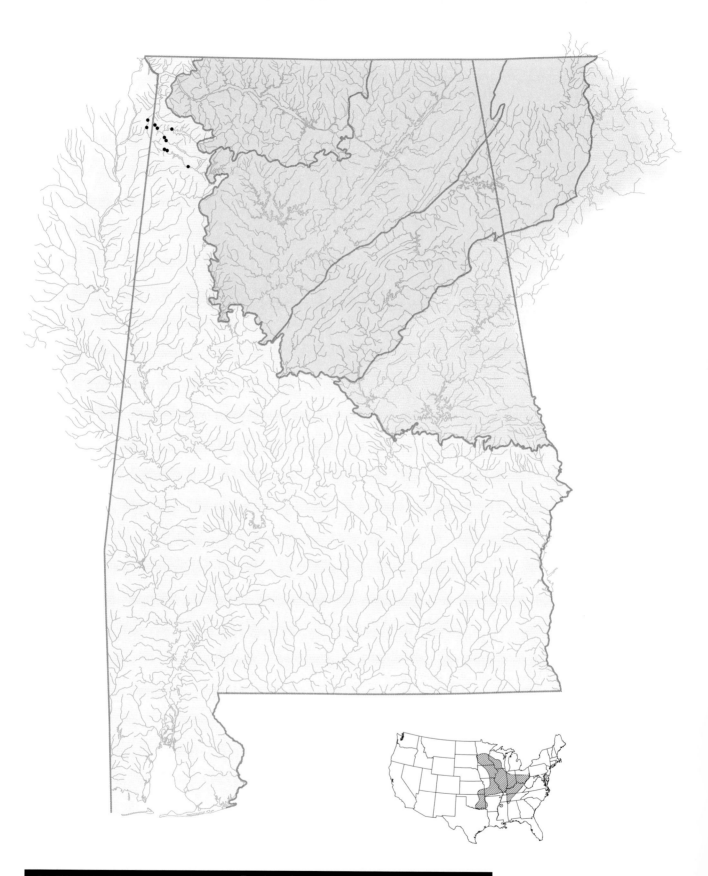

Percina phoxocephala

(Nelson, 1876)

ETYMOLOGY:

Percina—a diminutive of *Perca*, meaning perch

phoxocephala—tapered head

Cedar Creek, Franklin County, 10 March 1993, 2.0 in (50 mm) SL male, GSA 4370

CHARACTERISTICS: Slenderhead darters have moderately connected gill membranes, an orange submarginal band in the spiny dorsal fin, a wide frenum on the upper lip, and a single spot at the base of the caudal fin. The snout is moderately pointed. The sides have from 10 to 16 round or oval blotches. The back and sides are yellow-brown, and the venter is white or light yellow. Beyond occasional light stippling, the fins are clear.

ADULT SIZE: 2 to 3.1 in (50 to 80 mm)

DISTRIBUTION: *Percina phoxocephala* is found throughout the Mississippi River basin from Ohio to South Dakota and south to Oklahoma and Alabama. Records of this uncommon species in the study area are limited to the Bear Creek system of the Tennessee River drainage in Alabama and Mississippi.

HABITAT AND BIOLOGY: Page and Smith (1971) report a variable habitat preference for this species, ranging from small-stream riffles to large rocky riffles and sandy pools of large rivers. The preferred habitat includes a moderate to swift current over gravel raceways in large streams and small rivers. We collected this species only in knee- to waist-deep pools over a sandy, silty bottom with detritus. We have no life history information for this species in Alabama, owing to the fact that Alabama is at the southern periphery of its range and individuals are somewhat rare. Page and Smith (1971) indicate peak spawning during late May and June in gravel riffles for an Illinois population. Thomas (1970) reports a longer spawning season, perhaps extending into August. The life span of most individuals is two to three years (Page and Smith, 1971; Thomas, 1970; Karr, 1963). Midges, blackflies, mayflies, and caddisflies are primary food items.

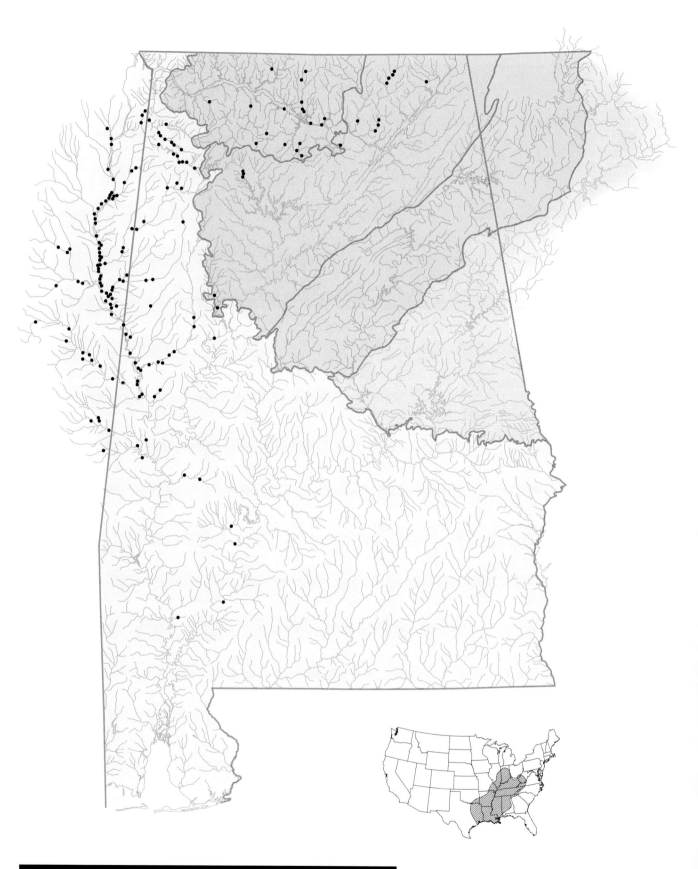

DUSKY DARTER *Percina sciera* **166 STATIONS**

Percina sciera

(Swain, 1883)

ETYMOLOGY:

Percina—a diminutive of

Perca, meaning perch

sciera—dusky

Piney Creek, Limestone County, 20 May 1993, 3.7 in (95 mm) SL male, GSA 4477

CHARACTERISTICS: The dusky darter is distinguished by moderately joined gill membranes, three vertical spots at the base of the caudal fin, which may be fused, and oval lateral blotches. The cheeks, opercles, and nape are usually scaled. Bright nuptial color does not develop in this species, although individuals are frequently marked and mottled with dark pigment. Males develop a distinctive row of mid-ventral scales. The body is olive, with around eight dark saddles on the back and eight to 12 dusky oval blotches on the sides. Banding is usually weak or absent in the fins; breeding males occasionally develop a yellow or orange band near the margin of the spiny dorsal fin.

ADULT SIZE: 1.6 to 4.3 in (40 to 110 mm)

DISTRIBUTION: The range of the dusky darter extends through the Mississippi basin south to the Gulf of Mexico and from the Mobile basin west to the Guadalupe River drainage in Texas. Most collections from the upper Tombigbee River proper date from before construction

of the Tennessee-Tombigbee Waterway; current population status is unknown. We have recently collected specimens at several locations in the Tennessee River drainage and lower Alabama River system.

HABITAT AND BIOLOGY: *Percina sciera* inhabits shoal areas of large streams and rivers with gravel and small rubble substrates and a moderate to swift current. Suttkus and Ramsey (1967) report that when *P. sciera* and the blackbanded darter, *P. nigrofasciata,* occur together, the dusky darter appears more common over clean sand, silt, and gravel substrates with no aquatic plants, whereas *P. nigrofasciata* inhabits vegetated areas with a variable substrate. Our observations indicate that spawning occurs in Alabama from March through June, whereas Page and Smith (1970) report peak spawning from May through July in Illinois. They also report that fertilized eggs are scattered over gravel substrates, individuals have a life span of three or four years, and adults consume midge larvae, blackflies, caddisflies, mayflies, and stoneflies.

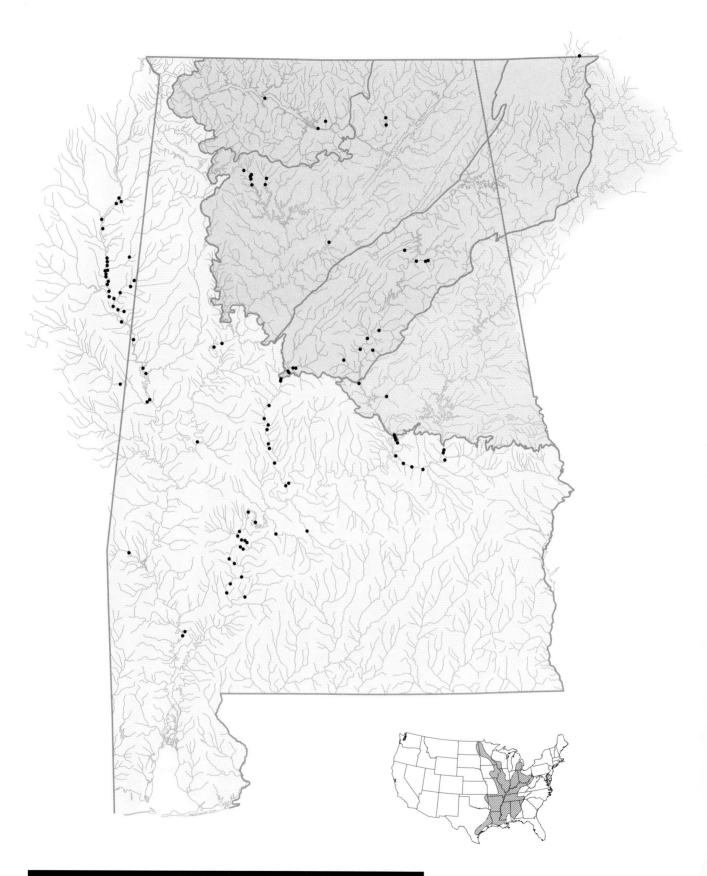

Percina shumardi

(Girard, 1859)

ETYMOLOGY:

Percina—a diminutive of *Perca*, meaning perch *shumardi*—in honor of the discoverer of the species, George Shumard, surgeon and naturalist of the U.S. Pacific Railroad Survey

Paint Rock River, Marshall County, 30 June 1992, 2.1 in (53 mm) SL male, GSA 4493

CHARACTERISTICS: The sides of *Percina shumardi* have eight to 15 vertically elongate bars that are crowded under the pectoral fins and become more oval toward the tail. Mottling on the back produces a characteristic dusky appearance. The head has a moderately pointed snout with a distinctive bar under the eye. In breeding males the anal fin is enlarged and heavily tuberculate. The dorsal fins are clear with light stippling or banding, while nuptial males have a prominent curved golden band in the posterior part of the spiny dorsal fin. The river darter is the only member of *Imostoma* that does not have the distinct dorsal saddles characteristic of other species found in Alabama and the Mobile basin, including the snail darter, *P. tanasi*; amber darter, *P. antesella*; and saddleback darter, *P. vigil*.

ADULT SIZE: 1.8 to 3.1 in (45 to 80 mm)

DISTRIBUTION: The river darter occurs from central Canada southward to the Gulf Coast in the Mississippi basin and in Gulf Coast tributaries from San Antonio Bay in Texas east to the Mobile basin. Most collection records of this riverine species in Alabama are from the main channel and larger tributaries of the Tombigbee and Alabama river drainages, primarily below the Fall Line. Collections are known above the Fall Line in the Black Warrior and Coosa river systems, but this species is notably absent from the upper Tallapoosa River system. Recent records in the Tennessee River drainage are limited to our 1992 collection in the Paint Rock River system.

HABITAT AND BIOLOGY: The habitat of this species is medium to large streams and rivers with a moderate to swift current and substrates of gravel, rubble, or partially exposed bedrock, as commonly encountered at the head or foot of riffles and shoals. In addition to occupying turbid waters typical of large flowing streams, rivers, and impounded rivers, this species apparently persists in tailwaters below some peaking hydroelectric facilities. Spawning occurs from February through April in swift riffles of small rubble or gravel. Thomas (1970) reports longevity of three to four years and a diet consisting of midges, blackflies, mayflies, and snails.

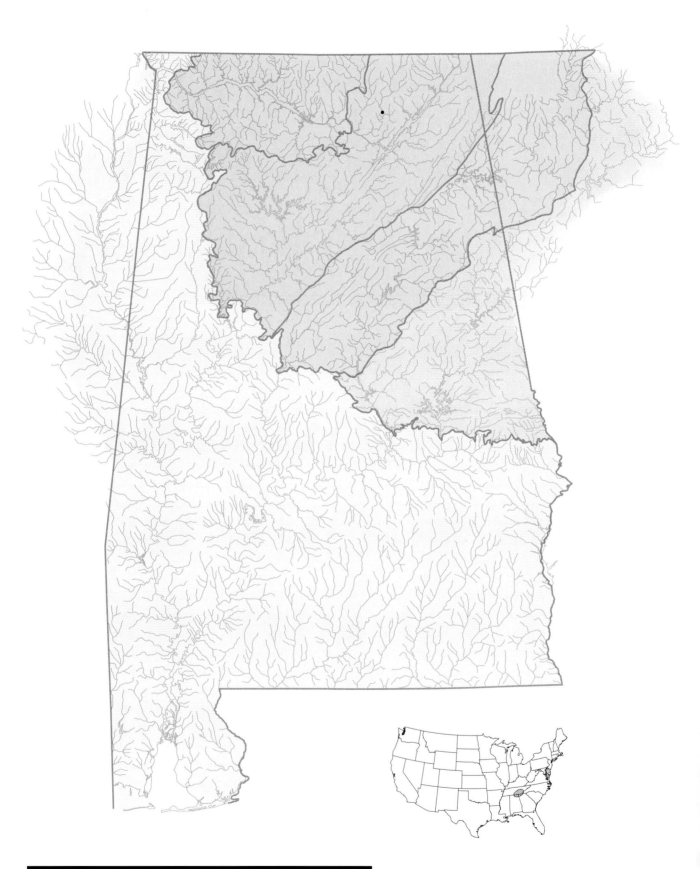

Percina tanasi
Etnier, 1976

ETYMOLOGY:
Percina—a diminutive of *Perca*, meaning perch *tanasi*—a former Cherokee settlement on the Little Tennessee River, this species' type locality; derivation of the word *tanasi* gave rise to the name Tennessee

Holston River, Knox County, Tennessee, 8 April 1991, 2.5 in (63 mm) SL male. Photograph courtesy of Richard T. Bryant and Wayne C. Starnes

CHARACTERISTICS: *Percina tanasi* is characterized by eyes placed toward the top of the head, four distinct dorsal saddles, a blunt snout, and short, rounded pectoral and pelvic fins. The back is speckled brown with four dark saddles under the spiny dorsal fin. Nine to 12 round or oval dark blotches form a variously developed lateral band. The venter is white or light green. The spiny dorsal fin has a gray margin and basal band; remaining fins lack distinct banding. Breeding males have an enlarged and tuberculate anal fin.

ADULT SIZE: 2.2 to 3.1 in (55 to 80 mm)

DISTRIBUTION: Snail darters were originally thought to occur only in the lower Little Tennessee River and adjacent Tennessee River. Introduction and subsequent sampling expanded their range into Chickamauga Creek, a downstream segment of the Tennessee River, and the Sequatchie, Hiwassee, Holston, and Elk river systems. The only confirmed location in Alabama is from the lower Paint Rock River in Jackson County.

HABITAT AND BIOLOGY: Starnes (1977) presents a comprehensive life study of the snail darter. *Percina tanasi* is found over gravel and sand shoals with moderate current in large tributaries and free-flowing rivers. Spawning occurs in gravel shoals from February until April. Eggs are deposited in the sand and gravel. Juveniles usually inhabit quiet pool areas, migrating to shoals by three to four months of age. Life span varies from two to four years, with most individuals living about two years. As its common name implies, the primary food item of this species is aquatic snails, which comprised more than 60 percent of the food volume consumed in the Little Tennessee River population. Other prey items include caddisflies, midges, and blackflies.

REMARKS: The snail darter is listed as a threatened species by the U.S. Fish and Wildlife Service.

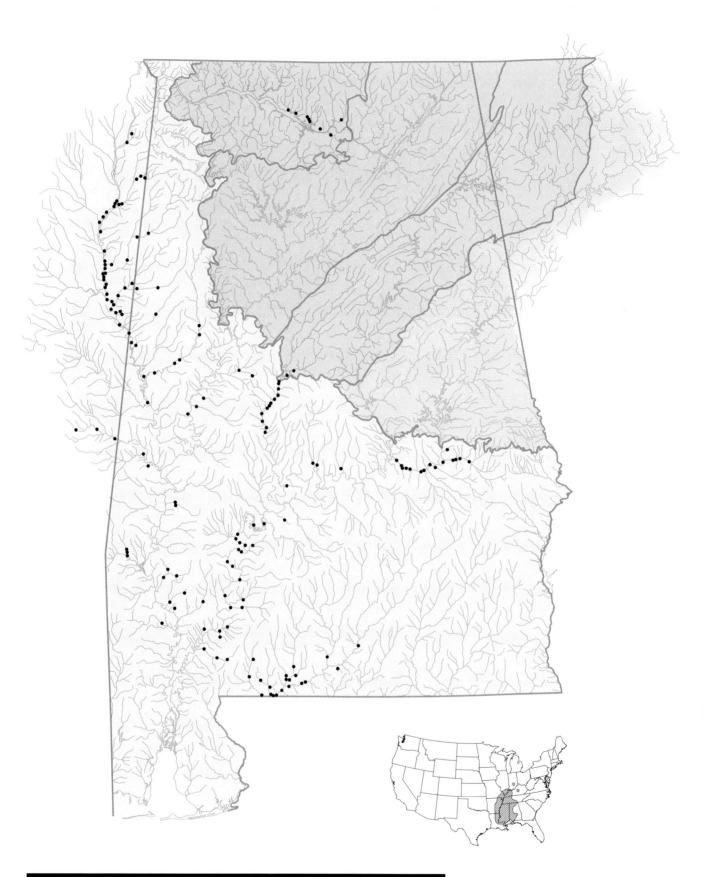

Percina vigil

(Hay, 1882)

ETYMOLOGY:

Percina—a diminutive of

Perca, meaning perch

vigil—wide awake

Little Escambia Creek, Escambia County, 12 November 1980, 2.2 in (56 mm) SL male, GSA 6153

CHARACTERISTICS: The saddleback darter has eyes set more on top of the head and less pigmentation than other members of *Imostoma*. It has separate to slightly connected gill membranes, a narrow frenum, and an elongate anal fin on breeding males. The back has four distinct dorsal saddles and a small, less defined saddle near the tail. On the sides are eight to 10 roughly square blotches that are separate from the saddles. The back is yellow to olive, and the venter is white or very light yellow. Distinct bars are present in front of and below the eye. The spiny dorsal fin is black at its base and margin; other fins are faintly banded or clear. A small but distinct spot is present at the base of the caudal fin. See Hay (1883) for original description.

ADULT SIZE: 1.6 to 2.4 in (40 to 60 mm)

DISTRIBUTION: *Percina vigil* occurs from Lake Pontchartrain east to the Escambia River and north in Mississippi River drainages to Illinois. Most of our collection records of the saddleback darter in the Mobile basin are from below the Fall Line. Populations are also known from the Tennessee River drainage. Healthy populations occur in the middle reaches of the Cahaba and lower Tallapoosa river systems. *Percina vigil* is fairly widespread and often abundant in the Conecuh River and several of its main tributaries.

HABITAT AND BIOLOGY: The saddleback darter is found in moderate to swift large rivers and streams over gravel and sand substrates. Chutes with swift current bisecting extensive shoal areas appear to be preferred microhabitats. Mettee et al. (1987) report collections of gravid males and gravid females in Little Escambia Creek in late February, with spawning extending from February through April. As with other *Imostoma*, eggs are deposited in sand and gravel shoals. Length-frequency data from Little Escambia Creek populations indicate a maximum age of two to three years. Examination of a few stomachs from this population revealed that individuals almost exclusively consumed caddisfly larvae (*Cheumatopsyche, Oxyethira*) in the fall, whereas the summer diet was more varied and included beetles, mayflies, and stoneflies. Interestingly, no midges were found in any of the stomachs examined.

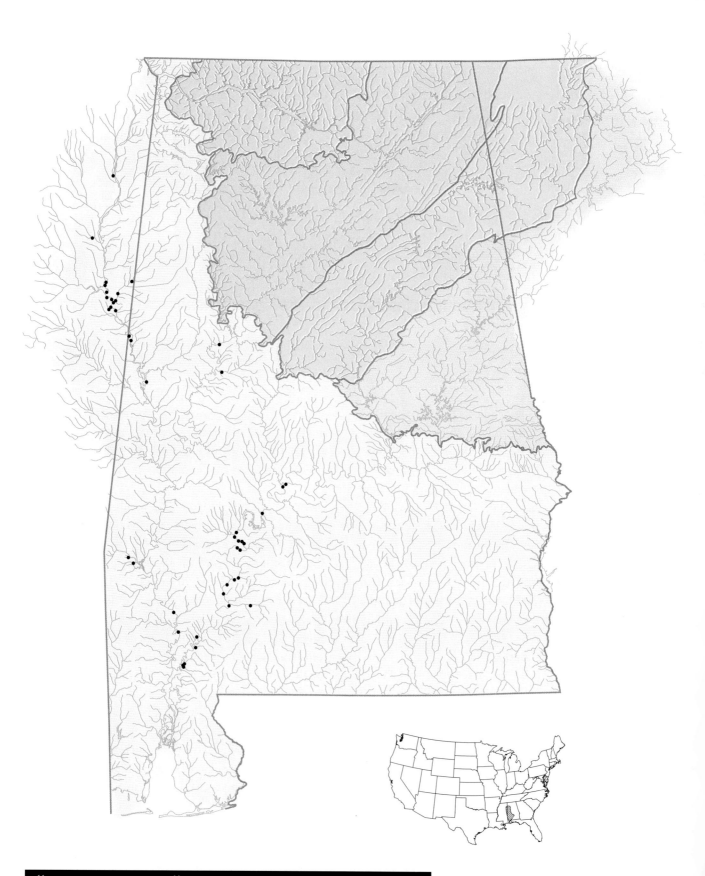

"GULF LOGPERCH"   *Percina* species   **43 STATIONS**

***Percina* species**

ETYMOLOGY:

Percina—a diminutive of
Perca, meaning perch

Five Mile Creek, Hale County, 14 May 1992, 3.2 in (81 mm) SL male, GSA 4317

CHARACTERISTICS: The "gulf logperch" has a conical snout that projects well beyond the upper jaw, a wide frenum, tigerlike vertical banding along the sides, and a single spot at the base of the caudal fin. The back has 16 to 22 full- and half-length thin bands continuing down the sides. The body is yellowish brown to yellow-green along the back and sides, changing to light green to white along the venter. The soft dorsal and caudal fins are banded with black. A single thin reddish orange submarginal band in the spiny dorsal fin distinguishes this species and the "Mobile logperch" from the similar *Percina caprodes* found in the Tennessee River drainage. In the "Mobile logperch," the body bars are generally wider than in the "gulf logperch," with the longest ones expanded into the characteristic blotch, and the submarginal red band in the spiny dorsal fin is generally wider than in the "gulf logperch."

ADULT SIZE: 2.8 to 4.8 in (70 to 123 mm)

DISTRIBUTION: The "gulf logperch" occurs in Gulf coastal drainages from Lake Pontchartrain east to the Mobile basin. All of our collection records in the Mobile basin are from below the Fall Line. Populations of the "gulf logperch" and "Mobile logperch" occur syntopically at certain locations in the Alabama, Black Warrior, and upper and lower Tombigbee river systems.

HABITAT AND BIOLOGY: The "gulf logperch" inhabits a variety of aquatic environments, from small tributaries to large rivers and impoundments and is more often found in main channel habitats. Individuals commonly occur over gravel or sand in moderate current, or in lakes over sand and mud substrates. Little is known of the biology of this species, but it is thought to be similar to the "Mobile logperch." Spawning is likely from mid-January through late February, similar to other species of logperch in Alabama. "gulf logperch" feed on aquatic insect larvae.

725

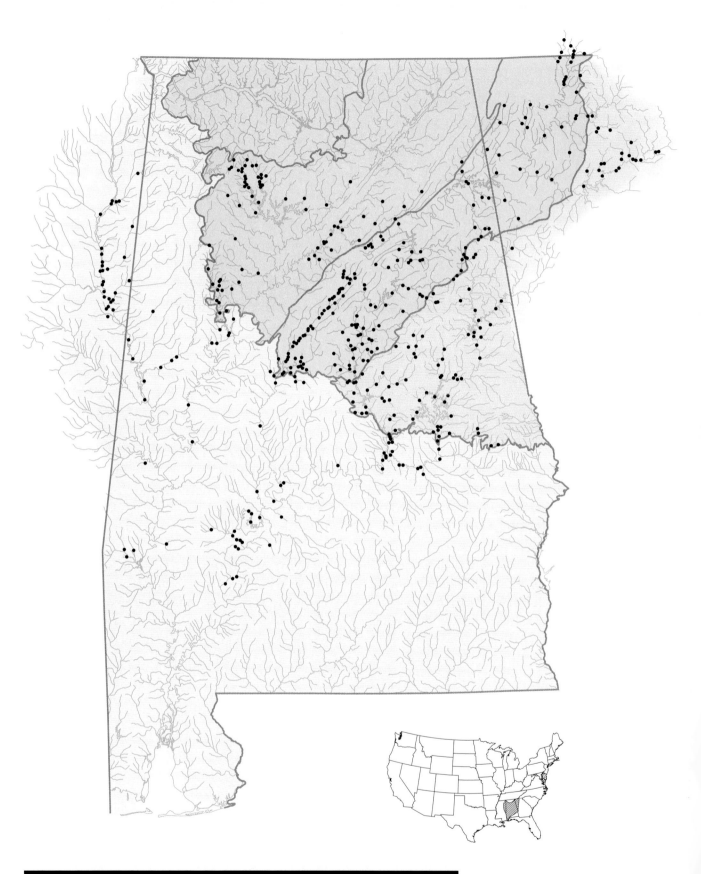

"MOBILE LOGPERCH"   *Percina* species   **436 STATIONS**

Percina species

ETYMOLOGY:

Percina—a diminutive of
Perca, meaning perch

Beeswax Creek, Shelby County, 21 April 1993, 4.4 in (113 mm) SL male, GSA 4436

CHARACTERISTICS: The "Mobile logperch" has a conical snout that projects well beyond the upper jaw, a wide frenum, obvious tigerlike vertical banding along the sides with the longer bands expanded into a diffuse blotch, and a single spot at the base of the caudal fin. A single, wide reddish orange submarginal band in the spiny dorsal fin, bordered by a thin black band on the margin and a broad black band at the base, distinguishes this species and the "Gulf logperch" from the similar *Percina caprodes* found in the Tennessee River drainage and *P. jenkinsi* in the upper Coosa River system, both of which lack colored bands. The back has 16 to 22 full- and half-length bands, some which are dark and wide, resembling saddles, that continue down the sides. The body is yellowish brown to yellow-green along the back and sides, changing to light green to white along the venter. The soft dorsal and caudal fins are banded with black.

ADULT SIZE: 3.1 to 6.3 in (80 to 160 mm)

DISTRIBUTION: The "Mobile logperch" is endemic to all river systems of the Mobile basin in Mississippi, Alabama, Tennessee, and Georgia. It is particularly widespread in the upper Cahaba and Coosa river systems. Populations of the "Mobile logperch" and "Gulf logperch" occur together at certain locations in the Alabama, Black Warrior, and upper and lower Tombigbee river systems.

HABITAT AND BIOLOGY: We have collected individuals of this undescribed form in a variety of habitats, from small tributaries to large rivers and impoundments. Greatest densities occur over gravel or sand substrates in moderate current or in lakes over sand and mud substrates. Large numbers of reservoir-based individuals frequently migrate upstream into small flowing streams from late February into May to spawn, an event we observed in Carrolls Creek, a tributary of Lake Tuscaloosa, Tuscaloosa County. Females are thought to bury eggs in riffles or shoals of sand or gravel. "Mobile logperch" may live three to four years. Young individuals consume small crustaceans, while adults feed on midge larvae, mayflies, and caddisflies. This and other logperch species flip small stones scattered along the bottom in search of food.

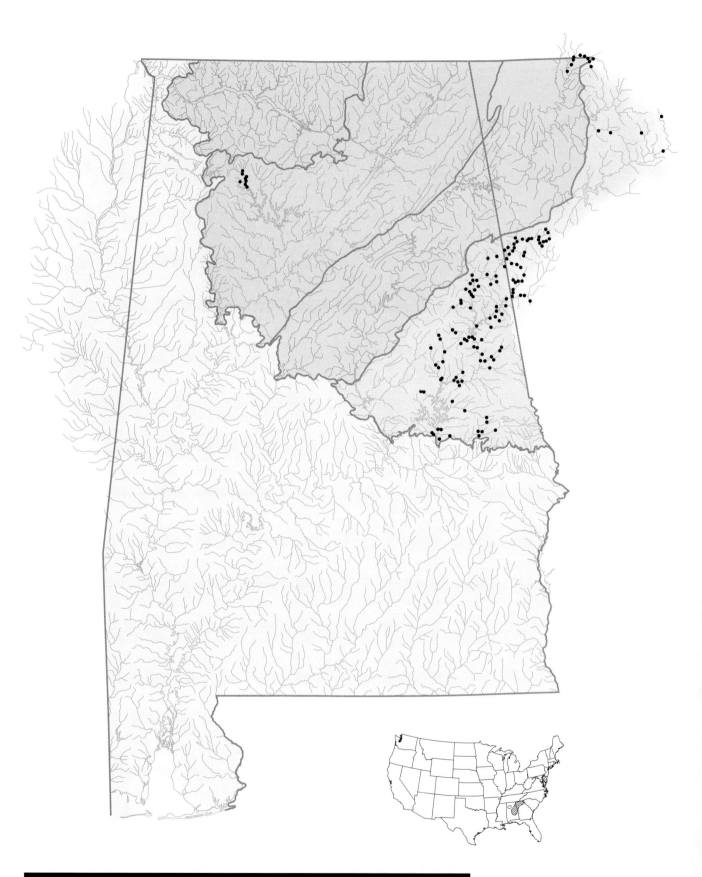

"MUSCADINE DARTER"   *Percina* species   **142 STATIONS**

728

Percina **species**

ETYMOLOGY:

Percina—a diminutive of
Perca, meaning perch

Josie Leg Creek, Tallapoosa County, 24 June 1992, 2.2 in (56 mm) SL male, GSA 4322

CHARACTERISTICS: The "muscadine darter" is an undescribed, although long recognized, species of the subgenus *Alvordius*. Individuals are characterized by separate or slightly connected gill membranes and no breeding tubercles. The back and upper sides are dusky tan with a pale to mottled venter. A thin mid-dorsal line extends from the head to the end of the soft dorsal fin; dorsal saddles are weakly developed. A dark lateral band, extending from the snout to the caudal fin base, is expanded into seven or eight lateral blotches. The spiny dorsal fin is low and somewhat arched, with dusky membranes in breeding males. The soft dorsal, caudal, and anal fins have dusky margins. Nuptial color is limited to darkened and dusky males. The "muscadine darter" is distinguishable from its near relative, the blackside darter, *Percina maculata*, by a scaled nape, modally 10 soft dorsal rays, and 56 to 65 lateral line scales. The blackside darter has a naked nape, modally 12 soft dorsal rays, and 66 to 75 lateral line scales.

ADULT SIZE: 1.8 to 2.3 in (45 to 58 mm)

DISTRIBUTION: This species occurs from disjunct populations in the Sipsey Fork of the Black Warrior River system and the Piedmont portion of the Tallapoosa River system. Etnier and Starnes (1993) recognize populations in the Conasauga River system in Georgia and Tennessee as another species, the "bridled darter."

HABITAT AND BIOLOGY: "Muscadine darters" are found below riffles of large rubble in deeper runs with moderate to slow current over sand and gravel. This species is consistently found over swift gravel shoals of main river channels. Wieland and Ramsey (1987) report spawning from March through early June in Tallapoosa River tributaries, with peak activity in April. They estimate a life span of two to three years. Individuals consume stream drift of midges, blackflies, stoneflies, and mayflies, generally in the early evening hours. Because of its lower reproductive potential and diet diversity relative to other *Percina* in the Tallapoosa River system, Wieland and Ramsey (1987) indicate that this pollution-sensitive species may require regular monitoring throughout its range.

Stizostedion canadense
(Smith, 1834)

ETYMOLOGY:

Stizostedion—interpreted by Rafinesque (1820) as Greek for pungent throat, referring to the large canine teeth lining the jaws and roof of the mouth
canadense—Canadian

Cypress Creek, Lauderdale County, 16 July 1992, 10.5 in (270 mm) SL male, GSA 4282

CHARACTERISTICS: The sauger is a large species of the family Percidae prized for its sport fishing character and its flavor. Cylindrical in body form, the sauger has a large horizontal mouth and well-developed pointed teeth. The back and top of the head are mottled brown to golden olive, the lips are less mottled and appear distinctly speckled, and the lower sides and venter are white or light cream. Four dark saddles traverse the back and may be expanded along the sides to produce large lateral blotches, while the back and sides are variously speckled with pigment. The lining in the eye behind the retina appears silver, a trait characteristic of the genus and presumably an adaptation for night feeding. Membranes of the spiny dorsal fin have distinct spots that sometimes appear to be banding, while the soft dorsal fin and caudal fin rays are definitely pigmented, producing delicate banding. The sauger can be distinguished from the walleye, *Stizostedion vitreum*, by its fewer (17 to 20) soft dorsal rays (19 to 22 for the walleye), by lacking a pigment concentration at the spiny dorsal fin base, and by having the lower lobe of the caudal fin mottled, compared to a white tip for the walleye.

ADULT SIZE: 10 to 18 in (254 to 460 mm). The state angling record (5 lb, 2 oz) was caught in the tailwaters of Wilson Dam on the Tennessee River in 1972.

DISTRIBUTION: The sauger is widely distributed throughout Canada and the Mississippi River basin and introduced in Atlantic slope tributaries. In Alabama it is known only from the Tennessee River drainage.

HABITAT AND BIOLOGY: Life history information is summarized from Becker (1983). The sauger is found in quiet backwaters over sand, mud, or bedrock substrates, usually at tributary mouths and in deeper tailwaters over rock and rubble substrate downstream of dams. Spawning occurs from April through May in a variety of places with the tailwater areas providing good spawning habitat, as observed in the sport catch during this time of the year. Individuals taken on hook and line are generally 2 pounds or less, but may reach 5 pounds. Small sauger feed on microcrustaceans and aquatic insect larvae, while large adults feed almost exclusively on fish, including young walleye and saugers, white bass, crappies, yellow perch, and, in northern states, trout-perch and burbots.

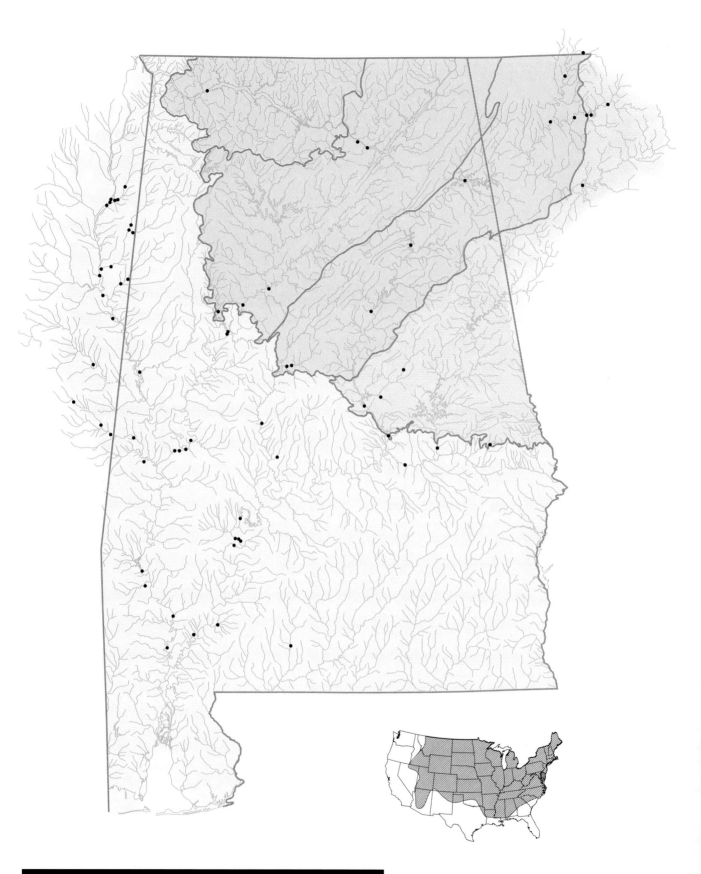

WALLEYE *Stizostedion vitreum* **69 STATIONS**

Stizostedion vitreum
(Mitchill, 1818)

ETYMOLOGY:

Stizostedion—interpreted by Rafinesque (1820) as Greek for pungent throat, referring to the large canine teeth lining the jaws and roof of the mouth

vitreum—glassy, referring to the large, silvery eye

North River, Tuscaloosa County, 1 March 1993, 12.2 in (310 mm) SL male, GSA 4379

CHARACTERISTICS: The walleye is similar in appearance to the sauger but can be distinguished by the large black spot at the posterior base of the walleye's spiny dorsal fin and by the white tip on the lower lobe of the caudal fin. Walleye have a large horizontal mouth with large pointed teeth. The body color is olive to brassy yellow with extensive mottling along the sides and a white or light cream venter. The six to seven saddles on the back are diffuse and ill-defined. The soft dorsal fin and caudal fin rays are pigmented, producing a somewhat mottled yet banded pattern. Spots on the spiny dorsal fin are small with no definite pattern or banding. Like the sauger, the walleye has a characteristic lining behind the retina that makes the eye look silver.

ADULT SIZE: 12 to 31 in (300 to 787 mm). The state angling record (10 lb, 14 oz) was caught in Weiss Reservoir on the Coosa River in 1980.

DISTRIBUTION: The walleye is widespread, naturally and from introductions, from the Mackenzie River in the Northwest Territories south to the lower Mississippi River basin and from the Atlantic Coast west to Nevada and Oregon. We have records of walleye throughout the Mobile basin both above and below the Fall Line. This species also occurs in the Tennessee River drainage as catches are commonly reported by fishermen, but our recent sampling has failed to capture walleye there.

HABITAT AND BIOLOGY: Life history information is summarized from Becker (1983). The walleye is associated with large rivers and stream tributaries and impoundments, frequently preferring clear, quiet backwaters over sand, gravel, mud, rubble, and silt. During spawning individuals move to shoal areas or tailwaters over riprap downstream of dams. Spawning occurs from March through May with eggs broadcast in open water over suitable spawning substrate. Inlet streams to impoundments are known spawning grounds in those habitats. A life span of seven years is common with a few individuals surviving to be 10 to 12 years of age. Young walleye feed on microcrustaceans and insect larvae, while larger individuals prey on fish, including white suckers, quillbacks, darters, and minnows. Feeding usually occurs at night when individuals migrate from deeper areas to shallow shoals.

DRUMS

Sciaenidae

There are at least 12 species of drums that inhabit Alabama's freshwater and nearshore marine environments. Several of these species have considerable economic significance. *Aplodinotus grunniens*, the only freshwater species in the family, is an important resource to anglers and commercial fishermen alike. Malvestuto et al. (1983) report anglers landing 92,631 pounds of freshwater drum in the Mobile Delta and lower Tombigbee River system in 1980 and 1981. Commercial fishermen harvested an additional 109,541 pounds in the same area during the same time.

Many commercially important marine drums rely on Alabama's estuaries as important spawning and nursery areas. These species include the sand seatrout, *Cynoscion arenarius*; silver trout, *C. nothus*; spot, *Leiostomus xanthurus*; southern kingfish, *Menticirrhus americanus*; gulf kingfish, *M. littoralis*; Atlantic croaker, *Micropogonias undulatus*; and black drum, *Pogonias cromis*. Spotted seatrout, *Cynoscion nebulosus*, and red drum, *Sciaenops ocellatus*, also inhabit these areas and are important game fishes for anglers. Marketing efforts aimed at promoting blackened red drum (locally known as redfish) throughout the United States were so successful in recent years that landing restrictions had to be imposed in the Gulf of Mexico to avoid overexploitation of offshore brood stocks.

Several characteristics distinguish members of the drum family from all other fish species in Alabama. The complete lateral line on most sciaenids continues onto the caudal fin. If present, the lateral line on all other species of fishes stops either along the side of the body or at the base of the caudal fin, never extending onto the caudal fin. All drum species usually have one or two stout anal spines. The second spine is usually thicker and stronger than the first. Other fish species may have no anal spines or up to eight, varying in length and thickness. Caudal fin shape also distinguishes drums from other fish species in Alabama. Most marine drums and the freshwater drum, *Aplodinotus grunniens*, have a convex or lance-shaped caudal fin because the middle caudal fin rays are distinctly longer than the upper and lower caudal rays. Other fish species in Alabama may have a forked, rounded, straight, or heterocercal tail, but none have a tail that is distinctly convex.

Drums are distributed in estuaries and nearshore areas throughout the world. They are usually associated with a variety of habitats including muddy and sandy bottoms, mud flats, rock reefs, and shallow grass bed environments. When removed from the water, most drums produce audible grunting or croaking sounds when their gas bladders are stroked with surrounding muscles, a characteristic that startles unsuspecting anglers. The study of sciaenids is rewarding because members of this diverse fish family occupy many marine and estuarine habitats and are popular with fisherman. As seasoned anglers will attest, these fishes are especially tasty when prepared soon after cleaning.

Only three species of drums are included in this work due to space limitations. We nevertheless decided to incorporate into the taxonomic key the identification of several additional species that, based on our sampling in the area, are fairly widespread and abundant and are likely to be encountered by recreational anglers.

KEY TO THE DRUMS

1a. Lower jaw with 1 or more barbel . . . . go to 2

1b. Lower jaw without barbels . . . . go to 3

2a. Many large barbels on lower jaw; body with approximately 5 wide, dark vertical bars . . . .
. . . . black drum, *Pogonias cromis*

2b. Row of small barbels on each side of lower jaw and small pits along jaw where barbels were formerly located;
body without wide vertical bars . . . . Atlantic croaker, *Micropogonias undulatus*

3a. Lower jaw projecting forward and upper jaw bearing one pair of enlarged canine teeth; upper sides of body
with well-defined spots. . . . . spotted seatrout, *Cynoscion nebulosus*

3b. Lower jaw not projecting forward, mouth terminal or inferior; no enlarged canine teeth in upper jaw . . . . .
. . . . go to 4

4a. Caudal fin base with a conspicuous black spot, and sometimes two or more; no shoulder spot . . . .
. . . . red drum, *Sciaenops ocellatus*

4b. No conspicuous black spots at caudal fin base . . . . go to 5

5a. Conspicuous spot present on shoulder; soft dorsal fin rays 30 to 34; lateral line scales 60 to 70. . . . .
. . . . spot, *Leiostomus xanthurus*

5b. No conspicuous spot on shoulder; soft dorsal fin rays 22 to 32; lateral line scales 50 to 56 . . . .
. . . . freshwater drum, *Aplodinotus grunniens*

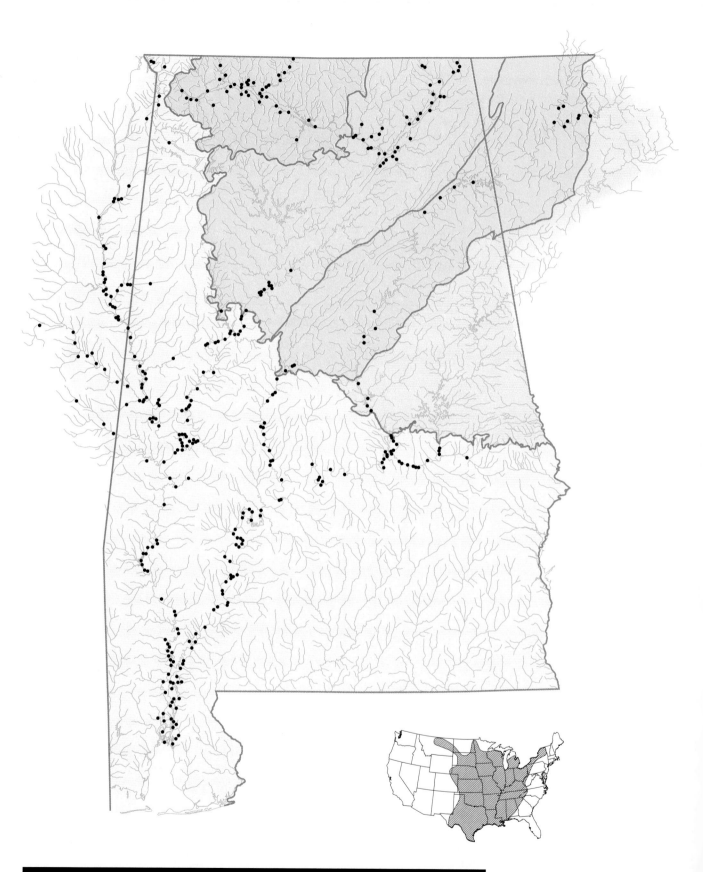

FRESHWATER DRUM   *Aplodinotus grunniens*   362 STATIONS

Aplodinotus grunniens
(Rafinesque, 1819)

ETYMOLOGY:

Aplodinotus—simple back, probably in reference to the single dorsal fin

grunniens—grunting, for the sounds they make

Short Creek, Marshall County, 9 June 1992, 5.5 in (140 mm) SL male, GSA 4246

CHARACTERISTICS: Also known as the gaspergou, the freshwater drum has a ventral surface that is essentially flat when viewed from the side. The body reaches its greatest depth near the dorsal fin origin, then tapers downward toward a somewhat slender caudal peduncle. The head is small with large eyes and an inferior mouth. The dorsal fin is long, extending from the pectoral fins almost to the base of the convex caudal fin. Most fins are dark gray to black on large individuals. Scales along the back are variously edged in black, producing a body color that varies from dusky gray to dull silvery white. *Aplodinotus grunniens* has marble-sized bony structures known as otoliths, or "head rocks," in its head that assist in maintaining balance. Anglers occasionally collect these curious objects from larger specimens.

ADULT SIZE: 28 in (711 mm) in length and 10 lb (4.6 kg) in weight. The state angling record (41 lb, 8 oz) was caught in Wilson Reservoir on the Tennessee River in 1949.

DISTRIBUTION: Freshwater drums are distributed across southern Canada, the central United States from the Mississippi basin eastward to the Appalachian Mountains, and southward to Guatemala. This species is known from numerous main-river collections in the Mobile basin, primarily below the Fall Line, and from the Tennessee River drainage. Records of this species are strangely absent from coastal drainages east of the Mobile basin.

HABITAT AND BIOLOGY: We routinely encounter small freshwater drum in backwaters and along the margins of rivers, reservoirs, and their large tributaries. Large individuals prefer swift areas below dams. Pelagic spawning occurs from May through mid-summer. Males produce a low-frequency drumming sound during spawning, perhaps to attract females and organize the reproduction activities. Females release large quantities of floating eggs during spawning. The freshwater drum is a bottom feeder, consuming aquatic insects, amphipods, fish, crayfish, and mollusks. This is a commercially important species for some freshwater fishermen, generally providing a major source of income. The life span of this species is estimated at 10 to 11 years.

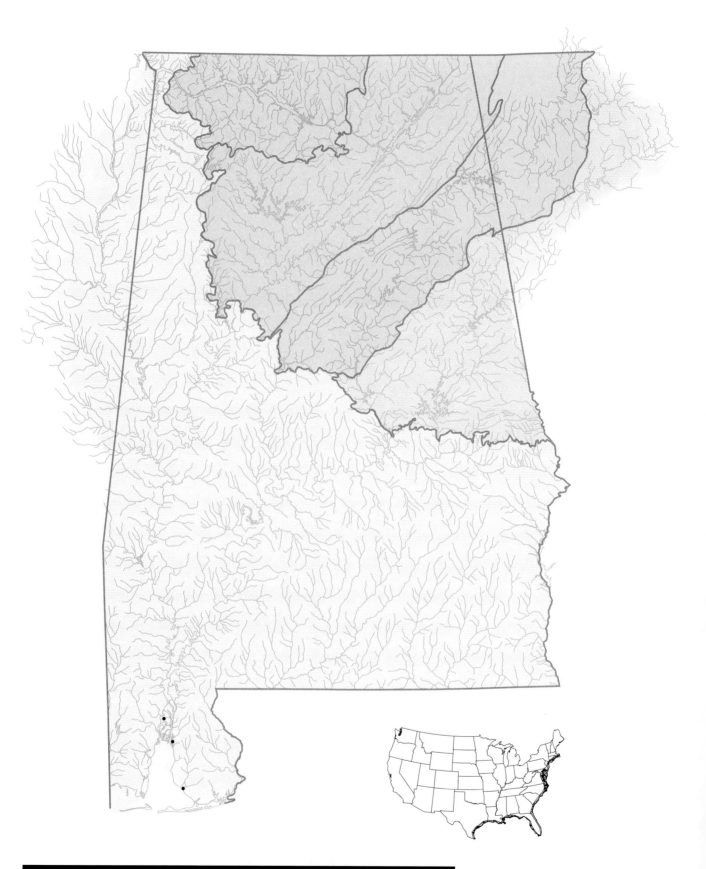

SPOTTED SEATROUT *Cynoscion nebulosus* **3 STATIONS**

Cynoscion nebulosus
(Cuvier, 1830)

ETYMOLOGY:
Cynoscion—doglike, probably referring to the large canine teeth
nebulosus—spotty, referring to the dark spots found along the sides of the body

Weeks Bay, Baldwin County, 20 August 1992, 2.7 in (68 mm) SL male, GSA 4471

CHARACTERISTICS: Locally known as "speck" or speckled trout, the spotted seatrout is distinguished by small spots arranged in oblique rows along the upper sides and back and by the presence of large canine teeth. The body is generally silvery and dark gray-green on the sides and back. The caudal fin of young individuals is shaped like a lance head, becoming straight-edged or slightly concave in adults. All fins are pale green to yellow-green, and the dorsal and anal fins have scattered black spots. The somewhat elongate snout has a prominent mouth sporting large canine teeth, testifying to a piscivorous mode of life. See Cuvier and Valenciennes (1830) for original description.

ADULT SIZE: 10 to 24 in (254 to 610 mm). The state angling record (12 lb, 4 oz) was caught in 1980.

DISTRIBUTION: The spotted seatrout occurs in coastal environments from New England southward in Atlantic Coast drainages through Florida and Gulf Coast drainages into Mexico. Although this is not reflected on the adjacent map due to the freshwater emphasis of our study, Shipp (1986) reports this species as abundant in coastal areas of Alabama.

HABITAT AND BIOLOGY: Specks usually inhabit large, shallow, grassy flats of estuarine waters. Adjacent channels and deep pools provide refuge during rapid temperature changes in winter months. Wade (1979) reports that spotted seatrout generally live within a 30-mile range, but movement of over 300 miles has been documented. Spawning occurs at night from May through September, with some adults reaching sexual maturity by the end of their first year. Spawning areas are thought to be deeper depressions and channels in bays adjacent to their preferred shallow, grassy flats. Foods of adult spotted seatrout include shrimp and small fin fish, while juveniles feed primarily on invertebrates.

REMARKS: The spotted seatrout is an extremely important game fish in the Mobile Delta. Malvestuto et al. (1983) report that anglers and commercial fishermen landed 108,361 pounds in the fall of 1980 and 1981.

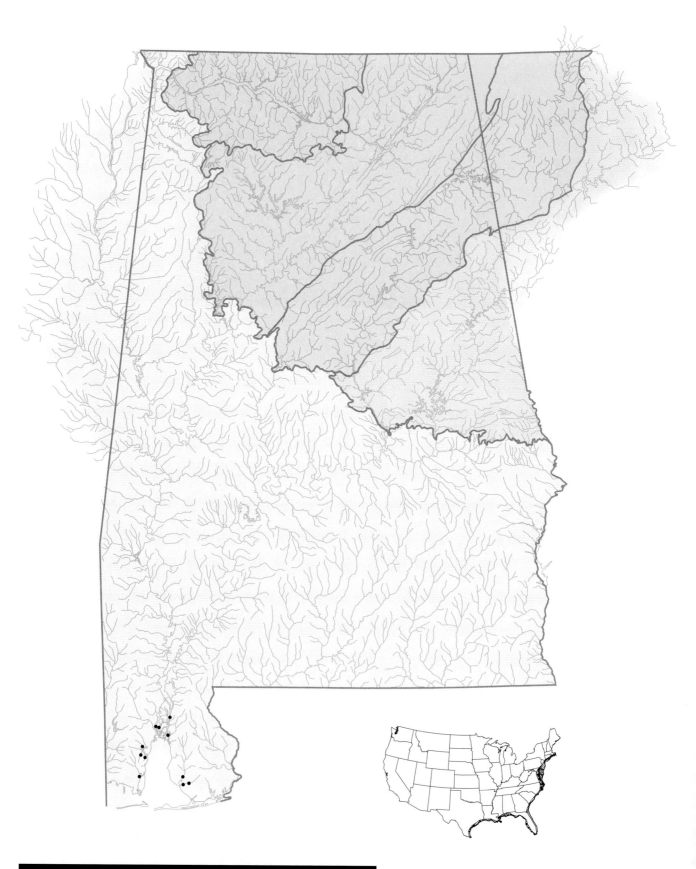

RED DRUM *Sciaenops ocellatus* **11 STATIONS**

Sciaenops ocellatus

(Linnaeus, 1766)

ETYMOLOGY:

Sciaenops—shade appearance
ocellatus—eye-like spots,
referring to the caudal spots

Claude Petite Mariculture Center, Baldwin County, 17 June 1993, 10 in (254 mm) SL male, GSA 4489

CHARACTERISTICS: The red drum, locally known as redfish, is distinguished by a prominent black spot at the base of the caudal fin and, rarely, a few smaller spots anteriorly. The predorsal region is not extremely elevated, as on other drum species. The head is conical in shape; the large, inferior mouth lacks barbels. Body color of this species varies from a pale to shiny silver in young individuals and to a brassy reddish or pinkish silver in older adults.

ADULT SIZE: 10 to 35 in (254 to 890 mm). Large adults may be 40 lb (18.1 kg). The state angling record (43 lb) was caught in 1982.

DISTRIBUTION: We encountered small rat reds in the Mobile Delta and in the Fish and Magnolia rivers in September and October. The distribution of this species in estuarine areas of Alabama is more extensive than indicated on the adjacent map; most of our collection efforts were confined to freshwater reaches of coastal streams.

HABITAT AND BIOLOGY: Large red drum are found in the deep parts of estuaries and island passes, while young individuals frequent shallow areas near grass beds, jetties, and piers. A spawning migration occurs in late summer and fall toward shallow, open-water spawning grounds offshore. Foods of this species include crustaceans such as shrimp and crabs. Large schools of spawning adults were overharvested in the 1980s to satisfy a growing demand for blackened redfish. Fearing that brood stock levels could be adversely affected by uncontrolled harvest, marine fisheries biologists recommended strict seasonal and tonnage limitations along the Gulf Coast that have improved the population status of this desirable species.

REMARKS: Smaller redfish in the 1- to 6-pound class provide a good seasonal sport fishery in the Mobile Delta and tributaries to Mobile Bay. Malvestuto et al. (1983) report that anglers caught 11,452 pounds in the fall of 1980 and 1981.

MULLETS

Mugilidae

Species in the family Mugilidae inhabit coastal areas of all continents except Antarctica. Other than a larger body size, the mullets closely resemble the silversides in the family Atherinidae. Members of both families generally have a stiff spinous finlet in front of the larger dorsal fin, and their pectoral fins are placed much higher on their bodies than on other fish species in Alabama. The body is fusiform with a reduced or absent lateral line. Like herrings, mullets have adipose eyelids.

Mullets are known for their schooling behavior. Artful cast netters can usually catch more than enough striped mullet, *Mugil cephalus*, for dinner in only a few minutes. They are extremely tasty fish, especially when cleaned and cooked immediately. Commercial fishermen catch large numbers of mullet by rapidly surrounding them with long nets discharged from the rear deck of a small, open boat. These boats are usually powered with an outboard motor mounted in the center of the hull to avoid fouling the net as it is deployed.

Striped mullet are extremely abundant in coastal Alabama, and we regularly encounter individuals as far inland as the upper Tombigbee River in Pickens County, the Black Warrior River in Tuscaloosa County, and the Cahaba River in Bibb County. White mullet, *M. curema*, are seasonal inhabitants of coastal Alabama, becoming more abundant during the fall and winter. These fishes are also excellent when cleaned and cooked immediately.

About 100 species of mullets are known worldwide. However, only three species occur in the northern Gulf: the mountain mullet (*Agonostomus monticola*), the striped mullet (*Mugil cephalus*), and the white mullet (*M. curema*). Although mullets are estuarine species and offshore spawners, several species have a tolerance of fresh water, frequently invading larger rivers for several hundred miles. Only the striped mullet is discussed in this work because this species is the only one of the three to penetrate fresh water with regularity.

KEY TO THE MULLETS

1a. Anal fin with 3 spines and 8 rays (very young may have 2 spines and 9 rays); sides with dark longitudinal stripes; soft dorsal and anal fins of adults with few or no scales . . . . striped mullet, *Mugil cephalus*
1b. Anal fin with 3 spines and 9 rays (very young with 2 spines and 10 rays); sides without dark longitudinal stripes; soft dorsal and anal fins of adults with scales. . . . . white mullet, *M. curema*

CONECUH RIVER, ESCAMBIA COUNTY

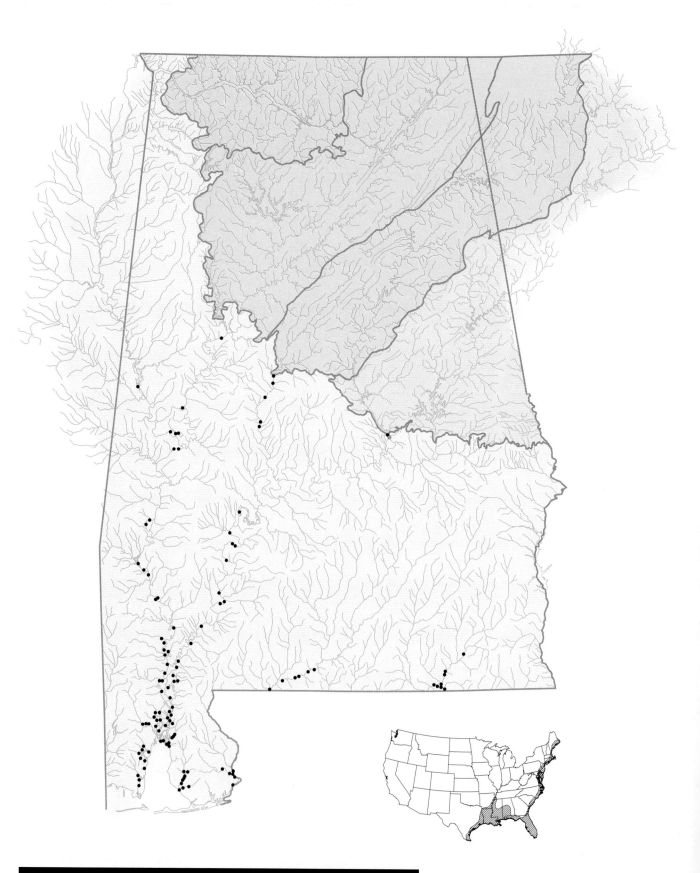

STRIPED MULLET   *Mugil cephalus*   113 STATIONS

744

Mugil cephalus

(Linnaeus, 1758)

ETYMOLOGY:

Mugil—from the word

mulgeo, meaning

to suck

cephalus—head

Weeks Bay, Baldwin County, 20 August 1992, 4.3 in (109 mm) SL male, GSA 4471

CHARACTERISTICS: The body of the striped mullet is somewhat compressed and robust with a stout caudal peduncle. The head is short and wide with a small, oblique mouth and a strongly developed adipose eyelid. Because this species is a filter feeder, numerous close-set gill rakers are found in the gill chamber. The scales extend well onto the caudal fin and only slightly onto the dorsal and anal fins. Adults are typically bluish gray on the back and silvery on the sides and venter. Scales on the sides have dusky centers, giving the appearance of distinct horizontal stripes. Juveniles are a bright silvery color. Brownish pigment in the iris is generally more dispersed than is the gold eye pigment found in the white mullet, *Mugil curema.*

ADULT SIZE: 9 to 15 in (226 to 380 mm)

DISTRIBUTION: Striped mullet are found worldwide in circumtropical areas. In the United States, this species is known from the Atlantic and Gulf coasts and in Pacific waters of southern California. Striped mullet are widespread in the lower reaches of the Alabama and lower Tombigbee rivers, decreasing in abundance near the Fall Line. We routinely encounter individuals in the Perdido, Conecuh, and Choctawhatchee rivers. Etnier and Starnes (1993) report striped mullet in the lower Tennessee River drainage, but we know of no collections from that drainage in Alabama at this time.

HABITAT AND BIOLOGY: Generally striped mullet prefer open water of estuarine and freshwater environments, where they can be observed traveling in schools near the surface. Spawning occurs offshore during late fall and winter, with small mullet entering nearshore coastal waters by early spring. Juveniles grow quickly in the food-rich estuaries, beginning their schooling efforts at this small size. Older adults usually move inland in late summer as river discharge decreases and salt water progressively moves upstream. The young of this species eat microcrustaceans and insect larvae, while older individuals feed strictly on plants and associated plant material that they process in a gizzard. Striped mullet are among the few fish species to possess such an organ.

LEFTEYE FLOUNDERS

Bothidae

The lefteye or left-handed flounder is so named because adults have both eyes located on the left side of the head. Likewise, righteye flounders in the family Pleuronectidae have both eyes on the right side. Larval flatfishes are born with an eye on either side of the head and a normally positioned mouth and internal body organs, looking much like other fishes. As metamorphosis begins one eye progressively migrates from one side of the body to the other. The mouth and internal organs shift to accommodate the new visual perspective. The top surface of the fish assumes a dark color with variously shaped light and dark spots, and the underside becomes white. Flounders have a remarkable ability to alter their body colors, which assists them in blending with their immediate habitat. On clean sand, individuals exhibit a light beige color, perhaps with a few darker spots of various sizes. On darker surfaces, they are light to dark brown, with irregularly scattered darker spots and mottling.

Fishing requires specialized gear and skill. It is nearly impossible to accurately discern a flounder's shape on the bottom because of its protective coloring and the fact that individuals usually cover themselves with a thin layer of sediment by rhythmically moving their fins. Serious anglers wade or pole small boats in shallow water from dusk until dawn, usually stopping only for a short while around midnight to rest and eat. They position strong bright lights just above or below the water surface. Successful anglers concentrate on the fish's eyes, which protrude slightly above the silty covering. The light reflects from them, revealing the fish's position. When the fish are spotted, anglers spear them with gigs mounted on long poles. Commercial fishermen usually catch flounder with gill nets in fresh water and with shrimp trawls in salt water.

Most species of righteye flounders occur on the Pacific Coast, although one species is known in the Gulf of Mexico. Lefteye flounders are more common along the Atlantic and Gulf coasts, with 32 recognized species in Canada and North America and about 24 or so species in the northern Gulf of Mexico. Several species occur in Alabama waters, the most common being the spotted whiff, *Citharichthys macrops*; bay whiff, *C. spilopterus*; fringed flounder, *Etropus crossotus*; Gulf flounder, *Paralichthys albigutta*; and the southern flounder, *P. lethostigma*, which is the fish usually served as fresh flounder in local restaurants.

Our sampling indicates that *P. lethostigma* probably intrudes farther upstream into Alabama's rivers than any other flounder species; hence its inclusion in this book. Although flounder are difficult to collect by seining and with boat-electrofishing gear, using gill nets we have successfully captured individuals as far upstream as the tailwaters of Claiborne Lock and Dam on the Alabama River and Coffeeville Lock and Dam on the lower Tombigbee River.

BON SECOUR BAY, BALDWIN COUNTY

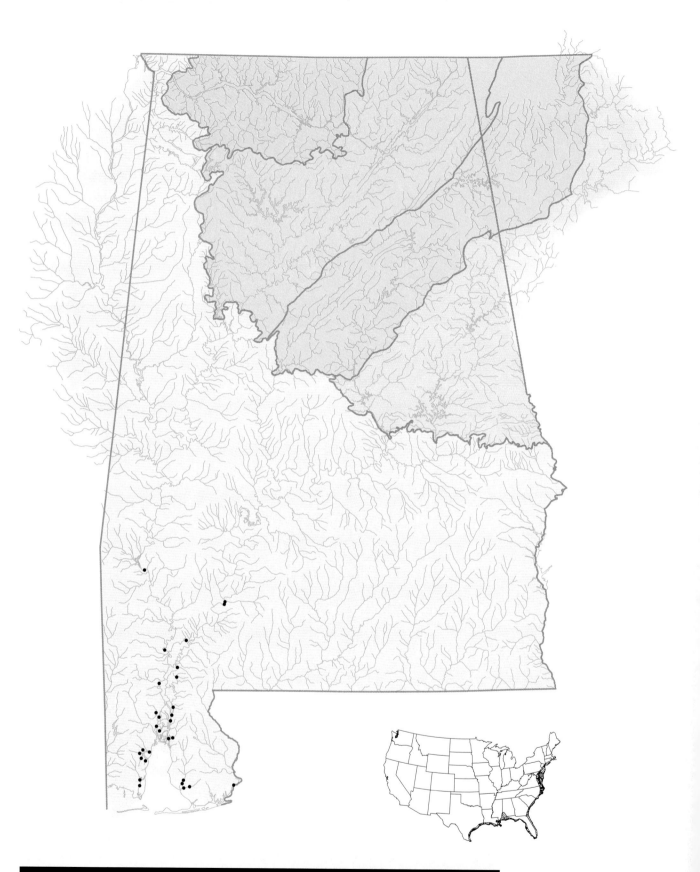

SOUTHERN FLOUNDER · *Paralichthys lethostigma* · **29 STATIONS**

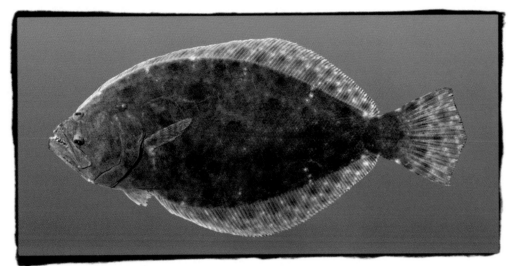

Paralichthys lethostigma

Jordan and Gilbert, 1884

ETYMOLOGY:

Paralichthys—parallel fish
lethostigma—forgotten
spots, referring to the grad-
ual disappearance of large
spots

Perdido Bay, Baldwin County, 17 June 1993, 13 in (330 mm) SL female, GSA 4488

CHARACTERISTICS: The southern flounder is a mod-erately large fish with prominent eyes and a large mouth containing sharp canine teeth. The eyed side is generally light to dark brown with diffuse small spots and blotches, while the blind side is dusky or white. The large ocel-lated spots present on other species of flounder are much more diffuse in the southern flounder and generally dis-appear in adult individuals. See Jordan and Meek (1884) for original description.

ADULT SIZE: 10 to 30 in (254 to 762 mm). Up to 10 lb (4.5 kg). Though not identified by species, the state angling record (13 lb, 3 oz), caught in 1975, was probably a southern flounder.

DISTRIBUTION: *Paralichthys lethostigma* is distributed in Atlantic coastal waters from North Carolina to Florida and in the Gulf of Mexico from Florida to Texas. This species is a common inhabitant of Alabama estuarine waters. Our collections of southern flounder in the lower Tombigbee River basin below Coffeeville Lock and Dam (river mile 116.6) and in the Alabama River below Clai-

borne Lock and Dam (river mile 117.5) are new inland records for this species in Alabama.

HABITAT AND BIOLOGY: The southern flounder gen-erally prefers muddy bottoms throughout most of the estuary, but it can occur in channels and bay mouths and also frequents areas around piers, pilings, and rock jetties. Migrations to offshore spawning grounds begin in late fall at the onset of cold weather, and spawning is completed during winter months. This species is the perfect preda-tor, lying in total camouflage on the bottom until unsus-pecting prey wander within reach and are captured with lightning quick movements. Foods of this species include shrimp and fishes.

REMARKS: Flounders are caught by both anglers and commercial fishermen in south Alabama. Malvestuto et al. (1983) report that anglers landed 8,425 pounds of floun-der, probably southern flounder, in the Mobile Delta and Mobile River in 1980 and 1981. An additional 1,414 pounds were landed by commercial fishermen during the same period.

SOLES

Soleidae

The Soleidae are a family of small, righteyed flatfish that have a small mouth, rough sides, and closely aligned eyes. Sixteen of the 17 species in the family (Robins et al., 1991) occur in the Atlantic Ocean and Gulf of Mexico. The California tonguefish is the only sole species found in the Pacific coastal waters off North America. Four species occur in coastal waters of Alabama, of which two—the lined sole, *Achirus lineatus*, and the hogchoker, *Trinectes maculatus*—intrude into fresh water.

The hogchoker, like the southern flounder, *Paralichthys lethostigma*, occurs farther inland than other species in the family, and for this reason is included in our species accounts. Because they spend most of their lives on the bottom and are generally too small to be caught with hook and line, hogchokers are not likely to be encountered by anglers. We formerly believed these small fishes were somewhat rare in riverine habitats, a misconception that changed when we observed thousands of individuals during a 1990 fish survey conducted at Claiborne Lock and Dam. Recent collections from the area between the Claiborne and Millers Ferry lock and dam installations clearly indicate that hogchokers navigate successfully through lock chambers. Although all of our collection records in the lower Tombigbee River are from downstream of Coffeeville Lock and Dam, we have an unverified record of a specimen observed at Demopolis Lock and Dam during a period when the lock chamber was dewatered for maintenance.

MAGNOLIA RIVER, BALDWIN COUNTY

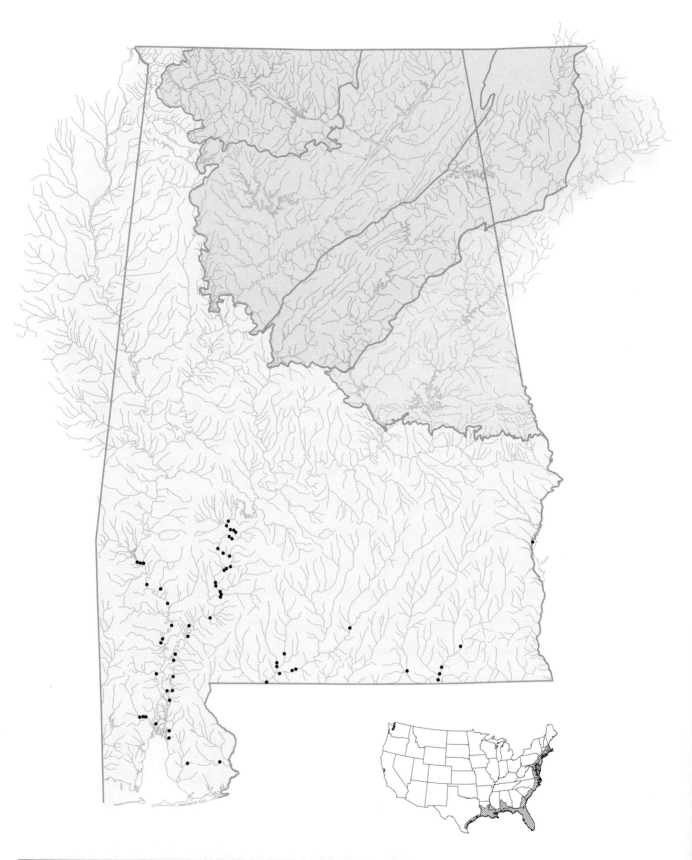

HOGCHOKER *Trinectes maculatus* **59 STATIONS**

Trinectes maculatus
(Bloch and Schneider, 1801)

ETYMOLOGY:

Trinectes—three swimming,
referring to the dorsal,
ventral, and caudal fins
maculatus—spotted

Blakeley River, Baldwin County, 20 August 1992, 2.4 in (60 mm) SL male, GSA 4470

CHARACTERISTICS: Besides being characterized by having its eyes and mouth on the right side of its body, the hogchoker lacks pectoral fins. The exposed side and fins are mottled in appearance. Six or seven dark vertical bars are present along the gray-green to brownish side, with more diffuse, less organized pigment found between the bars. A single row of spots extends along the lateral line from the gill cover to the caudal fin, and two large, diffuse spots are found on the sides in the middle of the body adjacent to the dorsal and anal fins. The hogchoker has small eyes with the top eye situated in front of the lower eye. The underside is white.

ADULT SIZE: 3 to 6 in (75 to 152 mm)

DISTRIBUTION: *Trinectes maculatus* is found from Massachusetts to Venezuela, including the Gulf of Mexico. In Alabama, the hogchoker occurs throughout estuarine and nearshore habitats and in fresh water, penetrating to Coffeeville Lock and Dam on the lower Tombigbee River and well upstream of Claiborne Lock and Dam on the Alabama River. Most collection records of this species in the Conecuh, Pea, and Choctawhatchee river systems were obtained during our sampling efforts from 1991-94.

HABITAT AND BIOLOGY: Small hogchokers are found well upstream in fresh tidal inlets and around grass beds near tidal creek mouths. Large individuals are found around bay mouths in deeper waters. Most spawning takes place during the summer in lower estuarine areas. However, our observations of many individuals less than 1 inch (25 mm) in total length during a 1990 fish survey at Claiborne Lock and Dam could indicate limited, though as yet unsubstantiated, freshwater spawnings. Inland abundance is also influenced by upstream larval migrations during late summer when river discharge decreases and a salt wedge moves upstream along the bottom of the Mobile and possibly the Alabama and lower Tombigbee rivers. Dove et al. (1969) suggest that small hogchokers remain in fresh water for up to three years and return to brackish nursery areas in their fourth year to spawn. This theory could explain the occurrence of large individuals in lower bay passes and would indicate habitat partitioning by fish of different ages. Food items of this species include small crustaceans and worms.

Unless preceded by an asterisk, each species is described in an account in the appropriate family chapter. For species followed by note numbers, see notes on page 776-77.

ABE—Apalachicola basin endemic   MBE—Mobile basin endemic   TDE—Tennessee drainage endemic

COUNTY NUMBERS

Species	1	2	3	4	5	6	7	8	9	10	11	12	13	14	15	16	17	18	19	20	21	22	23	24	25
PETROMYZONTIDAE LAMPREYS																									
Ichthyomyzon bdellium, Ohio lamprey																									
I. castaneus, chestnut lamprey				●						●		●	●				●	●				●			
I. gagei, southern brook lamprey	●	●	●	●	●		●	●	●		●	●	●	●	●	●		●		●		●			
I. greeleyi, mountain brook lamprey																									
Lampetra aepyptera, least brook lamprey		●		●			●	●		●	●	●	●	●			●			●	●	●		●	
L. appendix, American brook lamprey																	●								
CARCHARHINIDAE REQUIEM SHARKS																									
* Carcharhinus leucas, bull shark	●																								
DASYATIDAE STINGRAYS																									
* Dasyatis sabina, Atlantic stingray	●																								
ACIPENSERIDAE STURGEONS																									
Acipenser fulvescens, lake sturgeon																									
A. oxyrinchus desotoi, gulf sturgeon	●			●												●									
Scaphirhynchus platorynchus, shovelnose sturgeon																●									
S. suttkusi, Alabama sturgeon (MBE)													●			●						●			
POLYODONTIDAE PADDLEFISH																									
Polyodon spathula, paddlefish	●	●										●	●									●			
LEPISOSTEIDAE GARS																									
Lepisosteus oculatus, spotted gar	●	●		●	●					●		●	●				●		●	●	●	●	●		
L. osseus, longnose gar	●	●		●	●					●	●	●	●				●		●	●	●	●	●	●	
L. platostomus, shortnose gar																									
L. spatula, alligator gar	●												●												
AMIIDAE BOWFIN																									
Amia calva, bowfin	●		●		●							●	●				●			●	●		●	●	
HIODONTIDAE MOONEYES																									
Hiodon alosoides, goldeye																									
H. tergisus, mooneye	●	●		●									●				●						●		
ELOPIDAE TARPONS																									
* Elops saurus, ladyfish	●																								

1. Autauga
2. Baldwin
3. Barbour
4. Bibb
5. Blount
6. Bullock
7. Butler
8. Calhoun
9. Chambers
10. Cherokee
11. Chilton
12. Choctaw
13. Clarke
14. Clay
15. Cleburne
16. Coffee
17. Colbert
18. Conecuh
19. Coosa
20. Covington
21. Crenshaw
22. Cullman
23. Dale
24. Dallas
25. Dekalb
26. Elmore
27. Escambia
28. Etowah
29. Fayette
30. Franklin
31. Geneva
32. Greene
33. Hale
34. Henry
35. Houston
36. Jackson
37. Jefferson
38. Lamar
39. Lauderdale
40. Lawrence
41. Lee
42. Limestone
43. Lowndes
44. Macon
45. Madison
46. Marengo
47. Marion
48. Marshall
49. Mobile
50. Monroe
51. Montgomery
52. Morgan
53. Perry
54. Pickens
55. Pike
56. Randolph
57. Russell
58. St. Clair
59. Shelby
60. Sumter
61. Talladega
62. Tallapoosa
63. Tuscaloosa
64. Walker
65. Washington
66. Wilcox
67. Winston

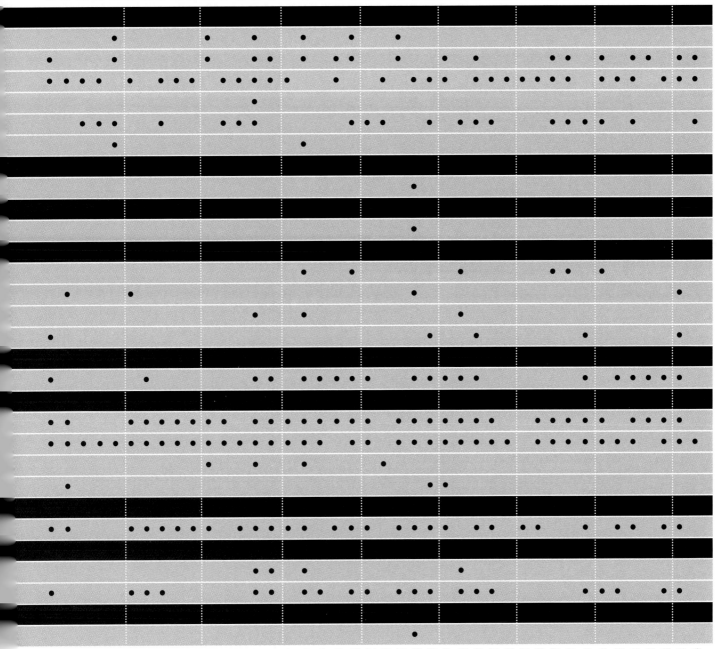

26 27 28 29 30 31 32 33 34 35 36 37 38 39 40 41 42 43 44 45 46 47 48 49 50 51 52 53 54 55 56 57 58 59 60 61 62 63 64 65 66 67

	1	2	3	4	5	6	7	8	9	10	11	12	13	14	15	16	17	18	19	20	21	22	23	24	25
ANGUILLIDAE — FRESHWATER EEL																									
Anguilla rostrata, American eel		●		●								●	●							●	●		●	●	
OPHICHTHYIDAE — SNAKE EELS																									
Myrophis punctatus, speckled worm eel		●																							
CLUPEIDAE — HERRINGS																									
Alosa alabamae, Alabama shad		●		●								●	●										●	●	
A. chrysochloris, skipjack herring	●	●	●	●								●	●				●						●		
Brevoortia patronus, gulf menhaden		●											●												
Dorosoma cepedianum, gizzard shad	●	●	●	●	●			●	●	●	●	●	●				●	●		●	●	●	●		
D. petenense, threadfin shad	●	●	●								●	●	●				●			●					
ENGRAULIDAE — ANCHOVIES																									
Anchoa mitchilli, bay anchovy		●										●	●												
CYPRINIDAE — CARPS AND MINNOWS																									
Campostoma oligolepis, largescale stoneroller	●			●	●		●	●	●	●	●			●		●		●			●			●	●
C. pauciradii, bluefin stoneroller (ABE)			●						●																
Carassius auratus, goldfish																									
Clinostomus funduloides, rosyside dace																	●								
Ctenopharyngodon idella, grass carp												●	●				●							●	
Cyprinella caerulea, blue shiner (MBE)				●				●		●							●								
C. callistia, Alabama shiner (MBE)	●			●	●			●	●	●	●	●	●	●								●		●	●
C. callitaenia, bluestripe shiner (ABE)			●																						
C. galactura, whitetail shiner																	●								●
C. gibbsi, Tallapoosa shiner (MBE)									●					●	●			●							
C. lutrensis, red shiner								●	●																
C. monacha, spotfin chub (TDE)																	●								
C. spiloptera, spotfin shiner																	●								●
C. trichroistia, tricolor shiner (MBE)	●			●				●			●	●		●	●			●							●
C. venusta, blacktail shiner	●	●	●	●	●		●	●	●	●	●	●	●	●	●			●	●	●				●	
C. whipplei, steelcolor shiner				●													●	●							
Cyprinus carpio, common carp	●	●		●							●	●	●	●		●		●		●				●	
Ericymba buccata, silverjaw minnow	●	●	●	●		●	●		●		●	●	●			●		●		●	●			●	●
Erimystax dissimilis, streamline chub																									
E. insignis, blotched chub																									

	1	2	3	4	5	6	7	8	9	10	11	12	13	14	15	16	17	18	19	20	21	22	23	24	25

ABE—Apalachicola basin endemic   MBE—Mobile basin endemic   TDE—Tennessee drainage endemic

1. Autauga	6. Bullock	11. Chilton	16. Coffee	21. Crenshaw	26. Elmore	31. Geneva
2. Baldwin	7. Butler	12. Choctaw	17. Colbert	22. Cullman	27. Escambia	32. Greene
3. Barbour	8. Calhoun	13. Clarke	18. Conecuh	23. Dale	28. Etowah	33. Hale
4. Bibb	9. Chambers	14. Clay	19. Coosa	24. Dallas	29. Fayette	34. Henry
5. Blount	10. Cherokee	15. Cleburne	20. Covington	25. Dekalb	30. Franklin	35. Houston

26 27 28 29 30 31 32 33 34 35 36 37 38 39 40 41 42 43 44 45 46 47 48 49 50 51 52 53 54 55 56 57 58 59 60 61 62 63 64 65 66 67

26 27 28 29 30 31 32 33 34 35 36 37 38 39 40 41 42 43 44 45 46 47 48 49 50 51 52 53 54 55 56 57 58 59 60 61 62 63 64 65 66 67

36. Jackson	41. Lee	46. Marengo	51. Montgomery	56. Randolph	61. Talladega	66. Wilcox
37. Jefferson	42. Limestone	47. Marion	52. Morgan	57. Russell	62. Tallapoosa	67. Winston
38. Lamar	43. Lowndes	48. Marshall	53. Perry	58. St. Clair	63. Tuscaloosa	
39. Lauderdale	44. Macon	49. Mobile	54. Pickens	59. Shelby	64. Walker	
40. Lawrence	45. Madison	50. Monroe	55. Pike	60. Sumter	65. Washington	

CYPRINIDAE — CARPS AND MINNOWS

Species	1	2	3	4	5	6	7	8	9	10	11	12	13	14	15	16	17	18	19	20	21	22	23	24	25
Hemitremia flammea, flame chub					●			●								●									
Hybognathus hayi, cypress minnow						●							●										●		
H. nuchalis, Mississippi silvery minnow	●	●		●		●						●	●				●						●		
Hybopsis amblops, bigeye chub																	●								
H. lineapunctata, lined chub (MBE)									●	●			●	●			●								
H. winchelli, clear chub	●	●		●			●			●	●	●					●						●		
H. sp. cf. winchelli[1]		●	●			●	●		●							●		●		●	●		●		
Hypopthalmichthys molitrix, silver carp																									
H. nobilis, bighead carp																									
Luxilus chrysocephalus, striped shiner	●	●		●	●			●	●	●	●	●	●	●		●	●	●			●			●	●
L. coccogenis, warpaint shiner																									
L. zonistius, bandfin shiner					●				●				●												
Lythrurus ardens, rosefin shiner							●										●				●				
L. atrapiculus, blacktip shiner					●		●	●								●	●			●	●	●			
L. bellus, pretty shiner	●			●	●	●	●		●		●	●	●		●			●			●		●		
L. fumeus, ribbon shiner																	●								
L. lirus, mountain shiner							●		●		●	●		●	●			●							
L. roseipinnis, cherryfin shiner		●											●												
Macrhybopsis aestivalis, speckled chub																									
M. storeriana, silver chub	●	●		●	●		●					●	●				●						●		
M. sp. cf. aestivalis (MBE)[2]	●	●		●			●						●				●								
M.sp. cf aestivalis[3]																●		●		●	●		●		
Nocomis leptocephalus, bluehead chub	●	●		●			●				●			●			●								
N. micropogon, river chub																									
Notemigonus crysoleucas, golden shiner	●	●	●	●	●	●	●	●	●	●	●	●	●	●	●	●	●	●	●	●	●				
Notropis albizonatus, palezone shiner																									
N. ammophilus, orangefin shiner	●	●		●		●	●				●	●	●								●				
N. ariommus, popeye shiner																									
N. asperifrons, burrhead shiner (MBE)						●	●		●			●		●	●				●			●			
N. atherinoides, emerald shiner	●	●		●	●			●				●	●	●			●		●			●		●	
N. baileyi, rough shiner	●	●		●			●				●	●	●	●			●	●	●					●	
N. boops, bigeye shiner																	●								

ABE—Apalachicola basin endemic   MBE—Mobile basin endemic   TDE—Tennessee drainage endemic

1. Autauga	6. Bullock	11. Chilton	16. Coffee	21. Crenshaw	26. Elmore	31. Geneva
2. Baldwin	7. Butler	12. Choctaw	17. Colbert	22. Cullman	27. Escambia	32. Greene
3. Barbour	8. Calhoun	13. Clarke	18. Conecuh	23. Dale	28. Etowah	33. Hale
4. Bibb	9. Chambers	14. Clay	19. Coosa	24. Dallas	29. Fayette	34. Henry
5. Blount	10. Cherokee	15. Cleburne	20. Covington	25. Dekalb	30. Franklin	35. Houston

26 27 28 29 30 31 32 33 34 35 36 37 38 39 40 41 42 43 44 45 46 47 48 49 50 51 52 53 54 55 56 57 58 59 60 61 62 63 64 65 66 67

26 27 28 29 30 31 32 33 34 35 36 37 38 39 40 41 42 43 44 45 46 47 48 49 50 51 52 53 54 55 56 57 58 59 60 61 62 63 64 65 66 67

36. Jackson
37. Jefferson
38. Lamar
39. Lauderdale
40. Lawrence

41. Lee
42. Limestone
43. Lowndes
44. Macon
45. Madison

46. Marengo
47. Marion
48. Marshall
49. Mobile
50. Monroe

51. Montgomery
52. Morgan
53. Perry
54. Pickens
55. Pike

56. Randolph
57. Russell
58. St. Clair
59. Shelby
60. Sumter

61. Talladega
62. Tallapoosa
63. Tuscaloosa
64. Walker
65. Washington

66. Wilcox
67. Winston

CYPRINIDAE — CARPS AND MINNOWS

Species	1	2	3	4	5	6	7	8	9	10	11	12	13	14	15	16	17	18	19	20	21	22	23	24	25
Notropis buchanani, ghost shiner																	•								
N. cahabae, Cahaba shiner (MBE)				•																					
N. candidus, silverside shiner (MBE)	•	•									•	•	•											•	
N. chalybaeus, ironcolor shiner		•											•								•				
N. chrosomus, rainbow shiner	•			•	•			•		•	•		•	•						•				•	•
N. cummingsae, dusky shiner																									
N. edwardraneyi, fluvial shiner (MBE)	•	•		•								•	•											•	
N. harperi, redeye chub				•				•									•		•		•	•			
N. hypsilepis, highscale shiner									•																
N. leuciodus, Tennessee shiner																									
N. longirostris, longnose shiner		•	•			•	•		•								•		•		•		•		
N. lutipinnis, yellowfin shiner	All sample stations occur in Georgia
N. maculatus, taillight shiner	•												•										•		
N. petersoni, coastal shiner	•																								
N. photogenis, silver shiner																									
N. rubellus, rosyface shiner																									
N. stilbius, silverstripe shiner				•	•			•	•	•	•	•	•	•				•			•			•	•
N. telescopus, telescope shiner																									
N. texanus, weed shiner	•	•	•	•	•	•	•	•									•		•	•	•			•	•
N. uranoscopus, skygazer shiner (MBE)				•																				•	
N. volucellus, mimic shiner																	•								
N. wickliffi, channel shiner																									
N. xaenocephalus, Coosa shiner (MBE)								•	•	•			•	•					•						•
N. sp. cf. *volucellus* (MBE)[4]	•		•	•				•											•						
N. species, "sawfin shiner"[5]																									
Opsopoeodus emiliae, pugnose minnow	•	•	•	•		•	•		•			•	•					•			•	•			
Phenacobius catostomus, riffle minnow (MBE)			•	•				•	•	•				•	•				•						
P. mirabilis, suckermouth minnow																									
P. uranops, stargazing minnow																									
Phoxinus erythrogaster, southern redbelly dace																	•								
Pimephales notatus, bluntnose minnow	•			•			•					•	•				•					•		•	
P. promelas, fathead minnow				•	•			•												•				•	

| | 1 | 2 | 3 | 4 | 5 | 6 | 7 | 8 | 9 | 10 | 11 | 12 | 13 | 14 | 15 | 16 | 17 | 18 | 19 | 20 | 21 | 22 | 23 | 24 | 25 |

ABE—Apalachicola basin endemic   MBE—Mobile basin endemic   TDE—Tennessee drainage endemic

1. Autauga	6. Bullock	11. Chilton	16. Coffee	21. Crenshaw	26. Elmore	31. Geneva
2. Baldwin	7. Butler	12. Choctaw	17. Colbert	22. Cullman	27. Escambia	32. Greene
3. Barbour	8. Calhoun	13. Clarke	18. Conecuh	23. Dale	28. Etowah	33. Hale
4. Bibb	9. Chambers	14. Clay	19. Coosa	24. Dallas	29. Fayette	34. Henry
5. Blount	10. Cherokee	15. Cleburne	20. Covington	25. Dekalb	30. Franklin	35. Houston

26 27 28 29 30 31 32 33 34 35 36 37 38 39 40 41 42 43 44 45 46 47 48 49 50 51 52 53 54 55 56 57 58 59 60 61 62 63 64 65 66 67

26 27 28 29 30 31 32 33 34 35 36 37 38 39 40 41 42 43 44 45 46 47 48 49 50 51 52 53 54 55 56 57 58 59 60 61 62 63 64 65 66 67

36. Jackson	41. Lee	46. Marengo	51. Montgomery	56. Randolph	61. Talladega	66. Wilcox
37. Jefferson	42. Limestone	47. Marion	52. Morgan	57. Russell	62. Tallapoosa	67. Winston
38. Lamar	43. Lowndes	48. Marshall	53. Perry	58. St. Clair	63. Tuscaloosa	
39. Lauderdale	44. Macon	49. Mobile	54. Pickens	59. Shelby	64. Walker	
40. Lawrence	45. Madison	50. Monroe	55. Pike	60. Sumter	65. Washington	

	1	2	3	4	5	6	7	8	9	10	11	12	13	14	15	16	17	18	19	20	21	22	23	24	25
CYPRINIDAE — CARPS AND MINNOWS																									
Pimephales vigilax, bullhead minnow	●	●		●	●		●		●	●	●	●	●	●	●		●		●			●		●	
Pteronotropis euryzonus, broadstripe shiner (ABE)																									
P. hypselopterus, sailfin shiner	●	●	●			●							●			●		●			●	●			
P. signipinnis, flagfin shiner		●	●									●	●				●			●					
P. welaka, bluenose shiner					●								●					●					●		
Rhinichthys atratulus, blacknose dace						●		●					●			●						●			●
Semotilus atromaculatus, creek chub	●	●		●	●		●	●	●	●	●	●	●	●	●		●		●		●				
S. thoreauianus, Dixie chub	●	●	●				●	●			●	●	●			●	●			●	●		●		
CATOSTOMIDAE — SUCKERS																									
Carpiodes carpio, river carpsucker																	●								
C. cyprinus, quillback[6]	●	●	●	●								●	●										●	●	
C. velifer, highfin carpsucker[7]	●	●		●							●	●	●				●			●	●			●	
Catostomus commersoni, white sucker																	●								
Cycleptus elongatus, blue sucker[8]	●	●		●								●	●											●	
Erimyzon oblongus, creek chubsucker	●			●	●		●					●					●	●	●				●		
E. sucetta, lake chubsucker		●				●						●	●							●			●	●	
E. tenuis, sharpfin chubsucker	●	●																		●	●				
Hypentelium etowanum, Alabama hog sucker	●	●		●	●		●	●	●	●	●	●	●	●	●			●				●		●	●
H. nigricans, northern hog sucker																	●								●
Ictiobus bubalus, smallmouth buffalo	●	●		●							●	●	●				●		●				●		
I. cyprinellus, bigmouth buffalo																	●								
I. niger, black buffalo																	●								
Lagochila lacera, harelip sucker																									
Minytrema melanops, spotted sucker	●	●	●	●	●	●		●	●	●	●	●	●	●	●	●	●	●	●	●	●	●	●	●	
Moxostoma anisurum, silver redhorse																	●								
M. carinatum, river redhorse						●											●							●	
M. duquesnei, black redhorse	●			●	●			●	●	●			●	●			●		●					●	
M. erythrurum, golden redhorse	●			●				●	●	●			●				●							●	
M. lachneri, greater jumprock (ABE)			●																						
M. macrolepidotum, shorthead redhorse																	●								
M. poecilurum, blacktail redhorse	●	●		●	●			●	●	●	●	●	●	●	●	●	●		●	●	●	●	●	●	
M. species, "grayfin redhorse" (ABE)[9]			●																						

	1	2	3	4	5	6	7	8	9	10	11	12	13	14	15	16	17	18	19	20	21	22	23	24	25

ABE—Apalachicola basin endemic   MBE—Mobile basin endemic   TDE—Tennessee drainage endemic

1. Autauga	6. Bullock	11. Chilton	16. Coffee	21. Crenshaw	26. Elmore	31. Geneva
2. Baldwin	7. Butler	12. Choctaw	17. Colbert	22. Cullman	27. Escambia	32. Greene
3. Barbour	8. Calhoun	13. Clarke	18. Conecuh	23. Dale	28. Etowah	33. Hale
4. Bibb	9. Chambers	14. Clay	19. Coosa	24. Dallas	29. Fayette	34. Henry
5. Blount	10. Cherokee	15. Cleburne	20. Covington	25. Dekalb	30. Franklin	35. Houston

26 27 28 29 30 31 32 33 34 35 36 37 38 39 40 41 42 43 44 45 46 47 48 49 50 51 52 53 54 55 56 57 58 59 60 61 62 63 64 65 66 67

36. Jackson	41. Lee	46. Marengo	51. Montgomery	56. Randolph	61. Talladega	66. Wilcox
37. Jefferson	42. Limestone	47. Marion	52. Morgan	57. Russell	62. Tallapoosa	67. Winston
38. Lamar	43. Lowndes	48. Marshall	53. Perry	58. St. Clair	63. Tuscaloosa	
39. Lauderdale	44. Macon	49. Mobile	54. Pickens	59. Shelby	64. Walker	
40. Lawrence	45. Madison	50. Monroe	55. Pike	60. Sumter	65. Washington	

	1	2	3	4	5	6	7	8	9	10	11	12	13	14	15	16	17	18	19	20	21	22	23	24	25
ICTALURIDAE BULLHEAD CATFISHES																									
Ameiurus brunneus, snail bullhead																									
A. catus, white catfish		●						●		●							●		●						
A. melas, black bullhead	●	●	●			●	●															●		●	
A. natalis, yellow bullhead	●	●	●	●			●	●	●		●	●	●	●	●	●	●		●	●	●	●	●	●	●
A. nebulosus, brown bullhead		●	●				●				●	●		●							●	●			
A. serracanthus, spotted bullhead			●																						
Ictalurus furcatus, blue catfish	●	●						●			●	●					●		●			●			
I. punctatus, channel catfish	●	●	●	●	●		●	●	●	●	●	●	●	●	●	●	●	●	●	●					
Noturus elegans, elegant madtom																	●								
N. eleutherus, mountain madtom																									
N. exilis, slender madtom																	●								
N. flavus, stonecat[10]																									
N. funebris, black madtom	●	●	●	●			●	●		●		●	●	●	●				●	●		●	●		
N. gyrinus, tadpole madtom			●	●							●	●	●							●			●		
N. leptacanthus, speckled madtom	●	●	●	●	●	●	●	●	●	●	●	●	●	●	●	●		●	●	●	●		●		
N. miurus, brindled madtom																	●								
N. munitus, frecklebelly madtom				●																					
N. nocturnus, freckled madtom				●								●	●											●	
Pylodictis olivaris, flathead catfish		●		●				●	●	●	●	●	●			●	●		●				●		
ARIIDAE SEA CATFISHES																									
* *Arius felis*, hardhead catfish		●																							
* *Bagre marinus*, gafftopsail catfish		●																							
ESOCIDAE PIKES																									
Esox americanus, redfin pickerel	●	●	●	●	●	●	●	●			●	●	●			●	●		●	●		●		●	
* *E. masquinongy*, muskellunge																									
E. niger, chain pickerel	●	●	●	●	●	●	●	●	●	●	●	●	●	●	●	●	●	●	●	●	●	●	●	●	●
SALMONIDAE TROUTS AND CHARS																									
Oncorhynchus mykiss, rainbow trout					●			●															●		
Salmo trutta, brown trout														●											
Salvelinus fontinalis, brook trout	— All sample stations occur in Georgia																								
APHREDODERIDAE PIRATE PERCH																									
Aphredoderus sayanus, pirate perch	●	●	●	●		●	●				●	●	●			●	●	●		●	●		●	●	

| | 1 | 2 | 3 | 4 | 5 | 6 | 7 | 8 | 9 | 10 | 11 | 12 | 13 | 14 | 15 | 16 | 17 | 18 | 19 | 20 | 21 | 22 | 23 | 24 | 25 |

ABE—Apalachicola basin endemic   MBE—Mobile basin endemic   TDE—Tennessee drainage endemic

1. Autauga	6. Bullock	11. Chilton	16. Coffee	21. Crenshaw	26. Elmore	31. Geneva
2. Baldwin	7. Butler	12. Choctaw	17. Colbert	22. Cullman	27. Escambia	32. Greene
3. Barbour	8. Calhoun	13. Clarke	18. Conecuh	23. Dale	28. Etowah	33. Hale
4. Bibb	9. Chambers	14. Clay	19. Coosa	24. Dallas	29. Fayette	34. Henry
5. Blount	10. Cherokee	15. Cleburne	20. Covington	25. Dekalb	30. Franklin	35. Houston

26 27 28 29 30 31 32 33 34 35 36 37 38 39 40 41 42 43 44 45 46 47 48 49 50 51 52 53 54 55 56 57 58 59 60 61 62 63 64 65 66 67

36. Jackson	41. Lee	46. Marengo	51. Montgomery	56. Randolph	61. Talladega	66. Wilcox
37. Jefferson	42. Limestone	47. Marion	52. Morgan	57. Russell	62. Tallapoosa	67. Winston
38. Lamar	43. Lowndes	48. Marshall	53. Perry	58. St. Clair	63. Tuscaloosa	
39. Lauderdale	44. Macon	49. Mobile	54. Pickens	59. Shelby	64. Walker	
40. Lawrence	45. Madison	50. Monroe	55. Pike	60. Sumter	65. Washington	

COUNTY NUMBERS

Family / Species	1	2	3	4	5	6	7	8	9	10	11	12	13	14	15	16	17	18	19	20	21	22	23	24	25
AMBLYOPSIDAE CAVEFISHES																									
Speoplatyrhinus poulsoni, Alabama cavefish (TDE)																									
Typhlichthys subterraneus, southern cavefish																	•								•
BELONIDAE NEEDLEFISH																									
Strongylura marina, Atlantic needlefish	•	•		•								•	•				•						•		
CYPRINODONTIDAE KILLIFISH																									
* *Cyprinodon variegatus*, sheepshead minnow		•																							
FUNDULIDAE TOPMINNOWS																									
Fundulus albolineatus, whiteline topminnow (TDE)																									
F. auroguttatus, banded topminnow		•																							
F. bifax, stippled studfish (MBE)									•										•						
F. blairae, southern starhead topminnow		•											•												
F. catenatus, northern studfish																•									
F. chrysotus, golden topminnow		•																							
F. dispar, northern starhead topminnow	•			•									•												
F. escambiae, russetfin topminnow		•	•			•														•		•			
* *F. grandis*, gulf killifish		•																							
F. notatus, blackstripe topminnow		•																					•		
F. notti, bayou topminnow	•	•									•	•													
F. olivaceus, blackspotted topminnow	•	•	•	•	•	•	•	•	•	•	•	•	•	•	•	•	•	•	•	•	•	•	•		
F. stellifer, southern studfish (MBE)				•						•		•		•		•				•					
Leptolucania ommata, pygmy killifish		•																							
Lucania goodei, bluefin killifish																									
L. parva, rainwater killifish		•											•												
POECILIIDAE LIVEBEARERS																									
Gambusia affinis, western mosquitofish[11]	•			•	•			•	•	•				•	•		•			•		•		•	•
G. holbrooki, eastern mosquitofish[11]		•	•			•	•					•	•				•		•	•	•	•			
Heterandria formosa, least killifish		•											•												
* *Poecilia latipinna*, sailfin molly		•																							
ATHERINIDAE SILVERSIDES																									
Labidesthes sicculus, brook silverside	•	•	•	•		•						•	•			•	•	•		•	•	•	•	•	•
Menidia beryllina, inland silverside		•																							

1 2 3 4 5 6 7 8 9 10 11 12 13 14 15 16 17 18 19 20 21 22 23 24 25

ABE—Apalachicola basin endemic   MBE—Mobile basin endemic   TDE—Tennessee drainage endemic

1. Autauga	6. Bullock	11. Chilton	16. Coffee	21. Crenshaw	26. Elmore	31. Geneva
2. Baldwin	7. Butler	12. Choctaw	17. Colbert	22. Cullman	27. Escambia	32. Greene
3. Barbour	8. Calhoun	13. Clarke	18. Conecuh	23. Dale	28. Etowah	33. Hale
4. Bibb	9. Chambers	14. Clay	19. Coosa	24. Dallas	29. Fayette	34. Henry
5. Blount	10. Cherokee	15. Cleburne	20. Covington	25. Dekalb	30. Franklin	35. Houston

26 27 28 29 30 31 32 33 34 35 36 37 38 39 40 41 42 43 44 45 46 47 48 49 50 51 52 53 54 55 56 57 58 59 60 61 62 63 64 65 66 67

36. Jackson	41. Lee	46. Marengo	51. Montgomery	56. Randolph	61. Talladega	66. Wilcox
37. Jefferson	42. Limestone	47. Marion	52. Morgan	57. Russell	62. Tallapoosa	67. Winston
38. Lamar	43. Lowndes	48. Marshall	53. Perry	58. St. Clair	63. Tuscaloosa	
39. Lauderdale	44. Macon	49. Mobile	54. Pickens	59. Shelby	64. Walker	
40. Lawrence	45. Madison	50. Monroe	55. Pike	60. Sumter	65. Washington	

Species	1	2	3	4	5	6	7	8	9	10	11	12	13	14	15	16	17	18	19	20	21	22	23	24	25
SYNGNATHIDAE — PIPEFISHES																									
Syngnathus scovelli, gulf pipefish		●																							
GASTEROSTEIDAE — STICKLEBACKS																									
Culaea inconstans, brook stickleback																									
COTTIDAE — SCULPINS																									
Cottus bairdi, mottled sculpin																									
C. carolinae, banded sculpin	●	●		●	●			●	●	●		●	●	●		●		●						●	●
C. pygmaeus, pygmy sculpin (MBE)								●																	
MORONIDAE — STRIPED BASSES																									
Morone chrysops, white bass	●	●	●					●	●	●						●		●	●	●		●			
M. mississippiensis, yellow bass		●											●				●								
M. saxatilis, striped bass	●	●	●					●		●			●					●						●	
M. chrysops x saxatilis, palmetto bass	●	●								●	●	●								●				●	
ELASSOMATIDAE — PYGMY SUNFISHES																									
Elassoma alabamae, spring pygmy sunfish (TDE)																									
E. evergladei, Everglades pygmy sunfish		●																							
E. zonatum, banded pygmy sunfish	●	●	●	●		●	●			●	●	●				●		●	●					●	●
CENTRARCHIDAE — SUNFISHES																									
Ambloplites ariommus, shadow bass	●	●		●	●			●	●							●	●	●		●				●	●
A. rupestris, rock bass																●									
Centrarchus macropterus, flier	●	●		●		●	●						●					●		●		●			
Enneacanthus gloriosus, bluespotted sunfish		●											●												
E. obesus, banded sunfish		●																							
Lepomis auritus, redbreast sunfish			●		●	●		●	●	●			●	●				●				●	●		
L. cyanellus, green sunfish	●	●	●	●	●	●	●	●	●	●	●	●	●	●	●	●	●	●	●	●	●	●	●	●	●
L. gulosus, warmouth		●	●	●	●	●	●	●	●	●	●	●	●	●	●	●	●	●	●	●	●	●	●	●	●
L. humilis, orangespotted sunfish												●	●				●						●		
L. macrochirus, bluegill	●	●	●	●	●	●	●	●	●	●	●	●	●	●	●	●	●	●	●	●	●	●	●	●	●
L. marginatus, dollar sunfish		●	●			●						●	●				●	●					●	●	
L. megalotis, longear sunfish	●	●	●	●	●	●	●	●	●	●	●	●	●	●	●	●	●	●	●	●	●	●	●	●	●
L. microlophus, redear sunfish	●	●	●	●	●	●	●	●	●	●	●	●	●	●	●	●	●	●	●	●	●	●	●	●	●
L. miniatus, redspotted sunfish	●	●	●			●	●			●	●					●	●	●		●		●	●	●	●
Micropterus coosae, redeye bass				●	●			●	●	●				●	●				●						●

ABE—Apalachicola basin endemic   MBE—Mobile basin endemic   TDE—Tennessee drainage endemic

1. Autauga	6. Bullock	11. Chilton	16. Coffee	21. Crenshaw	26. Elmore	31. Geneva
2. Baldwin	7. Butler	12. Choctaw	17. Colbert	22. Cullman	27. Escambia	32. Greene
3. Barbour	8. Calhoun	13. Clarke	18. Conecuh	23. Dale	28. Etowah	33. Hale
4. Bibb	9. Chambers	14. Clay	19. Coosa	24. Dallas	29. Fayette	34. Henry
5. Blount	10. Cherokee	15. Cleburne	20. Covington	25. Dekalb	30. Franklin	35. Houston

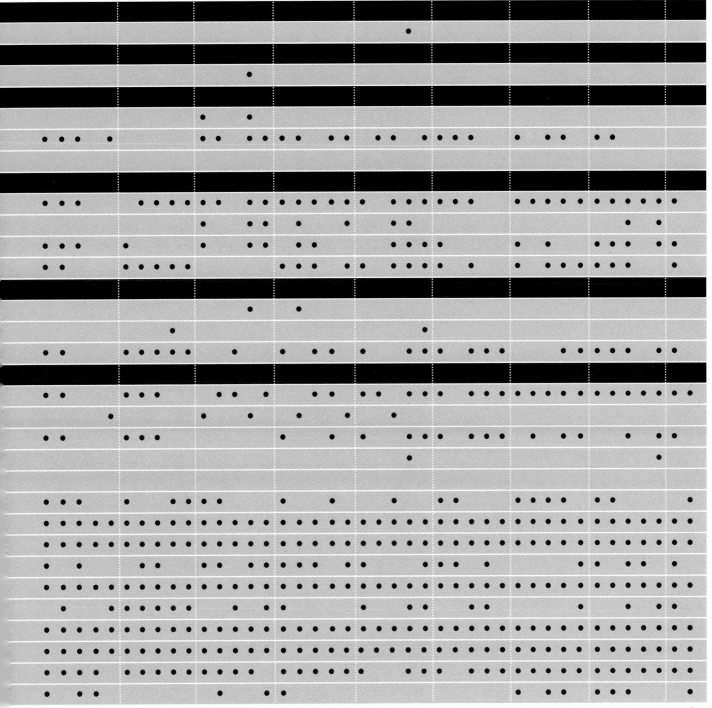

26 27 28 29 30 31 32 33 34 35 36 37 38 39 40 41 42 43 44 45 46 47 48 49 50 51 52 53 54 55 56 57 58 59 60 61 62 63 64 65 66 67

36. Jackson	41. Lee	46. Marengo	51. Montgomery	56. Randolph	61. Talladega	66. Wilcox
37. Jefferson	42. Limestone	47. Marion	52. Morgan	57. Russell	62. Tallapoosa	67. Winston
38. Lamar	43. Lowndes	48. Marshall	53. Perry	58. St. Clair	63. Tuscaloosa	
39. Lauderdale	44. Macon	49. Mobile	54. Pickens	59. Shelby	64. Walker	
40. Lawrence	45. Madison	50. Monroe	55. Pike	60. Sumter	65. Washington	

	1	2	3	4	5	6	7	8	9	10	11	12	13	14	15	16	17	18	19	20	21	22	23	24	25
CENTRARCHIDAE — SUNFISHES																									
Micropterus dolomieu, smallmouth bass																		●							●
M. punctulatus, spotted bass	●	●	●	●	●	●	●	●	●	●	●	●	●	●	●	●	●	●	●	●	●	●	●	●	
M. salmoides, largemouth bass	●	●	●	●	●	●	●	●	●	●	●	●	●	●	●	●	●	●	●	●	●	●	●	●	
M. species, "shoal bass" (ABE)[12]			●																						
Pomoxis annularis, white crappie	●	●		●	●			●					●			●	●	●			●	●	●	●	
P. nigromaculatus, black crappie	●	●	●	●	●		●	●	●	●	●	●	●			●	●	●		●	●	●	●	●	
PERCIDAE — PERCHES AND DARTERS																									
Ammocrypta beani, naked sand darter	●	●	●								●	●	●										●		
A. bifascia, Florida sand darter		●						●								●		●	●	●					
A. meridiana, southern sand darter (MBE)	●	●	●									●	●										●		
Crystallaria asprella, crystal darter	●	●	●									●	●										●		
Etheostoma bellator, Warrior darter (MBE)					●																				
E. blennioides, greenside darter																		●							
E. blennius, blenny darter (TDE)																									
E. boschungi, slackwater darter (TDE)																									
E. brevirostrum, holiday darter (MBE)								●						●											
E. caeruleum, rainbow darter																		●							
E. camurum, bluebreast darter																									
E. chermocki, vermilion darter (MBE)																									
E. chlorosomum, bluntnose darter							●					●	●											●	
E. chuckwachatte, lipstick darter (MBE)									●					●	●										
E. cinereum, ashy darter																									
E. colorosum, coastal darter		●	●			●	●									●		●		●	●		●		
E. coosae, Coosa darter (MBE)								●			●	●		●	●					●					●
E. corona, crown darter (TDE)																									
E. crossopterum, fringed darter																									
E. davisoni, Choctawhatchee darter			●			●	●									●	●		●		●		●		
E. ditrema, coldwater darter (MBE)								●		●											●				
E. douglasi, Tuskaloosa darter (MBE)					●																		●		
E. duryi, black darter (TDE)																	●								
E. edwini, brown darter		●	●			●										●		●		●		●			
E. etowahae, Etowah darter (MBE)	All sample stations occur in Georgia																								

	1	2	3	4	5	6	7	8	9	10	11	12	13	14	15	16	17	18	19	20	21	22	23	24	25

ABE—Apalachicola basin endemic   MBE—Mobile basin endemic   TDE—Tennessee drainage endemic

1. Autauga
2. Baldwin
3. Barbour
4. Bibb
5. Blount
6. Bullock
7. Butler
8. Calhoun
9. Chambers
10. Cherokee
11. Chilton
12. Choctaw
13. Clarke
14. Clay
15. Cleburne
16. Coffee
17. Colbert
18. Conecuh
19. Coosa
20. Covington
21. Crenshaw
22. Cullman
23. Dale
24. Dallas
25. Dekalb
26. Elmore
27. Escambia
28. Etowah
29. Fayette
30. Franklin
31. Geneva
32. Greene
33. Hale
34. Henry
35. Houston

26 27 28 29 30 31 32 33 34 35 36 37 38 39 40 41 42 43 44 45 46 47 48 49 50 51 52 53 54 55 56 57 58 59 60 61 62 63 64 65 66 67

36. Jackson	41. Lee	46. Marengo	51. Montgomery	56. Randolph	61. Talladega	66. Wilcox
37. Jefferson	42. Limestone	47. Marion	52. Morgan	57. Russell	62. Tallapoosa	67. Winston
38. Lamar	43. Lowndes	48. Marshall	53. Perry	58. St. Clair	63. Tuscaloosa	
39. Lauderdale	44. Macon	49. Mobile	54. Pickens	59. Shelby	64. Walker	
40. Lawrence	45. Madison	50. Monroe	55. Pike	60. Sumter	65. Washington	

PERCIDAE — PERCHES AND DARTERS	1	2	3	4	5	6	7	8	9	10	11	12	13	14	15	16	17	18	19	20	21	22	23	24	25
Etheostoma flabellare, fantail darter																									
E. fusiforme, swamp darter	●	●																●							
E. gracile, slough darter	All sample stations occur in Mississippi																								
E. histrio, harlequin darter				●							●	●								●				●	
E. jessiae, blueside darter (TDE)																									
E. jordani, greenbreast darter (MBE)				●				●		●	●			●	●				●						
E. kennicotti, stripetail darter																	●								
E. lachneri, Tombigbee darter (MBE)				●								●	●												
E. lynceum, brighteye darter																									
E. neopterum, lollipop darter (TDE)																									
E. nigripinne, blackfin darter (TDE)																	●								
E. nigrum, johnny darter				●		●					●	●					●						●		
E. nuchale, watercress darter (MBE)																									
E. parvipinne, goldstripe darter[13]	●		●	●						●	●	●				●	●	●		●	●				●
E. proeliare, cypress darter		●					●				●	●													●
E. ramseyi, Alabama darter (MBE)	●	●		●			●					●													●
E. rufilineatum, redline darter																	●								
E. rupestre, rock darter (MBE)	●			●	●		●					●	●	●					●						●
E. scotti, Cherokee darter (MBE)	All sample stations occur in Georgia																								
E. simoterum, snubnose darter																	●								
E. stigmaeum, speckled darter	●	●		●	●	●	●	●	●	●	●	●	●	●	●		●	●	●	●	●		●	●	
E. swaini, gulf darter	●	●	●	●		●	●				●	●	●			●		●							
E. tallapoosae, Tallapoosa darter (MBE)									●					●	●										
E. trisella, trispot darter (MBE)										●															
E. tuscumbia, Tuscumbia darter (TDE)																	●								
E. wapiti, boulder darter (TDE)																							●		●
E. whipplei, redfin darter	●			●	●		●					●	●	●											
E. zonale, banded darter																								●	
E. zonifer, backwater darter	●		●	●		●							●	●											
E. zonistium, bandfin darter[14]																	●								
Perca flavescens, yellow perch		●	●																						
Percina antesella, amber darter (MBE)	All sample stations occur in Georgia																								

| 1 | 2 | 3 | 4 | 5 | 6 | 7 | 8 | 9 | 10 | 11 | 12 | 13 | 14 | 15 | 16 | 17 | 18 | 19 | 20 | 21 | 22 | 23 | 24 | 25 |

ABE—Apalachicola basin endemic   MBE—Mobile basin endemic   TDE—Tennessee drainage endemic

1. Autauga	6. Bullock	11. Chilton	16. Coffee	21. Crenshaw	26. Elmore	31. Geneva
2. Baldwin	7. Butler	12. Choctaw	17. Colbert	22. Cullman	27. Escambia	32. Greene
3. Barbour	8. Calhoun	13. Clarke	18. Conecuh	23. Dale	28. Etowah	33. Hale
4. Bibb	9. Chambers	14. Clay	19. Coosa	24. Dallas	29. Fayette	34. Henry
5. Blount	10. Cherokee	15. Cleburne	20. Covington	25. Dekalb	30. Franklin	35. Houston

26 27 28 29 30 31 32 33 34 35 36 37 38 39 40 41 42 43 44 45 46 47 48 49 50 51 52 53 54 55 56 57 58 59 60 61 62 63 64 65 66 67

36. Jackson	41. Lee	46. Marengo	51. Montgomery	56. Randolph	61. Talladega	66. Wilcox
37. Jefferson	42. Limestone	47. Marion	52. Morgan	57. Russell	62. Tallapoosa	67. Winston
38. Lamar	43. Lowndes	48. Marshall	53. Perry	58. St. Clair	63. Tuscaloosa	
39. Lauderdale	44. Macon	49. Mobile	54. Pickens	59. Shelby	64. Walker	
40. Lawrence	45. Madison	50. Monroe	55. Pike	60. Sumter	65. Washington	

PERCIDAE — PERCHES AND DARTERS

Species	1	2	3	4	5	6	7	8	9	10	11	12	13	14	15	16	17	18	19	20	21	22	23	24	25
Percina aurolineata, goldline darter (MBE)				●																					
P. austroperca, southern logperch																				●	●				
P. brevicauda, coal darter (MBE)				●	●														●						
P. burtoni, blotchside logperch																									
P. caprodes, logperch																	●								
P. evides, gilt darter																									
P. jenkinsi, Conasauga logperch (MBE)	All sample stations occur in Georgia																								
P. lenticula, freckled darter				●						●															
P. maculata, blackside darter						●	●				●	●	●				●					●			
P. nigrofasciata, blackbanded darter[15]	●	●	●	●	●	●	●	●	●	●	●	●	●	●				●	●	●	●	●	●		
P. palmaris, bronze darter (MBE)								●	●	●	●			●											●
P. phoxocephala, slenderhead darter																									
P. sciera, dusky darter													●				●								
P. shumardi, river darter				●	●			●			●	●	●					●					●		
P. tanasi, snail darter (TDE)																									
P. vigil, saddleback darter	●	●		●							●	●						●		●			●		
P. species, "gulf logperch" (MBE)	●	●										●	●												
P. species, "Mobile logperch" (MBE)	●			●	●			●	●	●	●	●	●	●				●				●		●	●
P. species, "muscadine darter" (MBE)								●					●	●				●							
Stizostedion canadense, sauger																									
S. vitreum, walleye				●						●	●	●	●				●	●	●					●	

LUTJANIDAE — SNAPPERS

Species	1	2	3	4	5	6	7	8	9	10	11	12	13	14	15	16	17	18	19	20	21	22	23	24	25
Lutjanus griseus, gray snapper		●																							

GERREIDAE — MOJARRAS

Species	1	2	3	4	5	6	7	8	9	10	11	12	13	14	15	16	17	18	19	20	21	22	23	24	25
Eucinostomus argenteus, spotfin mojarra		●																							

SPARIDAE — PORGIES

Species	1	2	3	4	5	6	7	8	9	10	11	12	13	14	15	16	17	18	19	20	21	22	23	24	25
Archosargus probatocephalus, sheepshead		●																							
Lagodon rhomboides, pinfish		●																							

SCIAENIDAE — DRUMS

Species	1	2	3	4	5	6	7	8	9	10	11	12	13	14	15	16	17	18	19	20	21	22	23	24	25
Aplodinotus grunniens, freshwater drum	●	●		●						●	●	●	●					●		●				●	
Bairdiella chrysoura, silver perch																									
Cynoscion nebulosus, spotted seatrout		●																							

ABE—Apalachicola basin endemic   MBE—Mobile basin endemic   TDE—Tennessee drainage endemic

1. Autauga	6. Bullock	11. Chilton	16. Coffee	21. Crenshaw	26. Elmore	31. Geneva
2. Baldwin	7. Butler	12. Choctaw	17. Colbert	22. Cullman	27. Escambia	32. Greene
3. Barbour	8. Calhoun	13. Clarke	18. Conecuh	23. Dale	28. Etowah	33. Hale
4. Bibb	9. Chambers	14. Clay	19. Coosa	24. Dallas	29. Fayette	34. Henry
5. Blount	10. Cherokee	15. Cleburne	20. Covington	25. Dekalb	30. Franklin	35. Houston

26 27 28 29 30 31 32 33 34 35 36 37 38 39 40 41 42 43 44 45 46 47 48 49 50 51 52 53 54 55 56 57 58 59 60 61 62 63 64 65 66 67

26 27 28 29 30 31 32 33 34 35 36 37 38 39 40 41 42 43 44 45 46 47 48 49 50 51 52 53 54 55 56 57 58 59 60 61 62 63 64 65 66 67

36. Jackson	41. Lee	46. Marengo	51. Montgomery	56. Randolph	61. Talladega	66. Wilcox
37. Jefferson	42. Limestone	47. Marion	52. Morgan	57. Russell	62. Tallapoosa	67. Winston
38. Lamar	43. Lowndes	48. Marshall	53. Perry	58. St. Clair	63. Tuscaloosa	
39. Lauderdale	44. Macon	49. Mobile	54. Pickens	59. Shelby	64. Walker	
40. Lawrence	45. Madison	50. Monroe	55. Pike	60. Sumter	65. Washington	

	1	2	3	4	5	6	7	8	9	10	11	12	13	14	15	16	17	18	19	20	21	22	23	24	25
SCIAENIDAE DRUMS																									
Leiostomus xanthurus, spot		●																							
Micropogonias undulatus, Atlantic croaker		●																							
Pogonias cromis, black drum		●																							
Sciaenops ocellatus, red drum		●																							
CICHLIDAE CICHLIDS																									
Oreochromis aureus, blue tilapia																									
MUGILIDAE MULLETS																									
Mugil cephalus, striped mullet		●		●								●	●										●		
Mugil curema, silver mullet																									
ELEOTRIDAE SLEEPERS																									
Dormitator maculatus, fat sleeper		●																							
Eleotris pisonis, spinycheek sleeper		●																							
BOTHIDAE, LEFTEYE FLOUNDERS																									
Paralichthys lethostigma, southern flounder		●										●	●												
SOLEIDAE SOLES																									
Trinectes maculatus, hogchoker		●										●	●							●		●			
TOTAL SPECIES PER COUNTY	94	142	59	115	59	52	53	70	60	67	86	108	131	58	59	39	104	47	81	66	56	47	56	117	34

	1	2	3	4	5	6	7	8	9	10	11	12	13	14	15	16	17	18	19	20	21	22	23	24	25

ABE—Apalachicola basin endemic   MBE—Mobile basin endemic   TDE—Tennessee drainage endemic

1. Autauga	11. Chilton	21. Crenshaw	31. Geneva	41. Lee	51. Montgomery	61. Talladega
2. Baldwin	12. Choctaw	22. Cullman	32. Greene	42. Limestone	52. Morgan	62. Tallapoosa
3. Barbour	13. Clarke	23. Dale	33. Hale	43. Lowndes	53. Perry	63. Tuscaloosa
4. Bibb	14. Clay	24. Dallas	34. Henry	44. Macon	54. Pickens	64. Walker
5. Blount	15. Cleburne	25. Dekalb	35. Houston	45. Madison	55. Pike	65. Washington
6. Bullock	16. Coffee	26. Elmore	36. Jackson	46. Marengo	56. Randolph	66. Wilcox
7. Butler	17. Colbert	27. Escambia	37. Jefferson	47. Marion	57. Russell	67. Winston
8. Calhoun	18. Conecuh	28. Etowah	38. Lamar	48. Marshall	58. St. Clair	
9. Chambers	19. Coosa	29. Fayette	39. Lauderdale	49. Mobile	59. Shelby	
10. Cherokee	20. Covington	30. Franklin	40. Lawrence	50. Monroe	60. Sumter	

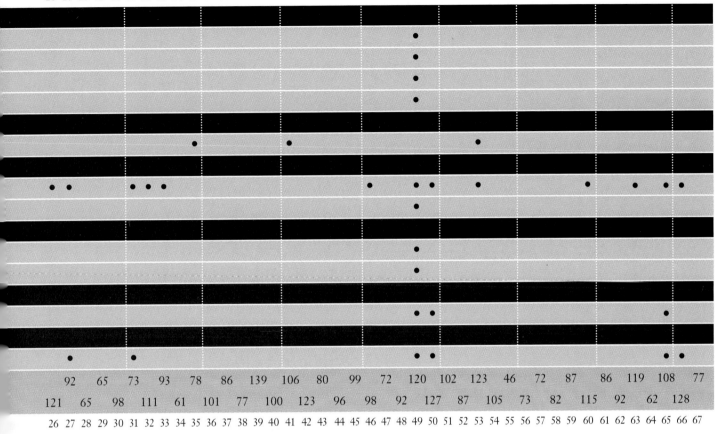

26 27 28 29 30 31 32 33 34 35 36 37 38 39 40 41 42 43 44 45 46 47 48 49 50 51 52 53 54 55 56 57 58 59 60 61 62 63 64 65 66 67

92 65 73 93 78 86 139 106 80 99 72 120 102 123 46 72 87 86 119 108 77
121 65 98 111 61 101 77 100 123 96 98 92 127 87 105 73 82 115 92 62 128

26 27 28 29 30 31 32 33 34 35 36 37 38 39 40 41 42 43 44 45 46 47 48 49 50 51 52 53 54 55 56 57 58 59 60 61 62 63 64 65 66 67

NOTES

1. Clear chub populations inhabiting coastal drainages east of the Mobile basin are a new species (Clemmer, 1979).

2. One, possibly two, new species of speckled chubs have been recognized in the Mobile basin.

3. Speckled chubs in the Choctawhatchee and Escambia Bay drainages have been recognized as a new species (Gilbert, 1992).

4. One, possibly two, new species of mimic shiners have been recognized in the Mobile basin.

5. The "sawfin shiner" will soon be described as a new species.

6. Quillback carpsuckers in the Choctawhatchee, Conecuh, and Chattahoochee river drainages are a new species.

7. Highfin carpsuckers in the Choctawhatchee and Conecuh river drainages are a new species.

8. Blue suckers in the Mobile basin have been recognized as a new species.

9. The "grayfin redhorse" in the Chattahoochee River drainage is a new species (Jenkins, 1970)

10. Based on our comparisons of color patterns and distributional data provided in Page and Burr (1991), stonecats in Shoal Creek and the Elk River may represent a new species.

11. Angus and Howell (1996) delinated the ranges of two species of mosquitofishes in Alabama. *Gambusia affinis* occurs in the Tennessee River drainage and the northern two-thirds of the Mobile basin; *G. holbrooki* occurs in coastal drainages lying east of the Mobile basin. Intergrades of both species occur in the lower reaches of the Alabama and lower Tombigbee drainages, the Mobile Delta and Mobile Bay tributaries, and the Perdido River drainage.

12. The "shoal bass" in the Chattahoochee River drainage is a new species (Gilbert, 1992).

13. Goldstripe darters in Doe Branch (Black Warrior River system) are a new species.

14. Populations of the bandfin darter from upper tributaries of Bear Creek (Tennessee River drainage) and Hubbard Creek (Black Warrior River system) may represent a new species.

15. Blackbanded darters in Uchee Creek (Chattahoochee River drainage) have been recognized as a distinct new species and may be more closely related to the bronze darter.

LITERATURE CITED

Abbott, C. C. 1860. Descriptions of new species of American fresh-water fishes. Proceedings of the Academy of Natural Sciences of Philadelphia 12: 325–328.

Agassiz, L. 1850. Lake Superior: Its physical character, vegetation and animals, compared with those of other and similar regions . . . with a narrative of the tour by J. Elliot Cabot and contributions by other scientific gentlemen. Gould, Kendall, and Lincoln, Boston. 428 p.

———. 1854. Notice of a collection of fishes from the southern bend of the Tennessee River, in the State of Alabama. American Journal of Science and Arts, 2nd Series, 17: 297–308, 353–369.

———. 1855. Synopsis of the ichthyological fauna of the Pacific Slope of North America, chiefly from collections made by the expedition under the command of Capt. C. Wilkes, with recent additions and comparisons with eastern types. American Journal of Science and Arts, 2nd Series, 19: 71–99, 215–231.

Angus, R. A., and W. M. Howell. 1996. Geographical distributions of eastern and western mosquitofishes (Poeciliidae: *Gambusia*). Delineation of ranges using fin ray contents. Southeastern Fishes Council Proceedings. 33: 1-6.

Applegate, R. L., J. W. Mullan, and D. I. Morais. 1967. Food and growth of six centrarchids from shoreline areas of Bull Shoals Reservoir. Proceedings of the 20th Annual Conference of Southeastern Game and Fish Commissioners. 469–482.

Arndt, R. G. E. 1971. Ecology and behavior of the cyprinodont fishes *Adinia xenica*, *Lucania parva*, *Lucania goodei* and *Leptolucania ommata*. Ph.D. Dissertation. Cornell University, Ithaca. 364 p.

Axelrod, H. R., and L. P. Schultz. 1971. Handbook of tropical aquarium fishes. T.F.H. Publications, Jersey City. 718 p.

Bailey, R. M. 1938. A systematic revision of the centrarchid fishes with a discussion of their distribution, variation, and probable interrelationships. Ph.D. Dissertation. University of Michigan, Ann Arbor. 256 p.

———. 1940. *Hadropterus palmaris*, a new darter from the Alabama River system. Journal of the Washington Academy of Science 30: 524–530.

Bailey, R. M., and F. B. Cross. 1954. River sturgeons of the American genus *Scaphirhynchus*: characters, distribution, and synonymy. Papers of the Michigan Academy of Science 39: 169–208.

Bailey, R. M., and D. A. Etnier. 1988. Comments on the subgenera of darters (Percidae) with descriptions of two new species of *Etheostoma* (*Ulocentra*) from the southeastern United States. Miscellaneous Publications of the University of Michigan Museum of Zoology 175. 48 p.

Bailey, R. M., and R. H. Gibbs, Jr. 1956. *Notropis callitaenia*, a new cyprinid fish from Alabama, Florida, and Georgia. Occasional Papers of the University of Michigan Museum of Zoology 576. 14 p.

Bailey, R. M., and W. A. Gosline. 1955. Variation and systematic significance of vertebral counts in the American fishes of the family Percidae. Miscellaneous Publications of the University of Michigan Museum of Zoology 93. 44 p.

Bailey, R. M., and W. J. Richards. 1963. Status of *Poecilichthys hopkinsi* Fowler and *Etheostoma trisella*, new species, percid fishes from Alabama, Georgia, and South Carolina. Occasional Papers of the University of Michigan Museum of Zoology 630. 21 p.

Bailey, R. M., and R. D. Suttkus. 1952. *Notropis signipinnis*, a new cyprinid fish from southeastern United States. Occasional Papers of the University of Michigan Museum of Zoology 542. 14 p.

Bailey, R. M., H. E. Winn, and C. L. Smith. 1954. Fishes from the Escambia River, Alabama and Florida, with ecologic and taxonomic notes. Proceedings of the

Academy of Natural Sciences of Philadelphia 106: 109–164.

Baird, S. F. 1855. Report on the fishes observed on the coasts of New Jersey and Long Island during the summer of 1854. Ninth Annual Report (1854), Smithsonian Institution. 317–352.

Baird, S. F., and C. Girard. 1853a. Description of new species of fishes, collected by Captains R. B. Marcy, and Geo. B. McClellan, in Arkansas. Proceedings of the Academy of Natural Sciences of Philadelphia 6: 390–392.

———. 1853b. Description of new species of fishes collected by Mr. John C. Clark, on the U.S. and Mexican Boundary Survey, under Lt. Col. Jas. D. Graham. Proceedings of the Academy of Natural Sciences of Philadelphia 6: 387–390.

Barney, R. L., and B. J. Anson. 1922. Life history and ecology of the orange-spotted sunfish, *Lepomis humilis*. Report of the U.S. Fish Commission, Document 938. 16 p.

Bart, H. L., Jr., and L. M. Page. 1991. Morphology and adaptive significance of fin knobs in egg-clustering darters. Copeia 1991: 80–86.

Bass, D. G., and V. G. Hitt. 1974. Ecological aspects of the redbreast sunfish, *Lepomis auritus*, in Florida. Proceedings of the 28th Annual Conference of Southeastern Game and Fish Commissioners. 296–307.

Bauer, B. H., D. A. Etnier, and N. M. Burkhead. 1995. *Etheostoma* (*Ulocentra*) *scotti* (Osteichthys: Percidae), a new darter from the Etowah River system in Georgia. Bulletin of the Alabama Museum of Natural History 17: 1–16.

Beamish, F. W., and L. S. Austin. 1985. Growth of the mountain brook lamprey *Ichthyomyzon greeleyi* Hubbs and Trautman. Copeia 1985: 881–890.

Becker, G. C. 1983. Fishes of Wisconsin. University of Wisconsin Press, Madison. 1,052 p.

Beckham, E. C., III. 1973. A study of the fishes of the Escatawpa River in Alabama and Mississippi. M.S. Thesis. University of Alabama, Tuscaloosa. 73 p.

———. 1980. *Percina gymnocephala*, a new percid fish of the subgenus *Alvordius*, from the New River in North Carolina, Virginia, and West Virginia. Occasional Papers of the Museum of Zoology, Louisiana State University 57. 11 p.

Bell, D., and T. J. Timmons. 1991. Life history of the bright-eye darter *Etheostoma lynceum* (Pisces: Percidae), in Terrapin Creek, Kentucky. Southeastern Fishes Council Proceedings 23: 1–6.

Berra, T. M. 1981. An atlas of distribution of the freshwater fish families of the world. University of Nebraska Press, Lincoln. 197 p.

Berra, T. M., and G. E. Gunning. 1972. Seasonal movement and home range of the longear sunfish, *Lepomis megalotis* (Rafinesque) in Louisiana. American Midland Naturalist 88: 368–375.

Birdsong, R. S., and R. W. Yerger. 1967. A natural population of *Lepomis macrochirus* x *Chaenobryttus gulosus*. Copeia 1967: 62–71.

Black, A., and W. M. Howell. 1978. A distinctive chromosomal race of the cyprinodontid fish, *Fundulus notatus*, from the upper Tombigbee River system of Alabama and Mississippi. Copeia 1978: 280–288.

———. 1979. The North American mosquitofish, *Gambusia affinis*: a unique case in sex chromosome evolution. Copeia 1979: 509–513.

Bloch, M. E., and J. M. Schneider. 1801. M. E. Bloch . . . Systema Ichthyologiae iconibus ex illustratum. Berolini. 584 p.

Bollman, C. H. 1887. Notes on a collection of fishes from the Escambia River, with description of a new species of *Zygonectes* (*Zygonectes escambiae*). Proceedings of the U.S. National Museum 9(585): 402–465.

Boschung, H. T. 1957. The fishes of Mobile Bay and the Gulf Coast of Alabama. Ph.D. Dissertation. University of Alabama, Tuscaloosa. 626 p.

———. 1992. Catalog of freshwater and marine fishes of Alabama. Bulletin of the Alabama Museum of Natural History 14. 266 p.

Boschung, H. T., R. L. Mayden, and J. R. Tomelleri. 1992. *Etheostoma chermocki*, a new species of darter (Teleostei: Percidae) from the Black Warrior River drainage of Alabama. Bulletin of the Alabama Museum of Natural History 13: 11–20.

Boulinger, G. A. 1895. A catalogue of the fishes of the British Museum. Order of Trustees, London. 349 p.

Bowman, M. L. 1970. Life history of the black redhorse, *Moxostoma duquesnei* (Lesueur), in Missouri. Transactions of the American Fisheries Society 99: 546–559.

Braasch, M. E., and R. L. Mayden. 1985. Review of the subgenus *Catonotus* (Percidae) with descriptions of two new darters of the *Etheostoma squamiceps* species group. Occasional Papers of the University of Kansas Museum of Natural History 119. 83 p.

Braasch, M. E., and P. W. Smith. 1965. Relationships of the topminnows *Fundulus notatus* and *Fundulus olivaceus* in the upper Mississippi River Valley. Copeia 1965: 46–53.

———. 1967. The life history of the slough darter, *Etheostoma gracile* (Pisces, Percidae). Illinois Natural History Survey Biological Notes 58. 12 p.

Branson, B. A., and G. A. Moore. 1962. The lateralis components of the acoustico-lateralis system in the family Centrarchidae. Copeia 1962: 1–108.

Brayton, S. L. 1981. Reproductive biology, energy content of tissues, and annual production of rainbow trout (*Salmo gairdneri*) in the South Fork of the Holston River, Virginia. M.S. Thesis. Virginia Polytechnic Institute and State University, Blacksburg.

Breder, C. M., and A. C. Redmond. 1929. The blue-spotted sunfish: a contribution to the life history and habits of *Enneacanthus* with notes on other Lepominae. Zoologica (New York) 9: 379–401.

Breder, C. M., and D. E. Rosen. 1966. Modes of reproduction in fishes. Natural History Press, New York. 941 p.

Bresnick, G. I., and D. C. Heins. 1977. The age and growth of the weed shiner, *Notropis texanus* (Girard). American Midland Naturalist 98: 495–499.

Brown, J. L. 1957. A key to the species and subspecies of the cyprinodont genus *Fundulus* in the United States and Canada east of the Continental Divide. Journal of the Washington Academy of Science 47: 69–77.

Bryant, R. T. 1979. The life history and comparative ecology of the sharphead darter, *Etheostoma acuticeps*. Tennessee Wildlife Resources Agency Report 79-50: 60 p.

Burgess, G. H., and C. R. Gilbert. 1978. *Amia calva* Linnaeus. p. 53 in D. S. Lee et al., Atlas of North American freshwater fishes. North Carolina State Museum of Natural History Publication 1980-12.

Burke, J. S., and J. S. Ramsey. 1985. Status survey of the Alabama shovelnose sturgeon (*Scaphirhynchus* sp. cf. *platorynchus*) in the Mobile Bay drainage. Unpublished report. U.S. Fish and Wildlife Service, Jackson, Mississippi. 61 p.

———. 1995. Present and recent historic habitat of the Alabama sturgeon, *Scaphirhynchus suttkusi* Williams and Clemmer, in the Mobile basin. Bulletin of the Alabama Museum of Natural History 17: 17–24.

Burkhead, N. M., R. E. Jenkins, and E. G. Maurakis. 1980. New records, distribution and diagnostic characters of Virginia ictalurid catfishes with an adnexed adipose fin. Brimleyana 4: 75–93.

Burr, B. M. 1978. Systematics of the percid fishes of the subgenus *Microperca*, genus *Etheostoma*. Bulletin of the Alabama Museum of Natural History 4: 53 p.

———. 1979a. Observations on spawning and breeding coloration of *Moxostoma lachneri* in the Chattahoochee River, Georgia. Georgia Journal of Science 37: 205–207.

———. 1979b. Systematics and life history aspects of the percid fish *Etheostoma blennius* with description of a new subspecies from the Sequatchie River, Tennessee. Copeia 197: 191–203.

Burr, B. M., and R. C. Cashner. 1983. *Campostoma pauciradii*, a new cyprinid fish from southeastern United States, with a review of related forms. Copeia 1983: 101–116.

Burr, B. M., and W. W. Dimmick. 1981. Nests, eggs, and larvae of the elegant madtom *Noturus elegans* from the Barren River drainage, Kentucky (Pisces, Ictaluridae). Transactions of the Kentucky Academy of Science 42: 116–118.

Burr, B. M., and R. L. Mayden. 1982a. Status of the cypress minnow, *Hybognathus hayi* Jordan, in Illinois. Chicago Academy of Science Natural History Miscellanea 215: 1–10.

———. 1982b. Life history of the brindled madtom *Noturus miurus* in Mill Creek, Illinois (Pisces, Ictaluridae). American Midland Naturalist 107: 25–41.

———. 1982c. Life history of the freckled madtom, *Noturus nocturnus*, in Mill Creek, Illinois (Pisces, Ictaluridae). Occasional Papers of the University of Kansas Museum of Natural History 98. 15 p.

Burr, B. M., and M. A. Morris. 1977. Spawning behavior of the shorthead redhorse, *Moxostoma macrolepidotum*, in Big Rock Creek, Illinois. Transactions of the American Fisheries Society 106: 80–82.

Burr, B. M., and L. M. Page. 1978. The life history of the cypress darter, *Etheostoma proeliare*, in Max Creek, Illinois. Illinois Natural History Survey Biological Notes 106. 15 p.

Burr, B. M., and M. L. Warren, Jr. 1986. A distributional

atlas of Kentucky fishes. Kentucky Natural Preserves Commission Scientific and Technical Series 4. 398 p.

Campbell, R. D., and B. A. Branson. 1978. Ecology and population dynamics of the black bullhead, *Ictalurus melas* (Rafinesque), in central Kentucky. Tulane Studies in Zoology and Botany 20: 99–136.

Carlander, K. D. 1969. Handbook of freshwater fishery biology, vol. 1. Iowa State University Press, Ames. 752 p.

———. 1977. Handbook of freshwater fishery biology, vol. 2. Iowa State University Press, Ames. 431 p.

Carney, D. A., and B. M. Burr. 1989. Life histories of the bandfin darter, *Etheostoma zonistium*, and the firebelly darter, *Etheostoma pyrrhogaster*, in western Kentucky. Illinois Natural History Survey Biological Notes 134: 1–16.

Cashner, R. C. 1979. *Ambloplites ariommus* Viosca. p. 578 in D. S. Lee et al., Atlas of North American freshwater fishes. North Carolina State Museum of Natural History Publication 1980-12.

Cashner, R. C., J. S. Rogers, and J. M. Grady. 1988. *Fundulus bifax*, a new species of the subgenus *Xenisma* from the Tallapoosa and Coosa river systems of Alabama and Georgia. Copeia 1988: 674–683.

———. 1992. Phylogenetic studies of the genus *Fundulus*. p. 421–437 in R. L. Mayden, editor, Systematics, historical ecology, and North American freshwater fishes. Stanford University Press. 969 p.

Cashner, R. C., and R. D. Suttkus. 1977. *Ambloplites constellatus*, a new species of rock bass from the Ozark Upland of Arkansas and Missouri with a review of western rock bass populations. American Midland Naturalist 98: 147–161.

Cavender, T. M., and M. M. Coburn. 1992. Phylogenetic relationships of North American Cyprinidae. p. 293–327 in R. L. Mayden, editor, Systematics, historical ecology, and North American freshwater fishes. Stanford University Press. 969 p.

Childers, W. F. 1967. Hybridization of four species of sunfishes (Centrarchidae). Illinois Natural History Survey Bulletin 29: 159–214.

Clemmer, G. H. 1971. The systematics and biology of the *Hybopsis amblops* complex. Ph.D. Dissertation. Tulane University, New Orleans. 155 p.

———. 1980. *Hybopsis winchelli* (Girard). p. 195 in D. S. Lee et al., Atlas of North American freshwater fishes. North Carolina State Museum of Natural History Publication 1980-12.

Clemmer, G. H., and R. D. Suttkus. 1971. *Hybopsis lineapunctata*, a new cyprinid fish from the upper Alabama River system. Tulane Studies in Zoology and Botany 17: 21–30.

Cole, C. F. 1967. A study of the eastern johnny darter, *Etheostoma olmstedi* Storer (Teleostei, Percidae). Chesapeake Science 8: 28–51.

Collette, B. B. 1962. The swamp darters of the subgenus *Hololepis* (Pisces, Percidae). Tulane Studies in Zoology 9: 115–211.

Collette, B. B., and P. Banarescu. 1977. Systematics and zoogeography of the fishes of the family Percidae. Journal of the Fisheries Research Board of Canada 34: 1,450–1,463.

Collette, B. B., and R. W. Yerger. 1962. The American percid fishes of the subgenus *Villora*. Tulane Studies in Zoology 9: 213–230.

Cook, F. A. 1959. Freshwater fishes in Mississippi. Mississippi Game and Fish Commission, Jackson. 239 p.

Cooper, J. E. 1990. Alabama cavefish, *Speoplatyrhinus poulsoni* Cooper and Kuehne 1974, (Second revision) recovery plan. U.S. Fish and Wildlife Service, Jackson, Mississippi. 17 p.

Cooper, J. E., and R. A. Kuehne. 1974. *Speoplatyrhinus poulsoni*, a new genus and species of subterranean fish from Alabama. Copeia 1974: 486–493.

Cope, E. D. 1865a. Partial catalogue of the cold-blooded vertebrata of Michigan, pt. 1. Proceedings of the Academy of Natural Sciences of Philadelphia 16: 276–285.

———. 1865b. Partial catalogue of the cold-blooded vertebrata of Michigan, pt. 2. Proceedings of the Academy of Natural Sciences of Philadelphia 17: 78–88.

———. 1867. [Description of a new genus of Cyprinoid fish from Virginia]. Proceedings of the Academy of Natural Sciences of Philadelphia 19: 95–97.

———. 1868a. On the genera of fresh-water fishes *Hypsilepis* Baird and *Photogenis* Cope, their species and distribution. Proceedings of the Academy of Natural Sciences of Philadelphia 19: 156–166.

———. 1868b. On the distribution of fresh-water fishes in the Allegheny region of southwestern Virginia. Journal of the Academy of Natural Sciences of Philadelphia, Series 2, 6, pt. 3, article 5: 207–247.

———. 1869a. Synopsis of the Cyprinidae of Pennsylvania.

Transactions of the American Philosophical Society, New Series 13, article 13: 351–399.

———. 1869b. Supplement: On some species of American and African fishes. Transactions of the American Philosophical Society, 13(13): 400–407.

———. 1870a. On some etheostomine perch from Tennessee and North Carolina. Proceedings of the American Philosophical Society 11: 261-270.

———. 1870b. A partial synopsis of the fishes of the fresh waters of North Carolina. Proceedings of the American Philosophical Society 11: 448-495.

Cordes, L. E., and L. M. Page. 1980. Feeding chronology and diet composition of two darters (Percidae) in the Iroquois River system, Illinois. American Midland Naturalist 104: 202–206.

Cowell, B. C., and B. S. Barnett. 1974. Life history of the taillight shiner, *Notropis maculatus*, in central Florida. American Midland Naturalist 91: 282–293.

Cross, F. B. 1967. Handbook of fishes of Kansas. Miscellaneous Publications of the Kansas Museum of Natural History 45. 357 p.

Crossman, E. J. 1966. A taxonomic study of *Esox americanus* and its subspecies in eastern North America. Copeia 1966: 1–20.

Crossmann, E. J. 1978. Taxonomy and distribution of North American Esocids. American Fisheries Society Special Publication 11: 13–26.

Cuvier, G., and A. Valenciennes. 1829. Histoire Naturelle des Poissons. Vol 3. Paris. 500 p.

———. 1830. Histoire Naturelle des Poissons. Vol. 5. Paris. 499 p.

———. 1836. Histoire Naturelle des Poissons. Vol 9. Paris.

———. 1840. Histoire Naturelle des Poissons. Vol.15. Paris. 540 p.

———. 1844. Histoire Naturelle des Poissons. Vol.17 Paris. 497 p.

———. 1848. Histoire Naturelle des Poissons. Vol. 21 Paris. 536 p.

Davis, J. R. 1972. The spawning behavior, fecundity rates, and food habits of the redbreast sunfish in southeastern North Carolina. Proceedings of the 25th Annual Conference of Southeastern Game and Fish Commissioners. 556–560.

Davis, J. R., and D. E. Louder. 1971. Life history and ecology of the cyprinid fish *Notropis petersoni* in North Carolina waters. Transactions of the American Fisheries Society 100: 726–733.

DeKay, J. E. 1842. Natural History of New York. Vol. 1: Zoology, pt IV: Fishes. New York, Albany, W. A. White and J. Visscher. 415 p.

DeMont, D. J. 1982. Use of *Lepomis macrochirus* Rafinesque nests by spawning *Notemigonus crysoleucas* (Mitchill) (Pisces: Centrarchidae and Cyprinidae). Brimleyana 8: 61–63.

Dendy, J. C., and D. C. Scott. 1953. Distribution, life history, and morphological variations of the southern brook lamprey, *Ichthyomyzon gagei*. Copeia 1953: 152–162.

Denoncourt, R. F. 1976. Sexual dimorphism and geographic variation in the bronze darter, *Percina palmaris* (Pisces: Percidae). Copeia 1976: 54–59.

Dobson, T. L. 1994. An ichthyofaunal survey of the Little River drainage in Alabama with notes on *Cyprinella caerulea* (Jordan). M.S. Thesis. Jacksonville State University, Jacksonville. 165 p.

Douglas, N. H. 1968. A new record size for darters. Proceedings of the Louisiana Academy of Science 31: 41–42.

Douglas, N. H. 1974. Freshwater fishes of Louisiana. Claitor's Publishing Division, Baton Rouge. 443 p.

Dovel, W. L., J. A. Mihursky, and A. J. McErlean. 1969. Life history aspects of the hogchoker, *Trinectes maculatus*, in the Patuxent River estuary, Maryland. Chesapeake Science 10: 104–119.

Duckett, C. R. 1972. The freshwater fishes of the Mulberry Fork of the Black Warrior River in Alabama. M.S. Thesis. Samford University, Birmingham. 80 p.

Eaton, T. H. 1953. Pygmy sunfishes and the meaning of pygmism. Journal of the Elisha Mitchell Scientific Society 69: 98–99.

Eaton, T. H. 1956. Notes on the olfactory organs in Centrarchidae. Copeia 1956: 196–199.

Eigenmann, C. H. 1877. Notes on the specific names of certain North American fishes. Proceedings of the Academy of Natural Sciences of Philadelphia 39: 295–296.

Etnier, D. A. 1976. *Percina (Imostoma) tanasi*, a new percid fish from the Little Tennessee River, Tennessee. Proceedings of the Biological Society of Washington 88: 469–488.

Etnier, D. A., and W. C. Starnes. 1986. *Etheostoma lynceum* removed from the synonymy of *E. zonale* (Pisces,

Percidae). Copeia 1986: 832–836.

———. 1993. The fishes of Tennessee. University of Tennessee Press, Knoxville. 681 p.

Etnier, D. A., W. C. Starnes, and B. H. Bauer. 1979. Whatever happened to the silvery minnow (*Hybognathus nuchalis*) in the Tennessee River? Southeastern Fishes Council Proceedings 2: 1–3.

Etnier, D. A., and J. D. Williams. 1989. *Etheostoma (Nothonotus) wapiti* (Osteichthys: Percidae), a new darter from the southern bend of the Tennessee River system in Alabama and Tennessee. Proceedings of the Biological Society of Washington 102: 987–1,000.

Evermann, B. W. 1892. A report upon investigations made in Texas in 1891. Bulletin of the U.S. Fish Commission (1891) 11: 61–90.

———. 1896. Description of a new species of shad (*Alosa alabamae*) from Alabama. Report of the U.S. Fish Commission (1895) 21: 203–205.

Evermann, B. W., and W. C. Kendall. 1898. Descriptions of new or little-known genera and species of fishes from the United States. Bulletin of the U.S. Fish Commission (1897) 17: 125–133.

Fahy, W. E. 1954. The life history of the northern greenside darter, *Etheostoma blennioides blennioides* Rafinesque. Journal of the Elisha Mitchell Scientific Society 70: 139–205.

Feeman, J. C. 1987. Results of fish surveys in the Tennessee River drainage, 1979–1981. Brimleyana 13: 99–121.

Fenneman, N. M. 1938. Physiography of eastern United States. McGraw-Hill, New York. 714 p.

Ferguson, M. T. 1989. Crevice spawning behavior of *Cyprinella trichroistia*, *C. gibbsi*, and *C. callistia*. Association of Southeastern Biologists Bulletin 36: 66 (abstract).

Fingerman, S. W., and R. D. Suttkus. 1961. Comparison of *Hybognathus hayi* Jordan and *Hybognathus nuchalis* Agassiz. Copeia 1961: 462–467.

Fiorino, K. L. 1991. Systematics of the *Lythrurus ardens* species complex (Cyprinidae), with recognition of phylogenetic species. M.S. Thesis. Southern Illinois University, Carbondale. 63 p.

Fisher, J. W. 1981. Ecology of *Fundulus catenatus* in three interconnected stream orders. American Midland Naturalist 106: 372–378.

Forbes, S. A. 1903. On the food of young fishes, 2nd edition.

Reprint and emendment of the Bulletin of the Illinois State Laboratory of Natural History 1(3): 71–85.

Forbes, S. A., and R. E. Richardson. 1920. The fishes of Illinois, 2nd edition. Illinois Natural History Survey, Urbana. 357 p.

Fowler, H. W. 1941. A collection of freshwater fishes obtained in Florida, 1939–1940, by Francis Harper. Proceedings of the Academy of Natural Sciences of Philadelphia 92: 227–244.

———. 1942. Descriptions of six new fresh-water fishes (Cyprinidae and Percidae) from the southeastern United States. Notulae Naturae of the Academy of Natural Sciences of Philadelphia 107: 11 p.

———. 1945. A study of the fishes of the southern Piedmont and Coastal Plain. Philadelphia Academy of Natural Sciences Monograph 7. 408 p.

Frazer, K. S., H. T. Boschung, and R. L. Mayden. 1989. Diet of juvenile bowfin, *Amia calva* Linnaeus, in the Sipsey River, Alabama. Southeastern Fishes Council Proceedings 20: 13–15.

Freeman, B. J. 1983. Final report on the status of *Etheostoma trisella*, the trispot darter, and *Percina antesella*, the amber darter, in the upper Coosa River system in AL, GA, TN. Unpublished report. U.S. Fish and Wildlife Service, Jackson, Mississippi. 77 p.

Gale, W. F. 1986. Indeterminate fecundity and spawning behavior of captive red shiners—fractional, crevice spawners. Transactions of the American Fisheries Society 115: 429–437.

Gale, W. F., and C. A. Gale. 1977. Spawning habits of spotfin shiner (*Notropis spilopterus*)—a fractional crevice spawner. Transactions of the American Fisheries Society 106: 170–177.

Gerald, J. W. 1971. Sound production during courtship in six species of sunfish (Centrarchidae). Evolution 25: 75–87.

Gibbs, R. H. 1957. Cyprinid fishes of the subgenus *Cyprinella* of *Notropis*. Pt. 3. Variation and subspecies of *Notropis venustus* (Girard). Tulane Studies in Zoology 5: 175–203.

Gilbert, C. H. 1884. A list of fishes collected in the East Fork of White River, Indiana, with descriptions of two new species. Proceedings of the U.S. National Museum 7(423): 199–205.

———. 1887. Descriptions of new and little known

etheostomids. Proceedings of the U.S. National Museum 10(607): 47–64.

———. 1891. Notes on explorations made in Alabama in 1889, with notes on the fishes of the Tennessee, Alabama, and Escambia Rivers. Bulletin of the U.S. Fish Commission (1889) 9: 143–159.

Gilbert, C. R. 1964. The American cyprinid fishes of the subgenus *Luxilus* (genus *Notropis*). Bulletin of the Florida State Museum Biological Sciences 8: 95–194.

———. 1992. Atlantic sturgeon *Acipenser oxyrinchus*. p. 31–39 in C. R. Gilbert, editor, Rare and endangered biota of Florida. University Press of Florida, Gainesville. 247 p.

———,. editor. 1992. Rare and endangered biota of Florida. University Press of Florida, Gainesville. 247 p.

Gilbert, C. R., and R. M. Bailey. 1972. Systematics and zoogeography of the American cyprinid fish *Notropis* (*Opsopoeodus*) *emiliae*. Occasional Papers of the University of Michigan Museum of Zoology 664. 35 p.

Gilbert, C. R., R. C. Cashner, and E. O. Wiley. 1992. Taxonomic and nomenclatural status of the banded topminnow, *Fundulus cingulatus* (Cyprinodontiformes: Cyprinodontidae). Copeia 1992: 747–759.

Gilbert, C. R., and F. F. Snelson. 1992. Grayfin redhorse *Moxostoma*. sp. cf. *poecilurum*. p. 45–48 in C. R. Gilbert, editor, Rare and endangered biota of Florida. University Press of Florida. 247 p.

Gilbert, R. J. 1973. Systematics of *Micropterus p. punctulatus* and *M. p. henshalli* and life history of *M. p. henshalli*. Ph.D. Dissertation. Auburn University, Auburn. 146 p.

Gill, T. N. 1861. Observations on the genus *Cottus*, and descriptions of two new species. Proceedings of the Boston Society of Natural History 8: 40–42.

Gilliams, J. 1824. Description of a new species of fish of the Linnean genus *Perca*. Journal of the Academy of Natural Sciences of Philadelphia 4(1): 80–82.

Girard, C. F. 1850. A monograph of the fresh water *Cottus* of North America. Proceedings of the American Association for the Advancement of Science (1849) 2: 409–411.

———. 1854. Descriptions of some new species of fish from the state of Massachusetts [*Pomotis obesus, Boleosoma fusiformis*, and *Esox ornatus*]. Proceedings of the Boston Society of Natural History 5: 40–41.

———. 1856. Researches upon the cyprinoid fishes inhabiting the fresh waters of the United States, west of the Mississippi Valley, from specimens in the museum of the Smithsonian Institution. Proceedings of the Academy of Natural Sciences of Philadelphia 8: 165–213.

———. 1858a. Part IV, Fishes, in General report upon the zoology of the several Pacific railroad routes. U.S. House of Representatives 10, Washington, D.C. 400 p.

———. 1858b. Notice upon new genera and new species of marine and fresh-water fishes from western North America. Proceedings of the Academy of Natural Sciences of Philadelphia 9: 200–202.

———. 1859. Ichthyological notices. Proceedings of the Academy of Natural Sciences of Philadelphia 11: 56–68, 100–104, 157–161.

Glodek, G. S. 1979a. *Ictalurus catus* (Linnaeus). p. 438 in D. S. Lee et al., Atlas of North American freshwater fishes. North Carolina State Museum of Natural History Publication 1980-12.

Glodek, G. S. 1979b. *Ictalurus nebulosus* (Lesueur). p. 443 in D. S. Lee et al., Atlas of North American freshwater fishes. North Carolina State Museum of Natural History Publication 1980-12.

Glodek, G. S. 1979c. *Ictalurus furcatus* (Lesueur). p. 439, in D. S. Lee et al., Atlas of North American freshwater fishes. North Carolina State Museum of Natural History Publication 1980-12.

Gmelin, J. F., editor. 1788. Systema Naturae, 13th edition. Lipsiae, vol. 1, pt. 3, pp. 1,126–1,516. Total work is 3 vols., 9 parts.

Goode, G. B. 1878. A revision of the American species of the genus *Brevoortia*, with a description of a new species from the Gulf of Mexico. Proceedings of the U.S. National Museum 1(15): 30–42.

Grady, J. M., and W. H. LeGrande. 1992. Phylogenetic relationships, modes of speciation, and historical biogeography of the madtom catfishes, genus *Noturus* Rafinesque (Siluriformes: Ictaluridae). p. 747–777 in R. L. Mayden, editor, Systematics, historical ecology, and North American freshwater fishes. Stanford University Press. 969 p.

Greenwood, P. H., D. E. Rosen, S. H. Weitzman, and G. S. Meyers. 1966. Phyletic studies of teleostean fishes, with a provisional classification of living forms. Bulletin of the American Museum of Natural History 131:

341–355.

Guillory, V. 1978. *Ctenopharyngodon idella* Valenciennes. p. 151 in D. S. Lee et al., Atlas of North American freshwater fishes. North Carolina State Museum of Natural History Publication 1980-12.

Gunning, G. E., and W. M. Lewis. 1955. The fish population of a spring-fed swamp in the Mississippi bottoms of southern Illinois. Ecology 36: 552–558.

Gunter, G. 1945. Studies on the marine fishes of Texas. Publication of the Marine Institute, University of Texas 1: 90 p.

Gunter, G., and G. E. Hall. 1963. Biological investigations of the St. Lucie estuary (Florida) in connection with Lake Okeechobee discharges through the St. Lucie canal. Gulf Research Reports 1(5): 189–307.

Günther, A. 1859. Catalogue of the Acanthopterygii fishes in the collection of the British Museum. Catalogue of the fishes in the British Museum, Vol. 1.Taylor and Francis, London. 524 p.

———. 1862. Catalogue of the Acanthopterygii, Pharyngognathi and Anacanthini in the collection of the British Museum. Catalogue of the fishes in the British Museum, Vol. 4. Taylor and Francis, London. 534 p.

———. 1866. Catalogue of the Physostomi. . . Catalogue of the fishes in the British Museum, Vol. 6. Taylor and Francis, London. 368 p.

———. 1868. Catalogue of the Physostomi. . . Catalogue of the fishes in the British Museum, Vol. 7. Taylor and Francis, London. 512 p.

Hackney, P. A., G. R. Cooper, and J. F. Webb. 1971. Spawning behavior, age and growth, and sport fishery for the silver redhorse, *Moxostoma anisurum* (Rafinesque) in the Flint River, Alabama. Proceedings of the 24th Annual Conference of Southeastern Game and Fish Commissioners. 569–576.

Hackney, P. A., W. M. Tatum, and S. L. Spencer. 1968. Life history study of the river redhorse, *Moxostoma carinatum* (Cope) in the Cahaba River, Alabama, with notes on the management of the species as a sport fish. Proceedings of the 21st Annual Conference of Southeastern Game and Fish Commissioners. 324–332.

Harper, R. M. 1920. Resources of southern Alabama. Alabama Geological Survey Special Report 11. 152 p.

———. 1942. Natural resources of the Tennessee Valley region in Alabama. Alabama Geological Survey Special Report 17. 93 p.

———. 1943. Forests of Alabama. Alabama Geological Survey Monograph 10. 230 p.

Harrington, R. W. 1956. An experiment on the effects of contrasting daily photoperiods on gametogenesis and reproduction of the centrarchid fish, *Enneacanthus obesus* (Girard). Journal of Experimental Zoology 131: 203–223.

Harris, J. L. 1986. Systematics, distribution, and biology of fishes currently allocated to *Erimystax* Jordan, a subgenus of *Hybopsis* (Cyprinidae). Ph.D. Dissertation. University of Tennessee, Knoxville. 335 p.

Hastings, R. W., and R. W. Yerger. 1971. Ecology and life history of the diamond killifish, *Adinia xenica* (Jordan and Gilbert). American Midland Naturalist 86: 276–291.

Hay, O. P. 1881. On a collection of fishes from eastern Mississippi. Proceedings of the U.S. National Museum 3(170): 488–515.

———. 1883. On a collection of fishes from the lower Mississippi valley. Bulletin of the U.S. Fish Commission (1882) 2: 57–75.

———. 1885. Notes on a collection of fishes from Florida, with descriptions of new or little known species. Proceedings of the U.S. National Museum 8(537): 552–559.

Heins, D. C. 1985. Life history traits of the Florida sand darter *Ammocrypta bifascia*, and comparisons with the naked sand darter *Ammocrypta beani*. American Midland Naturalist 113: 209–216. p.

Heins, D. C., and G. I. Bresnick. 1975. The ecological life history of the cherryfin shiner, *Notropis roseipinnis*. Transactions of the American Fisheries Society 104: 516–523.

Heins, D. C., and G. H. Clemmer. 1975. Ecology, foods, and feeding of the longnose shiner, *Notropis longirostris* (Hay) in Mississippi. American Midland Naturalist 94: 284–295.

———. 1976. The reproductive biology, age and growth of the North American cyprinid, *Notropis longirostris* (Hay). Journal of Fish Biology 1976: 365–379.

Heins, D. C., G. E. Gunning, and J. D. Williams. 1980. Reproduc-tion and population structure of an undescribed species of *Notropis* (Pisces: Cyprinidae) from the Mobile Bay drainage, Alabama. Copeia 1980: 822–830.

Heins, D. C., and M. D. Machado. 1993. Spawning season, clutch characteristics, sexual dimorphism and sex ratio in the redfin darter *Etheostoma whipplei*. American Midland Naturalist 129: 161–171.

Hemphill, A. F. 1960. A survey of the fishes of the lower coastal plain of Alabama. Ph.D. Dissertation. University of Alabama, Tuscaloosa. 368 p.

Henshall, J. A. 1889. On a collection of fishes from east Tennessee. Journal of the Cincinnati Society of Natural History 12: 31–33.

Hermann, J. 1804. Observationes zoologicae, quibus novae complures, aliaeque animalium species describuntur et illustrantur: opus posthuman edidit Fr. L. Hammer. Argentorati 4: 290–332.

Hildebrand, S. F. 1963. Family Clupeidae. p. 257–454 in Fishes of the western North Atlantic. Memoirs of the Sears Foundation for Marine Research, Yale University, New Haven 1 (3).

Hildebrand, S. F., and W. C. Schroeder. 1928. Fishes of Chesapeake Bay. Bulletin of the U.S. Bureau of Fisheries 43. 388 p.

Hocutt, C. H., and E. O. Wiley, editors. 1986. The zoogeography of North American freshwater fishes. Wiley-Interscience, New York. 866 p.

Hoese, H. D., and R. H. Moore. 1977. Fishes of the Gulf of Mexico, Texas, Louisiana, and adjacent waters. Texas A&M University Press, College Station. 327 p.

Holbrook, J. E. 1855a. An account of several species of fish observed in Florida, Georgia, etc. Journal of the Academy of Natural Sciences of Philadelphia 3(1): 47–58.

———. 1855b. Ichthyology of South Carolina. John Russell, Charleston, South Carolina. 182 p.

Howell, H. H. 1957. A taxonomic and distributional study of the genus *Notropis* in Alabama. Ph.D. Dissertation. University of Alabama, Tuscaloosa. 113 p.

Howell, W. M. 1968. Taxonomy and distribution of the percid fish *Etheostoma stigmaeum* (Jordan), with the validation and redescription of *Etheostoma davisoni* Hay. Ph.D. Dissertation. University of Alabama, Tuscaloosa. 113 p.

Howell, W. M., and A. Black. 1981. Karyotypes in populations of the cyprinodontid fishes of the *Fundulus notatus* species complex: a geographic analysis. Bulletin of the Alabama Museum of Natural History 6: 19–30.

Howell, W. M., H. T. Boschung, J. S. Ramsey, and L. E. Walls. 1980. Watercress darter (*Etheostoma nuchale*) recovery plan. Unpublished report. U.S. Fish and Wildlife Service, Jackson, Mississippi. 24 p.

Howell, W. M., and R. D. Caldwell. 1965. *Etheostoma (Oligocephalus) nuchale*, a new darter from a limestone spring in Alabama. Tulane Studies in Zoology 12: 101–108.

———. 1967. Discovery of a second specimen of the darter, *Etheostoma trisella*. Copeia 1967: 235–236.

Howell, W. M., and G. Dingerkus. 1978. *Etheostoma neopterum*, a new percid fish from the Tennessee River system in Alabama and Tennessee. Bulletin of the Alabama Museum of Natural History 3: 13–26.

Howell, W. M. and J. D. Williams. 1971. *Notropis gibbsi*, a new cyprinid fish from the Tallapoosa River system in Alabama and Georgia. Copeia 1971: 55–64.

Hubbs, C. L. 1921. An ecological study of the life history of the freshwater atherine fish *Labidesthes sicculus*. Ecology 2: 262–276.

Hubbs, C. L. 1926. Studies on the fishes of the order Cyprinodontes VI. Miscellaneous Publications of the University of Michigan Museum of Zoology 16. 87 p.

Hubbs, C. L. 1936. An older name for the black-nosed dace. Copeia 1936: 124–125.

Hubbs, C. L. 1955. Hybridization between fish species in nature. Systematic Zoology 4: 1–20.

Hubbs, C. L., and R. M. Bailey. 1938. The smallmouthed bass. Cranbrook Institute of Science Bulletin 10. 92 p.

Hubbs, C. L., and R. M. Bailey. 1940. A revision of the black basses (*Micropterus* and *Huro*) with descriptions of four new forms. Miscellaneous Publications of the University of Michigan Museum of Zoology 48: 1–51.

Hubbs, C. L., and M. D. Cannon. 1935. The darters of the genera *Hololepis* and *Villora*. Miscellaneous Publications of the University of Michigan Museum of Zoology 30: 1-93.

Hubbs, C. L., and W. R. Crowe. 1956. Preliminary analysis of the American cyprinid fishes, seven new, referred to the genus *Hybopsis*, subgenus *Erimystax*. Occasional Papers of the University of Michigan Museum of Zoology 578. 8 p.

Hubbs, C. L., and C. W. Greene. 1935. Two new subspecies of fishes from Wisconsin. Transactions of the Wisconsin Academy of Sciences, Arts and Letters 29: 89–101.

Hubbs, C. L., and K. F. Lagler. 1958. Fishes of the Great Lakes region. Cranbrook Institute of Science Bulletin 26. 213 p.

Hubbs, C. L., and E. C. Raney. 1951. Status, subspecies, and variations of *Notropis cummingsae*, a cyprinid fish of the southeastern United States. Occasional Papers of the University of Michigan Museum of Zoology 535. 25 p.

Hubbs, C. L., and M. B. Trautman. 1937. A revision of the lamprey genus *Ichthyomyzon*. Miscellaneous Publications of the University of Michigan Museum of Zoology 35. 109 p.

Hubbs, C. L., and B. W. Walker. 1942. Habitat and breeding behavior of the American cyprinid fish *Notropis longirostris*. Copeia 1942: 101–104.

Hubert, W. A. 1977. Comparative food habits of smallmouth and largemouth basses in Pickwick Reservoir. Journal of the Alabama Academy of Science 48: 167–17

Huff, J. A. 1975. Life history of the Gulf of Mexico sturgeon, *Acipenser oxyrhynchus desotoi* in Suwannee River, Florida. Florida Marine Resources Publication 16. 32 p.

Hunt, B. P. 1953. Food relationships between Florida spotted gar and other organisms in the Tamiami canal, Dade County, Florida. Transactions of the American Fisheries Society 82: 13–33.

Hurley, S. T., W. A. Hubert, and J. G. Nickum. 1987. Habitats and movements of shovelnose sturgeons in the upper Mississippi River. Transactions of the American Fisheries Society 116: 655–662.

Jandebeur, T. S. 1972. A study of the fishes of the Elk River drainage system in Alabama and Tennessee. M.S. Thesis. University of Alabama, Tuscaloosa. 153 p.

Jenkins, R. E. 1970. Systematic studies of the catostomid fish tribe Moxostomatini: Ph.D. Dissertation. Cornell University, Ithaca. 799 p.

———. 1980a. *Moxostoma anisurum* (Rafinesque). p. 409 in D. S. Lee et al., Atlas of North American freshwater fishes. North Carolina State Museum of Natural History Publication 1980-12.

———. 1980b. *Moxostoma macrolepidotum* (Lesueur). p. 427 D. S. Lee in et al., Atlas of North American freshwater fishes. North Carolina State Museum of Natural History Publication 1980-12.

Jenkins, R. E., and N. M. Burkhead. 1984. Description, biology, and distribution of the spotfin chub, *Hybopsis monacha*, a threatened cyprinid fish of the Tennessee River drainage. Bulletin of the Alabama Museum of Natural History 8: 1–30.

———. 1993. Freshwater fishes of Virginia. American Fisheries Society, Bethesda. 1,079 p.

Johnson, G. D. 1984. Percodei: development and relationships. p. 464–498 in Moser et al., editors, Ontogeny and systematics of fishes. American Society of Ichthyologists and Herpetologists Publication. 1. 970 p.

Johnson, W. D. 1930. Physical divisions of northern Alabama. Alabama Geological Survey Bulletin 38. 48 p.

Johnston, C. E., and W. S. Birkhead. 1988. Spawning in the bandfin shiner, *Notropis zonistius* (Pisces: Cyprinidae). Journal of the Alabama Academy of Science 59: 30–33.

Johnston, C. E., and K. J. Kleiner. 1994. Reproductive behavior of the rainbow shiner (*Notropis chrosomus*) and the rough shiner (*Notropis baileyi*), nest associates of the bluehead chub (*Nocomis leptocephalus*)(Pisces: Cyprinidae) in the Alabama River drainage. Journal of the Alabama Academy of Science 65: 230–240.

Johnston, C. E., and L. M. Page. 1992. The evolution of complex reproductive strategies in North American minnows (Cyprinidae). p. 600–621 in R. L. Mayden, editor, Systematics, historical ecology, and North American freshwater fishes. Stanford University Press. 969 p.

Johnston, C. E., and J. S. Ramsey. 1990. Redescription of *Semotilus thoreauianus* Jordan, 1877, a cyprinid fish of the southeastern United States. Copeia 1990: 119–130.

Jordan, D. S. 1877a. A partial synopsis of the fishes of upper Georgia, with supplementary papers on fishes of Tennessee, Kentucky, and Indiana. Annals of the New York Lyceum of Natural History 11: 307–377.

———. 1877b. Contributions to North American ichthyology based primarily on the collections of the United States National Museum. II. A. Notes on Cottidae, Etheostomatidae, Percidae, Centrarchidae, Aphredoderidae, Dorasomatidae, and Cyprinidae, with revisions of the genera and descriptions of new or little known species. B. Synopsis of the fresh-water Siluridae of the United States. Bulletin of the U.S. National Museum 10. 120 p.

———. 1877c. On the fishes of northern Indiana. Proceedings of the Academy of Natural Sciences of Philadelphia 29: 42–82.

———. 1878a. A manual of the vertebrates of the northern

United States, including the district east of the Mississippi River, and north of North Carolina and Tennessee, exclusive of marine species, 2nd edition. Jansen, McClurg, and company, Chicago. 407 p.

———. 1878b. A catalogue of the fishes of Illinois: Bulletin of the Illinois State Laboratory of Natural History 1: 37-70.

———. 1880. Description of new species of North American Fishes. Proceedings of the U.S. National Museum 2: 235–241.

———. 1882. Report on the fishes of Ohio. Geological Society of Ohio 4: 738–1,002.

———. 1884a. List of fishes collected in Lake Jessup, and Indian River, Florida, by Mr. R. E. Earll, with descriptions of two new species. Proceedings of the U.S. National Museum 7(438): 322–324.

———. 1884b. Descriptions of four new species of *Poecilichthys* in the United States National Museum. Proceedings of the U.S. National Museum 7(451): 477 480.

———. 1885a. A catalogue of the fishes known to inhabit the waters of North America north of the Tropic of Cancer, with notes on the species discovered in 1883 and 1884. Report of the Commissioner for (1885).U.S. Commission of Fish and Fisheries, pt. 13, 789–973.

———. 1885b. Description of a new species of *Hybognathus* (*Hybognathus hayi*) from Mississippi. Proceedings of the U.S. National Museum 7(467): 548–550.

———. 1889. Report on explorations made during the summer of 1888, in the Allegheny region of Virginia, North Carolina and Tennessee, and in western Indiana, with an account of the fishes found in each of the river basins in those regions. Bulletin of the U.S. Fish Commission 8 (1888): 97–173.

Jordan, D. S., and A. W. Brayton. 1877. On *Lagochila*, a new genus of catostomid fish. Proceedings of the Academy of Natural Sciences of Philadelphia 29: 280–283.

———. 1878. Contributions to North American ichthyology, based primarily on collections of the United States National Museum. III. A. On the distribution of the fishes of the Allegheny region of South Carolina, Georgia, and Tennessee, with descriptions of new or little known species. Bulletin of the U.S. National Museum 12. 95 p.

Jordan, D. S., and B. W. Evermann. 1896–1900. The fishes of North and Middle America: a descriptive catalogue of the fish-like vertebrates found in the waters of North America, north of the Isthmus of Panama. Bulletin of the U.S. National Museum 47. 3,313 p.

———. 1908. American food and game fishes. Doubleday, Page, New York. 572 p.

Jordan, D. S., and C. H. Gilbert. 1882. Synopsis of the fishes of North America. Bulletin of the U.S. National Museum 16. 1,018 p.

———. 1886. List of fishes collected in Arkansas, Indian Territory, and Texas, in September 1884, with notes and descriptions. Proceedings of the U.S. National Museum 9(549): 1–25.

Jordan, D. S., and S. E. Meek. 1884. List of fishes observed in the Saint John's River at Jackonsville, Florida. Proceedings of the U.S. National Museum 8(483): 44–67.

Karr, J. R. 1963. Age, growth, and food habits of johnny, slenderhead, and blacksided darters of Boone County, Iowa. Iowa Academy of Science 70: 228–236.

———. 1964. Age, growth, fecundity, and food habits of fantail darters in Boone County, Iowa. Iowa Academy of Science 71: 274–280.

Keast, A., and D. Webb. 1966. Mouth and body form relative to feeding ecology in the fish fauna of a small lake, Lake Opinicon, Ontario. Journal of the Fisheries Research Board of Canada 23: 1345–1374.

Kemp, R. J., and Carl Hubbs. 1954. First record of the cypress minnow (*Hybognathus hayi* Jordan) in Texas. Texas Journal of Science 6: 113.

Kilken, R. H. 1972. Food habits and growth of fingerling blacktail redhorse *Moxostoma poecilurum* (Jordan) in ponds. Proceedings of the Louisiana Academy of Science 35: 12–20.

Kirtland, J. P. 1840. Descriptions of the fishes of the Ohio River and its tributaries. Boston Journal of Natural History 3(10): 338–352.

———. 1845. Description of *Leuciscus storerianus*, sp. nov., from Ohio [this species has confusing authorship and this reference is the first complete description of the species]. Proceedings of the Boston Society of Natural History 1(1841–1844): 199–200.

Klippart, J. H. 1878. Descriptions of Ohio fishes, arranged from manuscript notes of Professor D. S. Jordan, by his assistant, Ernest R. Copeland. Second Annual Report of the Ohio State Fish Commission (1877). 83–116.

Koch, L. M. 1978. Aspects of life history of *Etheostoma (Psychromaster) tuscumbia* in Buffler Spring, Lauderdale County, Alabama. M.S. Thesis. University of North Alabama, Tuscaloosa, 75 p.

Kramer, R. H., and L. L. Smith. 1960. Utilization of nests of largemouth bass, *Micropterus salmoides*, by golden shiners, *Notemigonus crysoleucas*. Copeia 1960: 73–74.

Krotzer, M. J. 1990. Variation and systematics of *Etheostoma nigrum* Rafinesque, the johnny darter (Pisces: Percidae). Ph.D. Dissertation. University of Tennessee, Knoxville. 192 p.

Krotzer, R. S. 1984. The ecological life history of the blue shiner, *Notropis caeruleus* (Jordan), from the upper Conasauga River, Georgia. M.S. Thesis. Samford University, Birmingham. 37 p.

Krumholtz, L. A. 1948. Reproduction of the western mosquitofish, *Gambusia affinis* (Baird and Girard), and its use in mosquito control. Ecological Monographs 18: 43 p.

Kuehne, R. A., and R. W. Barbour. 1983. The American darters. University Press of Kentucky, Lexington. 177 p.

Kuhajda, B. R., and M. L. Warren. 1989. Life history aspects of the harlequin darter, *Etheostoma histrio*, in western Kentucky. Association of Southeastern Biologists Bulletin 36: 66–67.

Lacepède, B. G. E. 1801. Histoire naturelle des poissons, vol. 3.

———. 1802. Histoire naturelle des poissons, vol. 4.

———. 1803. Histoire naturelle des poissons, vol. 5.

Lachner, E. A. 1952. Studies of the biology of the cyprinid fishes of the chub genus *Nocomis* of northeastern United States. American Midland Naturalist 48: 433–466.

Lachner, E. A., and R. E. Jenkins. 1971. Systematics, distribution, and evolution of the chub genus *Nocomis* Girard (Pisces: Cyprinidae) of eastern United States, with descriptions of new species. Smithsonian Contributions to Zoology 85: 97 p.

Lachner, E. A., E. F. Westlake, and P. S. Handwerk. 1950. Studies on the biology of some percid fishes from western Pennsylvania. American Midland Naturalist 43: 92–111.

Lake, C. T. 1936. The life history of the fan-tailed darter *Catonotus flabellaris flabellaris* (Rafinesque). American Midland Naturalist 17: 816–830.

Larimore, R. W. 1957. Ecological life history of the war-mouth (Centrarchidae). Illinois Natural History Survey Bulletin 27:1–83

Lauder, G. V. 1983. Functional and morphological bases of trophic specialization in sunfishes (Teleostei, Centrarchidae). Journal of Morphology 178: 1–21.

Laurence, G. C., and R. W. Yerger. 1967. Life history of the Alabama shad (*Alosa alabamae*) in the Apalachicola River, Florida. Proceedings of the 20th Annual Conference of Southeastern Game and Fish Commissioners. 260–273.

Layman, S. R. 1994. Phylogenetic systematics and biogeography of the subgenus *Doration* (Percidae: *Etheostoma*). Ph.D. Dissertation. University of Alabama, Tuscaloosa. 299 p.

Lee, D. S. 1978a. *Lepisosteus platostomus* Rafinesque. p. 50 in D.S. Lee et al., Atlas of North American freshwater fishes. North Carolina State Museum of Natural History Publication 1980-12.

———. 1978b. *Anguilla rostrata* (Lesueur). p. 59 in D. S. Lee et al., Atlas of North American freshwater fishes. North Carolina State Museum of Natural History Publication 1980-12.

———. 1978c. *Lepomis auritus* (Linnaeus). p. 590 in D. S. Lee et al., Atlas of North American freshwater fishes. North Carolina State Museum of Natural History Publication 1980-12.

———. 1979. *Ictiobus bubalus* (Rafinesque). p. 404 in D. S. Lee et al., Atlas of North American freshwater fishes. North Carolina State Museum of Natural History Publication 1980-12.

Lee, D. S., and B. M. Burr. 1985. Observations of life history of the dollar sunfish, *Lepomis marginatus* (Holbrook). Association of Southeastern Biologists Bulletin 32: 58.

Lee, D. S., C. R. Gilbert, C. H. Hocutt, R. E. Jenkins, D. E. McAllister, and J. R. Stauffer, Jr. 1980. Atlas of North American freshwater fishes. North Carolina Museum of Natural History Publication 1980-12, Raleigh. 867 p.

Lee, D. S., and S. T. Kucas. 1978. *Catostomus commersoni* (Lacepède). p. 375 in D. S. Lee et al., Atlas of North American freshwater fishes. North Carolina State Museum of Natural History, Publication 1980-12.

Lee, D. S., and S. P. Platania. 1978a. *Carpiodes carpio* (Rafinesque). p. 367 in D. S. Lee et al., Atlas of North American freshwater fishes. North Carolina State Museum of Natural History Publication 1980-12.

———. 1978b. *Carpiodes velifer* (Rafinesque). p. 369 in D. S.

Lee et al., Atlas of North American freshwater fishes. North Carolina State Museum of Natural History Publication 1980-12.

Lentinen, S., and A. A. Echelle. 1979. Reproductive cycle of *Notropis boops* (Pisces: Cyprinidae) in Brier Creek, Marshall County, Oklahoma. American Midland Naturalist 102: 237–243.

Lesueur———. 1817a. A short description of five (supposed) new species of the genus *Muraena*, discovered by Mr. Lesueur, in the year 1816. Journal of the Academy of Natural Sciences of Philadelphia 1(1): 81–83.

———. 1817b. A new genus of fishes, of the order Abdominales, proposed, under the name *Catostomus*; and the characters of this genus, with those of its species, indicated. Journal of the Academy of Natural Sciences of Philadelphia 1(1): 88–96, 102–111.

———. 1818a. Descriptions of several new species of North American fishes. Journal of the Academy of Natural Sciences of Philadelphia 1(2): 222–235, 359–368.

———. 1818b. Descriptions of several new species of the genus *Esox*, of North America. Journal of the Academy of Natural Sciences of Philadelphia 1(2): 413–417.

———. 1819. Notice sur quelques poissons découverts dans les lacs du Haut Canada, durant l'été de 1816. Mémoires du Museum d'Histoire Naturelle (Paris) 5: 148–161.

———. 1821. Description of a new genus, and of several new species of freshwater fish, indigenous to the United States. Journal of the Academy of Natural Sciences of Philadelphia 2(1): 2–8.

Lewis, W. M., and G. E. Gunning. 1959 Notes on the life history of the steelcolor shiner, *Notropis whipplei* (Girard). Transactions of the Illinois Academy of Science 52: 59–64.

Linnaeus, C. 1758. Systema Naturae per regna tria naturae, secundum classes, ordines, genera, species cum characteribus, differentiis, synonymis, locis, 10th edition. Laurentii Salvii Publishers, Stockholm, Sweden. 824 p.

——— 1766. Systema Naturae . . . , 12th edition. Laurentii Salvii Publishers, Stockholm, Sweden.

Malvestuto, S. P., G. M. Lucas, G. M. Sullivan, and W. D. Davies. 1983. Survey of the sport and commercial fisheries of the lower Tombigbee River and Mobile River Delta. U.S. Army Corps of Engineers, Contract No. DACW01-81-C-0047, Mobile District, Alabama. 163 p.

Mansueti, A. J. 1963. Some changes in morphology during ontogeny in the pirateperch, *Aphredoderus s. sayanus*. Copeia 1963: 546–557.

Marshall, N. 1947. Studies on the life history and ecology of *Notropis chalybaeus* (Cope). Quarterly Journal of the Florida Academy of Science 9: 163–188.

Martin, F. D. 1978. *Heterandria formosa* Agassiz. p. 547 in D. S. Lee et al., Atlas of North American freshwater fishes. North Carolina State Museum of Natural History Publication 1980-12.

Martin, F. D., and C. Hubbs. 1973. Observations on the development of pirate perch, *Aphredoderus sayanus* (Pisces: Aphredoderidae) with comments on yolk circulation patterns as a possible taxonomic tool. Copeia 1973: 377–379.

Matheson, R. E., and J. D. McEachran. 1984. Taxonomic studies of the *Eucinostomus argenteus* complex (Pisces: Gerreidae): preliminary studies of external morphology. Copeia 1984: 893–902.

Mathur, D. 1973a. Some aspects of life history of the blackbanded darter, *Percina nigrofasciata* (Agassiz) in Halawakee Creek, Alabama. American Midland Naturalist 89: 381–393.

———. 1973b. Food habits and feeding chronology of the blackbanded darter, *Percina nigrofasciata* (Agassiz) in Halawakee Creek, Alabama. Transactions of the American Fisheries Society 102: 48–55.

Mathur, D., and J. S. Ramsey. 1974a. Reproductive biology of the rough shiner, *Notropis baileyi*, in Halawakee Creek, Alabama. Transactions of the American Fisheries Society 103: 88–93.

———. 1974b. Food habits of the rough shiner, *Notropis baileyi* Suttkus and Raney, in Halawakee Creek, Alabama. American Midland Naturalist 92: 84–93.

Mayden, R. L. 1989. Phylogenetic studies of North American minnows, with emphasis on the genus *Cyprinella* (Teleostei: Cypriniformes). Miscellaneous Publications of the University of Kansas Museum of Natural History 80. 189 p.

———. 1993. *Elassoma alabamae*, a new species of pygmy sunfish endemic to the Tennessee River drainage of Alabama (Teleostei: Elassomatidae). Bulletin of the Alabama Museum of Natural History 16: 1–14.

———, editor. 1992. Systematics, historical ecology, and North American freshwater fishes. Stanford University Press, Stanford, California. 969 p.

Mayden, R. L., and B. M. Burr. 1981. Life history of the slender madtom, *Noturus exilis*, in southern Illinois (Pisces: Ictaluridae). Occasional Papers of the University of Kansas Museum of Natural History 93. 64 p.

Mayden, R. L., and B. R. Kuhajda. 1989. Systematics of *Notropis cahabae*, a new cyprinid fish endemic to the Cahaba River of the Mobile basin. Bulletin of the Alabama Museum of Natural History 9: 1–16.

Mayden, R. L., R. H. Matson, B. R. Kuhajda, J. M. Pierson, M. F. Mettee, and K. S. Frazer. 1989. The chestnut lamprey, *Ichthyomyzon castaneus* Girard, in the Mobile basin. Southeastern Fishes Council Proceedings 20: 10–12.

McAuliffe, J. R., and D. H. Bennett. 1981. Observations on the spawning habits of the yellowfin shiner, *Notropis lutipinnis*. Journal of the Elisha Mitchell Scientific Society 97: 200–203.

McCaskill, M. L., J. E. Thomerson, and P. R. Mills. 1972. Food of the northern studfish, *Fundulus catenatus*, in the Missouri Ozarks. Transactions of the American Fisheries Society 101: 375–377.

McCormick, F. H., and N. Aspinwall. 1983. Habitat selection in three species of darters. Environmental Biology of Fishes 8: 279–282.

McGeehan, L. T. 1985. Multivariate and univariate analyses of the geographical variation with *Etheostoma flabellare* of eastern North America. Ph.D. Dissertation. Ohio State University, Columbus. 156 p.

McGregor, S. W., and T. E. Shepard. 1995. Investigations of slackwater darter, *Etheostoma boschungi*, populations, 1992–1994. Alabama Geological Survey Circular 184. 33 p.

McHugh, J. J. 1990. Responses of bluegills and crappies to reduced abundance of largemouth bass in two Alabama impoundments. North American Journal of Fish Management 10: 344–351.

McLane, W. M. 1950. Notes on the food of the largemouth black bass, *Micropterus salmoides floridanus* (LeSueur), in a Florida lake. Quarterly Journal of the Florida Academy of Science 12: 195–201.

McLane, W. M. 1955. The fishes of the St. Johns River system. Ph.D. Dissertation. University of Florida, Gainesville. 361 p.

McSwain, L. E., and R. W. Pasch. 1972. Life history studies of stream fishes: age and growth, reproduction, food habits, and abundance and distribution of the grayfin

redhorse. Federal Aid (Dingell-Johnson) Progress Report, Georgia Project F21-4 (mimeograph).

Meek, S. E. 1896. A list of fishes and mollusks collected in Arkansas and Indian Territory in 1894. Bulletin of the U.S. Fish Commission (1895) 15: 341–349.

Menhinick, E. F. 1991. The freshwater fishes of North Carolina. University of North Carolina Press, Charlotte. 177 p.

Mettee, M. F. 1974. A study on the reproductive behavior, embryology, and larval development of the pygmy sunfishes in the genus *Elassoma*. Ph.D. Dissertation. University of Alabama, Tuscaloosa. 130 p.

Mettee, M. F., and E. C. Beckham. 1978. Notes on the breeding behavior, embryology and larval development of *Cyprinodon variegatus* Lacepede in aquaria. Tulane Studies in Zoology and Botany 20: 137–148.

Mettee, M. F., P. E. O'Neil, J. M. Pierson, and R.D. Suttkus. 1989. Fishes of the Black Warrior River System in Alabama. Alabama Geological Survey Bulletin 133. 201 p.

Mettee, M. F., P. E. O'Neil, J. M. Pierson, and R. D. Suttkus. 1989. Fishes of the Black Warrior River system in Alabama. Alabama Geological Survey Bulletin 133. 201 p.

Mettee, M. F., P. E. O'Neil, R. D. Suttkus, and J. M. Pierson. 1987. Fishes of the lower Tombigbee River system in Alabama and Mississippi. Alabama Geological Survey Bulletin 107. 186 p.

Mettee, M. F., and J. J. Pulliam. 1986. Reintroduction of an undescribed species of *Elassoma* into Pryor Branch, Limestone County, Alabama. Southeastern Fishes Council Proceedings 4: 14–15.

Miller, G. L. 1984. Trophic ecology of the frecklebelly madtom *Noturus munitus* in the Tombigbee River, Mississippi. American Midland Naturalist 110: 299–313.

Miller, R. J., and H. W. Robison. 1973. The fishes of Oklahoma. Oklahoma State University Press, Stillwater. 246 p.

Miller, R. V. 1968. A systematic study of the greenside darter *Etheostoma blennioides* Rafinesque (Pisces: Percidae). Copeia 1968: 1–40.

Mills, J. G., Jr. 1972. Biology of the Alabama shad in northwest Florida. Florida Department of Natural Resources Division of Marine Resources, Technical Series 68. 24 p.

Minckley, W. L. 1959. Fishes of the Big Blue River basin, Kansas. University of Kansas Museum of Natural

History Publication 11: 401–442.

Minckley, W. L., J. E. Johnson, J. N. Rinne, and S. E. Willoughby. 1970. Foods of buffalofishes, genus *Ictiobus*, in central Arizona reservoirs. Transactions of the American Fisheries Society 99: 333–342.

Mitchill, S. L. 1814. Report, in part, of Samuel L. Mitchill, M.D., on the fishes of New York. D. Carlisle, New York. 28 p.

———. 1815. The fishes of New York, described and arranged. Transactions of the Literary and Philosophical Society of New York 1: 355–492.

———. 1817. Report on the ichthyology of the Wallkill, from specimens of fishes presented to the society . . . by Dr. B. Akerly. American Monthly Magazine and Critical Review 1(4): 289–290.

———. 1818. Memoir on ichthyology: the fishes of New York described and arranged. American Monthly Magazine and Critical Review 2(4): 241–248 and 2(5): 321–328.

Moore, G. A., and M. E. Sisk. 1963. The spectacle of *Elassoma zonatum* Jordan. Copeia 1963: 346–350.

Morris, M. A., and L. M. Page. 1981. Variation in western logperches (Pisces: Percidae), with description of a new subspecies from the Ozarks. Copeia 1981: 95–108.

Moser, H. G., W. J. Richards, D. M. Cohen, M. P. Fehay, A. W. Kendall, and S. L. Richardson, editors. 1984. Ontogeny and systematics of fishes. American Society of Ichthyologists and Herpetologists Special Publication 1. 760 p.

Moss, J. L. 1985. Summer selection of thermal refuges by striped bass in Alabama reservoirs and tailwaters. Transactions of the American Fisheries Society 114: 77–83.

Moss, J. L. 1995. Watercress darter population monitoring, October 1, 1994 through September 30, 1995. Annual performance report, endangered species program, grant no. E-1, segment 5. Alabama Department of Conservation and Natural Resources, Game and Fish Division. 13 p.

Mount, D. I. 1959. Spawning behavior of the bluebreast darter, *Etheostoma camurum* (Cope). Copeia 1959: 240–243.

Mount, R. H. 1986. Vertebrate animals of Alabama in need of special attention. Auburn Agricultural Experiment Station, Auburn. 124 p.

Moyle, P. B. 1973. Ecological segregation among three species of minnows (Cyprinidae) in a Minnesota Lake. Transactions of the American Fisheries Society 102: 794–805.

Munro, I. S. R. 1967. The fishes of New Guinea. Department of Agriculture, Stock, and Fisheries, Port Moresby, New Guinea.

Myers, G. S. 1925. *Notropis cummingsae*, a new minnow from Wilmington, North Carolina. American Museum Novitates 168: 1–4.

———. 1931. The primary groups of oviparous cyprinodont fishes. Stanford University Publication 6: 1-14.

———. 1955. Notes on the classification and names of the cyprinodont fishes. Tropical Fish Magazine 4: 7.

Nagel, J. W. 1980. Life history of the mottled sculpin, *Cottus bairdi*, in northeastern Tennessee (Osteichthys: Cottidae). Brimleyana 4: 115–121.

Neill, W. T. 1950. An estivating bowfin. Copeia 1950: 240.

Nelson, E. W. 1876. A partial catalogue of the fishes of Illinois. Bulletin of the Illinois Museum of Natural History 1: 33–52.

Nelson, J. S. 1968. Life history of the brook silverside, *Labidesthes sicculus*, in Crooked Lake, Indiana. Transactions of the American Fisheries Society 97: 293–296.

———. 1994. Fishes of the world, 3rd edition. Wiley-Interscience, New York. 600 p.

Nieland, D. L. 1981. Food habits of *Etheostoma boschungi* (Pisces: Percidae) from Cypress Creek watershed, Alabama and Tennessee, with comparisons of food habits in its nonbreeding and breeding habitats. Unpublished report. University of Alabama, Tuscaloosa. 32 p.

Nieman, R. L., and D. C. Wallace. 1974. The age and growth of the blackstripe topminnow, *Fundulus notatus* Rafinesque. American Midland Naturalist 92: 203–205.

O'Neil, P. E. 1980. Life histories and resource partitioning patterns of three species of fishes (Percidae: *Etheostoma*). M.S. Thesis. University of Alabama, Tuscaloosa. 64 p.

———. 1981. Life history of *Etheostoma coosae* (Pisces: Percidae) in Barbaree Creek, Alabama. Tulane Studies in Zoology and Botany 23: 75–84.

Orr, J. W., and J. S. Ramsey. 1990. Reproduction in the greenbreast darter, *Etheostoma jordani* (Teleostei: Percidae). Copeia 1990: 100–107.

Osborne, W. E., M. W. Szabo, C. W. Copeland, and T. L. Neathery, compilers. 1989. Geologic map of Alabama. Alabama Geological Survey Special Map 221.

Outten, L. M. 1957. A study of the life history of the cyprinid fish *Notropis coccogenis*. Journal of the Elisha Mitchell Scientific Society 74: 68–84.

———. 1958. Studies of the life history of the cyprinid fishes *Notropis galacturus* and *rubricroceus*. Journal of the Elisha Mitchell Scientific Society 74: 122–134.

———. 1962. Some observations on the spawning coloration and behavior of *Notropis leuciodus*. Journal of the Elisha Mitchell Scientific Society 78: 101–102.

Page, L. M. 1974a. The subgenera of *Percina* (Percidae: Etheostomatini). Copeia 1974: 66–86.

———. 1974b. The life history of the spottail darter, *Etheostoma squamiceps*, in Big Creek, Illinois, and Ferguson Creek, Kentucky. Illinois Natural History Survey Biological Notes 89. 20 p.

———. 1975 The life history of the stripetail darter, *Etheostoma kennicotti*, in Big Creek, Illinois. Illinois Natural History Survey Biological Notes 93. 15 p.

———. 1981 The genera and subgenera of darters (Percidae, Etheostomatini). Occasional Papers of the University of Kansas Museum of Natural History 90. 69 p.

———. 1983. Handbook of darters. T. F. H. Publications, Jersey City. 271 p.

———. 1985. Evolution of reproductive behaviors in percid fishes. Illinois Natural History Survey Bulletin 33: 275—295.

Page, L. M., and H. L. Bart, Jr. 1989. Egg-mimics in darters (Pisces: Percidae). Copeia 1989: 514–516.

Page, L. M., and B. M. Burr. 1979. The smallest species of darter (Pisces: Percidae). American Midland Naturalist 101: 452–453.

———. 1991. A field guide to freshwater fishes of North America north of Mexico. Houghton Mifflin, Boston. 432 p.

Page, L. M., and P.A. Ceas. 1989. Egg attachment in *Pimephales* (Pisces: Cyprinidae). Copeia 1989: 1,074–1,077.

Page, L. M., P. A. Ceas, D. L. Swofford, and D. G. Buth. 1992. Evolutionary relationships within the *Etheostoma squamiceps* complex (Percidae: subgenus *Catonotus*) with descriptions of five new species. Copeia 1992: 615–646.

Page, L. M., and C. E. Johnston. 1990a. The breeding behavior of *Opsopoeodus emiliae* (Cyprinidae) and its phylogenetic implications. Copeia 1990: 1,176–1,180.

———. 1990b. The breeding behavior of *Erimyzon oblongus* with a review of the spawning behavior of suckers (Catostomidae). Evolutionary Biology of Fishes 27: 265–272.

Page, L. M., and R. L. Mayden. 1981. The life history of the Tennessee snubnose darter, *Etheostoma simoterum*, in Brush Creek, Tennessee. Illinois Natural History Survey Biological Notes 117. 11 p.

Page, L. M., M. E. Retzer, and R. A. Stiles. 1982. Spawning behavior in seven species of darters (Pisces: Percidae). Brimleyana 8: 135–143.

Page, L. M., and P. W. Smith. 1970. The life history of the dusky darter, *Percina sciera*, in the Embarras River, Illinois. Illinois Natural History Survey Biological Notes 69. 15 p.

———. 1971. The life history of the slenderhead darter, *Percina phoxocephala*, in the Embarras River, Illinois. Illinois Natural History Survey Biological Notes 74. 14 p.

Page, L. M., and G. S. Whitt. 1973. Lactate dehydrogenase isozymes, malate dehydrogenase isozymes, and tetrazolium oxidase mobilities of darters (Etheostomatini). Comparative Biochemistry and Physiology 44B: 611–623.

Parenti, L. R. 1981. A phylogenetic and biogeographic analysis of cyprinodontiform fishes (Teleostei, Atherinomorpha). Bulletin of the American Museum of Natural History 168: 341–557.

Patterson, C., and D. E. Rosen. 1989. The Paracanthopterygii revisited: order and disorder. p. 536 in D. M. Cohen, editor, Papers on systematics of gadiform fishes. Natural History Museum of Los Angeles County Scientific Series 32. 262 p.

Peterson, M. S. 1993. Notes on the habitat characteristics of the backwater darter, *Etheostoma zonifer* (Hubbs and Cannon). Southeastern Fishes Council Proceedings 28: 1–6.

Petravicz, W. P. 1938. The breeding habits of the blacksided darter, *Hadropterus maculatus* Girard. Copeia 1938: 40–44.

Pfeiffer, R. A., 1955. Studies on the life history of the rosyface shiner, *Notropis rubellus*. Copeia 1955: 95–104.

Pflieger, W. L. 1965. Reproductive behavior of the minnows, *Notropis spilopterus* and *Notropis whipplei*. Copeia

1965: 1–8.

Pflieger, W. L. 1975. The fishes of Missouri. Missouri Department of Conservation, Jefferson City. 343 p.

Pierce, L. B. 1966. Surface water in southwestern Alabama. Alabama Geological Survey Bulletin 84. 182 p.

Pierson, J. M., W. M. Howell, R. A. Stiles, M. F. Mettee, P. E. O'Neil, R. D. Suttkus, and J. S. Ramsey. 1989. Fishes of the Cahaba River system in Alabama. Alabama Geological Survey Bulletin 134. 183 p.

Pierson, J. M., and R. S. Krotzer. 1987. The distribution, relative abundance and life history of the blue shiner, *Notropis caeruleus* (Jordan). Unpublished report. Alabama Department of Conservation and Natural Resources, Wildlife Section. 105 p.

Pierson, J. M., R. S. Krotzer, and E. J. Tybergein. 1986. Fishes of the upper Tallapoosa River and three of its major tributaries in Alabama. Journal of the Alabama Academy of Science 57: 1–18.

Platania, S. P., and R. E. Jenkins. 1978. *Carpiodes cyprinus* (Lesueur). p. 368 in D. S. Lee et al., Atlas of North American freshwater fishes. North Carolina State Museum of Natural History Publication 1980-12.

Poulson, T. L. 1963. Cave adaptation in amblyopsid fishes. American Midland Naturalist 70: 257–290.

Priegel, G. R. 1975. Age and growth of yellow bass in Lake Poygan, Wisconsin. Transactions of the American Fisheries Society 104: 513–515.

Probst, W. E., C. F. Rabeni, W. G. Covington, and R. E. Marteney. 1984. Resource use by stream-dwelling rock bass and smallmouth bass. Transactions of the American Fisheries Society 113: 283–294.

Putnam, F. W. 1863. List of fishes sent by the museum to different institutions, in exchange for other specimens, with annotations. Bulletin of the Museum of Comparative Zoology 1(1): 2–16.

Rafinesque, C.S. 1817a. Additions to the observations on the sturgeons of North America. American Monthly Magazine and Critical Review 1: 288.

———. 1817b. First decade of new North American fishes. American Monthly Magazine and Critical Review 2(2): 120–121.

———. 1818a. Description of two new genera of North American fishes, *Opsanus* and *Notropis*. American Monthly Magazine and Critical Review 2(3): 203–204.

———. 1818b. Discoveries in natural history made during a journey through the western region of the United States. American Monthly Magazine and Critical Review 3(5): 354–356.

———. 1818c. Further account of discoveries in natural history in the western states, by Constantine Samuel Rafinesque, Esq. American Monthly Magazine and Critical Review 4(1): 39–42.

———. 1819. Prodome de 70 nouveaux genres d'animaux découverts dans l'intérieur des Etats-Unis d'Amérique, durant l'année 1818. Journal de Physique, de Chimie, d'Histoire Naturelle, et des Arts, Paris. 88: 417–429.

———. 1820. Ichthyologia Ohiensis, or natural history of the fishes inhabiting the Ohio River and its tributary streams, preceded by a physical description of the Ohio and its branches. W. G. Hunt, Lexington. 90 p.

Ramsey, J. C. 1986. Frecklebelly madtom. p. 13–14 in R. H. Mount, editor, Vertebrate animals in Alabama in need of special attention. Auburn Agricultural Extension Station, Auburn.

Ramsey, J. S., and R. D. Suttkus. 1965. *Etheostoma ditrema*, a new darter of the subgenus *Oligocephalus* (Percidae) from springs of the Alabama River basin in Alabama and Georgia. Tulane Studies in Zoology 12: 65–77.

Raney, E. C. 1939. The breeding habits of the silvery minnow, *Hybognathus regius* Girard. American Midland Naturalist 21: 674–680.

Rauchenberger, M. 1989. Systematics and biogeography of the genus *Gambusia* (Cyprinodontiformes, Poeciliidae). American Museum Novitates 2591. 74 p.

Redmond, W. L., and L. A. Krumholz. 1978. Age, growth, condition, and maturity of sunfishes of Doe Run, Meade County, Kentucky. Transactions of the Kentucky Academy of Science 39: 60–73.

Reimer, R. D. 1970. A food study of *Heterandria formosa* Agassiz. American Midland Naturalist 83: 311–315.

Relyea, K. 1983. A systematic study of two species complexes of the genus *Fundulus* (Pisces: Cyprinodontidae). Bulletin of the Florida State Museum Biological Sciences 29: 1-64.

Richards, W. J., and L. W. Knapp. 1964. *Percina lenticula*, a new percid fish, with a redescription of the subgenus *Hadropterus*. Copeia 1964: 690–701.

Richardson, J. 1845. Ichthyology. p. 51–150 in R. B. Hinds, editor, The zoology of the voyage of H.M.S. "Sulphur," under the command of Captain Sir Edward Belcher, during the years 1836–42. London.

Roberts, F. L. 1964. A chromosome study of twenty species of Centrarchidae. Journal of Morphology 115: 410–418.

Robins, C. R., R. M. Bailey, C. E. Bond, J. R. Brooker, E. A. Lachner, R. N. Lea, and W. B. Scott. 1991. A list of common and scientific names of fishes from the United States and Canada. American Fisheries Society Special Report 20. 183 p.

Robins, C. R., D. M. Cohen, and C. H. Robins. 1979. The eels, *Anguilla* and *Histiobranchus*, photographed on the floor of the deep Atlantic in the Bahamas. Bulletin of Marine Science 29: 401–405.

Robins, C. R., and E. C. Raney. 1956. Studies of the catostomid fishes of the genus *Moxostoma*, with descriptions of two new species. Cornell University Agricultural Station Memoir 343. 56 p.

Robison, H. W. 1986. Zoogeographic implications of the Mississippi River basin. p. 267–285 in C. H. Hocutt and E. O. Wiley, editors, Zoogeography of North American freshwater fishes. Wiley-Interscience, New York.

Robison, H. W., and T. M. Buchanan. 1988. Fishes of Arkansas. University of Arkansas Press, Fayetteville. 536 p.

Rohde, F. C. 1978a. *Noturus eleutherus* Jordan. p. 451 in D. S. Lee et al., Atlas of North American freshwater fishes. North Carolina State Museum of Natural History Publication 1980-12.

———. 1978b. *Noturus funebris* Gilbert and Swain. p. 456 in D. S. Lee et al., Atlas of North American freshwater fishes. North Carolina State Museum of Natural History Publication 1980-12.

Rohde, F. C., and J. Lantrigne-Courchene. 1978a. *Ichthyomyzon castaneus* Girard. p. 16 in D. S. Lee et al., Atlas of North American freshwater fishes. North Carolina State Museum of Natural History Publication 1980-12.

———. 1978b. *Ichthyomyzon greeleyi* Hubbs and Trautman. p. 19 in D. S. Lee et al., Atlas of North American freshwater fishes. North Carolina State Museum of Natural History Publication 1980-12.

———. 1979. *Ichthyomyzon bdellium* (Jordan). p. 15 in D. S. Lee et al., Atlas of North American freshwater fishes. North Carolina State Museum of Natural History Publication 1980-12.

Rosen, D. E., and R. M. Bailey. 1963. The poeciliid fishes (Cyprinodontiformes), their structure, zoogeography, and systematics. Bulletin of the American Museum of Natural History 126: 1–176.

Ross, M. R. 1976. Nest-entry behavior of female creek chubs (*Semotilus atromaculatus*) in different habitats. Copeia 1976: 378–380.

———. 1977. Aggression as a social mechanism in the creek chub (*Semotilus atromaculatus*). Copeia 1977: 393-397.

Rupprecht, R. L., and L. A. Jahn. 1980. Biological notes on blue suckers in the Mississippi River. Transactions of the American Fisheries Society 109: 323–326.

Ryon, M. G. 1981. The life history and ecology of *Etheostoma trisella* (Pisces: Percidae). M.S. Thesis. University of Tennessee, Knoxville. 79 p.

Sandon, J. T., D. R. Holder, and L. M. McSwain. 1974. Ecological aspects of the redbreast sunfish in the Satilla River, Georgia. Proceedings of the 28th Annual Conference of Southeastern Game and Fish Commissioners. 279–295.

Sapp, C .D., and J. Emplaincourt. 1975. Physiographic regions of Alabama. Alabama Geological Survey Special Map 168.

Schmidt, R. E., and W. R. Whitworth. 1979. Distribution and habitat of the swamp darter (*Etheostoma fusiforme*) in southern New England. American Midland Naturalist 102: 408–413.

Schoffman, R.J. 1940. Age and growth of black and white crappie, the warmouth bass, and the yellow bass in Reelfoot Lake, Tennessee. Journal of the Tennessee Academy of Science 15: 22–42.

———. 1965. Age and growth of white crappie in Reelfoot Lake, Tennessee, for 1959 and 1964. Journal of the Tennessee Academy of Science 40: 6–8.

Schwartz, F. J. 1958. The breeding behavior of the southern blacknose dace, *Rhinichthys atratulus obtusus* Agassiz. Copeia 1958: 141–143.

Scott, W. B., and E. J. Crossman. 1973. Freshwater fishes of Canada. Fishery Research Board of Canada Bulletin 184. 966 p.

Seagle, H. H., Jr., and J. W. Nagel. 1982. Life history and fecundity of the American brook lamprey, *Lampetra appendix*, in Tennessee. Copeia 1982: 362–366.

Seesock, W. C. 1979. Some aspects of the life history and ecology of the coldwater darter, *Etheostoma ditrema*, from Glencoe spring, Etowah County, Alabama. M.S.

Thesis. Auburn University, Auburn. 70 p.

Settles, W. H., and R. D. Hoyt. 1978. The reproductive biology of the southern redbelly dace, *Chrosomus erythrogaster* Rafinesque, in a spring-fed stream in Kentucky. American Midland Naturalist 99: 290–298.

Shelton, C. T., and J. W. Cottier. 1983. Origins of Mobile, archaeological excavations at the courthouse site, Mobile, Alabama. Auburn University Archeological Monograph 5. 180 p.

Shemske, M. R. 1974. Age, length, and fecundity of the creek chub, *Semotilus atromaculatus* (Mitchill), in central Illinois. American Midland Naturalist 92: 505–509.

Shepard, M. E., and M. T. Huish. 1978. Age, growth, and diet of the pirate perch in a Coastal Plain stream of North America. Transactions of the American Fisheries Society 107: 457–459.

Shepard, T. E., and B. M. Burr. 1984. Systematics, status, and life history aspects of the ashy darter, *Etheostoma cinereum* (Pisces: Percidae). Proceedings of the Biological Society of Washington 97: 693–715.

Shepard, T. E., S. W. McGregor, M. F. Mettee, and P. E. O'Neil. 1995. Status survey of the bluestripe shiner (*Cyprinella callitaenia*) in Alabama, 1994–95. Alabama Geological Survey open file report. 78 p.

Shepard, T. E., S. W. McGregor, and P. E. O'Neil. 1994. Status survey of the Cahaba shiner, *Notropis cahabae*, 1992–93. Alabama Geological Survey Circular 181. 14 p.

Shipp, R. L. 1986. Dr. Bob Shipp's guide to fishes of the Gulf of Mexico. Marine Environmental Sciences Consortium of Alabama, Dauphin Island. 256 p.

Shute, J. R. 1978. *Ictiobus niger* (Rafinesque). p. 406 in D. S. Lee et al., Atlas of North American freshwater fishes. North Carolina State Museum of Natural History Publication 1980-12.

Simon, T. P., and E. J. Tyberghein. 1991. Contributions to the early life history of the spotted gar, *Lepisosteus oculatus* Winchell, from Hatchet Creek, Alabama. Transactions of the Kentucky Academy of Science 52: 124–131.

Simon, T. P., E. J. Tyberghein, K. J. Scheidegger, and C. E. Johnston. 1992. Descriptions of protolarvae of the sand darters (Percidae: *Ammocrypta* and *Crystallaria*) with comments on systematic relationships. Ichthyological Explorations of Freshwaters 3: 347–358.

Simons, A. M. 1991. Phylogenetic relationships of the crystal darter, *Crystallaria asprella* (Teleostei: Percidae). Copeia 1991: 927–936.

Simpson, D. G., and G. Gunter. 1956. Notes on the habitats, systematic characters and life histories of Texas salt water cyprinodontes. Tulane Studies in Zoology 4: 115–134.

Smith, B. G. 1908. The spawning habits of *Chrosomus erythrogaster* Rafinesque. Biological Bulletin 15: 8–18.

Smith, C. H. 1834. The class Pisces, with supplementary additions by Edward Griffith . . . [published as vol. 10 of Cuvier's Animal Kingdom, 1827–1835, London]

Smith, D. G. 1968. The occurrence of larvae of the American eel, *Anguilla rostrata*, in the Straits of Florida and nearby areas. Bulletin of Marine Science 18: 280–293.

———. 1989. Order Anguilliformes, family Anguillidae, freshwater eels. p. 25–46 in Fishes of the western North Atlantic. no. 1, pt. 9, vol 1. Memoirs of the Sears Foundation for Marine Research. Yale University, New Haven.

Smith, G. R., and R. F. Stearley. 1989. The classification and scientific names of rainbow and cutthroat trouts. Fisheries 14: 4–10.

Smith, H. M. 1907. The fishes of North Carolina. North Carolina Geologic and Economic Survey, Raleigh. 453 p.

Smith, P. W. 1979. The fishes of Illinois. University of Illinois Press, Urbana. 314 p.

Smith-Vaniz, W. F. 1968. Freshwater fishes of Alabama. Auburn University Agricultural Experiment Station, Auburn. 211 p.

Snelson, F. F., Jr., 1972. Systematics of the subgenus *Lythrurus*, genus *Notropis* (Pisces: Cyprinidae). Bulletin of the Florida State Museum Biological Sciences 17: 1–92.

———. 1973. Systematics and distribution of the ribbon shiner, *Notropis fumeus* (Cyprinidae) from the central United States. American Midland Naturalist 89: 166–191.

———. 1980. Systematic review of the cyprinid fish, *Notropis lirus*. Copeia 1980: 323–334.

———. 1990. Redescription, geographic variation, and subspecies of the minnow *Notropis ardens* (Pisces: Cyprinidae). Copeia 1990: 966–984.

Sossamon, M. K. 1990. The life history of the flame chub, *Hemitremia flammea* (Jordan and Gilbert) in Pond

Creek, Loudon County, Tennessee. M.S. Thesis. University of Tennessee, Knoxville. 52 p.

Starnes, L. B., and W. C. Starnes. 1981. Biology of the blacknose dace *Phoxinus cumberlandensis*. American Midland Naturalist 106: 360–371.

———. 1985. Ecology and life history of the mountain madtom, *Noturus eleutherus* (Pisces: Ictaluridae). American Midland Naturalist 106: 360–371.

Starnes, W. C. 1977. The ecology and life history of the endangered snail darter, *Percina (Imostoma) tanasi* Etnier. Tennessee Wildlife Resources Agency Technical Report 77–52. 144 p.

Starnes, W. C., and D. A. Etnier. 1986. Drainage evolution and fish biogeography of the Tennessee and Cumberland river drainages. p. 325–361 in C. H. Hocutt and E. O. Wiley, editors, Zoogeography of North American freshwater fishes. Wiley-Interscience, New York.

Starrett, W. C. 1950. Food relationships of the minnows of the Des Moines River, Iowa. Ecology 31: 216–233.

Steindachner, F. 1864. Ichthyologische Mitteilungen VII. Verhandlungen der Zoologischen-Botanischen Gesellschaft in Wien 14: 223–232.

Stevens, R. E. 1959. The white and channel catfishes of the Santee-Cooper Reservoir and tailrace sanctuary. Proceedings of the 11th Annual Conference of Southeastern Game and Fish Commissioners. 203–219.

Stiles, R. A. 1972. The comparative ecology of three species of *Nothonotus* (Percidae: *Etheostoma*) in Tennessee's Little River. Ph.D. Dissertation. University of Tennessee, Knoxville. 97 p.

———. 1990. A preliminary report on the current status of the goldline darter, *Percina aurolineata*, and the Cahaba shiner, *Notropis cahabae*, in the Little Cahaba and Cahaba rivers of Alabama. Unpublished report. U.S. Fish and Wildlife Service, Jackson, Mississippi. 28 p.

Storer, D. H. 1845a. [Description of hitherto undescribed species of fish, from Mr. S. C. Clark, of Chicago.] Proceedings of the Boston Society of Natural History 2: 47–48.

———. 1845b. [Descriptions of species of fishes received, together with drawings, from Mr. Charles A. Hentz, of Florence, Alabama.] Proceedings of the Boston Society of Natural History 2: 48–49, 51.

———. 1846. A synopsis of the fishes of North America.

Memoirs of the American Academy of Arts and Sciences 2(7): 253–550.

Stoye, F. H. 1935. Tropical fishes for the home and their care and propagation, 2nd edition. Carl Mertens, New York. 284 p.

Surat, E. M., W. J. Matthews, and J. R. Bek. 1982. Comparative ecology of *Notropis albeolus*, *N. ardens* and *N. cerasinus* (Cyprinidae) in the upper Roanoke Drainage, Virginia. American Midland Naturalist 107: 13–24.

Suttkus, R. D. 1955. *Notropis euryzonus*, a new cyprinid fish from the Chattahoochee River system of Georgia and Alabama. Tulane Studies in Zoology 3: 85–100.

———. 1959. *Notropis uranoscopus*, a new cyprinid fish from the Alabama River system. Copeia 1959: 7–11.

———. 1980. *Notropis candidus*, a new cyprinid fish from the Mobile Bay basin, and a review of the nomenclatural history of *Notropis shumardi* (Girard). Bulletin of the Alabama Museum of Natural History 5: 1–15.

Suttkus, R. D., and R. M. Bailey. 1993. *Etheostoma colorosum* and *E. bellator*, two new darters, subgenus *Ulocentra*, from the southeastern United States. Tulane Studies in Zoology and Botany 29: 1–28.

Suttkus, R. D., R. M. Bailey, and H. L. Bart, Jr., 1994. Three new species of *Etheostoma*, subgenus *Ulocentra*, from the Gulf Coastal Plain of southeastern United States. Tulane Studies in Zoology and Botany 29: 97–150.

Suttkus, R. D., and H. T. Boschung. 1990. *Notropis ammophilus*, a new cyprinid fish from southeastern United States. Tulane Studies in Zoology and Botany 27: 49–63.

Suttkus, R. D., and G. H. Clemmer. 1968. *Notropis edwardraneyi*, a new cyprinid fish from the Alabama and Tombigbee river systems and a discussion of related species. Tulane Studies in Zoology and Botany 15: 18–39.

Suttkus, R. D., and D. A. Etnier. 1991. *Etheostoma tallapoosae* and *E. brevirostrum*, two new darters, subgenus *Ulocentra*, from the Alabama River drainage. Tulane Studies in Zoology and Botany 28: 1–24.

Suttkus, R. D., and J. S. Ramsey. 1967. *Percina aurolineata*, a new percid fish from the Alabama River system and a discussion of ecology, distribution, and hybridization of darters of the subgenus *Hadropterus*. Tulane Studies in Zoology 13: 129–145.

Suttkus, R. D., and E. C. Raney. 1955a. *Notropis asperifrons*, a new cyprinid fish from the Mobile Bay drainage of Alabama and Georgia, with studies of related species. Tulane Studies in Zoology 3: 3–33.

———.1955b. *Notropis baileyi*, a new cyprinid fish from the Pascagoula and Mobile Bay drainages of Mississippi and Alabama. Tulane Studies in Zoology 2: 71–86.

———. 1955c. *Notropis hypsilepis*, a new cyprinid fish from the Apalachicola River system of Georgia and Alabama. Tulane Studies in Zoology 2: 161–170.

Suttkus, R. D., and W. R. Taylor. 1965. *Noturus munitus*, a new species of madtom, family Ictaluridae, from southern United States. Proceedings of the Biological Society of Washington 78: 169–178.

Suttkus, R. D., B. A. Thompson, and H. L. Bart. 1994. Two new darters, *Percina* (*Cottogaster*), from the southeastern United States, with a review of the subgenus. Occasional Papers of the Tulane University Museum of Natural History 4. 46 p.

Swain, J. 1883. A description of a new species of *Hadropterus* (*Hadropterus scierus*) from southern Indiana. Proceedings of the U.S. National Museum 6(379): 252.

Swift, C. C. 1970. A review of the eastern North American cyprinid fishes of the *Notropis texanus* species group (subgenus *Alburnops*), with a definition of the subgenus *Hydrophlox*, and materials for a revision of the subgenus *Alburnops*. Ph.D. Dissertation. Florida State University, Tallahassee. 476 p.

Swift, C. C., C. R. Gilbert, S. A. Bortone, H. G. Burgess, and R. W. Yerger. 1986. Zoogeography of the freshwater fishes of the southeastern United States: Savannah River to Lake Pontchartrain. p. 213–255 in C. H. Hocutt and E. O. Wiley, editors, Zoogeography of North American freshwater fishes. Wiley-Interscience, New York.

Swift, C. C., R. W. Yerger, and P. R. Parrish. 1977. Distribution and natural history of the fresh and brackish water fishes of the Ochlockonee River, Florida and Georgia. Bulletin of the Tall Timbers Research Station 20.

Swingle, H. A. 1971. Biology of Alabama estuarine areas–Cooperative Gulf of Mexico estuarine inventory. Alabama Marine Resources Bulletin 5. 123 p.

Swingle, H. A., and D. G. Bland. 1974. A study of the watercourses of Alabama. Alabama Marine Resources Bulletin 10: 17–102.

Taylor, W. R. 1969. A revision of the catfish genus *Noturus* Rafinesque, with an analysis of higher groups in the Ictaluridae. Bulletin of the U.S. National Museum 282. 315 p.

Tennessee Valley Authority. 1971. Tennessee valley streams: their fish, bottom fauna, and aquatic habitat, Flint River drainage basin, 1969. Tennessee Valley Authority Division of Forestry, Fisheries, and Wildlife Development, Norris.

Thomas, D. L. 1970. An ecological study of four darters of the genus *Percina* (Percidae) in the Kaskaskia River, Illinois. Illinois Natural History Survey Biological Notes 70. 18 p.

Thomerson, J. E. 1969. Variation and relationships of the studfishes, *Fundulus catenatus* and *Fundulus stellifer* (Cyprinodontidae, Pisces). Tulane Studies in Zoology and Botany 16: 1-21.

Thomerson, J. E., and D. P. Wooldridge. 1970. Food habits of allotopic and syntopic populations of the topminnows *Fundulus olivaceus* and *Fundulus notatus*. American Midland Naturalist 84: 573-576.

Thompson, B. A. 1985. *Percina jenkinsi*, a new species of logperch (Pisces: Percidae) from the Conasauga River, Tennessee and Georgia. Occasional Papers of the Louisiana State University Museum of Zoology 61. 23 p.

———. 1995. *Percina austroperca*, a new species of logperch (Percidae, subgenus *Percina*) from the Choctawhatchee and Escambia Rivers in Alabama and Florida. Occasional Papers of the Louisiana State University Museum of Natural Science 69. 19 p.

Timmons, T. J. 1982. Initial changes in fish species composition in two lakes of the Tennessee-Tombigbee Waterway, Alabama-Mississippi. Southeastern Fishes Council Proceedings 4: 1–4.

Trauth, S. E., G. L. Miller, and J. S. Williams. 1981. Seasonal gonadal changes and population structure of *Noturus munitus* (Pisces, Ictaluridae) in Mississippi. Association of Southeastern Biologists Bulletin 28: 66.

Trautman, M. B. 1981. The fishes of Ohio, revised edition. Ohio State University Press, Columbus. 782 p.

Traver, J. R. 1929. The habits of the black-nosed dace, *Rhinichthys atronasus* (Mitchill). Journal of the Elisha Mitchell Scientific Society 45: 101–129.

Tsai, C. 1968. Variation and distribution of the rock darter, *Etheostoma rupestre*. Copeia 1968: 346–353.

Tsai, C., and E. C. Raney. 1974. Systematics of the banded darter, *Etheostoma zonale* (Pisces: Percidae). Copeia 1974: 1-24.

U.S. Commission of Fish and Fisheries. 1898. Report of the Commissioner for the year ending June 30, 1896. Part XXII. Government Printing Office, Washington, D.C. 493–533.

U.S. Commission of Fish and Fisheries. 1905. Report of the Commissioner for the year ending June 30, 1903. Part XXIX. Government Printing Office, Washington, D.C. 493–533.

Viosca, P. Jr. 1936. A new rock bass from Louisiana and Mississippi. Copeia 1936: 37–45.

Vladykov, V. D. 1955. A comparison of Atlantic sea sturgeons with a new subspecies from the Gulf of Mexico (*Acipenser oxyrhynchus desotoi*). Journal of the Fisheries Research Board of Canada 12(5): 754–761.

———. 1971. Homing of the American eel, *Anguilla rostrata*, as evidenced by returns of transplanted tagged eels in New Brunswick. Canadian Field Naturalist 85: 241–248.

Vogt, G. E., Jr., and T. G. Coon. 1990. A comparison of the foraging behavior of two darter (*Etheostoma*) species. Copeia 1990: 41–49.

Wade, C. W. 1979. A summary of information pertinent to the Mobile Bay recreational finfishery and a review of the spotted seatrout's life history. p. 177–183 in H. A. Loyacano and J. P. Smith, editors, Symposium on the natural resources of the Mobile estuary, Alabama. U.S. Army Corps of Engineers, Mobile District.

Walbaum, J. J. 1792. Genera Piscium [in quibus systema totum ichthyologiae proponitur cum classicus, ordinibus, generum, characteribus, specierum differentiis, observationibus plurimis]. In Artedi, Petri, Ichthyologiae pars III a Iohanne Iulio Walbaum. Grypeswaldie, impensis Ant. Fer. Rose. 723 p.

Wall, B. R. 1968. Studies on the fishes of the Bear Creek drainage of the Tennessee River system. M.S. Thesis. University of Alabama, Tuscaloosa. 96 p.

Wall, B. R., and C. R. Gilbert. 1980. *Erimyzon oblongus* (Mitchill). p. 397 in D. S. Lee et al., Atlas of North American freshwater fishes. North Carolina State Museum of Natural History Publication 1980-12.

Wall, B. R., and J. D. Williams. 1974. *Etheostoma boschungi*, a new percid fish from the Tennessee River drainage in northern Alabama and western Tennessee. Tulane Studies in Zoology and Botany 18: 172–182.

Wallace, C. R. 1967. Observations on the reproductive behavior of the black bullhead (*Ictalurus melas*). Copeia 1967: 852–853.

Wallace, D. C. 1973. Reproduction of the silverjaw minnow, *Ericymba buccata* Cope. Transactions of the American Fisheries Society 102: 786–793.

Wallace, R. K., and J. S. Ramsey. 1981. Reproductive behavior and biology of the bluestripe shiner (*Notropis callitaenia*) in Uchee Creek, Alabama. American Midland Naturalist 106: 197–200.

Walsh, S. J., and B. M. Burr. 1984. Life history of the banded pygmy sunfish, *Elassoma zonatum* Jordan (Pisces, Centrarchidae) in western Kentucky. Bulletin of the Alabama Museum of Natural History 8: 31–52.

———. 1985. Biology of the stonecat, *Noturus flavus* (Siluriformes: Ictaluridae), in central Illinois and Missouri streams and comparison with Great Lakes populations and congeners. Ohio Journal of Science 85: 85–96.

Warren, M. L., Jr., 1992. Variation of the spotted sunfish, *Lepomis punctatus* complex (Centrarchidae): meristics, morphometrics, pigmentation and species limits. Alabama Museum of Natural History Bulletin 12. 47 p.

Warren, M. L., and B. M. Burr. 1990. Status survey of the palezone shiner, *Notropis* sp. cf. *procne*, a federal candidate for listing. Open file report. U.S. Fish and Wildlife Service, Office of Endangered Species, Asheville, North Carolina. 27 p.

Warren, M. L., B. M. Burr, and J. M. Grady. 1994. *Notropis albizonatus*, a new cyprinid fish endemic to the Tennessee and Cumberland river drainages, with a phylogeny of the *Notropis procne* species group. Copeia 1994: 868–886.

Warren, M. L., B. M. Burr, and B. R. Kuhajda. 1986. Mississippi River sturgeons: new Kentucky records and comments on status. Transactions of the Kentucky Academy of Science 47: 83–98.

Wenner, C. A., and J. A. Musick. 1975. Food habits and seasonal abundance of the American eel, *Anguilla rostrata*, from the lower Chesapeake Bay. Chesapeake Science 16: 62–66.

Widlak, J. C., and R. J. Neves. 1985. Age, growth, food habits, and reproduction of the redline darter *Etheostoma rufilineatum* (Cope) (Perciformes: Percidae) in Virginia. Brimleyana 11: 69–80.

Wieland, W. 1982. Life history of the bronze darter, *Percina palmaris*, in Alabama. American Society of Ichthyologists and Herpetologists 62nd annual meeting (abstract).

———. 1983. Interactive life histories of three species of *Percina* (Pisces: Percidae) in the Alabama River system. Ph.D. Dissertation. Auburn University, Auburn. 137 p.

Wieland, W., and J. S. Ramsey. 1987. Ecology of the muscadine darter, *Percina* sp. cf. *macrocephala*, in the Tallapoosa River, Alabama, with comments on related species. Southeastern Fishes Council Proceedings 17: 5–11.

Wiley, E. O. 1977. The phylogeny and systematics of the *Fundulus notti* species group (Teleostei: Cyprinodontidae). Occasional Papers of the University of Kansas Museum of Natural History 66. 31 p.

———. 1979. *Lepisosteus osseus* (Linnaeus). P. 49 in D. S. Lee et al., Atlas of North American freshwater fishes. North Carolina State Museum of Natural History Publication 1980-12.

———. 1986. A study of the evolutionary relationships of *Fundulus* topminnows (Teleostei: Fundulidae). American Zoologist 26: 121–130.

———. 1992. Phylogenetic relationships of the Percidae (Teleostei: Perciformes): a preliminary hypothesis. p. 247–267 in R. L. Mayden, editor, Systematics, historical ecology, and North American freshwater fishes. Stanford University Press, Stanford, California.

Wiley, E. O., and D. D. Hall. 1975. *Fundulus blairae*, a new species of the *Fundulus nottii* complex (Teleostei, Cyprinodontidae). American Museum Novitates 2577. 13 p.

Williams, J. D. 1968. A new species of sculpin, *Cottus pygmaeus*, from a spring in the Alabama River basin. Copeia 1968: 334–342.

———. 1975. Systematics of the percid fishes of the subgenus *Ammocrypta*, genus *Ammocrypta*, with descriptions of two new species. Bulletin of the Alabama Museum of Natural History 1. 56 p.

Williams, J. D., and G. H. Clemmer. 1991. *Scaphirhynchus suttkusi*, a new sturgeon (Pisces: Acipenseridae) from the Mobile Basin of Alabama and Mississippi. Bulletin of the Alabama Museum of Natural History 10: 17–31.

Williams, J. D., and D. A. Etnier. 1977. *Percina (Imostoma) antesella*, a new percid fish from the Coosa River system in Tennessee and Georgia. Proceedings of the Biological Society of Washington 90: 6–18.

———. 1982. Description of a new species, *Fundulus julisia*, with a redescription of *Fundulus albolineatus* and a diagnosis of the subgenus *Xenisma* (Teleostei: Cyprinodontidae). Occasional Papers of the University of Kansas Museum of Natural History 102: 1–20.

Williams, J. D., and H. W. Robison. 1980. *Ozarka*, a new subgenus of *Etheostoma* (Pisces: Percidae). Brimleyana 4: 149–156.

Williams, J. D., J. E. Johnson, D. A. Hendrickson, S. Contreras-Balderas, J. D. Williams, M. Navarrro-Mendoza, D. E. McAllister, and J. E. Deacon. 1989. Fishes of North America endangered, threatened, or special concern. Fisheries 14: 2–20.

Williams, J. S. 1976. Life history of the brown darter, *Etheostoma edwini* (Pisces: Percidae), in northwestern Florida. M.S. Thesis. University of West Florida, Pensacola. 39 p.

Wilson, A. 1967. River discharge to the sea from the shores of the conterminous United States. U.S. Geological Survey Hydrological Investigations Atlas HA-282.

Winchell, A. 1864. Description of a garpike, supposed to be new: *Lepisosteus (Cylindrosteus) oculatus*. Proceedings of the Academy of Natural Sciences of Philadelphia 16: 183–185.

Winn, H. E. 1958a. Comparative reproductive behavior and ecology of fourteen species of darters (Pisces: Percidae). Ecological Monographs 28: 155–191.

———. 1958b. Observations on the reproductive habits of darters (Pisces: Percidae). American Midland Naturalist 59: 190–212.

Wood, R. M., and R. L. Mayden. 1993. Systematics of the *Etheostoma jordani* species group (Teleostei: Percidae), with descriptions of three new species. Bulletin of the Alabama Museum of Natural History 16: 31–46.

Woolcott, W. S., and E. G. Maurakis. 1988. Pit-ridge construction and spawning behaviors of *Semotilus lumbee* and *Semotilus thoreauianus*. Southeastern Fishes Council Proceedings 18: 1–3.

Wooten, M. C., K. T. Scribner, and M. H. Smith. 1988. Genetic variability and systematics of *Gambusia* in the southeastern United States. Copeia 1988: 283–289.

Wrenn, W. B. 1969. Life history aspects of smallmouth buffalo and freshwater drum in Wheeler Reservoir,

Alabama. Proceedings of the 22nd Annual Conference of the Southeastern Game and Fish Commissioners. 479–495.

Yeager, B. L., and K. J. Semmens. 1987. Early development of the blue sucker *Cycleptus elongatus*. Copeia 1987: 312–316.

Yerger, R. W., and K. Relyea. 1968. The flat-headed bullheads (Pisces: Ictaluridae) of the southeastern United States, and a new species of *Ictalurus* from the Gulf Coast. Copeia 1968: 361–384.

SEINING IN HUBBARD CREEK, LAWRENCE COUNTY

GLOSSARY

For additional detail on fish anatomy, see pages 41–47.

Acute - Sharp or pointed.

ADCNR - Alabama Department of Conservation and Natural Resources.

Adipose (fin, eyelid) - Pertaining to fat, referring to a fleshy accessory appendage or membrane.

Adnate - Attached, referring to the attached adipose fin of madtom catfishes.

AGFD - Alabama Game and Fish Division of the Alabama Department of Conservation and Natural Resources.

Algae - Any one of a diversity of single-celled aquatic plants belonging to the phyla Cyanophyta, Pyrrophyta, Chrysophyta, Phaeophyta, Rhodophyta, and Chlorophyta.

Alkalinity - The measure of water's ability to neutralize acid. Highly alkaline waters usually have excess carbonate and bicarbonate in solution.

Allometric - Relative growth of a body part in relation to the entire organism.

Allopatric - A distributional relationship where species with nonoverlapping ranges do not occur together.

Allotopic - A distributional relationship where species with overlapping ranges do not occur together.

Ammocoete - Larval lamprey.

Anadromous - Referring to species that migrate from estuarine or marine areas into fresh water to spawn.

Anal fin - A median fin just behind the anus.

Annulus - A year mark on a scale or other body part.

Anterior - Situated toward the front.

Anticoagulant - A substance that hinders clotting of blood.

Anus - The terminal point of the digestive system.

Attenuate - To make thin or slender, extended.

Axillary Process - An elongate scale at the insertion of the pelvic fin.

Backpack shocker - An electroshocking device mounted on a backpack frame for sampling fishes in small streams.

Backwater - Pooled water separated from the main stream channel.

Barbel - A fleshy, tapered sensory organ found around the mouth or on the head in some fishes.

Basicaudal - At the base of the caudal fin.

Basin - A major group of drainages interconnected by a master river or estuary (i.e., Mobile basin).

Bedrock - A general term for a stream bottom characterized by unfractured rock.

Benthic - Of the bottom.

Binomial - Two names, referring to the practice of applying two Latin names to classify species.

Biogeography - The study of the distribution of plants and animals and the forces that influence them.

Blackfly - A family of aquatic insects, Simuliidae, in the order Diptera.

Blackwater - Water that is stained dark from the leaching of organic compounds such as tannins and lignins.

Blue Ridge - A physiographic province with upland characteristics lying between the Piedmont and the Valley and Ridge. Only occurs in Georgia for this study area.

Boulder - A substrate type of large rocks 12 inches in diameter or greater.

Branchiostegal membrane - The paired membranes located on the posterioventral surface of the head, which close the lower opening of the gill cavity.

Breeding tubercle - A small protuberance, usually pointed and hard, occurring on the body, head, or fins of breeding males and some female fishes, usually in large numbers. They are used for territorial aggression, sexual stimulation, or to maintain contact during breeding.

Buccal cavity - The mouth or oral cavity.

Caddisfly - A group of aquatic insects, order Trichoptera.

Canine - A large, conical tooth.

Cartilaginous - Referring to cartilage, a tough, elastic tissue constituting the skeleton of embryos and primitivevertebrates.

Cast net - A small throw net used to capture fishes such as mullet or shad.

Catadromous - Freshwater species that migrate to salt water to spawn.

Caudal fin - Tail fin.

Characins - A family of freshwater fishes common to Africa and South America.

Cheek - The part of the head below and slightly behind the eye.

Chromatophore - A cell with pigment giving color to the surrounding tissue.

Cirrus (plural, *cirri*) - A featherlike branched structure arising from the skin.

Claystone - A hardened clay with the appearance of shale.

Coastal Plain - A physiographic region in south Alabama composed of sedimentary deposits extending from the sea to the Fall Line, drained by the Mobile basin and all other rivers flowing to the Gulf of Mexico.

Contact organ - A small dermal growth on scales, fin rays, or the body. Similar to breeding tubercles.

Copepod - A member of a group of small Crustacea common in marine and fresh waters.

Ctenii - Tiny spines on ctenoid scales.

Ctenoid scale - A scale with ctenii on the exposed surface.

Cumberland Plateau - An upland plateau of sandstone and shale in north-central Alabama, through which the upper Black Warrior River flows.

Cycloid scale - A scale with a smooth exposed surface.

Depauperate - A biogeographic term referring to an area with relatively few species.

Diptera - A large order of winged insects including aquatic forms such as mosquitoes, gnats, and midges.

Distal - Toward or near the outer edge or margin.

Diverse - Biotas having a substantial number of species or a wide range of biological characteristics.

Dorsal (*dorsum*) - Back or upper body.

Dorsal fin - The median fin(s) on the back supported by rays and/or spines.

Drainage - A group of interconnected stream systems the main channel of which enters an ocean, estuary, or the mainstem of a basin.

Electrofishing - The sampling procedure whereby electrical currents are used to stun fish for sampling.

Emarginate - Having a notched margin.

Embedded scales - Scales hidden under the skin.

Endangered - A protective status for taxa that are threatened with extinction.

Endemic - Restricted to a given area, drainage, or basin.

Entire - Having a smooth or straight margin.

Escarpment - A continuous steep face that breaks the continuity of the land's surface.

Estivate - To spend a period of time, usually summer months, in a state of inactivity.

Estuary - A partially enclosed body of water that has a connection with the sea and is diluted by fresh water.

Eutrophic - A body of water with a high rate of productivity.

Exotic - Non-native, introduced species.

Extant - Still living or present.

Extinct - A taxon no longer living.

Extirpated - A nonextant population of an extant taxon.

Fall Line - The boundary between unconsolidated Coastal Plain sediments and harder rocks of the Appalachian Highlands.

Family - The taxonomic category between order and genus, ending in -*idae* for animal groups.

Fauna - Animals or animal life, distinguished from flora or plant life.

Fecundity - Female reproductive potential.

FL - Fork length.

Fluvial - Flowing.

Fyke net - A long bag net kept open by a series of rigid loops.

Game fish - Any one of a variety of fishes made legal catch by specific legislation.

Gamete - The mature sexual reproductive cell.

Ganoid scale - A bony scale found in gars that is rhomboid shaped and hard on the surface.

Genital papilla - A fleshy structure bearing the external genital opening.

Genus (plural, *genera*) - A taxonomic category between family and species containing common characteristics.

Gill net - A flat net suspended vertically in the water with meshes that allow the fish head to pass through but that entangle the gill covers.

Gonopodium - Modified anal fin rays in male livebearers that are used to transfer sperm to the female.

Gravid - The reproductive status of females where many of the oocytes are fully or almost fully developed.

Groundwater - Water held in storage under the land surface.

GSA - Geological Survey of Alabama. The notation GSA 0000 refers to the catalog number under which fish samples are accessioned to the GSA voucher collection.

Highland Rim - An upland plateau in north Alabama through which the Tennessee River flows.

Hybrid - The offspring of mating between different species.

Ichthy (prefix) - Of or pertaining to fish.

Ichthyofauna - Fish species of a given area.

Immaculate - Lacking pigmentation, stippling, or spotting.

Impoundment - A body of water created by a dam, with lake characteristics.

Indigenous - Native to an area.

Intergrade - The offspring of interbreeding between subspecies of the same species.

Intermittent - Ceasing for a period of time, as in headwater streamflow.

Interradial membranes - Membranes between rays in fins.

Invertebrate - A division of the animal kingdom containing organisms in which the nerve cord is not enclosed in a segmented backbone.

Invertivore - Feeding on invertebrates.

Kype - An enlargement of the lower jaw of male salmon and trout.

Lachrymal groove - A small groove on the lower side of the snout caused by skin folding around the lachrymal bone.

Lacustrine - Referring to lakes and their properties.

Larva - A developmental stage between hatching and the juvenile stage.

Leaf litter - Accumulations of leaves in streams, rivers, and lakes.

Leucisin - A term for North American minnows.

Live well - A container for holding living fishes.

Lowland - Flat or rolling terrain with streams of very low gradient.

Mandible - Lower jaw.

Mandibular pores - Canal openings on ventral surface of mandible.

Mayfly - A group of aquatic insects, order Ephemeroptera.

Maxilla - Upper jaw.

Melanistic - Dark or black.

Melanophore - A color cell with melanin.

Migration - A cyclic, directed movement for the purpose of breeding, feeding, or other life history needs.

Milt - Gametes and fluids released from a ripe male.

Mollusk - A large phylum of invertebrate animals including snails, mussels, and chitons characterized by a hard shell.

Monophyletic - Derived from a single common parent form.

Mouthbreeder - Species of fish which provide nursery for young in their mouths.

Myomere - Mussel segments.

Naked - Lacking scales.

Nape - The dorsal area between the posterior end of the head and the dorsal fin origin.

Nares - Nostrils.

Native - Naturally occurring in a given area.

Neuromast - An exposed receptive cell of the nervous system.

Nuptial - In reproductive condition.

Ocellus - A round spot contrasting with a lighter or darker color.

Oocyte - A reproductive cell that can develop into a mature ovum or egg.

Opercle - The largest bone of the gill cover.

Opercular flap - A posterior projection of the operculum common in sunfishes.

Operculum - The gill cover composed of several bones.

Oral disk - The circular mouth area of lampreys.

Origin - The anterior point of fin attachment to the body.

Palatine teeth - Small teeth on the paired palatine bone on the roof of the mouth.

Papilla - (plural, *papillae*) A small, fleshy, knoblike protuberance.

Papillate (*papillose*) - Bearing papillae.

Parasite - An organism living in or on another organism, usually causing harm.

Pectoral fin - The most anterior or most dorsal paired fin.

Pelagic - A term for species that live in open water.

Pelvic fin - A paired fin on the ventral surface between the pectoral and anal fins.

Pentamerous - Consisting of five parts or sections.

Periphyton - Organisms that live attached to objects underwater.

Pharyngeal - Relating to or found in the region of the pharynx (throat).

Phoxinin - A term for European minnows.

Piedmont - An upland plateau of metamorphic rock in east Alabama through which the Tallapoosa and Chattahoochee rivers flow.

Piscivorous - Feeding on fish.

Planktivore - A fish that eats plankton.

Pleistocene - The earlier of the two epochs of the Quaternary Period lasting from 1.6 million years ago to 10,000 years before the present. Periods of glaciation were common.

Plicate - Possessing parallel ridges and grooved like a fan, as in the lips of certain suckers.

Pool - A type of stream habitat characterized by moderate to deep water, slow to no flow, and sediments on the bottom.

Posterior - Situated toward the back or rear.

Premaxilla - A bone on the upper jaw preceding the maxilla.

Protractile - A condition when the premaxilla is free to protrude beyond the snout when the mouth is open.

Proximal - Toward the point of attachment.

Ray - A fin support element that is segmented, bilateral, branched or unbranched, and usually flexible.

Recurved - Curved backward or inward.

Redd - Spawning ground or nest.

Riffle - A stream habitat characterized by shallow depth, broken substrate, and swift flow.

Riparian - The shore of a body of water.

Ripe - A state of reproductive readiness when females usually extrude egss and males extrude sperm on light abnominal pressure.

Riprap - Large crushed rock used for stabilizing exposed banks.

Riverine - A term generally used to describe attributes of species found in large rivers.

Run - A stream habitat that is transitional between fast, shallow riffles and slow, deeper pools.

Runoff - Another term for water entering a stream after rainfall.

Salinity - A measure of the salt or dissolved solids content of water.

Sandbar - A shallow deposition of sand in a stream or river, usually found on the inside of bends.

Sedimentation - The process in which fine sediments are deposited and accumulated in layers on the bottom of a body of water.

Seine - A fine mesh net attached to straight poles and pulled through the water to capture fish.

Serrate - Notched or toothed on the edge.

SL - Standard length.

Slabrock - Large pieces of flat rock on stream bottoms.

sp. - Species; spp. refers to more than one species.

Species - The basic lower unit of classification, consisting of a population or series of populations of similar and closely related organisms. Classical definitions of biological species have the important requirement of reproductive isolation, meaning that individuals are capable of interbreeding freely with one another but not with members of other species.

Species richness - The number of species living in an area.

Spent - Adults that have recently completed spawning.

Spine - A fin support element that is unpaired, unsegmented, unbranched, and usually stiff.

Sport fish - A fish of importance primarily for the sport it affords anglers.

Spring run - A small stream leaving a spring.

Stonefly - A group of aquatic insects, order Plecoptera.

Stream capture (or *piracy*) - The natural diversion of headwater stream channels into the channel of another stream with greater erosional activity and flowing at a lower level.

Stream order - A classification of the relative position of a stream in a channel network. Headwater streams are ranked 1, while large streams and rivers may rank from 4 to 7.

Streamflow - The volume of water moving down a stream channel.

Subspecies - A formally named subdivision of a species.

Substrate - Bottom material in lakes, streams, and rivers.

Subterete - Not precisely cylindrical.

Sympatric - A distributional relationship where the ranges of two taxa overlap considerably.

Syntopic - A distributional relationship where two species commonly occur together.

System (river system) - A smaller division of a drainage.

Systematics - The science of classifying organisms.

Tailrace (tailwater) - A section of swift-flowing river immediately downstream of a lock or dam.

Taxon (plural, taxa) - A named group of organisms at any rank such as a species, genus, or family.

Taxonomy - The theory and practice of describing organisms and ordering biological diversity into a relational system.

Terete - Cylindrical.

Threatened - A protective status for organisms at such low population levels that endangerment may occur in the future.

TL - Total length.

Trotline - A method of fishing using hooks suspended at regular intervals along a submerged line.

Tubercle, Tuberculate - see breeding tubercle suspended matte

Turbid - Waters that are clouded by the presence of suspended matter, either organic or inorganic in origin.

TVA - Tennessee Valley Authority.

Type locality - The place where specimens were taken for the original scientific description.

Ubiquitous - A zoogeographic term describing species that are widely distributed and generally common and abundant.

Upland - Hilly terrain of moderate relief with streams of moderate gradient.

Urogenital pore - A common external opening carrying the products of both excretion and reproduction.

USFWS - United States Fish and Wildlife Service.

Valley and Ridge - A system of parallel ridges and adjoining valleys in northeast Alabama, through which flow the upper Cahaba and Coosa rivers.

Vent - Another term for the urogenital pore.

Venter - Underside.

Vermiculate - Wormlike in appearance, marked with irregular wavy lines.

Watershed - The region drained by or contributing water to a stream, river, or lake.

Wingwall - A lateral retaining wall usually parallel to the stream.

Young-of-the-year - Fishes usually hatched within the past 12 months.

Zoogeography - A division of biogeography that applies to animals.

Zooplankton - Microscopic animals that live suspended in water.

CAHABA RIVER, BIBB COUNTY

INDEX TO FAMILY AND SPECIES ACCOUNTS

ABOUT THE AUTHORS

MAURICE F. METTEE lives in Tuscaloosa, Alabama, and grew up in Demopolis. He became interested in fishes at a young age, spending much of his time catching minnows in the Whitfield canal. He received a B.S. in biology from Spring Hill College, an M.A. in secondary education, an M.S. in biology, and a Ph.D. in biology from the University of Alabama. Mettee has been employed by the Geological Survey of Alabama since 1975, and has served as Director of the Environmental Geology Division since 1977. His career has been devoted to assessing the impacts of energy resource development and other manmade activities on the aquatic resources of Alabama. He has observed, collected, and identified Alabama fishes for more than 25 years, resulting in publication of numerous technical and semi-technical reports on their distributions, habits, and habitats.

PATRICK E. O'NEIL lives in Tuscaloosa, Alabama, and was born in Athens, Tennessee. His early years in Tennessee, Mississippi, and Alabama were spent wandering neighborhood streams in search of "sucker mouth minnows." He attended the University of Alabama, where he received a B.S. in biology, an M.S. in vertebrate zoology, and a Ph.D. in civil engineering emphasizing water-quality assessment monitoring. He was employed by the Geological Survey of Alabama in 1979 as a staff biologist and is now chief of the Biological Resources section. During his time at the Survey he has authored or coauthored over 50 publications concerning Alabama's aquatic fauna and water quality.

J. MALCOLM PIERSON lives in Calera, Alabama, and was born in Tuscaloosa. He received a B.S. in biology from the University of Alabama and an M.S. in fisheries from Auburn University in 1982. He has been Senior Aquatic Biologist with Alabama Power Company's Environmental Affairs department since 1981. He has spent 21 years studying fisheries in the vicinity of electric generating facilities, conducting endangered and threatened species surveys and management, and delineating wetland identification and delineation. Pierson has authored and coauthored numerous reports on fishes and mollusks. His interests include studies on the distribution and biology of freshwater fishes, unionid mussels, and aquatic snails of the southeastern United States, and conservation of unique aquatic habitats.